Operations Research
An Introduction

Operations Research
An Introduction

Ninth Edition

Hamdy A. Taha
University of Arkansas, Fayetteville

PEARSON

Original Edition, entitled *Operations Research: An Introduction: International Version, Ninth Edition,* by Taha, Hamdy A., published by Pearson Education, Inc. publishing as Pearson, Copyright © 2011.

Indian edition published by Dorling Kindersley India Pvt. Ltd. Copyright © 2012.

ISBN 978-81-317-8594-2

First Impression, 2012
Second Impression

This edition is manufactured in India and is authorized for sale only in India, Bangladesh, Bhutan, Pakistan, Nepal, Sri Lanka and the Maldives. Circulation of this edition outside of these territories is UNAUTHORIZED.

Published by Dorling Kindersley (India) Pvt. Ltd., licensees of Pearson Education in South Asia.

Head Office: 7th Floor, knowledge Boulevard, A-8(A) Sector-62, Noida (U.P) 201309, India
Registered Office: 11 Community Centre, Panchsheel Park, New Delhi 110 017, India.

Printed in India by Manipal Technologies Limited.

To Karen

Los ríos no llevan agua,
el sol las fuentes secó . . .
¡Yo sé donde hay una fuente
que no ha de secar el sol!
La fuente que no se agota
es mi propio corazón . . .

—V. Ruiz Aguilera (1862)

Contents

Available on the Companion Website

(www.pearsonhighered.com/tahainternational)

Categorization by tool of Chapter files on the Companion Website

AMPL:

Assignment model, *AppenCFiles*
Appointments scheduling, *ch26Files*
Goal programming (interactive), *AppenCFiles*
Integer programming models
    B&B algorithm (interactive), *AppenCFiles*
    Job sequencing, *AppenCFiles*
    Manpower planning at Qantas, *ch26Files*
    Mt. Sinai Hospital, *ch26Files*
    PGF Glass optimization, *ch26Files*
    Set covering, *AppenCFiles*
    Ship routing, *ch26Files*
Linear Programming models
    Bus scheduling, *ch2Files*
    Fuel tankering, *ch26Files*
    Heart valves production, *ch26Files*
    Reddy Mikks model, *AppenCFiles*
    Urban renewal, *AppenCFiles*
Nonlinear programming models
    Constrained EOQ, *AppenCFiles*
    NLP, *AppenCFiles*
Network models
    CPM, *AppenCFiles* s
    Maximum flow, *AppenCFiles*
    Min-cost capacitated network, *AppenCFiles*
    Shortest route, *AppenCFiles*
Transportation model, *AppenCFiles*
Traveling salesperson problem (TSP)
    Branch and bound (interactive), *AppenCFiles*
    Cutting plane, *AppenCFiles*

Excel:
AHP, *ch15Files*
Bayes' probabilities, *ch15Files*
Decisions under uncertainty, *ch15Files*

Search methods
    Dichotomous, *ch21Files*
    Golden section, *ch21Files*
    Newton-Raphson, *ch20Files*
Heuristics,
    nearest neighbor in TSP, *ch11Files*
    random walk, *ch11Files*
    reversals in TSP, *ch11Files*
Histogramming, *ch23Files*
Inventory,
    Continuous review, *ch16Files*
    EOQ, *ch11Files*
    General DP, *ch11Files*
    Wagner-Whitin DP, *ch11Files*
    Silver-Meal Heuristic, *ch11Files*
Knapsack problem, DP, *ch10Files*
Matrix manipulation, *AppenDFiles*
Markov chains
    Absolute probabilities, *ch17Files*
    Absorption probabilities, *ch17Files*
    First passage time, *ch17Files*
    n-step transition matrix, *ch17Files*
    steady-state probabilities, *ch17Files*
Metaheuristics
    tabu ILP, *ch11Files*
    genetic ILP, *ch11Files*
simulated annealing ILP, *ch11Files*
Moving average method, *ch23Files*
Queues,
    Poisson, *ch18Files*
    P-K formula, *ch18Files*
Regression, *ch23Files*
Simulation,
    Monte Carlo (area of a circle), *ch19Files*
    Single server queue, *ch19Files*
    Multi-server queue, *ch19Files*
    Random number generator, *ch19Files*
    Regenerative (cycles) method, *ch19Files*
Statistical tables, "electronic", *ch14Files*
TSP
    metaheuristics. *See* Metaheuristics.
    heuristics. *See* Heuristics.

Solver:
Constrained EOQ inventory model, *ch11Files*
Integer programming B&B, *ch9Files*

Linear programming models
    TOYCO, *ch3Files*
    Reddy Mikks, *ch3Files*
    Sensitivity analysis, *ch3Files*
    Urban renewal, *ch2Files*
Network models
    Maximum flow, *ch6Files*
    Min-cost capacitated network, *ch22Files*
    Shortest route, *ch6Files*
Quadratic programming, *ch21Files*
Stochastic programming, *ch21Files*
Transportation model,

Tora:
Equipment replacement, *ch5Files*
Integer programming models
    B&B, *ch9Files*
    Capital budgeting, *ch9Files*
    Set covering, *ch9Files*
    Fixed Charge, *ch9Files*
    Either-or, *ch9Files*
    TSP cuts, *ch9Files*
Linear programming models
    Bounded variables, *Ch7Files*
    Diet, *ch2Files*
    M-method, *ch3Files*
    Reddy Mikks, *ch2Files*
    Sensitivity analysis, *ch3Files*
    TOYCO, *ch3Files*
Network models
    CPM, *ch6Files*
    Maximum flow, *ch6Files*
    PERT, *ch6Files*
    Shortest route, *ch6Files*
Queuing (Poisson) models, *ch18Files*
Transportation model, *ch5Files*
Zero-sum games, *ch15Files*

What's New in the Ninth Edition

The ninth edition continues to streamline both the text materials and the software support providing a broad focus on algorithmic and practical implementation of Operations Research techniques.

- For the first time in this book, the new Section 3.7 provides a comprehensive (math-free) framework of how the different LP algorithms (simplex, dual simplex, revised simplex, and interior point) are implemented in commercial codes (e.g., CPLEX and XPRESS) to provide the computational speed and accuracy needed to solve very large problems.

- The new Chapter 10 covers efficient heuristics/metaheuristics designed to find good approximate solutions for integer and combinatorial programming problems. The need for heuristics/metaheuristics is in recognition of the fact that the performance of the exact algorithms has been less than satisfactory from the computational standpoint.

- The new Chapter 11 is dedicated to the important traveling salesperson problem. The presentation includes a variety of applications and the development of exact and heuristic solution algorithms.

- All the algorithms in the new Chapters 10 and 11 are coded in Excel in a manner that permits convenient interactive experimentation with the models.

- All detailed AMPL models have been moved to Appendix C to complement the AMPL syntactical rules presented in the appendix. The models are cross-referenced opportunely in the book.

- Numerous new problems have been added throughout the book.

- The TORA software has been updated.

- In keeping with my commitment to maintain a reasonable count of printed pages, I found it necessary to move some material to the website, including the AMPL appendix.

Pearson offers many different products around the world to facilitate learning. In countries outside the United States, some products and services related to this textbook may not be available due to copyright and/or permissions restrictions. If you have questions, you can contact your local office by visiting www.pearsonhighered.com/international or you can contact your local Pearson representative.

Acknowledgments

I wish to acknowledge the importance of the ninth edition reviews provided by Professors Yahya Fathi (NCSU), Marc E. Posner (The Ohio State University), Charu Chandra (University of Michigan, Dearbon), Yasser Hosni (University of Central Florida), M. Jeya Chandra (Penn State University), and Manbir Sodhi (University of Rhode Island).

As always, I remain indebted to my friends and colleagues for their continual support over the years: John Ballard (University of Nebraska, Lincoln), David Elizandro (Tennessee Tech University), Rafael Gutiérrez (University of Texas El Paso), José Pablo Nuño de la Parra (Universidad Popular Autónoma del Estado de Puebla), and Jung-Fa Tsai (National Taipei University of Technology).

I wish to express my appreciation to Pearson's editorial and production personnel for their help during the production of this edition.

HAMDY A. TAHA
hat@uark.edu

About the Author

Hamdy A. Taha is a University Professor Emeritus of Industrial Engineering with the University of Arkansas, where he taught and conducted research in operations research and simulation. He is the author of three other books on integer programming and simulation, and his works have been translated to numerous languages. He is also the author of several book chapters, and his technical articles have appeared in *European Journal of Operations Research, IEEE Transactions on Reliability, IIE Transactions, Interfaces, Management Science, Naval Research Logistics Quarterly, Operations Research*, and *Simulation*.

Professor Taha was the recipient of the Alumni Award for excellence in research and the university-wide Nadine Baum Award for excellence in teaching, both from the University of Arkansas, and numerous other research and teaching awards from the College of Engineering, University of Arkansas. He was also named a Senior Fulbright Scholar to Carlos III University, Madrid, Spain. He is fluent in three languages and has held teaching and consulting positions in Europe, Mexico, and the Middle East.

Trademarks

AMPL is a registered trademark of AMPL Optimization, LLC, 900 Sierra Place SE, Albuquerque, NM 87108-3379, USA.

CPLEX is a registered trademark of ILOG, Inc., IBM Corporation, 1 New Orchard Road, Armonk, New York 10504-1722.

KNITRO is a registered trademark of Ziena Optimization Inc., 1801 Maple Ave, Suite 6320, Evanston, IL 60201.

LOQO is a trademark of Princeton University, Princeton University, Princeton, NJ, 08544.

Microsoft is a registered trademark and Windows and Excel are trademarks of Microsoft Corporation, One Microsoft Way Redmond, WA, 98052-7329.

MINOS is a trademark of Stanford University, 450 Serra Mall, Stanford, CA 94305.

Solver is a trademark of Frontline Systems, Inc., P.O. Box 4288, Incline Village, NV 89450.

TORA is a trademark of Hamdy A. Taha.

Operations Research
An Introduction

CHAPTER 1

What Is Operations Research?

1.1 INTRODUCTION

The first formal activities of Operations Research (OR) were initiated in England during World War II, when a team of British scientists set out to make scientifically based decisions regarding the best utilization of war materiel. After the war, the ideas advanced in military operations were adapted to improve efficiency and productivity in the civilian sector.

This chapter introduces the basic terminology of OR, including mathematical modeling, feasible solutions, optimization, and iterative computations. It stresses that defining the problem correctly is the most important (and most difficult) phase of practicing OR. The chapter also emphasizes that, while mathematical modeling is a cornerstone of OR, unquantifiable factors (such as human behavior) must be accounted for in the final decision. The book presents a variety of applications using solved examples and chapter problems. In particular, Chapter 26 on the website is entirely devoted to the presentation of fully developed case analyses.

1.2 OPERATIONS RESEARCH MODELS

Imagine that you have a 5-week business commitment between Fayetteville (FYV) and Denver (DEN). You fly out of Fayetteville on Mondays and return on Wednesdays. A regular round-trip ticket costs $400, but a 20% discount is granted if the round-trip dates span a weekend. A one-way ticket in either direction costs 75% of the regular price. How should you buy the tickets for the 5 week period?

We can look at the situation as a decision-making problem whose solution requires answering three questions:

1. What are the decision **alternatives?**
2. Under what **restrictions** is the decision made?
3. What is an appropriate **objective criterion** for evaluating the alternatives?

Three plausible alternatives come to mind:

1. Buy five regular FYV-DEN-FYV for departure on Monday and return on Wednesday of the same week.
2. Buy one FYV-DEN, four DEN-FYV-DEN that span weekends, and one DEN-FYV.
3. Buy one FYV-DEN-FYV to cover Monday of the first week and Wednesday of the last week and four DEN-FYV-DEN to cover the remaining legs. All tickets in this alternative span at least one weekend.

The restriction on these options is that you should be able to leave FYV on Monday and return on Wednesday of the same week.

An obvious objective criterion for evaluating the proposed alternative is the price of the tickets. The alternative that yields the smallest cost is the best. Specifically, we have

Alternative 1 cost = 5 × 400 = $2000

Alternative 2 cost = .75 × 400 + 4 × (.8 × 400) + .75 × 400 = $1880

Alternative 3 cost = 5 × (.8 × 400) = **$1600**

Alternative 3 is the best because it is the cheapest.

Though the preceding example illustrates the three main components of an OR model—alternatives, objective criterion, and constraints—situations differ in the details of how each component is developed and how the resulting model is solved. To illustrate this point, consider forming a maximum-area rectangle out of a piece of wire of length L inches. What should be the best width and height of the rectangle?

In contrast with the tickets example, the number of alternatives in the present example is not finite; namely, the width and height of the rectangle can assume an infinite number of values because they are continuous variables. To formalize this observation, the alternatives of the problem are identified by defining the width and height algebraically as

$$w = \text{width of the rectangle in inches}$$
$$h = \text{height of the rectangle in inches}$$

Based on these definitions, the restrictions of the situation can be expressed verbally as

1. Width of rectangle + Height of rectangle = Half the length of the wire
2. Width and height cannot be negative

These restrictions are translated algebraically as

1. $2(w + h) = L$
2. $w \geq 0, h \geq 0$

The only remaining component now is the objective of the problem; namely, maximization of the area of the rectangle. Let z be the area of the rectangle, then the complete model becomes

$$\text{Maximize } z = wh$$

subject to

$$2(w + h) = L$$
$$w, h \geq 0$$

Using differential calculus, the best solution of this model is $w = h = \frac{L}{4}$, which calls for constructing a square shape.

Based on the preceding two examples, the general OR model can be organized in the following general format:

> Maximize or minimize **Objective Function**
>
> subject to
>
> **Constraints**

A solution of the model is **feasible** if it satisfies all the constraints. It is **optimal** if, in addition to being feasible, it yields the best (maximum or minimum) value of the objective function. In the tickets example, the problem considers three feasible alternatives, with the third alternative yielding the optimal solution. In the rectangle problem, a feasible alternative must satisfy the condition $w + h = \frac{L}{2}$, where w and h are nonnegative variables. This definition leads to an infinite number of feasible solutions and, unlike the tickets problem, which uses simple price comparison, the optimum solution is determined by using differential calculus.

Though OR models are designed to "optimize" a specific objective criterion subject to a set of constraints, the quality of the resulting solution depends on the completeness of the model in representing the real system. Take, for example, the tickets model. If *all* the dominant alternatives for purchasing the tickets are not identified, then the resulting solution is optimum only relative to the choices represented in the model. To be specific, if alternative 3 is left out of the model, then the resulting "optimum" solution would call for purchasing the tickets for $1880, which is a **suboptimal** solution. The conclusion is that "the" optimum solution of a model is best only for *that* model. If the model happens to represent the real system reasonably well, then its solution is optimum also for the real situation.

PROBLEM SET 1.2A[1]

1. In the tickets example, identify a fourth feasible alternative.
   (a) Define an infeasible alternative.
   (b) Identify a fourth feasible alternative and determine its cost.
2. In the rectangle problem, identify three feasible solutions, and determine which one is better.
3. Determine the optimal solution of the rectangle problem (*Hint*: Use the constraint to express the objective function in terms of one variable, then use differential calculus.)
4. Amy, Jim, John, and Kelly are standing on the east bank of a river and wish to cross to the west side using a canoe. The canoe can hold at most two people at a time. Amy, being the most athletic, can row across the river in 1 minute. Jim, John, and Kelly would take 3, 6, and 9 minutes, respectively. If two people are in the canoe, the slower person dictates the crossing time. The objective is for all four people to be on the other side of the river in the shortest time possible.
   (a) Identify at least two feasible plans for crossing the river (remember, the canoe is the only mode of transportation, and it cannot be shuttled empty).
   (b) Define the criterion for evaluating the alternatives.
   *(c) What is the smallest time for moving all four people to the other side of the river?
*5. In a baseball game, Jim is the pitcher and Joe is the batter. Suppose that Jim can throw either a fast or a curve ball at random. If Joe correctly predicts a curve ball, he can maintain a .400 batting average, else if Jim throws a curve ball and Joe prepares for a fast ball, his batting average is kept down to .200. On the other hand, if Joe correctly predicts a fast ball, he gets a .250 batting average, else his batting average is only .125.
   (a) Define the alternatives for this situation.
   (b) Define the objective function for the problem, and discuss how it differs from the familiar optimization (maximization or minimization) of a criterion.
6. During the construction of a house, six joists of 24 feet each must be trimmed to the correct length of 23 feet. The operations for cutting a joist involve the following sequence:

Operation	Time (seconds)
1. Place joist on saw horses	15
2. Measure correct length (23 feet)	5
3. Mark cutting line for circular saw	5
4. Trim joist to correct length	20
5. Stack trimmed joist in a designated area	20

Three persons are involved: Two loaders must work simultaneously on operations 1, 2, and 5, and one cutter handles operations 3 and 4. There are two pairs of saw horses on which untrimmed joists are placed in preparation for cutting, and each pair can hold up to three side-by-side joists. Suggest a good schedule for trimming the six joists.

7. An upright symmetrical triangle is divided into four layers: The bottom layer consists of four (equally-spaced) dots, designated as A, B, C, and D. The next layer includes dots E, F,

---

[1]Asterisk designates problems whose solution is given in Appendix B.

and G, and the following layer has dots H and I. The top layer has dot J. You want to invert the triangle (bottom layer has one dot and top layer has four) by moving the dots around as necessary.

(a) Identify two feasible solutions.

(b) Determine the smallest number of moves needed to invert the triangle.[2]

8. You have five chains each consisting of four solid links. You need to make a bracelet by connecting all five chains. It costs 2 cents to break a link and 3 cents to resolder it.

(a) Identify two feasible solutions and evaluate them.

(b) Determine the cheapest cost for making the bracelet.

9. The squares of a rectangular board of 11 rows and 9 columns are numbered sequentially 1 through 99 with a *hidden* monetary reward between 0 and 50 dollars assigned to each square. A game using the board requires the player to choose a square by selecting any two-digits and then subtracting the sum of its two digits from the selected number. The player then receives the reward assigned to the selected square. What monetary values should be assigned to the 99 squares to minimize the player's reward (regardless of how many times the game is repeated)? To make the game interesting, the assignment of $0 to *all* the squares is not an option.

1.3   SOLVING THE OR MODEL

In OR, we do not have a single general technique to solve all mathematical models that can arise in practice. Instead, the type and complexity of the mathematical model dictate the nature of the solution method. For example, in Section 1.2 the solution of the tickets problem requires simple ranking of alternatives based on the total purchasing price, whereas the solution of the rectangle problem utilizes differential calculus to determine the maximum area.

The most prominent OR technique is **linear programming**. It is designed for models with linear objective and constraint functions. Other techniques include **integer programming** (in which the variables assume integer values), **dynamic programming** (in which the original model can be decomposed into smaller more manageable subproblems), **network programming** (in which the problem can be modeled as a network), and **nonlinear programming** (in which functions of the model are nonlinear). These are only a few among many available OR tools.

A peculiarity of most OR techniques is that solutions are not generally obtained in (formula-like) closed forms. Instead, they are determined by **algorithms**. An algorithm provides fixed computational rules that are applied repetitively to the problem, with each repetition (called **iteration**) moving the solution closer to the optimum. Because the computations associated with each iteration are typically tedious and voluminous, it is imperative that these algorithms be executed on the computer.

Some mathematical models may be so complex that it becomes impossible to solve them by any of the available optimization algorithms. In such cases, it may be necessary to abandon the search for the *optimal* solution and simply seek a *good* solution using **heuristics/metaheuristics** or *rules of thumb*.

---

[2]Problems 7 and 8 are adapted from Bruce Goldstein, *Cognitive Psychology: Mind, Research, and Everyday Experience*, Wadsworth Publishing, 2005.

1.4   QUEUING AND SIMULATION MODELS

Queuing and simulation deal with the study of waiting lines. They are not optimization techniques; rather, they determine measures of performance of waiting lines, such as average waiting time in queue, average waiting time for service, and utilization of service facilities.

Queuing models utilize probability and stochastic models to analyze waiting lines, and simulation estimates the measures of performance by imitating the behavior of the real system. In a way, simulation may be regarded as the next best thing to observing a real system. The main difference between queuing and simulation is that queuing models are purely mathematical and hence are subject to specific assumptions that limit their scope of application. Simulation, on the other hand, is flexible and can be used to analyze practically any queuing situation.

The use of simulation is not without drawbacks. The process of developing simulation models is costly in both time and resources. Moreover, the execution of simulation models, even on the fastest computer, is usually slow.

1.5   ART OF MODELING

The illustrative models developed in Section 1.1 are exact representations of real situations. This is a rare occurrence in OR, as the majority of applications usually involve (varying degrees of) approximations. Figure 1.1 depicts the levels of abstraction that characterize the development of an OR model. We abstract the assumed real world from the real situation by concentrating on the dominant variables that control the behavior of the real system. The model expresses in an amenable manner the mathematical functions that represent the behavior of the assumed real world.

To illustrate levels of abstraction in modeling, consider the Tyko Manufacturing Company, where a variety of plastic containers are produced. When a production order is issued to the production department, necessary raw materials are acquired

FIGURE 1.1

Levels of abstraction in model development

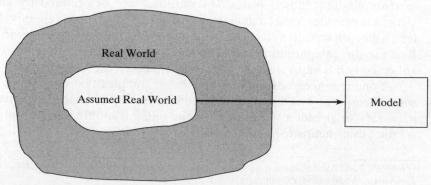

from the company's stocks or purchased from outside sources. Once the production batch is completed, the sales department takes charge of distributing the product to customers.

A viable question in the analysis of Tyko's situation is the determination of the size of a production batch. How can this situation be represented by a model?

Looking at the overall system, a number of variables can bear directly on the level of production, including the following (partial) list categorized by departments.

1. *Production Department*: Production capacity expressed in terms of available machine and labor hours, in-process inventory, and quality control standards.
2. *Materials Department*: Available stock of raw materials, delivery schedules from outside sources, and storage limitations.
3. *Sales Department*: Sales forecast, capacity of distribution facilities, effectiveness of the advertising campaign, and effect of competition.

Each of these variables affects the level of production at Tyko. Trying to establish explicit functional relationships between them and the level of production is a difficult task indeed.

A first level of abstraction requires defining the boundaries of the assumed real world. With some reflection, we can approximate the real system by two dominant parameters:

1. Production rate.
2. Consumption rate.

Determination of the production rate involves such data as production capacity, quality control standards, and availability of raw materials. The consumption rate is determined from the sales data. In essence, simplification from the real world to the assumed real world is achieved by "lumping" several real-world parameters into a single assumed-real-world parameter.

It is easier now to abstract a model from the assumed real world. From the production and consumption rates, measures of excess or shortage inventory can be established. The abstracted model may then be constructed to balance the conflicting costs of excess and shortage inventory—that is, to minimize the total cost of inventory.

1.6 MORE THAN JUST MATHEMATICS

Because of the mathematical nature of OR models, one tends to think that an OR study is *always* rooted in mathematical analysis. Though mathematical modeling is a cornerstone of OR, simpler approaches should be explored first. In some cases, a "commonsense" solution may be reached through simple observations. Indeed, since the human element invariably affects most decision problems, a study of the psychology of people may be key to solving the problem. Three illustrations are presented here to support this argument.

1. Responding to complaints of slow elevator service in a large office building, the OR team initially perceived the situation as a waiting-line problem that might require the use of mathematical queuing analysis or simulation. After studying the behavior of the people voicing the complaint, the psychologist on the team suggested installing full-length mirrors at the entrance to the elevators. Miraculously the complaints disappeared, as people were kept occupied watching themselves and others while waiting for the elevator.

2. In a study of the check-in counters at a large British airport, a U.S.–Canadian consulting team used queuing theory to investigate and analyze the situation. Part of the solution recommended the use of well-placed signs to urge passengers who were within 20 minutes from departure time to advance to the head of the queue and request immediate service. The solution was not successful because the passengers, being mostly British, were "conditioned to very strict queuing behavior" and hence were reluctant to move ahead of others waiting in the queue.

3. In a steel mill in India, ingots were first produced from iron ore and then used in the manufacture of steel bars and beams. The manager noticed a long delay between the ingots production and their transfer to the next manufacturing phase (where end products were manufactured). Ideally, to reduce the reheating cost, manufacturing should start soon after the ingots leave the furnaces. Initially the problem was perceived as a line-balancing situation, which could be resolved either by reducing the output of ingots or by increasing the capacity of the manufacturing process. The OR team used simple charts to summarize the output of the furnaces during the three shifts of the day. They discovered that, even though the third shift started at 11:00 P.M., most of the ingots were produced between 2:00 and 7:00 A.M. Further investigation revealed that third-shift operators preferred to get long periods of rest at the start of the shift and then make up for lost production during morning hours. The problem was solved by "leveling out" the production of ingots throughout the shift.

Three conclusions can be drawn from these illustrations:

1. Before embarking on sophisticated mathematical modeling, the OR team should explore the possibility of using "aggressive" ideas to resolve the situation. The solution of the elevator problem by installing mirrors is rooted in human psychology rather than in mathematical modeling. It is also simpler and less costly than any recommendation a mathematical model might have produced. Perhaps this is the reason OR teams usually include the expertise of "outsiders" from nonmathematical fields (psychology in the case of the elevator problem). This point was recognized and implemented by the first OR team in Britain during World War II.

2. Solutions are rooted in people and not in technology. Any solution that does not take human behavior into account is apt to fail. Even though the mathematical solution of the British airport problem may have been sound, the fact that the consulting team was not aware of the cultural differences between the United States and Britain (Americans and Canadians tend to be less formal) resulted in an unimplementable recommendation.

3. An OR study should not start with a bias toward using a specific mathematical tool before the use of the tool is rationally justified. For example, because linear programming is a successful technique, there is a tendency to use it as the tool of choice for modeling "any" situation. Such an approach usually leads to a mathematical model that is far removed from the real situation. It is thus imperative that we first analyze available data, using the simplest techniques where possible (e.g., averages, charts, and histograms), with the objective of pinpointing the source of the problem. Once the problem is defined, a decision can be made regarding the most appropriate tool for the solution.[3] In the steel mill problem, simple charting of the ingots production was all that was needed to clarify the situation.

1.7   PHASES OF AN OR STUDY

OR studies are rooted in *teamwork*, where the OR analysts and the client work side by side. The OR analysts' expertise in modeling must be complemented by the experience and cooperation of the client for whom the study is being carried out.

As a decision-making tool, OR is both a science and an art. It is a science by virtue of the mathematical techniques it embodies, and it is an art because the success of the phases leading to the solution of the mathematical model depends largely on the creativity and experience of the OR team. Willemain (1994) advises that "effective [OR] practice requires more than analytical competence: It also requires, among other attributes, technical judgment (e.g., when and how to use a given technique) and skills in communication and organizational survival."

It is difficult to prescribe specific courses of action (similar to those dictated by the precise theory of most mathematical models) for these intangible factors. We can, however, offer general guidelines for the implementation of OR in practice.

The principal phases for implementing OR in practice include the following:

1. Definition of the problem.
2. Construction of the model.
3. Solution of the model.
4. Validation of the model.
5. Implementation of the solution.

---

[3]Deciding on a specific mathematical model before justifying its use is like "putting the cart before the horse," and it reminds me of the story of a frequent air traveler who was paranoid about the possibility of a terrorist bomb on board the plane. He calculated the probability that such a misfortune could occur, and though quite small, it wasn't small enough to calm his anxieties. From then on, he always carried a bomb in his briefcase on the plane because, according to his calculations, the probability of having *two* bombs aboard the plane was practically zero!

Phase 3, dealing with *model solution*, is the best defined and generally the easiest to implement in an OR study, because it deals mostly with precise mathematical models. Implementation of the remaining phases is more an art than a theory.

Problem definition involves defining the scope of the problem under investigation. This function should be carried out by the entire OR team. The aim is to identify three principal elements of the decision problem: (1) description of the decision alternatives, (2) determination of the objective of the study, and (3) specification of the limitations under which the modeled system operates.

Model construction entails an attempt to translate the problem definition into mathematical relationships. If the resulting model fits one of the standard mathematical models, such as linear programming, we can usually reach a solution by using available algorithms. Alternatively, if the mathematical relationships are too complex to allow the determination of an analytic solution, the OR team may opt to simplify the model and use a heuristic approach, or the team may consider the use of simulation, if appropriate. In some cases, a mathematical, simulation, and heuristic models may be combined to solve the decision problem, as the case analyses in Chapter 26 on the website demonstrate.

Model solution is by far the simplest of all OR phases because it entails the use of well-defined optimization algorithms. An important aspect of the model solution phase is *sensitivity analysis*. It deals with obtaining additional information about the behavior of the optimum solution when the model undergoes some parameter changes. Sensitivity analysis is particularly needed when the parameters of the model cannot be estimated accurately. In these cases, it is important to study the behavior of the optimum solution in the neighborhood of the estimated parameters.

Model validity checks whether or not the proposed model does what it purports to do—that is, does it predict adequately the behavior of the system under study? Initially, the OR team should be convinced that the model's output does not include "surprises." In other words, does the solution make sense? Are the results intuitively acceptable? On the formal side, a common method for checking the validity of a model is to compare its output with historical output data. The model is valid if, under similar input conditions, it reasonably duplicates past performance. Generally, however, there is no assurance that future performance will continue to duplicate past behavior. Also, because the model is usually based on careful examination of past data, the proposed comparison is usually favorable. If the proposed model represents a new (nonexisting) system, no historical data would be available. In such cases, we may use simulation as an independent tool for verifying the output of the mathematical model.

Implementation of the solution of a validated model involves the translation of the results into understandable operating instructions to be issued to the people who will administer the recommended system. The burden of this task lies primarily with the OR team.

1.8   ABOUT THIS BOOK

Morris (1967) states that "the teaching of models is not equivalent to the teaching of modeling." I have taken note of this important statement during the preparation of the ninth edition, making every effort to introduce the art of modeling in OR by including realistic models throughout the book. Because of the importance of computations in OR, the book discusses how the theoretical algorithms fit in commercial computer codes (see Section 3.7). It also presents extensive tools for carrying out the computational task, ranging from tutorial-oriented TORA to the commercial packages Excel, Excel Solver, and AMPL.

OR is both an art and a science—the art of describing and modeling the problem and the science of solving the model using (precise) mathematical algorithms. A first course in the subject should give the student an appreciation of the importance of both areas. This will provide OR users with the kind of confidence that normally would be lacking if training is dedicated solely to the art aspect of OR, under the guise that computers can relieve the user from the need to *understand* why the solution algorithms work.

Modeling and computational capabilities can be enhanced by studying published practical cases. To assist you in this regard, Chapter 26 on the website includes 15 fully developed and analyzed cases that cover most of the OR models presented in this book. There are also some 50 cases that are based on real-life applications in Appendix E on the Website. Additional case studies are available in journals and publications. In particular, *Interfaces* (published by INFORMS) is a rich source of diverse OR applications.

BIBLIOGRAPHY

Altier, W., *The Thinking Manager's Toolbox: Effective Processes for Problem Solving and Decision Making*, Oxford University Press, New York, 1999.

Checkland, P., *Systems Thinking, System Practice,* Wiley, New York, 1999.

Evans, J., *Creative Thinking in the Decision and Management Sciences*, South-Western Publishing, Cincinnati, 1991.

Gass, S., "Model World: Danger, Beware the User as a Modeler," *Interfaces*, Vol. 20, No. 3, pp. 60–64, 1990.

Morris, W., "On the Art of Modeling," *Management Science*, Vol. 13, pp. B707–B717, 1967.

Paulos, J., *Innumeracy: Mathematical Illiteracy and Its Consequences*, Hill and Wang, New York, 1988.

Singh, S., *Fermat's Enigma*, Walker, New York, 1997.

Willemain, T., "Insights on Modeling from a Dozen Experts," *Operations Research*, Vol. 42, No. 2, pp. 213–222, 1994.

CHAPTER 2

Modeling with Linear Programming

Real-Life Application—Frontier Airlines Purchases Fuel Economically

The fueling of an aircraft can take place at any of the stopovers along a flight route. Fuel price varies among the stopovers, and potential savings can be realized by tankering (loading) extra fuel at a cheaper location for use on subsequent flight legs. The disadvantage is that the extra weight of tankered fuel will result in higher burn of gasoline. Linear programming (LP) and heuristics are used to determine the optimum amount of tankering that balances the cost of excess burn against the savings in fuel cost. The study, carried out in 1981, resulted in net savings of about $350,000 per year. Case 1 in Chapter 26 on the website provides the details of the study. Interestingly, with the recent rise in the cost of fuel, many airlines are now using LP-based tankering software to purchase fuel.

2.1 TWO-VARIABLE LP MODEL

This section deals with the graphical solution of a two-variable LP. Though two-variable problems hardly exist in practice, the treatment provides concrete foundations for the development of the general simplex algorithm presented in Chapter 3.

Example 2.1-1 (The Reddy Mikks Company)

Reddy Mikks produces both interior and exterior paints from two raw materials, $M1$ and $M2$. The following table provides the basic data of the problem:

	Tons of raw material per ton of		Maximum daily availability (tons)
	Exterior paint	*Interior paint*	
Raw material, $M1$	6	4	24
Raw material, $M2$	1	2	6
Profit per ton ($1000)	5	4	

A market survey indicates that the daily demand for interior paint cannot exceed that for exterior paint by more than 1 ton. Also, the maximum daily demand for interior paint is 2 tons.

Reddy Mikks wants to determine the optimum (best) product mix of interior and exterior paints that maximizes the total daily profit.

All OR models, LP included, consist of three basic components.

1. Decision **variables** that we seek to determine.
2. **Objective** (goal) that we need to optimize (maximize or minimize).
3. **Constraints** that the solution must satisfy.

The proper definition of the decision variables is an essential first step in the development of the model. Once done, the task of constructing the objective function and the constraints becomes more straightforward.

For the Reddy Mikks problem, we need to determine the daily amounts to be produced of exterior and interior paints. Thus the variables of the model are defined as

$$x_1 = \text{Tons produced daily of exterior paint}$$

$$x_2 = \text{Tons produced daily of interior paint}$$

The goal of Reddy Mikks is to *maximize* (i.e., increase as much as possible) the total daily profit of both paints. The two components of the total daily profit are expressed in terms of the variables x_1 and x_2 as:

$$\text{Profit from exterior paint} = 5x_1 \text{ (thousand) dollars}$$

$$\text{Profit from interior paint} = 4x_2 \text{ (thousand) dollars}$$

Letting z represent the total daily profit (in thousands of dollars), the objective (or goal) of Reddy Mikks is expressed as

$$\text{Maximize } z = 5x_1 + 4x_2$$

Next, we construct the constraints that restrict raw material usage and product demand. The raw material restrictions are expressed verbally as

$$\left(\begin{array}{c} \text{Usage of a raw material} \\ \text{by both paints} \end{array} \right) \leq \left(\begin{array}{c} \text{Maximum raw material} \\ \text{availability} \end{array} \right)$$

The daily usage of raw material $M1$ is 6 tons per ton of exterior paint and 4 tons per ton of interior paint. Thus

$$\text{Usage of raw material } M1 \text{ by both paints } = 6x_1 + 4x_2 \text{ tons/day}$$

In a similar manner,

$$\text{Usage of raw material } M2 \text{ by both paints } = 1x_1 + 2x_2 \text{ tons/day}$$

The maximum daily availabilities of raw materials $M1$ and $M2$ are 24 and 6 tons, respectively. Thus, the raw material constraints are

$$6x_1 + 4x_2 \leq 24 \quad \text{(Raw material } M1\text{)}$$

$$x_1 + 2x_2 \leq 6 \quad \text{(Raw material } M2\text{)}$$

The first restriction on product demand stipulates that the daily production of interior paint cannot exceed that of exterior paint by more than 1 ton, which translates to

$$x_2 - x_1 \leq 1 \quad \text{(Market limit)}$$

The second restriction limits the daily demand of interior paint to 2 tons—that is,

$$x_2 \leq 2 \quad \text{(Demand limit)}$$

An implicit (or "understood-to-be") restriction requires all the variables, x_1 and x_2, to assume zero or positive values only. The restrictions, expressed as $x_1 \geq 0$ and $x_2 \geq 0$, are referred to as **nonnegativity constraints**.

The complete Reddy Mikks model is

$$\text{Maximize } z = 5x_1 + 4x_2$$

subject to

$$
\begin{align*}
6x_1 + 4x_2 &\leq 24 & (1)\\
x_1 + 2x_2 &\leq 6 & (2)\\
-x_1 + x_2 &\leq 1 & (3)\\
x_2 &\leq 2 & (4)\\
x_1, x_2 &\geq 0 & (5)
\end{align*}
$$

Any values of x_1 and x_2 that satisfy *all* five constraints constitute a **feasible solution**. Otherwise, the solution is **infeasible**. For example, the solution, $x_1 = 3$ tons per day and $x_2 = 1$ ton per day, is feasible because it does not violate *any* of the five constraints. This result is confirmed by using the substitution $(x_1 = 3, x_2 = 1)$ in the left-hand side of each constraint. In constraint (1), we have $6x_1 + 4x_2 = 6 \times 3 + 4 \times 1 = 22$, which is less than the right-hand side of the constraint ($= 24$). Constraints 2 to 5 are checked in a similar manner (verify!). On the other hand, the solution $x_1 = 4$ and $x_2 = 1$ is infeasible because it does not satisfy at least one constraint. For example, in constraint (1), $6 \times 4 + 4 \times 1 = 28$, which is larger than the right-hand side ($= 24$).

The goal of the problem is to find the **optimum**, the best *feasible* solution that maximizes the total profit z. We first use the graphical method (presented in Section 2.2) to show that the Reddy Mikks problem has an *infinite* number of feasible solutions, a property that is shared by all nontrivial LPs. This means that the problem cannot be solved by enumeration. Instead, we need an algorithm that finds the optimum in a finite number of steps. The graphical method in Section 2.2 and its algebraic generalization in Chapter 3 explain the details of the desired algorithm.

Remarks.   The objective and the constraint function in all LPs must be linear. Additionally, all the parameters (coefficients of the objective and constraint functions) of the model are known with certainty.

PROBLEM SET 2.1A

1. For the Reddy Mikks model, construct each of the following constraints, and express it with a linear left-hand side and a constant right-hand side:

   *(a) The daily demand for interior paint exceeds that of exterior paint by *at least* 1 ton.

   (b) The daily usage of raw material $M1$ in tons is *at most* 8 and *at least* 5.

*(c) The demand for exterior paint cannot be less than the demand for interior paint.

(d) The maximum quantity that should be produced of both the interior and the exterior paint is 15 tons.

*(e) The proportion of exterior paint to the total production of both interior and exterior paints must not exceed .5.

2. Determine the best *feasible* solution among the following (feasible and infeasible) solutions of the Reddy Mikks model:

   (a) $x_1 = 1, x_2 = 2$.

   (b) $x_1 = 3, x_2 = 1$.

   (c) $x_1 = 3, x_2 = 1.5$.

   (d) $x_1 = 2, x_2 = 1$.

   (e) $x_1 = 2, x_2 = -1$.

*3. For the feasible solution $x_1 = 1, x_2 = 2$ of the Reddy Mikks model, determine the unused amounts of raw materials $M1$ and $M2$.

4. Suppose that Reddy Mikks sells its exterior paint to a single wholesaler at a quantity discount. The profit per ton is $5000 if the contractor buys no more than 5 tons daily and $4300 otherwise. Express the objective function mathematically. Is the resulting function linear?

2.2   GRAPHICAL LP SOLUTION[1]

The graphical solution includes two steps:

1. Determination of the feasible solution space.
2. Determination of the optimum solution from among all the points in the solution space.

The presentation uses two examples to show how maximization and minimization objective functions are handled.

2.2.1   Solution of a Maximization Model

Example 2.2-1

This example solves the Reddy Mikks model of Example 2.1-1.

Step 1.   *Determination of the Feasible Solution Space*:
First, consider the nonnegativity constraints $x_1 \geq 0$ and $x_2 \geq 0$. In Figure 2.1, the horizontal axis x_1 and the vertical axis x_2 represent the exterior- and interior-paint variables, respectively. Thus, the nonnegativity constraints restrict the variables to the first quadrant (above the x_1-axis and to the right of the x_2-axis).

---

[1]The graphical solution of a two-variable LP, though hardly useful in practice, provides ideas that are crucial for understanding the general algebraic simplex method presented in Chapter 3. TORA interactive graphical module is especially helpful in experimenting with the graphical method. Section 2.3 introduces the commercial packages Excel Solver and AMPL. Their use is demonstrated by diverse practical LP applications in Section 2.4.

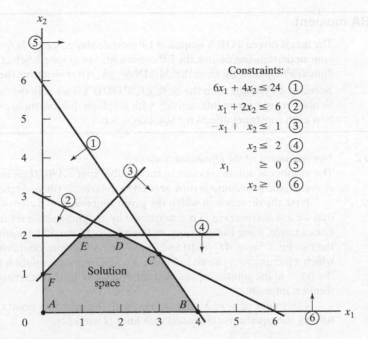

Constraints:

$$6x_1 + 4x_2 \leq 24 \quad ①$$
$$x_1 + 2x_2 \leq 6 \quad ②$$
$$-x_1 + x_2 \leq 1 \quad ③$$
$$x_2 \leq 2 \quad ④$$
$$x_1 \geq 0 \quad ⑤$$
$$x_2 \geq 0 \quad ⑥$$

FIGURE 2.1

Feasible space of the Reddy Mikks model

To account for the remaining four constraints, first replace each inequality with an equation, and then graph the resulting straight line by locating two distinct points. For example, after replacing $6x_1 + 4x_2 \leq 24$ with the straight line $6x_1 + 4x_2 = 24$, two distinct points are determined by setting $x_1 = 0$ to obtain $x_2 = \frac{24}{4} = 6$ and then by setting $x_2 = 0$ to obtain $x_1 = \frac{24}{6} = 4$. Thus the line $6x_1 + 4x_2 = 24$ passes through $(0, 6)$ and $(4, 0)$, as shown by line (1) in Figure 2.1.

Next, consider the effect of the inequality. It divides the (x_1, x_2)-plane into two half-spaces, one on each side of the graphed line. Only one of these two halves satisfies the inequality. To determine the correct side, choose $(0, 0)$ as a *reference point*. If $(0, 0)$ satisfies the inequality, then the side in which it lies is the feasible half-space; otherwise, the other side is. The use of the reference point $(0, 0)$ is illustrated with the constraint $6x_1 + 4x_2 \leq 24$. Because $6 \times 0 + 4 \times 0 = 0$ is less than 24, the half-space representing inequality (1) includes the origin (as the direction of the arrow in Figure 2.1 shows).

It is convenient computationally to select $(0, 0)$ as the reference point because it always renders a zero value for the left-hand side of the constraint. However, if the line happens to pass through the origin, then any other point not lying on the line can be used as a reference point.

Application of the reference-point procedure to all the constraints of the model produces the constraints shown in Figure 2.1 (verify!). The **feasible solution space** is the area in the first quadrant that satisfies all constraints simultaneously. In Figure 2.1, all points in or on the boundary of the area $ABCDEF$ define the feasible solution space. All points outside this area are infeasible.

TORA moment.

The menu-driven TORA graphical LP module should prove helpful in reinforcing your understanding of how the LP constraints are graphed. Select `Linear Programming` from the `MAIN menu`. After inputting the model, select `Solve ⇒ Graphical` from the `SOLVE/MODIFY` menu. In the output screen, you will be able to experiment interactively with graphing the constraints, one at a time, to see how each constraint affects the solution space.

Step 2. *Determination of the Optimum Solution*:

The number of solution points in the feasible space $ABCDEF$ in Figure 2.1 is *infinite*. A systematic procedure is thus needed to determine the optimum solution.

First, the direction in which the profit function $z = 5x_1 + 4x_2$ increases (recall that we are *maximizing z*) is determined by assigning arbitrary *increasing* values to z. For example, using (arbitrary) $z = 10$ and $z = 15$ would be equivalent to graphing the two lines $5x_1 + 4x_2 = 10$ and $5x_1 + 4x_2 = 15$, thus identifying the direction in which z increases, as shown in Figure 2.2. The optimum solution occurs at C, which is the point in the solution space beyond which any further increase will render the solution infeasible.

The values of x_1 and x_2 associated with the optimum point C are determined by solving the equations associated with lines (1) and (2):

$$6x_1 + 4x_2 = 24$$
$$x_1 + 2x_2 = 6$$

FIGURE 2.2

Optimum solution of the Reddy Mikks model

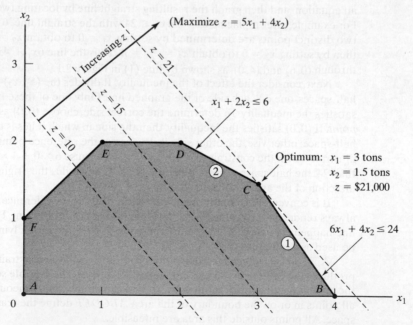

The solution is $x_1 = 3$ and $x_2 = 1.5$ with $z = 5 \times 3 + 4 \times 1.5 = 21$. This calls for a daily product mix of 3 tons of exterior paint and 1.5 tons of interior paint. The associated daily profit is \$21,000.

An important characteristic of the optimum LP solution is that it is *always* associated with a **corner point** of the solution space (where, in two dimensions, two lines intersect). This is true even if the objective function is parallel to a constraint. For example, if the objective function is $z = 6x_1 + 4x_2$, which is parallel to constraint 1, we can always say that the optimum occurs at either corner point B or C. Actually any point on the line segment BC will be an *alternative* optimum (see also Example 3.5-2), but the important observation here is that the line segment BC is totally defined by the *corner points B and C.*

TORA moment.

You can use TORA interactively to see that the optimum is always associated with a corner point. From the output screen, you can click ⟨View/Modify Input Data⟩ to modify the objective coefficients and re-solve the problem graphically. You may use the following objective functions to test the proposed idea:

(a) $z = 5x_1 + x_2$
(b) $z = 5x_1 + 4x_2$
(c) $z = x_1 + 3x_2$
(d) $z = -x_1 + 2x_2$
(e) $z = -2x_1 + x_2$
(f) $z = -x_1 - x_2$

The remarkable observation that the LP optimum is always associated with a corner point indicates that the search for the optimum can be limited to a finite (rather than infinite) number of points. Indeed, in this small example, the optimum solution can be found simply by enumerating all the corner points, as the following table shows:

Corner point	(x_1, x_2)	z
A	(0, 0)	0
B	(4, 0)	20
C	(3, 1.5)	21 (OPTIMUM)
D	(2, 2)	18
E	(1, 2)	13
F	(0, 1)	4

As the number of constraints and variables increases, the number of corner points also increases, and the proposed enumeration procedure becomes computationally impractical. Nevertheless, the observation regarding the role of the corner points in identifying the optimum is key to the development of the general algebraic algorithm, called the *simplex method*, which we will study in Chapter 3.

PROBLEM SET 2.2A

1. Determine the feasible space for each of the following independent constraints, given that $x_1, x_2 \geq 0$.

   *(a) $-3x_1 + x_2 \geq 6$

   (b) $x_1 - 2x_2 \leq 5$

   (c) $2x_1 - 3x_2 \geq 12$

   (d) $x_1 - x_2 \leq 0$

   *(e) $-x_1 + x_2 \geq 0$

2. Identify the direction of increase in z in each of the following cases:

   *(a) Maximize $z = x_1 - x_2$

   (b) Maximize $z = -8x_1 - 3x_2$

   (c) Maximize $z = -x_1 + 3x_2$

   *(d) Maximize $z = -3x_1 + x_2$

3. Determine the solution space and the optimum solution of the Reddy Mikks model for each of the following independent changes:

   (a) The maximum daily demand for interior paint is 1.9 tons and that for exterior paint is at most 2.5 tons.

   (b) The daily demand for interior paint is at least 2.5 tons.

   (c) The daily demand for interior paint is exactly 1 ton higher than that for exterior paint.

   (d) The daily availability of raw material $M1$ is at least 24 tons.

   (e) The daily availability of raw material $M1$ is at least 24 tons, and the daily demand for interior paint exceeds that for exterior paint by at least 1 ton.

4. A company that operates 10 hours a day manufactures two products on three sequential processes. The following table summarizes the data of the problem:

Product	Minutes per unit			Unit profit
	Process 1	*Process 2*	*Process 3*	
1	10	6	8	$20
2	5	20	10	$30

Determine the optimal mix of the two products.

*5. A company produces two products, A and B. The sales volume for A is at least 80% of the total sales of both A and B. However, the company cannot sell more than 110 units of A per day. Both products use one raw material, of which the maximum daily availability is 240 lb. The usage rates of the raw material are 2 lb per unit of A and 4 lb per unit of B. The profit units for A and B are $10 and $25, respectively. Determine the optimal product mix for the company.

6. Alumco manufactures aluminum sheets and aluminum bars. The maximum production capacity is estimated at either 800 sheets or 600 bars per day. The maximum daily demand is 550 sheets and 560 bars. The profit per ton is $40 per sheet and $35 per bar. Determine the optimal daily production mix.

*7. An individual wishes to invest $5000 over the next year in two types of investment: Investment A yields 5% and investment B yields 8%. Market research recommends an allocation of at least 25% in A and at most 50% in B. Moreover, investment in A should be at least half the investment in B. How should the fund be allocated to the two investments?

8. The Continuing Education Division at the Ozark Community College offers a total of 30 courses each semester. The courses offered are usually of two types: practical and humanistic. To satisfy the demands of the community, at least 10 courses of each type must be offered each semester. The division estimates that the revenues of offering practical and humanistic courses are approximately $1500 and $1000 per course, respectively.

   (a) Devise an optimal course offering for the college.

   (b) Show that the worth per additional course is $1500, which is the same as the revenue per practical course. What does this result mean in terms of offering additional courses?

9. ChemLabs uses raw materials I and II to produce two domestic cleaning solutions, A and B. The daily availabilities of raw materials I and II are 150 and 145 units, respectively. One unit of solution A consumes .5 unit of raw material I and .6 unit of raw material II, and one unit of solution B uses .5 unit of raw material I and .4 unit of raw material II. The profits per unit of solutions A and B are $8 and $10, respectively. The daily demand for solution A lies between 30 and 150 units and that for solution B between 40 and 200 units. Find the optimal production amounts of A and B.

10. In the Ma-and-Pa grocery store, shelf space is limited and must be used effectively to increase profit. Two cereal items, Grano and Wheatie, compete for a total shelf space of 60 ft^2. A box of Grano occupies .2 ft^2 and a box of Wheatie needs .4 ft^2. The maximum daily demands of Grano and Wheatie are 200 and 120 boxes, respectively. A box of Grano nets $1.00 in profit and a box of Wheatie $1.35. Ma-and-Pa thinks that because the unit profit of Wheatie is 35% higher than that of Grano, Wheatie should be allocated 35% more space than Grano, which amounts to allocating about 57% to Wheatie and 43% to Grano. What do you think?

11. Jack is an aspiring freshman at Ulern University. He realizes that "all work and no play make Jack a dull boy." Jack wants to apportion his available time of about 10 hours a day between work and play. He estimates that play is twice as much fun as work. He also wants to study at least as much as he plays. However, Jack realizes that if he is going to get all his homework assignments done, he cannot play more than 4 hours a day. How should Jack allocate his time to maximize his pleasure from both work and play?

12. Wild West produces two types of cowboy hats. A Type 1 hat requires twice as much labor time as a Type 2. If all the available labor time is dedicated to Type 2 alone, the company can produce a total of 400 Type 2 hats a day. The respective market limits for Type 1 and Type 2 are 150 and 200 hats per day, respectively. The profit is $8 per Type 1 hat and $5 per Type 2 hat. Determine the number of hats of each type that maximizes profit.

13. Show & Sell can advertise its products on local radio and television (TV). The advertising budget is limited to $10,000 a month. Each minute of radio advertising costs $15 and each minute of TV commercials $300. Show & Sell likes to advertise on radio at least twice as much as on TV. In the meantime, it is not practical to use more than 400 minutes of radio advertising a month. From past experience, advertising on TV is estimated to be 25 times as effective as on radio. Determine the optimum allocation of the budget to radio and TV advertising.

*14. Wyoming Electric Coop owns a steam-turbine power-generating plant. Because Wyoming is rich in coal deposits, the plant generates its steam from coal. This, however, may result in emission that does not meet the Environmental Protection Agency (EPA) standards. EPA regulations limit sulfur dioxide discharge to 2000 parts per million per ton of coal burned and smoke discharge from the plant stacks to 20 lb per hour. The Coop receives two grades of pulverized coal, $C1$ and $C2$, for use in the steam plant. The two grades are usually mixed together before burning. For simplicity, it can be assumed that the amount of sulfur pollutant discharged (in parts per million) is a weighted average of the proportion of each grade used in the mixture. The following data are based on consumption of 1 ton per hour of each of the two coal grades.

Coal grade	Sulfur discharge in parts per million	Smoke discharge in lb per hour	Steam generated in lb per hour
C1	1800	2.1	12,000
C2	2100	.9	9000

(a) Determine the optimal ratio for mixing the two coal grades.

(b) Determine the effect of relaxing the smoke discharge limit by 1 lb on the amount of generated steam per hour.

15. Top Toys is planning a new radio and TV advertising campaign. A radio commercial costs $300 and a TV ad costs $2000. A total budget of $20,000 is allocated to the campaign. However, to ensure that each medium will have at least one radio commercial and one TV ad, the most that can be allocated to either medium cannot exceed 80% of the total budget. It is estimated that the first radio commercial will reach 5000 people, with each additional commercial reaching only 2000 new ones. For TV, the first ad will reach 4500 people and each additional ad an additional 3000. How should the budgeted amount be allocated between radio and TV?

16. The Burroughs Garment Company manufactures men's shirts and women's blouses for Walmark Discount Stores. Walmark will accept all the production supplied by Burroughs. The production process includes cutting, sewing, and packaging. Burroughs employs 25 workers in the cutting department, 35 in the sewing department, and 5 in the packaging department. The factory works one 8-hour shift, 5 days a week. The following table gives the time requirements and profits per unit for the two garments:

Garment	Minutes per unit			Unit profit ($)
	Cutting	*Sewing*	*Packaging*	
Shirts	20	70	12	8
Blouses	60	60	4	12

Determine the optimal weekly production schedule for Burroughs.

17. A furniture company manufactures desks and chairs. The sawing department cuts the lumber for both products, which is then sent to separate assembly departments. Assembled items are sent for finishing to the painting department. The daily capacity of the sawing department is 200 chairs or 80 desks. The chair assembly department can produce 120 chairs daily and the desk assembly department 60 desks daily. The paint department has a daily capacity of either 150 chairs or 110 desks. Given that the profit per chair is $50 and that of a desk is $100, determine the optimal production mix for the company.

*18. An assembly line consisting of three consecutive stations produces two radio models: HiFi-1 and HiFi-2. The following table provides the assembly times for the three workstations.

	Minutes per unit	
Workstation	*HiFi-1*	*HiFi-2*
1	6	4
2	5	5
3	4	6

The daily maintenance for stations 1, 2, and 3 consumes 10%, 14%, and 12%, respectively, of the maximum 480 minutes available for each station each day. Determine the optimal product mix that will minimize the idle (or unused) times in the three workstations.

19. *TORA Experiment.* Enter the following LP into TORA, and select the graphic solution mode to reveal the LP graphic screen.

$$\text{Minimize } z = 3x_1 + 8x_2$$

subject to

$$
\begin{aligned}
x_1 + x_2 &\geq 8 \\
2x_1 - 3x_2 &\leq 0 \\
x_1 + 2x_2 &\leq 30 \\
3x_1 - x_2 &\geq 0 \\
x_1 &\leq 10 \\
x_2 &\geq 9 \\
x_1, x_2 &\geq 0
\end{aligned}
$$

Next, on a sheet of paper, graph and scale the x_1- and x_2-axes for the problem (you may also click Print Graph on the top of the right window to obtain a ready-to-use scaled sheet). Now, graph a constraint manually on the prepared sheet, then click it on the left window of the screen to check your answer. Repeat the same for each constraint, and then terminate the procedure with a graph of the objective function. The suggested process is designed to test and reinforce your understanding of the graphical LP solution through immediate feedback from TORA.

20. *TORA Experiment.* Consider the following LP model:

$$\text{Maximize } z = 5x_1 + 4x_2$$

subject to

$$
\begin{aligned}
6x_1 + 4x_2 &\leq 24 \\
6x_1 + 3x_2 &\leq 22.5 \\
x_1 + x_2 &\leq 5 \\
x_1 + 2x_2 &\leq 6 \\
-x_1 + x_2 &\leq 1 \\
x_2 &\leq 2 \\
x_1, x_2 &\geq 0
\end{aligned}
$$

In LP, a constraint is said to be *redundant* if its removal from the model leaves the feasible solution space unchanged. Use the graphical facility of TORA to identify the redundant constraints, then show that their removal (simply by not graphing them) does not affect the solution space or the optimal solution.

21. *TORA Experiment.* In the Reddy Mikks model, use TORA to show that the removal of the raw material constraints (constraints 1 and 2) would result in an *unbounded solution space*. What can be said in this case about the optimal solution of the model?

22. *TORA Experiment.* In the Reddy Mikks model, suppose that the following constraint is added to the problem.

$$x_2 \geq 3$$

Use TORA to show that the resulting model has conflicting constraints that cannot be satisfied simultaneously and hence it has *no feasible solution*.

2.2.2 Solution of a Minimization Model

Example 2.2-2   (Diet Problem)

Ozark Farms uses at least 800 lb of special feed daily. The special feed is a mixture of corn and soybean meal with the following compositions:

Feedstuff	lb per lb of feedstuff		Cost ($/lb)
	Protein	*Fiber*	
Corn	.09	.02	.30
Soybean meal	.60	.06	.90

The dietary requirements of the special feed are at least 30% protein and at most 5% fiber. The goal is to determine the daily minimum-cost feed mix.

The decision variables of the model are

$$x_1 = \text{ lb of corn in the daily mix}$$
$$x_2 = \text{ lb of soybean meal in the daily mix}$$

The objective is to minimize the total daily cost (in dollars) of the feed mix—that is,

$$\text{Minimize } z = .3x_1 + .9x_2$$

The constraints represent the daily amount of the mix and the dietary requirements. Ozark Farms needs at least 800 lb of feed a day—that is,

$$x_1 + x_2 \geq 800$$

The amount of protein included in x_1 lb of corn and x_2 lb of soybean meal is $(.09x_1 + .6x_2)$ lb. This quantity should equal at least 30% of the total feed mix $(x_1 + x_2)$ lb—that is,

$$.09x_1 + .6x_2 \geq .3(x_1 + x_2)$$

In a similar manner, the fiber requirement of at most 5% is represented as

$$.02x_1 + .06x_2 \leq .05(x_1 + x_2)$$

The constraints are simplified by moving the terms in x_1 and x_2 to the left-hand side of each inequality, leaving only a constant on the right-hand side. The complete model is

$$\text{Minimize } z = .3x_1 + .9x_2$$

subject to

$$x_1 + x_2 \geq 800$$

$$.21x_1 - .30x_2 \leq 0$$

$$.03x_1 - .01x_2 \geq 0$$

$$x_1, x_2 \geq 0$$

Figure 2.3 provides the graphical solution of the model. The second and third constraints pass through the origin. Thus, unlike the Reddy Mikks model of Example 2.2-1, the determination of the feasible half-spaces of these two constraints require using a reference point other than $(0, 0)$ [e.g., $(100, 0)$ or $(0, 100)$].

Solution:

The model minimizes the value of the objective function by reducing z in the direction shown in Figure 2.3. The optimum solution is the intersection of the two lines $x_1 + x_2 = 800$ and $.21x_1 - .3x_2 = 0$, which yields $x_1 = 470.6$ 1b and $x_2 = 329.4$ 1 b. The minimum cost of the feed mix is $z = .3 \times 470.6 + .9 \times 329.4 = \$437.64$ per day.

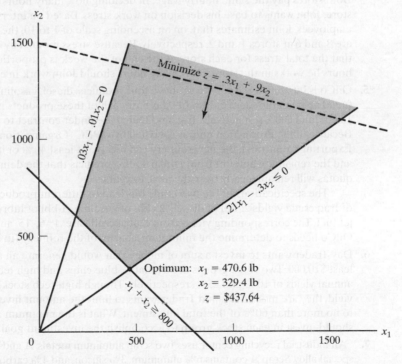

FIGURE 2.3

Graphical solution of the diet model

Remarks. One may wonder why the constraint $x_1 + x_2 \geq 800$ cannot be replaced with $x_1 + x_2 = 800$ because it would not be optimum to produce more than the minimum quantity. Although the solution of the present model did satisfy the equation, a more complex model may impose additional restrictions that would require mixing more than the minimum amount. More importantly, the inequality, by definition, is inclusive of the equality case, so that the equation can be chosen if optimality requires it. The conclusion is that one should not "preguess" the solution by imposing the additional equality restriction.

PROBLEM SET 2.2B

1. Identify the direction of decrease in z in each of the following cases:
   *(a) Minimize $z = 4x_1 - 2x_2$
   (b) Minimize $z = -6x_1 + 2x_2$
   (c) Minimize $z = -3x_1 - 6x_2$

2. For the diet model, suppose that the daily availability of corn is limited to 400 lb. Identify the new solution space, and determine the new optimum solution.

3. For the diet model, determine the optimum solution given the feed mix does not exceed 500 lb a day? Does the solution make sense?

4. John must work at least 20 hours a week to supplement his income while attending school. He has the opportunity to work in two retail stores. In store 1, he can work between 4.5 and 12 hours a week, and in store 2, he is allowed between 5.5 and 10 hours. Both stores pay the same hourly wage. In deciding how many hours to work in each store, John wants to base his decision on work stress. Based on interviews with present employees, John estimates that, on an ascending scale of 1 to 10, the stress factors are 8 and 6 at stores 1 and 2, respectively. Because stress mounts by the hour, he assumes that the total stress for each store at the end of the week is proportional to the number of hours he works in the store. How many hours should John work in each store?

*5. OilCo is building a refinery to produce four products: diesel, gasoline, lubricants, and jet fuel. The minimum demand (in bbl/day) for each of these products is 14,000, 30,000, 10,000, and 8000, respectively. Iraq and Dubai are under contract to ship crude to OilCo. Because of the production quotas specified by OPEC (Organization of Petroleum Exporting Countries), the new refinery can receive at least 40% of its crude from Iraq and the remaining amount from Dubai. OilCo predicts that the demand and crude oil quotas will remain steady over the next 10 years.
   The specifications of the two crude oils lead to different product mixes: One barrel of Iraq crude yields .2 bbl of diesel, .25 bbl of gasoline, .1 bbl of lubricant, and .15 bbl of jet fuel. The corresponding yields from Dubai crude are .1, .6, .15, and .1, respectively. OilCo needs to determine the minimum capacity of the refinery (in bbl/day).

6. Day Trader wants to invest a sum of money that would generate an annual yield of at least $10,000. Two stock groups are available: blue chips and high tech, with average annual yields of 10% and 25%, respectively. Though high-tech stocks provide higher yield, they are more risky, and Trader wants to limit the amount invested in these stocks to no more than 60% of the total investment. What is the minimum amount Trader should invest in each stock group to accomplish the investment goal?

7. *An industrial recycling center uses two scrap aluminum metals, A and B, to produce a special alloy. Scrap A contains 6% aluminum, 3% silicon, and 4% carbon. Scrap B has 3% aluminum, 6% silicon, and 3% carbon. The costs per ton for scraps A and B are $100 and $80, respectively. The specifications of the special alloy require that (1) the aluminum content

must be at least 3% and at most 6%, (2) the silicon content must lie between 3% and 5%, and (3) the carbon content must be between 3% and 7%. Determine the optimum mix of the scraps that should be used in producing 1000 tons of the alloy.

8. *TORA Experiment.* Consider the Diet Model, and let the objective function be given as

$$\text{Minimize } z = .8x_1 + .8x_2$$

Use TORA to show that the optimum solution is associated with *two* distinct corner points and that both points yield the same objective value. In this case, the problem is said to have *alternative optima.* Explain the conditions leading to this situation, and show that, in effect, the problem has an infinite number of alternative optima, then provide a formula for determining all such solutions.

2.3   COMPUTER SOLUTION WITH SOLVER AND AMPL

In practice, where typical LP models may involve thousands of variables and constraints, computer is the only viable venue for solving LP problems. This section presents two commonly used software systems: Excel Solver and AMPL. Solver is particularly appealing to spreadsheet users. AMPL is an algebraic modeling language that, like all higher-order programming languages, requires more expertise. Nevertheless, AMPL, and similar languages,[2] offers great modeling flexibility. Although the presentation in this section concentrates on LPs, both AMPL and Solver can handle integer and nonlinear problems, as will be shown in later chapters.

2.3.1   LP Solution with Excel Solver

In Excel Solver, the spreadsheet is the input and output medium for the LP. Figure 2.4 shows the layout of the data for the Reddy Mikks model (file *solverRM1.xls*). The top of the figure includes four types of information: (1) input data cells (B5:C9 and F6:F9), (2) cells representing the variables and the objective function (B13:D13), (3) algebraic definitions of the objective function and the left-hand side of the constraints (cells D5:D9), and (4) cells that provides explanatory names or symbols. Solver requires the first three types only. The fourth type enhances readability but serves no other purpose. The relative positioning of the four types of information on the spreadsheet (as suggested in Figure 2.4) is convenient for proper cell cross-referencing in Solver, and its use is recommended.

How does Solver link to the spreadsheet data? First, we provide "algebraic" definitions of the objective function and the left-hand side of the constraints using the input data (cells B5:C9 and F6:F9) and the objective function and variables (cells B13:D13). Next, we place the resulting formulas appropriately in cells D5:D9, as the following table shows:

	Algebraic expression	Spreadsheet formula	Entered in cell
Objective, z	$5x_1 + 4x_2$	$=B5*\$B\$13+C5*\$C\$13$	D5
Constraint 1	$6x_1 + 4x_2$	$=B6*\$B\$13+C6*\$C\$13$	D6
Constraint 2	$x_1 + 2x_2$	$=B7*\$B\$13+C7*\$C\$13$	D7
Constraint 3	$-x_1 + x_2$	$=B8*\$B\$13+C8*\$C\$13$	D8
Constraint 4	$0x_1 + x_2$	$=B9*\$B\$13+C9*\$C\$13$	D9

---

[2]Other known commercial packages include AIMMS, GAMS, LINGO, MPL, OPL Studio, and Xpress-Mosel.

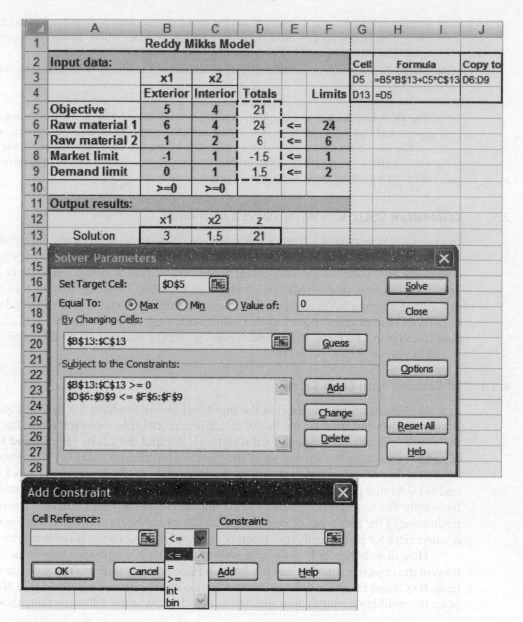

FIGURE 2.4

Defining the Reddy Mikks model with Excel Solver (file *solverRM1.xls*)

Actually, you only need to enter the formula for cell D5 and then copy it into cells D6:D9. To do so correctly, it is necessary to use *fixed referencing* of the cells representing x_1 and x_2 (i.e., $B$13 and $C$13, respectively).

The explicit formulas just described are impractical for large LPs. Instead, the formula in cell D5 can be written compactly as

$$= \text{SUMPRODUCT(B5:C5,}\$B\$13:\$C\$13)$$

The new formula can then be copied into cells D6:D9.

All the elements of the LP model are now ready to execute the model. Click Solver from the spreadsheet menu bar[3] to access **Solver Parameters** dialogue box (shown in the middle of Figure 2.4). Next, update the dialogue box as follows:

Set Target Cell: $D$5
Equal To: ⊙ Max
By Changing Cells: $B$13:$C$13

This information tells Solver that the LP variables (cells $B$13 and $C$13) are determined by maximizing the objective function in cell $D$5.

To set up the constraints, click Add in the dialogue box to display the **Add Constraint** box (see the bottom of Figure 2.4) and then enter the left-hand side, inequality type, and right-hand side of the constraints as[4]

$$\$D\$6:\$D\$9 <= \$F\$6:\$F\$9$$

For the nonnegativity restrictions, click Add once again and enter

$$\$B\$13:\$C\$13 >= 0$$

Another way to enter the nonnegative constraints is to click Options in the **Solver Parameters** box to access **Solver Options** (see Figure 2.5) and then check ☑ Assume Non-Negative. ☑ Assume Linear Model.

In general, the remaining default settings in **Solver Options** need not be changed. However, the default precision of .000001 may be too "high" for some problems, and

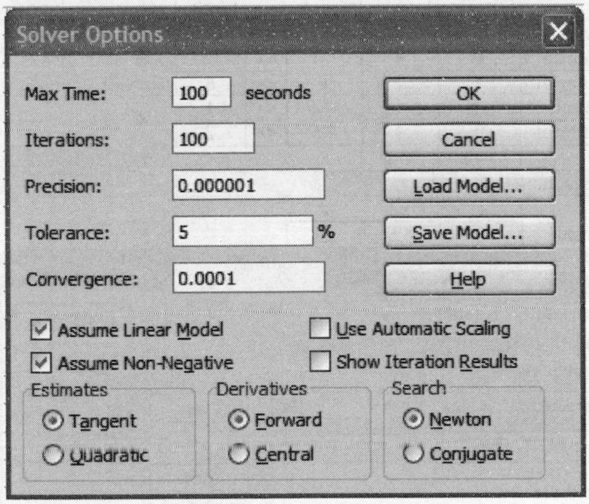

FIGURE 2.5
Solver options dialogue box

[3]It may be necessary first to check Solver as an add-in in Excel.
[4]In the **Add Constraint** box in Figure 2.4, the two additional options, **int** and **bin**, which stand for **int**eger and **bin**ary, are used with integer programs to restrict variables to integer or binary values (see Chapter 9).

Solver may incorrectly return the message "Solver could not find a feasible solution." In such cases, less precision (i.e., larger value) needs to be specified. If the message persists, then the problem may be infeasible.

Descriptive Excel range names can be used to enhance readability. A range is created by highlighting the desired cells, typing the range name in the top left box of the sheet, and then pressing Return. Figure 2.6 (file *solverRM2.xls*) provides the details with a summary of the range names used in the model. The model should be contrasted with the file *solverRM1.xls* to see how ranges are used in the formulas.

To solve the problem, click Solve on **Solver Parameters**. A new dialogue box, **Solver Results**, then gives the status of the solution. If the model setup is correct, the optimum value of z will appear in cell D5 and the values of x_1 and x_2 will go to cells B13 and C13, respectively. For convenience, cell D13 exhibits the optimum value of z by entering the formula $= D5$ in cell D13, thus displaying the entire optimum solution in contiguous cells.

If a problem has no feasible solution, Solver will issue the explicit message "Solver could not find a feasible solution." If the optimal objective value is unbounded (not finite), Solver will issue the somewhat ambiguous message "The Set Cell values do not converge." In either case, the message indicates that there is something wrong with the formulation of the model, as will be discussed in Section 3.5.

FIGURE 2.6

Use of range names in Excel Solver (file *solverRM2.xls*)

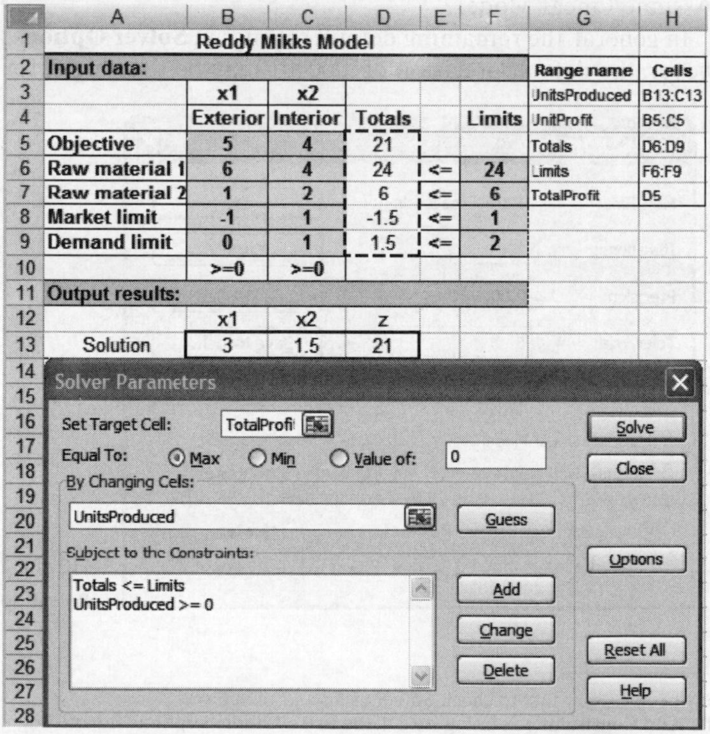

The **Solver Results** dialogue box provides the opportunity to request further details about the solution, including the important sensitivity analysis report. We will discuss these additional results in Section 3.6.4.

The solution of the Reddy Mikks by Solver is straightforward. Other models may require a "bit of ingenuity" before they can be set up. A class of LP models that falls in this category deals with network optimization, as will be demonstrated in Chapter 6.

PROBLEM SET 2.3A

1. Modify the Reddy Mikks Solver model of Figure 2.4 to account for a third type of paint named "marine." Requirements per ton of raw materials 1 and 2 are .6 and .85 ton, respectively. The daily demand for the new paint lies between .6 ton and 1.9 tons. The profit per ton is $3.7 (thousand).

2. Develop the Excel Solver model for the following problems:
   (a) The diet model of Example 2.2-2
   (b) Problem 17, Set 2.2a
   (c) Problem 7, Set 2.2b

2.3.2 LP Solution with AMPL[5]

This section provides a brief introduction to AMPL. The material in Appendix C on the website details AMPL syntax. It will be cross-referenced with the presentation in this section and with other AMPL presentations in the book. The two examples presented here deal with the basics of AMPL.

Reddy Mikks Problem—a Rudimentary Model. AMPL provides a facility for modeling an LP in a rudimentary longhand format. Figure 2.7 gives the self-explanatory code for the Reddy Mikks model (file *amplRM1.txt*). All reserved keywords are in bold. All other names are user generated. The objective function and each of the constraints must have distinct (user-generated) names followed by a colon. Each statement closes with a semicolon.

The longhand format is problem specific, in the sense that a new code is needed whenever the input data are changed. For practical problems (with complex structure and a large number of variables and constraints), the longhand format is at best cumbersome. AMPL alleviates this difficulty by devising a code that divides the problem into two components: (1) A general algebraic model for a specific class of problems applicable to any number of variables and constraints, and (2) data for driving the algebraic model. The implementation of these two points is addressed in the following section using the Reddy Mikks problem.

---

[5]For convenience, the AMPL student version is on the website. Future updates may be downloaded from www.ampl.com. AMPL uses line commands and does not operate in Windows environment.

```
maximize z: 5*x1+4*x2;
subject to
   c1: 6*x1+4*x2<=24;
   c2: x1+2*x2<=6;
   c3: -x1+x2<=1;
   c4: x2<=2;
solve;
display z,x1,x2;
```

FIGURE 2.7

Rudimentary AMPL model for the Reddy Mikks problem (file *amplRM1.txt*)

Reddy Mikks Problem—an Algebraic Model. Figure 2.8 lists the statements of the model (file *amplRM2.txt*). The file must be strictly text (ASCII). The symbol # designates the start of explanatory comments. Comments may appear either on a separate line or following the semicolon at the end of a statement. The language is case sensitive, and all its keywords, with few exceptions, are in lower case. (Section C.2 on the website provides more details.)

```
#--------------------------------------------algebraic model
param m;
param n;
param c{1..n};
param b{1..m};
param a{1..m,1..n};

var x{1..n}>=0;

maximize z: sum{j in 1..n}c[j]*x[j];
subject to restr{i in 1..m}:
          sum{j in 1..n}a[i,j]*x[j]<=b[i];
#--------------------------------------------specify model data
data;
param n:=2;
param m:=4;
param c:=1 5 2 4;
param b:=1 24  2 6  3 1  4 2;
param a:       1     2 :=
           1   6     4
           2   1     2
           3  -1     1
           4   0     1;
#--------------------------------------------solve the problem
solve;
display z, x;
```

FIGURE 2.8

AMPL model of the Reddy Mikks problem using hard-coded input data (file *amplRM2.txt*)

The algebraic model in AMPL views the general LP problem with n variables and m constraints in the following generic format:

$$\text{Maximize } z: \sum_{j=1}^{n} c_j x_j$$

$$\textbf{subject to } restr_i: \sum_{j=1}^{n} a_{ij} x_j \leq b_i, i = 1, 2, \ldots, m$$

$$x_j \geq 0, j = 1, 2, \ldots, n$$

It gives the objective function and constraint i the (user-specified) names z and $restr_i$.

The model starts with the `param` statements that declare m, n, c, b, and a_{ij} as parameters (or constants) whose specific values are given in the input data section of the model. It translates $c_j(j = 1, 2, \ldots, n)$ as c{1..n}, $b_i(i = 1, 2, \ldots, m)$ as b{1..m}, and $a_{ij}(i = 1, 2, \ldots, m, j = 1, 2, \ldots, n)$ as a{1..m,1..n}. Next, the variables $x_j(j = 1, 2, \ldots, n)$ together with the nonnegativity restriction are defined by the `var` statement

```
var x{1..n}>=0;
```

A variable is considered unrestricted if >=0 is removed from its definition. The notation in {} represents the *set* of subscripts over which a `param` or a `var` is a defined.

The model is developed in terms of the parameters and the variables in the following manner. The objective function and constraints carry distinct names followed by a colon (:). The objective statement is a direct translation of maximize $z = \sum_{j=1}^{n} c_j x_j$:

```
maximize z: sum{j in 1..n}c[j]*x[j];
```

Constraint i is given the root name `restr` indexed over the set {1..m}:

```
restr{i in 1..m}:sum{j in 1..n}a[i,j]*x[j]<=b[i];
```

The statement is a direct translation of $restr_i \sum_{j=1}^{n} a_{ij} x_j \leq b_i$.

The algebraic model may now be used with any set of applicable data that can be entered following the statement data;. For the Reddy Mikks model, the data tell AMPL that the problem has 2 variables (param n:=2;) and 4 constraints (param m:=4;). The compound operator := must be used, and the statement must start with the keyword param. For the single-subscripted parameters, c and b, each element is represented by its index followed by its value and separated by at least one blank space. Thus, $c_1 = 5$ and $c_2 = 4$ are entered as

```
param c:= 1 5 2 4;
```

The data for param b are entered in a similar manner.

For the double-subscripted parameter a_{ij}, that data set reads as a two-dimensional matrix with its rows designating i and its columns designating j. The top line defines the subscript j, and the subscript i is entered at the start of each row as

```
param a:   1    2 :=
       1   6    4
       2   1    2
       3  -1    1
       4   0    1;
```

The data set must terminate with a semicolon. Note the *mandatory* location of the separator : and the compound operator := after param a.

The model and its data are now ready. The command solve; invokes the solution algorithm and the command display z, x; provides the solution.

To execute the model, first invoke AMPL (by clicking ampl.exe in the AMPL directory). At the ampl: prompt, enter the following **model** command, then press Return:

```
model amplRM2.txt;
```

The output of the system will then appear on the screen as follows:

```
MINOS 5.5: Optimal solution found.
2 iterations, objective = 21

z = 21
x[*]:=

1 = 3
2 = 1.5
```

The bottom four lines are the result of executing display z,x;. Actually, AMPL has formatting capabilities that enhance the readability of the output results (see Section C.5.2 on the website).

AMPL allows separating the algebraic model and the data into two independent files. This arrangement is more convenient because only the data file needs to be changed once the model has been developed. See the end of Section C.2 for details.

AMPL offers a wide range of programming capabilities. For example, the input/output data can be secured from/sent to external files, spreadsheets, and databases, and the model can be executed interactively for a wide variety of options. The details are given in Appendix C on the website.

PROBLEM SET 2.3B

1. In the Reddy Mikks model, suppose that a third type of paint, named "marine," is produced. The requirements per ton of raw materials $M1$ and $M2$ are .7 and .95 ton, respectively. The daily demand for the new paint lies between .4 ton and 2.1 tons, and the profit per ton is $4.5 (thousand). Modify the Excel Solver model *solverRM2.xls* and the

AMPL model *amplRM2.txt* to account for the new situation and determine the optimum solution. Compare the additional effort associated with each modification.

2. Develop AMPL models for the following problems:
   (a) The diet problem of Example 2.2-2 and find the optimum solution.
   (b) Problem 18, Set 2.2a
   (c) Problem 7, Set 2.2b

2.4 LINEAR PROGRAMMING APPLICATIONS

This section presents realistic LP models in which the definition of the variables and the construction of the objective function and the constraints are not as straightforward as in the case of the two-variable model. The areas covered by these applications include the following:

1. Investment.
2. Production planning and inventory control.
3. Manpower planning.
4. Urban development planning.
5. Oil refining and blending.

Each model is detailed, and its optimum solution is interpreted.

2.4.1 Investment

Multitudes of investment opportunities are available to today's investor. Examples of investment problems are capital budgeting for projects, bond investment strategy, stock portfolio selection, and establishment of bank loan policy. In many of these situations, LP can be used to select the optimal mix of opportunities that will maximize return while meeting requirements set by the investor and the market.

Example 2.4-1 (Bank Loan Model)

Bank One is in the process of devising a loan policy that involves a maximum of $12 million. The following table provides the pertinent data about available loans.

Type of loan	Interest rate	Bad-debt ratio
Personal	.140	.10
Car	.130	.07
Home	.120	.03
Farm	.125	.05
Commercial	.100	.02

Bad debts are unrecoverable and produce no interest revenue.

Competition with other financial institutions dictates the allocation of at least 40% of the funds to farm and commercial loans. To assist the housing industry in the region, home loans must equal at least 50% of the personal, car, and home loans. The bank limits the overall ratio of bad debts on all loans to at most 4%.

Mathematical Model: The situation deals with determining the amount of loan in each category, thus leading to the following definitions of the variables:

$$x_1 = \text{personal loans (in millions of dollars)}$$

$$x_2 = \text{car loans}$$

$$x_3 = \text{home loans}$$

$$x_4 = \text{farm loans}$$

$$x_5 = \text{commercial loans}$$

The objective of the Bank One is to maximize net return, the difference between interest revenue and lost bad debts. Interest revenue is accrued on loans in good standing. For example, when 10% of personal loans are lost to bad debt, the bank will receive interest on 90% of the loan—that is, it will receive 14% interest on $.9x_1$ of the original loan x_1. The same reasoning applies to the remaining four types of loans. Thus,

$$\text{Total interest} = .14(.9x_1) + .13(.93x_2) + .12(.97x_3) + .125(.95x_4) + .1(.98x_5)$$

$$= .126x_1 + .1209x_2 + .1164x_3 + .11875x_4 + .098x_5$$

We also have

$$\text{Bad debt} = .1x_1 + .07x_2 + .03x_3 + .05x_4 + .02x_5$$

The objective function combines interest revenue and bad debt as

$$\text{Maximize } z = \text{Total interest} - \text{Bad debt}$$

$$= (.126x_1 + .1209x_2 + .1164x_3 + .11875x_4 + .098x_5)$$

$$- (.1x_1 + .07x_2 + .03x_3 + .05x_4 + .02x_5)$$

$$= .026x_1 + .0509x_2 + .0864x_3 + .06875x_4 + .078x_5$$

The problem has five constraints:

1. *Total funds should not exceed $12 (million):*

$$x_1 + x_2 + x_3 + x_4 + x_5 \leq 12$$

2. *Farm and commercial loans equal at least 40% of all loans:*

$$x_4 + x_5 \geq .4(x_1 + x_2 + x_3 + x_4 + x_5)$$

or

$$.4x_1 + .4x_2 + .4x_3 - .6x_4 - .6x_5 \leq 0$$

3. *Home loans should equal at least 50% of personal, car, and home loans:*

$$x_3 \geq .5(x_1 + x_2 + x_3)$$

or

$$.5x_1 + .5x_2 - .5x_3 \leq 0$$

4. *Bad debts should not exceed 4% of all loans:*

$$.1x_1 + .07x_2 + .03x_3 + .05x_4 + .02x_5 \leq .04(x_1 + x_2 + x_3 + x_4 + x_5)$$

or

$$.06x_1 + .03x_2 - .01x_3 + .01x_4 - .02x_5 \leq 0$$

5. *Nonnegativity:*

$$x_1 \geq 0, x_2 \geq 0, x_3 \geq 0, x_4 \geq 0, x_5 \geq 0$$

A subtle assumption in the preceding formulation is that all loans are issued at approximately the same time. It allows us to ignore differences in the time value of the funds allocated to the different loans.

Solution:

The optimal solution is computed using AMPL (file *amplEx2.4-1.txt*):

$$z = .99648, x_1 = 0, x_2 = 0, x_3 = 7.2, x_4 = 0, x_5 = 4.8$$

Remarks.

1. You may be wondering why we did not define the right-hand side of the second constraint as $.4 \times 12$ instead of $.4(x_1 + x_2 + x_3 + x_4 + x_5)$. After all, it appears plausible that the bank would want to loan out all \$12 (million). The answer is that the usage given in the formulation does not disallow this possibility. But there are two more reasons why you should not use $.4 \times 12$: (1) If other constraints in the model are such that all \$12 (million) *cannot* be used (e.g., the bank may set caps on the different loans), then the choice $.4 \times 12$ could lead to an infeasible or incorrect solution. (2) If you want to experiment with the effect of changing available funds (say from \$12 to \$13 million) on the optimum solution, there is a real chance that you may forget to change $.4 \times 12$ to $.4 \times 13$, in which case the solution will not be correct. A similar reasoning applies to the left-hand side of the fourth constraint.

2. The optimal solution calls for allocating all \$12 million: \$7.2 million to home loans and \$4.8 million to commercial loans. The remaining categories receive none. The return on the investment is

$$\text{Rate of return} = \frac{z}{12} = \frac{.99648}{12} = .08034$$

This shows that the combined annual rate of return is 8.034%, which is less than the best *net* interest rate (= 8.64% for home loans), and one wonders why the model does not take full advantage of this opportunity. The answer is that the stipulation that farm and commercial loans must account for at least 40% of all loans (constraint 2) forces the solution to allocate \$4.8 million to commercial loans at the lower *net* rate of 7.8%, hence lowering the overall interest rate to $100 \left(\frac{.0864 \times 7.2 + .078 \times 4.8}{12} \right) = 8.034\%$. In fact, if we remove constraint 2, the optimum will allocate all the funds to home loans at the higher 8.64% rate (try it using the AMPL model!).

PROBLEM SET 2.4A

1. Fox Enterprises is considering six projects for possible construction over the next 4 years. Fox can undertake any of the projects partially or completely. A partial undertaking of a

project will prorate both the return and cash outlays proportionately. The expected (present value) returns and cash outlays for the projects are given in the following table.

Project	Cash outlay ($1000)				Return ($1000)
	Year 1	Year 2	Year 3	Year 4	
1	10.5	14.4	2.2	2.4	324.0
2	8.3	12.6	9.5	3.1	358.0
3	10.2	14.2	5.6	4.2	177.5
4	7.2	10.5	7.5	5.0	148.0
5	12.3	10.1	8.3	6.3	182.0
6	9.2	7.8	6.9	5.1	123.5
Available funds ($1000)	60.0	70.0	35.0	20.0	

(a) Formulate the problem as a linear program, and determine the optimal project mix that maximizes the total return using AMPL, Solver, or TORA. Ignore the time value of money.

(b) Suppose that if a portion of project 2 is undertaken, then at least an equal portion of project 6 must be undertaken. Modify the formulation of the model, and find the new optimal solution.

(c) In the original model, suppose that any funds left at the end of a year are used in the next year. Find the new optimal solution, and determine how much each year "borrows" from the preceding year. For simplicity, ignore the time value of money.

(d) Suppose in the original model the yearly funds available for any year can be exceeded, if necessary, by borrowing from other financial activities within the company. Ignoring the time value of money, reformulate the LP model, and find the optimum solution. Would the new solution require borrowing in any year? If so, what is the rate of return on borrowed money?

*2. Investor Doe has $10,000 to invest in four projects. The following table gives the cash flow for the four investments.

Project	Cash flow ($1000) at the start of				
	Year 1	Year 2	Year 3	Year 4	Year 5
1	−1.00	0.50	0.30	1.80	1.20
2	−1.00	0.60	0.20	1.50	1.30
3	0.00	−1.00	0.80	1.90	0.80
4	−1.00	0.40	0.60	1.80	0.95

The information in the table can be interpreted as follows: For project 1, $1.00 invested at the start of year 1 will yield $.50 at the start of year 2, $.30 at the start of year 3, $1.80 at the start of year 4, and $1.20 at the start of year 5. The remaining entries can be interpreted similarly. The entry 0.00 indicates that no transaction is taking place. Doe has the additional option of investing in a bank account that earns 6.5% annually. All funds accumulated at the end of 1 year can be reinvested in the following year. Formulate the problem as a linear program to determine the optimal allocation of funds to investment opportunities. Solve the model using Solver of AMPL.

3. HiRise Construction can bid on two 1-year projects. The following table provides the quarterly cash flow (in millions of dollars) for the two projects.

	Cash flow (in millions of $) at				
Project	January 1	April 1	July 1	October 1	December 31
I	−1.0	−3.1	−1.5	1.8	5.0
II	−3.0	−2.5	1.5	1.8	2.8

HiRise has cash funds of $10 million at the beginning of each quarter and may borrow at most $1 million at a 10% nominal annual interest rate. Any borrowed money must be returned at the end of the quarter. Surplus cash can earn quarterly interest at an 8% nominal annual rate. Net accumulation at the end of one quarter is invested in the next quarter.

(a) Assume that HiRise is allowed partial or full participation in the two projects. Determine the level of participation that will maximize the net cash accumulated on December 31. Solve the model using Solver or AMPL.

(b) Is it possible in any quarter to borrow money and simultaneously end up with surplus funds? Explain.

4. In anticipation of the immense college expenses, Joe and Jill started an annual investment program on their child's eighth birthday that will last until the eighteenth birthday. They plan to invest the following amounts at the beginning of each year:

Year	1	2	3	4	5	6	7	8	9	10
Amount ($)	2000	2000	2500	2500	3000	3500	3500	4000	4000	5000

To avoid unpleasant surprises, they want to invest the money safely in the following options: Insured savings with 7.5% annual yield, 6-year government bonds that yield 7.9% and have a current market price equal to 98% of face value, and 9-year municipal bonds yielding 8.5% and having a current market price of 1.02 of face value. How should the money be invested?

*5. A business executive has the option to invest money in two plans: Plan A guarantees that each dollar invested will earn $.70 a year later, and plan B guarantees that each dollar invested will earn $2 after 2 years. In plan A, investments can be made annually, and in plan B, investments are allowed for periods that are multiples of 2 years only. How should the executive invest $100,000 to maximize the earnings at the end of 3 years? Solve the model using Solver of AMPL.

6. A gambler plays a game that requires dividing bet money among four choices. The game has three outcomes. The following table gives the corresponding gain or loss per dollar for the different options of the game.

	Return per dollar deposited in choice			
Outcome	1	2	3	4
1	−3	4	−7	15
2	5	−3	9	4
3	3	−9	10	−8

The gambler has a total of $1500, which may be played only once. The exact outcome of the game is not known a priori. Because of this uncertainty, the gambler's strategy is to maximize the *minimum* return produced by the three outcomes. How should the gambler allocate the $1500 among the four choices? Solve the model using Solver of AMPL. (*Hint*: The gambler's net return may be positive, zero, or negative.)

7. *Lewis (1996).* Monthly bills in a household are received monthly (e.g., utilities and home mortgage), quarterly (e.g., estimated tax payments), semiannually (e.g., insurance), or annually (e.g., subscription renewals and dues). The following table provides the monthly bills for next year.

Month	Jan.	Feb.	Mar.	Apr.	May	June	July	Aug.	Sep.	Oct.	Nov.	Dec.	Total
$	800	1200	400	700	600	900	1500	1000	900	1100	1300	1600	12000

To account for these expenses, the family sets aside $1000 per month, which is the average of the total divided by 12 months. If the money is deposited in a regular savings account, it can earn 4% annual interest, provided it stays in the account at least 1 month. The bank also offers 3-month and 6-month certificates of deposit that can earn 5.5% and 7% annual interest, respectively. Develop a 12-month investment schedule that will maximize the family's total return for the year. State any assumptions or requirements needed to reach a feasible solution. Solve the model using Solver of AMPL.

2.4.2 Production Planning and Inventory Control

There is a wealth of LP applications to production planning and inventory control. This section presents three examples. The first deals with production scheduling to meet a single-period demand. The second deals with the use of inventory in a multiperiod production system to meet future demand, and the third deals with the use of inventory and worker hiring/firing to "smooth" production over a multiperiod planning horizon.

Example 2.4-2   (Single-Period Production Model)

In preparation for the winter season, a clothing company is manufacturing parka and goose overcoats, insulated pants, and gloves. All products are manufactured in four different departments: cutting, insulating, sewing, and packaging. The company has received firm orders for its products. The contract stipulates a penalty for undelivered items. Devise an optimal production plan for the company based on the following data:

Department	Time per units (hr)				Capacity (hr)
	Parka	*Goose*	*Pants*	*Gloves*	
Cutting	.30	.30	.25	.15	1000
Insulating	.25	.35	.30	.10	1000
Sewing	.45	.50	.40	.22	1000
Packaging	.15	.15	.1	.05	1000
Demand	800	750	600	500	
Unit profit	$30	$40	$20	$10	
Unit penalty	$15	$20	$10	$8	

Mathematical Model: The variables of the problem are

$$x_1 = \text{number of parka jackets}$$

$$x_2 = \text{number of goose jackets}$$

$$x_3 = \text{number of pairs of pants}$$

$$x_4 = \text{number of pairs of gloves}$$

The company is penalized for not meeting demand. The objective then is to maximize the net profit, defined as

$$\text{Net profit} = \text{Total profit} - \text{Total penalty}$$

The total profit is $30x_1 + 40x_2 + 20x_3 + 10x_4$. To compute the total penalty, the demand constraints can be written as

$$x_1 + s_1 = 800, \ x_2 + s_2 = 750, \ x_3 + s_3 = 600, \ x_4 + s_4 = 500,$$

$$x_j \geq 0, s_j \geq 0, j = 1, 2, 3, 4$$

The new variable s_j represents the shortage in demand for product j, and the total penalty can be computed as $15s_1 + 20s_2 + 10s_3 + 8s_4$. The complete model thus becomes

$$\text{Maximize } z = 30x_1 + 40x_2 + 20x_3 + 10x_4 - (15s_1 + 20s_2 + 10s_3 + 8s_4)$$

subject to

$$.30x_1 + .30x_2 + .25x_3 + .15x_4 \leq 1000$$

$$.25x_1 + .35x_2 + .30x_3 + .10x_4 \leq 1000$$

$$.45x_1 + .50x_2 + .40x_3 + .22x_4 \leq 1000$$

$$.15x_1 + .15x_2 + .10x_3 + .05x_4 \leq 1000$$

$$x_1 + s_1 = 800, \ x_2 + s_2 = 750, \ x_3 + s_3 = 600, \ x_4 + s_4 = 500$$

$$x_j \geq 0, s_j \geq 0, j = 1, 2, 3, 4$$

Solution:

The optimum solution (obtained using file *amplEx2.4-2.txt*) is $z = \$64{,}625$, $x_1 = 800$, $x_2 = 750$; $x_3 = 387.5$, $x_4 = 500$, $s_1 = s_2 = s_4 = 0$, $s_3 = 212.5$. The solution satisfies all the demand for both types of jackets and the gloves. A shortage of 213 (rounded up from 212.5) pairs of pants will result in a penalty cost of $213 \times \$10 = \$2130$.

Example 2.4-3 (Multiple Period Production-Inventory Model)

Acme Manufacturing Company has a contract to deliver 100, 250, 190, 140, 220, and 110 home windows over the next 6 months. Production cost (labor, material, and utilities) per window varies by period and is estimated to be $50, $45, $55, $48, $52, and $50 over the next 6 months. To take advantage of the fluctuations in manufacturing cost, Acme can produce more windows than needed in a given month and hold the extra units for delivery in later months. This will incur a storage cost at the rate of $8 per window per month, assessed on end-of-month inventory. Develop a linear program to determine the optimum production schedule.

Mathematical Model: The variables of the problem include the monthly production amount and the end-of-month inventory. For $i = 1, 2, \ldots, 6$, let

$$x_i = \text{Number of units produced in month } i$$

$$I_i = \text{Inventory units left at the end of month } i$$

The relationship between these variables and the monthly demand over the 6-month horizon is represented schematically in Figure 2.9. The system starts empty ($I_0 = 0$).

The objective is to minimize the total cost of production and end-of-month inventory.

$$\text{Total production cost} = 50x_1 + 45x_2 + 55x_3 + 48x_4 + 52x_5 + 50x_6$$

$$\text{Total inventory (storage) cost} = 8(I_1 + I_2 + I_3 + I_4 + I_5 + I_6)$$

Thus the objective function is

$$\text{Minimize } z = 50x_1 + 45x_2 + 55x_3 + 48x_4 + 52x_5 + 50x_6$$

$$+ 8(I_1 + I_2 + I_3 + I_4 + I_5 + I_6)$$

The constraints of the problem can be determined directly from the representation in Figure 2.9. For each period we have the following balance equation:

$$\text{Beginning inventory} + \text{Production amount} - \text{Ending inventory} = \text{Demand}$$

This is translated mathematically for the individual months as

$$x_1 - I_1 = 100 \quad \text{(Month 1)}$$

$$I_1 + x_2 - I_2 = 250 \quad \text{(Month 2)}$$

$$I_2 + x_3 - I_3 = 190 \quad \text{(Month 3)}$$

$$I_3 + x_4 - I_4 = 140 \quad \text{(Month 4)}$$

$$I_4 + x_5 - I_5 = 220 \quad \text{(Month 5)}$$

$$I_5 + x_6 = 110 \quad \text{(Month 6)}$$

$$x_i, i = 1, 2, \ldots, 6, I_i \geq 0, i = 1, 2, \ldots, 5$$

Note that the initial inventory, I_0, is zero. Also, in any optimal solution, the ending inventory I_6 will be zero because it is not economical to incur unnecessary additional storage cost.

FIGURE 2.9

Schematic representation of the production-inventory system

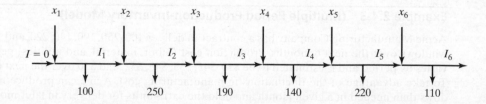

FIGURE 2.10

Optimum solution of the production-inventory problem

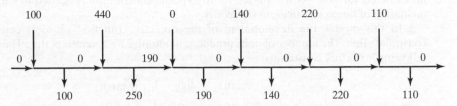

Solution:

The optimum solution (obtained using file *amplEx2.4-3.txt*) is summarized in Figure 2.10. It shows that each month's demand is satisfied from the same month's production, except for month 2 where the production quantity (= 440 units) covers the demand for both months 2 and 3. The total associated cost is $z = \$49{,}980$.

Example 2.4-4 (Multiperiod Production Smoothing Model)

A company is planning the manufacture of a product for March, April, May, and June of next year. The demand quantities are 520, 720, 520, and 620 units, respectively. The company has a steady workforce of 10 employees but can meet fluctuating production needs by hiring and firing temporary workers. The extra costs of hiring and firing a temp in any month are $200 and $400, respectively. A permanent worker produces 12 units per month, and a temporary worker, lacking equal experience, produces 10 units per month. The company can produce more than needed in any month and carry the surplus over to a succeeding month at a holding cost of $50 per unit per month. Develop an optimal hiring/firing policy over the 4-month planning horizon.

Mathematical Model: This model is similar to that of Example 2.4-3 in the sense that each month has its production, demand, and ending inventory. The only exception deals with handling permanent versus the temporary workforce.

The ten permanent workers can be accounted for by subtracting the units they produce from the respective monthly demand. The remaining demand is then satisfied through hiring and firing of temps. Thus

$$\text{Remaining demand for March} = 520 - 12 \times 10 = 400 \text{ units}$$
$$\text{Remaining demand for April} = 720 - 12 \times 10 = 600 \text{ units}$$
$$\text{Remaining demand for May} = 520 - 12 \times 10 = 400 \text{ units}$$
$$\text{Remaining demand for June} = 620 - 12 \times 10 = 500 \text{ units}$$

The variables of the model for month i can be defined as

$$x_i = \text{Net number of temps at the start of month } i \text{ after any hiring or firing}$$
$$S_i = \text{Number of temps hired or fired at the start of month } i$$
$$I_i = \text{Units of ending inventory for month } i$$

By definition, x_i and I_i are nonnegative, whereas S_i is *unrestricted in sign* because it equals the number of hired or fired workers in month i. This is the first instance in this chapter of using an unrestricted variable. As we will see shortly, special substitution is needed to allow the implementation of hiring and firing in the model.

In this model, the development of the objective function requires constructing the constraints first. The number of units produced in month i by x_i temps is $10x_i$. Thus, we have the following inventory constraints:

$$10x_1 = 400 + I_1 \quad \text{(March)}$$
$$I_1 + 10x_2 = 600 + I_2 \quad \text{(April)}$$
$$I_2 + 10x_3 = 400 + I_3 \quad \text{(May)}$$
$$I_3 + 10x_4 = 500 \quad\quad\ \text{(June)}$$
$$x_1, x_2, x_3, x_4 \geq 0, I_1, I_2, I_3 \geq 0$$

For hiring and firing, the temp workforce starts with x_1 workers at the beginning of March. At the start of April, x_1 will be adjusted (up or down) by S_2 temps to generate x_2. The same idea applies to x_3 and x_4, thus leading to the following constraint equations

$$x_1 = S_1$$
$$x_2 = x_1 + S_2$$
$$x_3 = x_2 + S_3$$
$$x_4 = x_3 + S_4$$
$$S_1, S_2, S_3, S_4 \text{ unrestricted in sign}$$
$$x_1, x_2, x_3, x_4 \geq 0$$

Next, we develop the objective function. The goal is to minimize the inventory cost plus the cost of hiring and firing. As in Example 2.4-3,

$$\text{Inventory holding cost} = 50(I_1 + I_2 + I_3)$$

Modeling the cost of hiring and firing is a bit involved. Given the costs of hiring and firing a temp are $200 and $400, respectively, we have

$$\begin{pmatrix} \text{Cost of hiring} \\ \text{and firing} \end{pmatrix} = 200\begin{pmatrix} \text{Number of } hired \text{ temps} \\ \text{at the start of each month} \end{pmatrix} + 400\begin{pmatrix} \text{Number of } fired \text{ temps} \\ \text{at the start of each month} \end{pmatrix}$$

If the variable S_i is positive, hiring takes place in month i. If it is negative, then firing occurs. This "qualitative" assessment can be translated mathematically by using the substitution

$$S_i = S_i^- - S_i^+, \text{ where } S_i^-, S_i^+ \geq 0$$

The unrestricted variable S_i is now the difference between the two nonnegative variables S_i^- and S_i^+. We can think of S_i^- as the number of temps hired and S_i^+ as the number fired. For example, if $S_i^- = 5$ and $S_i^+ = 0$, then $S_i = 5 - 0 = +5$, which represents hiring. If $S_i^- = 0$ and $S_i^+ = 7$, then $S_i = 0 - 7 = -7$, which represents firing. In the first case, the corresponding cost of hiring is $200S_i^- = 200 \times 5 = \$1000$, and in the second case, the corresponding cost of firing is $400S_i^+ = 400 \times 7 = \$2800$.

The substitution $S_i = S_i^- - S_i^+$ is the basis for the development of cost of hiring and firing. First we need to address a possible question: What if both S_i^- and S_i^+ are positive? The answer is that this cannot happen because it implies both hiring and firing in the same month. Interestingly, the theory of LP (see Chapter 7) tells us that S_i^- and S_i^+ cannot be positive simultaneously, a mathematical result that confirms intuition.

We can now write the total cost of hiring and firing as:

$$\text{Cost of hiring} = 200(S_1^- + S_2^- + S_3^- + S_4^-)$$

$$\text{Cost of firing} = 400(S_1^+ + S_2^+ + S_3^+ + S_4^+)$$

The complete model is

$$\text{Minimize } z = 50(I_1 + I_2 + I_3 + I_4) + 200(S_1^- + S_2^- + S_3^- + S_4^-)$$
$$+ 400(S_1^+ + S_2^+ + S_3^+ + S_4^+)$$

subject to

$$10x_1 = 400 + I_1$$

$$I_1 + 10x_2 = 600 + I_2$$

$$I_2 + 10x_3 = 400 + I_3$$

$$I_3 + 10x_4 = 500$$

$$x_1 = S_1^- - S_1^+$$

$$x_2 = x_1 + S_2^- - S_2^+$$

$$x_3 = x_2 + S_3^- - S_3^+$$

$$x_4 = x_3 + S_4^- - S_4^+$$

$$S_1^-, S_1^+, S_2^-, S_2^+, S_3^-, S_3^+, S_4^-, S_4^+ \geq 0$$

$$x_1, x_2, x_3, x_4 \geq 0$$

$$I_1, I_2, I_3 \geq 0$$

Solution:

The optimum solution (obtained using file *amplEx2.4-4.txt*) is z = \$19,500, x_1 = 50, x_2 = 50, x_3 = 45, x_4 = 45, S_1^- = 50, S_3^+ = 5, I_1 = 100, I_3 = 50. All the remaining variables are zero. The solution calls for hiring 50 temps in March (S_1^- = 50) and holding the workforce steady till May when 5 temps are fired (S_3^+ = 5). No further hiring or firing is recommended until the end of June when, presumably, all temps are terminated. This solution requires 100 units of inventory to be carried into May and 50 units to be carried into June.

PROBLEM SET 2.4B

1. Toolco has contracted with AutoMate to supply their automotive discount stores with wrenches and chisels. AutoMate's weekly demand consists of at least 1570 wrenches and 1250 chisels. Toolco cannot produce all the requested units with its present one-shift capacity and must use overtime and possibly subcontract with other tool shops. The result

is an increase in the production cost per unit, as shown in the following table. Market demand restricts the ratio of chisels to wrenches to at least 2:1.

Tool	Production type	Weekly production range (units)	Unit cost ($)
Wrenches	Regular	0–500	2.00
	Overtime	501–800	2.80
	Subcontracting	801–∞	3.00
Chisel	Regular	0–620	2.10
	Overtime	621–900	3.20
	Subcontracting	901–∞	4.20

(a) Formulate the problem as a linear program, and determine the optimum production schedule for each tool.

(b) Explain why the validity of the model is dependent on the fact that the unit production cost is an increasing function of the production quantity.

(c) Solve the model using AMPL, Solver, or TORA.

2. Four products are processed sequentially on three machines. The following table gives the pertinent data of the problem:

Machine	Cost per hr ($)	Manufacturing time (hr) per unit				Capacity (hr)
		Product 1	Product 2	Product 3	Product 4	
1	10	2	3	4	2	500
2	5	3	2	1	2	380
3	4	7	3	2	1	450
Unit selling price ($)		75	70	55	45	

Formulate the problem as an LP model, and find the optimum solution using AMPL, Solver, or TORA.

*3. A manufacturer produces three models, I, II, and III, of a certain product using raw materials A and B. The following table gives the data for the problem:

Raw material	Requirements per unit			Availability
	I	II	III	
A	2	3	5	4000
B	4	2	7	6000
Minimum demand	200	200	150	
Price per unit ($)	30	20	50	

The labor time per unit of model I is twice that of II and three times that of III. The entire labor force of the factory can produce the equivalent of 1500 units of model I. Market requirements specify the ratios 3:2:5 for the production of the three respective models. Formulate the problem as a linear program, and find the optimum solution using AMPL, Solver, or TORA.

4. The demand for ice cream during the three summer months (June, July, and August) at All-Flavors Parlor is estimated at 500, 600, and 400 20-gallon cartons, respectively. Two wholesalers, 1 and 2, supply All-Flavors with its ice cream. Although the flavors from the two suppliers are different, they are interchangeable. The maximum number of cartons either supplier can provide is 400 per month. Also, the price the two suppliers charge change from one month to the next according to the following schedule:

	Price per carton in month		
	June	*July*	*August*
Supplier 1	$100	$110	$120
Supplier 2	$115	$108	$125

To take advantage of price fluctuation, All-Flavors can purchase more than is needed for a month and store the surplus to satisfy the demand in a later month. The cost of refrigerating an ice-cream carton is $5 per month. It is realistic in the present situation to assume that the refrigeration cost is a function of the average number of cartons on hand during the month. Develop a model to determine the optimum schedule for buying ice cream from the two suppliers, and find the optimum solution using TORA, Solver, or AMPL.

5. The demand for an item over the next four quarters is 300, 400, 450, and 250 units, respectively. The price per unit starts at $20 in the first quarter and increases by $3.00 each quarter thereafter. The supplier can provide no more than 400 units in any one quarter. Although we can take advantage of lower prices in early quarters, a storage cost of $3.80 is incurred per unit per quarter. In addition, the number of units that can be held over from one quarter to the next must be 80 or less. Develop an LP model to determine the optimum schedule for purchasing the item to meet the demand, and find the optimum solution using AMPL, Solver, or TORA.

6. A company has contracted to produce two products, A and B, over the months of June, July, and August. The total production capacity (expressed in hours) varies monthly. The following table provides the basic data of the situation:

	June	July	August
Demand for *A* (units)	500	5000	750
Demand for *B* (units)	1000	1200	1200
Capacity (hr)	3000	3500	3000

The production rates in units per hour are .75 and 1 for products A and B, respectively. All demand must be met. However, demand for a later month may be filled from the production in an earlier one. For any carryover from one month to the next, holding costs of $.90 and $.75 per unit per month are charged for products A and B, respectively. The unit production costs for the two products are $30 and $28 for A and B, respectively. Develop an LP model to determine the optimum production schedule for the two products, and find the optimum solution using AMPL, Solver, or TORA.

*7. The manufacturing process of a product consists of two successive operations, I and II. The following table provides the pertinent data over the months of June, July, and August:

	June	July	August
Finished product demand (units)	500	450	600
Capacity of operation I (hr)	800	700	550
Capacity of operation II (hr)	1000	850	700

Producing a unit of the product takes .6 hour on operation I plus .8 hour on operation II. Overproduction of either the semifinished product (operation I) or the finished product (operation II) in any month is allowed for use in a later month. The corresponding holding costs are $.20 and $.40 per unit per month. The production cost varies by operation and by month. For operation 1, the unit production cost is $10, $12, and $11 for June, July, and August, respectively. For operation 2, the corresponding unit production cost is $15, $18, and $16. Develop an LP model to determine the optimal production schedule for the two operations over the 3-month horizon, and find the optimum solution using AMPL, Solver, or TORA.

8. Two products are manufactured sequentially on two machines. The time available on each machine is 8 hours per day and may be increased by up to 4 hours of overtime, if necessary, at an additional cost of $110 per hour. The following table gives the production rate on the two machines as well as the price per unit of the two products.

	Production rate (units/hr)	
	Product 1	Product 2
Machine 1	5	5
Machine 2	8	4
Price per unit ($)	120	128

Develop an LP model to determine the optimum production schedule and the recommended use of overtime, if any. Solve the problem using AMPL, Solver, or TORA.

2.4.3 Manpower Planning

Fluctuations in a labor force to meet variable demand over time can be achieved through the process of hiring and firing, as demonstrated in Example 2.4-4. There are situations in which the effect of fluctuations in demand can be "absorbed" by adjusting the start and end times of a work shift. For example, instead of following the traditional three 8-hour-shift start times at 8:00 A.M., 3:00 P.M., and 11:00 P.M., we can use overlapping 8-hour shifts in which the start time of each is made in response to increase or decrease in demand.

The idea of redefining the start of a shift to accommodate fluctuation in demand can be extended to other operating environments as well. Example 2.4-5 deals with the determination of the minimum number of buses needed to meet rush-hour and off-hour transportation needs.

Real-Life Application—Telephone Sales Manpower Planning at Qantas Airways

Australian airline Qantas operates its main reservation offices from 7:00 till 22:00 using 6 shifts that start at different time of the day. Qantas used LP (with imbedded queuing analysis) to staff its main telephone sales reservation office efficiently while providing convenient service to its customers. The study, carried out in the late 70s, resulted in annual savings of over 200,000 Australian dollars per year. The study is detailed in Case 15, Chapter 26, on the website.

Example 2.4-5   (Bus Scheduling Model)

Progress City is studying the feasibility of introducing a mass-transit bus system to reduce in-city driving. The study seeks the minimum number of buses that can handle the transportation needs. After gathering necessary information, the city engineer noticed that the minimum number of buses needed fluctuated with time of the day and that the required number of buses could be approximated by constant values over successive 4-hour intervals. Figure 2.11 summarizes the engineer's findings. To carry out the required daily maintenance, each bus can operate 8 successive hours a day only.

Mathematical Model: The variables of the model are the number of buses needed in each shift, and the constraints deal with satisfying demand. The objective is to minimize the number of buses in operation.

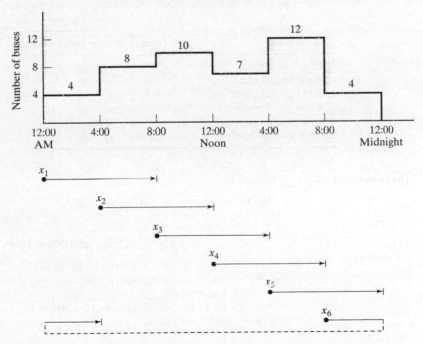

FIGURE 2.11

Number of buses as a function of the time of the day

The stated definition of the variables is somewhat "vague." We know that each bus will run for 8 consecutive hours, but we do not know when a shift should start. If we follow a normal three-shift schedule (8:01 A.M. to 4:00 P.M., 4:01 P.M. to 12:00 midnight, and 12:01 A.M. to 8:00 A.M.) and assume that x_1, x_2, and x_3 are the number of buses starting in the first, second, and third shifts, we can see in Figure 2.11 that $x_1 \geq 10$, $x_2 \geq 12$, and $x_3 \geq 8$. The corresponding minimum number of daily buses is $x_1 + x_2 + x_3 = 10 + 12 + 8 = 30$.

The given solution is acceptable only if the shifts *must* coincide with the normal three-shift schedule. However, it may be advantageous to allow the optimization process to choose the "best" starting time for a shift. A reasonable way to accomplish this goal is to allow a shift to start every 4 hours. The bottom of Figure 2.11 illustrates this idea with overlapping 8-hour shifts starting at 12:01 A.M., 4:01 A.M., 8:01 A.M., 12:01 P.M., 4:01 P.M., and 8:01 P.M. Thus, the variables are defined as

$$x_1 = \text{number of buses starting at 12:01 A.M.}$$

$$x_2 = \text{number of buses starting at 4:01 A.M.}$$

$$x_3 = \text{number of buses starting at 8:01 A.M.}$$

$$x_4 = \text{number of buses starting at 12:01 P.M.}$$

$$x_5 = \text{number of buses starting at 4:01 P.M.}$$

$$x_6 = \text{number of buses starting at 8:01 P.M.}$$

We can see from Figure 2.11 that because of the overlapping of the shifts, the number of buses for the successive 4-hour periods can be computed as follows:

Time period	Number of buses in operation
12:01 A.M. to 4:00 A.M.	$x_1 + x_6$
4:01 A.M. to 8:00 A.M.	$x_1 + x_2$
8:01 A.M. to 12:00 noon	$x_2 + x_3$
12:01 P.M. to 4:00 P.M.	$x_3 + x_4$
4:01 P.M. to 8:00 P.M.	$x_4 + x_5$
8:01 A.M. to 12:00 A.M.	$x_5 + x_6$

The complete model thus becomes

$$\text{Minimize } z = x_1 + x_2 + x_3 + x_4 + x_5 + x_6$$

subject to

$$
\begin{aligned}
x_1 \qquad\qquad\qquad\quad\;\; + x_6 &\geq 4 \quad (\text{12:01 A.M.-4:00 A.M.}) \\
x_1 + x_2 \qquad\qquad\qquad\quad &\geq 8 \quad (\text{4:01 A.M.-8:00 A.M.}) \\
x_2 + x_3 + \qquad\qquad\quad &\geq 10 \quad (\text{8:01 A.M.-12:00 noon}) \\
x_3 + x_4 + \qquad\quad &\geq 7 \quad (\text{12:01 P.M.-4:00 P.M.}) \\
x_4 + x_5 \qquad &\geq 12 \quad (\text{4:01 P.M.-8:00 P.M.}) \\
x_5 + x_6 &\geq 4 \quad (\text{8:01 P.M.-12:00 P.M.}) \\
x_j \geq 0, j = 1, 2, \ldots, 6
\end{aligned}
$$

Solution:

The optimal solution (obtained using file *amplEx2.4-5.txt, solverEx2.4-5.xls*, or *toraEx2.4-5.txt*) calls for scheduling 26 buses (compared with 30 buses when the three traditional shifts are used). The schedule calls for $x_1 = 4$ buses to start at 12:01 A.M., $x_2 = 10$ at 4:01 A.M., $x_4 = 8$ at 12:01 P.M., and $x_5 = 4$ at 4:01 P.M. (*Note*: File *solverEx2.4-5.xls* yields the alternative optimum $x_1 = 2$, $x_2 = 6$, $x_3 = 4$, $x_4 = 6$, $x_5 = 6$, and $x_6 = 2$, with $z = 26$.)

PROBLEM SET 2.4C

*1. In the bus scheduling example suppose that buses can run either 8- or 12-hour shifts. If a bus runs for 12 hours, the driver must be paid for the extra hours at 150% of the regular hourly pay. Do you recommend the use of 12-hour shifts? Solve the new model using AMPL, Solver, or TORA.

2. A hospital employs volunteers to staff the reception desk between 8:00 A.M. and 10:00 P.M. Each volunteer works three consecutive hours except for those starting at 8:00 P.M. who work for 2 hours only. The minimum need for volunteers is approximated by a step function over 2-hour intervals starting at 8:00 A.M. as 5, 8, 6, 4, 8, 6. Because most volunteers are retired individuals, they are willing to offer their services at any hour of the day (8:00 A.M. to 10:00 P.M.). However, because of the large number of charities competing for their service, the number needed must be kept as low as possible. Determine an optimal schedule (using AMPL, Solver, or TORA) for the start time of the volunteers.

3. In Problem 2, suppose that no volunteers will start at 2:00 P.M. or 8:00 P.M. to allow for lunch and dinner. Develop the LP, and determine the optimal schedule using AMPL, Solver, or TORA.

4. In an LTL (less-than-truckload) trucking company, terminal docks include *casual* workers who are hired temporarily to account for peak loads. At the Omaha, Nebraska, dock, the minimum demand for casual workers during the 7 days of the week (starting on Monday) is 18, 15, 19, 10, 20, 16 workers. Each worker is contracted to work 5 consecutive days. Develop the LP model and determine an optimal weekly hiring practice of casual workers for the company using AMPL, Solver, or TORA.

*5. On most United States university campuses, students are contracted by academic departments to do office errands. The need for such service fluctuates during work hours (8:00 A.M. to 5:00 P.M.). In one department, the minimum number of students needed is 2 between 8:00 A.M. and 10:00 A.M., 4 between 10:01 A.M. and 11:00 A.M., 3 between 11:01 A.M. and 1:00 P.M., and 2 between 1:01 P.M. and 5:00 P.M. Each student is allotted 3 consecutive hours (except for those starting at 3:01 who work for 2 hours, and those who start at 4:01 who work for 1 hour). Because of their flexible schedule, students can usually start at any hour during the workday, except at lunchtime (12:00 noon). Develop the LP model, and determine a time schedule specifying the time of the day and the number of students reporting to work. Use AMPL, Solver, or TORA to determine the solution.

6. A large department store operates 7 days a week. The manager estimates that the minimum number of salespersons required to provide prompt service is 12 for Monday, 18 for Tuesday, 20 for Wednesday, 28 for Thursday, 32 for Friday, and 40 for each of Saturday and Sunday. Each salesperson works 5 days a week, with the two consecutive off-days staggered throughout the week. For example, if 10 salespersons start on Monday, 2 can take their off-days on Tuesday and Wednesday, 5 on Wednesday and Thursday, and 3 on Saturday and Sunday. How many salespersons should be contracted, and how should their off-days be allocated? Use AMPL, Solver, or TORA to find the solution.

2.4.4   Urban Development Planning[6]

Urban planning deals with three general areas: (1) building new housing developments, (2) upgrading inner-city deteriorating housing and recreational areas, and (3) planning public facilities (such as schools and airports). The constraints associated with these projects are both economic (land, construction, and financing) and social (schools, parks, and income level). The objectives in urban planning vary. In new housing developments, profit is usually the motive for undertaking the project. In the remaining two categories, the goals involve social, political, economic, and cultural considerations. Indeed, in a publicized case in 2004, the mayor of a city in Ohio wanted to condemn an old area of the city to make way for a luxury housing development. The motive was to increase tax collection to help alleviate budget shortages. The example presented in this section is fashioned after the Ohio case.

Example 2.4-6   (Urban Renewal Model)

The city of Erstville is faced with a severe budget shortage. Seeking a long-term solution, the city council votes to improve the tax base by condemning an inner-city housing area and replacing it with a modern development.

The project involves two phases: (1) demolishing substandard houses to provide land for the new development and (2) building the new development. The following is a summary of the situation.

1. As many as 300 substandard houses can be demolished. Each house occupies a .25-acre lot. The cost of demolishing a condemned house is $2000.

2. Lot sizes for new single-, double-, triple-, and quadruple-family homes (units) are .18, .28, .4, and .5 acre, respectively. Streets, open space, and utility easements account for 15% of available acreage.

3. In the new development, the triple and quadruple units account for at least 25% of the total. Single units must be at least 20% of all units and double units at least 10%.

4. The tax levied per unit for single, double, triple, and quadruple units is $1000, $1900, $2700, and $3400, respectively.

5. The construction cost per unit for single-, double-, triple-, and quadruple-family homes is $50,000, $70,000, $130,000, and $160,000, respectively. Financing through a local bank is limited to $15 million.

How many units of each type should be constructed to maximize tax collection?

Mathematical Model: Besides determining the number of units to be constructed of each type of housing, we also need to decide how many houses must be demolished to make room for the new development. Thus, the variables of the problem can be defined as follows:

$$x_1 = \text{Number of units of single-family homes}$$

$$x_2 = \text{Number of units of double-family homes}$$

[6]This section is based on Laidlaw (1972)

$$x_3 = \text{Number of units of triple-family homes}$$

$$x_4 = \text{Number of units of quadruple-family homes}$$

$$x_5 = \text{Number of old homes to be demolished}$$

The objective is to maximize total tax collection from all four types of homes—that is,

$$\text{Maximize } z = 1000x_1 + 1900x_2 + 2700x_3 + 3400x_4$$

The first constraint of the problem deals with land availability.

$$\begin{pmatrix} \text{Acreage used for new} \\ \text{homes construction} \end{pmatrix} \leq \begin{pmatrix} \text{Net available} \\ \text{acreage} \end{pmatrix}$$

From the data of the problem, we have

$$\text{Acreage needed for new homes} = .18x_1 + .28x_2 + .4x_3 + .5x_4$$

To determine the available acreage, each demolished home occupies a .25-acre lot, thus netting $.25x_5$ acres. Allowing for 15% open space, streets, and easements, the net acreage available is $.85(.25x_5) = .2125x_5$. The resulting constraint is

$$.18x_1 + .28x_2 + .4x_3 + .5x_4 \qquad \leq .2125x_5$$

or

$$.18x_1 + .28x_2 + .4x_3 + .5x_4 - .2125x_5 \leq 0$$

The number of demolished homes cannot exceed 300, which translates to

$$x_5 \leq 300$$

Next we add the constraints limiting the number of units of each home type.

$$(\text{Number of single units}) \geq (20\% \text{ of all units})$$

$$(\text{Number of double units}) \geq (10\% \text{ of all units})$$

$$(\text{Number of triple and quadruple units}) \geq (25\% \text{ of all units})$$

These constraints translate mathematically to

$$x_1 \geq .2(x_1 + x_2 + x_3 + x_4)$$

$$x_2 \geq .1(x_1 + x_2 + x_3 + x_4)$$

$$x_3 + x_4 \geq .25(x_1 + x_2 + x_3 + x_4)$$

The only remaining constraint deals with keeping the demolition/construction cost within the allowable budget—that is,

$$(\text{Construction and demolition cost}) \leq (\text{Available budget})$$

Expressing all the costs in thousands of dollars, we get

$$(50x_1 + 70x_2 + 130x_3 + 160x_4) + 2x_5 \leq 15000$$

The complete model thus becomes

$$\text{Maximize } z = 1000x_1 + 1900x_2 + 2700x_3 + 3400x_4$$

subject to

$$.18x_1 + .28x_2 + .4x_3 + .5x_4 - .2125x_5 \le 0$$

$$x_5 \le 300$$

$$-.8x_1 + .2x_2 + .2x_3 + .2x_4 \qquad \le 0$$

$$.1x_1 - .9x_2 + .1x_3 + .1x_4 \qquad \le 0$$

$$.25x_1 + .25x_2 - .75x_3 - .75x_4 \qquad \le 0$$

$$50x_1 + 70x_2 + 130x_3 + 160x_4 + 2x_5 \le 15000$$

$$x_1, x_2, x_3, x_4, x_5 \ge 0$$

Solution:

The optimum solution (obtained using file *amplEX2.4-6.txt* or *solverEx2.4-6.xls*) is:

> Total tax collection = z = \$343,965
> Number of single homes = x_1 = 35.83 $\simeq$ 36units
> Number of double homes = x_2 = 98.53 $\simeq$ 99 units
> Number of triple homes = x_3 = 44.79 $\simeq$ 45 units
> Number of quadruple homes = x_4 = 0 unit
> Number of homes demolished = x_5 = 244.49 $\simeq$ 245 units

Remarks.   Linear programming does not guarantee an integer solution automatically, and this is the reason for rounding the continuous values to the closest integer. The rounded solution calls for constructing 180 (= 36 + 99 + 45) units and demolishing 245 old homes, which yields \$345,600 in taxes. Keep in mind, however, that, in general, the rounded solution may not be feasible. In fact, the current rounded solution violates the budget constraint by \$70,000 (verify!). Interestingly, the true optimum integer solution (using the algorithms in Chapter 9) is x_1 = 36, x_2 = 98, x_3 = 45, x_4 = 0, and x_5 = 245 with z = \$343,700. Carefully note that the rounded solution yields a better objective value, which appears contradictory. The reason is that the rounded solution calls for producing an extra double home, which is feasible only if the budget is increased by \$70,000.

PROBLEM SET 2.4D

1. A realtor is developing a rental housing and retail area. The housing area consists of efficiency apartments, duplexes, and single-family homes. Maximum demand by potential renters is estimated to be 500 efficiency apartments, 300 duplexes, and 250 single-family homes, but the number of duplexes must equal at least 50% of the number of efficiency apartments and single homes. Retail space is proportionate to the number of home units at the rates of at least 12 ft^2, 18 ft^2, and 20 ft^2 for efficiency, duplex, and single-family units, respectively. However, land availability limits retail space to no more than 15,000 ft^2. The monthly rental income is estimated at \$650, \$800, and \$1500 for efficiency-, duplex-, and single-family units, respectively. The retail space rents for \$120/ft^2. Develop an LP model to determine the optimal retail space area and the number of family residences, and find the solution using AMPL, Solver, or TORA.

2. The city council of Fayetteville is in the process of approving the construction of a new 220,000-ft^2 convention center. Two sites have been proposed, and both require

exercising the "eminent domain" law to acquire the property. The following table provides data about proposed (contiguous) properties in both sites together with the acquisition cost.

	Site 1		Site 2	
Property	*Area* (1000 ft^2)	*Cost* ($1000)	*Area* (1000 ft^2)	*Cost* ($1000)
1	20	1000	80	2800
2	50	2100	60	1900
3	50	2350	50	2800
4	30	1850	70	2500
5	60	2950		

Partial acquisition of property is allowed. At least 80% of property 4 must be acquired if site 1 is selected, and at least 60% of property 3 must be acquired if site 2 is selected. Although site 1 property is more expensive (on a per ft^2 basis), the construction cost is less than at site 2, because the infrastructure at site 1 is in a much better shape. Construction cost is $30 million at site 1 and $32 million at site 2. Which site should be selected, and what properties should be acquired? Find the solution using AMPL, Solver, or TORA

*3. A city will undertake five urban renewal housing projects over the next 5 years. Each project has a different starting year and a different duration. The following table provides the basic data of the situation:

	Year 1	Year 2	Year 3	Year 4	Year 5	Cost (million $)	Annual income (million $)
Project 1	Start		End			5.0	.05
Project 2		Start			End	8.0	.07
Project 3	Start				End	15.0	.15
Project 4				Start	End	1.2	.02
Budget (million $)	3.0	6.0	7.0	7.0	7.0		

Projects 1 and 4 must be finished completely within their durations. The remaining two projects can be finished partially within budget limitations, if necessary. However, each project must be at least 25% completed within its duration. At the end of each year, the completed section of a project is immediately occupied by tenants, and a proportional amount of income is realized. For example, if 40% of project 1 is completed in year 1 and 60% in year 3, the associated income over the 5-year planning horizon is .4 × $50,000 (for year 2) + .4 × $50,000 (for year 3) + (.4 + .6) × $50,000 (for year 4) + (.4 + .6) × $50,000 (for year 5) = (4 × .4 + 2 × .6) × $50,000. Develop an LP model to determine the schedule for the projects that will maximize the total income over the 5-year horizon, and find the solution using AMPL, Solver, or TORA. For simplicity, disregard the time value of money.

4. The city of Fayetteville is embarking on an urban renewal project that will include lower- and middle-income row housing, upper-income luxury apartments, and public housing. The project also includes a public elementary school and retail facilities. The size of the elementary school (number of classrooms) is proportional to the number of pupils, and

the retail space is proportional to the number of housing units. The following table provides the pertinent data of the situation:

	Lower income	Middle income	Upper income	Public housing	School room	Retail unit
Minimum number of units	100	125	75	300		0
Maximum number of units	200	190	260	600		25
Lot size per unit (acre)	.05	.07	.03	.025	.045	.1
Average number of pupils per unit	1.3	1.2	.5	1.4		
Retail demand per unit (acre)	.023	.034	.046	.023	.034	
Annual income per unit ($)	7000	12,000	20,000	5000	—	15,000

The new school can occupy a maximum space of 2 acres at the rate of at most 25 pupils per room. The operating annual cost per schoolroom is $10,000. The project will be located on a 50-acre vacant property owned by the city. Additionally, the project can make use of an adjacent property occupied by 200 condemned slum homes. Each condemned home occupies .25 acre. The cost of buying and demolishing a slum unit is $7000. Open space, streets, and parking lots consume 15% of total available land.

Develop a linear program to determine the optimum plan for the project, and find the solution using AMPL, Solver, or TORA.

5. Realco owns 900 acres of undeveloped land on a scenic lake in the heart of the Ozark Mountains. In the past, little or no regulation was imposed upon new developments around the lake. The lake shores are now dotted with vacation homes, and septic tanks, most of them improperly installed, are in extensive use. Over the years, seepage from the septic tanks led to severe water pollution. To curb further degradation of the lake, county officials have approved stringent ordinances applicable to all future developments: (1) Only single-, double-, and triple-family homes can be constructed, with single-family homes accounting for at least 50% of the total. (2) To limit the number of septic tanks, minimum lot sizes of 2, 3, and 5 acres are required for single-, double-, and triple-family homes, respectively. (3) Recreation areas of 1 acre each must be established at the rate of one area per 220 families. (4) To preserve the ecology of the lake, underground water may not be pumped out for house or garden use. The president of Realco is studying the possibility of developing the 800-acre property. The new development will include single-, double-, and triple-family homes. It is estimated that 15% of the acreage will be allocated to streets and utility easements. Realco estimates the returns from the different housing units as follows:

Housing unit	Single	Double	Triple
Net return per unit ($)	12,000	15,000	18,000

The cost of connecting water service to the area is proportionate to the number of units constructed. However, the county charges a minimum of $120,000 for the project. Additionally, the expansion of the water system beyond its present capacity is limited to 220,000 gallons per day during peak periods. The following data summarize the water service connection cost as well as the water consumption, assuming an average size family:

Housing unit	Single	Double	Triple	Recreation
Water service connection cost per unit ($)	1000	1200	1400	800
Water consumption per unit (gal/day)	400	600	840	450

Develop an LP model to determine the optimal plan for Realco, and find the solution using AMPL, Solver, or TORA.

6. Consider the Realco model of Problem 5. Suppose that an additional 100 acres of land can be purchased for $450,000, which will increase the total acreage to 900 acres. Is this a profitable deal for Realco?

2.4.5 Blending and Refining

A number of LP applications deal with blending different input materials to manu-facture products that meet certain specifications while minimizing cost or maximiz-ing profit. The input materials could be ores, metal scraps, chemicals, or crude oils, and the output products could be metal ingots, paints, or gasoline of various grades. This section presents a (simplified) model for oil refining. The process starts with dis-tilling crude oil to produce intermediate gasoline stocks and then blending these stocks to produce final gasoline products. The final products must satisfy certain quality specifications (such as octane rating). In addition, distillation capacities and demand limits can directly affect the level of production of the different grades of gasoline. One goal of the model is to determine the optimal mix of final products that will maximize an appropriate profit function. In some cases, the goal may be to mini-mize a cost function.

Example 2.4-7 (Crude Oil Refining and Gasoline Blending)

Shale Oil, located on the island of Aruba, has a capacity of 1,500,000 bbl of crude oil per day. The final products from the refinery include three types of unleaded gasoline with different octane numbers (ON): regular with ON = 87, premium with ON = 89, and super with ON = 92. The refining process encompasses three stages: (1) a distillation tower that produces feedstock (ON = 82) at the rate of .2 bbl per bbl of crude oil, (2) a cracker unit that produces gasoline stock (ON = 98) by using a portion of the feedstock produced from the distillation tower at the rate of .5 bbl per bbl of feedstock, and (3) a blender unit that blends the gasoline stock from the cracker unit and the feedstock from the distillation tower. The company estimates the net prof-it per barrel of the three types of gasoline to be $6.70, $7.20, and $8.10, respectively. The input capacity of the cracker unit is 200,000 barrels of feedstock a day. The demand limits for regular, premium, and super gasoline are 50,000, 30,000, and 40,000 barrels, respectively, per day. Develop a model for determining the optimum production schedule for the refinery.

Mathematical Model: Figure 2.12 summarizes the elements of the model. The variables can be defined in terms of two input streams to the blender (feedstock and cracker gasoline) and the three final products. Let

$$x_{ij} = \text{bbl/day of input stream } i \text{ used to blend final product } j, i = 1, 2; j = 1, 2, 3$$

Using this definition, we have

$$\text{Daily production of regular gasoline} = x_{11} + x_{21} \text{ bbl/day}$$

$$\text{Daily production of premium gasoline} = x_{12} + x_{22} \text{ bbl/day}$$

$$\text{Daily production of super gasoline} = x_{13} + x_{23} \text{ bbl/day}$$

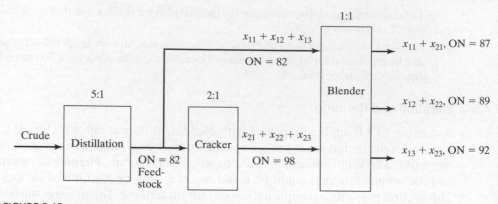

FIGURE 2.12

Product flow in the refinery problem

$$\begin{pmatrix} \text{Daily output} \\ \text{of blender unit} \end{pmatrix} = \begin{pmatrix} \text{Daily production} \\ \text{of regular gas} \end{pmatrix} + \begin{pmatrix} \text{Daily production} \\ \text{of premium gas} \end{pmatrix}$$

$$+ \begin{pmatrix} \text{Daily production} \\ \text{of super gas} \end{pmatrix}$$

$$= (x_{11} + x_{21}) + (x_{12} + x_{22}) + (x_{13} + x_{23}) \text{ bbl/day}$$

$$\begin{pmatrix} \text{Daily feedstock} \\ \text{to blender} \end{pmatrix} = x_{11} + x_{12} + x_{13} \text{ bbl/day}$$

$$\begin{pmatrix} \text{Daily cracker unit} \\ \text{feed to blender} \end{pmatrix} = x_{21} + x_{22} + x_{23} \text{ bbl/day}$$

$$\begin{pmatrix} \text{Daily feedstock} \\ \text{to cracker} \end{pmatrix} = 2(x_{21} + x_{22} + x_{23}) \text{ bbl/day}$$

$$\begin{pmatrix} \text{Daily crude oil used} \\ \text{in the refinery} \end{pmatrix} = 5(x_{11} + x_{12} + x_{13}) + 10(x_{21} + x_{22} + x_{23}) \text{ bbl/day}$$

The objective of the model is to maximize the total profit resulting from the sale of all three grades of gasoline. From the definitions given earlier, we get

$$\text{Maximize } z = 6.70(x_{11} + x_{21}) + 7.20(x_{12} + x_{22}) + 8.10(x_{13} + x_{23})$$

The constraints of the problem are developed as follows:

1. *Daily crude oil supply does not exceed 1,500,000 bbl/day*:

$$5(x_{11} + x_{12} + x_{13}) + 10(x_{21} + x_{22} + x_{23}) \le 1,500,000$$

2. *Cracker unit input capacity does not exceed 200,000 bbl/day*:

$$2(x_{21} + x_{22} + x_{23}) \le 200,000$$

3. *Daily demand for regular does not exceed 50,000 bbl*:

$$x_{11} + x_{21} \le 50,000$$

4. *Daily demand for premium does not exceed 30,000*:

$$x_{12} + x_{22} \le 30,000$$

5. *Daily demand for super does not exceed 40,000 bbl*:

$$x_{13} + x_{23} \le 40,000$$

6. *Octane number (ON) for regular is at least 87*:

The octane number of a gasoline product is the weighted average of the octane numbers of the input streams used in the blending process and can be computed as

$$\left(\begin{array}{c} \text{Average ON of} \\ \text{regular gasoline} \end{array} \right) =$$

$$\frac{\text{Feedstock ON} \times \text{feedstock bbl/day} + \text{Cracker unit ON} \times \text{Cracker unit bbl/day}}{\text{Total bbl/day of regular gasoline}}$$

$$= \frac{82x_{11} + 98x_{21}}{x_{11} + x_{21}}$$

Thus, octane number constraint for regular gasoline becomes

$$\frac{82x_{11} + 98x_{21}}{x_{11} + x_{21}} \ge 87$$

The constraint is linearized as

$$82x_{11} + 98x_{21} \ge 87(x_{11} + x_{21})$$

7. *Octane number (ON) for premium is at least 89*:

$$\frac{82x_{12} + 98x_{22}}{x_{12} + x_{22}} \ge 89$$

which is linearized as

$$82x_{12} + 98x_{22} \ge 89(x_{12} + x_{22})$$

8. *Octane number (ON) for super is at least 92*:

$$\frac{82x_{13} + 98x_{23}}{x_{13} + x_{23}} \ge 92$$

or

$$82x_{13} + 98x_{23} \ge 92(x_{13} + x_{23})$$

The complete model is thus summarized as

$$\text{Maximize } z = 6.70(x_{11} + x_{21}) + 7.20(x_{12} + x_{22}) + 8.10(x_{13} + x_{23})$$

subject to

$$5(x_{11} + x_{12} + x_{13}) + 10(x_{21} + x_{22} + x_{23}) \le 1,500,000$$

$$2(x_{21} + x_{22} + x_{23}) \le 200,000$$

$$x_{11} + x_{21} \leq 50{,}000$$

$$x_{12} + x_{22} \leq 30{,}000$$

$$x_{13} + x_{23} \leq 40{,}000$$

$$82x_{11} + 98x_{21} \geq 87(x_{11} + x_{21})$$

$$82x_{12} + 98x_{22} \geq 89(x_{12} + x_{22})$$

$$82x_{13} + 98x_{23} \geq 92(x_{13} + x_{23})$$

$$x_{11}, x_{12}, x_{13}, x_{21}, x_{22}, x_{23} \geq 0$$

The last three constraints can be simplified to produce a constant right-hand side.

Solution:

The optimum solution (obtained using file *toraEx2.4-7.txt* or *amplEx2.4-7.txt*) is $z = 875{,}000$, $x_{11} = 34{,}375$, $x_{21} = 15{,}625$, $x_{12} = 16{,}875$, $x_{22} = 13{,}125$, $x_{13} = 15{,}000$, $x_{23} = 25{,}000$. This translates to

Daily profit $= \$ 875{,}000$
Daily amount of regular gasoline $= x_{11} + x_{21} = 34{,}375 + 13{,}125 = 30{,}000$ bbl/day
Daily amount of premium gasoline $= x_{12} + x_{22} = 16{,}875 + 13{,}125 = 30{,}000$ bbl/day
Daily amount of regular gasoline $= x_{13} + x_{23} = 15{,}000 + 25{,}000 = 40{,}000$ bbl/day

The solution shows that regular gasoline production is 20,000 bbl/day short of satisfying the maximum demand. The demand for the remaining two grades is satisfied.

PROBLEM SET 2.4E

1. Hi-V produces three types of canned juice drinks, *A*, *B*, and *C*, using fresh strawberries, grapes, and apples. The daily supply is limited to 200 tons of strawberries, 90 tons of grapes, and 150 tons of apples. The cost per ton of strawberries, grapes, and apples is $210, $110, and $100, respectively. Each ton makes 1500 lb of strawberry juice, 1200 lb of grape juice, and 1000 lb of apple juice. Drink *A* is a 1:1 mix of strawberry and apple juice. Drink *B* is 1:1:2 mix of strawberry, grape, and apple juice. Drink *C* is a 2:3 mix of grape and apple juice. All drinks are canned in 16-oz (1 lb) cans. The price per can is $1.15, $1.25, and $1.20 for drinks *A*, *B*, and *C*. Develop an LP model to determine the optimal production mix of the three drinks, and find the solution using AMPL, Solver, or TORA.

*2. A hardware store packages handyman bags of screws, bolts, nuts, and washers. Screws come in 100-lb boxes and cost $120 each, bolts come in 100-lb boxes and cost $175 each, nuts come in 80-lb boxes and cost $75 each, and washers come in 30-lb boxes and cost $25 each. The handyman package weighs at least 1 lb and must include, by weight, at least 10% screws and 25% bolts, and at most 15% nuts and 10% washers. To balance the package, the number of bolts cannot exceed the number of nuts or the number of washers. A bolt weighs 10 times as much as a nut and 50 times as much as a washer. Develop an LP model to determine the optimal mix of the package, and find the solution using AMPL, Solver, or TORA.

3. All-Natural Coop makes three breakfast cereals, *A*, *B*, and *C*, from four ingredients: rolled oats, raisins, shredded coconuts, and slivered almonds. The daily availabilities of the ingredients are 5 tons, 2 tons, 1 ton, and 1 ton, respectively. The corresponding costs per ton are $100, $120, $110, and $200. Cereal *A* is a 50:5:2 mix of oats, raisins, and almond.

Cereal B is a 60:2:3 mix of oats, coconut, and almond. Cereal C is a 60:3:4:2 mix of oats, raisins, coconut, and almond. The cereals are produced in jumbo 5-lb sizes. All-Natural sells A, B, and C at $2, $2.50, $3.00 per box, respectively. The minimum daily demand for cereals A, B, and C is 500, 600, and 500 boxes, respectively. Develop an LP model to determine the optimal production mix of the cereals and the associated amounts of ingredients, and find the solution using AMPL, Solver, or TORA.

4. A refinery manufactures two grades of jet fuel, F1 and F2, by blending four types of gasoline, A, B, C, and D. Fuel F1 uses gasolines A, B, C, and D in the ratio 1:1:2:4, and fuel F2 uses the ratio 2:2:1:3. The supply limits for A, B, C, and D are 1000, 1200, 900, and 1500 bbl/day, respectively. The costs per bbl for gasolines A, B, C, and D are $120, $90, $100, and $150, respectively. Fuels F1 and F2 sell for $200 and $250 per bbl, respectively. The minimum demand for F1 and F2 is 200 and 400 bbl/day, respectively. Develop an LP model to determine the optimal production mix for F1 and F2, and find the solution using AMPL, Solver, or TORA.

*5. An oil company distills two types of crude oil, A and B, to produce regular and premium gasoline and jet fuel. There are limits on the daily availability of crude oil and the minimum demand for the final products. If the production is not sufficient to cover demand, the shortage must be made up from outside sources at a penalty. Surplus production will not be sold immediately and will incur storage cost. The following table provides the data of the situation:

Crude	Fraction yield per bbl			Price/bbl ($)	bbl/day
	Regular	Premium	Jet		
Crude A	.20	.1	.25	30	2500
Crude B	.25	.3	.10	40	3000
Demand (bbl/day)	500	700	400		
Revenue ($/bbl)	50	70	120		
Storage cost for surplus production ($/bbl)	2	3	4		
Penalty for unfilled demand ($/bbl)	10	15	20		

Develop an LP model to determine the optimal product mix for the refinery, and find the solution using AMPL, Solver, or TORA.

6. In the refinery situation of Problem 5, suppose that the distillation unit actually produces the intermediate products naphtha and light oil. One bbl of crude A produces .35 bbl of naphtha and .6 bbl of light oil, and one bbl of crude B produces .45 bbl of naphtha and .5 bbl of light oil. Naphtha and light oil are blended to produce the three final gasoline products: One bbl of regular gasoline has a blend ratio of 2:1 (naphtha to light oil), one bbl of premium gasoline has a blend ratio of 1:1, and one bbl of jet fuel has a blend ratio of 1:2. Develop an LP model to determine the optimal production mix, and find the solution using AMPL, Solver, or TORA.

7. Hawaii Sugar Company produces brown sugar, processed (white) sugar, powdered sugar, and molasses from sugar cane syrup. The company purchases 4000 tons of syrup weekly and is contracted to deliver at least 25 tons weekly of each type of sugar. The production process starts by manufacturing brown sugar and molasses from the syrup. A ton of syrup produces .3 ton of brown sugar and .1 ton of molasses. White sugar is produced by processing brown sugar. It takes 1 ton of brown sugar to produce .8 ton of white sugar. Powdered sugar is produced from white sugar through a special grinding process that has a 95%

conversion efficiency (1 ton of white sugar produces .95 ton of powdered sugar). The profits per ton for brown sugar, white sugar, powdered sugar, and molasses are $150, $200, $230, and $35, respectively. Formulate the problem as a linear program, and determine the weekly production schedule using AMPL, Solver, or TORA.

8. Shale Oil refinery blends two petroleum stocks, A and B, to produce two high-octane gasoline products, I and II. Stocks A and B are produced at the maximum rates of 450 and 700 bbl/hour, respectively. The corresponding octane numbers are 98 and 89, and the vapor pressures are 10 and 8 lb/in^2. Gasoline I and gasoline II must have octane numbers of at least 91 and 93, respectively. The vapor pressure associated with both products should not exceed 12 lb/in^2. The profits per bbl of I and II are $7 and $10, respectively. Develop an LP model to determine the optimum production rate for I and II and their blend ratios from stocks A and B, and find the solution using AMPL, Solver, or TORA. (*Hint*: Vapor pressure, like the octane number, is the weighted average of the vapor pressures of the blended stocks.)

9. A foundry smelts steel, aluminum, and cast iron scraps to produce two types of metal ingots, I and II, with specific limits on the aluminum, graphite, and silicon contents. Aluminum and silicon briquettes may be used in the smelting process to meet the desired specifications. The following tables set the specifications of the problem:

Input item	Contents (%)			Cost/ton ($)	Available (tons/day)
	Aluminum	*Graphite*	*Silicon*		
Steel scrap	10	5	4	110	1100
Aluminum scrap	95	1	2	160	600
Cast iron scrap	0	15	8	85	2600
Aluminum briquette	100	0	0	910	Any amount
Silicon briquette	0	0	100	390	Any amount

Ingredient	Ingot I		Ingot II	
	Minimum (%)	*Maximum* (%)	*Minimum* (%)	*Maximum* (%)
Aluminum	8.1	10.8	6.2	8.9
Graphite	1.5	3.0	4.1	∞
Silicon	2.5	∞	2.8	4.1
Demand (tons/day)		130		250

Develop an LP model to determine the optimal input mix the foundry should smelt, and find the solution using AMPL, Solver, or TORA.

10. Two alloys, A and B, are made from four metals, I, II, III, and IV, according to the following specifications:

Alloy	Specifications	Selling price ($)
A	At most 80% of I	200
	At most 30% of II	
	At least 50% of IV	
B	Between 40% and 60% of II	300
	At least 30% of III	
	At most 70% of IV	

The four metals are extracted from three ores according to the following data:

Ore	Maximum quantity (tons)	Constituents (%)					Price/ton ($)
		I	II	III	IV	Others	
1	1000	20	10	30	30	10	30
2	2000	10	20	30	30	10	40
3	3000	5	5	70	20	0	50

Develop an LP model to determine how much of each type of alloy should be produced, and find the solution using AMPL, Solver, or TORA. (*Hint*: Let x_{kj} be tons of ore i allocated to alloy k, and define w_k as tons of alloy k produced.)

2.4.6 Additional LP Applications

The preceding sections have demonstrated representative LP applications in five areas. Problem Set 2.4f in this section provides additional areas of application, ranging from agriculture to military.

PROBLEM SET 2.4F

1. *Shelf Space Allocation.* A grocery store must decide on the shelf space to be allocated to each of five types of breakfast cereals. The maximum daily demand is 110, 80, 150, and 100 boxes, respectively. The shelf space in square inches for the respective boxes is 15, 25, 16, 20, and 22. The total available shelf space is 5000 in^2. The profit per unit is $1.10, $1.30, $1.08, $1.25, and $1.20, respectively. Determine the optimal space allocation for the five cereals.

2. *Voting on Issues.* In a particular county in the State of Arkansas, four election issues are on the ballot: Build new highways, increase gun control, increase farm subsidies, and increase gasoline tax. The county includes 100,000 urban voters, 250,000 suburban voters, and 50,000 rural voters, all with varying degrees of support for and opposition to election issues. For example, rural voters are opposed to gun control and gas tax and in favor of road building and farm subsidies. The county is planning a TV advertising campaign with a budget of $120,000 at the cost of $1800 per ad. The following table summarizes the impact of a single ad in terms of the number of pro and con votes as a function of the different issues:

Issue	Expected number of pro (+) and con (−) votes per ad		
	Urban	Suburban	Rural
New highways	−35,000	+60,000	I 30,000
Gun control	+80,000	+35,000	−45,000
Smog control	+45,000	+10,000	0
Gas tax	+90,000	0	−28,000

An issue will be adopted if it garners at least 51% of the votes. Which issues will be approved by voters, and how many ads should be allocated to these issues?

3. *Assembly-Line Balancing.* A product is assembled from three different parts. The parts are manufactured by two departments at different production rates as given in the following table:

Department	Capacity (hr/wk)	Production rate (units/hr)		
		Part 1	*Part 2*	*Part 3*
1	100	6	6	12
2	90	6	12	4

Determine the maximum number of final assembly units that can be produced weekly. (*Hint*: Assembly units-min {units of part 1, units of part 2, and units of part 3}. Maximize $z = \min \{x_1, x_2\}$ is equivalent to max z subject to $z \leq x_1$ and $z \leq x_2$.)

4. *Pollution Control.* Three types of coal, C1, C2, and C3, are pulverized and mixed together to produce 50 tons per hour needed to power a plant for generating electricity. The burning of coal emits sulfur oxide (in parts per million) which must meet the EPA specifications of at most 2000 parts per million. The following table summarizes the data of the situation:

	C1	C2	C3
Sulfur (parts per million)	2500	1500	1600
Pulverizer capacity (ton/hr)	30	30	30
Cost per ton	\$30	\$35	\$33

Determine the optimal mix of the coals.

*5. *Traffic Light Control, Stark and Nicholes (1972).* Automobile traffic from three highways, H1, H2, and H3, must stop and wait for a green light before exiting to a toll road. The tolls are \$4, \$5, and \$6 for cars exiting from H1, H2, and H3, respectively. The flow rates from H1, H2, and H3 are 550, 650, and 450 cars per hour. The traffic light cycle may not exceed 2.2 minutes, and the green light on any highway must be on for at least 22 seconds. The yellow light is on for 10 seconds. The toll gate can handle a maximum of 500 cars per hour. Assuming that no cars move on yellow, determine the optimal green time interval for the three highways that will maximize toll gate revenue per traffic cycle.

6. *Fitting a Straight Line into Empirical Data (Regression).* In a 10-week typing class for beginners, the average speed per student (in words per minute) as a function of the number of weeks in class is given in the following table:

Week, x	1	2	3	4	5	6	7	8	9	10
Words per minute, y	5	9	15	19	21	24	26	30	31	35

Determine the coefficients a and b in the straight-line relationship, $\hat{y} = ax + b$, that best fit the given data. (*Hint*: Minimize the sum of the *absolute value* of the deviations between theoretical $\hat{y}$ and empirical y. Min $|w|$ is equivalent to min z subject to $z \geq w$ and $z \geq -w, z \geq 0$. Alternatively, min $|w|$ is equivalent to min $(z^+ + z^-)$ subject to $w = z^+ - z^-$ with $z^+, z^- \geq 0$.)

7. *Leveling the Terrain for a New Highway, Stark and Nicholes (1972).* The Arkansas Highway Department is planning a new 10-mile highway on uneven terrain as shown by the profile in Figure 2.13. The width of the construction terrain is approximately 50 yards.

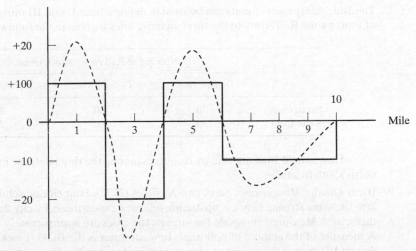

FIGURE 2.13

Terrain profile for Problem 7

To simplify the situation, the terrain profile can be replaced by a step function as shown in the figure. Using heavy machinery, earth removed from high terrain is hauled to fill low areas. There are also two burrow pits, I and II, located at the ends of the 10-mile stretch from which additional earth can be hauled, if needed. Pit I has a capacity of 20,000 cubic yards and pit II a capacity of 15,000 cubic yards. The costs of removing earth from pits I and II are, respectively, $1.50 and $1.90 per cubic yard. The transportation cost per cubic yard per mile is $.15, and the cost of using heavy machinery to load hauling trucks is $.20 per cubic yard. This means that a cubic yard from pit I hauled 1 mile will cost a total of $(1.5 + .20) + 1 \times .15 = \$1.85$ and a cubic yard hauled 1 mile from a hill to a fill area will cost $.20 + 1 \times .15 = \$.35$. Develop a minimum cost plan for leveling the 10-mile stretch.

8. *Military Planning, Shepard and Associates (1988)*. The Red Army (R) is trying to invade the territory defended by the Blue Army (B). Blue has three defense lines and 200 regular combat units and can draw also on a reserve pool of 200 units. Red plans to attack on two fronts, north and south, and Blue has set up three east–west defense lines, I, II, and III. The purpose of defense lines 1 and 2 is to delay the Red Army attack by at least 4 days in each line and to maximize the total duration of the battle. The advance time of the Red Army is estimated by the following empirical formula:

$$\text{Battle duration in days} = a + b\left(\frac{\text{Blue units}}{\text{Red units}}\right)$$

The constants a and b are a function of the defense line and the north/south front as the following table shows:

	a			b		
	I	II	III	I	II	III
North front	.5	.75	.55	8.8	7.9	10.2
South front	1.1	1.3	1.5	10.5	8.1	9.2

The Blue Army reserve units can be used in defense lines II and III only. The allocation of units by the Red Army to the three defense lines is given in the following table:

	Number of Red Army attack units		
	Defense line 1	*Defense line 2*	*Defense line 3*
North front	30	60	20
South front	30	40	20

How should Blue allocate its resources among the three defense lines and the north/south fronts?

9. *Water Quality Management, Stark and Nicholes (1972).* Four cities discharge wastewater into the same stream. City 1 is upstream, followed downstream by city 2, then city 3, and then city 4. Measured alongside the stream, the cities are approximately 15 miles apart. A measure of the amount of pollutants in wastewater is the BOD (biochemical oxygen demand), which is the weight of oxygen required to stabilize the waste constituent in water. A higher BOD indicates worse water quality. The EPA sets a maximum allowable BOD loading, expressed in lb BOD per gallon. The removal of pollutants from wastewater takes place in two forms: (1) natural decomposition activity stimulated by the oxygen in the air, and (2) treatment plants at the points of discharge before the waste reaches the stream. The objective is to determine the most economical efficiency of each of the four plants that will reduce BOD to acceptable levels. The maximum possible plant efficiency is 99%.

To demonstrate the computations involved in the process, consider the following definitions for plant 1:

Q_1 = Stream flow (gal/hr) on the 15-mile reach 1-2 leading to city 2

p_1 = BOD discharge rate (in lb/hr)

x_1 = efficiency of plant 1 ($\leq .99$)

b_1 = maximum allowable BOD loading in reach 1-2 (in lb BOD/gal)

To satisfy the BOD loading requirement in reach 1-2, we must have

$$p_1(1 - x_1) \leq b_1 Q_1$$

In a similar manner, the BOD loading constraint for reach 2-3 takes the form

$$(1 - r_{12})\left(\begin{array}{c}\text{BOD discharge} \\ \text{rate in reach 1-2}\end{array}\right) + \left(\begin{array}{c}\text{BOD discharge} \\ \text{rate in reach 2-3}\end{array}\right) \leq b_2 Q_2$$

or

$$(1 - r_{12})p_1(1 - x_1) + p_2(1 - x_2) \leq b_2 Q_2$$

The coefficient r_{12} (<1) represents the fraction of waste removed in reach 1-2 by decomposition. For reach 2-3, the constraint is

$$(1 - r_{23})[(1 - r_{12})p_1(1 - x_1) + p_2(1 - x_2)] + p_3(1 - x_3) \leq b_3 Q_3$$

Determine the most economical efficiency for the four plants using the following data (the fraction of BOD removed by decomposition is 6% for all four reaches):

	Reach 1–2 ($i = 1$)	Reach 2–3 ($i = 2$)	Reach 2–3 ($i = 3$)	Reach 3–4 ($i = 4$)
Q_i (gal/hr)	215,000	220,000	200,000	210,000
p_i (lb/hr)	500	3000	6000	1000
b_i (lb BOD/gal)	.00085	.0009	.0008	.0008
Treatment cost ($/lb BOD removed)	.20	.25	.15	.18

10. *Loading Structure, Stark and Nichole (1972).* The overhead crane in Figure 2.14 with two lifting yokes is used to transport mixed concrete to a yard for casting concrete barriers. The concrete bucket hangs at midpoint from the yoke. The crane end rails can support a maximum of 25 kip each, and the yoke cables have a 20-kip capacity each. Determine the maximum load capacity, W_1 and W_2. (*Hint:* At equilibrium, the sum of moments about any point on the girder or yoke is zero.)

11. *Allocation of Aircraft to Routes.* Consider the problem of assigning aircraft to four routes according to the following data:

Aircraft type	Capacity (passengers)	Number of aircraft	Number of daily trips on route			
			1	*2*	*3*	*4*
1	50	5	3	2	2	1
2	30	8	4	3	3	2
3	20	10	5	5	4	2
Daily number of customers			1000	2000	900	1200

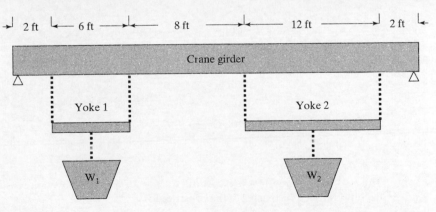

FIGURE 2.14
Overhead crane with two yokes (Problem 11)

The associated costs, including the penalties for losing customers because of space unavailability, are

	Operating cost ($) per trip on route			
Aircraft type	1	2	3	4
1	1000	1100	1200	1500
2	800	900	1000	1000
3	600	800	800	900
Penalty ($) per lost customer	40	50	45	70

Determine the optimum allocation of aircraft to routes, and determine the associated number of trips.

BIBLIOGRAPHY

Dantzig, G. and M. Thapa, *Linear Programming 1: Introduction*, Springer, New York, 1997.

Fourer, R., D. Gay, and B. Kernighan, *AMPL, A Modeling Language for Mathematical Programming*, 2nd ed., Brooks/Cole-Thomson, Pacific Grove, CA, 2003.

Laidlaw, C. *Linear Programming for Urban Development Plan Evaluation*, Praegers, London, 1972.

Lewis, T., "Personal Operations Research: Practicing OR on Ourselves," *Interfaces*, Vol. 26, No. 5, pp. 34–41, 1996.

Shepard, R., D. Hartley, P. Hasman, L. Thorpe, and M. Bathe, *Applied Operations Research*, Plenum Press, New York, 1988.

Stark, R., and R. Nicholes, *Mathematical Programming Foundations for Design: Civil Engineering Systems*, McGraw-Hill, New York, 1972.

CHAPTER 3

The Simplex Method and Sensitivity Analysis

Real-Life Application—Optimization of Heart Valve Production

Biological heart valves in different sizes are bioprostheses manufactured from porcine hearts for human implantation. On the supply side, porcine hearts cannot be "produced" to specific sizes. On the other hand, the exact size of a manufactured valve cannot be determined until the biological component of pig heart has been processed. As a result, some sizes may be overstocked and others understocked. A linear programming model was developed to reduce overstocked sizes and increase understocked sizes. The resulting savings exceeded $1,476,000 in 1981, the year the study was made. The details of this study are presented in Case 2, Chapter 26 on the website.

3.1 LP MODEL IN EQUATION FORM

The development of the simplex method computations is facilitated by imposing two requirements on the LP constraints:

1. All the constraints are equations with nonnegative right-hand side.
2. All the variables are nonnegative.[1]

Converting inequalities into equations with nonnegative right-hand side. In an economic LP model, the right-hand side represents the availability of a resource, and the left-hand side represents the usage of the resource by all the model activities (variables). The excess amount of the right-hand side over the left-hand side then yields the *unused* amount of the resource.

---

[1]Commercial packages (and TORA) directly accept inequality constraints, nonnegative right-hand side, and unrestricted variables. Any preconditioning of the constraints and the variables is done internally in the software before the simplex method solves the problem.

To convert a ($\leq$)-inequality to an equation, a nonnegative **slack variable** is added to the left-hand side of the constraint. For example, the $M1$-constraint of the Reddy Mikks model (Example 2.1-1) is converted into an equation as

$$6x_1 + 4x_2 + s_1 = 24, s_1 \geq 0$$

The nonnegative variable s_1 is the slack (or unused amount) of resource $M1$.

Next, a ($\geq$)-constraint sets a lower limit on the economic activities of the LP, so that the amount by which the left-hand side exceeds the minimum limit represents a *surplus*. Thus, the conversion from ($\geq$) to ($=$) is achieved by subtracting a nonnegative **surplus variable** from the left-hand side of the inequality. For example, in the diet model (Example 2.2-2), the surplus variable S_1 (≥ 0) converts the ($\geq$) feed mix constraint to the equation

$$x_1 + x_2 - S_1 = 800, S_1 \geq 0$$

The only remaining requirement is for the right-hand side of the resulting equation to be nonnegative. If the right-hand side happens to be negative, the requirement can be satisfied by multiplying both sides of the equation by -1.

PROBLEM SET 3.1A

*1. In the Reddy Mikks model (Example 2.2-1), consider the feasible solution $x_1 = 2$ tons and $x_2 = 2$ tons. Determine the value of the associated slacks for raw materials $M1$ and $M2$.

2. In the diet model (Example 2.2-2), determine the surplus amount of feed consisting of 525 lb of corn and 425 lb of soybean meal.

3. Consider the following inequality

$$22x_1 - 4x_2 \geq -7$$

Show that multiplying both sides of the inequality by -1 and then converting the resulting inequality into an equation is the same as converting it first to an equation and then multiplying both sides by -1.

*4. Two different products, $P1$ and $P2$, can be manufactured by one or both of two different machines, $M1$ and $M2$. The unit processing time of either product on either machine is the same. The daily capacity of machine $M1$ is 200 units (of either $P1$ or $P2$, or a mixture of both), and the daily capacity of machine $M2$ is 250 units. The shop supervisor wants to balance the production schedule of the two machines such that the total number of units produced on one machine is within 5 units of the number produced on the other. The profit per unit of $P1$ is \$10 and that of $P2$ is \$15. Set up the problem as an LP in equation form.

5. Show how the following objective function can be presented in equation form:

$$\text{Minimize } z = \max \{|x_1 - x_2 + 3x_3|, |-x_1 + 3x_2 - x_3|\}$$
$$x_1, x_2, x_3 \geq 0$$

(*Hint:* $|a| \leq b$ is equivalent to $a \leq b$ and $a \geq -b$.)

6. Show that the m equations

$$\sum_{j=1}^{n} a_{ij}x_j = b_i, \ i = 1, 2, \ldots, m$$

are equivalent to the following $m + 1$ inequalities:

$$\sum_{j=1}^{n} a_{ij}x_j \leq b_i, \, i = 1, 2, \ldots, m$$

$$\sum_{j=1}^{n} \left(\sum_{i=1}^{m} a_{ij} \right) x_j \geq \sum_{i=1}^{m} b_i$$

Dealing with unrestricted variables. The use of an unrestricted variable in an LP model is demonstrated in the multiperiod production smoothing model of Example 2.4-4, where the unrestricted variable S_i represents the number of workers hired or fired in period i. In the same example, we explained that the unrestricted variable can be replaced by two nonnegative variables by using the substitution

$$S_i = S_i^- - S_i^+, S_i^- \geq 0, S_i^+ \geq 0$$

In this case, S_i^- represents the number of workers hired and S_i^+ the number of workers fired. As explained in Example 2.4-4, it is impossible (both intuitively and mathematically) that S_i^- and S_i^+ assume positive values simultaneously.

PROBLEM SET 3.1B

1. McBurger fast-food restaurant sells quarter-pounders and cheeseburgers. A quarter-pounder uses a quarter of a pound of meat, and a cheeseburger uses only .2 lb. The restaurant starts the day with 250 lb of meat but may order more at an additional cost of 28 cents per pound to cover the delivery cost. Any surplus meat at the end of the day is donated to charity. McBurger's profits are 2022 cents for a quarter-pounder and 18 cents for a cheeseburger. McBurger does not expect to sell more than 950 sandwiches in any one day. How many of each type sandwich should McBurger plan for the day? Solve the problem using TORA, Solver, or AMPL.

2. Two products are manufactured in a machining center. The production times per unit of products 1 and 2 are 10 and 12 minutes, respectively. The total regular machine time is 2400 minutes per day. In any one day, the manufacturer can produce between 150 and 200 units of product 1, but no more than 45 units of product 2. Overtime may be used to meet the demand at an additional cost of $1 per minute. Assuming that the unit profits for products 1 and 2 are $12 and $15, respectively, formulate the problem as an LP model, then solve with TORA, Solver, or AMPL to determine the optimum production level for each product as well as any overtime needed in the center.

*3. JoShop manufactures three products whose unit profits are $2, $5, and $3, respectively. The company has budgeted 80 hours of labor time and 65 hours of machine time for the production of three products. The labor requirements per unit of products 1, 2, and 3 are 2, 1, and 2 hours, respectively. The corresponding machine-time requirements per unit are 1, 1, and 2 hours. JoShop regards the budgeted labor and machine hours as goals that may be exceeded, if necessary, but at the additional cost of $15 per labor hour and $10 per machine hour. Formulate the problem as an LP, and determine its optimum solution using TORA, Solver, or AMPL.

4. In an LP in which there are several unrestricted variables, a transformation of the type $x_j = x_j^- - x_j^+, x_j^-, x_j^+ \geq 0$ will double the corresponding number of nonnegative

variables. We can, instead, replace k unrestricted variables with exactly $k + 1$ nonnegative variables by using the substitution $x_j = x_j' - w$, x_j', $w \geq 0$. Use TORA, Solver, or AMPL to show that the two methods produce the same solution for the following LP:

$$\text{Maximize } z = -2x_1 + 3x_2 - 2x_3$$

subject to

$$4x_1 - x_2 - 5x_3 = 10$$
$$2x_1 + 3x_2 + 2x_3 = 12$$
$$x_1 \geq 0, \; x_2, \; x_3 \text{ unrestricted}$$

3.2   TRANSITION FROM GRAPHICAL TO ALGEBRAIC SOLUTION

The development of the algebraic simplex method is based on ideas conveyed by the graphical LP solution in Section 2.2. Figure 3.1 compares the two methods. In the graphical method, the solution space is the intersection of the half-spaces representing the constraints, and in the simplex method, the solution space is represented by m simultaneous linear equations and n nonnegative variables. We can see visually that the graphical solution space has an infinite number of solution points, but how can we draw a similar conclusion from the algebraic representation of the solution space? The answer is that, in all nontrivial LPs, the number of equations m is always *less than* the number of variables n, thus yielding an infinite number of solutions (provided the equations are

FIGURE 3.1

Transition from graphical to algebraic solution

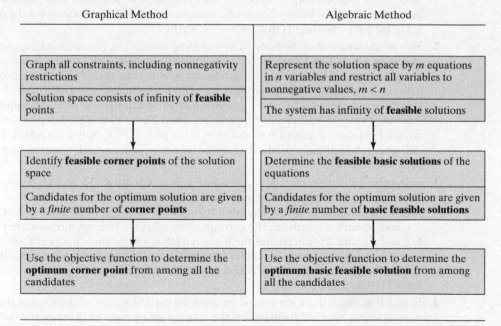

consistent)[2]. For example, the equation $x + y = 1$ has $m = 1$ and $n = 2$ and yields an infinite number of solutions because any point on the straight line $x + y = 1$ is a solution.

In the algebraic solution space (defined by $m \times n$ equations, $m < n$), **basic solutions** correspond to the *corner points* in the graphical solution space. They are determined by setting $n - m$ variables equal to zero and solving the m equations for the remaining m variables, *provided the resulting solution is unique*. This means that the *maximum* number of corner points is

$$C_m^n = \frac{n!}{m!(n - m)!}$$

As with corner points, the basic feasible solutions completely define the candidates for the optimum solution in the algebraic solutions space.

Example 3.2-1

Consider the following LP with two variables:

$$\text{Maximize } z = 2x_1 + 3x_2$$

subject to

$$2x_1 + x_2 \leq 4$$

$$x_1 + 2x_2 \leq 5$$

$$x_1, x_2 \geq 0$$

Figure 3.2 provides the graphical solution space for the problem.

Algebraically, the solution space of the LP is represented by the following $m = 2$ equations and $n = 4$ variables:

$$2x_1 + x_2 + s_1 = 4$$

$$x_1 + 2x_2 + s_2 = 5$$

$$x_1, x_2, s_1, s_2 \geq 0$$

The basic solutions are determined by setting $n - m = 4 - 2 = 2$ variables equal to zero and solving for the remaining $m = 2$ variables. For example, if we set $x_1 = 0$ and $x_2 = 0$, the equations provide the unique basic solution

$$s_1 = 4, s_2 = 5$$

This solution corresponds to point A in Figure 3.2 (convince yourself that $s_1 = 4$ and $s_2 = 5$ at point A). Another point can be determined by setting $s_1 = 0$ and $s_2 = 0$ and then solving the resulting two equations

$$2x_1 + x_2 = 4$$

$$x_1 + 2x_2 = 5$$

The associated basic solution is ($x_1 = 1, x_2 = 2$), or point C in Figure 3.2.

---

[2]If the number of equations m equals the number of variables n (and the equations are consistent), the system has exactly one solution. If m is larger than n, then at least $m - n$ equations must be redundant.

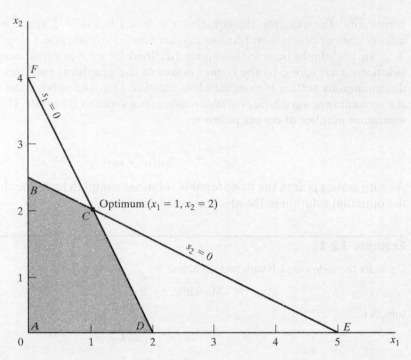

FIGURE 3.2

LP Solution space of Example 3.2-1

You probably are wondering which $n - m$ variables should be set equal to zero to target a specific corner point. Without the benefit of the graphical solution space (which is available only for at most three variables), we cannot specify the $(n - m)$ zero variables associated with a given corner point. But that does not prevent enumerating *all* the corner points of the solution space. Simply consider *all* combinations in which $n - m$ variables equal zero and solve the resulting equations. Once done, the optimum solution is the *feasible* basic solution (corner point) with the best objective value.

In the present example, we have $C_2^4 = \frac{4!}{2!2!} = 6$ corner points. Looking at Figure 3.2, we can spot the four corner points A, B, C, and D. So, where are the remaining two? In fact, points E and F also are corner points. But, they are *infeasible*, and, hence, are not candidates for the optimum.

To complete the transition from the graphical to the algebraic solution, the zero $n - m$ variables are known as **nonbasic variables**. The remaining m variables are called **basic variables**, and their solution (obtained by solving the m equations) is referred to as **basic solution**. The following table provides all the basic and nonbasic solutions of the current example.

Nonbasic (zero) variables	Basic variables	Basic solution	Associated corner point	Feasible?	Objective value, z
(x_1, x_2)	(s_1, s_2)	$(4, 5)$	A	Yes	0
(x_1, s_1)	(x_2, s_2)	$(4, -3)$	F	No	—
(x_1, s_2)	(x_2, s_1)	$(2.5, 1.5)$	B	Yes	7.5
(x_2, s_1)	(x_1, s_2)	$(2, 3)$	D	Yes	4
(x_2, s_2)	(x_1, s_1)	$(5, -6)$	E	No	—
(s_1, s_2)	(x_1, x_2)	$\mathbf{(1, 2)}$	C	**Yes**	**8**
					(optimum)

Remarks.   We can see from the preceding illustration that, as the size of the problem increases, enumerating all the corner points becomes a prohibitive task. For example, for $m = 10$ and $n = 20$, it is necessary to solve $C_{10}^{20} = 184{,}756$ sets of 10×10 equations, a staggering task, particularly when we realize that a (10×20)-LP is a very small size (real-life LPs can include thousands of variables and constraints). The simplex method alleviates this computational burden dramatically by investigating only a subset of all possible basic feasible solutions (corner points). This is what the simplex algorithm does.

PROBLEM SET 3.2A

1. Consider the following LP:

$$\text{Maximize } z = 2x_1 + 3x_2$$

subject to

$$x_1 + 3x_2 \leq 12$$
$$3x_1 + 2x_2 \leq 12$$
$$x_1, x_2 \geq 0$$

   (a) Express the problem in equation form.

   (b) Determine all the basic solutions of the problem, and classify them as feasible and infeasible.

   (c) Use direct substitution in the objective function to determine the optimum basic feasible solution.

   (d) Verify graphically that the solution obtained in (c) is the optimum LP solution— hence, conclude that the optimum solution can be determined algebraically by considering the basic feasible solutions only.

   (e) Show how the *infeasible* basic solutions are represented on the graphical solution space.

2. Determine the optimum solution for each of the following LPs by enumerating all the basic solutions.

   (a) Maximize $z = 2x_1 - 4x_2 + 5x_3 - 6x_4$

   subject to

   $$x_1 + 4x_2 - 2x_3 + 8x_4 \leq 2$$
   $$- x_1 + 2x_2 + 3x_3 + 4x_4 \leq 1$$
   $$x_1, x_2, x_3, x_4 \geq 0$$

   (b) Minimize $z = x_1 + 2x_2 - 3x_3 - 2x_4$

   subject to

   $$x_1 + 2x_2 - 3x_3 + x_4 = 4$$
   $$x_1 + 2x_2 + x_3 + 2x_4 = 4$$
   $$x_1, x_2, x_3, x_4 \geq 0$$

*3. Show algebraically that all the basic solutions of the following LP are infeasible.

$$\text{Maximize } z = x_1 + x_2$$

subject to

$$x_1 + 2x_2 \le 3$$
$$2x_1 + x_2 \le 8$$
$$x_1, x_2 \ge 0$$

4. Consider the following LP:

$$\text{Maximize } z = 2x_1 + 3x_2 + 5x_3$$

subject to

$$-6x_1 + 7x_2 - 9x_3 \ge 4$$
$$x_1 + x_2 + 4x_3 = 10$$
$$x_1, x_3 \ge 0$$
$$x_2 \text{ unrestricted}$$

Conversion to the equation form involves using the substitution $x_2 = x_2^- - x_2^+$. Show that a basic solution cannot include both x_2^- and x_2^+ simultaneously.

5. Consider the following LP:

$$\text{Maximize } z = x_1 + 3x_2$$

subject to

$$x_1 + x_2 \le 2$$
$$-x_1 + x_2 \le 4$$
$$x_2 \text{ unrestricted}$$
$$x_2 \ge 0$$

   (a) Determine all the basic feasible solutions of the problem.
   (b) Use direct substitution in the objective function to determine the best basic solution.
   (c) Solve the problem graphically, and verify that the solution obtained in (c) is the optimum.

3.3   THE SIMPLEX METHOD

Rather than enumerating *all* the basic solutions (corner points) of the LP problem (as we did in Section 3.2), the simplex method investigates only a "select few" of these solutions. Section 3.3.1 describes the *iterative* nature of the method, and Section 3.3.2 provides the computational details of the simplex algorithm.

3.3.1 Iterative Nature of the Simplex Method

Figure 3.3 provides the solution space of the LP of Example 3.2-1. Normally, the simplex method starts at the origin (point A), where $x_1 = x_2 = 0$ and the objective value, z, is zero. The logical question now is whether an increase in nonbasic x_1 and/or x_2 above their current zero values can improve (increase) the value of z. We can answer this question by investigating the objective function:

$$\text{Maximize } z = 2x_1 + 3x_2$$

An increase in x_1 or x_2(or both) above their current zero values will *improve* the value of z. The design of the simplex method does not allow simultaneous increase in variables. Instead, it targets the variables *one at a time*. The variable slated for increase is the one with the *largest rate of improvement* in z. In the present example, the *rate* of improvement in the value of z is 2 for x_1 and 3 for x_2. We thus elect to increase x_2(the variable with the largest rate of improvement among all nonbasic variables). Figure 3.3 shows that the value of x_2 must be increased until corner point B is reached (recall that stopping short of corner point B is not an option because a candidate for the optimum must be a corner point). At point B, the simplex method will then increase the value of x_1 to reach the improved corner point C, which is the optimum.

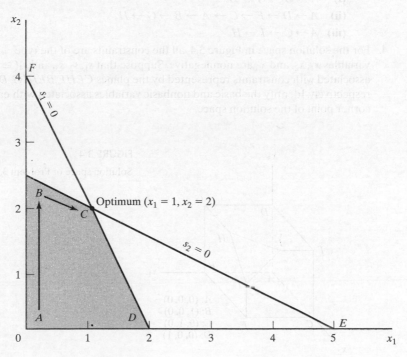

FIGURE 3.3

Iterative process of the simplex method

The path of the simplex algorithm is defined as $A \rightarrow B \rightarrow C$. Each corner point along the path is associated with an **iteration**. It is important to note that the simplex method moves alongside the **edges** of the solution space, which means that the method cannot cut across the solution space, going from A to C directly.

PROBLEM SET 3.3A

1. In Figure 3.3, suppose that the objective function is changed to

$$\text{Maximize } z = -4x_1 + 7x_2$$

   Identify the path of the simplex method and the basic and nonbasic variables that define this path.

2. Consider the graphical solution of the Reddy Mikks model given in Figure 2.2. Identify the path of the simplex method and the basic and nonbasic variables that define this path.

*3. Consider the three-dimensional LP solution space in Figure 3.4, whose feasible extreme points are $A, B, \ldots,$ and J.

   (a) Which of the following pairs of corner points cannot represent *successive* simplex iterations: $(A, B), (H, I), (E, H)$, and (A, I)? Explain why.

   (b) Suppose that the simplex iterations start at A and that the optimum occurs at H. Indicate whether any of the following paths are *not* legitimate for the simplex algorithm, and state the reason.

   (i) $A \rightarrow B \rightarrow G \rightarrow H$

   (ii) $A \rightarrow D \rightarrow F \rightarrow C \rightarrow A \rightarrow B \rightarrow G \rightarrow H$

   (iii) $A \rightarrow C \rightarrow I \rightarrow H$

4. For the solution space in Figure 3.4, all the constraints are of the type $\leq$, and all the variables $x_1, x_2,$ and x_3 are nonnegative. Suppose that $s_1, s_2, s_3,$ and $s_4 (\geq 0)$ are the slacks associated with constraints represented by the planes $CEIJF, BEIHG, DFJHG,$ and IJH, respectively. Identify the basic and nonbasic variables associated with each feasible corner point of the solution space.

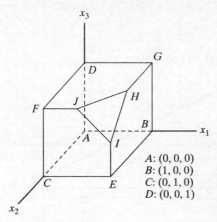

FIGURE 3.4

Solution space of Problem 3, Set 3.2b

A: (0, 0, 0)
B: (1, 0, 0)
C: (0, 1, 0)
D: (0, 0, 1)

5. For each of the given objective functions and the solution space in Figure 3.4, select the nonbasic variable that leads to the next simplex corner point, and determine the associated improvement in z.

   *(a) Maximize $z = x_1 - 2x_2 + 3x_3$

   (b) Maximize $z = 5x_1 + 2x_2 + 4x_3$

   (c) Maximize $z = -2x_1 + 7x_2 + 2x_3$

   (d) Maximize $z = x_1 + x_2 + x_3$

3.3.2 Computational details of the Simplex algorithm

This section provides the computational details of a simplex iteration. The vehicle of explanation is a numerical example.

Example 3.3-1

Consider the Reddy Mikks model (Example 2.1-1) expressed in equation form:

$$\text{Maximize } z = 5x_1 + 4x_2 + 0s_1 + 0s_2 + 0s_3 + 0s_4$$

subject to

$$6x_1 + 4x_2 + s_1 \qquad\qquad = 24 \quad \text{(Raw material } M1)$$
$$x_1 + 2x_2 \qquad + s_2 \qquad\qquad = 6 \quad \text{(Raw material } M2)$$
$$- x_1 + x_2 \qquad\qquad + s_3 \qquad = 1 \quad \text{(Market limit)}$$
$$x_2 \qquad\qquad\qquad + s_4 = 2 \quad \text{(Demand limit)}$$

$$x_1, x_2, s_1, s_2, s_3, s_4 \geq 0$$

The variables s_1, s_2, s_3, and s_4 are the slacks associated with the respective constraints. Next, we write the objective equation as

$$z - 5x_1 - 4x_2 = 0$$

In this manner, the starting simplex tableau can be represented as follows:

Basic	z	x_1	x_2	s_1	s_2	s_3	s_4	Solution	
z	1	−5	−4	0	0	0	0	0	z-row
s_1	0	6	4	1	0	0	0	24	s_1-row
s_2	0	1	2	0	1	0	0	6	s_2-row
s_3	0	−1	1	0	0	1	0	1	s_3-row
s_4	0	0	1	0	0	0	1	2	s_4-row

The layout of the simplex tableau automatically provides the solution at the starting iteration. The solution starts at the origin $(x_1, x_2) = (0, 0)$, thus defining (x_1, x_2) as the nonbasic variables and (s_1, s_2, s_3, s_4) as the basic variables. The objective variable z and the basic variables are listed in the rightmost (Basic) column. Their values are given directly by the right-hand sides of the model's equations, as shown in the rightmost (Solution) column of the tableau—that is, $z = 0$, $s_1 = 24$, $s_2 = 6$, $s_3 = 1$, $s_4 = 2$. The result can be seen by setting the nonbasic variables (x_1, x_2) equal to zero in all the equations and also by noting the special identity-matrix arrangement of the constraint coefficients of the basic variables (all diagonal elements are 1, and all off-diagonal elements are 0).

Is the starting solution optimal? The objective function $z = 5x_1 + 4x_2$ shows that the solution can be improved by increasing the value of nonbasic x_1 or x_2 above zero. Using the argument in Section 3.3.1, x_1 is to be increased because it has the *most positive* objective coefficient. Equivalently, in the simplex tableau where the objective function is written as $z - 5x_1 - 4x_2 = 0$, the selected variable is the nonbasic variable with the *most negative* coefficient in the objective equation. This rule defines the so-called **simplex optimality condition**. In the terminology of the simplex algorithm, x_1 is known as the **entering variable** because it enters the basic solution.

If x_1 is the entering variable, one of the current basic variables must leave—that is, it becomes nonbasic at zero level (recall that the number of nonbasic variable must always be $n - m$). The mechanics for determining the **leaving variable** calls for computing the **ratios** of the right-hand side of the equations (*Solution* column) to the corresponding (strictly) *positive* constraint coefficients under the entering variable, x_1, as the following table shows:

Basic	Entering x_1	Solution	Ratio (or intercept)
s_1	6	24	$x_1 = \frac{24}{6} = 4 \leftarrow$ minimum
s_2	1	6	$x_1 = \frac{6}{1} = 6$
s_3	-1	1	$x_1 = \frac{1}{-1} = -1$ (negative denominator, ignore)
s_4	0	2	$x_1 = \frac{2}{0} = \infty$ (zero denominator, ignore)

Conclusion: x_1 enters (at level 4) and s_1 leaves (at level zero)

How do the computed ratios determine the leaving variable and the value of the entering variable? Figure 3.5 shows that the computed ratios are actually the intercepts of the constraint lines with the (entering variable) x_1-axis. We can see that the value of x_1 must be increased to the smallest nonnegative intercept with the x_1-axis (= 4) to reach corner point B. Any increase beyond B is infeasible. At point B, the current basic variable s_1 associated with constraint 1 assumes a zero value and becomes the *leaving variable*. The rule associated with the ratio computations is referred to as the **simplex feasibility condition** because it guarantees the feasibility of the new solution.

The new solution point B is determined by "swapping" the entering variable x_1 and the leaving variable s_1 in the simplex tableau to yield

$$\text{Nonbasic (zero) variables at } B: (s_1, x_2)$$

$$\text{Basic variables at } B: (x_1, s_2, s_3, s_4)$$

The swapping process is based on the **Gauss-Jordan row operations**. It identifies the entering variable column as the **pivot column** and the leaving variable row as the **pivot row**. The intersection

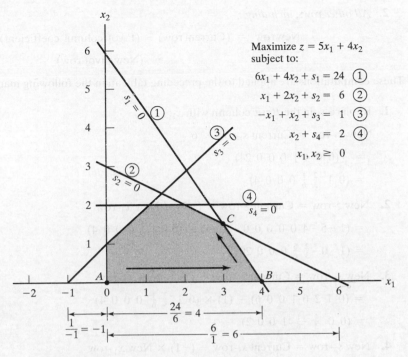

Maximize $z = 5x_1 + 4x_2$
subject to:

$$6x_1 + 4x_2 + s_1 = 24 \quad ①$$
$$x_1 + 2x_2 + s_2 = 6 \quad ②$$
$$-x_1 + x_2 + s_3 = 1 \quad ③$$
$$x_2 + s_4 = 2 \quad ④$$
$$x_1, x_2 \geq 0$$

FIGURE 3.5

Graphical interpretation of the simplex method ratios in the Reddy Mikks model

of the pivot column and the pivot row is called the **pivot element**. The following tableau is a restatement of the starting tableau with its pivot row and column highlighted.

	Basic	z	Enter ↓ x_1	x_2	s_1	s_2	s_3	s_4	Solution	
	z	1	−5	−4	0	0	0	0	0	
Leave ←	s_1	0	6	4	1	0	0	0	24	Pivot row
	s_2	0	1	2	0	1	0	0	6	
	s_3	0	−1	1	0	0	1	0	1	
	s_4	0	0	1	0	0	0	1	2	
			Pivot column							

The Gauss-Jordan computations needed to produce the new basic solution include two types.

1. *Pivot row*

   a. Replace the leaving variable in the *Basic* column with the entering variable.

   b. New pivot row = Current pivot row ÷ Pivot element

2. *All other rows, including z*

$$\text{New row} = (\text{Current row}) - (\text{Pivot column coefficient}) \times$$
$$(\text{New pivot row})$$

These computations are applied to the preceding tableau in the following manner:

1. Replace s_1 in the *Basic* column with x_1:

New x_1-row = Current s_1-row $\div$ 6

$= \frac{1}{6} (0\ 6\ 4\ 1\ 0\ 0\ 0\ 24)$

$= (0\ 1\ \frac{2}{3}\ \frac{1}{6}\ 0\ 0\ 0\ 4)$

2. New z-row = Current z-row $- (-5) \times$ New x_1-row

$= (1 -5 -4\ 0\ 0\ 0\ 0\ 0 - (-5) \times (0\ 1\frac{2}{3}\ \frac{1}{6}\ 0\ 0\ 0\ 4)$

$= (1\quad 0 -\frac{2}{3}\ \frac{5}{6}\ 0\ 0\ 0\ 20)$

3. New s_2-row = Current s_2-row $- (1) \times$ New x_1-row

$= (0\ 1\ 2\ 0\ 1\ 0\ 0\ 6) - (1) \times (0\ 1\ \frac{2}{3}\ \frac{1}{6}\ 0\ 0\ 0\ 4)$

$= (0\ 0\ \frac{4}{3} -\frac{1}{6}\ 1\ 0\ 0\ 2)$

4. New s_3-row = Current s_3-row $- (-1) \times$ New x_1-row

$= (0 -1\ 1\ 0\ 0\ 1\ 0\ 1) - (-1) \times (0\ 1\ \frac{2}{3}\ \frac{1}{6}\ 0\ 0\ 0\ 4)$

$= (0\ 0\ \frac{5}{3}\ \frac{1}{6}\ 0\ 1\ 0\ 5)$

5. New s_4-row = Current s_4-row $- (0) \times$ New x_1-row

$= (0\ 0\ 1\ 0\ 0\ 0\ 1\ 2) - (0)(0\ 1\ \frac{2}{3}\ \frac{1}{6}\ 0\ 0\ 0\ 4)$

$= (0\ 0\ 1\ 0\ 0\ 0\ 1\ 2)$

The new basic solution is (x_1, s_2, s_3, s_4), and the new tableau becomes

Basic	z	x_1	x_2	s_1	s_2	s_3	s_4	Solution
z	1	0	$-\frac{2}{3}$	$\frac{5}{6}$	0	0	0	20
x_1	0	1	$\frac{2}{3}$	$\frac{1}{6}$	0	0	0	4
s_2	0	0	$\frac{4}{3}$	$-\frac{1}{6}$	1	0	0	2
s_3	0	0	$\frac{5}{3}$	$\frac{1}{6}$	0	1	0	5
s_4	0	0	1	0	0	0	1	2

Observe that the structure of the new tableau is similar to that of the starting tableau, in the sense that the constraint coefficients of the basic variable form an identity matrix. As a result, when we set the new nonbasic variables x_2 and s_1 to zero, the *Solution* column automatically yields the new basic solution $(x_1 = 4, s_2 = 2, s_3 = 5, s_4 = 2)$.[3] This "conditioning" of the tableau is the result of the application of the Gauss-Jordan row operations. The corresponding new objective value is $z = 20$, which is consistent with

$$\text{New } z = \text{Old } z + \text{New } x_1\text{-value} \times \text{its objective coefficient}$$

$$= 0 + 4 \times 5 = 20$$

Alternatively, $z = 4 \times x_1$-value $+ 0 \times s_2$-value $+ 0 \times s_3$-value $+ 0 \times s_4$-value $= 4 \times 5 + 0 \times 2 + 0 \times 5 + 0 \times 2 = 20$

In the last tableau, the *optimality condition* shows that x_2 is the entering variable. The feasibility condition produces the following information:

Basic	Entering x_2	Solution	Ratio
x_1	$\frac{2}{3}$	4	$x_2 = 4 \div \frac{2}{3} = 6$
s_2	$\frac{4}{3}$	2	$x_2 = 2 \div \frac{4}{3} = 1.5 \,(\text{minimum})$
s_3	$\frac{5}{3}$	5	$x_2 = 5 \div \frac{5}{3} = 3$
s_4	1	2	$x_2 = 2 \div 1 = 2$

Thus, s_2 leaves the basic solution, and the new value of x_2 is 1.5. The corresponding increase in z is $\frac{2}{3} x_2 = \frac{2}{3} \times 1.5 = 1$, which yields new $z = 20 + 1 = 21$.

Replacing s_2 in the *Basic* column with entering x_2, the following Gauss-Jordan row operations are applied:

1. New pivot x_2-row = Current s_2-row $\div \frac{4}{3}$
2. New z-row = Current z-row $- (-\frac{2}{3}) \times$ New x_2-row
3. New x_1-row = Current x_1-row $- (\frac{2}{3}) \times$ New x_2-row
4. New s_3-row = Current s_3-row $- (\frac{5}{3}) \times$ New x_2-row
5. New s_4-row = Current s_4-row $- (1) \times$ New x_2-row

These computations produce the following tableau:

Basic	z	x_1	x_2	s_1	s_2	s_3	s_4	Solution
z	1	0	0	$\frac{3}{4}$	$\frac{1}{2}$	0	0	21
x_1	0	1	0	$\frac{1}{4}$	$-\frac{1}{2}$	0	0	3
x_2	0	0	1	$-\frac{1}{8}$	$\frac{3}{4}$	0	0	$\frac{3}{2}$
s_3	0	0	0	$\frac{3}{8}$	$-\frac{5}{4}$	1	0	$\frac{5}{2}$
s_4	0	0	0	$\frac{1}{8}$	$-\frac{3}{4}$	0	1	$\frac{1}{2}$

[3]Throughout my teaching experience, I have noticed that while students can carry out the tedious simplex method computations, in the end some cannot tell what the solution is. To assist in overcoming this potential difficulty, stress is made on "reading" the solution of the LP from the tableau.

Based on the optimality condition, *none* of the z-row coefficients are negative. Hence, the last tableau is optimal.

The optimum solution can be read from the simplex tableau in the following manner. The optimal values of the variables in the *Basic* column are given in the right-hand-side *Solution* column and can be interpreted as

Decision variable	Optimum value	Recommendation
x_1	3	Produce 3 tons of exterior paint daily
x_2	$\frac{3}{2}$	Produce 1.5 tons of interior paint daily
z	21	Daily profit is $21,000

The solution also gives the status of the resources. A resource is designated as **scarce** if its associated slack variable is zero—that is, the activities (variables) of the model have used the resource completely. Otherwise, if the slack is positive, then the resource is **abundant**. The following table classifies the constraints of the model:

Resource	Slack value	Status
Raw material, $M1$	$s_1 = 0$	Scarce
Raw material, $M2$	$s_2 = 0$	Scarce
Market limit	$s_3 = \frac{5}{2}$	Abundant
Demand limit	$s_4 = \frac{1}{2}$	Abundant

Remarks. The simplex tableau offers a wealth of additional information that include the following:

1. *Sensitivity analysis*, which deals with determining the conditions that will keep the current solution unchanged.

2. *Post-optimal analysis*, which deals with finding a new optimal solution when the data of the model are changed.

Section 3.6 deals with sensitivity analysis. Post-optimal analysis is covered in Chapter 4.

TORA moment.

The Gauss-Jordan computations are tedious, voluminous, and, above all, boring. Yet, they are the least important, because in practice these computations are carried out by the computer. What is important is that you understand *how* the simplex method works. TORA's interactive *user-guided* option (with instant feedback) can be of help because it allows you to specify the course of the simplex computations (i.e., determination of the entering and leaving variables) without the burden-some Gauss-Jordan calculations. To use TORA with the Reddy Mikks problem, enter the model and then, from the SOLVE/MODIFY menu, select Solve $\Rightarrow$ Algebraic $\Rightarrow$ Iterations $\Rightarrow$ All-Slack. (The All-Slack selection indicates that the starting basic solution consists of slack variables only. The remaining options will be presented in Sections 3.4, 4.3, and 7.4.2.) Next, click Go To Output Screen. You can generate one or all iterations by clicking Next Iteration or

All Iterations. If you opt to generate the iterations one at a time, you can interactively specify the entering and leaving variables by clicking the headings of their respective column and row. If your selections are correct, the column turns green and the row turns red. Else, an error message is posted.

3.3.3 Summary of the Simplex Method

So far we have dealt with the maximization case. In minimization problems, the *optimality condition* calls for selecting the entering variable as the nonbasic variable with the most *positive* objective coefficient in the objective equation, the exact opposite rule of the maximization case. This follows because max z is equivalent to min $(-z)$. As for the *feasibility condition* for selecting the leaving variable, the rule remains unchanged.

Optimality condition. The entering variable in a maximization (minimization) problem is the *nonbasic* variable with the most negative (positive) coefficient in the z-row. Ties are broken arbitrarily. The optimum is reached at the iteration where all the z-row coefficients are nonnegative (nonpositive).

Feasibility condition. For both the maximization and the minimization problems, the leaving variable is the *basic* variable associated with the smallest nonnegative ratio with *strictly positive* denominator. Ties are broken arbitrarily.

Gauss-Jordan row operations.

1. *Pivot row*

   a. Replace the leaving variable in the *Basic* column with the entering variable.
   b. New pivot row = Current pivot row ÷ Pivot element

2. *All other rows, including z*
   New row = (Current row) − (Its pivot column coefficient) × (New pivot row).

   The steps of the simplex method are

Step 0. Determine a starting basic feasible solution.

Step 1. Select an *entering variable* using the optimality condition. Stop if there is no entering variable; the last solution is optimal. Else, go to step 2.

Step 2. Select a *leaving variable* using the feasibility condition.

Step 3. Apply the Gauss-Jordan computations to determine the new basic solution. Go to step 1.

PROBLEM SET 3.3B

1. This problem is designed to reinforce your understanding of the simplex feasibility condition. In the first tableau in Example 3.3-1, we used the minimum (nonnegative) ratio test to determine the leaving variable. The condition guarantees feasibility (all the new values of the basic variables remain nonnegative as stipulated by the definition of

the LP). To demonstrate this point, force s_2, instead of s_1, to leave the basic solution, and carry out the Gauss-Jordan computations. In the resulting simplex tableau, s_1 is infeasible $(= -12)$.

2. Consider the following set of constraints:

$$x_1 + 2x_2 + 2x_3 + 4x_4 \le 40$$
$$2x_1 - x_2 + x_3 + 2x_4 \le 8$$
$$4x_1 - 2x_2 + x_3 - x_4 \le 10$$
$$x_1, x_2, x_3, x_4 \ge 0$$

Solve the problem for each of the following objective functions.

(a) Maximize $z = 2x_1 + x_2 - 3x_3 + 5x_4$.

(b) Maximize $z = 8x_1 + 6x_2 + 3x_3 - 2x_4$.

(c) Maximize $z = 3x_1 - x_2 + 3x_3 + 4x_4$.

(d) Minimize $z = 5x_1 - 4x_2 + 6x_3 - 8x_4$.

*3. Consider the following system of equations:

$$x_1 + 2x_2 - 3x_3 + 5x_4 + x_5 = 8$$
$$5x_1 - 2x_2 + 6x_4 + x_6 = 16$$
$$2x_1 + 3x_2 - 2x_3 + 3x_4 + x_7 = 6$$
$$-x_1 + x_3 - 2x_4 + x_8 = 0$$
$$x_1, x_2, \ldots, x_8 \ge 0$$

Let $x_5, x_6, \ldots$, and x_8 be a given initial basic feasible solution. Suppose that x_1 becomes basic. Which of the given basic variables must become nonbasic at zero level to guarantee that all the variables remain nonnegative, and what is the value of x_1 in the new solution? Repeat this procedure for x_2, x_3, and x_4.

4. Consider the following LP:

$$\text{Maximize } z = x_1$$

subject to

$$5x_1 + x_2 = 4$$
$$6x_1 + x_3 = 8$$
$$3x_1 + x_4 = 3$$
$$x_1, x_2, x_3, x_4 \ge 0$$

(a) Solve the problem *by inspection* (do not use the Gauss-Jordan row operations), and justify the answer in terms of the basic solutions of the simplex method.

(b) Repeat (a) assuming that the objective function calls for minimizing $z = x_1$.

5. Solve the following problem by *inspection*, and justify the method of solution in terms of the basic solutions of the simplex method.

$$\text{Maximize } z = 5x_1 - 6x_2 + 3x_3 - 5x_4 + 12x_5$$

subject to

$$x_1 + 3x_2 + 5x_3 + 6x_4 + 3x_5 \le 30$$

$$x_1, x_2, x_3, x_4, x_5 \ge 0$$

(*Hint*: A basic solution consists of one variable only.)

6. The following tableau represents a specific simplex iteration. All variables are nonnegative. The tableau is not optimal for either maximization or minimization. Thus, when a nonbasic variable enters the solution, it can either increase or decrease z or leave it unchanged, depending on the parameters of the entering nonbasic variable.

Basic	X_1	x_2	x_3	x_4	x_5	x_6	x_7	x_8	Solution
z	0	-5	0	4	-1	-10	0	0	620
x_8	0	3	0	-2	-3	-1	5	1	12
x_3	0	1	1	3	1	0	3	0	6
x_1	1	-1	0	0	6	-4	0	0	0

(a) Categorize the variables as basic and nonbasic, and provide the current values of all the variables.

*(b) Assuming that the problem is of the maximization type, identify the nonbasic variables that have the potential to improve the value of z. If each such variable enters the basic solution, determine the associated leaving variable, if any, and the associated change in z. Do not use the Gauss-Jordan row operations.

(c) Repeat part (b) assuming that the problem is of the minimization type.

(d) Which nonbasic variable(s) will not cause a change in the value of z when selected to enter the solution?

7. Consider the two-dimensional solution space in Figure 3.6.

(a) Suppose that the objective function is given as

$$\text{Maximize } z = 6x_1 + 3x_2$$

If the simplex iterations start at point A, identify the path to the optimum point D.

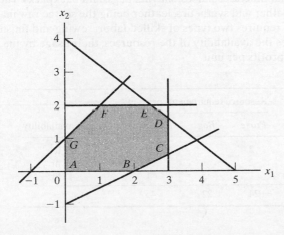

FIGURE 3.6

Solution Space for Problem 7, Set 3.3b

(b) Determine the entering variable, the corresponding ratios of the feasibility condition, and the change in the value of z, assuming that the starting iteration occurs at point A and that the objective function is given as

$$\text{Maximize } z = x_1 + 4x_2$$

(c) Repeat (b), assuming that the objective function is

$$\text{Maximize } z = 8x_1 + 2x_2$$

8. Consider the following LP:

$$\text{Maximize } z = 16x_1 + 15x_2$$

subject to

$$40x_1 + 31x_2 \leq 124$$

$$-x_1 + x_2 \leq 1$$

$$x_1 \leq 3$$

$$x_1, x_2 \geq 0$$

(a) Solve the problem by the simplex method, where the entering variable is the nonbasic variable with the *most* negative z-row coefficient.

(b) Resolve the problem by the simplex algorithm, always selecting the entering variable as the nonbasic variable with the *least* negative z-row coefficient.

(c) Compare the number of iterations in (a) and (b). Does the selection of the entering variable as the nonbasic variable with the *most* negative z-row coefficient lead to a smaller number of iterations? What conclusion can be made regarding the optimality condition?

(d) Suppose that the sense of optimization is changed to minimization by multiplying z by -1. How does this change affect the simplex iterations?

*9. In Example 3.3-1, show how the second-best optimal value of z can be determined from the optimal tableau.

10. Can you extend the procedure in Problem 9 to determine the third-best optimal value of z?

11. The Gutchi Company manufactures purses, shaving bags, and backpacks. The construction includes leather and synthetics, leather being the scarce raw material. The production process requires two types of skilled labor: sewing and finishing. The following table gives the availability of the resources, their usage by the three products, and the profits per unit.

Resource	Resource requirements per unit			Daily availability
	Purse	*Bag*	*Backpack*	
Leather (ft^2)	2	1	3	42 ft^2
Sewing (hr)	2	1	2	40 hr
Finishing (hr)	1	.5	1	45 hr
Selling price ($)	24	22	45	

(a) Formulate the problem as a linear program, and find the optimum solution (using TORA, Excel Solver, or AMPL).

(b) From the optimum solution, determine the status of each resource.

12. *TORA experiment.* Consider the following LP:

$$\text{Maximize } z = x_1 + x_2 + 3x_3 + 2x_4$$

subject to

$$x_1 + 2x_2 - 3x_3 + 5x_4 \leq 4$$
$$5x_1 - 2x_2 \qquad + 6x_4 \leq 8$$
$$2x_1 + 3x_2 - 2x_3 + 3x_4 \leq 3$$
$$-x_1 \qquad + x_3 + 2x_4 \leq 0$$
$$x_1, x_2, x_3, x_4 \geq 0$$

(a) Use TORA's iterations option to determine the optimum tableau.

(b) Select any nonbasic variable to "enter" the basic solution, and click Next Iteration to produce the associated iteration. How does the new objective value compare with the optimum in (a). The idea is to show that the tableau in (a) is optimum because none of the nonbasic variables can improve the objective value.

13. *TORA experiment.* In Problem 12, use TORA to find the next-best optimal solution.

3.4   ARTIFICIAL STARTING SOLUTION

As demonstrated in Example 3.3-1, LPs in which all the constraints are ($\leq$) with nonnegative right-hand sides offer a convenient all-slack starting basic feasible solution. Models involving (=) and/or ($\geq$) constraints do not.

The procedure for starting "ill-behaved" LPs with (=) and ($\geq$) constraints is to use **artificial variables** that play the role of slacks at the first iteration. The artificial variables are then disposed of at a later iteration. Two closely related methods are introduced here: the *M*-method and the two-phase method.

3.4.1   *M*-Method[4]

The *M*-method starts with the LP in equation form (Section 3.1). If equation i does not have a slack (or a variable that can play the role of a slack), an artificial variable, R_i, is added to form a starting solution similar to the all-slack basic solution. However, the artificial variables are not part of the original problem, and a modeling "trick" is needed to force them to zero by the time the optimum iteration is reached (assuming the problem has a feasible solution). The desired goal is achieved by *penalizing* these variables in the objective function using the following rule:

---

[4]The *M*-method, one of the oldest LP techniques, is never used in commercial codes because of its inherent machine roundoff error problem. Instead, the two-phase method (Section 3.4.2) is the preferred technique. Nevertheless, the use of penalty, as advanced by the *M*-method, is an important concept in many OR modeling instances.

Penalty rule for artificial variables.

Given M, a sufficiently large positive value (mathematically, $M \to \infty$), the objective coefficient of an artificial variable represents an appropriate **penalty** if:

$$\text{Artificial variable objective coefficient} = \begin{cases} -M, & \text{in maximization problems} \\ M, & \text{in minimization problems} \end{cases}$$

Example 3.4-1

$$\text{Minimize } z = 4x_1 + x_2$$

subject to

$$3x_1 + x_2 = 3$$
$$4x_1 + 3x_2 \geq 6$$
$$x_1 + 2x_2 \leq 4$$
$$x_1, x_2 \geq 0$$

Using x_3 as a surplus in the second constraint and x_4 as a slack in the third constraint, the equation form of the problem is given as

$$\text{Minimize } z = 4x_1 + x_2$$

subject to

$$3x_1 + x_2 \qquad\qquad = 3$$
$$4x_1 + 3x_2 - x_3 \qquad = 6$$
$$x_1 + 2x_2 \qquad + x_4 = 4$$
$$x_1, x_2, x_3, x_4 \geq 0$$

The third equation has its slack variable, x_4, but the first and second equations do not. Thus, we add the artificial variables R_1 and R_2 in the first two equations and penalize them in the objective function with $MR_1 + MR_2$ (because we are minimizing). The resulting LP is given as

$$\text{Minimize } z = 4x_1 + x_2 + MR_1 + MR_2$$

subject to

$$3x_1 + x_2 \qquad\qquad + R_1 \qquad = 3$$
$$4x_1 + 3x_2 - x_3 \qquad\qquad + R_2 = 6$$
$$x_1 + 2x_2 \qquad + x_4 \qquad\qquad = 4$$
$$x_1, x_2, x_3, x_4, R_1, R_2 \geq 0$$

The starting basic solution is $(R_1, R_2, x_4) = (3, 6, 4)$.

From a computational standpoint, solving the problem on the computer requires replacing M with a (sufficiently large) numeric value. Yet, in all textbook treatments, including the first seven editions of this book, M is manipulated algebraically in the simplex tableau. The result is an added, and an unnecessary, layer of difficulty that can be avoided by substituting an appropriate numeric value for M (which is what we need to do anyway when we use the computer). We break away from the long tradition of manipulating M algebraically and use a numerical substitution instead. The intent, of course, is to simplify the presentation without losing substance.

What value of M should we use? The answer depends on the data of the original LP. Recall that the penalty M must be sufficiently large *relative to the original objective coefficients* to force the artificial variables to zero in the optimal solution. At the same time, since computers are the main tool for solving LPs, we do not want M to be unnecessarily too large as this may lead to severe roundoff error. In the present example, the objective coefficients of x_1 and x_2 are 4 and 1, respectively, and it appears reasonable to set $M = 100$.[5]

Using $M = 100$, the starting simplex tableau is given as follows (for convenience, the z-column is eliminated because it does not change in all the iterations):

Basic	x_1	x_2	x_3	R_1	R_2	x_4	Solution
z	-4	-1	0	-100	-100	0	0
R_1	3	1	0	1	0	0	3
R_2	4	3	-1	0	1	0	6
x_4	1	2	0	0	0	1	4

Before proceeding with the simplex method computations, the z-row must be made consistent with the rest of the tableau. The right-hand side of the z-row in the tableau currently shows $z = 0$. However, given the nonbasic solution $x_1 = x_2 = x_3 = 0$, the current basic solution is $R_1 = 3$, $R_2 = 6$, and $x_4 = 4$, which yields $z = 100 \times 3 + 100 \times 6 + 4 \times 0 = 900$. This inconsistency stems from the fact that R_1 and R_2 have nonzero coefficients $(-100, -100)$ in the z-row (compare with the all-slack starting solution in Example 3.3-1, where the z-row coefficients of the slacks are zero).

To eliminate the inconsistency, we need to substitute out R_1 and R_2 in the z-row using the following row operation:

$$\text{New } z\text{-row} = \text{Old } z\text{-row} + (100 \times R_1\text{-row} + 100 \times R_2\text{-row})$$

(Convince yourself that this operation is the same as substituting out $R_1 = 3 - 3x_1 - x_2$ and $R_2 = 6 - 4x_1 - 3x_2 + x_3$ in the z-row.)

The modified tableau thus becomes (verify!):

Basic	x_1	x_2	x_3	R_1	R_2	x_4	Solution
z	696	399	-100	0	0	0	900
R_1	3	1	0	1	0	0	3
R_2	4	3	-1	0	1	0	6
x_4	1	2	0	0	0	1	4

[5]Technically, the M-method need not involve substituting out M numerically. Instead, the ith objective row coefficient in a simplex tableau reduces to computing the constants a_i and b_i in the algebraic expression $a_i M + b_i$. Comparison of two algebraic expressions will then be based on conditions involving the constants a_i and b_i only. The reason this procedure is not used in practice is the potentially tremendous computational overhead associated with computing (and comparing) the constants a_i and b_i.

The result is that R_1 and R_2 are now substituted out (have zero coefficients) in the z-row with $z = 900$ as desired.

The last tableau is ready for the application of the simplex optimality and the feasibility conditions, exactly as explained in Section 3.3.2. Because the objective function is minimized, the variable x_1 having the most *positive* coefficient in the z-row ($= 696$) enters the solution. The minimum ratio of the feasibility condition specifies R_1 as the leaving variable (verify!).

Once the entering and the leaving variables have been determined, the new tableau can be computed by using the familiar Gauss-Jordan operations.

Basic	x_1	x_2	x_3	R_1	R_2	x_4	Solution
z	0	167	-100	-232	0	0	204
x_1	1	$\frac{1}{3}$	0	$\frac{1}{3}$	0	0	1
R_2	0	$\frac{5}{3}$	-1	$-\frac{4}{3}$	1	0	2
x_4	0	$\frac{5}{3}$	0	$-\frac{1}{3}$	0	1	3

The last tableau shows that x_2 and R_2 are the entering and leaving variables, respectively. Continuing with the simplex computations, two more iterations are needed to reach the optimum: $x_1 = \frac{2}{5}$, $x_2 = \frac{9}{5}$, $z = \frac{17}{5}$ (verify with TORA!).

Note that the artificial variables R_1 and R_2 leave the basic solution (i.e., become equal to zero) promptly in the first and second iterations, a result that is consistent with the concept of penalizing them in the objective function.

Remarks. The use of the penalty M will not force an artificial variable to zero in the final simplex iteration if the LP does not have a feasible solution (i.e., the constraints cannot be satisfied simultaneously). In this case, the final simplex iteration will include at least one artificial variable with a positive value. Section 3.5.4 explains this situation.

PROBLEM SET 3.4A

1. Use hand computations to complete the simplex iteration of Example 3.4-1 and obtain the optimum solution.

2. *TORA experiment.* Generate the simplex iterations of Example 3.4-1 using TORA's Iterations ⟹ M-method module (file *toraEx3.4-1.txt*). Compare the effect of using $M = 1, M = 10$, and $M = 1000$ on the solution. What conclusion can be drawn from this experiment?

3. In Example 3.4-1, identify the starting tableau for each of the following (independent) cases, and develop the associated z-row after substituting out all the artificial variables:

   *(a) The third constraint is $x_1 + 2x_2 \geq 4$.

   *(b) The second constraint is $4x_1 + 3x_2 \leq 6$.

   (c) The second constraint is $4x_1 + 3x_2 = 6$.

   (d) The objective function is to maximize $z = 4x_1 + x_2$.

4. Consider the following set of constraints:

$$-2x_1 + 3x_2 = 3 \quad (1)$$
$$4x_1 + 5x_2 \geq 10 \quad (2)$$
$$x_1 + 2x_2 \leq 5 \quad (3)$$
$$6x_1 + 7x_2 \leq 3 \quad (4)$$
$$4x_1 + 8x_2 \geq 5 \quad (5)$$
$$x_1, x_2 \geq 0$$

For each of the following problems, develop the z-row after substituting out the artificial variables:

(a) Maximize $z = 5x_1 + 6x_2$ subject to (1), (3), and (4).
(b) Maximize $z = 2x_1 - 7x_2$ subject to (1), (2), (4), and (5).
(c) Minimize $z = 3x_1 + 6x_2$ subject to (3), (4), and (5).
(d) Minimize $z = 4x_1 + 6x_2$ subject to (1), (2), and (5).
(e) Minimize $z = 3x_1 + 2x_2$ subject to (1) and (5).

5. Consider the following set of constraints:

$$x_1 + x_2 + x_3 = 7$$
$$2x_1 - 5x_2 + x_3 \geq 10$$
$$x_1, x_2, x_3 \geq 0$$

Solve the problem for each of the following objective functions:

(a) Maximize $z = 2x_1 + 3x_2 - 5x_3$.
(b) Minimize $z = 2x_1 + 3x_2 - 5x_3$.
(c) Maximize $z = x_1 + 2x_2 + x_3$.
(d) Minimize $z = 4x_1 - 8x_2 + 3x_3$.

*6. Consider the problem

$$\text{Maximize } z = 2x_1 + 4x_2 + 4x_3 - 3x_4$$

subject to

$$x_1 + x_2 + x_3 \quad = 4$$
$$x_1 + 4x_2 + \quad x_4 = 8$$
$$x_1, x_2, x_3, x_4 \geq 0$$

Solve the problem with x_3 and x_4 as the starting basic variables and *without using any artificial variables*. (*Hint*: x_3 and x_4 play the role of slack variables. The main difference is that they have nonzero objective coefficients.)

7. Solve the following problem using x_3 and x_4 as starting basic feasible variables. As in Problem 6, do *not* use any artificial variables.

$$\text{Minimize } z = 3x_1 + 2x_2 + 3x_3$$

subject to

$$x_1 + 4x_2 + x_3 \geq 14$$
$$2x_1 + x_2 + x_4 \geq 20$$
$$x_1, x_2, x_3, x_4 \geq 0$$

8. Consider the problem

$$\text{Maximize } z = x_1 + 5x_2 + 3x_3$$

subject to

$$x_1 + 2x_2 + x_3 = 6$$
$$2x_1 - x_2 = 8$$
$$x_1, x_2, x_3 \geq 0$$

The variable x_3 plays the role of a slack. Thus, no artificial variable is needed in the first constraint. In the second constraint, an artificial variable, R, is needed. Solve the problem using x_3 and R as the starting variables.

9. Show that the M-method will conclude that the following problem has no feasible solution.

$$\text{Maximize } z = 2x_1 + 5x_2$$

subject to

$$3x_1 + 2x_2 \geq 6$$
$$2x_1 + x_2 \leq 2$$
$$x_1, x_2 \geq 0$$

3.4.2 Two-Phase Method

In the M-method, the use of the penalty, M, can result in computer roundoff error. The two-phase method eliminates the use of the constant M altogether. As the name suggests, the method solves the LP in two phases: Phase I attempts to find a starting basic feasible solution, and, if one is found, Phase II is invoked to solve the original problem.

Summary of the Two-Phase Method

Phase I. Put the problem in equation form, and add the necessary artificial variables to the constraints (exactly as in the M-method) to secure a starting basic solution. Next, find a basic solution of the resulting equations that *always* minimizes the sum of the artificial variables, regardless of whether the LP is maximization or minimization. If the minimum value of the sum is positive, the LP problem has no feasible solution. Otherwise, proceed to Phase II.

Phase II. Use the feasible solution from Phase I as a starting basic feasible solution for the *original* problem.

Example 3.4-2

We use the same problem in Example 3.4-1.

Phase I

$$\text{Minimize } r = R_1 + R_2$$

subject to

$$3x_1 + x_2 + R_1 = 3$$
$$4x_1 + 3x_2 - x_3 + R_2 = 6$$
$$x_1 + 2x_2 + x_4 = 4$$
$$x_1, x_2, x_3, x_4, R_1, R_2 \geq 0$$

The associated tableau is

Basic	x_1	x_2	x_3	R_1	R_2	x_4	Solution
r	0	0	0	-1	-1	0	0
R_1	3	1	0	1	0	0	3
R_2	4	3	-1	0	1	0	6
x_4	1	2	0	0	0	1	4

As in the M-method, R_1 and R_2 are substituted out in the r-row by using the following row operations:

$$\text{New } r\text{-row} = \text{Old } r\text{-row} + (1 \times R_1\text{-row} + 1 \times R_2\text{-row})$$

The new r-row is used to solve Phase I of the problem, which yields the following optimum tableau (verify with TORA's Iterations $\Rightarrow$ Two-phase Method):

Basic	x_1	x_2	x_3	R_1	R_2	x_4	Solution
r	0	0	0	-1	-1	0	0
x_1	1	0	$\frac{1}{5}$	$\frac{3}{5}$	$-\frac{1}{5}$	0	$\frac{3}{5}$
x_2	0	1	$-\frac{3}{5}$	$-\frac{4}{5}$	$\frac{3}{5}$	0	$\frac{6}{5}$
x_4	0	0	1	1	-1	1	1

Because minimum $r = 0$, Phase I produces the basic feasible solution $x_1 = \frac{3}{5}$, $x_2 = \frac{6}{5}$, and $x_4 = 1$. At this point, the artificial variables have completed their mission, and we can eliminate their columns altogether from the tableau and move on to Phase II.

Phase II

After deleting the artificial columns, we write the *original* problem as

$$\text{Minimize } z = 4x_1 + x_2$$

subject to

$$x_1 + \tfrac{1}{5}x_3 \qquad = \tfrac{3}{5}$$

$$x_2 - \tfrac{3}{5}x_3 \qquad = \tfrac{6}{5}$$

$$x_3 + x_4 = 1$$

$$x_1, x_2, x_3, x_4 \geq 0$$

Essentially, Phase I has transformed the original constraint equations in a manner that provides a starting basic feasible solution for the problem, if one exists. The tableau associated with Phase II problem is thus given as

Basic	x_1	x_2	x_3	x_4	Solution
z	-4	-1	0	0	0
x_1	1	0	$\tfrac{1}{5}$	0	$\tfrac{3}{5}$
x_2	0	1	$-\tfrac{3}{5}$	0	$\tfrac{6}{5}$
x_4	0	0	1	1	1

Again, because the basic variables x_1 and x_2 have nonzero coefficients in the z-row, they must be substituted out, using the following operations.

$$\text{New } z\text{-row} = \text{Old } z\text{-row} + (4 \times x_1\text{-row} + 1 \times x_2\text{-row})$$

The initial tableau of Phase II is thus given as

Basic	x_1	x_2	x_3	x_4	Solution
z	0	0	$\tfrac{1}{5}$	0	$\tfrac{18}{5}$
x_1	1	0	$\tfrac{1}{5}$	0	$\tfrac{3}{5}$
x_2	0	1	$-\tfrac{3}{5}$	0	$\tfrac{6}{5}$
x_4	0	0	1	1	1

Because we are minimizing, x_3 must enter the solution. Application of the simplex method will produce the optimum in one iteration (verify with TORA).

Remarks. The removal of the artificial variables and their columns at the end of Phase I can take place only when they are all *nonbasic* (as Example 3.4-2 illustrates). If one or more artificial variables are *basic* (at *zero* level) at the end of Phase I, then their removal requires the following additional steps:

Step 1. Select a zero artificial variable to leave the basic solution and designate its row as the *pivot row*. The entering variable can be *any* nonbasic (and nonartificial) variable with a *nonzero* (positive or negative) coefficient in the pivot row. Perform the associated simplex iteration.

Step 2. Remove the column of the (just-leaving) artificial variable from the tableau. If all the zero artificial variables have been removed, go to Phase II. Otherwise, go back to Step 1.

The logic behind step 1 is that the feasibility of the remaining basic variables will not be affected when a zero artificial variable is made nonbasic regardless of whether the pivot element is positive or negative. Problems 5 and 6, Set 3.4b illustrate this situation. Problem 7 provides an additional detail about Phase I calculations.

PROBLEM SET 3.4B

*1. In Phase I, if the LP is of the maximization type, explain why we do not maximize the sum of the artificial variables in Phase I.

2. For each case in Problem 4, Set 3.4a, write the corresponding Phase I objective function.

3. Solve Problem 5, Set 3.4a, by the two-phase method.

4. Write Phase I for the following problem, and then solve (with TORA for convenience) to show that the problem has no feasible solution.

$$\text{Maximize } z = 2x_1 + 5x_2$$

subject to

$$3x_1 + 2x_2 \geq 12$$

$$2x_1 + x_2 \leq 4$$

$$x_1, x_2 \geq 0$$

5. Consider the following problem:

$$\text{Maximize } z = 2x_1 + 2x_2 + 4x_3$$

subject to

$$2x_1 + x_2 + x_3 \leq 2$$

$$3x_1 + 4x_2 + 2x_3 \geq 8$$

$$x_1, x_2, x_3 \geq 0$$

   (a) Show that Phase I will terminate with an artificial *basic* variable at zero level (you may use TORA for convenience).

   (b) Remove the zero artificial variable prior to the start of Phase II, then carry out Phase II iterations.

6. Consider the following problem:

$$\text{Maximize } z = 3x_1 + 2x_2 + 3x_3$$

subject to

$$2x_1 + x_2 + x_3 = 4$$
$$x_1 + 3x_2 + x_3 = 12$$
$$3x_1 + 4x_2 + 2x_3 = 16$$
$$x_1, x_2, x_3 \geq 0$$

(a) Show that Phase I terminates with two zero artificial variables in the basic solution (use TORA for convenience).

(b) Show that when the procedure of Problem 5(b) is applied at the end of Phase I, only one of the two zero artificial variables can be made nonbasic.

(c) Show that the original constraint associated with the zero artificial variable that cannot be made nonbasic in (b) must be redundant—hence, its row and column can be removed at the start of Phase II.

*7. Consider the following LP:

$$\text{Maximize } z = 3x_1 + 2x_2 + 3x_3$$

subject to

$$2x_1 + x_2 + x_3 \leq 2$$
$$3x_1 + 4x_2 + 2x_3 \geq 8$$
$$x_1, x_2, x_3 \geq 0$$

The optimal simplex tableau at the end of Phase I is

Basic	x_1	x_2	x_3	x_4	x_5	R	Solution
r	-5	0	-2	-1	-4	0	0
x_2	2	1	1	0	1	0	2
R	-5	0	-2	-1	-4	1	0

Explain why the nonbasic variables $x_1, x_3, x_4,$ and x_5 can never assume positive values at the end of Phase II. Hence, conclude that their columns can be dropped before we start Phase II. In essence, the removal of these variables reduces the constraint equations of the problem to $x_2 = 2$—meaning that it necessary to carry out Phase II in this problem.

8. Consider the LP model

$$\text{Minimize } z = 2x_1 - 4x_2 + 3x_3$$

subject to

$$5x_1 - 6x_2 + 2x_3 \geq 5$$
$$-x_1 + 3x_2 + 5x_3 \geq 8$$
$$2x_1 + 5x_2 - 4x_3 \leq 4$$
$$x_1, x_2, x_3 \geq 0$$

Show how the inequalities can be modified to a set of equations that requires the use of single artificial variable only (instead of two).

3.5 SPECIAL CASES IN THE SIMPLEX METHOD

This section considers four special cases that arise in the use of the simplex method.

1. Degeneracy
2. Alternative optima
3. Unbounded solutions
4. Nonexisting (or infeasible) solutions

The remainder of this section presents a *theoretical* explanation of these situations. It also provides an interpretation of what these special results mean in a real-life problem.

3.5.1 Degeneracy

In the application of the feasibility condition of the simplex method, a tie for the minimum ratio may occur and can be broken arbitrarily. When this happens, at least one *basic* variable will be zero in the next iteration, and the new solution is said to be **degenerate**.

Degeneracy can cause the simplex iterations to **cycle** indefinitely, thus never terminating the algorithm. The condition also reveals that the model has at least one *redundant* constraint (see also Remark 2 following this example).

The following example explains the practical and theoretical impacts of degeneracy.

Example 3.5-1 (Degenerate Optimal Solution)

$$\text{Maximize } z = 3x_1 + 9x_2$$

subject to

$$x_1 + 4x_2 \le 8$$
$$x_1 + 2x_2 \le 4$$
$$x_1, x_2 \ge 0$$

Using the slack variables x_3 and x_4, the solution tableaus are

In iteration 0, x_3 and x_4 tie for the leaving variable, leading to degeneracy in iteration 1 because the basic variable x_4 assumes a zero value. The optimum is reached in one additional iteration.

Iteration	Basic	x_1	x_2	x_3	x_4	Solution
0	z	-3	-9	0	0	0
x_2 enters	x_3	1	4	1	0	8
x_3 leaves	x_4	1	2	0	1	4
1	z	$-\frac{3}{4}$	0	$\frac{9}{4}$	0	18
x_1 enters	x_2	$\frac{1}{4}$	1	$\frac{1}{4}$	0	2
x_4 leaves	x_4	$\frac{1}{2}$	0	$-\frac{1}{2}$	1	0
2	z	0	0	$\frac{3}{2}$	$\frac{3}{2}$	18
(optimum)	x_2	0	1	$\frac{1}{2}$	$-\frac{1}{2}$	2
	x_1	1	0	-1	2	0

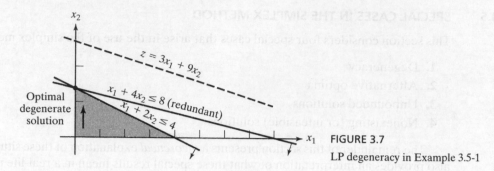

FIGURE 3.7

LP degeneracy in Example 3.5-1

Remarks.

1. What is the practical implication of degeneracy? Look at the graphical solution in Figure 3.7. Three lines pass through the optimum point ($x_1 = 0$, $x_2 = 2$). Because this is a two-dimensional problem, the point is *overdetermined*, and one of the constraints is redundant.[6] In practice, the mere knowledge that some resources are superfluous can be valuable during the implementation phase of the solution. The information may also lead to discovering irregularities in the construction of the model. Unfortunately, there are no efficient computational techniques for identifying redundant constraints directly from the tableau.

2. From the theoretical standpoint, degeneracy can lead to **cycling**. In simplex iterations 1 and 2, the objective value does not improve ($z = 18$), and it is thus possible for the simplex method to enter a repetitive sequence of iterations, never improving the objective value and never satisfying the optimality condition (see Problem 4, Set 3.5a). Although there are methods for eliminating cycling, these methods lead to drastic slowdown in computations.[7]

3. Although an LP model may not start with redundant constraints (in the direct sense shown in Figure 3.7), computer roundoff error may actually create degeneracy-like conditions during the course of solving a real-life LP. In such cases, the iterations will "stall" at a solution point, thus mimicking cycling. Commercial codes attempt to alleviate the problem by periodically perturbing the values of the basic variables (see Section 3.7 for more details about how commercial codes are developed).

PROBLEM SET 3.5A

*1. Consider the graphical solution space in Figure 3.8. Suppose that the simplex iterations start at A and that the optimum solution occurs at D. Further, assume that the objective function is defined such that at A, x_1 enters the solution first.

(a) Identify (on the graph) the corner points that define the simplex method path to the optimum point.

(b) Determine the maximum possible number of simplex iterations needed to reach the optimum solution, assuming no cycling.

---

[6]Redundancy generally implies that constraints can be removed without affecting the feasible solution space. A sometimes-quoted counterexample is $x + y \leq 1$, $x \geq 1$, $y \geq 0$, where the removal of any one constraint will change the feasible space from a single point to a region. Suffice it to say that this condition is true only if the solution space consists of a single feasible point, a highly unlikely occurrence in large (real-life) LPs.
[7]See Bland, R., "New Finite Pivoting Rules for the Simplex Method," *Mathematics of Operations Research*, Vol. 2, No. 2, pp. 103–107, 1977.

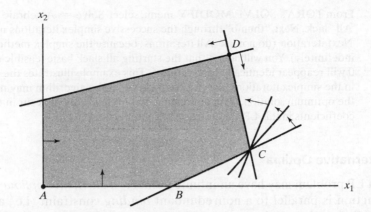

FIGURE 3.8

Solution space of Problem 1, Set 3.5a

2. Consider the following LP:

$$\text{Maximize } z = 3x_1 + 2x_2$$

subject to

$$4x_1 - x_2 \leq 4$$

$$4x_1 + 3x_2 \leq 6$$

$$4x_1 + x_2 \leq 4$$

$$x_1, x_2 \geq 0$$

(a) Show that the associated simplex iterations are temporarily degenerate (you may use TORA for convenience).

(b) Verify the result by solving the problem graphically (TORA's Graphic module can be used here).

3. *TORA experiment.* Consider the LP in Problem 2.

(a) Use TORA to generate the simplex iterations. How many iterations are needed to reach the optimum?

(b) Interchange constraints (1) and (3) and re-solve the problem with TORA. How many iterations are needed to solve the problem?

(c) Explain why the numbers of iterations in (a) and (b) are different.

4. *TORA Experiment.* Consider the following LP (authored by E.M. Beale to demonstrate cycling):

$$\text{Maximize } z = \tfrac{3}{4}x_1 - 20x_2 + \tfrac{1}{2}x_3 - 6x_4$$

subject to

$$\tfrac{1}{4}x_1 - 8x_2 - x_3 + 9x_4 \leq 0$$

$$\tfrac{1}{2}x_1 - 12x_2 - \tfrac{1}{2}x_3 + 3x_4 \leq 0$$

$$x_3 \leq 1$$

$$x_1, x_2, x_3, x_4 \geq 0$$

From TORA's SOLVE/MODIFY menu, select Solve ⟹ Algebraic ⟹ Iterations ⟹ All-slack. Next, "thumb" through the successive simplex iterations using the command Next iteration (do not use All iterations, because the simplex method will then cycle indefinitely). You will notice that the starting all-slack basic feasible solution at iteration 0 will reappear identically in iteration 6. This example illustrates the occurrence of cycling in the simplex iterations and the possibility that the algorithm may never converge to the optimum solution. (It is interesting that cycling will not occur in this example if all the coefficients in this LP are converted to integer—try it!)

3.5.2 Alternative Optima

An LP problem may have an infinite number of *alternative optima* when the objective function is parallel to a nonredundant *binding* constraint (i.e., a constraint that is satisfied as an equation at the optimal solution). The next example demonstrates the practical significance of such solutions.

Example 3.5-2 (Infinite Number of solutions)

$$\text{Maximize } z = 2x_1 + 4x_2$$

subject to

$$x_1 + 2x_2 \leq 5$$
$$x_1 + x_2 \leq 4$$
$$x_1, x_2 \geq 0$$

Figure 3.9 demonstrates how alternative optima can arise in the LP model when the objective function is parallel to a binding constraint. Any point on the *line segment BC* represents an alternative optimum with the same objective value $z = 10$.

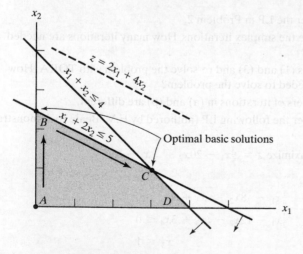

FIGURE 3.9

LP alternative optima in Example 3.5-2

The iterations of the model are given by the following tableaus.

Iteration	Basic	x_1	x_2	x_3	x_4	Solution
0	z	-2	-4	0	0	0
x_2 enters	x_3	1	2	1	0	5
x_3 leaves	x_4	1	1	0	1	4
1 (optimum)	z	0	0	2	0	10
x_1 enters	x_2	$\frac{1}{2}$	1	$\frac{1}{2}$	0	$\frac{5}{2}$
x_4 leaves	x_4	$\frac{1}{2}$	0	$-\frac{1}{2}$	1	$\frac{3}{2}$
2	z	0	0	2	0	10
(alternative optimum)	x_2	0	1	1	-1	1
	x_1	1	0	-1	2	3

Iteration 1 gives the optimum solution $x_1 = 0$, $x_2 = \frac{5}{2}$, and $z = 10$ (point B in Figure 3.9). The existence of alternative can be detected in the optimal tableau by examining the z-equation coefficients of the *non*basic variables. The zero coefficient of nonbasic x_1 indicates that x_1 can be made basic, altering the values of the basic variables without changing the value of z. Iteration 2 does just that, using x_1 and x_4 as the entering and leaving variables, respectively. The new solution point occurs at $C(x_1 = 3, x_2 = 1, z = 10)$. (TORA's Iterations option allows determining one alternative optimum.)

The simplex method deals with corner point optima only—namely, points B and C in the present example. Mathematically, we can determine all the points (x_1, x_2) on the line segment BC as a nonnegative weighted average of points $B(x_1 = 0, x_2 = \frac{5}{2})$ and $C(x_1 = 3, x_2 = 1)$—that is,

$$\left.\begin{aligned}\hat{x}_1 &= \alpha(0) + (1 - \alpha)(3) = 3 - 3\alpha \\ \hat{x}_2 &= \alpha\left(\tfrac{5}{2}\right) + (1 - \alpha)(1) = 1 + \tfrac{3}{2}\alpha\end{aligned}\right\}, 0 \le \alpha \le 1$$

Remarks.   In practice, alternative optima are useful because we can choose from many solutions without experiencing deterioration in the objective value. For instance, in the present example, the solution at B shows that activity 2 only is at a positive level. At C, both activities are at a positive level. If the example represents a product-mix situation, it may be advantageous to market two products instead of one.

PROBLEM SET 3.5B

*1. For the following LP, identify three alternative optimal basic solutions, and then write a general expression for all the nonbasic alternative optima comprising these three basic solutions.

$$\text{Maximize } z = x_1 + 2x_2 + 3x_3$$

subject to

$$x_1 + 2x_2 + 3x_3 \leq 10$$

$$x_1 + x_2 \leq 5$$

$$x_1 \leq 1$$

$$x_1, x_2, x_3 \geq 0$$

Note: Although the problem has more than three alternative basic solution optima, you are only required to identify three of them. You may use TORA for convenience.

2. Solve the following LP:

$$\text{Maximize } z = 2x_1 - x_2 + 3x_3$$

subject to

$$x_1 - x_2 + 5x_3 \leq 5$$

$$2x_1 - x_2 + 3x_3 \leq 20$$

$$x_1, x_2, x_3 \geq 0$$

From the optimal tableau, show that all the alternative optima are not corner points (i.e., nonbasic). Give a two-dimensional graphical demonstration of the type of solution space and objective function that will produce this result. (You may use TORA for convenience.)

3. For the following LP, show that the optimal solution is degenerate and that none of the alternative solutions are corner points (you may use TORA for convenience).

$$\text{Maximize } z = 3x_1 + x_2$$

subject to

$$x_1 + 2x_2 \leq 5$$

$$x_1 + x_2 - x_3 \leq 2$$

$$7x_1 + 3x_2 - 5x_3 \leq 20$$

$$x_1, x_2, x_3 \geq 0$$

3.5.3 Unbounded Solution

In some LP models, the solution space is *unbounded* in at least one variable—meaning that variables may be increased indefinitely without violating any of the constraints. The associated objective value may also be unbounded in this case.

An unbounded solution space usually is a sign that the model is poorly constructed. The most likely irregularity in such models is that some key constraints have not been accounted for. Another possibility is that estimates of the constraint coefficients may not be accurate.

Example 3.5-3   (Unbounded Objective Value)

$$\text{Maximize } z = 2x_1 + x_2$$

subject to

$$x_1 - x_2 \le 10$$
$$2x_1 \quad\;\; \le 40$$
$$x_1, x_2 \ge 0$$

Starting Iteration

Basic	x_1	x_2	x_3	x_4	Solution
z	-2	-1	0	0	0
x_3	1	-1	1	0	10
x_4	2	0	0	1	40

In the starting tableau, both x_1 and x_2 have negative z-equation coefficients, which means that an increase in their values will increase the objective value. Although x_1 should be the entering variable (it has the most negative z-coefficient), we note that *all* the *constraint* coefficients under x_2 are ≤ 0—meaning that x_2 can be increased indefinitely without violating any of the constraints (compare with the graphical interpretation of the minimum ratio in Figure 3.5). The result is that z can be increased indefinitely. Figure 3.10 shows the unbounded solution space and also that x_2 and z can be increased indefinitely.

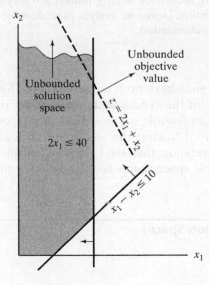

FIGURE 3.10

LP unbounded solution in Example 3.5-3

Remarks.   Had x_1 been selected as the entering variable in the starting iteration (per the optimality condition), a later iteration would eventually have produced an entering variable with the same properties as x_2. See Problem 1, Set 3.5c.

PROBLEM SET 3.5C

1. *TORA Experiment.* Solve Example 3.5-3 using TORA's Iterations option and show that even though the solution starts with x_1 as the entering variable (per the optimality condition), the simplex algorithm will point eventually to an unbounded solution.

*2. Consider the LP:

$$\text{Maximize } z = 20x_1 + 5x_2 + x_3$$

subject to

$$3x_1 + 5x_2 - 5x_3 \leq 50$$

$$x_1 \qquad\qquad \leq 10$$

$$x_1 + 3x_2 - 4x_3 \leq 20$$

$$x_1, x_2, x_3 \geq 0$$

   (a) By inspecting the constraints, determine the direction (x_1, x_2, or x_3) in which the solution space is unbounded.

   (b) Without further computations, what can you conclude regarding the optimum objective value?

3. In some ill-constructed LP models, the solution space may be unbounded even though the problem may have a bounded objective value. Such an occurrence points to possible irregularities in the construction of the model. In large problems, it may be difficult to detect "unboundedness" by inspection. Devise an analytic procedure for determining whether or not a solution space is unbounded.

3.5.4   Infeasible Solution

LP models with inconsistent constraints have no feasible solution. This situation does not occur if *all* the constraints are of the type $\leq$ with nonnegative right-hand sides because the slacks provide an obvious feasible solution. For other types of constraints, penalized artificial variables are used to start the solution. If at least one artificial variable is *positive* in the optimum iteration, then the LP has no feasible solution. From the practical standpoint, an infeasible space points to the possibility that the model is not formulated correctly.

Example 3.5-4   (Infeasible Solution Space)

Consider the following LP:

$$\text{Maximize } z = 3x_1 + 2x_2$$

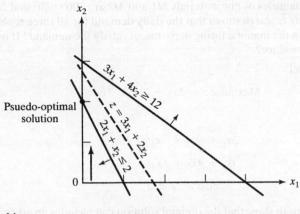

FIGURE 3.11

Infeasible solution of Example 3.5-4

subject to

$$2x_1 + x_2 \leq 2$$

$$3x_1 + 4x_2 \geq 12$$

$$x_1, x_2 \geq 0$$

Using the penalty $M = 100$ for the artificial variable R, the following tableau provide the simplex iterations of the model.

Iteration	Basic	x_1	x_2	x_4	x_3	R	Solution
0	z	−303	−402	100	0	0	−1200
x_2 enters	x_3	2	1	0	1	0	2
x_3 leaves	R	3	4	−1	0	1	12
1	z	501	0	100	402	0	−396
(pseudo-optimum)	x_2	2	1	0	1	0	2
	R	−5	0	−1	−4	1	4

Optimum iteration 1 shows that the artificial variable R is *positive* (= 4)—meaning that the LP is infeasible. Figure 3.11 depicts the infeasible solution space. By allowing the artificial variable to be positive, the simplex method has in effect reversed the direction of the inequality from $3x_1 + 4x_2 \geq 12$ to $3x_1 + 4x_2 \leq 12$ (can you explain how?). The result is what we may call a **pseudo-optimal** solution.

PROBLEM SET 3.5D

1. *Toolco produces three types of tools, $T1$, $T2$, and $T3$. The tools use two raw materials, $M1$ and $M2$, according to the data in the following table:

	Number of units of raw materials per tool		
Raw material	$T1$	$T2$	$T3$
$M1$	3	5	6
$M2$	5	3	4

The available daily quantities of raw materials $M1$ and $M2$ are 2000 units and 2400 units, respectively. Marketing research shows that the daily demand for all three tools must be at least 1000 units. Can the manufacturing department satisfy the demand? If not, what is the most Toolco can produce?

2. Consider the LP model

$$\text{Maximize } z = 3x_1 + 2x_1 + 3x_3$$

subject to

$$2x_1 + x_2 + x_3 \le 4$$

$$3x_1 + 4x_2 + 2x_3 \ge 16$$

$$x_1, x_2, x_3 \ge 0$$

Use hand computations to show that the optimal solution can includes an artificial basic variable at zero level. Does the problem have a *feasible* optimal solution?

3.6   SENSITIVITY ANALYSIS

In LP, the parameters (input data) of the model can change within certain limits without causing changes in the optimum. This is referred to as *sensitivity analysis* and will be the subject matter of this section. Later, Chapter 4 will study *post-optimal* analysis, which deals with determining the new optimum solution when targeted input data are changed.

The presentation explains the basic ideas of sensitivity analysis using the more concrete graphical solution. These ideas are then extended to the general LP problem using the simplex tableau results.

3.6.1   Graphical Sensitivity Analysis

This section demonstrates the general idea of sensitivity analysis. Two cases will be considered:

1. Sensitivity of the optimum solution to changes in the availability of the resources (right-hand side of the constraints).

2. Sensitivity of the optimum solution to changes in unit profit or unit cost (coefficients of the objective function).

We will use individual examples to explain the two cases.

Example 3.6-1   (Changes in the Right-Hand Side)

JOBCO manufactures two products on two machines. A unit of product 1 requires 2 hours on machine 1 and 1 hour on machine 2. For product 2, one unit requires 1 hour on machine 1 and 3 hours on machine 2. The revenues per unit of products 1 and 2 are $30 and $20, respectively. The total daily processing time available for each machine is 8 hours.

Letting x_1 and x_2 represent the daily number of units of products 1 and 2, respectively, the LP model is given as

$$\text{Maximize } z = 30x_1 + 20x_2$$

subject to

$$2x_1 + x_2 \le 8 \quad \text{(Machine 1)}$$
$$x_1 + 3x_2 \le 8 \quad \text{(Machine 2)}$$
$$x_1, x_2 \ge 0$$

Figure 3.12 illustrates the change in the optimum solution when changes are made in the capacity of machine 1. If the daily capacity is increased from 8 hours to 9 hours, the new optimum will move to point G. The rate of change in optimum z resulting from changing machine 1 capacity from 8 hours to 9 hours can be computed as:

$$\begin{pmatrix} \text{Rate of revenue change} \\ \text{resulting from increasing} \\ \text{machine 1 capacity by 1 hr} \\ \text{(point } C \text{ to point } G) \end{pmatrix} = \frac{z_G - z_C}{\text{(Capacity change)}} = \frac{142 - 128}{9 - 8} = \$14/\text{hr}$$

FIGURE 3.12

Graphical sensitivity of optimal solution to changes in the availability of resources (right-hand side of the constraints)

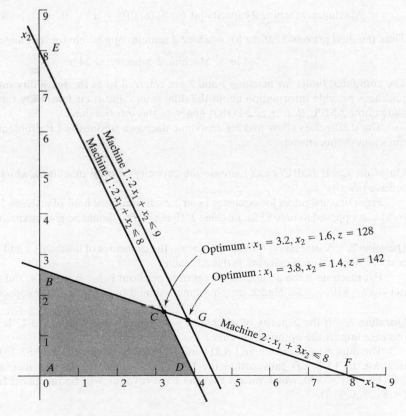

Optimum : $x_1 = 3.2, x_2 = 1.6, z = 128$

Optimum : $x_1 = 3.8, x_2 = 1.4, z = 142$

The computed rate provides a *direct* link between the model input (resources) and its output (total revenue). It says that a unit increase (decrease) in machine 1 capacity will increase (decrease) revenue by $14.00.

The name **unit worth of a resource** is an apt description of the rate of change of the objective function per unit change of a resource. Nevertheless, early LP developments have coined the abstract name **dual (or shadow) price**, and this name is now standard in all the LP literature and software packages. The presentation in this book conforms to this standard.

Looking at Figure 3.12, we can see that the dual price of $14/hr remains valid for changes (increases or decreases) in machine 1 capacity that move its constraint parallel to itself to any point on the line segment *BF*. We compute machine 1 capacities at points B and F as follows:

$$\text{Minimum machine 1 capacity [at } B = (0, 2.67)] = 2 \times 0 + 1 \times 2.67 = 2.67 \text{ hr}$$

$$\text{Maximum machine 1 capacity [at } F = (8, 0)] = 2 \times 8 + 1 \times 0 = 16 \text{ hr}$$

The conclusion is that the dual price of $14/hr remains valid in the range

$$2.67 \text{ hr} \leq \text{Machine 1 capacity} \leq 16 \text{ hr}$$

Changes outside this range produce a different dual price (worth per unit).

Using similar computations, you can verify that the dual price for machine 2 capacity is $2.00/hr, and it remains valid for changes in machine 2 capacity within the line segment *DE*. Now,

$$\text{Minimum machine 2 capacity [at } D = (4, 0)] = 1 \times 4 + 3 \times 0 = 4 \text{ hr}$$

$$\text{Maximum machine 2 capacity [at } E = (8, 0)] = 1 \times 0 + 3 \times 8 = 24 \text{ hr}$$

Thus, the dual price of $2.00/hr for machine 2 remains applicable for the range

$$4 \text{ hr} \leq \text{Machine 2 capacity} \leq 24 \text{ hr}$$

The computed limits for machine 1 and 2 are referred to as the **feasibility ranges**. All software packages provide information about the dual prices and their feasibility ranges. Section 3.6.4 shows how AMPL, Solver, and TORA generate this information.

The dual prices allow making economic decisions about the LP problem, as the following questions demonstrate:

Question 1.   If JOBCO can increase the capacity of both machines, which machine should receive priority?

From the dual prices for machines 1 and 2, each additional hour of machine 1 increases revenue by $14, as opposed to only $2 for machine 2. Thus, priority should be given to machine 1.

Question 2.   A suggestion is made to increase the capacities of machines 1 and 2 at the additional cost of $10/hr for each machine. Is this advisable?

For machine 1, the additional net revenue per hour is $14 - 10 = \$4$, and for machine 2, the net is $\$2 - \$10 = -\$8$. Hence, only machine 1 should be considered for capacity increase.

Question 3.   If the capacity of machine 1 is increased from 8 hours to 13 hours, how will this increase impact the optimum revenue?

The dual price for machine 1 is $14 and is applicable in the range (2.67, 16) hr. The proposed increase to 13 hours falls within the feasibility range. Hence, the increase in revenue is $\$14(13 - 8) = \$70$, which means that the total revenue will be increased from $128 to $198 (= \$128 + \$70).

Question 4. Suppose that the capacity of machine 1 is increased to 20 hours, how will this increase affect the optimum revenue?

The proposed change is outside the feasibility range (2.67, 16) hr. Thus, we can only make an immediate conclusion regarding an increase up to 16 hours. Beyond that, further calculations are needed to find the answer (see Chapter 4). Remember that falling outside the feasibility range does *not* mean that the problem has no solution. It only means that available information is not sufficient to make a complete decision.

Question 5. How can we determine the new optimum values of the variables associated with a change in a resource?

The optimum values of the variables will change. However, the procedure for determining these values requires additional computations, as will be shown in Section 3.6.2.

PROBLEM SET 3.6A

1. A company manufactures two products, A and B. The unit revenues are $2 and $3, respectively. Two raw materials, $M1$ and $M2$, used in the manufacture of the two products have daily availabilities of 8 and 18 units, respectively. One unit of A uses 2 units of $M1$ and 2 units of $M2$, and 1 unit of B uses 3 units of $M1$ and 6 units of $M2$.

   (a) Determine the dual prices of $M1$ and $M2$ and their feasibility ranges.

   (b) Suppose that 2 additional units of $M1$ can be acquired at the cost of 25 cents per unit. Would you recommend the additional purchase?

   (c) What is the most the company should pay per unit of $M2$?

   (d) If $M2$ availability is increased by 3 units, determine the associated optimum revenue.

*2. Wild West produces two types of cowboy hats. A Type 1 hat requires twice as much labor time as a Type 2. If all the available labor time is dedicated to Type 2 alone, the company can produce a total of 400 Type 2 hats a day. The respective market limits for the two types are 150 and 200 hats per day. The revenue is $8 per Type 1 hat and $5 per Type 2 hat.

   (a) Use the graphical solution to determine the number of hats of each type that maximizes revenue.

   (b) Determine the dual price of the production capacity (in terms of the Type 2 hat) and the range for which it is applicable.

   (c) If the daily demand limit on the Type 1 hat is decreased to 120, use the dual price to determine the corresponding effect on the optimal revenue.

   (d) What is the dual price of the market share of the Type 2 hat? By how much can the market share be increased while yielding the computed worth per unit?

Example 3.6-2 (Changes in the Objective Coefficients)

Figure 3.13 shows the graphical solution space of the JOBCO problem presented in Example 3.6-1. The optimum occurs at point $C(x_1 = 3.2, x_2 = 1.6, z = 128)$. Changes in revenue units (i.e., objective-function coefficients) will change the slope of z. However, as can be seen from the figure, the optimum solution at point C remains unchanged so long as the objective function lies between lines BF and DE.

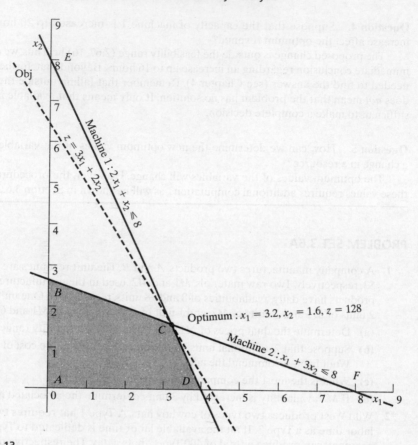

FIGURE 3.13

Graphical sensitivity of optimal solution to changes in the revenue units (coefficients of the objective function)

How can we determine ranges for the coefficients of the objective function that will keep the optimum solution unchanged at C? First, we write the objective function in the general format

$$\text{Maximize } z = c_1 x_1 + c_2 x_2$$

Imagine now that the line z is pivoted at C and that it can rotate clockwise and counterclockwise. The optimum solution will remain at point C so long as $z = c_1 x_1 + c_2 x_2$ lies between the two lines $x_1 + 3x_2 = 8$ and $2x_1 + x_2 = 8$. This means that the ratio $\frac{c_1}{c_2}$ can vary between $\frac{1}{3}$ and $\frac{2}{1}$, which yields the following **optimality range**:[8]

$$\frac{1}{3} \le \frac{c_1}{c_2} \le \frac{2}{1} \text{ or } .333 \le \frac{c_1}{c_2} \le 2$$

---

[8]The "ratio" condition works correctly in this situation because the slopes for the two lines passing through the optimum point C have the same sign. Other situations are more complex.

This information can provide immediate answers regarding the optimum solution as the following questions demonstrate:

Question 1. Suppose that the unit revenues for products 1 and 2 are changed to $35 and $25, respectively. Will the current optimum remain the same?

The new objective function is

$$\text{Maximize } z = 35x_1 + 25x_2$$

The solution at C will remain optimal because $\frac{c_1}{c_2} = \frac{35}{25} = 1.4$ remains within the optimality range (.333, 2). When the ratio falls outside this range, additional calculations are needed to find the new optimum (see Chapter 4). Notice that although the values of the variables at the optimum point C remain unchanged, the optimum value of z changes to $35 \times (3.2) + 25 \times (1.6) = \$152$.

Question 2. Suppose that the unit revenue of product 2 is fixed at its current value $c_2 = \$20$. What is the associated optimality range for the unit revenue for product 1, c_1, that will keep the optimum unchanged?

Substituting $c_2 = 20$ in the condition $\frac{1}{3} \leq \frac{c_1}{c_2} \leq 2$, we get

$$\tfrac{1}{3} \times 20 \leq c_1 \leq 2 \times 20 \text{ or } 6.67 \leq c_1 \leq 40$$

This range implicitly assumes that c_2 is fixed at $20.

We can similarly determine the optimality range for c_2 by fixing the value of c_1 at $30. Thus,

$$(c_2 \leq 30 \times 3 \text{ and } c_2 \geq \tfrac{30}{2}) \text{ or } 15 \leq c_2 \leq 90$$

As in the case of the right-hand side, all software packages provide the optimality ranges for each objective function coefficient. Section 3.6.4 shows how AMPL, Solver, and TORA generate these results.

Remarks. Although the material in this section has dealt only with two variables, the results lay the foundation for the development of sensitivity analysis for the general LP problem in Sections 3.6.2 and 3.6.3.

PROBLEM SET 3.6B

1. Consider Problem 1, Set 3.6a.
   (a) Determine the optimality condition for $\dfrac{c_A}{c_B}$ that will keep the optimum unchanged.
   (b) Determine the optimality ranges for c_A and c_B, assuming that the other coefficient is kept constant at its present value.
   (c) If the unit revenues c_A and c_B are changed simultaneously to $5 and $4, respectively, determine the new optimum solution.
   (d) If the changes in (c) are made one at a time, what can be said about the optimum solution?

2. In the Reddy Mikks model of Example 2.2-1:
   (a) Determine the range for the ratio of the unit revenue of exterior paint to the unit revenue of interior paint.

(b) If the revenue per ton of exterior paint remains constant at \$6000 per ton, determine the maximum unit revenue of interior paint that will keep the present optimum solution unchanged.

(c) If for marketing reasons the unit revenue of interior paint must be reduced to \$2500, will the current optimum production mix change?

*3. In Problem 2, Set 3.6a:

(a) Determine the optimality range for the unit revenue ratio of the two types of hats that will keep the current optimum unchanged.

(b) Using the information in (b), will the optimal solution change if the revenue per unit is the same for both types.

3.6.2 Algebraic Sensitivity Analysis—Changes in the Right-hand Side

In Section 3.6.1, we used the graphical solution to determine the *dual price* (unit worth of a resource) and its feasibility ranges. This section extends the analysis to the general LP model. A numeric example (the TOYCO model) will be used to facilitate the presentation.

Example 3.6-3 (TOYCO Model)

TOYCO uses three operations to assemble three types of toys—trains, trucks, and cars. The daily available times for the three operations are 430, 460, and 420 minutes, respectively, and the revenues per unit of toy train, truck, and car are \$3, \$2, and \$5, respectively. The assembly times per train at the three operations are 1, 3, and 1 minutes, respectively. The corresponding times per train and per car are $(2, 0, 4)$ and $(1, 2, 0)$ minutes (a zero time indicates that the operation is not used).

Letting x_1, x_2, and x_3 represent the daily number of units assembled of trains, trucks, and cars, respectively, the associated LP model is given as:

$$\text{Maximize } z = 3x_1 + 2x_2 + 5x_3$$

subject to

$$x_1 + 2x_2 + x_3 \leq 430 \text{ (Operation 1)}$$

$$3x_1 \quad\quad + 2x_3 \leq 460 \text{ (Operation 2)}$$

$$x_1 + 4x_2 \quad\quad \leq 420 \text{ (Operation 3)}$$

$$x_1, x_2, x_3 \geq 0$$

Using x_4, x_5, and x_6 as the slack variables for the constraints of operations 1, 2, and 3, respectively, the optimum tableau is

Basic	x_1	x_2	x_3	x_4	x_5	x_6	Solution
z	4	0	0	1	2	0	1350
x_2	$-\frac{1}{4}$	1	0	$\frac{1}{2}$	$-\frac{1}{4}$	0	100
x_3	$\frac{3}{2}$	0	1	0	$\frac{1}{2}$	0	230
x_6	2	0	0	-2	1	1	20

The solution recommends manufacturing 100 trucks and 230 cars but no trains. The associated revenue is $1350.

Determination of dual prices and feasibility ranges.   We will use the TOYCO model to show how this information is obtained from the optimal simplex tableau. Recognizing that the dual prices and their feasibility ranges are rooted in making changes in the right-hand side of the constraints, suppose that D_1, D_2, and D_3 are the (positive or negative) changes made in the allotted daily manufacturing time of operations 1, 2, and 3, respectively. The original TOYCO model can then be changed to

$$\text{Maximize } z = 3x_1 + 2x_2 + 5x_3$$

subject to

$$x_1 + 2x_2 + x_3 \le 430 + D_1 \quad \text{(Operation 1)}$$
$$3x_1 \qquad + 2x_3 \le 460 + D_2 \quad \text{(Operation 2)}$$
$$x_1 + 4x_2 \qquad \le 420 + D_3 \quad \text{(Operation 3)}$$

$$x_1, x_2, x_3 \ge 0$$

To express the optimum simplex tableau of the modified problem in terms of the changes D_1, D_2, and D_3, we first rewrite the starting tableau using the new right-hand sides, $430 + D_1$, $460 + D_2$, and $420 + D_3$.

Basic	x_1	x_2	x_3	x_4	x_5	x_6	RHS	D_1	D_2	D_3
									Solution	
z	-3	-2	-5	0	0	0	0	0	0	0
x_4	1	2	1	1	0	0	430	1	0	0
x_5	3	0	2	0	1	0	460	0	1	0
x_6	1	4	0	0	0	1	420	0	0	1

The two shaded areas are identical. Hence, if we repeat the *same* simplex iterations (with the *same* row operations) as in the *original* model, the columns in the two highlighted area will also be identical in the optimal tableau—that is,

Basic	x_1	x_2	x_3	x_4	x_5	x_6	RHS	D_1	D_2	D_3
									Solution	
z	4	0	0	1	2	0	1350	1	2	0
x_2	$-\frac{1}{4}$	1	0	$\frac{1}{2}$	$-\frac{1}{4}$	0	100	$\frac{1}{2}$	$-\frac{1}{4}$	0
x_3	$\frac{3}{2}$	0	1	0	$\frac{1}{2}$	0	230	0	$\frac{1}{2}$	0
x_6	2	0	0	-2	1	1	20	-2	1	1

The new optimum tableau provides the following optimal solution:

$$z = 1350 + D_1 + 2D_2$$
$$x_2 = 100 + \tfrac{1}{2}D_1 - \tfrac{1}{4}D_2$$
$$x_3 = 230 + \tfrac{1}{2}D_2$$
$$x_6 = 20 - 2D_1 + D_2 + D_3$$

We now use this solution to determine the dual prices and the feasibility ranges.

Dual prices: The value of the objective function can be written as

$$z = 1350 + \mathbf{1}D_1 + \mathbf{2}D_2 + \mathbf{0}D_3$$

The equation shows that

1. A unit change in operation 1 capacity ($D_1 = \pm 1$ min) changes z by \$1.
2. A unit change in operation 2 capacity ($D_2 = \pm 1$ min) changes z by \$2.
3. A unit change in operation 3 capacity ($D_3 = \pm 1$ min) changes z by \$0.

This means that, by definition, the corresponding dual prices are 1, 2, and 0 (\$/min) for operations 1, 2, and 3, respectively.

The coefficients of D_1, D_2, and D_3 in the optimal z-row are exactly those of the slack variables x_4, x_5, and x_6. This means that the dual prices equal the coefficients of the slack variables in the optimal z-row. There is no ambiguity as to which coefficient applies to which resource because each slack variable is uniquely identified with a constraint.

Feasibility range: The current solution remains feasible if all the basic variables remain nonnegative — that is,

$$x_2 = 100 + \tfrac{1}{2}D_1 - \tfrac{1}{4}D_2 \geq 0$$
$$x_3 = 230 + \tfrac{1}{2}D_2 \geq 0$$
$$x_6 = 20 - 2D_1 + D_2 + D_3 \geq 0$$

Simultaneous changes D_1, D_2, and D_3 that satisfy these inequalities will keep the solution feasible. The new optimum solution can be found by substituting out the values of D_1, D_2, and D_3.

To illustrate the use of these conditions, suppose that the manufacturing time available for operations 1, 2, and 3 are 480, 440, and 400 minutes, respectively. Then, $D_1 = 480 - 430 = 50$, $D_2 = 440 - 460 = -20$, *and* $D_3 = 400 - 420 = -20$. Substituting in the feasibility conditions, we get

$$x_2 = 100 + \tfrac{1}{2}(50) - \tfrac{1}{4}(-20) = 130 > 0 \qquad \text{(feasible)}$$
$$x_3 = 230 + \tfrac{1}{2}(-20) = 220 > 0 \qquad \text{(feasible)}$$
$$x_6 = 20 - 2(50) + (-20) + (-10) = -110 < 0 \quad \text{(infeasible)}$$

The calculations show that $x_6 < 0$, hence the current solution does not remain feasible. Additional calculations will be needed to find the new solution (see Chapter 4).

Alternatively, if the changes in the resources are such that $D_1 = -30$, $D_2 = -12$, and $D_3 = 10$, then

$$x_2 = 100 + \tfrac{1}{2}(-30) - \tfrac{1}{4}(-12) = 88 > 0 \qquad \text{(feasible)}$$

$$x_3 = 230 + \tfrac{1}{2}(-12) = 224 > 0 \qquad \text{(feasible)}$$

$$x_6 = 20 - 2(-30) + (-12) + (10) = 78 > 0 \quad \text{(feasible)}$$

The new (optimal) feasible solution is $x_1 = 88$, $x_3 = 224$, and $x_6 = 68$ with $z = 3(0) + 2(88) + 5(224) = \$1296$. Notice that the optimum objective value can also be computed using the dual prices as $z = 1350 + 1(-30) + 2(-12) + 0(10) = \$1296$.

The given conditions can produce the individual *feasibility ranges* associated with changing the resources *one at a time* (as defined in Section 3.6.1). For example, a change in operation 1 time only means that $D_2 = D_3 = 0$. The simultaneous conditions thus reduce to

$$\left. \begin{array}{l} x_2 = 100 + \tfrac{1}{2}D_1 \geq 0 \Rightarrow D_1 \geq -200 \\ x_3 = 230 > 0 \\ x_6 = 20 - 2D_1 \geq 0 \Rightarrow D_1 \leq 10 \end{array} \right\} \Rightarrow -200 \leq D_1 \leq 10$$

This means that the dual price for operation 1 is valid in the feasibility range $-200 \leq D_1 \leq 10$.

We can show in a similar manner that the feasibility ranges for operations 2 and 3 are $-20 \leq D_2 \leq 400$ and $-20 \leq D_3 < \infty$, respectively (verify!).

We can now summarize the dual prices and their feasibility ranges for the TOYCO model as follows:[9]

Resource	Dual price ($)	Feasibility range	Resource amount (minutes)		
			Minimum	*Current*	*Maximum*
Operation 1	1	$-200 \leq D_1 \leq 10$	230	430	440
Operation 2	2	$-20 \leq D_2 \leq 400$	440	440	860
Operation 3	0	$-20 \leq D_3 < \infty$	400	420	∞

It is important to notice that the dual prices will remain applicable for any *simultaneous* changes that keep the solution feasible, even if the changes violate the individual ranges. For example, the changes $D_1 = 30, D_2 = -12$, and $D_3 = 100$ will keep the solution feasible even though $D_1 = 30$ violates the feasibility range $-200 \leq D_1 \leq 10$, as the following computations show:

$$x_2 = 100 + \tfrac{1}{2}(30) - \tfrac{1}{4}(-12) = 118 > 0 \qquad \text{(feasible)}$$

$$x_3 = 230 + \tfrac{1}{2}(-12) = 224 > 0 \qquad \text{(feasible)}$$

$$x_6 = 20 - 2(30) + (-12) + (100) = 48 > 0 \quad \text{(feasible)}$$

---

[9]Available LP packages usually present this information as standard output. Practically none provide the case of simultaneous conditions, presumably because its display is cumbersome for large LPs.

This means that the dual prices will remain applicable, and we can compute the new optimum objective value from the dual prices as $z = 1350 + 1(30) + 2(-12) + 0(100) = \$1356$.

PROBLEM SET 3.6C[10]

1. In the TOYCO model, suppose that the changes D_1, D_2, and D_3 are made *simultaneously* in the three operations.

   (a) If the availabilities of operations 1, 2, and 3 are changed to 440, 490, and 400 minutes, respectively, use the simultaneous conditions to show that the current basic solution remains feasible, and determine the change in the optimal revenue by using the optimal dual prices.

   (b) If the availabilities of the three operations are changed to 460, 440, and 370 minutes, respectively, use the simultaneous conditions to show that the current basic solution is infeasible.

*2. Consider the TOYCO model.

   (a) Suppose that any additional time for operation 1 beyond its current capacity of 430 minutes per day must be done on an overtime basis at $50 an hour. The hourly cost includes both labor and the operation of the machine. Is it economically advantageous to use overtime with operation 1?

   (b) Suppose that the operator of operation 2 has agreed to work 2 hours of overtime daily at $45 an hour. Additionally, the cost of the operation itself is $10 an hour. What is the net effect of this activity on the daily revenue?

   (c) Is overtime needed for operation 3?

   (d) Suppose that the daily availability of operation 1 is increased to 440 minutes. Any overtime used beyond the current maximum capacity will cost $40 an hour. Determine the new optimum solution, including the associated net revenue.

   (e) Suppose that the availability of operation 2 is decreased by 15 minutes a day and that the hourly cost of the operation during regular time is $30. Is it advantageous to decrease the availability of operation 2?

3. A company manufactures three products, *A, B,* and *C.* The sales volume for *A* is at least 50% of the total sales of all three products. However, the company cannot sell more than 80 units of *A* per day. The three products use one raw material, of which the maximum daily availability is 240 lb. The usage rates of the raw material are 2 lb per unit of *A,* 4 lb per unit of *B,* and 3 lb per unit of *C.* The unit prices for *A, B,* and *C* are $20, $50, and $35, respectively.

   (a) Determine the optimal product mix for the company.

   (b) Determine the dual price of the raw material resource and its allowable range. If available raw material is increased by 120 lb, determine the optimal solution and the change in total revenue using the dual price.

   (c) Use the dual price to determine the effect of changing the maximum demand for product *A* by ± 10 units.

---

[10]In this problem set, you may find it convenient to generate the optimal simplex tableau with TORA.

4. A company that operates 10 hours a day manufactures three products on three processes. The following table summarizes the data of the problem:

Product	Minutes per unit			Unit price
	Process 1	Process 2	Process 3	
1	10	6	8	$4.50
2	5	8	10	$5.00
3	6	9	12	$4.00

(a) Determine the optimal product mix.

(b) Use the dual prices to prioritize the three processes for possible expansion.

(c) If additional production hours can be allocated, what would be a fair cost per additional hour for each process?

5. The Continuing Education Division at the Ozark Community College offers a total of 30 courses each semester. The courses offered are usually of two types: practical, such as woodworking, word processing, and car maintenance, and humanistic, such as history, music, and fine arts. To satisfy the demands of the community, at least 10 courses of each type must be offered each semester. The division estimates that the revenues of offering practical and humanistic courses are approximately $1500 and $1000 per course, respectively.

(a) Devise an optimal course offering for the college.

(b) Show that the dual price of an additional course is $1500, which is the same as the revenue per practical course. What does this result mean in terms of offering additional courses?

(c) How many more courses can be offered while guaranteeing that each will contribute $1500 to the total revenue?

(d) Determine the change in revenue resulting from increasing the minimum requirement of humanistics by one course.

***6.** Show & Sell can advertise its products on local radio and television (TV), or in newspapers. The advertising budget is limited to $10,000 a month. Each minute of advertising on radio costs $15 and each minute on TV costs $300. A newspaper ad costs $50. Show & Sell likes to advertise on radio at least twice as much as on TV. In the meantime, the use of at least 5 newspaper ads and no more than 400 minutes of radio advertising a month is recommended. Past experience shows that advertising on TV is 50 times more effective than on radio and 10 times more effective than in newspapers.

(a) Determine the optimum allocation of the budget to the three media.

(b) Are the limits set on radio and newspaper advertising justifiable economically?

(c) If the monthly budget is increased by 50%, would this result in a proportionate increase in the overall effectiveness of advertising?

7. The Burroughs Garment Company manufactures men's shirts and women's blouses for Walmark Discount Stores. Walmark will accept all the production supplied by Burroughs. The production process includes cutting, sewing, and packaging. Burroughs employs 25 workers in the cutting department, 35 in the sewing department, and 5 in the packaging department. The factory works one 8-hour shift, 5 days a week. The following table gives the time requirements and prices per unit for the two garments:

| Garment | Minutes per unit | | | Unit price ($) |
	Cutting	Sewing	Packaging	
Shirts	20	70	12	8.00
Blouses	60	60	4	12.00

(a) Determine the optimal weekly production schedule for Burroughs.

(b) Determine the worth of 1 hour of cutting, sewing, and packaging in terms of the total revenue.

(c) If overtime can be used in cutting and sewing, what is the maximum hourly rate Burroughs should pay for overtime?

8. ChemLabs uses raw materials *I* and *II* to produce two domestic cleaning solutions, *A* and *B*. The daily availabilities of raw materials *I* and *II* are 150 and 145 units, respectively. One unit of solution *A* consumes .5 unit of raw material *I* and .6 unit of raw material *II*, and one unit of solution *B* uses .5 unit of raw material *I* and .4 unit of raw material *II*. The prices per unit of solutions *A* and *B* are $8 and $10, respectively. The daily demand for solution *A* lies between 30 and 150 units and that for solution *B* between 40 and 200 units.

(a) Find the optimal amounts of *A* and *B* that ChemLab should produce.

(b) Use the dual prices to determine which demand limits on products *A* and *B* should be relaxed to improve profitability.

(c) If additional units of raw material can be acquired at $20 per unit, is this advisable? Explain.

(d) A suggestion is made to increase raw material *II* by 25% to remove a bottleneck in production. Is this advisable? Explain.

9. An assembly line consisting of three consecutive workstations produces two radio models: DiGi-1 and DiGi-2. The following table provides the assembly times for the three workstations.

| Workstation | Minutes per unit | |
	DiGi-1	DiGi-2
1	6	4
2	5	4
3	4	6

The daily maintenance for workstations 1, 2, and 3 consumes 10%, 14%, and 12%, respectively, of the maximum 480 minutes available for each workstation each day.

(a) The company wishes to determine the optimal product mix that will minimize the idle (or unused) times in the three workstations. Determine the optimum utilization of the workstations. [*Hint*: Express the sum of the idle times (slacks) for the three operations in terms of the original variables.]

(b) Determine the worth of decreasing the daily maintenance time for each workstation by 1.5 percentage point.

(c) It is proposed that the operation time for all three workstations be increased to 600 minutes per day at the additional cost of $1.50 per minute. Can this proposal be improved?

10. The Gutchi Company manufactures purses, shaving bags, and backpacks. The construction of the three products requires leather and synthetics, with leather being the limiting raw material. The production process uses two types of skilled labor: sewing and finishing. The following table gives the availability of the resources, their usage by the three products, and the prices per unit.

	Resource requirements per unit			
Resource	*Purse*	*Bag*	*Backpack*	Daily availability
Leather (ft^2)	2	1	3	42
Sewing (hr)	2	1	2	40
Finishing (hr)	1	.5	1	45
Price ($)	24	22	45	

Formulate the problem as a linear program, and find the optimum solution. Next, indicate whether the following changes in the resources will keep the current solution feasible. For the cases where feasibility is maintained, determine the new optimum solution (values of the variables and the objective function).

(a) Available leather is increased to 45 ft^2.

(b) Available leather is decreased by 1 ft^2.

(c) Available sewing hours are changed to 38 hours.

(d) Available sewing hours are changed to 46 hours.

(e) Available finishing hours are decreased to 15 hours.

(f) Available finishing hours are increased to 50 hours.

(g) Would you recommend hiring an additional sewing worker at $15 an hour?

11. HiDec produces two models of electronic gadgets that use resistors, capacitors, and chips. The following table summarizes the data of the situation:

	Unit resource requirements		
Resource	*Model 1 (units)*	*Model 2 (units)*	Maximum availability (units)
Resistor	2	3	1200
Capacitor	2	1	1000
Chips	0	4	800
Unit price ($)	3	4	

Let x_1 and x_2 be the amounts produced of Models 1 and 2, respectively. Following are the LP model and its associated optimal simplex tableau.

$$\text{Maximize } z = 3x_1 + 4x_2$$

subject to

$$2x_1 + 3x_2 \leq 1200 \qquad \text{(Resistors)}$$
$$2x_1 + x_2 \leq 1000 \qquad \text{(Capacitors)}$$
$$4x_2 \leq 800 \qquad \text{(Chips)}$$
$$x_1, x_2 \geq 0$$

Handwritten margin notes:

$Z: 1750 + \frac{5}{4}D_1 + \frac{1}{4}D_2 + 0D_3 \geq 0$

$x_1: 450 - \frac{1}{4}D_1 + \frac{3}{4}D_2 \geq 0$

$S_3: 400 - 2D_1 + 2D_2 + D_3 \geq 0$

$x_2: 100 + \frac{1}{2}D_1 - \frac{1}{2}D_2 \geq 0$

$D_3 \geq -400$

$D_2, D_3 = 0 \quad 450 \geq \frac{1}{4}D_1 \rightarrow D_1 \leq 1800$

$400 - 2D_1 \geq 0 \rightarrow D_1 \leq 800$

$100 + \frac{1}{2}D_1 \geq 0 \rightarrow D_1 \geq -200$

$-200 \leq D_1 \leq 800$

$D_1, D_3 = 0$

$450 + \frac{3}{4}D_2 \geq 0 \rightarrow D_2 \geq -600$

$400 + 2D_2 \geq 0 \rightarrow D_2 \geq -800$

$100 - \frac{1}{2}D_2 \geq 0 \rightarrow D_2 \leq 200$

$-600 \leq D_2 \leq 200$

Basic	x_1	x_2	s_1	s_2	s_3	Solution
z	0	0	$\frac{5}{4}$	$\frac{1}{4}$	0	1750
x_1	1	0	$-\frac{1}{4}$	$\frac{3}{4}$	0	450
s_3	0	0	-2	2	1	400
x_2	0	1	$\frac{1}{2}$	$-\frac{1}{2}$	0	100

*(a) Determine the status of each resource.

*(b) In terms of the optimal revenue, determine the dual prices for the resistors, capacitors, and chips.

(c) Determine the feasibility ranges for the dual prices obtained in (b).

(d) If the available number of resistors is increased to 1300 units, find the new optimum solution.

*(e) If the available number of chips is reduced to 350 units, will you be able to determine the new optimum solution directly from the given information? Explain.

(f) If the availability of capacitors is limited by the feasibility range computed in (c), determine the corresponding range of the optimal revenue and the corresponding ranges for the numbers of units to be produced of Models 1 and 2.

(g) A new contractor is offering to sell HiDec additional resistors at 40 cents each, but only if HiDec would purchase at least 500 units. Should HiDec accept the offer?

12. *The 100% feasibility rule.* A simplified rule based on the *individual* changes D_1, $D_2, \ldots$, and D_m in the right-hand side of the constraints can be used to test whether or not *simultaneous* changes will maintain the feasibility of the current solution. Assume that the right-hand side b_i of constraint i is changed to $b_i + D_i$ *one at a time*, and that $p_i \leq D_i \leq q_i$ is the corresponding feasibility range obtained by using the procedure in Section 3.6.2. By definition, we have $p_i \leq 0 (q_i \geq 0)$ because it represents the maximum allowable decrease (increase) in b_i. Next, define r_i to equal $\frac{D_i}{p_i}$ if D_i is negative and $\frac{D_i}{q_i}$ if D_i is positive. By definition, we have $0 \leq r_i \leq 1$. The 100% rule thus says that, given the changes $D_1, D_2, \ldots$, and D_m, a *sufficient* (but not necessary) condition for the current solution to remain feasible is that $r_1 + r_2 + \ldots + r_m \leq 1$. If the condition is not satisfied, then the current solution may or may not remain feasible. The rule is not applicable if D_i falls outside the range (p_i, q_i).

In reality, the 100% rule is too weak to be consistently useful. Even in the cases where feasibility can be confirmed, we still need to obtain the new solution using the regular simplex feasibility conditions. Besides, the direct calculations associated with simultaneous changes given in Section 3.6.2 are straightforward and manageable.

To demonstrate the weakness of the rule, apply it to parts (a) and (b) of Problem 1 in this set. The rule fails to confirm the feasibility of the solution in (a) and does not apply in (b) because the changes in D_i are outside the admissible ranges. Problem 13 further demonstrates this point.

13. Consider the problem

$$\text{Maximize } z = x_1 + x_2$$

subject to

$$2x_1 + x_2 \leq 6$$

$$x_1 + 2x_2 \leq 6$$

$$x_1 + x_2 \geq 0$$

(a) Show that the optimal basic solution includes both x_1 and x_2 and that the feasibility ranges for the two constraints, considered one at a time, are $-3 \leq D_1 \leq 6$ *and* $-3 \leq D_2 \leq 6$.

(b) *Suppose that the two resources are increased simultaneously by $\Delta > 0$ each. First, show that the basic solution remains feasible for all $\Delta > 0$. Next, show that the 100% rule will confirm feasibility only if the increase is in the range $0 < \Delta \leq 3$ units. Otherwise, the rule fails for $3 < \Delta \leq 6$ and does not apply for $\Delta > 6$.

3.6.3 Algebraic Sensitivity Analysis—Objective function

In Section 3.6.1, we used graphical sensitivity analysis to determine the conditions that will maintain the optimality of the solution of a two-variable LP. In this section, we extend these ideas to the general LP problem.

Definition of reduced cost. To facilitate the explanation of the objective function sensitivity analysis, first we need to define *reduced costs*. In the TOYCO model (Example 3.6-2), the objective z-equation in the optimal tableau can be written as

$$z = 1350 - 4x_1 - x_4 - 2x_5$$

The optimal solution does not produce toy trains ($x_1 = 0$). The reason can be seen from the z-equation, where a unit increase in x_1 (above its current zero value) decreases z by 4—namely, $z = 1350 - 4 \times (1) - 1 \times (0) - 2 \times (0) = \$1346$.

We can think of the coefficient of x_1 in the z-equation ($= 4$) as a unit *cost* because it causes a reduction in the revenue z. But where does this "cost" come from? We know that the revenue per unit of x_1 is \$3 (per the original model). We also know that the production of toy train incurs cost because it consumes resources (operations time). Thus, from the standpoint of optimization, the "attractiveness" of x_1 depends on the cost of consumed resources relative to revenue. This relationship defines the so-called **reduced cost** and is formalized in the LP literature as

$$\begin{pmatrix} \text{Reduced cost} \\ \text{per unit} \end{pmatrix} = \begin{pmatrix} \text{Cost of consumed} \\ \text{resources per unit} \end{pmatrix} - (\text{Revenue per unit})$$

To appreciate the significance of this definition, in the original TOYCO model the revenue per unit for toy trucks ($= \$2$) is less than that for toy trains ($= \$3$). Yet the optimal solution recommends producing toy trucks ($x_2 = 100$ units) and no toy trains ($x_1 = 0$). The reason is that the cost of the resources used by one toy truck (i.e., operations time) is smaller than its unit price. The opposite applies in the case of toy trains.

With the given definition of *reduced cost*, we can see that an unprofitable variable (such as x_1) can be made profitable in two ways:

1. By increasing the unit revenue.
2. By decreasing the unit cost of consumed resources.

In most situations, the price per unit is dictated by market conditions and may be difficult to increase at will. On the other hand, reducing the consumption of resources is a more viable option because the manufacturer may be able to reduce cost by making the production process more efficient.

Determination of the optimality ranges. We now turn our attention to determining the conditions that will keep a solution optimal. The development is based on the definition of *reduced cost*.

In the TOYCO model, let $d_1, d_2,$ and d_3 represent the change in unit revenues for toy trucks, trains, and cars, respectively. The objective function then becomes

$$\text{Maximize } z = (3 + d_1)x_1 + (2 + d_2)x_2 + (5 + d_3)x_3$$

We first consider the general situation in which all the objective coefficients are changed *simultaneously*.

With the simultaneous changes, the z-row in the starting tableau appears as:

Basic	x_1	x_2	x_3	x_4	x_5	x_6	Solution
z	$-3 - d_1$	$-2 - d_2$	$-5 - d_3$	0	0	0	0

When we generate the simplex tableaus with the same sequence of entering and leaving variables used in the original model (before the changes d_j are made), the optimal iteration will appear as follows (convince yourself that this is indeed the case by carrying out the simplex row operations):

Basic	x_1	x_2	x_3	x_4	x_5	x_6	Solution
z	$4 - \frac{1}{4}d_2 + \frac{3}{2}d_3 - d_1$	0	0	$1 + \frac{1}{2}d_2$	$2 - \frac{1}{4}d_2 + \frac{1}{2}d_3$	0	$1350 + 100d_2 + 230d_3$
x_2	$-\frac{1}{4}$	1	0	$\frac{1}{2}$	$-\frac{1}{4}$	0	100
x_3	$\frac{3}{2}$	0	1	0	$\frac{1}{2}$	0	230
x_6	$-\frac{1}{4}$	0	0	-2	1	1	20

The new optimal tableau is the same as in the *original* optimal tableau, except for the *reduced costs* (z-equation coefficients). This means that *changes in the objective-function coefficients can affect the optimality of the problem only*. (Compare with Section 3.6.2, where changes in the right-hand side affect feasibility only.)

You really do not need to carry out the simplex row operation to compute the new reduced costs. An examination of the new z-row shows that the coefficients of d_j are taken directly from the constraint coefficients of the optimum tableau. A convenient way for computing the new reduced cost is to add a new top row and a new leftmost column to the optimum tableau, as shown by the shaded areas in the following illustration.

		d_1	d_2	d_3	0	0	0	
	Basic	x_1	x_2	x_3	x_4	x_5	x_6	Solution
1	z	4	0	0	1	2	0	1350
d_2	x_2	$-\frac{1}{4}$	1	0	$\frac{1}{2}$	$-\frac{1}{4}$	0	100
d_3	x_3	$\frac{3}{2}$	0	1	0	$\frac{1}{2}$	0	230
0	x_6	2	0	0	-2	1	1	20

The entries in the top row are the change d_j associated with variable x_j. For the leftmost column, the top element is 1 in the z-row followed by change d_i for basic variable x_i. Keep in mind that $d_i = 0$ for slack variable x_i.

To compute the new reduced cost for any variable (or the value of z), multiply the elements of its column by the corresponding elements in the leftmost column, add them up, and subtract the top-row element from the sum. For example, for x_1, we have

$$\text{Reduced cost for } x_1 = [4 \times 1 + (-\tfrac{1}{4}) \times d_2 + \tfrac{3}{2} \times d_3 + 2 \times 0] - d_1$$
$$= 4 - \tfrac{1}{4} d_2 + \tfrac{3}{2} d_3 - d_1$$

The current solution remains optimal so long as the new reduced costs (z-equation coefficients) remain nonnegative (maximization case). We thus have the following *simultaneous optimality conditions* corresponding to nonbasic x_1, x_4, and x_5:

$$4 - \tfrac{1}{4} d_2 + \tfrac{3}{2} d_3 - d_1 \geq 0$$
$$1 + \tfrac{1}{2} d_2 \geq 0$$
$$2 - \tfrac{1}{4} d_2 + \tfrac{1}{2} d_3 \geq 0$$

Remember that the reduced cost for a basic variable is always zero, as the modified optimal tableau shows.

To illustrate the use of these conditions, suppose that the objective function of TOYCO is changed from $z = 3x_1 + 2x_2 + 5x_3$ to $z = 2x_1 + x_2 + 6x_3$. Then, $d_1 = 2 - 3 = -\$1$, $d_2 = 1 - 2 = -\$1$, and $d_3 = 6 - 5 = \$1$. Substitution in the given conditions yields

$$4 - \tfrac{1}{4} d_2 + \tfrac{3}{2} d_3 - d_1 = 4 - \tfrac{1}{4}(-1) + \tfrac{3}{2}(1) - (-1) = 6.75 > 0 \text{ (satisfied)}$$
$$1 + \tfrac{1}{2} d_2 = 1 + \tfrac{1}{2}(-1) = .5 > 0 \qquad\qquad\qquad \text{(satisfied)}$$
$$2 - \tfrac{1}{4} d_2 + \tfrac{1}{2} d_3 = 2 - \tfrac{1}{4}(-1) + \tfrac{1}{2}(1) = 2.75 > 0 \qquad \text{(satisfied)}$$

The results show that the proposed changes will keep the current solution ($x_1 = 0$, $x2 = 100, x_3 = 230$) optimal (with a new value of $z = 1350 + 100d_2 + 230d_3 = 1350 + 100 \times -1 + 230 \times 1 = \$1480$). If any condition is not satisfied, a new solution must be determined (see Chapter 4).

The preceding discussion has dealt with the maximization case. The only difference in the minimization case is that the reduced costs (z-equations coefficients) must be ≤ 0 to maintain optimality.

The *optimality ranges* dealing with changing d_j *one at a time* can be developed from the simultaneous optimality conditions.[11] For example, suppose that the objective coefficient of x_2 only is changed to $2 + d_2$—meaning that $d_1 = d_3 = 0$. The simultaneous optimality conditions thus reduce to

$$\left. \begin{array}{l} 4 - \frac{1}{4}d_2 \geq 0 \Rightarrow d_2 \leq 16 \\ 1 + \frac{1}{2}d_2 \geq 0 \Rightarrow d_2 \geq -2 \\ 2 - \frac{1}{4}d_2 \geq 0 \Rightarrow d_2 \leq 8 \end{array} \right\} \Rightarrow -2 \leq d_2 \leq 8$$

In a similar manner, you can verify that the individual changes $(3 + d_1)$ and $(5 + d_3)$ for x_1 and x_3 yield the optimality ranges $d_1 < 4$ and $d_3 \geq -\frac{8}{3}$, respectively.

The given individual conditions can be translated to total unit revenue ranges. For example, for toy trucks (variable x_2), the total unit revenue is $2 + d_2$, and its optimality range $-2 \leq d_2 \leq 8$ translates to

$$\$0 \leq (\text{Unit revenue of toy truck}) \leq \$10$$

It assumes that the unit revenues for toy trains and toy cars remain fixed at \$3 and \$5, respectively.

It is important to notice that the changes $d_1, d_2,$ and d_3 may be within their allowable individual ranges without satisfying the simultaneous conditions and vice versa. For example, consider $z = 6x_1 + 8x_2 + 3x_3$. Here $d_1 = 6 - 3 = \$3, d_2 = 8 - 2 = \$6,$ and $d_3 = 3 - 5 = -\$2$, which are all within the permissible individual ranges $(-\infty < d_1 \leq 4, -2 \leq d_2 \leq 8, and -\frac{8}{3} \leq d_3 < \infty)$. However, the corresponding simultaneous conditions yield

$$4 - \tfrac{1}{4}d_2 + \tfrac{3}{2}d_3 - d_1 = 4 - \tfrac{1}{4}(6) + \tfrac{3}{2}(-2) - 3 = -3.5 < 0 \quad \text{(not satisfied)}$$
$$1 + \tfrac{1}{2}d_2 = 1 + \tfrac{1}{2}(6) = 4 > 0 \quad \text{(satisfied)}$$
$$2 - \tfrac{1}{4}d_2 + \tfrac{1}{2}d_3 = 2 - \tfrac{1}{4}(6) + \tfrac{1}{2}(-2) = -.5 < 0 \quad \text{(not satisfied)}$$

---

[11]The individual ranges are standard outputs in all LP software. Simultaneous conditions usually are not part of the output, presumably because they are cumbersome for large problems.

PROBLEM SET 3.6d[12]

1. In the TOYCO model, determine if the current solution will change in each of the following cases:

   (i) $z = x_1 + x_2 + 4x_3$

   (ii) $z = 4x_1 + 6x_2 + x_3$

   (iii) $z = 6x_1 + 3x_2 + 9x_3$

*2. B&K grocery store sells three types of soft drinks: the brand names A1 Cola and A2 Cola and the cheaper store brand BK Cola. The price per can for A1, A2, and BK are 80, 70, and 60 cents, respectively. On the average, the store sells no more than 500 cans of all colas a day. Although A1 is a recognized brand name, customers tend to buy more A2 and BK because they are cheaper. It is estimated that at least 100 cans of A1 are sold daily and that A2 and BK combined outsell A1 by a margin of at least 4:2.

   (a) Show that the optimum solution does not call for selling the A3 brand.

   (b) By how much should the price per can of A3 be increased to be sold by B&K.

   (c) To be competitive with other stores, B&K decided to lower the price on all three types of cola by 5 cents per can. Recompute the reduced costs to determine if this promotion will change the current optimum solution.

3. Baba Furniture Company employs four carpenters for 10 days to assemble tables and chairs. It takes 2 person-hours to assemble a table and .5 person-hour to assemble a chair. Customers usually buy one table and four to six chairs. The prices are $135 per table and $50 per chair. The company operates one 8-hour shift a day.

   (a) Determine the 10-day optimal production mix.

   (b) If the present unit prices per table and chair are each reduced by 10%, use sensitivity analysis to determine if the optimum solution obtained in (a) will change.

   (c) If the present unit prices per table and chair are changed to $120 and $25, will the solution in (a) change?

4. The Bank of Elkins is allocating a maximum of $200,000 for personal and car loans during the next month. The bank charges 14% for personal loans and 12% for car loans. Both types of loans are repaid at the end of a 1-year period. Experience shows that about 3% of personal loans and 2% of car loans are not repaid. The bank usually allocates at least twice as much to car loans as to personal loans.

   (a) Determine the optimal allocation of funds between the two loans and the net rate of return on all the loans.

   (b) If the percentages of personal and car loans are changed to 4% and 3%, respectively, use sensitivity analysis to determine if the optimum solution in (a) will change.

*5. Electra produces four types of electric motors, each on a separate assembly line. The respective capacities of the lines are 500, 500, 800, and 750 motors per day. Type 1 motor uses 8 units of a certain electronic component, type 2 motor uses 5 units, type 3 motor uses 4 units, and type 4 motor uses 6 units. The supplier of the component can

---

[12]In this problem set, you may find it convenient to generate the optimal simplex tableau with TORA.

provide 8000 pieces a day. The prices per motor for the respective types are $60, $40, $25, and $30.

(a) Determine the optimum daily production mix.

(b) The present production schedule meets Electra's needs. However, because of competition, Electra may need to lower the price of type 2 motor. What is the most reduction that can be effected without changing the present production schedule?

(c) Electra has decided to slash the price of all motor types by 25%. Use sensitivity analysis to determine if the optimum solution remains unchanged.

(d) Currently, type 4 motor is not produced. By how much should its price be increased to be included in the production schedule?

6. Popeye Canning is contracted to receive daily 50,000 lb of ripe tomatoes at 7 cents per pound from which it produces canned tomato juice, tomato sauce, and tomato paste. The canned products are packaged in 24-can cases. A can of juice uses 1 lb of fresh tomatoes, a can of sauce uses $\frac{1}{2}$ lb, and a can of paste uses $\frac{3}{4}$ lb. The company's daily share of the market is limited to 1500 cases of juice, 1500 cases of sauce, and 1000 cases of paste. The wholesale prices per case of juice, sauce, and paste are $21, $9, and $12, respectively.

(a) Develop an optimum daily production program for Popeye.

(b) If the price per case for juice and paste remains fixed as given in the problem, use sensitivity analysis to determine the unit price range Popeye should charge for a case of sauce to keep the optimum product mix unchanged.

7. Dean's Furniture Company assembles regular and deluxe kitchen cabinets from precut lumber. The regular cabinets are painted white, and the deluxe are varnished. Both painting and varnishing are carried out in one department. The daily capacity of the assembly department is 400 regular cabinets and 300 deluxe. Varnishing a deluxe unit takes twice as much time as painting a regular one. If the painting/varnishing department is dedicated to the deluxe units only, it can complete 360 units daily. The company estimates that the revenues per unit for the regular and deluxe cabinets are $100 and $140, respectively.

(a) Formulate the problem as a linear program, and find the optimal production schedule per day.

(b) Suppose that competition dictates that the price per unit of each of regular and deluxe cabinets be reduced to $90. Use sensitivity analysis to determine whether or not the optimum solution in (a) remains unchanged.

8. *The 100% Optimality Rule.* A rule similar to the *100% feasibility rule* outlined in Problem 12, Set 3.6c, can also be developed for testing the effect of simultaneously changing all c_j to $c_j + d_j, j = 1, 2, \ldots, n$, on the optimality of the current solution. Suppose that $u_j \leq d_j \leq v_j$ is the optimality range obtained as a result of changing each c_j to $c_j + d_j$ one at a time, using the procedure in Section 3.6.3. In this case, $u_j \leq 0 \ (v_j \geq 0)$, because it represents the maximum allowable decrease (increase) in c_j that will keep the current solution optimal. For the cases where $u_j \leq d_j \leq v_j$, define r_j equal to $\frac{d_j}{v_j}$ if d_j is positive and $\frac{d_j}{u_j}$ if d_j is negative. By definition, $0 \leq r_j \leq 1$. The 100% rule says that a sufficient (but not necessary) condition for the current solution to remain optimal is that $r_1 + r_2 + \ldots + r_n \leq 1$. If the condition is not satisfied, the current solution may or may not remain optimal. The rule does not apply if d_j falls outside the specified ranges.

Demonstrate that the 100% optimality rule is too weak to be consistently reliable as a decision-making tool by applying it to the following cases:

(a) Parts (ii) and (iii) of Problem 1

(b) Part (b) of Problem 7.

3.6.4 Sensitivity Analysis with Tora, Solver, and Ampl

We now have all the tools to decipher the output provided by LP software, particularly with regard to sensitivity analysis. We will use the TOYCO example to demonstrate the TORA, Solver, and AMPL output.

TORA's LP output report provides the sensitivity analysis data automatically as shown in Figure 3.14 (file *toraTOYCO.txt*). The output includes the reduced costs and the dual prices as well as their allowable optimality and feasibility ranges.

Figure 3.15 provides the Solver TOYCO model (file *solverTOYCO.xls*) and its sensitivity analysis report. After you click Solve in the **Solver Parameters** dialogue box, you can request sensitivity analysis report in the new dialogue box **Solver Results**. You can then click **Sensitivity Report 1** to view the results. The report is similar to that of TORA's, with three exceptions: (1) The reduced cost carries an opposite sign. (2) It uses the name *shadow price* instead of *dual price*. (3) The optimality ranges are for the changes d_j and D_i rather than for the total objective coefficients and constraint right-hand sides. The differences are minor, and the interpretation of the results remains the same.

In AMPL, the sensitivity analysis report is readily available. File *amplTOYCO.txt* provides the code necessary to determine the sensitivity analysis output. It requires the following additional statements (the report is sent to file a.out):

```
option solver cplex;
option cplex_options 'sensitivity';
solve;
#——————————sensitivity analysis
display oper.down,oper.current,oper.up,oper.dual>a.out;
display x.down,x.current,x.up,x.rc>a.out;
```

FIGURE 3.14

TORA sensitivity analysis for the TOYCO model

Sensitivity Analysis				
Variable	CurrObjCoeff	MinObjCoeff	MaxObjCoeff	Reduced Cost
x1:	3.00	-infinity	7.00	4.00
x2:	2.00	0.00	10.00	0.00
x3:	5.00	2.33	infinity	0.00
Constraint	Curr RHS	Min RHS	Max RHS	Dual Price
1(<):	430.00	230.00	440.00	1.00
2(<):	460.00	440.00	860.00	2.00
3(<):	420.00	400.00	infinity	0.00

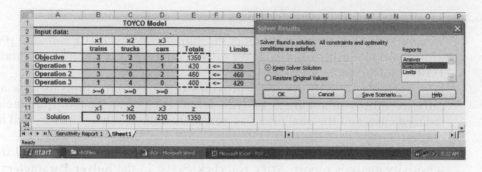

FIGURE 3.15

Excel Solver sensitivity analysis report for the TOYCO model

		Final	Reduced	Objective	Allowable	Allowable
Cell	Name	Value	Cost	Coefficient	Increase	Decrease
$B$12	Solution x1	0	-4	3	4	1E+30
$C$12	Solution x2	100	0	2	8	2
$D$12	Solution x3	230	0	5	1E+30	2.666666667

Constraints

		Final	Shadow	Constraint	Allowable	Allowable
Cell	Name	Value	Price	R.H. Side	Increase	Decrease
$E$6	Operation 1 Totals	430	1	430	10	200
$E$7	Operation 2 Totals	460	2	460	400	20
$E$8	Operation 3 Totals	400	0	420	1E+30	20

The CPLEX `option` statements are needed to obtain the standard sensitivity analysis report. In the TOYCO model, the indexed variables and constraints use the root names x and `oper`, respectively. Using these names, the suggestive suffixes `.down`, `.current`, and `.up` in the `display` statements automatically generate the formatted sensitivity analysis report in Figure 3.16. The suffixes `.dual` and `.rc` provide the dual price and the reduced cost.

```
: oper.down  oper.current  oper.up  oper.dual    :=
1     230          430         440        1
2     440          460         860        2
3     400          420       1e+20p       0

:      x.down  x.current      x.up   x.rc   :=
1     -1e+20          3           7     -4
2          0          2          10      0
3     2.33333          5       1e+20      0
```

FIGURE 3.16

AMPL sensitivity analysis report for the TOYCO model

PROBLEM SET 3.6E[13]

1. Consider Problem 1, Set 2.4a (Chapter 2). Use the dual price to decide if it is worthwhile to increase the funding for year 4.

---

[13]Before answering the problems in this set, you are expected to generate the sensitivity analysis report using AMPL, Solver, or TORA.

2. Consider Problem 2, Set 2.4a (Chapter 2).

   (a) Use the dual prices to determine the overall return on investment.

   (b) If you wish to spend $2000 on pleasure at the end of year 1, how would this affect the accumulated amount at the start of year 5?

3. Consider Problem 3, Set 2.4a (Chapter 2).

   (a) Give an economic interpretation of the dual prices of the model.

   (b) Show how the dual price associated with the upper bound on borrowed money at the beginning of the third quarter can be derived from the dual prices associated with the balance equations representing the in-out cash flow at the five designated dates of the year.

4. Consider Problem 4, Set 2.4a (Chapter 2). Use the dual prices to determine the rate of return associated with each year.

*5. Consider Problem 5, Set 2.4a (Chapter 2). Use the dual price to determine if it is worthwhile for the executive to invest more money in the plans.

6. Consider Problem 6, Set 2.4a (Chapter 2). Use the dual price to decide if it is advisable for the gambler to bet an additional $400.

7. Consider Problem 1, Set 2.4b (Chapter 2). Relate the dual prices to the unit production costs of the model.

8. Consider Problem 2, Set 2.4b (Chapter 2). Suppose that any additional capacity of machines 1 and 2 can be acquired only by using overtime. What is the maximum cost per hour the company should be willing to incur for either machine?

*9. Consider Problem 3, Set 2.4b (Chapter 2).

   (a) Suppose that the manufacturer can purchase additional units of raw material A at $12 per unit. Would it be advisable to do so?

   (b) Would you recommend that the manufacturer purchase additional units of raw material B at $5 per unit?

10. Consider Problem 10, Set 2.4e (Chapter 2).

   (a) Which of the specification constraints impacts the optimum solution adversely?

   (b) Is it economical for the compny to purchase ore 1 at $100/ton. Explain in terms of dual prices.

3.7 COMPUTATIONAL ISSUES IN LINEAR PROGRAMMING[14]

This chapter has presented the details of the simplex algorithm. Subsequent chapters present other algorithms: The dual simplex (Chapter 4), the revised simplex (Chapter 7), and the interior point (Chapter 22 on the website). Why the variety? The reason is that each algorithm has specific features that can be beneficial in the development of robust computer codes.

An LP code is deemed robust if it satisfies two requirements:

1. Speed

2. Accuracy

Both requirements present challenges even on the most advanced computers. The reasons stem from the nature of the algorithmic computations and the limitations of

---

[14]This section has benefited from R. Bixby, "Solving Real-World Linear Programs: A Decade and More of Progress," *Operations Research*, Vol. 50, No. 1, pp. 3–15, 2002.

the computer. To be sure, the simplex tableau format presented in this chapter is not *numerically stable*, meaning that computer round-off error and digit loss present serious computational problems, particularly when the coefficients of the LP model differ widely in magnitude. Despite these challenges, the different LP algorithms have in fact been integrated cleverly to produce highly efficient codes for solving extremely large LPs.

This section explains the transition from basic textbook presentations to current state-of-the-art robust LP codes. It addresses the issues that affect speed and accuracy and presents remedies for alleviating the problems. It also presents a comprehensive framework regarding the roles of the different LP algorithms (simplex, dual simplex, revised simplex, and interior point) in the development of numerically stable computer codes. The presentation is purposely kept math free to concentrate on the key concepts underlying successful LP codes.

1. Simplex entering variable (pivot) rule. A new simplex iteration determines the entering and leaving variables by using the *optimality* and *feasibility* criteria. Once the two variables are determined, pivot-row operations are used to generate the next simplex tableau.

Actually, the *optimality criterion* presented in Section 3.3.2 is but one of several used in the development of LP codes. The following table summarizes the three prominent criteria:

Entering variable rule	Description
Classical (Section 3.3.2)	The entering variable is the one having the most favorable *reduced cost* among all nonbasic variables.
Most improvement	The entering variable is the one yielding the largest *total improvement* in the objective value among all nonbasic variables.
Steepest edge[15]	The entering variable is the one that yields the most favorable *normalized reduced cost* among all nonbasic variables. The algorithm moves along the *steepest edge* leading from the current to a neighboring extreme point.

For the *classical rule*, the objective row of the simplex tableau readily provides the reduced costs of all the nonbasic variables with no additional computations. On the other hand, the *most improvement rule* requires considerable additional computing that first determines the value at which a nonbasic variable enters the solution and then the resulting total improvement in the objective value. The idea of the *steepest edge rule*, though in the "spirit" of the *most improvement rule* (in the sense that it indirectly takes into account the value of the entering variable), requires much less computational overhead.

---

[15]See D. Goldfarb and J. Reid, "A Practicable Steepest Edge Simplex Algorithm," *Mathematical Programming*, Vol. 12, No. 1, pp. 361–371, 1977.

The trade-off among the three rules is that the *classical rule* is the least costly computationally but, in all likelihood, requires the most number of iterations to reach the optimum. On the other hand, the *most improvement rule* is the most costly computationally but, most likely, entails the smallest number of simplex iterations. The *steepest edge rule* seems to represent a happy medium in terms of the amount of additional computations and the number of simplex iterations. Interestingly, test results show that the payoff from the additional computations in the *most improvement rule* seems no better than for the *steepest edge rule*. For this reason, the *most improvement rule* is rarely implemented in LP codes.

Although the *steepest edge rule* is the most common default for the selection of the entering variable, successful LP codes tend to use *hybrid pricing*. Initially, the simplex iterations use (a variation of) the *classical rule*. As the number of iterations increases, a switch is made to (a variation of) the *steepest edge rule*. Extensive computational experience indicates that this strategy pays off in terms of the total computer time needed to solve an LP.

2. Primal vs. dual simplex algorithm. Chapter 3 has mainly concentrated on the details of what is sometimes referred to in the literature as the *primal simplex* method. In the primal algorithm, the starting basic solution is feasible but nonoptimal. Successive iterations remain feasible as they move toward the optimum. A subsequent algorithm, called the *dual simplex*, was developed for LPs that start infeasible but (better than) optimal and move toward feasibility, all the while maintaining optimality. The final iteration occurs when feasibility is restored. The details of the dual algorithm are given in Chapter 4 (Section 4.4.1).

Initially, the dual algorithm was used primarily in LP post-optimal analysis (Section 4.5) and integer linear programming (Chapter 9), but not as a standalone algorithm for solving the LPs. The main reason is that its rule for selecting the leaving variable was weak. This all changed, however, when the idea of the primal steepest edge rule was adapted to determine the leaving variable in the dual simplex algorithm.[16] Today, the dual simplex with the steepest-edge adaptation is proven in the majority of tests to be twice as fast as the primal simplex, and it is currently the dominant all-purpose simplex algorithm in the major commercial codes.

3. Revised simplex vs. tableau simplex. The simplex computations presented early in this chapter (and also in Chapter 4 for the dual simplex) generate the next simplex tableau from the immediately preceding one. The result is that the tableaus are not numerically stable for three reasons:

    a. Most practical LP models are highly sparse (i.e., contain a high percentage of zero coefficients in the starting iteration). Available numerical methods can reduce the amount of local computations by economizing (even eliminating) arithmetic operations involving zero coefficients, which in turn can

---

[16]See J. Forrest and D. Goldfarb, "Steepest-Edge Simplex Algorithm for Linear Programming," *Mathematical Programming*, Vol. 57, No. 3, pp. 341–374, 1992.

speed up computations substantially. This is a serious missed opportunity in tableau computations because successive tableaus can quickly populate the tableau with nonzero elements.

b. The machine roundoff error and digit loss, inherent in all computers, can propagate quickly as the number of iterations increases, possibly leading to serious loss of accuracy, particularly in large LPs.

c. Simplex row operations carry out more computations than needed to generate the next tableau (recall that all that is needed in an iteration is the entering and leaving variables). These extra computations represent wasted computer time.

The revised simplex algorithm presented in Section 7.2 improves on these drawbacks. Though the method uses the exact pivoting rules as in the tableau method, the main difference is that it carries out the computations using matrix algebra. In an m-constraint model, each extreme (corner) point solution is computed by solving the set of $m \times m$ equations $\mathbf{B}\mathbf{X}_B = \mathbf{b}$ for the basic vector $\mathbf{X}_B$. The basic matrix $\mathbf{B}$ is determined from the constraint columns of the *original* model, and $\mathbf{b}$ is the *original* right-hand side of the constraints. In essence, only $\mathbf{B}$ changes between iterations. This very property makes it possible to control the roundoff/digit loss error, take advantage of the sparseness of the original model, and speed up the computations. Indeed, numerical analysis in matrix algebra provides robust and efficient methods for solving $\mathbf{B}\mathbf{X}_B = \mathbf{b}$ by factoring $\mathbf{B}$ into a lower, $\mathbf{L}$, and an upper, $\mathbf{U}$, triangular matrices such that $\mathbf{B} = \mathbf{L}\mathbf{U}$. The method, aptly called L-U decomposition, is particularly suited for sparse matrices.[17]

It is for these reasons that the tableau format is never used in any of the leading LP codes available today.

4. Barrier (interior point) algorithm vs. simplex algorithm. The interior point algorithm (see Section 22.3 on the website) is totally different from the simplex algorithm in that it cuts across the feasible space and gradually moves (in the limit) to the optimum. Computationally, the algorithm is *polynomial* in problem size. The simplex algorithm, on the other hand, is *exponential* in problem size (hypothetical examples have been constructed where the simplex algorithm visits *every* corner point of the solution space before reaching the optimum).

The interior point algorithm was initially introduced in 1984 and, surprisingly, was patented by AT&T and sold on a specialized computer (apparently for an exuberant fee) without releasing its computational details. Eventually, the scientific community "got busy" and discovered that the interior point method had roots in earlier nonlinear programming algorithms of the 1960s (see, e.g., the SUMT algorithm in Section 21.2.5). The result is the so-called *barrier method* with several algorithmic variations.

For extremely large problems, the barrier method has proven to be considerably faster than the fastest dual simplex algorithm. The disadvantage is that the barrier

---

[17]See J. Bunch and J. Hopcroft, "Triangular Factorization and Inversion by Fast Matrix Multiplication," *Mathematics of Computation*, Vol. 28, pp. 231–236, 1974. See also, E. Hellerman and D. Rarick, "Reinversion with the Preassigned Pivot Procedure," *Mathematical Programming*, Vol. 1, pp. 195–216, 1971.

algorithm does not produce corner-point solutions, a restriction that limits its application in post-optimal analysis (Chapter 4) and also in integer programming (Chapter 9). Although methods to convert a barrier optimum interior point to a corner-point solution have been developed, the associated computational overhead is enormous, limiting its use in such applications as integer programming, where the frequent need for locating corner-point solutions is fundamental to the algorithm. Nevertheless, all commercial codes include the barrier algorithm as a tool for solving large LPs.

5. Degeneracy. As explained in Section 3.5.1, degenerate basic solutions can result in cycling, which can cause the simplex iterations to stall indefinitely at a degenerate corner point without ever reaching termination. In early versions of the simplex algorithm, degeneracy and cycling were not incorporated in most codes because of the assumption that their occurrence in practice was rare. As instances of more difficult and larger problems (particularly in the area of integer programming) were tested, computer roundoff error gave rise to degeneracy/cycling-like behavior that caused the computations to "stall" at the same objective value. The problem was circumvented by interjecting conditional random perturbation and shifting in the values of the basic variables.[18]

6. Input model conditioning (presolving). All commercial LP modeling languages and solvers attempt to condition the input data prior to actually solving it. The goal is to "simplify" the model in two key ways:[19]
  a. Reduction in the model size (rows and columns) by identifying and removing redundant constraints and by possibly fixing and substituting out variables.
  b. Scaling the coefficients of the model that are widely different in magnitude to mitigate the adverse effect of digit loss when manipulating real numbers of widely different magnitudes.

Figure 3.17 summarizes the stages of solving an LP problem. The input model can be fed by way of a pre-solver to a solver, such as CPLEX or XPRESS. Alternatively, a convenient modeling language, such as AMPL, GAMS, MOSEL, or MPL, can be used to model the LP algebraically and then internally pre-solve and translate its input data to fit the format of the solver. The solver then produces the output results in terms of the variables and constraints of the *original* LP model.

7. Advances in computers. It is not surprising that in the last quarter of a century, computer speed has increased by more than one-thousand fold. Today, a desktop

FIGURE 3.17

Components of an LP Numerical

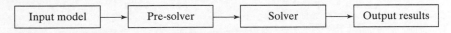

---

[18]See P. Harris, "Pivot Selection Methods of the devex LP Code," *Mathematical Programming*, Vol. 5, pp. 1–28, 1974.
[19]See L. Bearley, L., Mitra, and H. Williams, "Analysis of Mathematical Programming Problems Prior to Applying the Simplex Algorith," *Mathematical Programming*, Vol. 8, pp. 54–83, 1975.

computer has more power and speed than the supercomputers of yesteryears. These hardware advances (together with the algorithmic advances cited earlier) have made it possible to solve huge LPs in a matter of seconds as opposed to days (yes, days!) in the past.

BIBLIOGRAPHY

Bazaraa, M., J. Jarvis, and H. Sherali, *Linear Programming and Network Flows*, 4th ed., Wiley, New York, 2009.

Chvátal, V., *Linear Programming*, Freeman, New York, 1983.

Dantzig, G., *Linear Programming and Extensions*, Princeton University Press, Princeton, NJ, 1963.

Dantzig, G., and M. Thapa, *Linear Programming 1: Introduction,* Springer, New York, 1997.

Nering, E., and A. Tucker, *Linear Programming and Related Problems*, Academic Press, Boston, 1992.

Taha, H., "Linear Programming," Chapter II-1 in *Handbook of Operations Research*, J. Moder and S. Elmaghraby (eds.), Van Nostrand Reinhold, New York, 1987.

CHAPTER 4

Duality and Post-Optimal Analysis

4.1 DEFINITION OF THE DUAL PROBLEM

The **dual** problem is defined systematically from the **primal** (or original) LP model. The two problems are closely related, in the sense that the optimal solution of one problem automatically provides the optimal solution to the other.

In most LP treatments, the dual is defined for various forms of the primal depending on the sense of optimization (maximization or minimization), types of constraints ($\leq$, $\geq$, or =), and sign of the variables (nonnegative or unrestricted). This chapter offers a *single* definition that automatically subsumes *all* forms of the primal.

Our definition of the dual problem requires expressing the primal problem in the *equation form* presented in Section 3.1 (all the constraints are equations with nonnegative right-hand side, and all the variables are nonnegative). This requirement is consistent with the format of the simplex starting tableau. Hence, any results obtained from the primal optimal solution apply directly to the associated dual problem.

The key ideas for constructing the dual from the primal are summarized as follows:

1. Assign a dual variable for each primal (equality) constraint.
2. Construct a dual constraint for each primal variable.
3. The (column) constraint coefficients and the objective coefficient of the *j*th primal variable respectively define the left-hand and the right-hand sides of the *j*th dual constraint.
4. The dual objective coefficents equal the right-hand sides of the primal constraint equations.
5. The sense of optimization, direction of inequalities, and the signs of the variables in the dual are governed by the rules in Table 4.1. An easy way to remember the constraint type in the dual (i.e., $\leq$, or $\geq$) is that if the dual objective is *minimization* (i.e., pointing *down*), then the constraints are all of the type $\geq$ (i.e., pointing *up*). The opposite applies when the dual objective is maximization.

TABLE 4.1   Rules for Constructing the Dual Problem

Primal problem objective[a]	Dual problem		
	Objective	Constraints type	Variables sign
Maximization	Minimization	$\geq$	Unrestricted
Minimization	Maximization	$\leq$	Unrestricted

[a]All primal constraints are equations with nonnegative right-hand side, and all the variables are nonnegative.

The following examples demonstrate the use of the rules in Table 4.1. The examples also show that our definition incorporates all forms of the primal automatically.

Example 4.1-1

Primal	Primal in equation form	Dual variables
Maximize $z = 5x_1 + 12x_2 + 4x_3$ subject to	Maximize $z = 5x_1 + 12x_2 + 4x_3 + 0x_4$ subject to	
$\begin{aligned} x_1 + 2x_2 + x_3 &\leq 10 \\ 2x_1 - x_2 + 3x_3 &= 8 \\ x_1, x_2, x_3 &\geq 0 \end{aligned}$	$\begin{aligned} x_1 + 2x_2 + x_3 + x_4 &= 10 \\ 2x_1 - x_2 + 3x_3 + 0x_4 &= 8 \\ x_1, x_2, x_3, x_4 &\geq 0 \end{aligned}$	y_1 y_2

Dual Problem

$$\text{Minimize } w = 10y_1 + 8y_2$$

subject to

$$y_1 + 2y_2 \geq 5$$

$$2y_1 - y_2 \geq 12$$

$$y_1 + 3y_2 \geq 4$$

$$\left. \begin{array}{l} y_1 + 0y_2 \geq 0 \\ y_1, y_2 \text{ unrestricted} \end{array} \right\} \Rightarrow (y_1 \geq 0,\ y_2 \text{ unrestricted})$$

Example 4.1-2

Primal	Primal in equation form	Dual variables
Minimize $z = 15x_1 + 12x_2$ subject to	Minimize $z = 15x_1 + 12x_2 + 0x_3 + 0x_4$ subject to	
$\begin{aligned} x_1 + 2x_2 &\geq 3 \\ 2x_1 - 4x_2 &\leq 5 \\ x_1, x_2 &\geq 0 \end{aligned}$	$\begin{aligned} x_1 + 2x_2 - x_3 + 0x_4 &= 3 \\ 2x_1 - 4x_2 + 0x_3 + x_4 &= 5 \\ x_1, x_2, x_3, x_4 &\geq 0 \end{aligned}$	y_1 y_2

Dual Problem

$$\text{Maximize } w = 3y_1 + 5y_2$$

subject to

$$y_1 + 2y_2 \leq 15$$

$$2y_1 - 4y_2 \leq 12$$

$$\left.\begin{array}{r} -y_1 \qquad \leq 0 \\ y_2 \leq 0 \\ y_1, y_2 \text{ unrestricted} \end{array}\right\} \Rightarrow (y_1 \geq 0, y_2 \leq 0)$$

Example 4.1-3

Primal	Primal in equation form	Dual variables
	Substitute $x_1 = x_1^- - x_1^+$	
Maximize $z = 5x_1 + 6x_2$	Maximize $z = 5x_1^- - 5x_1^+ + 6x_2$	
subject to	subject to	
$x_1 + 2x_2 = 5$	$x_1^- - x_1^+ + 2x_2 \qquad = 5$	y_1
$-x_1 + 5x_2 \geq 3$	$-x_1^- + x_1^+ + 5x_2 - x_3 \qquad = 3$	y_2
$4x_1 + 7x_2 \leq 8$	$4x_1^- - 4x_1^+ + 7x_2 \qquad + x_4 = 8$	y_3
x_1 unrestricted, $x_2 \geq 0$	$x_1^-, x_1^+, x_2, x_3, x_4 \geq 0$	

Dual Problem

$$\text{Minimize } z = 5y_1 + 3y_2 + 8y_3$$

subject to

$$\left.\begin{array}{r} y_1 - y_2 + 4y_3 \geq 5 \\ -y_1 + y_2 - 4y_3 \geq -5 \end{array}\right\} \Rightarrow \left.\begin{array}{r} y_1 - y_2 + 4y_3 \geq 5 \\ y_1 - y_2 + 4y_3 \leq 5 \end{array}\right\} \Rightarrow y_1 - y_2 + 4y_3 = 5$$

$$2y_1 + 5y_2 + 7y_3 \geq 6$$

$$\left.\begin{array}{r} -y_2 \qquad \geq 0 \\ y_3 \geq 0 \\ y_1, y_2, y_3 \text{ unrestricted} \end{array}\right\} \Rightarrow (y_1 \text{ unrestricted}, y_2 \leq 0, y_3 \geq 0)$$

The first and second constraints are replaced by an equation. The general rule is that an unrestricted primal variable always corresponds to an equality dual constraint. Conversely, a primal equation produces an unrestricted dual variable, as the first primal constraint demonstrates.

Summary of the Rules for Constructing the Dual.   Table 4.2 summarizes the primal–dual rules as they are usually presented in the literature. It is a good exercise to verify that these explicit rules are subsumed by the two rules in Table 4.1.

TABLE 4.2   Rules for Constructing the dual problem

Maximization problem		Minimization problem
Constraints		*Variables*
$\geq$	$\Leftrightarrow$	≤ 0
$\leq$	$\Leftrightarrow$	≥ 0
$=$	$\Leftrightarrow$	Unrestricted
Variables		*Constraints*
≥ 0	$\Leftrightarrow$	$\geq$
≤ 0	$\Leftrightarrow$	$\leq$
Unrestricted	$\Leftrightarrow$	$=$

Note that the column headings in the table do not use the designation primal and dual. What matters here is the sense of optimization. If the primal is maximization, then the dual is minimization, and vice versa. Note also that no provision is made for including artificial variables in the primal. The reason is that artificial variables would not change the definition of the dual (see Problem 5, Set 4.1a).

PROBLEM SET 4.1A

1. In Example 4.1-1, derive the associated dual problem if the sense of optimization in the primal problem is changed to minimization.

*2. In Example 4.1-2, derive the associated dual problem given that the primal problem is augmented with a third constraint, $3x_1 + x_2 = 4$.

3. In Example 4.1-3, show that even if the sense of optimization in the primal is changed to minimization, an unrestricted primal variable always corresponds to an equality dual constraint.

4. Write the dual for each of the following primal problems:

    (a) Maximize $z = 66x_1 - 22x_2$
    subject to

$$-x_1 + x_2 \leq -2$$
$$2x_1 + 3x_2 \leq 5$$
$$x_1, x_2 \geq 0$$

    (b) Minimize $z = 6x_1 + 3x_2$
    subject to

$$6x_1 - 3x_2 + x_3 \geq 25$$
$$3x_1 + 4x_2 + x_3 \geq 55$$
$$x_1, x_2, x_3 \geq 0$$

    *(c) Maximize $z = x_1 + x_2$
    subject to

$$2x_1 + x_2 = 5$$
$$3x_1 - x_2 = 6$$
$$x_1, x_2 \text{ unrestricted}$$

*5. Consider Example 4.1-1. The application of the simplex method to the primal requires the use of an artificial variable in the second constraint of the standard primal to secure a starting basic solution. Show that the presence of an artificial primal in equation form variable does not affect the definition of the dual because it leads to a redundant dual constraint.

6. True or False?

   (a) The dual of the dual problem yields the original primal.

   (b) If the primal constraint is originally in equation form, the corresponding dual variable is not necessarily unrestricted.

   (c) If the primal constraint is of the type ≤, the corresponding dual variable will be nonnegative (nonpositive) if the primal objective is maximization (minimization).

   (d) If the primal constraint is of the type ≥, the corresponding dual variable will be nonnegative (nonpositive) if the primal objective is minimization (maximization).

   (e) An unrestricted primal variable may result in an inequality dual constraint.

4.2 PRIMAL–DUAL RELATIONSHIPS

Changes made in the data of an LP model can affect the optimality and/or the feasibility of the current optimum solution. This section introduces a number of primal–dual relationships that can be used to recompute the elements of the optimal simplex tableau. These relationships form the basis for the economic interpretation of the LP model and for post-optimality analysis.

The section starts with a brief review of matrices, a convenient tool for carrying out the simplex tableau computations. A more detailed review of matrices is given in Appendix D on the website.

4.2.1 Review of Simple Matrix Operations

The simplex tableau can be generated by three elementary matrix operations: (row vector) × (matrix), (matrix) × (column vector), and (scalar) × (matrix). These operations are summarized here for convenience. First, we introduce some matrix definitions:

1. A *matrix*, $\mathbf{A}$, of size $(m \times n)$ is a rectangular array of elements with m rows and n columns.

2. A *row vector*, $\mathbf{V}$, of size m is a $(1 \times m)$ matrix.

3. A *column vector*, $\mathbf{P}$, of size n is an $(n \times 1)$ matrix.

These definitions can be represented mathematically as

$$\mathbf{V} = (v_1, v_2, \ldots, v_m), \mathbf{A} = \begin{pmatrix} a_{11} & a_{12} & \cdots & a_{1n} \\ a_{21} & a_{22} & \cdots & a_{2n} \\ \cdots & \cdots & \cdots & \cdots \\ a_{m1} & a_{m2} & \cdots & a_{mn} \end{pmatrix}, \mathbf{P} = \begin{pmatrix} p_1 \\ p_2 \\ \cdots \\ p_n \end{pmatrix}$$

1. **(Row vector $\times$ matrix, VA).** The operation is valid only if the size of the row vector $\mathbf{V}$ and the number of rows of $\mathbf{A}$ are equal. For example,

$$(11, 22, 33)\begin{pmatrix} 1 & 2 \\ 3 & 4 \\ 5 & 6 \end{pmatrix} = (1 \times 11 + 3 \times 22 + 5 \times 33, 2 \times 11 + 4 \times 22 + 6 \times 33)$$

$$= (242, 308)$$

2. **(Matrix $\times$ column vector, AP).** The operation is valid only if the number of columns of $\mathbf{A}$ and the size of column vector $\mathbf{P}$ are equal. For example,

$$\begin{pmatrix} 1 & 3 & 5 \\ 2 & 4 & 6 \end{pmatrix}\begin{pmatrix} 11 \\ 22 \\ 33 \end{pmatrix} = \begin{pmatrix} 1 \times 11 + 3 \times 22 + 5 \times 33 \\ 2 \times 11 + 4 \times 22 + 6 \times 33 \end{pmatrix} = \begin{pmatrix} 242 \\ 308 \end{pmatrix}$$

3. **(Scalar $\times$ matrix, αA).** Given the scalar (or constant) quantity α, the multiplication operation $\alpha \mathbf{A}$ results in a matrix of the same size as matrix $\mathbf{A}$. For example, given $\alpha = 10$,

$$(10)\begin{pmatrix} 1 & 2 & 3 \\ 4 & 5 & 6 \end{pmatrix} = \begin{pmatrix} 10 & 20 & 30 \\ 40 & 50 & 60 \end{pmatrix}$$

PROBLEM SET 4.2A

1. Consider the following matrices:

$$\mathbf{A} = \begin{pmatrix} 1 & 4 \\ 2 & 5 \\ 3 & 6 \end{pmatrix}, \mathbf{P}_1 = \begin{pmatrix} 10 \\ 20 \end{pmatrix}, \mathbf{P}_2 = \begin{pmatrix} 10 \\ 20 \\ 30 \end{pmatrix}$$

$$\mathbf{V}_1 = (11, 22), \mathbf{V}_2 = (-2, -4, -6)$$

In each of the following cases, indicate whether the given matrix operation is legitimate, and, if so, calculate the result.

*(a) $\mathbf{AV}_1$

(b) $\mathbf{AP}_1$

(c) $\mathbf{AP}_2$

(d) $\mathbf{V}_1\mathbf{A}$

*(e) $\mathbf{V}_2\mathbf{A}$

(f) $\mathbf{P}_1\mathbf{P}_2$

(g) $\mathbf{V}_1\mathbf{P}_1$

4.2.2   Simplex Tableau Layout

The simplex tableau in Chapter 3 is the basis for the presentation in this chapter. Figure 4.1 represents the *starting* and *general* simplex tableaus schematically. In the starting tableau, the constraint coefficients under the starting variables form an **identity matrix** (all main-diagonal elements are 1, and all off-diagonal elements

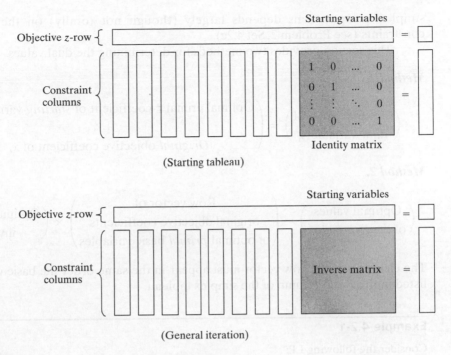

FIGURE 4.1

Schematic representation of the starting and general simplex tableaus

are zero). With this arrangement, subsequent iterations of the simplex tableau generated by the Gauss-Jordan row operations (see Chapter 3) modify the elements of the identity matrix to produce what is known as the **inverse matrix**. As we will see in the remainder of this chapter, the inverse matrix is key to computing all the elements of the associated simplex tableau.

PROBLEM SET 4.2B

1. Consider the optimal tableau of Example 3.3-1.
   (a)* Identify the optimal inverse matrix.
   (b) Show that the right-hand side equals the inverse multiplied by the original right-hand side vector of the original constraints.
2. Repeat Problem 1 for the optimal tableau of Phase 1 in Example 3.4-2.

4.2.3 Optimal Dual Solution

The primal and dual solutions are closely related, in the sense that the optimal solution of either problem yields the optimal solution to the other. Thus, in an LP model in which the number of variables is considerably smaller than the number of constraints, computational savings may be realized by solving the dual because the amount of simplex computations depends largely (though not totally) on the number of constraints (see Problem 2, Set 4.2c).

This section provides two methods for determining the dual values.

Method 1.

$$\begin{pmatrix} \text{Optimal value of} \\ \text{dual variable } y_i \end{pmatrix} = \begin{pmatrix} \text{Optimal primal } z\text{-coefficient of } \textit{starting} \text{ variable } x_i \\ + \\ \textit{Original} \text{ objective coefficient of } x_i \end{pmatrix}$$

Method 2.

$$\begin{pmatrix} \text{Optimal values} \\ \text{of } \textit{dual} \text{ variables} \end{pmatrix} = \begin{pmatrix} \text{Row vector of} \\ \text{original objective coefficients} \\ \text{of optimal } \textit{primal} \text{ basic variables} \end{pmatrix} \times \begin{pmatrix} \text{Optimal } \textit{primal} \\ \text{inverse} \end{pmatrix}$$

The elements of the row vector must appear in the same order the basic variables are listed in the *Basic* column of the simplex tableau.

Example 4.2-1

Consider the following LP:

$$\text{Maximize } z = 5x_1 + 12x_2 + 4x_3$$

Subject to

$$x_1 + 2x_2 + x_3 \leq 10$$
$$2x_1 - x_2 + 3x_3 = 8$$
$$x_1, x_2, x_3 \geq 0$$

To prepare the problem for solution by the simplex method, we add a slack x_4 in the first constraint and an artificial R in the second. The resulting primal and the associated dual problems are thus defined as follows:

Primal	Dual
Maximize $z = 5x_1 + 12x_2 + 4x_3 - MR$ subject to $\quad x_1 + 2x_2 + x_3 + x_4 \quad\quad = 10$ $\quad 2x_1 - x_2 + 3x_3 \quad + R = 8$ $\quad x_1, x_2, x_3, x_4, R \geq 0$	Minimize $w = 10y_1 + 8y_2$ subject to $\quad y_1 + 2y_2 \geq 5$ $\quad 2y_1 - y_2 \geq 12$ $\quad y_1 + 3y_2 \geq 4$ $\quad y_1 \quad\quad \geq 0$ $\quad y_2 \geq -M \ (\Rightarrow y_2 \text{ unrestricted})$

Table 4.3 provides the optimal primal tableau.

We now show how the optimal dual values are determined using the two methods described at the start of this section.

TABLE 4.3   Optimal Tableau of the Primal of Example 4.2-1

Basic	x_1	x_2	x_3	x_4	R	Solution
z	0	0	$\frac{3}{5}$	$\frac{29}{5}$	$-\frac{2}{5} + M$	$54\frac{4}{5}$
x_2	0	1	$-\frac{1}{5}$	$\frac{2}{5}$	$-\frac{1}{5}$	$\frac{12}{5}$
x_1	1	0	$\frac{7}{5}$	$\frac{1}{5}$	$\frac{2}{5}$	$\frac{26}{5}$

Method 1. In Table 4.3, the starting primal variables x_4 and R uniquely correspond to the dual variables y_1 and y_2, respectively. Thus, we determine the optimum dual solution as follows:

Starting primal basic variables	x_4	R
z-equation coefficients	$\frac{29}{5}$	$-\frac{2}{5} + M$
Original objective coefficient	0	$-M$
Dual variables	y_1	y_2
Optimal dual values	$\frac{29}{5} + 0 = \frac{29}{5}$	$-\frac{2}{5} + M + (-M) = -\frac{2}{5}$

Method 2. The optimal inverse matrix, highlighted in Table 4.3 under the starting variables x_4 and R, is

$$\text{Optimal inverse} = \begin{pmatrix} \frac{2}{5} & -\frac{1}{5} \\ \frac{1}{5} & \frac{2}{5} \end{pmatrix}$$

The order of the optimal primal basic variables in the *Basic* column is x_2 followed by x_1. The elements of the original objective coefficients for the two variables must appear in the same order—namely,

$$(\text{Original objective coefficients}) = (\text{Coefficient of } x_2, \text{coefficient of } x_1)$$
$$= (12, 5)$$

The optimal dual values are

$$(y_1, y_2) = \begin{pmatrix} \text{Original objective} \\ \text{coefficients of } x_2, x_1 \end{pmatrix} \times (\text{Optimal inverse})$$

$$= (12, 5) \begin{pmatrix} \frac{2}{5} & -\frac{1}{5} \\ \frac{1}{5} & \frac{2}{5} \end{pmatrix}$$

$$= \left(\frac{29}{5}, -\frac{2}{5} \right)$$

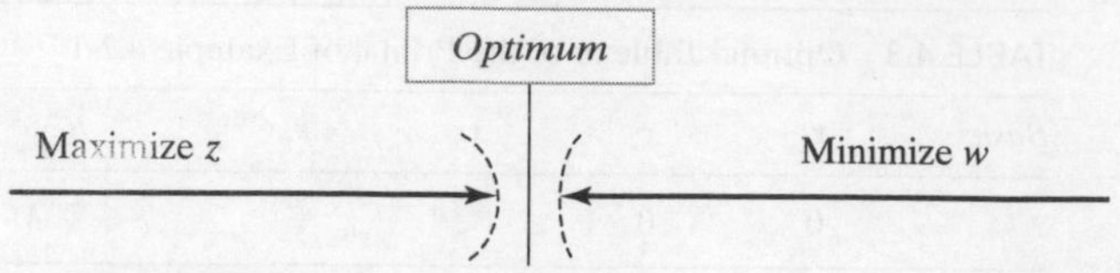

FIGURE 4.2

Relationship between maximum z and minimum w

Primal–dual objective values. For any pair of *feasible* primal and dual solutions,

$$\begin{pmatrix} \text{Objective value in the} \\ maximization \text{ problem} \end{pmatrix} \leq \begin{pmatrix} \text{Objective value in the} \\ minimization \text{ problem} \end{pmatrix}$$

At the optimum, the relationship holds as a strict equation, meaning that the two objective values are equal. Note that the relationship does not specify which problem is primal and which is dual. Only the sense of optimization (maximization or minimization) is important in this case.

The optimum cannot occur with z strictly less than w (i.e., $z < w$) because, no matter how close z and w are, there is always room for improvement, which contradicts optimality as Figure 4.2 demonstrates.

Example 4.2-2

In Example 4.2-1, $(x_1 = 0, x_2 = 0, x_3 = \frac{8}{3})$ and $(y_1 = 6, y_2 = 0)$ are (arbitrary) feasible primal and dual solutions. The associated values of the objective functions are

$$z = 5x_1 + 12x_2 + 4x_3 = 5(0) + 12(0) + 4(\tfrac{8}{3}) = 10\tfrac{2}{3}$$
$$w = 10y_1 + 8y_2 = 10(6) + 8(0) = 60$$

Thus, $z\ (= 10\tfrac{2}{3})$ for the maximization problem (primal) is less than $w\ (=60)$ for the minimization problem (dual). The optimum value of $z\ (= 54\tfrac{4}{5})$ falls in the range $(10\tfrac{2}{3}, 60)$.

PROBLEM SET 4.2C

1. Find the optimal value of the objective function for the following problem by inspecting only its dual. (Do not solve the dual by the simplex method.)

$$\text{Minimize } z = 10x_1 + 4x_2 + 5x_3$$

subject to

$$5x_1 - 7x_2 + 3x_3 \geq 25$$
$$x_1, x_2, x_3 \geq 0$$

2. Solve the dual of the following problem, then find the optimal primal solution from the solution of the dual. Does the solution of the dual offer computational advantages over solving the primal directly?

$$\text{Minimize } z = 50x_1 + 60x_2 + 30x_3$$

subject to

$$5x_1 + 5x_2 + 3x_3 \geq 50$$
$$x_1 + x_2 - x_3 \geq 20$$
$$7x_1 + 6x_2 - 9x_3 \geq 30$$
$$5x_1 + 5x_2 + 5x_3 \geq 35$$
$$2x_1 + 4x_2 - 15x_3 \geq 10$$
$$12x_1 + 10x_2 \geq 90$$
$$x_2 - 10x_3 \geq 20$$
$$x_1, x_2, x_3 \geq 0$$

*3. Consider the following LP:

$$\text{Maximize } z = 5x_1 + 2x_2 + 3x_3$$

subject to

$$x_1 + 5x_2 + 2x_3 = 30$$
$$x_1 - 5x_2 - 6x_3 \leq 40$$
$$x_1, x_2, x_3 \geq 0$$

Given that the artificial variable x_4 and the slack variable x_5 form the starting basic variables and that M was set equal to 100 when solving the problem, the *optimal* tableau is given as:

Basic	x_1	x_2	x_3	x_4	x_5	Solution
z	0	23	7	105	0	150
x_1	1	5	2	1	0	30
x_5	0	-10	-8	-1	1	10

Write the associated dual problem, and determine its optimal solution in two ways.

4. Consider the following LP:

$$\text{Minimize } z = 4x_1 + x_2$$

subject to

$$3x_1 + x_2 = 30$$
$$4x_1 + 3x_2 \geq 60$$
$$x_1 + 2x_2 \leq 40$$
$$x_1, x_2 \geq 0$$

The starting solution consists of artificial x_4 and x_5 for the first and second constraints and slack x_6 for the third constraint. Using $M = 100$ for the artificial variables, the optimal tableau is given as

Basic	x_1	x_2	x_3	x_4	x_5	x_6	Solution
z	0	0	0	−98.6	−100	−.2	34
x_1	1	0	0	.4	0	−.2	4
x_2	0	1	0	.2	0	.6	18
x_3	0	0	1	1	−1	1	10

Write the associated dual problem, and determine its optimal solution in two ways.

5. Consider the following LP:

$$\text{Maximize } z = 2x_1 + 4x_2 + 4x_3 - 3x_4$$

subject to

$$x_1 + x_2 + x_3 \quad = 4$$
$$x_1 + 4x_2 \quad + x_4 = 8$$
$$x_1, x_2, x_3, x_4 \geq 0$$

Using x_3 and x_4 as starting variables, the optimal tableau is given as

Basic	x_1	x_2	x_3	x_4	Solution
z	2	0	0	3	16
x_3	.75	0	1	−.25	2
x_2	.25	1	0	.25	2

Write the associated dual problem, and determine its optimal solution in two ways.

*6. Consider the following LP:

$$\text{Maximize } z = x_1 + 5x_2 + 3x_3$$

subject to

$$x_1 + 2x_2 + x_3 = 3$$
$$2x_1 - x_2 \quad = 4$$
$$x_1, x_2, x_3 \geq 0$$

The starting solution consists of x_3 in the first constraint and an artificial x_4 in the second constraint with $M = 100$. The optimal tableau is given as

Basic	x_1	x_2	x_3	x_4	Solution
z	0	2	0	99	5
x_3	1	2.5	1	−.5	1
x_1	0	−.5	0	.5	2

Write the associated dual problem, and determine its optimal solution in two ways.

7. Consider the following set of inequalities:

$$2x_1 + 3x_2 \leq 12$$

$$-3x_1 + 2x_2 \leq -4$$

$$3x_1 - 5x_2 \leq 2$$

$$x_1 \text{ unrestricted}$$

$$x_2 \geq 0$$

A feasible solution can be found by augmenting the trivial objective function, maximize $z = x_1 + x_2$, and then solving the problem. Another way is to solve the dual, from which a solution for the set of inequalities can be found. Apply the two methods.

8. Estimate a range for the optimal objective value for the following LPs:

   *(a) Minimize $z = 5x_1 + 2x_2$

   subject to

$$x_1 - x_2 \geq 3$$

$$2x_1 + 3x_2 \geq 5$$

$$x_1, x_2 \geq 0$$

   (b) Maximize $z = x_1 + 5x_2 + 3x_3$

   subject to

$$x_1 + 2x_2 + x_3 = 30$$

$$2x_1 - x_2 = 40$$

$$x_1, x_2, x_3 \geq 0$$

   (c) Maximize $z = 2x_1 + x_2$

   subject to

$$x_1 - x_2 \leq 2$$

$$2x_1 \leq 8$$

$$x_1, x_2 \geq 0$$

   (d) Maximize $z = 3x_1 + 2x_2$

   subject to

$$2x_1 + x_2 \leq 3$$

$$3x_1 + 4x_2 \leq 12$$

$$x_1, x_2 \geq 0$$

9. In Problem 7(a), let y_1 and y_2 be the dual variables. Determine whether the following pairs of primal–dual solutions are optimal:

   (a)* $(x_1 = 3, x_2 = 1; y_1 = 4, y_2 = 1)$

   (b) $(x_1 = 4, x_2 = 1; y_1 = 1, y_2 = 0)$

   (c) $(x_1 = 3, x_2 = 0; y_1 = 5, y_2 = 0)$

4.2.4 Simplex Tableau Computations

This section shows how *any iteration* of the simplex tableau can be generated from the *original* data of the problem, the *inverse* associated with the iteration, and the dual problem. Using the layout of the simplex tableau in Figure 4.1, we can divide the computations into two types:

1. Constraint columns (left- and right-hand sides).
2. Objective z-row.

Formula 1: Constraint column computations. In any simplex iteration, a left-hand or a right-hand side column is computed as follows:

$$\begin{pmatrix} \text{Constraint column} \\ \text{in iteration } i \end{pmatrix} = \begin{pmatrix} \text{Inverse in} \\ \text{iteration } i \end{pmatrix} \times \begin{pmatrix} \text{Original} \\ \text{constraint column} \end{pmatrix}$$

Formula 2: Objective z-row computations. In any simplex iteration, the objective equation coefficient (reduced cost) of x_j is computed as follows:

$$\begin{pmatrix} \textit{Primal } z\text{-equation} \\ \text{coefficient of variable } x_j \end{pmatrix} = \begin{pmatrix} \text{Left-hand side of} \\ j\text{th } \textit{dual} \text{ constraint} \end{pmatrix} - \begin{pmatrix} \text{Right-hand side of} \\ j\text{th } \textit{dual} \text{ constraint} \end{pmatrix}$$

Example 4.2-3

We use the LP in Example 4.2-1 to illustrate the application of Formulas 1 and 2. From the optimal tableau in Table 4.3, we have

$$\text{Optimal inverse} = \begin{pmatrix} \frac{2}{5} & -\frac{1}{5} \\ \frac{1}{5} & \frac{2}{5} \end{pmatrix}$$

$$\begin{pmatrix} x_1\text{-column in} \\ \text{optimal iteration} \end{pmatrix} = \begin{pmatrix} \text{Inverse in} \\ \text{optimal iteration} \end{pmatrix} \times \begin{pmatrix} \text{original} \\ x_1\text{-column} \end{pmatrix}$$

$$= \begin{pmatrix} \frac{2}{5} & -\frac{1}{5} \\ \frac{1}{5} & \frac{2}{5} \end{pmatrix} \times \begin{pmatrix} 1 \\ 2 \end{pmatrix} = \begin{pmatrix} 0 \\ 1 \end{pmatrix}$$

Similar computation can be used to generate the optimal columns for x_2, x_3, x_4, R, and the right-hand side (verify!).

Next, we demonstrate how the objective row computations are carried out with Formula 2. The optimal values of the dual variables, $(y_1, y_2) = \left(\frac{29}{5}, -\frac{2}{5}\right)$, were computed in Example 4.2-1. These values are used in Formula 2 to compute all the z-coefficients, as illustrated here for x_1 and R.

$$z \text{ - cofficient of } x_1 = y_1 + 2y_2 - 5 = \frac{29}{5} + 2 \times -\frac{2}{5} - 5 = 0$$

$$z \text{ - cofficient of } R = y_2 - (-M) \quad = -\frac{2}{5} - (-M) \quad = -\frac{2}{5} + M$$

Similar computations can be used to determine the z-coefficients of x_2, x_3, and x_4 (verify!).

PROBLEM SET 4.2D

1. Generate the first simplex iteration of Example 4.2-1 (you may use TORA's Iterations $\Rightarrow$ M-method with $M = 100$ for convenience), then use Formulas 1 and 2 to verify all the elements of the resulting tableau.

2. Consider the following LP model:

$$\text{Maximize } z = 4x_1 + 14x_2$$

subject to

$$2x_1 + 7x_2 + x_3 \qquad = 21$$
$$7x_1 + 2x_2 \qquad + x_4 = 21$$
$$x_1, x_2, x_3, x_4 \geq 0$$

Check the optimality and feasibility of each of the following basic solutions.

*(a) Basic variables $= (x_2, x_4)$, Inverse $= \begin{pmatrix} \frac{1}{7} & 0 \\ -\frac{2}{7} & 1 \end{pmatrix}$

(b) Basic variables $= (x_2, x_3)$, Inverse $= \begin{pmatrix} 0 & \frac{1}{2} \\ 1 & -\frac{7}{2} \end{pmatrix}$

(c) Basic variables $= (x_2, x_1)$, Inverse $= \begin{pmatrix} \frac{7}{45} & -\frac{2}{45} \\ -\frac{2}{45} & \frac{7}{45} \end{pmatrix}$

(d) Basic variables $= (x_1, x_4)$, Inverse $= \begin{pmatrix} \frac{1}{2} & 0 \\ -\frac{7}{2} & 1 \end{pmatrix}$

3. Consider the following LP model:

$$\text{Maximize } z = 3x_1 + 2x_2 + 5x_3$$

subject to

$$x_1 + 2x_2 + x_3 + x_4 \qquad = 30$$
$$3x_1 \qquad + 2x_3 \qquad + x_5 \qquad = 60$$
$$x_1 + 4x_2 \qquad\qquad + x_6 = 20$$
$$x_1, x_2, x_3, x_4, x_5, x_6 \geq 0$$

Check the optimality and feasibility of the following basic solutions:

(a) Basic variables $- (x_4, x_3, x_6)$, Inverse $= \begin{pmatrix} 1 & -\frac{1}{2} & 0 \\ 0 & \frac{1}{2} & 0 \\ 0 & 0 & 1 \end{pmatrix}$

(b) Basic variables $= (x_2, x_3, x_1)$, Inverse $= \begin{pmatrix} \frac{1}{4} & -\frac{1}{8} & \frac{1}{8} \\ \frac{3}{2} & -\frac{1}{4} & -\frac{3}{4} \\ -1 & \frac{1}{2} & \frac{1}{2} \end{pmatrix}$

(c) Basic variables = (x_2, x_3, x_6), Inverse = $\begin{pmatrix} \frac{1}{2} & -\frac{1}{4} & 0 \\ 0 & \frac{1}{2} & 0 \\ -2 & 1 & 1 \end{pmatrix}$

*4. Consider the following LP model:

$$\text{Minimize } z = 2x_1 + x_2$$

subject to

$$3x_1 + x_2 - x_3 \qquad\qquad = 3$$
$$4x_1 + 3x_2 \qquad - x_4 \qquad = 6$$
$$x_1 + 2x_2 \qquad\qquad + x_5 = 3$$
$$x_1, x_2, x_3, x_4, x_5 \geq 0$$

Compute the entire simplex tableau associated with the following basic solution, and check it for optimality and feasibility.

$$\text{Basic variables} = (x_1, x_2, x_5), \text{Inverse} = \begin{pmatrix} \frac{3}{5} & -\frac{1}{5} & 0 \\ -\frac{4}{5} & \frac{3}{5} & 0 \\ 1 & -1 & 1 \end{pmatrix}$$

5. Consider the following LP model:

$$\text{Maximize } z = 5x_1 + 12x_2 + 4x_3$$

subject to

$$x_1 + 2x_2 + x_3 + x_4 = 5$$
$$2x_1 - x_2 + 3x_3 \qquad = 1$$
$$x_1, x_2, x_3, x_4 \geq 0$$

(a) Identify the best solution from among the following basic feasible solutions:

   (i)   Basic variables = (x_4, x_3), Inverse = $\begin{pmatrix} 1 & -\frac{1}{3} \\ 0 & \frac{1}{3} \end{pmatrix}$

   (ii) Basic variables = (x_2, x_1), Inverse = $\begin{pmatrix} \frac{2}{5} & -\frac{1}{5} \\ \frac{1}{5} & \frac{2}{5} \end{pmatrix}$

   (iii) Basic variables = (x_2, x_3), Inverse = $\begin{pmatrix} \frac{3}{7} & -\frac{1}{7} \\ \frac{1}{7} & \frac{2}{7} \end{pmatrix}$

(b) Is the best solution obtained in (a) optimum for the LP model?

6. Consider the following LP model:

$$\text{Maximize } z = 5x_1 + 2x_2 + 3x_3$$

subject to

$$x_1 + 5x_2 + 2x_3 \leq b_1$$
$$x_1 - 5x_2 - 6x_3 \leq b_2$$
$$x_1, x_2, x_3 \geq 0$$

The following optimal tableau corresponds to specific values of b_1 and b_2:

Basic	x_1	x_2	x_3	x_4	x_5	Solution
z	0	a	7	d	e	15
x_1	1	b	2	1	0	3
x_5	0	c	-8	-1	1	1

Determine the following:

  (a) The right-hand-side values, b_1 and b_2.

  (b) The optimal dual solution.

  (c) The elements $a, b, c, d,$ and e.

*7. The following is the optimal tableau for a maximization LP model with three ($\leq$) constraints and all nonnegative variables. The variables $x_3, x_4,$ and x_5 are the slacks associated with the three constraints. Determine the associated optimal objective value in two different ways by using the primal and dual objective functions.

Basic	x_1	x_2	x_3	x_4	x_5	Solution
z	0	0	0	3	2	?
x_3	0	0	1	1	-1	2
x_2	0	1	0	1	0	6
x_1	1	0	0	-1	1	2

8. Consider the following LP:

$$\text{Maximize } z = x_1 + 2x_2 + 4x_3 - 3x_4$$

subject to

$$x_1 + x_2 + x_3 \qquad = 4$$
$$x_1 + 4x_2 \qquad + x_4 = 8$$
$$x_1, x_2, x_3, x_4 \geq 0$$

Use the dual problem to show that the basic solution (x_1, x_2) is not optimal.

9. Show that Method 1 in Section 4.2.3 for determining the optimal dual values is actually based on the Formula 2 in Section 4.2.4.

4.3   ECONOMIC INTERPRETATION OF DUALITY

The LP problem can be viewed as a resource allocation model that seeks to maximize revenue under limited resources. Looking at the problem from this standpoint, the associated dual problem offers interesting economic interpretations of the resource allocation model.

To formalize the discussion, consider the following representation of the general primal and dual problems:

Primal	Dual
Maximize $z = \sum_{j=1}^{n} c_j x_j$	Minimize $w = \sum_{i=1}^{m} b_i y_i$
subject to	subject to
$\sum_{j=1}^{n} a_{ij} x_j \leq b_i,\ i = 1, 2, \ldots, m$	$\sum_{i=1}^{m} a_{ij} y_i \geq c_j,\ j = 1, 2, \ldots, n$
$x_j \geq 0,\ j=1, 2, \ldots, n$	$y_i \geq 0,\ i = 1, 2, \ldots, m$

Viewed as a resource allocation model, the primal problem has n economic activities and m resources. The coefficient c_j in the primal represents the revenue per unit of activity j. Resource i with availability b_i is consumed at the rate a_{ij} units per unit of activity j.

4.3.1 Economic Interpretation of Dual Variables

Section 4.2.3 states that for any two primal and dual *feasible* solutions, the values of the objective functions, when finite, must satisfy the following inequality:

$$z = \sum_{j=1}^{n} c_j x_j \leq \sum_{i=1}^{m} b_i y_i = w$$

At the optimum, the two objective values are equal—that is, $z = w$.

In terms of the resource allocation model, z represents \$ revenue, and b_i represents available units of resource i. Thus, dimensionally, $z = w$ implies

$$\$\ \text{revenue} = \sum_{i=1}^{m} b_i y_i = \sum_{i=1}^{m} (\text{units of resource } i) \times (\$\text{ per unit of resource } i)$$

This means that the dual variable, y_i, represents the **worth per unit** of resource i.

As stated in Section 3.6, the standard name **dual** (or **shadow**) **price** of resource i replaces the (suggestive) name *worth per unit* in all LP literature and software packages, and hence the standard name is adopted in this book as well.

Using the same dimensional analysis, we can interpret the inequality $z < w$ (for any two feasible primal and dual solution) as

$$(\text{Revenue}) < (\text{Worth of resources})$$

This relationship says that so long as the total revenue from all the activities is less than the worth of the resources, the corresponding primal and dual solutions are not optimal. Optimality is reached only when the resources have been exploited completely. This can happen only when the input (worth of the resources) equals the output (revenue dollars).

Example 4.3-1

The Reddy Mikks model (Example 2.1-1) and its dual are given as follows:

Reddy Mikks primal	Reddy Mikks dual
Maximize $z = 5x_1 + 4x_2$	Minimize $w = 24y_1 + 6y_2 + y_3 + 2y_4$
subject to	subject to
$6x_1 + 4x_2 \leq 24$ (resource 1, $M1$)	$6y_1 + y_2 - y_3 \geq 5$
$x_1 + 2x_2 \leq 6$ (resource 2, $M2$)	$4y_1 + 2y_2 + y_3 + y_4 \geq 4$
$-x_1 + x_2 \leq 1$ (resource 3, market)	$y_1, y_2, y_3, y_4 \geq 0$
$x_2 \leq 2$ (resource 4, demand)	
$x_1, x_2 \geq 0$	
Optimum solution:	Optimum solution:
$x_1 = 3, x_2 = 1.5, z = 21$	$y_1 = .75, y_2 = 0.5, y_3 = y_4 = 0, w = 21$

The Reddy Mikks model deals with the production of two types of paint (interior and exterior) using two raw materials $M1$ and $M2$ (resources 1 and 2) and subject to the market and demand limits represented by the third and fourth constraints. The model determines the amounts (in tons/day) of exterior and interior paints that maximize the daily revenue (expressed in thousands of dollars).

The optimal dual solution shows that the dual price (worth per unit) of raw material $M1$ (resource 1) is $y_1 = .75$ (or \$750 per ton) and that of raw material $M2$ (resource 2) is $y_2 = .5$ (or \$500 per ton). These results hold true for specific *feasibility ranges* as was shown in Section 3.6. For resources 3 and 4, representing the market and demand limits, the dual prices are both zero, which indicates that their associated resources are abundant (i.e., they are not critical in determining the optimum and, hence, their worth per unit, or dual price, is zero).

PROBLEM SET 4.3A

1. In Example 4.3-1, compute the change in the optimal revenue in each of the following cases (use TORA output to obtain the feasibility ranges):

   (a) The constraint for raw material $M1$ (resource 1) is $6x_1 + 4x_2 \leq 20$.

   (b) The constraint for raw material $M2$ (resource 2) is $x_1 + 2x_2 \leq 5$.

   (c) The market condition represented by resource 4 is $x_2 \leq 4$.

2.* NWAC Electronics manufactures four types of simple cables for a defense contractor. Each cable must go through four sequential operations: splicing, soldering, sleeving, and inspection. The following table gives the pertinent data of the situation.

	Minutes per unit				
Cable	Splicing	Soldering	Sleeving	Inspection	Unit revenue (\$)
SC320	10.5	20.4	3.2	5.0	9.40
SC325	9.3	24.6	2.5	5.0	10.80
SC340	11.6	17.7	3.6	5.0	8.75
SC370	8.2	26.5	5.5	5.0	7.80
Daily capacity (minutes)	4800.0	9600.0	4700.0	4500.0	

The contractor guarantees a minimum production level of 100 units for each of the four cables.

(a) Formulate the problem as a linear programming model, and determine the optimum production schedule.

(b) Based on the dual prices, do you recommend making increases in the daily capacities of any of the four operations? Explain.

(c) Does the minimum production requirements for the four cables represent an advantage or a disadvantage for NWAC Electronics? Provide an explanation based on the dual prices.

(d) Can the present unit contribution to revenue as specified by the dual price be guaranteed if we increase the capacity of soldering by 10%?

3. BagCo produces leather jackets and handbags. A jacket requires 8 m^2 of leather, and a handbag only 2 m^2. The labor requirements for the two products are 12 and 5 hours, respectively. The current weekly supplies of leather and labor are limited to 600 m^2 and 925 hours. The company sells the jackets and handbags at \$350 and \$120, respectively. The objective is to determine the production schedule that maximizes the net revenue.

(a) Determine the optimum solution.

(b) BagCo is considering an expansion of production. What is the maximum purchase price the company should pay for additional leather? For additional labor?

4.3.2   Economic Interpretation of Dual Constraints

The economic meaning of the dual constraints can be achieved by using Formula 2 in Section 4.2.4, which states that at any primal iteration,

$$\text{Objective coefficient of } x_j = \left(\begin{array}{c}\text{Left-hand side of}\\ \text{dual constraint } j\end{array}\right) - \left(\begin{array}{c}\text{Right-hand side of}\\ \text{dual constraint } j\end{array}\right)$$

$$= \sum_{i=1}^{m} a_{ij}y_i - c_j$$

We use dimensional analysis once again to interpret this equation. The revenue per unit, c_j, of activity j is in dollars per unit. Hence, for consistency, the quantity $\sum_{i=1}^{m} a_{ij}y_i$ must also be in dollars per unit. Next, because c_j represents revenue, the quantity $\sum_{i=1}^{m} a_{ij}y_i$, with opposite sign, must represent cost. Thus we have

$$\$ \text{ cost} = \sum_{i=1}^{m} a_{ij}y_i = \sum_{i=1}^{m} \left(\begin{array}{c}\text{Usage of resource } i\\ \text{per unit of activity } j\end{array}\right) \times \left(\begin{array}{c}\text{Cost per unit}\\ \text{of resource } i\end{array}\right)$$

The conclusion is that the dual variable y_i represents what is known in the LP literature as the **imputed cost** per unit of resource i, and we can think of the quantity $\sum_{i=1}^{m} a_{ij}y_i$ as the imputed cost of all the resources needed to produce one unit of activity j. As stated in Section 3.6, the quantity $\sum_{i=1}^{m} a_{ij}y_i - c_j$ (= imputed cost of activity j − c_j) is known by the standard name **reduced cost** of activity j. The maximization optimality condition of the simplex method says that an increase in the level of an unused (nonbasic) activity j can improve revenue only if its *reduced cost* is negative. In terms of the preceding interpretation, this condition states that

$$\left(\begin{array}{c}\text{Imputed cost of} \\ \text{resources used by} \\ \text{one unit of activity } j\end{array}\right) < \left(\begin{array}{c}\text{Revenue per unit} \\ \text{of activity } j\end{array}\right)$$

Thus, the maximization optimality condition says that it is economically advantageous to increase the level of an activity if its unit revenue exceeds its unit imputed cost.

Example 4.3-2

TOYCO assembles three types of toys: trains, trucks, and cars, using three operations. Available assembly times for the three operations are 430, 460, and 420 minutes per day, respectively, and the revenues per toy train, truck, and car are \$3, \$2, and \$5, respectively. The assembly times per train for the three operations are 1, 3, and 1 minutes, respectively. The corresponding times per truck and per car are $(2, 0, 4)$ and $(1, 2, 0)$ minutes (a zero time indicates that the operation is not used).

Letting x_1, x_2, and x_3 represent the daily number of units assembled of trains, trucks, and cars, the associated LP model and its dual are given as follows:

TOYCO primal	TOYCO dual
Maximize $z = 3x_1 + 2x_2 + 5x_3$	Minimize $w = 430y_1 + 460y_2 + 420y_3$
subject to	subject to
$x_1 + 2x_2 + x_3 \leq 430$ (Operation 1)	$y_1 + 3y_2 + y_3 \geq 3$
$3x_1 \quad\quad + 2x_3 \leq 460$ (Operation 2)	$2y_1 \quad\quad + 4y_3 \geq 2$
$x_1 + 4x_2 \quad\quad \leq 420$ (Operation 3)	$y_1 + 2y_2 \quad\quad \geq 5$
$x_1, x_2, x_3 \geq 0$	$y_1, y_2, y_3 \geq 0$
Optimal solution:	Optimal solution:
$x_1 = 0, x_2 = 100, x_3 = 230, z = \$1350$	$y_1 = 1, y_2 = 2, y_3 = 0, w = \$1350$

The optimal primal solution calls for producing no toy trains, 100 toy trucks, and 230 toy cars.

Suppose that TOYCO is interested in producing toy trains (x_1) as well. How can this be achieved? Looking at the *reduced cost* for x_1, a toy train becomes attractive economically only if its unit imputed cost is strictly less than its unit revenue. TOYCO can achieve this by increasing the unit price. It can also decrease the imputed cost of the consumed resources $(= y_1 + 3y_2 + y_3)$.

A decrease in the unit imputed cost entails reducing the assembly times used by a unit toy train on the three operations. Let r_1, r_2, and r_3 represent the reduction ratios on operations 1, 2, and 3, respectively. The goal is to determine the values of r_1, r_2, and r_3 such that the new imputed cost per toy train is less than its unit revenue—that is,

$$1(1 - r_1)y_1 + 3(1 - r_2)y_2 + 1(1 - r_3)y_3 < 3$$

$$0 \leq r_1 \leq 1, 0 \leq r_2 \leq 1, 0 \leq r_3 \leq 1$$

For the optimal dual values, $y_1 = 1$, $y_2 = 2$, and $y_3 = 0$, this inequality reduces to

$$r_1 + 6r_2 > 4, 0 \leq r_1 \leq 1, 0 \leq r_2 \leq 1$$

Any values of r_1 and r_2 that satisfy these conditions will make toy trains profitable. Note, however, that this goal may not be attainable because it requires impractically large reductions in the times of operations 1 and 2. For example, even a 50% reduction (i.e., $r_1 = r_2 = .5$) fails to satisfy the given condition. The logical conclusion then is that TOYCO should not produce toy trains unless the time reductions are accompanied with increase in unit revenue.

PROBLEM SET 4.3B

1. In Example 4.3-2, suppose that for toy trains the per-unit time of operation 2 can be reduced from 3 minutes to at most 1.3 minutes. By how much must the per-unit time of operation 1 be reduced to make toy trains just profitable?

*2. In Example 4.3-2, suppose that TOYCO is studying the possibility of introducing a fourth toy: fire trucks. The assembly does not make use of operation 1. Its unit assembly times on operations 2 and 3 are 1 and 3 minutes, respectively. The revenue per unit is $4. Would you advise TOYCO to introduce the new product?

*3. JoShop uses lathes and drill presses to produce four types of machine parts, PP1, PP2, PP3, and PP4. The following table summarizes the pertinent data.

Machine	Machining time in minutes per unit of				
	PP1	PP2	PP3	PP4	Capacity (min)
Lathes	2	5	3	4	5300
Drill presses	3	4	6	4	5300
Unit revenue ($)	3	6	5	4	

For the parts that are not produced by the present optimum solution, determine the rate of deterioration in the optimum revenue per unit increase of each of these products.

4. Consider the optimal solution of JoShop in Problem 3. The company estimates that for each part that is not produced (per the optimum solution), an across-the-board 20% reduction in machining time can be realized through process improvements. Would these improvements make these parts profitable? If not, what is the minimum percentage reduction needed to realize profitability?

4.4   ADDITIONAL SIMPLEX ALGORITHMS

Chapter 3 presents the (primal) simplex algorithm that starts feasible and continues to be feasible until the optimum is reached. This section presents two additional algorithms: The **dual simplex** starts *infeasible* (but better than optimal) and remains infeasible until feasibility is restored, and the **generalized simplex** combines the primal and dual simplex methods, starting both nonoptimal and infeasible. All three algorithms are used with post-optimal analysis in Section 4.5.

4.4.1   Dual Simplex Algorithm

The dual simplex method starts with a better than optimal and infeasible basic solution. The optimality and feasibility conditions are designed to preserve the optimality of the basic solutions as the solution move toward feasibility.

Dual feasibility condition.   The leaving variable, x_r, is the basic variable having the most negative value (ties are broken arbitrarily). If all the basic variables are nonnegative, the algorithm ends.[1]

Dual optimality condition.   Given that x_r is the leaving variable, let $\bar{c}_j$ be the reduced cost of nonbasic variable x_j and α_{rj} the constraint coefficient in the x_r-row and x_j-column of the tableau. The entering variable is the nonbasic variable with $\alpha_{rj} < 0$ that corresponds to

$$\min_{\text{Nonbasic } x_j} \left\{ \left| \frac{\bar{c}_j}{\alpha_{rj}} \right|, \alpha_{rj} < 0 \right\}$$

(Ties are broken arbitrarily.) If $\alpha_{rj} \geq 0$ for all nonbasic x_j, the problem has no feasible solution.

To start the LP optimal and infeasible, two requirements must be met:

1. The objective function must satisfy the optimality condition of the regular simplex method (Chapter 3).
2. All the constraints must be of the type ($\leq$).

Inequalities of the type ($\geq$) are converted to ($\leq$) by multiplying both sides of the inequality by -1. If the LP includes ($=$) constraints, the equation can be replaced by two inequalities. For example, $x_1 + x_2 = 1$ is equivalent to $x_1 + x_2 \leq 1, x_1 + x_2 \geq 1$ or $x_1 + x_2 \leq 1, -x_1 - x_2 \leq -1$. The starting solution is infeasible if at least one of the right-hand sides of the inequalities is negative.

Example 4.4-1

$$\text{Minimize } z = 3x_1 + 2x_2 + x_3$$

subject to

$$3x_1 + x_2 + x_3 \geq 3$$

$$-3x_1 + 3x_2 + x_3 \geq 6$$

$$x_1 + x_2 + x_3 \leq 3$$

$$x_1, x_2, x_3 \geq 0$$

---

[1]As explained in Section 3.7, a different feasibility condition, called the *steepest edge*, has so improved the computational efficiency of the dual simplex algorithm that it is now the dominant (simplex-based) algorithm for solving LPs in all commercial codes.

In the present example, the first two inequalities are multiplied by –1 to convert them to ($\leq$) constraints. The starting tableau is thus given as follows:

Basic	x_1	x_2	x_3	x_4	x_5	x_6	Solution
z	-3	-2	-1	0	0	0	0
x_4	-3	-1	-1	1	0	0	-3
x_5	3	-3	-1	0	1	0	-6
x_6	1	1	1	0	0	1	3

The tableau is optimal because all the reduced costs in the z-row are ≤ 0 ($\bar{c}_1 = -3$, $\bar{c}_2 = -2$, $\bar{c}_3 = -1$, $\bar{c}_4 = 0$, $\bar{c}_5 = 0$, $\bar{c}_6 = 0$). It is also infeasible because at least one of the basic variables is negative ($x_4 = -3$, $x_5 = -6$, $x_6 = 3$).

According to the dual feasibility condition, $x_5 (= -6)$ is the leaving variable. The next table shows how the dual optimality condition is used to determine the entering variable.

	$j = 1$	$j = 2$	$j = 3$
Nonbasic variable	x_1	x_2	x_3
z-row ($\bar{c}_j$)	-3	-2	-1
x_5-row, α_{4j}	3	-3	-1
Ratio, $\left\|\frac{\bar{c}_j}{\alpha_{5j}}\right\|$, $\alpha_{5j} < 0$	—	$\frac{2}{3}$	1

The ratios show that x_2 is the entering variable.

The next tableau is obtained by using the familiar row operations, which give

Basic	x_1	x_2	x_3	x_4	x_5	x_6	Solution
z	-5	0	$-\frac{1}{3}$	0	$-\frac{2}{3}$	0	4
x_4	-4	0	$-\frac{2}{3}$	1	$-\frac{1}{3}$	0	-1
x_2	-1	1	$\frac{1}{3}$	0	$-\frac{1}{3}$	0	2
x_6	2	0	$\frac{2}{3}$	0	$\frac{1}{3}$	1	1
Ratio	$\frac{5}{4}$	—	$\frac{1}{2}$	—	2	—	

The preceding tableau shows that x_4 leaves and x_3 enters, thus yielding the following tableau, which is both optimal and feasible:

Basic	x_1	x_2	x_3	x_4	x_5	x_6	Solution
z	-3	0	0	$-\frac{1}{2}$	$-\frac{1}{2}$	0	$\frac{9}{2}$
x_3	6	0	1	$-\frac{3}{2}$	$\frac{1}{2}$	0	$\frac{3}{2}$
x_2	-3	1	0	$\frac{1}{2}$	$-\frac{1}{2}$	0	$\frac{3}{2}$
x_6	-2	0	0	1	0	1	0

Notice how the dual simplex works. In all the iterations, optimality is maintained (all reduced costs are ≤ 0) as each new iteration moves the solution toward feasibility. At iteration 3, feasibility is restored for the first time, and the process ends with the optimal feasible solution given as $x_1 = 0, x_2 = \frac{3}{2}, x_2 = \frac{3}{2}$, and $z = \frac{9}{2}$.

TORA moment.

TORA provides a tutorial module for the dual simplex method. From the SOLVE/MODIFY menu select Solve $\Rightarrow$ Algebraic $\Rightarrow$ Iterations $\Rightarrow$ Dual Simplex. Remember that you need to convert $(=)$ constraints to inequalities. You do not need to convert $(\geq)$ constraints because TORA will do the conversion internally.

PROBLEM SET 4.4A[2]

1. Consider the solution space in Figure 4.3, where it is desired to find the optimum extreme point that uses the *dual* simplex method to minimize $z = 2x_1 + x_2$. The optimal solution occurs at point $F = (0.5, 1.5)$ on the graph.

    (a) Can the dual simplex start at point A?

    ***(b)** If the starting basic (infeasible but better than optimum) solution is given by point G with the optimum given by point F, would it be possible for the iterations of the dual simplex method to follow the path $G \rightarrow E \rightarrow F$? Explain.

    (c) If the starting basic (infeasible) solution starts at point L, identify a possible path of the dual simplex method that leads to the optimum feasible point at point F.

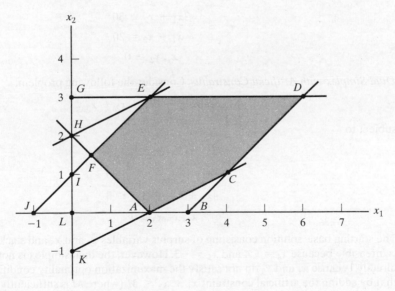

FIGURE 4.3

Solution space for Problem 1, Set 4.4a

---

[2]You are encouraged to use TORA's tutorial mode where possible to avoid the tedious simplex computations.

2. Generate the dual simplex iterations for the following problems (using TORA for convenience), and trace the path of the algorithm on the graphical solution space.

(a) Minimize $z = 2x_1 + 3x_2$

subject to

$$2x_1 + 2x_2 \leq 3$$
$$x_1 + 2x_2 \geq 1$$
$$x_1, x_2 \geq 0$$

(b) Minimize $z = 5x_1 + 6x_2$

subject to

$$x_1 + x_2 \geq 20$$
$$4x_1 + x_2 \geq 40$$
$$x_1, x_2 \geq 0$$

(c) Minimize $z = 4x_1 + 2x_2$

subject to

$$x_1 + x_2 = 10$$
$$3x_1 - x_2 \geq 20$$
$$x_1, x_2 \geq 0$$

(d) Minimize $z = 2x_1 + 3x_2$

subject to

$$2x_1 + x_2 \geq 30$$
$$x_1 + x_2 = 20$$
$$x_1, x_2 \geq 0$$

3. *Dual Simplex with Artificial Constraints.* Consider the following problem:

$$\text{Maximize } z = 2x_1 - x_2 + x_3$$

subject to

$$2x_1 + 3x_2 - 5x_3 \geq 4$$
$$-x_1 + 9x_2 - x_3 \geq 3$$
$$4x_1 + 6x_2 + 3x_3 \leq 8$$
$$x_1, x_2, x_3 \geq 0$$

The starting basic solution consisting of surplus variables x_4 and x_5 and slack variable x_6 is infeasible because $x_4 = -4$ and $x_5 = -3$. However, the dual simplex is not applicable directly, because x_1 and x_3 do not satisfy the maximization optimality condition. Show that by adding the artificial constraint $x_1 + x_3 \leq M$ (where M is sufficiently large not to eliminate any feasible points in the original solution space), and then using the new constraint as a pivot row, the selection of x_1 as the entering variable (because it has the most negative objective coefficient) will render an all-optimal objective row. Next, carry out the regular dual simplex method on the modified problem.

4. Using the artificial constraint procedure introduced in Problem 3, solve the following problems by the dual simplex method. In each case, indicate whether the resulting solution is feasible, infeasible, or unbounded.

(a) Maximize $z = 2x_3$

subject to

$$-x_1 + 2x_2 - 2x_3 \geq 4$$
$$-x_1 + x_2 + x_3 \leq 2$$
$$2x_1 - x_2 + 4x_3 \leq 5$$
$$x_1, x_2, x_3 \geq 0$$

(b) Maximize $z = x_1 - 3x_2$

subject to

$$x_1 - x_2 \leq 20$$
$$x_1 + x_2 \geq 40$$
$$2x_1 - 2x_2 \geq 30$$
$$x_1, x_2 \geq 0$$

*(c) Minimize $z = -x_1 + x_2$

subject to

$$x_1 - 4x_2 \geq 5$$
$$x_1 - 3x_2 \leq 1$$
$$2x_1 - 5x_2 \geq 1$$
$$x_1, x_2 \geq 0$$

(d) Maximize $z = 2x_3$

subject to

$$-x_1 + 3x_2 - 7x_3 \geq 50$$
$$-x_1 + x_2 - x_3 \leq 10$$
$$3x_1 + x_2 - 10x_3 \leq 80$$
$$x_1, x_2, x_3 \geq 0$$

5. Solve the following LP in three different ways (use TORA for convenience). Which method appears to be the most efficient computationally?

$$\text{Minimize } z = 6x_1 + 7x_2 + 3x_3 + 5x_4$$

subject to

$$5x_1 + 6x_2 - 3x_3 + 4x_4 \geq 12$$
$$x_2 - 5x_3 - 6x_4 \geq 10$$
$$2x_1 + 5x_2 + x_3 + x_4 \geq 8$$
$$x_1, x_2, x_3, x_4 \geq 0$$

4.4.2   Generalized Simplex Algorithm

The (primal) simplex algorithm in Chapter 3 starts feasible but nonoptimal. The dual simplex (Section 4.4.1) starts better than optimal and infeasible. What if an LP model starts both nonoptimal and infeasible? Of course we can use artificial variables and artificial constraints to secure a starting solution. This is not mandatory, however, because the key idea of both the primal and dual simplex methods is that the optimum feasible solution, when finite, always occurs at a corner point (or a basic solution). This suggests that a new simplex algorithm can be developed based on tandem use of the dual simplex and the primal simplex methods. First, use the dual algorithm to get rid of infeasibility (without worrying about optimality). Once feasibility is restored, the primal simplex can be used to find the optimum. Alternatively, we can first apply the primal simplex to secure optimality (without worrying about feasibility) and then use the dual simplex to seek feasibility.

Example 4.4-2

Consider the maximization LP model of Problem 4(a), Set 4.4a. The model can be put in the following tableau format in which the starting basic solution (x_4, x_5, x_6) is both nonoptimal (because of nonbasic x_3) and infeasible (because of basic x_4).

Basic	x_1	x_2	x_3	x_4	x_5	x_6	Solution
z	0	0	−2	0	0	0	0
x_4	1	−2	2	1	0	0	−8
x_5	−1	1	1	0	1	0	4
x_6	2	−1	4	0	0	1	10

We can solve the problem without the use of any artificial variables or artificial constraints, first securing feasibility using the dual simplex and then seeking optimality using the primal simplex. The dual simplex selects x_4 as the leaving variable. The entering variable can be *any* nonbasic variable with a negative constraint coefficient in the x_4-row. In the present example, x_2 has a negative coefficient in the x_4-row and is selected as the entering variable. The next tableau is thus computed as

Basic	x_1	x_2	x_3	x_4	x_5	x_6	Solution
z	0	0	−2	0	0	0	0
x_2	$-\frac{1}{2}$	1	−1	$-\frac{1}{2}$	0	0	4
x_5	$-\frac{1}{2}$	0	2	$\frac{1}{2}$	1	0	0
x_6	$\frac{3}{2}$	0	3	$-\frac{1}{2}$	0	1	14

The new solution is now feasible but nonoptimal, and we can use the primal simplex to determine the optimal solution. In general, had we not restored feasibility in the preceding tableau, we would repeat the procedure as necessary until feasibility is satisfied or until there is evidence that the problem has no feasible solution (which happens if a basic variable is negative and all its constraint coefficients are nonnegative).

Remarks. The essence of Example 4.4-2 is that the simplex method is not rigid. The literature abounds with variations of the simplex method (e.g., the primal–dual method, the symmetrical method, the criss-cross method, and the multiplex method) that give the impression that each procedure is different, when, in fact, they all seek a corner-point solution, with a slant toward automated computations and, perhaps, computational efficiency.

PROBLEM SET 4.4B

1. The LP model of Problem 4(c), Set 4.4a, has no feasible solution. Show how this condition is detected by the *generalized simplex procedure*.
2. The LP model of Problem 4(d), Set 4.4a, has no bounded solution. Show how this condition is detected by the *generalized simplex procedure*.

4.5   POST-OPTIMAL ANALYSIS

In Section 3.6, we dealt with the sensitivity of the optimum solution by determining the ranges for the different LP parameters that would keep the optimum basic variables unchanged. In this section, we deal with making changes in the parameters of the model and finding the new optimum solution. Take, for example, a case in the poultry industry, where an LP model is commonly used to determine the optimal feed mix per broiler (see Example 2.2-2). The weekly consumption per broiler varies from .26 lb (120 grams) for a 1-week-old bird to 2.1 lb (950 grams) for an 8-week-old bird. Additionally, the cost of the ingredients in the mix may change periodically. These changes require periodic re-calculation of the optimum solution. *Post-optimal analysis* determines the new solution in an efficient way. The new computations are rooted in the use duality and the primal–dual relationships given in Section 4.2.

The following table lists the cases that can arise in post-optimal analysis and the actions needed to obtain the new solution (assuming one exists):

Condition after parameters change	Recommended action
Current solution remains optimal and feasible.	No further action is necessary.
Current solution becomes infeasible.	Use dual simplex to recover feasibility.
Current solution becomes nonoptimal.	Use primal simplex to recover optimality.
Current solution becomes both nonoptimal and infeasible.	Use the generalized simplex method to recover optimality and feasibility.

The first three cases are investigated in this section. The fourth case, being a combination of cases 2 and 3, is treated in Problem 6, Set 4.5a.

The TOYCO model of Example 4.3-2 will be used to explain the different procedures. Recall that the problem deals with the assembly of three types of toys: trains, trucks, and cars. Three operations are involved in the assembly. The model and its dual are repeated here for convenience.

TOYCO primal	TOYCO dual
Maximize $z = 3x_1 + 2x_2 + 5x_3$	Minimize $z = 430y_1 + 460y_2 + 420y_3$
subject to	subject to
$x_1 + 2x_2 + x_3 \leq 430$ (Operation 1)	$y_1 + 3y_2 + y_3 \geq 3$
$3x_1 \qquad + 2x_3 \leq 460$ (Operation 2)	$2y_1 \qquad + 4y_3 \geq 2$
$x_1 + 4x_2 \qquad \leq 420$ (Operation 3)	$y_1 + 2y_2 \qquad \geq 5$
$x_1, x_2, x_3 \geq 0$	$y_1, y_2, y_3 \geq 0$
Optimal solution:	Optimal solution:
$x_1 = 0, x_2 = 100, x_3 = 230, z = \$1350$	$y_1 = 1, y_2 = 2, y_3 = 0, w = \$1350$

The associated optimum tableau for the primal is given as

Basic	x_1	x_2	x_3	x_4	x_5	x_6	Solution
z	4	0	0	1	2	0	1350
x_2	$-\frac{1}{4}$	1	0	$\frac{1}{2}$	$-\frac{1}{4}$	0	100
x_3	$\frac{3}{2}$	0	1	0	$\frac{1}{2}$	0	230
x_6	2	0	0	-2	1	1	20

4.5.1 Changes Affecting Feasibility

The feasibility of the current optimum solution is affected only if the right-hand side of the constraints is changed, or a new constraint is added to the model. In both cases, infeasibility occurs when one or more of the current basic variables become negative.

Changes in the right-hand side. This change requires recomputing the right-hand side of the tableau using Formula 1 in Section 4.2.4:

$$\begin{pmatrix} \text{New right-hand side of} \\ \text{tableau in iteration } i \end{pmatrix} = \begin{pmatrix} \text{Inverse in} \\ \text{iteration } i \end{pmatrix} \times \begin{pmatrix} \text{New right-hand} \\ \text{side of constraints} \end{pmatrix}$$

Recall that the right-hand side of the tableau gives the values of the basic variables.

Example 4.5-1

Situation 1. Suppose that TOYCO is increasing the daily capacity of operations 1, 2, and 3 to 600, 640, and 590 minutes, respectively. How would this change affect the total revenue?

With these increases, the only change that will take place in the optimum tableau is the right-hand side of the constraints (and the optimum objective value). Thus, the new basic solution is computed as follows:

$$\begin{pmatrix} x_2 \\ x_3 \\ x_6 \end{pmatrix} = \begin{pmatrix} \frac{1}{2} & -\frac{1}{4} & 0 \\ 0 & \frac{1}{2} & 0 \\ -2 & 1 & 1 \end{pmatrix} \begin{pmatrix} 600 \\ 640 \\ 590 \end{pmatrix} = \begin{pmatrix} 140 \\ 320 \\ 30 \end{pmatrix}$$

Thus, the current basic variables, x_2, x_3, and x_6, remain feasible at the new values 140, 320, and 30 units, respectively. The associated optimum revenue is $1880.

Situation 2. Although the new solution is appealing from the standpoint of increased revenue, TOYCO recognizes that its implementation may take time. Another proposal shifts the slack capacity of operation 3 ($x_6 = 20$ minutes) to the capacity of operation 1. How would this change impact the optimum solution?

The capacity mix of the three operations changes to 450, 460, and 400 minutes, respectively. The resulting solution is

$$\begin{pmatrix} x_2 \\ x_3 \\ x_6 \end{pmatrix} = \begin{pmatrix} \frac{1}{2} & -\frac{1}{4} & 0 \\ 0 & \frac{1}{2} & 0 \\ -2 & 1 & 1 \end{pmatrix} \begin{pmatrix} 450 \\ 460 \\ 400 \end{pmatrix} = \begin{pmatrix} 110 \\ 230 \\ -40 \end{pmatrix}$$

The resulting solution is infeasible because $x_6 = -40$, which requires applying the dual simplex method to recover feasibility. First, we modify the right-hand side of the tableau as shown by the shaded column. Notice that the associated value of $z = 3 \times 0 + 2 \times 110 + 5 \times 230 = \$1370$.

Basic	x_1	x_2	x_3	x_4	x_5	x_6	Solution
z	4	0	0	1	2	0	1370
x_2	$-\frac{1}{4}$	1	0	$\frac{1}{2}$	$-\frac{1}{4}$	0	110
x_3	$\frac{3}{2}$	0	1	0	$\frac{1}{2}$	0	230
x_6	2	0	0	-2	1	1	-40

From the dual simplex, x_6 leaves and x_4 enters, which yields the following optimal feasible tableau (in general, the dual simplex may take more than one iteration to recover feasibility).

Basic	x_1	x_2	x_3	x_4	x_5	x_6	Solution
z	5	0	0	0	$\frac{5}{2}$	$\frac{1}{2}$	1350
x_2	$\frac{1}{4}$	1	0	0	0	$\frac{1}{4}$	100
x_3	$\frac{3}{2}$	0	1	0	$\frac{1}{2}$	0	230
x_4	-1	0	0	1	$-\frac{1}{2}$	$-\frac{1}{2}$	20

The optimum solution (in terms of x_1, x_2, and x_3) remains the same as in the original model. This means that the proposed shift in capacity allocation is not advantageous because it simply shifts the surplus capacity from operation 3 to a surplus capacity in operation 1. The conclusion then is that operation 2 is the bottleneck, and it may be advantageous to shift the surplus to operation 2 instead (see Problem 1, Set 4.5a).

PROBLEM SET 4.5A

1. In the TOYCO model listed at the start of Section 4.5, would it be more advantageous to assign the 20-minute excess capacity of operation 3 to operation 2 instead of operation 1?

2. Suppose that TOYCO wants to change the capacities of the three operations according to the following cases:

$$
\textbf{(a)} \begin{pmatrix} 460 \\ 500 \\ 400 \end{pmatrix} \quad
\textbf{(b)} \begin{pmatrix} 500 \\ 400 \\ 600 \end{pmatrix} \quad
\textbf{(c)} \begin{pmatrix} 300 \\ 800 \\ 200 \end{pmatrix} \quad
\textbf{(d)} \begin{pmatrix} 450 \\ 700 \\ 350 \end{pmatrix}
$$

Use post-optimal analysis to determine the optimum solution in each case.

3. Consider the Reddy Mikks model of Example 2.1-1. Its optimal tableau is given in Example 3.3-1. If the daily availabilities of raw materials $M1$ and $M2$ are increased to 35 and 10 tons, respectively, use post-optimal analysis to determine the new optimal solution.

*4. The Ozark Farm has 20,000 broilers that are fed for 8 weeks before being marketed. The weekly feed per broiler varies according to the following schedule:

Week	1	2	3	4	5	6	7	8
lb/broiler	.26	.48	.75	1.00	1.30	1.60	1.90	2.10

For the broiler to reach a desired weight gain in 8 weeks, the feedstuffs must satisfy specific nutritional needs. Although a typical list of feedstuffs is large, for simplicity we will limit the model to three items only: limestone, corn, and soybean meal. The nutritional needs will also be limited to three types: calcium, protein, and fiber. The following table summarizes the nutritive content of the selected ingredients together with the cost data.

Ingredient	Content (lb) per lb of			$ per lb
	Calcium	Protein	Fiber	
Limestone	.380	.00	.00	.12
Corn	.001	.09	.02	.45
Soybean meal	.002	.50	.08	1.60

The feed mix must contain at least .8% but not more than 1.2% calcium, at least 22% protein, and at most 5% crude fiber.

Solve the LP for week 1 and then use post-optimal analysis to develop an optimal schedule for the remaining 7 weeks.

5. Show that the 100% feasibility rule in Problem 12, Set 3.6c (Chapter 3) is based on the condition

$$
\begin{pmatrix} \text{Optimum} \\ \text{inverse} \end{pmatrix} \begin{pmatrix} \text{Original right-hand} \\ \text{side vector} \end{pmatrix} \geq 0
$$

6. *Post-optimal Analysis for Cases Affecting Both Optimality and Feasibility.* Suppose that you are given the following simultaneous changes in the Reddy Mikks model: The revenue per ton of exterior and interior paints are $2000 and $5000, respectively, and

the maximum daily availabilities of raw materials, $M1$ and $M2$, are 35 and 10 tons, respectively.

(a) Show that the proposed changes will render the current optimal solution both nonoptimal and infeasible.

(b) Use the *generalized simplex algorithm* (Section 4.4.2) to determine the new optimal feasible solution.

Addition of a new constraint. The addition of a new constraint can never improve the current optimum objective value. If the new constraint is *redundant*, it will have no effect on the current solution. Else, the current solution does not satisfy the new constraint, and a new solution must be determined by the dual simplex method.

Example 4.5-2

Situation 1. Suppose that TOYCO is changing the design of its toys and that the change will require the addition of a fourth assembly operation. The daily capacity of the new operation is 500 minutes and the times per unit for the three products on this operation are 3, 1, and 1 minutes, respectively.

The new constraint for operation 4 is

$$3x_1 + x_2 + x_3 \le 500$$

This constraint is redundant because it is satisfied by the current optimum solution $x_1 = 0$, $x_2 = 100$, and $x_3 = 230$. Hence, the current optimum solution remains unchanged.

Situation 2. Suppose, instead, that TOYCO unit times on the fourth operation are changed to 3, 3, and 1 minutes, respectively. All the remaining data of the model remain the same.

The new constraint for operation 4 is

$$3x_1 + 3x_2 + x_3 \le 500$$

This constraint is not satisfied by the current optimum solution, and it is added to the current optimum tableau as follows (x_7 is a slack variable):

Basic	x_1	x_2	x_3	x_4	x_5	x_6	x_7	Solution
z	4	0	0	1	2	0	0	1350
x_2	$-\frac{1}{4}$	1	0	$\frac{1}{2}$	$-\frac{1}{4}$	0	0	100
x_3	$\frac{3}{2}$	0	1	0	$\frac{1}{2}$	0	0	230
x_6	2	0	0	-2	1	1	0	20
x_7	3	3	1	0	0	0	1	500

The tableau shows that $x_7 = 500$, which is not consistent with the values of x_2 and x_3 in the rest of the tableau. The reason is that the basic variables x_2 and x_3 have not been substituted out in the new constraint. This substitution is achieved by performing the following operation:

$$\text{New } x_7\text{-row} = \text{Old } x_7\text{-row} - [3 \times (x_2\text{-row}) + 1 \times (x_3\text{-row})]$$

This operation is exactly the same as using the substitution

$$x_2 = 100 - (-\tfrac{1}{4} x_1 + \tfrac{1}{2} x_4 - \tfrac{1}{4} x_5)$$

$$x_3 = 230 - (\tfrac{3}{2} x_1 + \tfrac{1}{2} x_5)$$

The new tableau is thus given as

Basic	x_1	x_2	x_3	x_4	x_5	x_6	x_7	Solution
z	4	0	0	1	2	0	0	1350
x_2	$-\tfrac{1}{4}$	1	0	$\tfrac{1}{2}$	$-\tfrac{1}{4}$	0	0	100
x_3	$\tfrac{3}{2}$	0	1	0	$\tfrac{1}{2}$	0	0	230
x_6	2	0	0	-2	1	1	0	20
x_7	$\tfrac{9}{4}$	0	0	$-\tfrac{3}{2}$	$\tfrac{1}{4}$	0	1	-30

Application of the dual simplex method will produce the new optimum solution $x_1 = 0, x_2 = 90$, $x_3 = 230$, and $z = \$1370$ (verify!). The solution shows that the addition of operation 4 worsens the revenues from $1350 to $1330.

PROBLEM SET 4.5B

1. In the TOYCO model, suppose the fourth operation has the following specifications: The maximum production rate based on 480 minutes a day is 120 units of product 1, 480 units of product 2, or 240 units of product 3. Determine the optimal solution, assuming that the daily capacity is limited to

   *(a) 565 minutes.

   (b) 548 minutes.

2. *Secondary Constraints*. Instead of solving a problem using all of its constraints, we can start by identifying the so-called *secondary constraints*. These are the constraints that we suspect are least restrictive in terms of the optimum solution. The model is solved using the remaining (primary) constraints. We may then add the secondary constraints one at a time. A secondary constraint is discarded if it satisfies the available optimum. The process is repeated until all the secondary constraints are accounted for.

   Apply the proposed procedure to the following LP:

   $$\text{Maximize } z = 5x_1 + 6x_2 + 3x_2$$

   subject to

   $$5x_1 + 5x_2 + 3x_3 \leq 50$$
   $$x_1 + x_2 - x_3 \leq 20$$
   $$7x_1 + 6x_2 - 9x_3 \leq 30$$
   $$5x_1 + 5x_2 + 5x_3 \leq 35$$
   $$12x_1 + 6x_2 \leq 90$$
   $$x_2 - 9x_3 \leq 20$$
   $$x_1, x_2, x_3 \geq 0$$

4.5.2   Changes Affecting Optimality

This section considers making changes in the objective coefficients and the addition of a new economic activity (variable).

Changes in the objective function coefficients.   These changes affect only the optimality of the solution and require recomputing the z-row coefficients (reduced costs) according to the following procedure:
1. Compute the dual values using Method 2, Section 4.2.3.
2. Substitute the new dual values in Formula 2, Section 4.2.4, to determine the new reduced costs (z-row coefficients).

If the new z-row satisfies the optimality condition, the solution remains unchanged (the optimum objective value may change, however). If it is not, the primal simplex is used to recover optimality.

Example 4.5-3

Situation 1.   In the TOYCO model, suppose that the company has a new pricing policy to meet the competition. The unit revenues are \$2, \$3, and \$4 for train, truck, and car toys, respectively.
The new objective function is

$$\text{Maximize } z = 2x_1 + 3x_2 + 4x_3$$

Thus,

$$(\text{New objective coefficients of basic } x_2, x_3, \text{ and } x_6) = (3, 4, 0)$$

Using Method 2, Section 4.2.3, the new dual variables are computed as

$$(y_1, y_2, y_3) = (3, 4, 0)\begin{pmatrix} \frac{1}{2} & -\frac{1}{4} & 0 \\ 0 & \frac{1}{2} & 0 \\ -2 & 1 & 1 \end{pmatrix} = \left(\frac{3}{2}, \frac{5}{4}, 0\right)$$

The z-row coefficients are determined as the difference between the left- and right-hand sides of the dual constraints (Formula 2, Section 4.2.4). It is not necessary to recompute the objective-row coefficients of the basic variables ($x_2, x_3,$ and x_6) because they are always zero regardless of any changes made in the objective coefficients (verify!).

$$\text{Reduced cost of } x_1 = y_1 + 3y_2 + y_3 - 2 = \frac{3}{2} + 3\left(\frac{5}{4}\right) + 0 - 2 = \frac{13}{4}$$

$$\text{Reduced cost of } x_4 = y_1 - 0 = \frac{3}{2}$$

$$\text{Reduced cost of } x_5 = y_2 - 0 = \frac{5}{4}$$

Note that the right-hand side of the first dual constraint is 2, the *new* coefficient in the modified objective function.
    The computations show that the current solution, $x_1 = 0$ train, $x_2 = 100$ trucks, and $x_3 = 230$ cars, remains optimal. The corresponding new revenue is computed as $2 \times 0 + 3 \times 100 + 4 \times 230 = \$1220$. The new pricing policy is not recommended because it lowers revenue.

Situation 2. Suppose now that the TOYCO objective function is changed to

$$\text{Maximize } z = 6x_1 + 3x_2 + 4x_3$$

Will the optimum solution change?

We have

$$(y_1, y_2, y_3) = (3, 4, 0) \begin{pmatrix} \frac{1}{2} & -\frac{1}{4} & 0 \\ 0 & \frac{1}{2} & 0 \\ -2 & 1 & 1 \end{pmatrix} = \left(\frac{3}{2}, \frac{5}{4}, 0\right)$$

Reduced cost of $x_1 = y_1 + 3y_2 + y_3 - 6 = \frac{3}{2} + 3\left(\frac{5}{4}\right) + 0 - 6 = -\frac{3}{4}$

Reduced cost of $x_4 = y_1 - 0 = \frac{3}{2}$

Reduced cost of $x_5 = y_2 - 0 = \frac{5}{4}$

The new reduced cost of x_1 shows that the current solution is not optimum.

To determine the new solution, the z-row is changed as highlighted in the following tableau:

Basic	x_1	x_2	x_3	x_4	x_5	x_6	Solution
z	$-\frac{3}{4}$	0	0	$\frac{3}{2}$	$\frac{5}{4}$	0	1220
x_2	$-\frac{1}{4}$	1	0	$\frac{1}{2}$	$-\frac{1}{4}$	0	100
x_3	$\frac{3}{2}$	0	1	0	$\frac{1}{2}$	0	230
x_6	2	0	0	-2	1	1	20

The highlighted elements are the new reduced costs and the new objective value. All the remaining elements are the same as in the original optimal tableau. The new optimum solution is then determined by letting x_1 enter and x_6 leave, which yields the solution $x_1 = 10$, $x_2 = 102.5, x_3 = 215$, and $z = \$12270.50$ (verify!). Although the new solution recommends the production of all three toys, the optimum revenue is less than that when only two toys are manufactured.

PROBLEM SET 4.5C

1. Investigate the optimality of the TOYCO solution for each of the following objective functions. Where necessary, use post-optimal analysis to determine the new optimum. (The optimum tableau of TOYCO is given at the start of Section 4.5.)

   (a) $z = 4x_1 + 2x_2 + 8x_3$

   (b) $z = 3x_1 + 6x_2 + x_3$

   (c) $z = 16x_1 + 6x_2 + 18x_3$

2. Investigate the optimality of the Reddy Mikks solution (Example 4.3-1) for each of the following objective functions. If necessary, use post-optimal analysis to determine the new optimum. (The optimal tableau of the model is given in Example 3.3-1.)

   *(a) $z = 3x_1 + 2x_2$

(b) $z = 8x_1 + 10x_2$

(c) *$z = 2x_1 + 5x_2$

3. Show that the 100% optimality rule (Problem 8, Set 3.6d, Chapter 3) is derived from (reduced costs) ≥ 0 for maximization problems and (reduced costs) ≤ 0 for minimization problems.

Addition of a new activity. A new activity signifies adding a new variable to the model. Intuitively, the addition of a new activity is desirable only if it is profitable. This condition can be checked by using Formula 2, Section 4.2.4, to compute the reduced cost of the new variable. The new activity is not profitable if it satisfies the optimality condition. Else, the new activity will increase revenue.

Example 4.5-4

TOYCO recognizes that toy trains are not currently in production because they are not profitable. The company wants to replace toy trains with a new product, a toy fire engine, to be assembled on the existing facilities. TOYCO estimates the revenue per toy fire engine to be $4 and the assembly times per unit to be 1 minute on each of operations 1 and 2 and 2 minutes on operation 3.

Let x_7 represent the new fire engine product. Given that $(y_1, y_2, y_3) = (1, 2, 0)$ are the optimal dual values, we get

$$\text{Reduced cost of } x_7 = 1y_1 + 1y_2 + 2y_3 - 4 = 1 \times 1 + 1 \times 2 + 2 \times 0 - 4 = -1$$

The result shows that it is profitable to include x_7 in the optimal basic solution. To obtain the new optimum, we first compute its column constraint using Formula 1, Section 4.2.4, as

$$x_7\text{-constraint colum} = \begin{pmatrix} \frac{1}{2} & -\frac{1}{4} & 0 \\ 0 & \frac{1}{2} & 0 \\ -2 & 1 & 1 \end{pmatrix}\begin{pmatrix} 1 \\ 1 \\ 2 \end{pmatrix} = \begin{pmatrix} \frac{1}{4} \\ \frac{1}{2} \\ 1 \end{pmatrix}$$

Thus, the current simplex tableau must be modified as follows:

Basic	x_1	x_2	x_3	x_7	x_4	x_5	x_6	Solution
z	4	0	0	-1	1	2	0	1350
x_2	$-\frac{1}{4}$	1	0	$\frac{1}{4}$	$\frac{1}{2}$	$-\frac{1}{4}$	0	100
x_3	$\frac{3}{2}$	0	1	$\frac{1}{2}$	0	$\frac{1}{2}$	0	230
x_6	2	0	0	1	-2	1	1	20

The new optimum is determined by letting x_7 enter the basic solution, in which case x_6 must leave. The new solution is $x_1 = 0, x_2 = 0, x_3 = 125, x_7 = 210$, and $z = \$1465$ (verify!), which improves the revenues by $115.

PROBLEM SET 4.5D

*1. In the original TOYCO model, toy trains are not part of the optimal product mix. The company recognizes that market competition will not allow raising the unit price of the toy. Instead, the company wants to concentrate on improving the assembly operation itself. This entails reducing the assembly time per unit in each of the three operations by a specified percentage, $p\%$. Determine the value of p that will make toy trains just profitable. (The optimum tableau of the TOYCO model is given at the start of Section 4.5.)

2. In the TOYCO model, suppose that the company can reduce the unit times on operations 1, 2, and 3 for toy trains from the current levels of 1, 3, and 1 minutes to .5, 1, and .5 minutes, respectively. The revenue per unit is unchanged to $4. Determine the new optimum solution.

3. In the TOYCO model, suppose that a new toy (fire engine) requires 3, 2, and 4 minutes, respectively, on operations 1, 2, and 3. Determine the optimal solution when the revenue per unit is given by

   *(a) $5

   (b) $10

4. In the Reddy Mikks model, the company is considering the production of a cheaper brand of exterior paint whose input requirements per ton include .75 ton of each of raw materials $M1$ and $M2$. Market conditions still dictate that the excess of interior paint over the production of *both* types of exterior paint be limited to 1 ton daily. The revenue per ton of the new exterior paint is $3500. Determine the new optimal solution. (The model is explained in Example 4.5-1, and its optimum tableau is given in Example 3.3-1.)

BIBLIOGRAPHY

Bradley, S., A. Hax, and T. Magnanti, *Applied Mathematical Programming*, Addison-Wesley, Reading, MA, 1977.

Bazaraa, M., J. Jarvis, and H. Sherali, *Linear Programming and Network Flows*, 4th ed., Wiley, New York, 2009.

Diwckar, U., *Introduction to Applied Optimization*, Kluwer Academic Publishers, Boston, 2003.

Nering, E., and A. Tucker, *Linear Programming and Related Problems*, Academic Press, Boston, 1992.

Vanderbei, R., *Linear Programming: Foundation and Extensions*, 3rd ed., Springer, New York, 2008.

CHAPTER 5

Transportation Model and Its Variants

Real-Life Application—Scheduling Appointments at Australian Trade Events

The Australian Tourist Commission (ATC) organizes trade events around the world to provide a forum for Australian sellers to meet international buyers of tourism products. During these events, sellers are stationed in booths and are visited by buyers according to scheduled appointments. Because of the limited number of time slots available in each event and the fact that the number of buyers and sellers can be quite large (one such event held in Melbourne in 1997 attracted 620 sellers and 700 buyers), ATC attempts to schedule the seller–buyer appointments in advance of the event in a manner that maximizes preferences. The model has resulted in greater satisfaction for both the buyers and sellers. Case 3 in Chapter 26 on the website contains details of the study.

5.1 DEFINITION OF THE TRANSPORTATION MODEL

The problem is represented by the network in Figure 5.1. There are m sources and n destinations, each represented by a **node**. The **arcs** represent the routes linking the sources and the destinations. Arc (i, j) joining source i to destination j carries two pieces of information: the transportation cost per unit, c_{ij}, and the amount shipped, x_{ij}. The amount of supply at source i is a_i, and the amount of demand at destination j is b_j. The objective of the model is to minimize the total transportation cost while satisfying all the supply and demand restrictions.

Example 5.1-1

MG Auto has three plants in Los Angeles, Detroit, and New Orleans, and two major distribution centers in Denver and Miami. The quarterly capacities of the three plants are 1000, 1500, and 1200 cars, and the demands at the two distribution centers for the same period are 2300 and 1400 cars. The mileage chart between the plants and the distribution centers is given in Table 5.1.

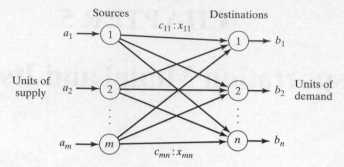

FIGURE 5.1

Representation of the transportation model with nodes and arcs

TABLE 5.1   Mileage Chart

	Denver	Miami
Los Angeles	1000	2690
Detroit	1250	1350
New Orleans	1275	850

The trucking company in charge of transporting the cars charges 8 cents per mile per car. The transportation costs per car on the different routes, rounded to the closest dollar, are given in Table 5.2.

The LP model of the problem is

$$\text{Minimize } z = 80x_{11} + 215x_{12} + 100x_{21} + 108x_{22} + 102x_{31} + 68x_{32}$$

subject to

$$x_{11} + x_{12} \qquad\qquad\qquad\qquad = 1000 \text{ (Los Angeles)}$$
$$x_{21} + x_{22} \qquad\qquad\qquad = 1500 \text{ (Detroit)}$$
$$+ x_{31} + x_{32} = 1200 \text{ (New Orleans)}$$
$$x_{11} \qquad + x_{21} \qquad + x_{31} \qquad = 2300 \text{ (Denver)}$$
$$x_{12} \qquad + x_{22} \qquad + x_{32} = 1400 \text{ (Miami)}$$
$$x_{ij} \geq 0, i = 1, 2, 3, j = 1, 2$$

These constraints are all equations because the total supply from the three sources (= 1000 + 1500 + 1200 = 3700 cars) equals the total demand at the two destinations (= 2300 + 1400 = 3700 cars).

TABLE 5.2   Transportation Cost per Car

	Denver (1)	Miami (2)
Los Angeles (1)	$80	$215
Detroit (2)	$100	$108
New Orleans (3)	$102	$68

TABLE 5.3 MG Transportation Model

	Denver	Miami	Supply
Los Angeles	80 x_{11}	215 x_{12}	**1000**
Detroit	100 x_{21}	108 x_{22}	**1500**
New Orleans	102 x_{31}	68 x_{32}	**1200**
Demand	**2300**	**1400**	

The special structure of the transportation problem allows a compact representation of the problem using the **transportation tableau** format in Table 5.3. This format is convenient for modeling many situations that do not deal with transporting goods, as demonstrated by the examples in Section 5.2.

The optimal solution in Figure 5.2 (obtained by TORA[1]) ships 1000 cars from Los Angeles to Denver ($x_{11} = 1000$), 1300 from Detroit to Denver ($x_{21} = 1300$), 200 from Detroit to Miami ($x_{22} = 200$), and 1200 from New Orleans to Miami ($x_{32} = 1000$). The associated minimum transportation cost is computed as $1000 \times \$80 + 1300 \times \$100 + 200 \times \$108 + 1200 \times \$68 = \$313,200$.

Balancing the transportation model. The transportation tableau representation assumes that model is balanced, meaning that the total demand equals to the total supply. If the model is unbalanced, we can add a dummy source or a dummy destination to restore balance.

Example 5.1-2

In the MG model, suppose that the Detroit plant capacity is 1300 cars (instead of 1500). The total supply (= 3500 cars) is less than the total demand (= 3700 cars), meaning that part of the demand at Denver and Miami will not be satisfied.

Because the demand exceeds the supply, a dummy source (plant) with a capacity of 200 cars (= 3700 − 3500) is added to balance the transportation model. The unit

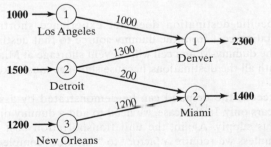

FIGURE 5.2

Optimal solution of MG Auto model

---

[1]To use TORA, from Main Menu select Transportation Model . From the SOLVE/MODIFY menu, select Solve ⇒ Final solution to obtain a summary of the optimum solution. A detailed description of the iterative solution of the transportation model is given in Section 5.3.3.

TABLE 5.4   MG Model with Dummy Plant

	Denver	Miami	Supply
Los Angeles	80 / **1000**	215	1000
Detroit	100 / **1300**	108	1300
New Orleans	102	68 / **1200**	1200
Dummy Plant	0	0 / **200**	200
Demand	2300	1400	

TABLE 5.5   MG Model with Dummy Destination

	Denver	Miami	Dummy	
Los Angeles	80 / **1000**	215	0	1000
Detroit	100 / **900**	108 / **200**	0 / **400**	1500
New Orleans	102	68 / **1200**	0	1200
Demand	1900	1400	400	

transportation cost from the dummy plant to the two destinations is zero because the plant does not exist.

Table 5.4 gives the balanced model together with its optimum solution. The solution shows that the dummy plant ships 200 cars to Miami, which means that Miami will be 200 cars short of satisfying its demand of 1400 cars.

We can make sure that a specific destination does not experience shortage by assigning a very high unit transportation cost from the dummy source to that destination. For example, a penalty of $1000 in the dummy-Miami cell will prevent shortage at Miami. Of course, we cannot use this "trick" with all the destinations, because shortage must take place somewhere.

The case where the supply exceeds the demand can be demonstrated by assuming that the demand at Denver is 1900 cars only. In this case, we need to add a dummy distribution center to "receive" the surplus supply. Again, the unit transportation cost to the dummy distribution center is zero, unless we require a factory to "ship out" completely. In this case, a high unit transportation cost is assigned from the designated factory to the dummy destination.

Table 5.5 gives the new model and its optimal solution (obtained by TORA). The solution shows that the Detroit plant will have a surplus of 400 cars.

PROBLEM SET 5.1A[2]

1. True or False?
   (a) To balance a transportation model, it is necessary to add a dummy source or a dummy destination bur never both.
   (b) The amounts shipped to a dummy destination represent surplus at the shipping source.
   (c) The amounts shipped from a dummy source represent shortages at the receiving destinations.

2. In each of the following cases, determine whether a dummy source or a dummy destination must be added to balance the model.
   (a) Supply: $a_1 = 100$, $a_2 = 50$, $a_3 = 40$, $a_4 = 60$
       Demand: $b_1 = 100$, $b_2 = 50$, $b_3 = 70$, $b_4 = 90$
   (b) Supply: $a_1 = 15$, $a_2 = 44$
       Demand: $b_1 = 25$, $b_2 = 15$, $b_3 = 10$

3. In Table 5.4 of Example 5.1-2, where a dummy plant is added, what does the solution mean when the dummy plant "ships" 150 cars to Denver and 50 cars to Miami?

*4. In Table 5.5 of Example 5.1-2, where a dummy destination is added, suppose that the Detroit plant must ship out *all* its production. How can this restriction be implemented in the model?

5. In Example 5.1-2, suppose that for the case where the demand exceeds the supply (Table 5.4), a penalty is levied at the rate of $300 and $190 for each undelivered car at Denver and Miami, respectively. Additionally, no deliveries are made from the Los Angeles plant to the Miami distribution center. Set up the model, and determine the optimal shipping schedule for the problem.

*6. Three electric power plants with capacities of 25, 40, and 30 million kWh supply electricity to three cities. The maximum demands at the three cities are estimated at 30, 35, and 25 million kWh. The price per million kWh at the three cities is given in Table 5.6.
   During the month of August, there is a 20% increase in demand at each of the three cities, which can be met by purchasing electricity from another network at a premium rate of $1000 per million kWh. The network is not linked to city 3, however. The utility company wishes to determine the most economical plan for the distribution and purchase of additional energy.
   (a) Formulate the problem as a transportation model.
   (b) Determine an optimal distribution plan for the utility company.
   (c) Determine the cost of the additional power purchased by each of the three cities.

7. Solve Problem 6, assuming that there is a 10% power transmission loss through the network.

8. Three refineries with daily capacities of 6, 5, and 8 million gallons, respectively, supply three distribution areas with daily demands of 4, 8, and 7 million gallons, respectively. Gasoline is

TABLE 5.6 Price/Million kWh for Problem 6

	City		
	1	2	3
1	$600	$700	$400
Plant 2	$320	$300	$350
3	$500	$480	$450

---

[2]In this set, you may use TORA to find the optimum solution. AMPL and Solver models for the transportation problem will be introduced at the end of Section 5.3.2.

TABLE 5.7   Mileage Chart for Problem 8

		Distribution area		
		1	2	3
	1	180	180	—
Refinery	2	300	800	900
	3	220	200	120

transported to the three distribution areas through a network of pipelines. The transportation cost is 10 cents per 1000 gallons per pipeline mile. Table 5.7 gives the mileage between the refineries and the distribution areas. Refinery 1 is not connected to distribution area 3.

(a) Construct the associated transportation model.

(b) Determine the optimum shipping schedule in the network.

*9. In Problem 8, suppose that the capacity of refinery 3 is 6 million gallons only and that distribution area 1 must receive all its demand. Additionally, any shortages at areas 2 and 3 will incur a penalty of 5 cents per gallon.

(a) Formulate the problem as a transportation model.

(b) Determine the optimum shipping schedule.

10. In Problem 8, suppose that the daily demand at area 3 drops to 4 million gallons. Surplus production at refineries 1 and 2 is diverted to other distribution areas by truck. The transportation cost per 100 gallons is $1.50 from refinery 1 and $2.20 from refinery 2. Refinery 3 can divert its surplus production to other chemical processes within the plant.

(a) Formulate the problem as a transportation model.

(b) Determine the optimum shipping schedule.

11. Three orchards supply crates of oranges to four retailers. The daily demand amounts at the four retailers are 150, 150, 400, and 100 crates, respectively. Supplies at the three orchards are dictated by available regular labor and are estimated at 150, 200, and 250 crates daily. However, both orchards 1 and 2 have indicated that they could supply more crates, if necessary, by using overtime labor. Orchard 3 does not offer this option. The transportation costs per crate from the orchards to the retailers are given in Table 5.8.

(a) Formulate the problem as a transportation model.

(b) Solve the problem.

(c) How many crates should orchards 1 and 2 supply using overtime labor?

12. Cars are shipped from three distribution centers to five dealers. The shipping cost is based on the mileage between the sources and the destinations and is independent of whether the truck makes the trip with partial or full loads. Table 5.9 summarizes the mileage between the distribution centers and the dealers together with the monthly

TABLE 5.8   Transportation Cost/Crate for Problem 11

		Retailer			
		1	2	3	4
	1	$1	$2	$3	$2
Orchard	2	$2	$4	$1	$2
	3	$1	$3	$5	$3

TABLE 5.9 Mileage Chart and Supply and Demand for Problem 12

			Dealer			
	1	2	3	4	5	Supply
1	100	150	200	140	35	**400**
Center 2	50	70	60	65	80	**200**
3	40	90	100	150	130	**150**
Demand	**100**	**200**	**150**	**160**	**140**	

supply and demand figures given in *number* of cars. A full truckload includes 18 cars. The transportation cost per truck mile is $25.

(a) Formulate the associated transportation model.

(b) Determine the optimal shipping schedule.

13. MG Auto, of Example 5.1-1, produces four car models: $M1, M2, M3$, and $M4$. The Detroit plant produces models $M1, M2$, and $M4$. Models $M1$ and $M2$ are also produced in New Orleans. The Los Angeles plant manufactures models $M3$ and $M4$. The capacities of the various plants and the demands at the distribution centers are given in Table 5.10.

The mileage chart is the same as given in Example 5.1-1, and the transportation rate remains at 8 cents per car mile for all models. Additionally, it is possible to satisfy a percentage of the demand for some models from the supply of others according to the specifications in Table 5.11.

(a) Formulate the corresponding transportation model.

(b) Determine the optimum shipping schedule.

(*Hint*: Add four new destinations corresponding to the new combinations [$M1, M2$], [$M3, M4$], [$M1, M2$], and [$M2, M4$]. The demands at the new destinations are determined from the given percentages.)

TABLE 5.10 Capacities and Demands for Problem 13

		Model			
	$M1$	$M2$	$M3$	$M4$	Totals
Plant					
Los Angeles	—	—	700	300	1000
Detroit	500	600	—	400	1500
New Orleans	800	400	—	—	1200
Distribution center					
Denver	700	500	500	600	2300
Miami	600	500	200	100	1400

TABLE 5.11 Interchangeable Models for Problem 13

Distribution center	Percentage of demand	Interchangeable models
Denver	10	$M1, M2$
	20	$M3, M4$
Miami	10	$M1, M2$
	5	$M2, M4$

5.2 NONTRADITIONAL TRANSPORTATION MODELS

The application of the transportation model is not limited to *transporting* goods. This section presents two nontraditional applications in the areas of production-inventory control and tool sharpening service.

Example 5.2-1 (Production-Inventory Control)

Boralis manufactures backpacks for serious hikers. The demand for its product during the peak period of March to June of each year is 100, 200, 180, and 300 units, respectively. The company uses part-time labor to accommodate fluctuations in demand. It is estimated that Boralis can produce 50, 180, 280, and 270 units in March through June. A current month's demand may be satisfied in one of three ways.

1. Current month's production at the cost of $40 per pack.
2. Surplus production in an earlier month at an additional holding cost of $.50 per pack per month.
3. Surplus production in a later month (back-ordering) at an additional penalty cost of $2.00 per pack per month.

Boralis wishes to determine the optimal production schedule for the four months.

The following table summarizes the parallels between the elements of the production-inventory problem and the transportation model:

Transportation	Production-inventory
1. Source i	1. Production period i
2. Destination j	2. Demand period j
3. Supply amount at source i	3. Production capacity of period i
4. Demand at destination j	4. Demand for period j
5. Unit transportation cost from source i to destination j	5. Unit cost (production + holding + penalty) in period i for period j

The resulting transportation model is given in Table 5.12.

TABLE 5.12 Transportation Model for Example 5.2-1

	1	2	3	4	Capacity
1	$40.00	$40.50	$41.00	$41.50	**50**
2	$42.00	$40.00	$40.50	$41.00	**180**
3	$44.00	$42.00	$40.00	$40.50	**280**
4	$46.00	$44.00	$42.00	$40.00	**270**
Demand	**100**	**200**	**180**	**300**	

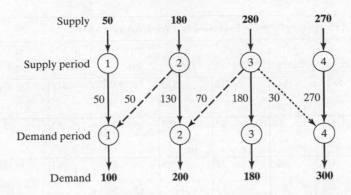

FIGURE 5.3

Optimal solution of the production-inventory model

The unit "transportation" cost from period i to period j is computed as

$$c_{ij} = \begin{cases} \text{Production cost in } i, i = j \\ \text{Production cost in } i + \text{holding cost from } i \text{ to } j, i < j \\ \text{Production cost in } i + \text{penaty cost from } i \text{ to } j, i > j \end{cases}$$

For example,

$$c_{11} = \$40.00$$

$$c_{24} = \$40.00 + (\$.50 + \$.50) = \$41.00$$

$$c_{41} = \$40.00 + (\$2.00 + \$2.00 + \$2.00) = \$46.00$$

The optimal solution is summarized in Figure 5.3. The dashed lines indicate back-ordering, the dotted lines indicate production for a future period, and the solid lines show production in a period for itself. The total cost is $31,455.

Example 5.2-2 (Tool Sharpening)

Arkansas Pacific operates a saw mill that produces boards from different types of lumber. Depending on the type of wood being milled, the demand for sharp blades varies from day to day according to the following 1-week (7-day) data:

Day	Mon.	Tue.	Wed.	Thu.	Fri.	Sat.	Sun.
Demand (blades)	24	12	14	20	18	14	22

The mill can satisfy the daily demand in four ways:

1. New blades at the cost of $12 a piece.
2. Overnight sharpening service for $6 a blade.
3. One-day sharpening service for $5 a blade.
4. Two-day sharpening service for $3 a blade.

The situation can be represented as a transportation model with eight sources and seven destinations. The destinations represent the 7 days of the week. The sources of the model are

TABLE 5.13   Tool Sharpening Problem Expressed as a Transportation Model

	1 Mon.	2 Tue.	3 Wed.	4 Thu.	5 Fri.	6 Sat.	7 Sun.	8 Disposal	
1-New	$12 **24**	$12 **12**	$12	$12	$12	$12	$12	$0 **88**	124
2-Mon.	M	$6	$5 **14**	$3 **10**	$3	$3	$3	$0	24
3-Tue.	M	M	$6	$5	$3 **12**	$3	$3	$0	12
4-Wed.	M	M	M	$6 **10**	$5 **4**	$3	$3	$0	14
5-Thu.	M	M	M	M	$6 **2**	$5 **18**	$3	$0	20
6-Fri.	M	M	M	M	M	$6 **14**	$5 **4**	$0	18
7-Sat.	M	M	M	M	M	M	$6 **0**	$0 **14**	14
8-Sun.	M	M	M	M	M	M	M	$0 **22**	22
	24	12	14	20	18	14	22	124	

defined as follows: Source 1 corresponds to buying new blades, which, in the extreme, can cover the demand for all 7 days (= 24 + 12 + 14 + 20 + 18 + 14 + 22 = 124). Sources 2 to 8 correspond to the 7 days of the week. The amount of supply for each of these sources equals the number of used blades at the end of the associated day. For example, source 2 (Monday) will have a supply of used blades equal to the demand for Monday. The unit "transportation cost" for the model is $12, $6, $5, or $3, depending on whether the blade is new or sharpened. The "disposal" column is a dummy destination for balancing the model. The complete model and its solution are given in Table 5.13.

The following table summarizes the optimum solution at a total cost of $818 (file *toraEx5.2-2.txt*).

	Number of sharp blades (Target day)				
Period	*New*	*Overnight*	*1-Day*	*2-Day*	Disposal
Mon.	24 (Mon.)	0	14 (Wed.)	10 (Thu.)	0
Tues.	12 (Tue.)	0	0	12 (Fri.)	0
Wed.	0	10 (Thu.)	4 (Fri.)	0	0
Thu.	0	2 (Fri.)	0	18 (Sun.)	0
Fri.	0	14 (Sat.)	4 (Sun.)	0	0
Sat.	0	0		0	14
Sun.	0	0		0	22

Remarks. The model in Table 5.13 assumes one week of operation only. For multiple weeks, the model must deal with the *rotational* nature of the days of the week, in the sense that this week's days can act as sources for next week's demand. One way to handle this situation is to assume that the very first week of operation starts with all new blades for each day. From there on, we use a model consisting of exactly 7 sources and 7 destinations corresponding to the days of the week. The new model will be similar to Table 5.13 less source "New" and destination "Disposal." Also, only diagonal cells will be blocked (unit cost = M). The remaining cells will have a unit cost of $3.00, $5.00, or $6.00.

Intuitively, and without solving the new transportation model at all, it is obvious that the cheapest sharpening service (2-day) can be used to satisfy all the demand starting from week 2 on. This intuitive conclusion can be confirmed by solving the new model (file *toraEx5.2-2a.txt*).

PROBLEM SET 5.2A[3]

1. In Example 5.2-1, suppose that the holding cost per unit is period dependent and is given by 20, 15, and 35 cents for periods 1, 2, and 3, respectively. The penalty cost is $1 per period and the production costs remain as given in the example. Determine the optimum solution and interpret the results.

*2. In Example 5.2-2, suppose that the sharpening service offers 3-day service for $1 a blade on Monday and Tuesday (days 1 and 2). Reformulate the problem, and interpret the optimum solution.

3. In Example 5.2-2, if a blade is not used the day it is sharpened, a holding cost of 50 cents per blade per day is incurred. Reformulate the model, and interpret the optimum solution.

4. JoShop wants to assign four different categories of machines to five types of tasks. The numbers of machines available in the four categories are 25, 30, 20, and 30. The numbers of jobs in the five tasks are 30, 10, 20, 25, and 20. Machine category 4 cannot be assigned to task type 4. Table 5.14 provides the unit cost (in dollars) of assigning a machine category to a task type. The objective of the problem is to determine the optimum number of machines in each category to be assigned to each task type. Solve the problem and interpret the solution.

*5. The demand for a perishable item over the next four months is 400, 300, 420, and 380 tons, respectively. The supply capacities for the same months are 500, 600, 200, and 300 tons. The

TABLE 5.14 Unit Costs for Problem 4

		Task type				
		1	2	3	4	5
	1	10	2	3	15	9
Machine category	2	5	10	15	2	4
	3	15	5	14	7	15
	4	20	15	13	—	8

---

[3]In this set, you may use TORA to find the optimum solution. AMPL and Solver models for the transportation problem will be introduced at the end of Section 5.3.2.

purchase price per ton varies from month to month and is estimated at $100, $140, $120, and $150, respectively. Because the item is perishable, a current month's supply must be consumed within 3 months (starting with current month). The storage cost per ton per month is $3. The nature of the item does not allow back-ordering. Solve the problem as a transportation model, and determine the optimum delivery schedule for the item over the next 4 months.

6. The demand for a special small engine over the next five quarters is 200, 150, 300, 250, and 400 units, respectively. The manufacturer supplying the engine has different production capacities estimated at 180, 230, 430, 300, and 300 for the five quarters. Back-ordering is not allowed, but the manufacturer may use overtime to fill the immediate demand, if necessary. The overtime capacity for each period is half the regular capacity. The production costs per unit for the five periods are $100, $96, $116, $102, and $106, respectively. The overtime production cost per engine is 50% higher than the regular production cost. If an engine is produced now for use in later periods, an additional storage cost of $4 per engine per period is incurred. Formulate the problem as a transportation model. Determine the optimum number of engines to be produced during regular time and overtime of each period.

7. Periodic preventive maintenance is carried out on aircraft engines, where an important component must be replaced. The numbers of aircraft scheduled for such maintenance over the next six months are estimated at 200, 180, 300, 198, 230, and 290, respectively. All maintenance work is done during the first day of the month, where a used component may be replaced with a new or an overhauled component. The overhauling of used components may be done in a local repair facility, where they will be ready for use at the beginning of next month, or they may be sent to a central repair shop, where a delay of 3 months (including the month in which maintenance occurs) is expected. The repair cost in the local shop is $120 per component. At the central facility, the cost is only $35 per component. An overhauled component used in a later month will incur an additional storage cost of $1.50 per unit per month. New components may be purchased at $200 each in month 1, with a 5% price increase every 2 months. Formulate the problem as a transportation model, and determine the optimal schedule for satisfying the demand for the component over the next six months.

8. The National Parks Service is receiving four bids for logging at three pine forests in Arkansas. The three locations include 20,000, 30,000, and 10,000 acres. A single bidder can bid for at most 50% of the total acreage available. The bids per acre at the three locations are given in Table 5.15. Bidder 2 does not wish to bid on location 1, and bidder 3 cannot bid on location 2.

   (a) In the present situation, we need to *maximize* the total bidding revenue for the Parks Service. Show how the problem can be formulated as a transportation model.

   (b) Determine the acreage that should be assigned to each of the four bidders.

TABLE 5.15 Bids per Acre for Problem 8

	Location		
	1	2	3
Bidder 1	$520	$210	$570
Bidder 2	–	$510	$495
Bidder 3	$650	–	$240
Bidder 4	$180	$430	$710

5.3 THE TRANSPORTATION ALGORITHM[4]

The basic steps of the transportation algorithm are exactly those of the simplex method (Chapter 3). However, instead of using the regular simplex tableau, we take advantage of the special structure of the transportation model to organize the computations in a more convenient form.

Step 1. Determine a *starting* basic feasible solution, and go to step 2.

Step 2. Use the optimality condition of the simplex method to determine the *entering variable* from among all the nonbasic variables. If the optimality condition is satisfied, stop. Otherwise, go to step 3.

Step 3. Use the feasibility condition of the simplex method to determine the *leaving variable* from among all the current basic variables, and find the new basic solution. Return to step 2.

The details of the algorithm are explained in Sections 5.3.1 and 5.3.2 using the following example.

Example 5.3-1 (SunRay Transport)

SunRay Transport Company ships truckloads of grain from three silos to four mills. The supply (in truckloads) and the demand (also in truckloads) together with the unit transportation costs per truckload on the different routes are summarized in Table 5.16. The unit transportation costs, c_{ij} (shown in the northeast corner of each box) are in hundreds of dollars. The model seeks the minimum-cost shipping schedule between the silos and the mills.

TABLE 5.16 SunRay Transportation Model

	Mill 1	2	3	4	Supply
1	10 x_{11}	2 x_{12}	20 x_{13}	11 x_{14}	15
Silo 2	12 x_{21}	7 x_{22}	9 x_{23}	20 x_{24}	25
3	4 x_{31}	14 x_{32}	16 x_{33}	18 x_{34}	10
Demand	5	15	15	15	

[4]The special transportation algorithm was developed early on when hand computations were the norm and shortcuts were warranted. Today, powerful computer codes can solve transportation models of any size as a regular LP. In fact, TORA handles all necessary computations in the background using the simplex method and uses the transportation model format only as a screen "veneer". Nevertheless, the transportation algorithm, aside from its historical significance, does provide insight into the use of the theoretical primal–dual relationships (introduced in Section 4.2) to achieve a practical end result—that of improving hand computations. The exercise is theoretically intriguing. Moreover, the special transportation tableau format can facilitate the modeling of a number of situations that do not deal directly with transporting goods, as Section 5.2 demonstrates.

5.3.1   Determination of the Starting Solution

A general transportation model with m sources and n destinations has $m + n$ constraint equations, one for each source and each destination. However, because the transportation model is always balanced (sum of the supply = sum of the demand), one of the equations is redundant, reducing the model to $m + n - 1$ independent equations and $m + n - 1$ basic variables. In Example 5.3-1, the starting solution has $3 + 4 - 1 = 6$ basic variables.

The special structure of the transportation problem allows securing a nonartificial starting basic solution using one of three methods:[5]

1. Northwest-corner method
2. Least-cost method
3. Vogel approximation method

The first method is "mechanical" in nature, and the remaining two are heuristics that seek a better-quality starting solution that yields a smaller objective value. In general, the Vogel heuristic is better than the least-cost heuristic. On the other hand, the northwest-corner method consistently gives the worst starting solution. The trade-off is that the northwest-corner method involves the least amount of computations.

Northwest-corner method.   The method starts at the *northwest-corner* cell (route) of the tableau (variable x_{11}).

Step 1.   Allocate as much as possible to the selected cell, and adjust the associated amounts of supply and demand by subtracting the allocated amount.

Step 2.   Cross out the row or column with zero supply or demand to indicate that no further assignments can be made in that row or column. If both a row and a column net to zero simultaneously, *cross out one only*, and leave a zero supply (demand) in the uncrossed-out row (column).

Step 3.   If *exactly one* row or column is left uncrossed out, stop. Otherwise, move to the cell to the right if a column has just been crossed out or below if a row has been crossed out. Go to step 1.

Example 5.3-2

The application of the procedure to the model of Example 5.3-1 gives the starting basic solution in Table 5.17. The arrows show the order in which the allocated amounts are generated.

The starting basic solution is

$$x_{11} = 5, \; x_{12} = 10$$

$$x_{22} = 5, \; x_{23} = 15, \; x_{24} = 5$$

$$x_{34} = 10$$

The associated cost of the schedule is

$$z = 5 \times 10 + 10 \times 2 + 5 \times 7 + 15 \times 9 + 5 \times 20 + 10 \times 18 = \$520.$$

---

[5]All three methods are featured in TORA. See the end of Section 5.3.3.

TABLE 5.17   North-West Corner Starting Solution

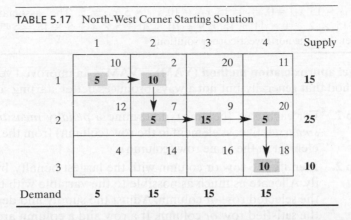

	1	2	3	4	Supply
1	10 **5**	2 **10**	20	11	15
2	12	7 **5**	9 **15**	20 **5**	25
3	4	14	16	18 **10**	10
Demand	5	15	15	15	

Least-cost method.   The least-cost method finds a better starting solution by targeting the cheapest routes. It assigns as much as possible to the cell with the smallest unit cost (ties are broken arbitrarily). Next, the satisfied row or column is crossed out and the amounts of supply and demand are adjusted accordingly. If both a row and a column are satisfied simultaneously, *only one is crossed out*, the same as in the northwest-corner method. Next, select the uncrossed-out cell with the smallest unit cost and repeat the process until exactly one row or column is left uncrossed out.

Example 5.3-3

The least-cost method is applied to Example 5.3-1.

1. Cell $(1, 2)$ has the least unit cost in the tableau (= \$2). The most that can be shipped through $(1, 2)$ is $x_{12} = 15$ truckloads, which happens to satisfy both row 1 and column 2 simultaneously. We arbitrarily cross out column 2 and adjust the supply in row 1 to 0.

2. Cell $(3, 1)$ has the smallest uncrossed-out unit cost (= \$4). Assign $x_{31} = 5$, and cross out column 1 because it is satisfied, and adjust the demand of row 3 to $10 - 5 = 5$ truckloads.

3. Continuing in the same manner, we successively assign 15 truckloads to cell $(2, 3)$, 0 truckloads to cell $(1, 4)$, 5 truckloads to cell $(3, 4)$, and 10 truckload to cell $(2, 4)$ (verify!).

The resulting starting solution is summarized in Table 5.18. The arrows show the order in which the allocations are made. The starting solution (consisting of 6 basic variables)

TABLE 5.18   Least-Cost Starting Solution

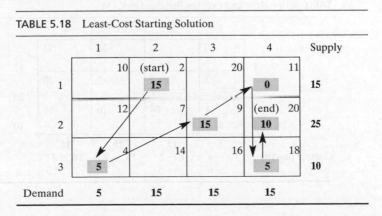

	1	2	3	4	Supply
1	10	(start) 2 **15**	20	11 **0**	15
2	12	7	9 **15**	(end) 20 **10**	25
3	4 **5**	14	16	18 **5**	10
Demand	5	15	15	15	

is $x_{12} = 15, x_{14} = 0, x_{23} = 15, x_{24} = 10, x_{31} = 5, x_{34} = 5$. The associated objective value is $z = 15 \times 2 + 0 \times 11 + 15 \times 9 + 10 \times 20 + 5 \times 4 + 5 \times 18 = \$475$, which happens to be better than the northwest-corner solution.

Vogel approximation method (VAM).   VAM is an improved version of the least-cost method that generally, but not always, produces better starting solutions.

Step 1.   For each row (column), determine a *penalty measure* by subtracting the *smallest* unit cost element in the row (column) from the *next smallest* unit cost element in the same row (column).

Step 2.   Identify the row or column with the largest penalty, breaking ties arbitrarily. Allocate as much as possible to the variable with the least unit cost in the selected row or column. Adjust the supply and demand, and cross out the satisfied row *or* column. If a row and a column are satisfied simultaneously, only one of the two is crossed out, and the remaining row (column) is assigned zero supply (demand).

Step 3.   **(a)**   If exactly one row or column with zero supply or demand remains uncrossed out, stop.

   (b)   If one row (column) with *positive* supply (demand) remains uncrossed out, determine the basic variables in the row (column) by the least-cost method. Stop.

   (c)   If all the uncrossed-out rows and columns have (remaining) zero supply and demand, determine the *zero* basic variables by the least-cost method. Stop.

   (d)   Otherwise, go to step 1.

Example 5.3-4

VAM is applied to Example 5.3-1. Table 5.19 computes the first set of penalties.

Because row 3 has the largest penalty ($= 10$) and cell $(3, 1)$ has the smallest unit cost in that row, the amount 5 is assigned to x_{31}. Column 1 is now satisfied and must be crossed out. Next, new penalties are recomputed as in Table 5.20.

TABLE 5.19   Row and Column Penalties in VAM

		1	2	3	4		Row penalty
		10	2	20	11		$10 - 2 = 8$
	1					15	
		12	7	9	20		$9 - 7 = 2$
	2					25	
		4	14	16	18		$14 - 4 = \boxed{10}$
	3	5				10	
		5	15	15	15		
Column penalty		$10 - 4$	$7 - 2$	$16 - 9$	$18 - 11$		
		$= 6$	$= 5$	$= 7$	$= 7$		

TABLE 5.20   First Assignment in VAM ($x_{31} = 5$)

	1	2	3	4		Row penalty
1	10	2	20	11	15	9
2	12	7	9	20	25	2
3	4 5	14	16	18	10	2
	5	15	15	15		
Column penalty	—	5	7	7		

Table 5.20 shows that row 1 has the highest penalty ($= 9$). Hence, we assign the maximum amount possible to cell $(1, 2)$, which yields $x_{12} = 15$ and simultaneously satisfies both row 1 and column 2. We arbitrarily cross out column 2 and adjust the supply in row 1 to zero.

Continuing in the same manner, row 2 will produce the highest penalty ($= 11$), and we assign $x_{23} = 15$, which crosses out column 3 and leaves 10 units in row 2. Only column 4 is left, and it has a positive supply of 15 units. Applying the least-cost method to that column, we successively assign $x_{14} = 0$, $x_{34} = 5$, and $x_{24} = 10$ (verify!). The associated objective value for this solution is

$$z = 15 \times 2 + 0 \times 11 + 15 \times 9 + 10 \times 20 + 5 \times 4 + 5 \times 18 = \$475$$

This solution happens to have the same objective value as in the least-cost method.

*(a)				(b)				(c)			
0	2	1	6	1	2	6	12	5	1	8	12
2	1	5	7	0	4	2	7	2	4	0	14
2	4	3	7	3	1	5	11	3	6	7	4
5	5	10		10	10	10		9	10	11	

PROBLEM SET 5.3A

1. Compare the starting solutions obtained by the northwest-corner, least-cost, and Vogel methods for each of the following models:

5.3.2 Iterative Computations of the Transportation Algorithm

After determining the starting solution (using one of the methods in Section 5.3.1), we use the following algorithm to determine the optimum solution:

Step 1. Use the simplex *optimality condition* to determine the *entering variable*. If the optimality condition is satisfied, stop. Otherwise, go to step 2.

Step 2. Determine the *leaving variable* using the simplex *feasibility condition*. Change the basis, and return to step 1.

The optimality and feasibility conditions do not involve the familiar row operations used in the simplex method. Instead, the special structure of the transportation model allows simpler (hand) computations.

TABLE 5.21   Starting Iteration

	1	2	3	4	Supply
1	10 **5**	2 **10**	20	11	15
2	12	7 **5**	9 **15**	20 **5**	25
3	4	14	16	18 **10**	10
Demand	**5**	**15**	**15**	**15**	

Example 5.3-5

Solve the transportation model of Example 5.3-1, starting with the northwest-corner solution.

Table 5.21 gives the northwest-corner starting solution as determined in Table 5.17, Example 5.3-2. The determination of the entering variable from among the current nonbasic variables (those that are not part of the starting basic solution) is done by computing the nonbasic coefficients in the z-row, using the **method of multipliers** (which, as shown in Section 5.3.3, is rooted in LP duality theory).

In the method of multipliers, we associate the multipliers u_i and v_j with row i and column j of the transportation tableau. For each current *basic* variable x_{ij}, these multipliers are shown in Section 5.3.3 to satisfy the following equations:

$$u_i + v_j = c_{ij}, \text{ for each } basic \ x_{ij}$$

As Table 5.21 shows, the starting solution has 6 basic variables, which leads to 6 equations in 7 unknowns. To solve these equations, the method of multipliers calls for setting any of the multiplier equal to zero. We will arbitrarily set $u_1 = 0$, and then solve for the remaining variables as shown in the following table:

Basic variable	(u,v)-Equation	Solution
x_{11}	$u_1 + v_1 = 10$	Set $u_1 = 0 \Rightarrow v_1 = 10$
x_{12}	$u_1 + v_2 = 2$	$u_1 = 0 \Rightarrow v_2 = 2$
x_{22}	$u_2 + v_2 = 7$	$v_2 = 2 \Rightarrow u_2 = 5$
x_{23}	$u_2 + v_3 = 9$	$u_2 = 5 \Rightarrow v_3 = 4$
x_{24}	$u_2 + v_4 = 20$	$u_2 = 5 \Rightarrow v_4 = 15$
x_{34}	$u_3 + v_4 = 18$	$v_4 = 15 \Rightarrow u_3 = 3$

To summarize, we have

$$u_1 = 0, \ u_2 = 5, \ u_3 = 3$$
$$v_1 = 10, \ v_2 = 2, \ v_3 = 4, \ v_4 = 15$$

Next, we use u_i and v_j to evaluate the nonbasic variables by computing

$$u_i + v_j - c_{ij}, \text{ for each } nonbasic \ x_{ij}$$

The results of these evaluations are shown in the following table:

Nonbasic variable	$u_i + v_j - c_{ij}$
x_{13}	$u_1 + v_3 - c_{13} = 0 + 4 - 20 = -16$
x_{14}	$u_1 + v_4 - c_{14} = 0 + 15 - 11 = 4$
x_{21}	$u_2 + v_1 - c_{21} = 5 + 10 - 12 = 3$
x_{31}	$u_3 + v_1 - c_{31} = 3 + 10 - 4 = 9$
x_{32}	$u_3 + v_2 - c_{32} = 3 + 2 - 14 = -9$
x_{33}	$u_3 + v_3 - c_{33} = 3 + 4 - 16 = -9$

The preceding information, together with the fact that $u_i + v_j - c_{ij} = 0$ for basic x_{ij}, is actually equivalent to computing the z-row of the simplex tableau, as the following summary shows:

Basic	x_{11}	x_{12}	x_{13}	x_{14}	x_{21}	x_{22}	x_{23}	x_{24}	x_{31}	x_{32}	x_{33}	x_{34}
z	0	0	−16	4	3	0	0	0	9	−9	−9	0

Because the transportation model *minimizes* cost, the entering variable is the one having the *most positive* coefficient in the z-row—namely, x_{31} is the entering variable.

All the preceding computations are usually done directly on the transportation tableau as shown in Table 5.22, meaning that it is not necessary to write the (u, v)-equations explicitly. Instead, we start by setting $u_1 = 0.$[6] Then we can compute the v-values of all the columns that have *basic* variables in row 1–namely, v_1 and v_2. Next, we compute u_2 based on the (u, v)-equation of basic x_{22}. Now, given u_2, we can compute v_3 and v_4. Finally, we determine u_3 using the basic equation of x_{33}. The next step is to evaluate the nonbasic variables by computing $u_i + v_j - c_{ij}$ for each nonbasic x_{ij}, as shown in Table 5.22 in the boxed southeast corner of each cell.

Having identified x_{31} as the entering variable, we need to determine the leaving variable. Remember that if x_{31} enters the solution to become basic, one of the current basic variables must leave as nonbasic (at zero level).

TABLE 5.22 Iteration 1 Calculations

	$v_1 = 10$	$v_2 = 2$	$v_3 = 4$	$v_4 = 15$	Supply
$u_1 = 0$	10 **5**	2 **10**	20 −16	11 4	15
$u_2 = 5$	12 3	7 **5**	9 **15**	20 **5**	25
$u_3 = 3$	4 9	14 −9	16 −9	18 **10**	10
Demand	5	15	15	15	

---

[6]The tutorial module of TORA is designed to demonstrate that assigning a zero initial value to any u or v produces the same $u + v - c$ for all the nonbasic variables. See *TORA moment* following this example.

The selection of x_{31} as the entering variable means shipping through this route reduces the total shipping cost. What is the most that we can ship through the new route? Observe in Table 5.22 that if route (3, 1) ships θ units (i.e., $x_{31} = \theta$), then the maximum value of θ is determined based on two conditions:

1. Supply limits and demand requirements remain satisfied.
2. Shipments through all routes remain nonnegative.

These two conditions determine the maximum value of θ and the leaving variable in the following manner. First, construct a *closed loop* that starts and ends at the entering variable cell, (3, 1). The loop consists of *connected* horizontal and vertical segments only (no diagonals are allowed) whose corner elements (excluding the entering variable cell) must coincide with a current basic variable.[7] Table 5.23 shows the loop for x_{31}. Exactly one loop exists for a given entering variable.

Next, we assign the amount θ to the entering variable cell (3, 1). For the supply and demand limits to remain satisfied, we must alternate between subtracting and adding the amount θ at the successive *corners* of the loop as shown in Table 5.23 (it is immaterial if the loop is traced in a clockwise or counterclockwise direction). For $\theta \geq 0$, the new values of all the variables remain nonnegative if

$$x_{11} = 5 - \theta \geq 0$$

$$x_{22} = 5 - \theta \geq 0$$

$$x_{34} = 10 - \theta \geq 0$$

The corresponding maximum value of θ is 5, which occurs when both x_{11} and x_{22} reach zero level. Either x_{11} or x_{22} leaves the solution, and we arbitrarily choose x_{11} as the leaving variable.

The values of the basic variables at the corners of the closed loop are adjusted to accommodate setting $x_{31} = 5$, as Table 5.24 shows. Because each unit shipped through route (3, 1) reduces the shipping cost by $9 (= u_3 + v_1 - c_{31})$, the total cost associated with the new schedule is $9 \times 5 = \$45$ less than in the previous schedule. Thus, the new cost is $520 - \$45 = \$475$.

Given the new basic solution, we repeat the computation of the multipliers u and v, as Table 5.24 shows. The entering variable is x_{14}. The closed loop shows that $x_{14} = 10$ and that the leaving variable is x_{24}.

TABLE 5.23 Determination of Closed Loop for x_{31}

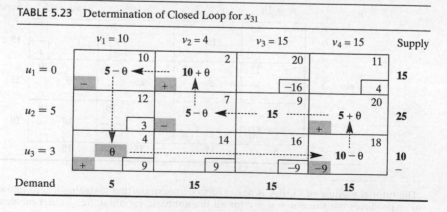

[7]TORA's tutorial module allows you to determine the corner cells of the *closed loop* interactively, with immediate feedback regarding the validity of your selections. See TORA Moment on p.196.

TABLE 5.24 Iteration 2 Calculations

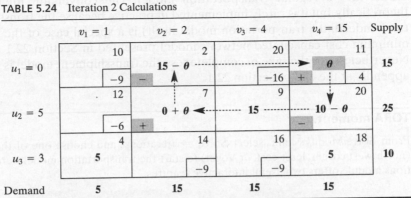

	$v_1 = 1$	$v_2 = 2$	$v_3 = 4$	$v_4 = 15$	Supply
$u_1 \equiv 0$	10 −9 −	2 $15 - \theta$	20 −16 +	11 θ 4	15
$u_2 = 5$	12 −6 +	7 $0 + \theta$	9 15	20 $10 - \theta$	25
$u_3 = 3$	4 5	14 −9	16 −9	18 5	10
Demand	5	15	15	15	

TABLE 5.25 Iteration 3 Calculations (Optimal)

	$v_1 = -3$	$v_2 = 2$	$v_3 = 4$	$v_4 = 11$	Supply
$u_1 \equiv 0$	10 −13	2 5	20 −16	11 10	15
$u_2 = 5$	12 −10	7 10	9 15	20 −4	25
$u_3 = 7$	4 5	14 −5	16 −5	18 5	10
Demand	5	15	15	15	

The new solution, shown in Table 5.25, costs $4 \times 10 = \$40$ less than the preceding one, thus yielding the new cost $\$475 - \$40 = \$435$. The new values of $u_i + v_j - c_{ij}$ are now negative for all nonbasic x_{ij}. Thus, the solution in Table 5.25 is optimal.

The following table summarizes the optimum solution.

From silo	To mill	Number of truckloads
1	2	5
1	4	10
2	2	10
2	3	15
3	1	5
3	4	5
	Optimal cost = $435	

Transshipment model. The transportation model assumes *direct* shipments between sources and destinations. This may not be the case in many situations where it may be cheaper to *transship* through intermediate nodes before reaching the final destination. A modeling trick based on the use of *buffers* can be used to convert the transshipment model into a regular transportation model. The conversion idea is interesting theoretically, but it is rarely implemented in practice because the transshipment model (and, indeed, the transportation model itself) is a special case of the highly efficient minimum cost capacitated network model presented in Section 22.1 on the website. Nevertheless, for the sake of completeness, the transshipment model is presented as an appendix at the end of Section 22.1.

TORA moment.

From Solve/Modify Menu , select Solve $\Rightarrow$ Iterations , and choose one of the three methods (north-west corner, least-cost, or Vogel) to start the transportation model iterations. The iterations module offers two useful interactive features:

1. You can set any u or v equal to zero before generating iteration 2 (the default is $u_1 = 0$). Although the values of u_i and v_j change, the evaluation of the nonbasic cells ($= u_i + v_j - c_{ij}$) remains the same.

2. You can test your understanding of the selection of the *closed loop* by clicking (in any order) the *corner* cells that comprise the path. If your selection is correct, the cell will change color (green for entering variable, red for leaving variable, and gray otherwise).

Solver moment.

Figure 5.4 provides the Excel Solver template for Example 5.3-1 (file *solverEx5.3-1.xls*), together with all the formulas and the definition of range names.

In the input section, data include unit cost matrix (cells B4:E6), source names (cells A4:A6), destination names (cells B3:E3), supply (cells F4:F6), and demand (cells B7:E7). In the output section, cells B11:E13 provides the optimal solution in matrix form. The total cost formula is in target cell A10.

AMPL moment.

Files *amplEx5.3-1a.txt* and *amplEx5.3-1b.txt* provide the AMPL model for Example 5.3-1. The details of the model are explained in Section C.9 on the website.

PROBLEM SET 5.3B

1. Consider the transportation models in Table 5.26.
   (a) Use the northwest-corner method to find the starting solution.
   (b) Develop the iterations that lead to the optimum solution.
   (c) *TORA Experiment.* Use TORA's Iterations module to compare the effect of using the northwest-corner rule, least-cost method, and Vogel method on the number of iterations leading to the optimum solution.
   (d) *Solver Experiment.* Solve the problem by modifying file *solverEx5.3-1.xls*.
   (e) *AMPL Experiment.* Solve the problem by modifying file *amplEx5.3-1b.txt*.

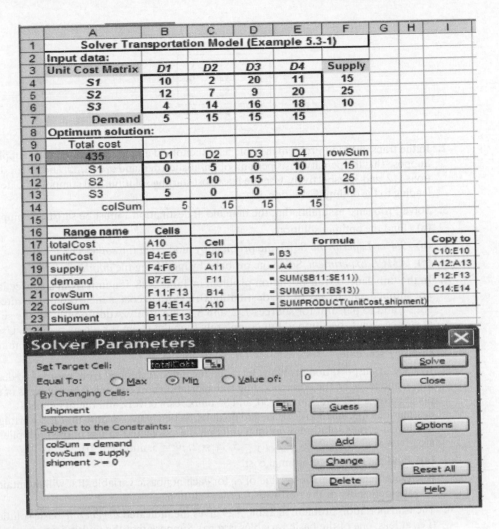

FIGURE 5.4

Excel Solver solution of the transportation model of Example 5.3-1 (File *solverEx5.3-1.xls*)

TABLE 5.26 Transportation Models for Problem 1

(i)				(ii)				(iii)			
$0	$2	$1	6	$10	$4	$2	8	—	$3	$5	4
$2	$1	$5	9	$2	$3	$4	5	$7	$4	$9	7
$2	$4	$3	5	$1	$2	$0	6	$1	$8	$6	19
5	5	10		7	6	6		5	6	19	

TABLE 5.27 Data for Problem 2

$5	$1	$7	**10**
$6	$4	$6	**80**
$3	$2	$5	**15**
75	**20**	**50**	

2. In the transportation problem in Table 5.27, the total demand exceeds the total supply. Suppose that the penalty costs per unit of unsatisfied demand are $2, $5, and $3 for destinations 1, 2, and 3, respectively. Use the least-cost starting solution, and compute the iterations leading to the optimum solution.

3. Solve Problem 2 assuming that the demand at destination 1 must be satisfied completely.
   (a) Find the optimal solution.
   (b) *Solver Experiment.* Solve the problem by modifying file *solverEx5.3-1.xls*.
   (c) *AMPL Experiment.* Solve the problem by modifying file *amplEx5.3-1b.txt*.

4. In the unbalanced transportation problem in Table 5.28, if a unit from a source is not shipped out (to any of the destinations), a storage cost is incurred at the rate of $5, $4, and $3 per unit for sources 1, 2, and 3, respectively. Additionally, all the supply at source 2 must be shipped out completely to make room for a new product. Use Vogel's starting solution, and determine all the iterations leading to the optimum shipping schedule.

*5. In a 3×3 transportation problem, let x_{ij} be the amount shipped from source i to destination j, and let c_{ij} be the corresponding transportation cost per unit. The amounts of supply at sources 1, 2, and 3 are 15, 30, and 85 units, respectively, and the demands at destinations 1, 2, and 3 are 20, 30, and 80 units, respectively. Assume that the starting northwest-corner solution is optimal and that the associated values of the multipliers are given as $u_1 = -2$, $u_2 = 3$, $u_3 = 5$, $v_1 = 2$, $v_2 = 5$, and $v_3 = 10$.
   (a) Find the associated optimal cost.
   (b) Determine the smallest value of c_{ij} for each nonbasic variable that will maintain the optimality of the northwest-corner solution.

6. The transportation problem in Table 5.29 gives the indicated *degenerate* basic solution (i.e., at least one of the basic variables is zero). Suppose that the multipliers associated

TABLE 5.28 Data for Problem 4

$1	$2	$1	**20**
$3	$4	$5	**40**
$2	$3	$3	**30**
30	**20**	**20**	

TABLE 5.29 Data for Problem 6

10			**10**
	20	**20**	**40**
10	**20**	**20**	

TABLE 5.30 Data for Problem 7

$1	$1	$2	5
$6	$5	$1	6
2	7	1	

with this solution are $u_1 = 1$, $u_2 = -1$, $v_1 = 2$, $v_2 = 2$, and $v_3 = 5$ and that the unit cost for all (basic and nonbasic) *zero* x_{ij} variables is given by

$$c_{ij} = i + j\theta, \; -\infty < \theta < \infty$$

(a) If the given solution is optimal, determine the associated optimal value of the objective function.

(b) Determine the value of θ that will guarantee the optimality of the given solution. (*Hint:* Locate the zero basic variable.)

7. Consider the problem

$$\text{Minimize } z = \sum_{i=1}^{m} \sum_{j=1}^{n} c_{ij} x_{ij}$$

subject to

$$\sum_{j=1}^{n} x_{ij} \geq a_i, \; i = 1, 2, \ldots, m$$

$$\sum_{i=1}^{m} x_{ij} \geq b_j, \; j = 1, 2, \ldots, n$$

$$x_{ij} \geq 0, \text{ all } i \text{ and } j$$

It may appear logical to assume that the optimum solution will require the first (second) set of inequalities to be replaced with equations if $\Sigma a_i \geq \Sigma b_j (\Sigma a_i \leq \Sigma b_j)$. The counterexample in Table 5.30 shows that this assumption is not correct.

Show that the application of the suggested procedure yields the solution $x_{11} = 2$, $x_{12} = 3$, $x_{22} = 4$, and $x_{23} = 2$, with $z = \$27$, which is worse than the feasible solution $x_{11} = 2$, $x_{12} = 7$, and $x_{23} = 6$, with $z = \$15$.

5.3.3 Simplex Method Explanation of the Method of Multipliers

The relationship between the method of multipliers and the simplex method can be explained based on the primal–dual relationships (Section 4.2). From the special structure of the LP representing the transportation model (see Example 5.1-1 for an illustration), the associated dual problem can be written as

$$\text{Maximize } z = \sum_{i=1}^{m} a_i u_i + \sum_{j=1}^{n} b_j v_j$$

subject to

$$u_i + v_j \leq c_{ij}, \text{ all } i \text{ and } j$$

$$u_i \text{ and } v_j \text{ unrestricted}$$

where

a_i = Supply amount at source i

b_j = Demand amount at destination j

c_{ij} = Unit transportation cost from source i to destination j

u_i = Dual variable of the constraint associated with source i

v_j = Dual variable of the constraint associated with destination j

From Formula 2, Section 4.2.4, the objective-function coefficients (reduced costs) of the variable x_{ij} equal the difference between the left- and right-hand sides of the corresponding dual constraint—that is, $u_i + v_j - c_{ij}$. However, we know that this quantity must equal zero for each *basic variable*, which produces the following result:

$$u_i + v_j = c_{ij}, \text{ for each } \textit{basic} \text{ variable } x_{ij}.$$

There are $m + n - 1$ such equations whose solution (after assuming an arbitrary value $u_1 = 0$) yields the multipliers u_i and v_j. Once these multipliers are computed, the entering variable is determined from all the *nonbasic* variables as the one having the largest positive $u_i + v_j - c_{ij}$.

The assignment of an arbitrary value to one of the dual variables (i.e., $u_1 = 0$) may appear inconsistent with the way the dual variables are computed using Method 2 in Section 4.2.3. Namely, for a given basic solution (and, hence, inverse), the dual values must be unique. Problem 2, Set 5.3c, addresses this point.

PROBLEM SET 5.3C

1. Write the dual problem for the LP of the transportation problem in Example 5.3-5 (Table 5.21). Compute the associated optimum *dual* objective value using the optimal dual values given in Table 5.25, and show that it equals the optimal cost given in the example.

2. In the transportation model, one of the dual variables assumes an arbitrary value. This means that for the same basic solution, the values of the associated dual variables are not unique. The result appears to contradict the theory of linear programming, where the dual values are determined as the product of the vector of the objective coefficients for the basic variables and the associated inverse basic matrix (see Method 2, Section 4.2.3). Show that for the transportation model, although the inverse basis is unique, the vector of *basic* objective coefficients need not be so. Specifically, show that if c_{ij} is changed to $c_{ij} + k$ for all i and j, where k is a constant, then the optimal values of x_{ij} will remain the same. Hence, the use of an arbitrary value for a dual variable is implicitly equivalent to assuming that a specific constant k is added to all c_{ij}.

5.4 THE ASSIGNMENT MODEL

The classical assignment model deals with matching workers (with varying skills) to jobs. Presumably, skill variation affects the cost of completing a job. The goal is to determine the minimum-cost assignment of workers to jobs. The general assignment model with n workers and n jobs is represented in Table 5.31. The element c_{ij} represents the cost of assigning worker i to job $j(i, j = 1, 2, ... n)$. There is no loss of

TABLE 5.31 Assignment Model

	Jobs				
	1	2	...	n	
1	c_{11}	c_{12}	...	c_{1n}	1
2	c_{21}	c_{22}	...	c_{2n}	1
Worker $\vdots$	$\vdots$	$\vdots$	$\vdots$	$\vdots$	$\vdots$
N	c_{n1}	c_{n2}	...	c_{nn}	1
	1	1	...	1	

generality in assuming that the number of workers and the number of jobs are equal, because we can always add fictitious workers or fictitious jobs to satisfy this assumption.

The assignment model is a special case of the transportation model, where workers represent sources and jobs represent destinations. The supply (demand) amount at each source (destination) exactly equals 1. The cost of "transporting" worker i to job j is c_{ij}. In effect, the assignment model can be solved directly as a regular transportation model (or as a regular LP). Nevertheless, the fact that all the supply and demand amounts equal 1 has led to the development of a simple solution algorithm called the **Hungarian method**. Although the new solution method appears totally unrelated to the transportation model, the algorithm is actually rooted in the simplex method, just as the transportation model is.

5.4.1 The Hungarian Method[8]

We will use two examples to present the mechanics of the new algorithm. The next section provides a simplex-based explanation of the procedure.

Example 5.4-1

Joe Klyne's three children, John, Karen, and Terri, want to earn some money for personal expenses. Mr. Klyne has chosen three chores for his children: mowing the lawn, painting the garage door, and washing the family cars. To avoid anticipated sibling competition, he asks them to submit individual (secret) bids for what they feel is fair pay for each of the three chores.

TABLE 5.32 Klyne's Assignment Problem

	Mow	Paint	Wash
John	$15	$10	$9
Karen	$9	$15	$10
Terri	$10	$12	$8

---

[8]As with the transportation model, the classical Hungarian method, designed primarily for *hand* computations, is something of the past and is presented here for historical reasons. Today, the need for such computational shortcuts is not warranted, as the problem can be solved by highly efficient LP computer codes. Perhaps the benefit from studying these classical techniques is that they are based on a sophisticated theory that reduce the solution steps to simple rules suitable for hand computations.

TABLE 5.33 Application of the Hungarian Method to the Assignment Problem of Example 5.4-1

Step 1:

	Mow	Paint	Wash	Row min
John	15	10	9	$p_1 = 9$
Karen	9	15	10	$p_2 = 9$
Terri	10	12	8	$p_3 = 8$

$\Rightarrow$

Step 2:

	Mow	Paint	Wash
John	6	1	0
Karen	0	6	1
Terri	2	4	0
Column max	$q_1 = 0$	$q_2 = 1$	$q_3 = 0$

$\Rightarrow$

Step 3:

	Mow	Paint	Wash
John	6	**0**	0
Karen	**0**	5	1
Terri	2	3	**0**

Table 5.32 summarizes the bids received. The children will abide by their father's decision regarding the assignment of chores.

The assignment problem will be solved by the Hungarian method.

Step 1. Determine p_i, the minimum cost element of row i in the original cost matrix, and subtract it from all the elements of row $i, i = 1, 2, 3$.

Step 2. For the matrix created in step 1, determine q_j, the minimum cost element of column j, and subtract it from all the elements of column $j, j = 1, 2, 3$.

Step 3. From the matrix in step 2, attempt to find a *feasible* assignment among all the resulting zero entries.

3a. If such an assignment can be found, it is optimal.

3b. Else, additional calculations are needed (as will be explained in Example 5.4-2).

Table 5.33 shows the application of the three steps to the current problem.

The cells with underscored zero entries in Step 3 provide the (feasible) optimum solution: John gets the paint job, Karen gets to mow the lawn, and Terri gets to wash the family cars. The total cost to Mr. Klyne is $9 + 10 + 8 = \$27$. This amount also will always equal $(p_1 + p_2 + p_3) + (q_1 + q_2 + q_3) = (9 + 9 + 8) + (0 + 1 + 0) = \$27$. (A justification of this result is given in the next section.)

As stated in step 3 of the Hungarian method, the zeros created by steps 1 and 2 may not yield a feasible solution directly. In this case, further steps are needed to find the optimal (feasible) assignment. The following example demonstrates this situation.

Example 5.4-2

Suppose that the situation discussed in Example 5.4-1 is extended to four children and four chores. Table 5.34 summarizes the cost elements of the problem.

TABLE 5.34   Assignment Model

		Chore		
	1	2	3	4
Child 1	$1	$4	$6	$3
2	$9	$7	$10	$9
3	$4	$5	$11	$7
4	$8	$7	$8	$5

TABLE 5.35   Reduced Assignment Matrix

		Chore		
	1	2	3	4
Child 1	0	3	2	2
2	2	0	0	2
3	0	1	4	3
4	3	2	0	0

The application of steps 1 and 2 to the matrix in Table 5.34 (using $p_1 = 1$, $p_2 = 7$, $p_3 = 4$, $p_4 = 5$, $q_1 = 0$, $q_2 = 0$, $q_3 = 3$, and $q_4 = 0$) yields the reduced matrix in Table 5.35 (verify!):

The locations of the zero entries do not allow assigning unique chores to all the children. For example, if we assign child 1 to chore 1, then column 1 will be eliminated, and child 3 will not have a zero entry in the remaining three columns. This obstacle can be accounted for by adding the following step to the procedure given in Example 5.4-1:

Step 3b. If no feasible zero-element assignments can be found,

(i)   Draw the *minimum* number of horizontal and vertical lines in the last reduced matrix to cover *all* the zero entries.

(ii) Select the *smallest un*covered entry, subtract it from every uncovered entry, and then add it to every entry at the intersection of two lines.

(iii) If no feasible assignment can be found among the resulting zero entries, repeat step 3a.

The application of step 3b to the last matrix produces the shaded cells in Table 5.36. The smallest unshaded entry (shown underscored) equals 1. This entry is added to the intersection cells and subtracted from the remaining shaded cells to produce the matrix in Table 5.37, and the optimal solution shown by underscored zeros.

TABLE 5.36   Application of Step 3b

		Chore		
	1	2	3	4
Child 1	0	3	2	2
2	2	0	0	2
3	0	1	4	3
4	3	2	0	0

TABLE 5.37   Optimal Assignment

	Chore			
	1	2	3	4
Child 1	**0**	2	1	1
Child 2	3	0	**0**	2
Child 3	0	**0**	3	2
Child 4	4	2	0	**0**

AMPL moment.

File *amplEx5.4-2.txt* provides the AMPL model for the assignment model. The model is similar to that of the transportation model.

PROBLEM SET 5.4A

1. Solve the assignment models in Table 5.38.
   (a) Solve by the Hungarian method.
   (b) *TORA Experiment.* Express the problem as an LP and solve it with TORA.
   (c) *TORA Experiment.* Use TORA to solve the problem as a transportation model.
   (d) *Solver Experiment.* Modify Excel file *solverEx5.3-1.xls* to solve the problem.
   (e) *AMPL Experiment.* Modify file *amplEx5.3b-1.txt* to solve the problem.
2. JoShop needs to assign 4 jobs to 4 workers. The cost of performing a job is a function of the skills of the workers. Table 5.39 summarizes the cost of the assignments. Worker 1 cannot do job 3, and worker 3 cannot do job 4. Determine the optimal assignment using the Hungarian method.

TABLE 5.38   Data for Problem 1

(i)					(ii)				
$9	$8	$2	$10	$3	$3	$12	$2	$2	$7
$6	$5	$2	$7	$5	$6	$1	$5	$8	$6
$6	$3	$2	$7	$5	$9	$4	$7	$13	$3
$8	$4	$12	$3	$5	$2	$5	$4	$2	$1
$7	$8	$6	$7	$7	$10	$6	$1	$4	$6

TABLE 5.39   Data for Problem 2

	Job			
	1	2	3	4
Worker 1	$50	$50	—	$20
Worker 2	$70	$40	$20	$30
Worker 3	$90	$30	$50	—
Worker 4	$70	$20	$60	$70

TABLE 5.40   Data for Problem 5

Departure date from Dallas	Return date to Dallas
Monday, June 3	Friday, June 7
Monday, June 10	Wednesday, June 12
Monday, June 17	Friday, June 21
Tuesday, June 25	Friday, June 28

3. In the JoShop model of Problem 2, suppose that an additional (fifth) worker becomes available for performing the four jobs at the respective costs of $70, $50, $30, and $90. Is it economical to replace one of the current four workers with the new one?

4. In the model of Problem 2, suppose that JoShop has just received a fifth job and that the respective costs of performing it by the four current workers are $20, $10, $20, and $80. Moreover, job 1 cannot be displaced by the newly arriving job. Should the new job take priority over any of the four jobs JoShop already has?

5. *A business executive must make the four round-trips listed in Table 5.40 between the head office in Dallas and a branch office in Atlanta.

The price of a round-trip ticket from Dallas is $400. A 25% discount is granted if the dates of arrival and departure of a ticket span a weekend (Saturday and Sunday). If the stay in Atlanta lasts more than 21 days, the discount is increased to 30%. A one-way ticket between Dallas and Atlanta (either direction) costs $250. How should the executive purchase the tickets?

*6. Figure 5.5 gives a schematic layout of a machine shop with its existing work centers designated by squares 1, 2, 3, and 4. Four new work centers, I, II, III, and IV are to be

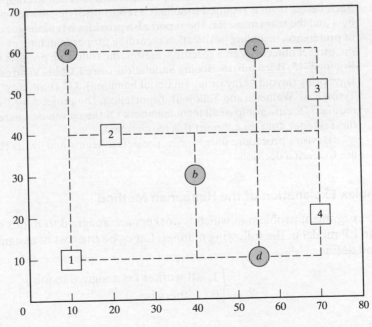

FIGURE 5.5

Machine shop layout for Problem 6, Set 5.4a

TABLE 5.41 Data for Problem 6

		New center			
		I	II	III	IV
	1	10	2	4	3
Existing	2	7	1	9	5
center	3	0	8	6	2
	4	11	4	0	7

added to the shop at the locations designated by circles a, b, c, d, and d. The objective is to assign the new centers to the proposed locations to minimize the total materials handling traffic between the existing centers and the proposed ones. Table 5.41 summarizes the frequency of trips between the new centers and the old ones. Materials handling equipment travels along the rectangular aisles intersecting at the locations of the centers. For example, the one-way travel distance (in meters) between center 1 and location b is $30 + 20 = 50$ m.

7. In the Industrial Engineering Department at the University of Arkansas, INEG 4904 is a capstone design course intended to allow teams of students to apply the knowledge and skills learned in the undergraduate curriculum to a practical problem. The members of each team select a project manager, identify an appropriate scope for their project, write and present a proposal, perform necessary tasks for meeting the project objectives, and write and present a final report. The course instructor identifies potential projects and provides appropriate information sheets for each, including contact at the sponsoring organization, project summary, and potential skills needed to complete the project. Each design team is required to submit a report justifying the selection of team members and the team manager. The report also provides a ranking for each project in order of preference, including justification regarding proper matching of the team's skills with the project objectives. In a specific semester, the following projects were identified: Boeing F-15, Boeing F-18, Boeing Simulation, Cargil, Cobb-Vantress, ConAgra, Cooper, DaySpring (layout), DaySpring (material handling), J.B. Hunt, Raytheon, Tyson South, Tyson East, Walmart, and Yellow Transportation. The projects for Boeing and Raytheon require U.S. citizenship of all team members. Of the eleven design teams available for this semester, four do not meet this requirement.

Devise a procedure for assigning projects to teams, and justify the arguments you use to reach a decision.

5.4.2 Simplex Explanation of the Hungarian Method

The assignment problem in which n workers are assigned to n jobs can be represented as an LP model in the following manner: Let c_{ij} be the cost of assigning worker i to job j, and define

$$x_{ij} = \begin{cases} 1, & \text{if worker } i \text{ is assigned to job } j \\ 0, & \text{otherwise} \end{cases}$$

Then the LP model is given as

$$\text{Minimize } z = \sum_{i=1}^{n}\sum_{j=1}^{n}c_{ij}x_{ij}$$

subject to

$$\sum_{j=1}^{n}x_{ij} = 1, i = 1, 2, \dots, n$$

$$\sum_{i=1}^{n}x_{ij} = 1, j = 1, 2, \dots, n$$

$$x_{ij} = 0 \text{ or } 1$$

The optimal solution of the preceding LP model remains unchanged if a constant is added to or subtracted from any row or column of the cost matrix (c_{ij}). To prove this point, let p_i and q_j be constants subtracted from row i and column j. Thus, the cost element c_{ij} is changed to

$$c'_{ij} = c_{ij} - p_i - q_j$$

Now

$$\sum_{i}\sum_{j}c'_{ij}x_{ij} = \sum_{i}\sum_{j}(c_{ij} - p_i - q_j)x_{ij} = \sum_{i}\sum_{j}c_{ij}x_{ij} - \sum_{i}p_i\left(\sum_{j}x_{ij}\right) - \sum_{j}q_j\left(\sum_{i}x_{ij}\right)$$

$$= \sum_{i}\sum_{j}c_{ij}x_{ij} - \sum_{i}p_i(1) - \sum_{j}q_j(1)$$

$$= \sum_{i}\sum_{j}c_{ij}x_{ij} - \text{constant}$$

Because the new objective function differs from the original by a constant, the optimum values of x_{ij} are the same in both cases. The development shows that steps 1 and 2 of the Hungarian method, which call for subtracting p_i from row i and then subtracting q_j from column j, produce an equivalent assignment model. In this regard, if a feasible solution can be found among the zero entries of the cost matrix created by steps 1 and 2, then it must be optimum (because the cost in the modified matrix cannot be less than zero).

If the created zero entries cannot yield a feasible solution (as Example 5.4-2 demonstrates), then step 2a (dealing with the covering of the zero entries) must be applied. The validity of this procedure is again rooted in the simplex method of linear programming and can be explained by duality theory (Chapter 4) and the complementary slackness theorem (Chapter 7). We will not present the details of the proof here because they are somewhat involved.

The reason $(p_1 + p_2 + \ldots + p_n) + (q_1 + q_2 + \ldots + q_n)$ gives the optimal objective value is that it represents the dual objective function of the assignment model. This result can be seen through comparison with the dual objective function of the transportation model given in Section 5.3.3. [See Bazaraa and Associates (2009) for the details.]

BIBLIOGRAPHY

Bazaraa, M., J. Jarvis, and H. Sherali, *Linear Programming and Network Flows*, 4th ed., Wiley, New York, 2009.

Dantzig, G., *Linear Programming and Extensions*, Princeton University Press, Princeton, N.J., 1963.

Hansen, P., and R. Wendell, "A Note on Airline Commuting," *Interfaces*, Vol. 12, No. 1, pp. 85–87, 1982.

Murty, K., *Network Programming*, Prentice Hall, Upper Saddle River, NJ, 1992.

CHAPTER 6

Network Model

Real-Life Application—Saving Federal Travel Dollars

U.S. Federal government offices are located in most cities in the United States, and federal employees are required to attend development conferences and training courses offered around the country. The location of the city hosting conferences/training events can impact travel costs. The goal of the study is to determine the optimal location of host city for a scheduled conference/training event. For fiscal year 1997, the developed model was estimated to save at least $400,000. Case 4 in Chapter 26 on the website provides the details.

6.1 SCOPE AND DEFINITION OF NETWORK MODELS

Many operations research situations can be modeled and solved as networks (nodes connected by branches):

1. Design of an offshore natural-gas pipeline network connecting well heads in the Gulf of Mexico to an inshore delivery point with the objective of minimizing the cost of constructing the pipeline.

2. Determination of the shortest route between two cities in an existing network of roads.

3. Determination of the maximum capacity (in tons per year) of a coal slurry pipeline network joining coal mines in Wyoming with power plants in Houston. (Slurry pipelines transport coal by pumping water through specially designed pipes.)

4. Determination of the time schedule (start and completion dates) for the activities of a construction project.

5. Determination of the minimum-cost flow schedule from oil fields to refineries through a pipeline network.

The solution of these situations is accomplished through a variety of network optimization algorithms. This chapter presents four of these algorithms.

1. Minimal spanning tree (situation 1)
2. Shortest-route algorithm (situation 2)
3. Maximal-flow algorithm (situation 3)
4. Critical path (CPM) algorithm (situation 4)

For the fifth situation, the minimum-cost capacitated network algorithm is presented in Section 22.1 on the website.

Network definitions. A network consists of a set of **nodes** linked by **arcs** (or **branches**). The notation for describing a network is (N, A), where N is the set of nodes, and A is the set of arcs. As an illustration, the network in Figure 6.1 is described as

$$N = \{1, 2, 3, 4, 5\}$$

$$A = \{(1, 2), (1, 3), (2, 3), (2, 5), (3, 4), (3, 5), (4, 2), (4, 5)\}$$

Associated with each network is a **flow** (e.g., oil products flow in a pipeline and automobile traffic flow in highways). The maximum flow in a network can be finite or infinite, depending on the capacity of its arcs.

An arc is said to be **directed** or **oriented** if it allows positive flow in one direction only. A **directed network** has all directed arcs.

A **path** is a set of arcs joining two distinct nodes, passing through other nodes in the network. For example, in Figure 6.1 arcs $(1, 2), (2, 3), (3, 4)$, and $(4, 5)$ form a path between nodes 1 and 5. A path forms a **cycle** or a **loop** if it connects a node back to itself through other nodes. In Figure 6.1, arcs $(2, 3), (3, 4)$, and $(4, 2)$ form a cycle.

A network is said to be **connected** if every two distinct nodes are linked by at least one path. The network in Figure 6.1 demonstrates this type of network. A **tree** is a *cycle-free* connected network comprised of a *subset* of all the nodes, and a **spanning tree** is a tree that links *all* the nodes of the network. Figure 6.2 provides examples of a tree and a spanning tree from the network in Figure 6.1.

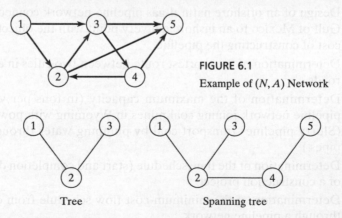

FIGURE 6.1

Example of (N, A) Network

Tree   Spanning tree

FIGURE 6.2

Examples of a tree and a spanning tree

Example 6.1-1   (Bridges of Königsberg)

The Prussian city of Königsberg (now Kalingrad in Russia) was founded in 1254 on the banks of river Pergel with seven bridges connecting its four sections (labeled *A, B, C,* and *D*) as shown in Figure 6.3. A question was raised as to whether a *round-trip* could be constructed to visit all four sections of the city, crossing each bridge exactly once. A section could be visited multiple times, if necessary.

In the mid-eighteenth century, the famed mathematician Leonhard Euler developed a special "path construction" argument to prove that it was impossible to construct such a trip. Later, in the early nineteenth century, the same problem was solved by representing the situation as a network with nodes representing the sections and (distinct) arcs representing the bridges, as shown in Figure 6.4.

The network representation facilitates finding an answer to the posed question: The number of arcs incident into each node is *odd*. This makes it impossible to enter and exit all sections using distinct bridges. Hence the desired round-trip cannot be constructed.[1]

FIGURE 6.3

Bridges of Königsberg

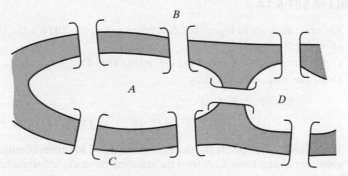

FIGURE 6.4

Network representation of Königsberg problem

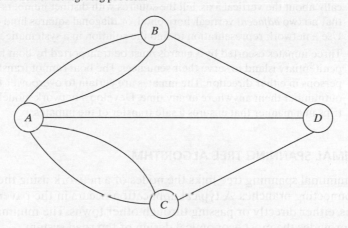

---

[1]General solution: A tour starting and ending at one node exists if the number of arcs incident into each node is *even*. A trip starting at one node and ending at *another* exists if the number of arcs incident into these two nodes is *odd*. Else, no solution exists. See B. Hopkins and R. Wilson, "The Truth about Königsberg," *College Math Journal*, Vol. 35, No. 3, pp. 198–207, 2004.

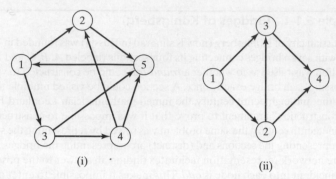

FIGURE 6.5

Networks for Problem 1, Set 6.1a

PROBLEM SET 6.1A

*1. For each network in Figure 6.5, determine (a) a path, (b) a cycle, (c) a tree, and (d) a spanning tree.

2. Determine the sets N and A for the networks in Figure 6.5.

3. Draw the network defined by

$$N = \{1, 2, 3, 4, 5\}$$

$$A = \{(1, 2), (1, 5), (2, 3), (2, 4), (3, 4), (3, 5), (4, 3), (4, 5), (5, 2)\}$$

4. In Example 6.1-1, specify the smallest number and locations of additional bridges needed to construct a round-trip. Construct the resulting network, and determine the legs of the trip.

*5. Consider eight equal squares arranged in three rows, with two squares in the first row, four in the second, and two in the third. The squares of each row are arranged symmetrically about the vertical axis. Fill the squares with distinct numbers in the range 1 to 8 so that no two *adjacent* vertical, horizontal, or diagonal squares hold consecutive numbers. Use a network representation to find the solution in a systematic way.

6. Three inmates escorted by 3 guards must be transported by boat from the mainland to a penitentiary island to serve their sentences. The boat cannot transfer more than two persons in either direction. The inmates are certain to overpower the guards if they outnumber them anywhere at any time. Develop a network model that designs the boat trips in a manner that ensures a safe transfer of the inmates.

6.2   MINIMAL SPANNING TREE ALGORITHM

The minimal spanning tree links the nodes of a network using the smallest total length of connecting branches. A typical application occurs in the pavement of roads linking towns, either directly or passing through other towns. The minimal spanning tree solution provides the most economical design of the road system.

Let $N = \{1, 2, \ldots, n\}$ be the set of nodes of the network and define

C_k = Set of nodes that have been permanently connected at iteration k

$\overline{C}_k$ = Set of nodes as yet to be connected permanently after iteration k

The following steps describe the minimal spanning tree algorithm:

Step 0.   Set $C_0 = \varnothing$ and $\overline{C}_0 = N$.

Step 1.   Start with *any* node i in the unconnected set $\overline{C}_0$ and set $C_1 = \{i\}$, rendering $\overline{C}_1 = N - \{i\}$. Set $k = 2$.

General step k.   Select a node, j^*, in the unconnected set $\overline{C}_{k-1}$ that yields the shortest arc to a node in the connected set C_{k-1}. Link j^* permanently to C_{k-1} and remove it from $\overline{C}_{k-1}$ to obtain C_k and $\overline{C}_k$, respectively. Stop if $\overline{C}_k$ is empty; else, set $k = k + 1$ and repeat the step.

Example 6.2-1

Midwest TV Cable Company is providing cable service to five new housing developments. Figure 6.6 depicts possible TV connections to the five areas, with cable miles affixed on each arc. The goal is to determine the most economical cable network.

The algorithm starts at node 1 (actually, any other node can be a starting point), which gives

$$C_1 = \{1\} \text{ and } \overline{C}_1 = \{2, 3, 4, 5, 6\}$$

The iterations of the algorithm are summarized in Figure 6.7. The thin arcs provide all the candidate links between C and $\overline{C}$. The thick arcs are the permanent links of the connected set C, and the dashed arc is the new (permanent) link added at each iteration. For example, in iteration 1, branch $(1, 2)$ is the shortest link ($= 1$ mile) among all the candidate branches from node 1 to nodes 2, 3, 4, 5, and 6 in the unconnected set $\overline{C}_1$. Hence, link $(1, 2)$ is made permanent and $j^* = 2$, which yields

$$C_2 = \{1, 2\}, \overline{C}_2 = \{3, 4, 5, 6\}$$

The solution is given by the minimal spanning tree shown in iteration 6 of Figure 6.7. The resulting minimum cable miles needed to provide the desired cable service are $1 + 3 + 4 + 3 + 5 = 16$ miles.

Remarks.   In theory, a minimal spanning tree can be formulated and solved as a linear program. However, LP is not a practical option because numerous constraints must be added to exclude all cycles, resulting in a huge LP, even for small networks.

FIGURE 6.6

Cable connections for Midwest TV Company

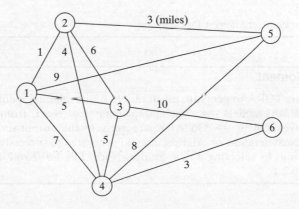

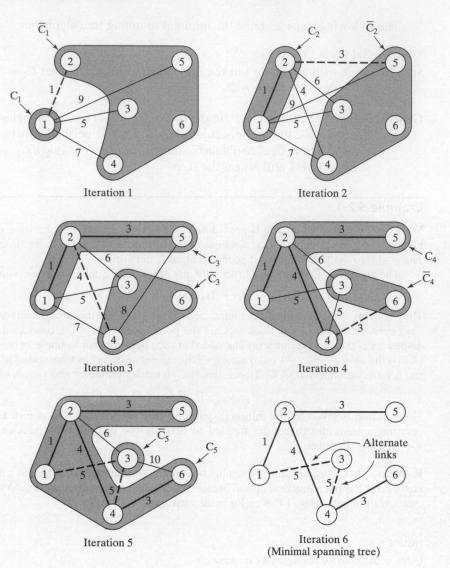

FIGURE 6.7

Solution iterations for Midwest TV Company

TORA Moment

You can use TORA to generate the iterations of the minimal spanning tree. From Main Menu, select Network models ⟹ Minimal spanning tree. Next, from SOLVE/MODIFY menu, select Solve problem ⟹ Go to output screen. In the output screen, select a Starting node, then use Next iteration or All iterations to generate the successive iterations. You can restart the iterations by selecting a new Starting Node. File *toraEx6.2-1.txt* gives TORA's data for Example 6.2-1.

PROBLEM SET 6.2A

1. Solve Example 6.2-1 starting at node 6 (instead of node 1), and show that the algorithm produces the same solution.
2. Determine the minimal spanning tree of the network of Example 6.2-1 under each of the following separate conditions:
  *(a) Nodes 5 and 6 are linked by a 2-mile cable.
  (b) Nodes 2 and 5 cannot be linked.
  (c) Nodes 2 and 6 are linked by a 4-mile cable.
  (d) The cable between nodes 1 and 2 is 8 miles long.
  (e) Nodes 3 and 5 are linked by a 2-mile cable.
  (f) Node 2 cannot be linked directly to nodes 3 and 5.
3. In intermodal transportation, loaded truck trailers are shipped between railroad termi-nals on special flatbed carts. Figure 6.8 shows the location of the main railroad terminals in the United States and the existing railroad tracks. The objective is to decide which tracks should be "revitalized" to handle the intermodal traffic. In particular, the Los Angeles (LA) terminal must be linked directly to Chicago (CH) to accommodate expected heavy traffic. Other than that, all the remaining terminals can be linked, directly or indirectly, such that the total length (in miles) of the selected tracks is minimized. Determine the segments of the railroad tracks that must be included in the revitalization program.
4. Figure 6.9 gives the mileage of the feasible links connecting nine offshore natural gas wellheads with an inshore delivery point. Because wellhead 1 is the closest to shore, it is equipped with sufficient pumping and storage capacity to pump the output of the remaining eight wells to the delivery point. Determine the minimum pipeline network that links the wellheads to the delivery point.
 *5. In Figure 6.9 of Problem 4, suppose that the wellheads can be divided into two groups depending on gas pressure: a high-pressure group that includes wells 2, 3, 4, and 7, and a low-pressure group that includes wells 5, 6, 8, and 9. Because of pressure difference, it is not possible to link the wellheads from the two groups. At the same time, both groups

FIGURE 6.8

Network for Problem 3, Set 6.2a

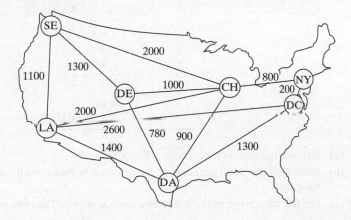

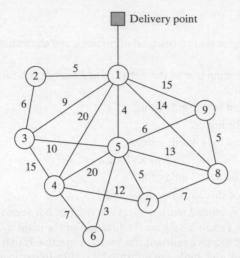

FIGURE 6.9

Network for Problem 4, Set 6.2a

must be connected to the delivery point through wellhead 1. Determine the minimum pipeline network for this situation assuming wellhead 3 is connected to wellhead 7 by and 8-mile link.

6. Electro produces 15 electronic parts on 10 machines. The company wants to group the machines into cells designed to minimize the "dissimilarities" among the parts processed in each cell. A measure of "dissimilarity," d_{ij}, among the parts processed on machines i and j can be expressed as

$$d_{ij} = 1 - \frac{n_{ij}}{n_{ij} + m_{ij}}$$

where n_{ij} is the number of parts shared between machines i and j, and m_{ij} is the number of parts that are used by either machine i or machine j only.

The following table assigns the parts to machines:

Machine	Assigned parts
1	1, 6
2	2, 3, 7, 8, 9, 12, 13, 15
3	3, 5, 10, 14
4	2, 7, 8, 11, 12, 13
5	3, 5, 10, 11, 14
6	1, 4, 5, 9, 10
7	2, 5, 7, 8, 9, 10
8	3, 4, 15
9	4, 10
10	3, 8, 10, 14, 15

(a) Express the problem as a network model.

(b) Show that the determination of the cells can be based on the minimal spanning tree solution.

(c) For the data given in the preceding table, construct the two- and three-cell solutions.

6.3 SHORTEST-ROUTE PROBLEM

The shortest-route problem determines the shortest route between a source and destination in a transportation network. Other situations can be represented by the same model, as illustrated by the following examples.

6.3.1 Examples of the Shortest-Route Applications

Example 6.3-1 (Equipment Replacement)

RentCar is developing a replacement policy for its car fleet over a 4-year planning horizon. At the start of each year, a car is either replaced or kept in operation for an extra year. A car must be in service from 1 to 3 years. The following table provides the replacement cost as a function of the year a car is acquired and the number of years in operation.

Equipment acquired at start of year	Replacement cost ($) for given years in operation		
	1	*2*	*3*
1	4000	5400	9800
2	4300	6200	8700
3	4800	7100	—
4	4900	—	—

The problem can be formulated as a network in which nodes 1 to 5 represent the start of years 1 to 5. Arcs from node 1 (year 1) can reach nodes 2, 3, and 4 because a car must be in operation from 1 to 3 years. The arcs from the other nodes can be interpreted similarly. The length of each arc equals the replacement cost. The solution of the problem is equivalent to finding the shortest route between nodes 1 and 5.

Figure 6.10 shows the resulting network. Using TORA,[2] the shortest route is $1 \rightarrow 3 \rightarrow 5$. The solution says that a car acquired at the start of year 1 (node 1) must be replaced after 2 years

FIGURE 6.10

Equipment replacement problem as a shortest-route model

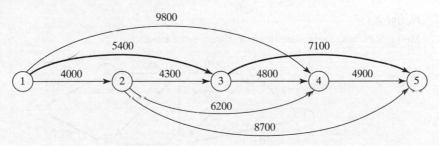

---

[2]From Main menu, select Network models $\Rightarrow$ Shortest route. From SOLVE/MODIFY menu, select Solve problem $\Rightarrow$ Shortest routes.

at the start of year 3 (node 3). The replacement car will then be kept in service until the end of year 4. The total cost of this replacement policy is $12,500 (=$5400 + $7100).

Example 6.3-2   (Most Reliable Route)

I. Q. Smart drives daily to work. Having just completed a course in network analysis, Smart is able to determine the shortest route to work. Unfortunately, the selected route is heavily patrolled by police, and with all the fines paid for speeding, the shortest route may not be the best choice. Smart has thus decided to choose a route that maximizes the probability of *not* being stopped by police.

The network in Figure 6.11 shows the possible routes from home to work, and the associated probabilities of not being stopped on each segment. The probability of not being stopped on a route is the product of the probabilities of its segments. For example, the probability of not receiving a fine on the route $1 \rightarrow 3 \rightarrow 5 \rightarrow 7$ is $.9 \times .3 \times .25 = .0675$. Smart's objective is to select the route that *maximizes* the probability of not being fined.

The problem can be formulated as a shortest-route model by using logarithmic transformation to convert the product probability into the sum of the logarithms of probabilities—that is, $p_{1k} = p_1 \times p_2 \times \cdots \times p_k$ is transformed to $\log p_{1k} = \log p_1 + \log p_2 + \cdots + \log p_k$.

The two functions p_{1k} and $\log p_{1k}$ are both monotone decreasing in k, thus maximizing p_{1k} is equivalent to maximizing $\log p_{1k}$, which in turn is equivalent to *minimizing* $-\log p_{1k}$. Thus, replacing p_j with $-\log p_j$ for all j in the network, the problem is converted to the shortest-route network in Figure 6.12.

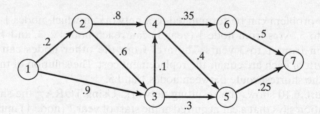

FIGURE 6.11

Most-reliable-route network model

FIGURE 6.12

Most-reliable-route representation as a shortest-route model

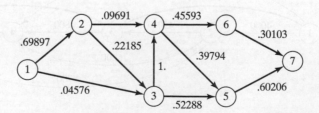

Using TORA, the shortest route in Figure 6.12 passes through nodes 1, 3, 5, and 7 with a corresponding "length" of 1.1707, or log $p_{17} = -1.1707$. Thus, the maximum probability of not being stopped is $p_{17} = 10^{-1.1707} = .0675$, not a very encouraging news for Smart!

Example 6.3-3   (Three-Jug Puzzle)

An 8-gallon jug is filled with fluid. Given two empty 5- and 3-gallon jugs, divide the 8 gallons of fluid into two equal parts using only the three jugs. What is the smallest number of transfers (decantations) needed to achieve this result?

You probably can solve this puzzle by inspection. Nevertheless, the solution process can be systematized by representing the problem as a shortest-route problem.

A node is defined by a triple index representing the amounts of fluid in the 8-, 5-, and 3-gallon jugs, respectively. This means that the network starts with node $(8, 0, 0)$ and terminates with the desired solution node $(4, 4, 0)$. A new node is generated from the current node by decanting fluid from one jug into another.

Figure 6.13 shows different routes that lead from the start node $(8, 0, 0)$ to the end node $(4, 4, 0)$. The arc between two successive nodes represents a single transfer, and hence it can be assumed to have a length of 1 unit. The problem thus reduces to determining the shortest route between node $(8, 0, 0)$ and node $(4, 4, 0)$.

The optimal solution, given by the bottom path in Figure 6.13, requires 7 decantations.

PROBLEM SET 6.3A

*1. Reconstruct the equipment replacement model of Example 6.3-1, assuming that a car must be kept in service for at least 2 years, with a maximum service life of 4 years. The planning horizon is from the start of year 1 to the end of year 5. The following table provides the necessary data.

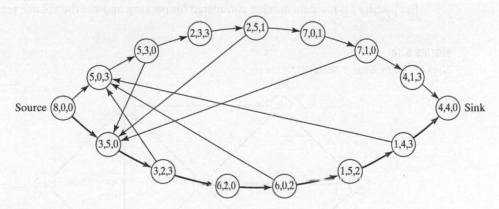

FIGURE 6.13

Three-jug puzzle representation as a shortest-route model

Year acquired	Replacement cost ($) for given years in operation		
	2	*3*	*4*
1	3800	4100	6900
2	4100	4890	7200
3	4200	5300	7300
4	4800	5800	—
5	5400	—	—

2. Figure 6.14 provides the communication network between two stations, 1 and 7. The probability that a link in the network will operate without failure is shown on each arc. Messages are sent from station 1 to station 7, and the objective is to determine the route that maximizes the probability of a successful transmission. Formulate the situation as a shortest-route model, and determine the optimum solution.

3. *Production Planning.* DirectCo sells an item whose demands over the next 4 months are 100, 140, 210, and 180 units, respectively. The company can stock just enough supply to meet each month's demand, or it can overstock to meet the demand for two or more consecutive months. In the latter case, a holding cost of $1.20 is charged per overstocked unit per month. DirectCo estimates the unit purchase prices for the next 4 months to be $15, $12, $10, and $14, respectively. A setup cost of $200 is incurred each time a purchase order is placed. The company wants to develop a purchasing plan that will minimize the total costs of ordering, purchasing, and holding the item in stock. Formulate the problem as a shortest-route model, and use TORA to find the optimum solution.

*4. *Knapsack Problem.* A hiker has a 5-ft^3 backpack and needs to decide on the most valuable items to take on the hiking trip. There are three items from which to choose. Their volumes are 2, 3, and 4 ft^3, and the hiker estimates their associated values on a scale from 0 to 100 as 30, 50, and 70, respectively. Express the problem as longest-route network, and find the optimal solution. (*Hint*: A node in the network may be defined as $[i, v]$, where i is the item number considered for packing, and v is the volume remaining

FIGURE 6.14

Network for Problem 2, Set 6.3a

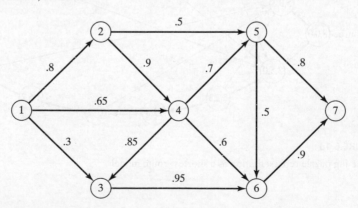

immediately before a decision is made on i. To solve with TORA, convert the longest-route to a shortest-route problem by using negative arc length.)

5. An old-fashioned electric toaster has two spring-loaded base-hinged doors. The two doors open outward in opposite directions away from the heating element. A slice of bread is toasted one side at a time by pushing open one of the doors with one hand and placing the slice with the other hand. After one side is toasted, the slice is turned over to get the other side toasted. The goal is to determine the sequence of operations (placing, toasting, turning, and removing) needed to toast three slices of bread in the shortest possible time. Formulate the problem as a shortest-route model, using the following elemental times for the different operations:

Operation	Time (seconds)
Place one slice in either side	3
Toast one side	30
Turn slice already in toaster	1
Remove slice from either side	3

6.3.2   Shortest-Route Algorithms

This section presents two algorithms for solving both cyclic (i.e., containing loops) and acyclic networks:

1. **Dijkstra's algorithm** for determining the shortest routes between the source node and every other node in the network.
2. **Floyd's algorithm** for determining the shortest route between *any* two nodes in the network.

Essentially, Floyd's algorithm subsumes Dijkstra's.

Dijkstra's algorithm.   Let u_i be the shortest distance from source node 1 to node i, and define d_{ij} (≥ 0) as the length of arc (i, j). The algorithm defines the label for an immediately succeeding node j as

$$[u_j, i] = [u_i + d_{ij}, i], d_{ij} \geq 0$$

The label for the starting node is $[0, -]$, indicating that the node has no predecessor.
   Node labels in Dijkstra's algorithm are of two types: *temporary* and *permanent*. A temporary label at a node is modified if a shorter route to the node can be found. Otherwise, the temporary status is changed to permanent.

Step 0.   Label the source node (node 1) with the *permanent* label $[0, -]$. Set $i = 1$.
General step i.
   (a)   Compute the *temporary* labels $[u_i + d_{ij}, i]$ for each node j with $d_{ij} > 0$, *provided j is not permanently labeled*. If node j already has an existing temporary label $[u_j, k]$ through another node k and if $u_i + d_{ij} < u_j$, replace $[u_j, k]$ with $[u_i + d_{ij}, i]$.

(b) If *all* the nodes have *permanent* labels, stop. Otherwise, select the label $[u_r, s]$ having the shortest distance ($= u_r$) among all the *temporary* labels (break ties arbitrarily). Set $i = r$ and repeat step i.

Example 6.3-4

The network in Figure 6.15 gives the permissible routes and their lengths in miles between city 1 (node 1) and four other cities (nodes 2 to 5). Determine the shortest routes between city 1 and each of the remaining four cities.

Iteration 0.   Assign the *permanent* label $[0, -]$ to node 1.

Iteration 1.   Nodes 2 and 3 can be reached from (the last permanently labeled) node 1. Thus, the list of labeled nodes (temporary and permanent) becomes

Node	Label	Status
1	**[0, −]**	**Permanent**
2	$[0 + 100, 1] = [100, 1]$	Temporary
3	$[0 + 30, 1] = [30, 1]$	Temporary

For the two temporary labels $[100, 1]$ and $[30, 1]$, node 3 yields the smaller distance ($u_3 = 30$). Thus, the status of node 3 is changed to permanent.

Iteration 2.   Nodes 4 and 5 can be reached from node 3, and the list of labeled nodes becomes

Node	Label	Status
1	[0, −]	Permanent
2	[100, 1]	Temporary
3	**[30, 1]**	**Permanent**
4	$[30 + 10, 3] = [40, 3]$	Temporary
5	$[30 + 60, 3] = [90, 3]$	Temporary

Temporary label $[40, 3]$ at node 4 is now permanent ($u_4 = 40$).

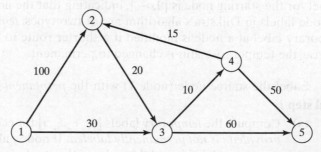

FIGURE 6.15

Network Example for Dijkstra's shortest-route algorithm

Iteration 3. Nodes 2 and 5 can be reached from node 4. Thus, the list of labeled nodes is updated as

Node	Label	Status
1	$[0, -]$	Permanent
2	$[40 + 15, 4] = [55, 4]$	Temporary
3	$[30, 1]$	Permanent
4	**$[40, 3]$**	**Permanent**
5	$[90, 3]$ or	
	$[40 + 50, 4] = [90, 4]$	Temporary

At node 2, the new label [55, 4] replaces the temporary label [100, 1] from iteration 1 because it provides a shorter route. Also, in iteration 3, node 5 has two alternative labels with the same distance ($u_5 = 90$). Temporary label [55, 4] at node 2 is now permanent ($u_2 = 55$).

Iteration 4. Only permanently labeled node 3 can be reached from node 2. Hence node 3 cannot be relabeled. The new list of labels remains the same as in iteration 3 except that the label at node 2 is now permanent. This leaves node 5 as the only temporary label. Because node 5 does not lead to other nodes, its label becomes permanent, and the process ends.

The computations of the algorithm can be carried out directly on the network, as Figure 6.16 demonstrates.

The shortest route between nodes 1 and any other node in the network is determined beginning at the desired destination node and backtracking to the starting node using the information in the permanent labels. For example, the following sequence determines the shortest route from node 1 to node 2:

$$(2) \rightarrow [55, 4] \rightarrow (4) \rightarrow [40, 3] \rightarrow (3) \rightarrow [30, 1] \rightarrow (1)$$

Thus, the desired route is $1 \rightarrow 3 \rightarrow 4 \rightarrow 2$ with a total length of 55 miles.

FIGURE 6.16

Dijkstra's labeling procedure

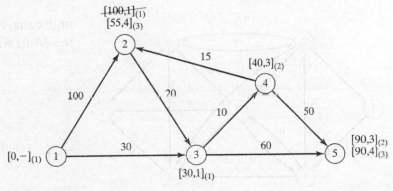

( ) = iteration

TORA Moment

TORA can be used to generate Dijkstra's iterations. From **SOLVE/MODIFY** menu, select Solve problem ⇒ Iterations ⇒ Dijkstra's algorithm. File *toraEx6.3-4.txt* provides TORA's data for Example 6.3-4.

PROBLEM SET 6.3B

1. The network in Figure 6.17 gives the distances in miles between pairs of cities 1, 2, . . . , and 8. Use Dijkstra's algorithm to find the shortest route between the following cities:

   (a) Cities 1 and 7

   (b) Cities 1 and 6

   *(c) Cities 4 and 8

   (d) Cities 2 and 7

2. Use Dijkstra's algorithm to find the shortest route between node 1 and every other node in the network of Figure 6.18.

3. Use Dijkstra's algorithm to determine the optimal solution of each of the following problems:

   (a) Problem 1, Set 6.3a.

   (b) Problem 2, Set 6.3a.

   (c) Problem 4, Set 6.3a.

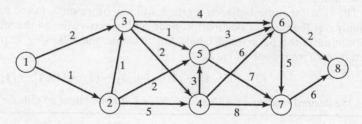

FIGURE 6.17

Network for Problem 1, Set 6.3b

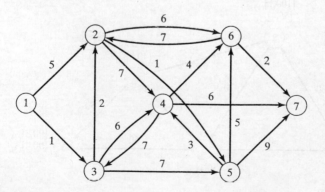

FIGURE 6.18

Network for Problem 2, Set 6.3b

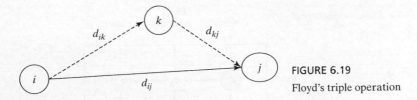

FIGURE 6.19

Floyd's triple operation

Floyd's algorithm. Floyd's algorithm is more general than Dijkstra's because it determines the shortest route between *any* two nodes in the network. The algorithm represents an *n*-node network as a square matrix with *n* rows and *n* columns. Entry (i, j) of the matrix gives the distance d_{ij} from node i to node j, which is finite if i is linked directly to j, and infinite otherwise.

The idea of Floyd's algorithm is straightforward. Given three nodes i, j, and k in Figure 6.19 with the connecting distances shown on the three arcs, it is shorter to reach j from i passing through k if

$$d_{ik} + d_{kj} < d_{ij}$$

In this case, it is optimal to replace the direct route from $i \rightarrow j$ with the indirect route $i \rightarrow k \rightarrow j$. This **triple operation** exchange is applied to the distance matrix using the following steps:

Step 0. Define the starting distance matrix D_0 and node sequence matrix S_0 (all diagonal elements are blocked). Set $k = 1$.

$$
D_0 =
\begin{array}{c|ccccc}
 & 1 & 2 & \cdots & j & \cdots & n \\
\hline
1 & - & d_{12} & \cdots & d_{ij} & \cdots & d_{1n} \\
2 & d_{21} & - & \cdots & d_{2j} & \cdots & d_{2n} \\
\vdots & \vdots & \vdots & \vdots & \vdots & \vdots & \vdots \\
i & d_{i1} & d_{i2} & \cdots & d_{ij} & \cdots & d_{in} \\
\vdots & \vdots & \vdots & \vdots & \vdots & \vdots & \vdots \\
N & D_{n1} & d_{n2} & \cdots & d_{nj} & \cdots & - \\
\end{array}
$$

$$
S_0 =
\begin{array}{c|ccccc}
 & 1 & 2 & \cdots & j & \cdots & n \\
\hline
1 & - & 2 & \cdots & j & \cdots & n \\
2 & 1 & - & \cdots & j & \cdots & n \\
\vdots & \vdots & \vdots & \vdots & \vdots & \vdots & \vdots \\
i & 1 & 2 & \cdots & j & \cdots & n \\
\vdots & \vdots & \vdots & \vdots & \vdots & \vdots & \vdots \\
n & 1 & 2 & \cdots & j & \cdots & - \\
\end{array}
$$

General step k. Define row k and column k as *pivot row* and *pivot column*. Apply the *triple operation* to each element d_{ij} in D_{k-1}, for all i and j. If the condition

$$d_{ik} + d_{kj} < d_{ij}, (i \neq k, j \neq k, \text{and } i \neq j)$$

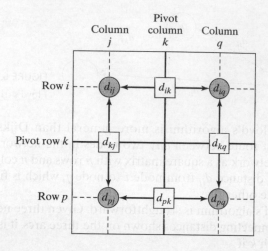

FIGURE 6.20

Implementation of triple operation in matrix form

is satisfied, make the following changes:

a. Create D_k by replacing d_{ij} in D_{k-1} with $d_{ik} + d_{kj}$.

b. Create S_k by replacing s_{ij} in S_{k-1} with k. Set $k = k + 1$. If $k = n + 1$, stop; else repeat step k.

Step k of the algorithm can be explained by representing D_{k-1} as shown in Figure 6.20. Here, row k and column k define the current pivot row and column. Row i represents any of the rows $1, 2, \ldots$, and $k - 1$, and row p represents any of the rows $k + 1$, $k + 2, \ldots$, and n. Similarly, column j represents any of the columns $1, 2, \ldots$, and $k - 1$, and column q represents any of the columns $k + 1, k + 2, \ldots$, and n. The *triple operation* can be applied as follows: If the sum of the elements on the pivot row and the pivot column (shown by squares) is smaller than the associated intersection element (shown by a circle), then it is optimal to replace the intersection distance by the sum of the pivot distances.

After n steps, we can determine the shortest route between nodes i and j from the matrices D_n and S_n using the following rules:

1. From D_n, d_{ij} gives the shortest distance between nodes i and j.

2. From S_n, determine the intermediate node $k = s_{ij}$ that yields the route $i \rightarrow k \rightarrow j$. If $s_{ik} = k$ and $s_{kj} = j$, stop; all the intermediate nodes of the route have been found. Otherwise, repeat the procedure between nodes i and k and between nodes k and j.

Example 6.3-5

For the network in Figure 6.21, find the shortest routes between every two nodes. The distances (in miles) are given on the arcs. Arc (3, 5) is directional—no traffic is allowed from node 5 to node 3. All the other arcs allow two-way traffic.

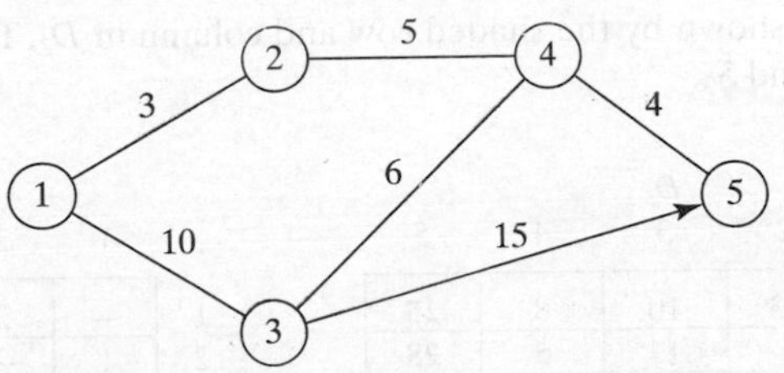

FIGURE 6.21

Network for Example 6.3-5

Iteration 0. The matrices D_0 and S_0 give the initial representation of the network. D_0 is symmetrical, except that $d_{53} = \infty$ because no traffic is allowed from node 5 to node 3.

D_0	1	2	3	4	5
1	—	3	10	∞	∞
2	3	—	∞	5	∞
3	10	∞	—	6	15
4	∞	5	6	—	4
5	∞	∞	∞	4	—

S_0	1	2	3	4	5
1	—	2	3	4	5
2	1	—	3	4	5
3	1	2	—	4	5
4	1	2	3	—	5
5	1	2	3	4	—

Iteration 1. Set $k = 1$. The pivot row and column are shown by the lightly shaded first row and first column in the D_0-matrix. The darker cells, d_{23} and d_{32}, are the only ones that can be improved by the *triple operation*. Thus, D_1 and S_1 are obtained from D_0 and S_0 in the following manner:

1. Replace d_{23} with $d_{21} + d_{13} = 3 + 10 = 13$ and set $s_{23} = 1$.
2. Replace d_{32} with $d_{31} + d_{12} = 10 + 3 = 13$ and set $s_{32} = 1$.

These changes are shown in bold in matrices D_1 and S_1.

D_1	1	2	3	4	5
1	—	3	10	∞	∞
2	3	—	**13**	5	∞
3	10	**13**	—	6	15
4	∞	5	6	—	4
5	∞	∞	∞	4	—

S_1	1	2	3	4	5
1	—	2	3	4	5
2	1	—	**1**	4	5
3	1	**1**	—	4	5
4	1	2	3	—	5
5	1	2	3	4	—

Iteration 2. Set $k = 2$, as shown by the lightly shaded row and column in D_1. The *triple operation* is applied to the darker cells in D_1 and S_1. The resulting changes are shown in bold in D_2 and S_2.

D_2	1	2	3	4	5
1	—	3	10	**8**	∞
2	3	—	13	5	∞
3	10	13	—	6	15
4	**8**	5	6	—	4
5	∞	∞	∞	4	—

S_2	1	2	3	4	5
1	—	2	3	**2**	5
2	1	—	1	4	5
3	1	1	—	4	5
4	**2**	2	3	—	5
5	1	2	3	4	—

Iteration 3.   Set $k = 3$, as shown by the shaded row and column in D_2. The new matrices are given by D_3 and S_3.

D_3

	1	2	3	4	5
1	—	3	10	8	25
2	3	—	13	5	28
3	10	13	—	6	15
4	8	5	6	—	4
5	∞	∞	∞	4	—

S_3

	1	2	3	4	5
1	—	2	3	2	3
2	1	—	1	4	3
3	1	1	—	4	5
4	2	2	3	—	5
5	1	2	3	4	—

Iteration 4.   Set $k = 4$, as shown by the shaded row and column in D_3. The new matrices are given by D_4 and S_4.

D_4

	1	2	3	4	5
1	—	3	10	8	12
2	3	—	11	5	9
3	10	11	—	6	10
4	8	5	6	—	4
5	12	9	10	4	—

S_4

	1	2	3	4	5
1	—	2	3	2	4
2	1	—	4	4	4
3	1	4	—	4	4
4	2	2	3	—	5
5	4	4	4	4	—

Iteration 5.   Set $k = 5$, as shown by the shaded row and column in D_4. No further improvements are possible in this iteration.

The final matrices D_4 and S_4 contain all the information needed to determine the shortest route between any two nodes in the network. For example, from D_4, the shortest distance from node 1 to node 5 is $d_{15} = 12$ miles. To determine the associated route, recall that a segment (i, j) represents a direct link only if $s_{ij} = j$. Otherwise, i and j are linked through at least one other intermediate node. Because $s_{15} = 4 \neq 5$, the route is initially given as $1 \rightarrow 4 \rightarrow 5$. Now, because $s_{14} = 2 \neq 4$, the segment $(1, 4)$ is not a *direct* link, and $1 \rightarrow 4$ is replaced with $1 \rightarrow 2 \rightarrow 4$, and the route $1 \rightarrow 4 \rightarrow 5$ now becomes $1 \rightarrow 2 \rightarrow 4 \rightarrow 5$. Next, because $s_{12} = 2$, $s_{24} = 4$, and $s_{45} = 5$, no further "dissecting" is needed, and $1 \rightarrow 2 \rightarrow 4 \rightarrow 5$ defines the shortest route.

TORA Moment

As in Dijkstra's algorithm, TORA can be used to generate Floyd's iterations. From SOLVE/MODIFY menu, select Solve problem ⇒ Iterations ⇒ Floyd's algorithm. File *toraEx6.3-5.txt* provides TORA's data for Example 6.3-5.

PROBLEM SET 6.3C

1. In Example 6.3-5, use the final D_4 and S_4 matrices of Floyd's algorithm to determine the shortest routes between each of the following pairs of nodes:

    *(a) From node 5 to node 1.

    (b) From node 3 to node 5.

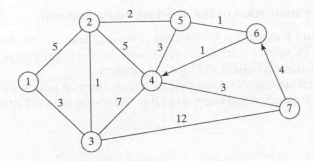

FIGURE 6.22

Network for Problem 2, Set 6.3c

(c) From node 1 to node 4.

(d) From node 3 to node 2.

2. Apply Floyd's algorithm to the network in Figure 6.22. Arcs (7, 6) and (6, 4) are unidirectional, and all the distances are in miles. Determine the shortest route between the following pairs of nodes:

(a) From node 1 to node 7.

(b) From node 7 to node 1.

(c) From node 6 to node 7.

3. The Tell-All mobile-phone company services six geographical areas. The satellite distances (in miles) among the six areas are given in Figure 6.23. Tell-All needs to determine the most efficient message routes that should be established between each two areas in the network.

*4. Six kids, Joe, Kay, Jim, Bob, Rae, and Kim, play a variation of *hide and seek*. The hiding place of a child is known only to a select few of the other children. A child is then paired with another with the objective of finding the partner's hiding place. This may be achieved through a chain of other kids who eventually will lead to discovering where the designated child is hiding. For example, suppose that Joe needs to find Kim and that Joe knows where Jim is hiding, who in turn knows where Kim is. Thus, Joe can find Kim by first finding Jim, who in turn will lead Joe to Kim. The following list provides the whereabouts of the children:

Joe knows the hiding places of Bob and Kim.

Kay knows the hiding places of Bob, Jim, and Rae.

Jim and Bob each know the hiding place of Kay only.

Rae knows where Kim is hiding.

Kim knows where Joe and Bob are hiding.

Devise a plan for each child to find every other child using the smallest number of contacts. What is the largest number of contacts?

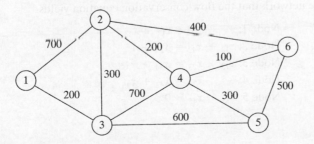

FIGURE 6.23

Network for Problem 3, Set 6.3c

6.3.3 Linear Programming Formulation of the Shortest-Route Problem

This section provides an LP model for the shortest-route problem. The model is general in the sense that it can be used to find the shortest route between any two nodes in the network. In this regard, it is equivalent to Floyd's algorithm.

We wish to determine the shortest route between any two nodes s and t in an n-node network. The LP assumes that one unit of flow enters the network at node s and leaves at node t.

Define

$$x_{ij} = \text{amount of flow in arc } (i, j)$$

$$= \begin{cases} 1, \text{ if arc } (i, j) \text{ is on the shortest route} \\ 0, \text{ otherwise} \end{cases}$$

$$c_{ij} = \text{length of arc } (i, j)$$

Thus, the objective function of the linear program becomes

$$\text{Minimize } z = \sum_{\substack{\text{all defined} \\ \text{arcs } (i, j)}} c_{ij} x_{ij}$$

The constraints represent the **conservation-of-flow equation** at each node:

$$\text{Total input flow} = \text{Total output flow}$$

Mathematically, this translates for node j to

$$\left(\begin{array}{c} \text{External } input \\ \text{into node } j \end{array} \right) + \sum_{\substack{i \\ \text{all defined} \\ \text{arcs } (i, j)}} x_{ij} = \left(\begin{array}{c} \text{External } output \\ \text{from node } j \end{array} \right) + \sum_{\substack{k \\ \text{all defined} \\ \text{arcs } (j, k)}} x_{jk}$$

Example 6.3-6

In the network of Example 6.3-4, suppose that we want to determine the shortest route from node 1 to node 2—that is, $s = 1$ and $t = 2$. Figure 6.24 shows how the unit of flow enters at node 1 and leaves at node 2.

We can see from the network that the flow-conservation equation yields

$$
\begin{aligned}
&\text{Node 1:} && 1 = x_{12} + x_{13} \\
&\text{Node 2: } x_{12} + x_{42} = x_{23} + 1 \\
&\text{Node 3: } x_{13} + x_{23} = x_{34} + x_{35} \\
&\text{Node 4:} && x_{34} = x_{42} + x_{45} \\
&\text{Node 5: } x_{35} + x_{45} = 0
\end{aligned}
$$

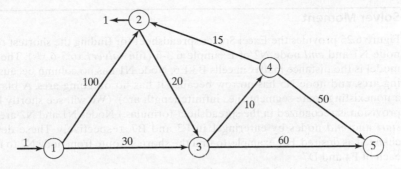

FIGURE 6.24

Insertion of unit flow to determine shortest route between node $s = 1$ and node $t = 2$

The complete LP can be expressed as

	x_{12}	x_{13}	x_{23}	x_{34}	x_{35}	x_{42}	x_{45}		
Minimize $z =$	100	30	20	10	60	15	50		
Node 1	1	1						=	1
Node 2	-1		1			-1		=	-1
Node 3		-1	-1	1	1			=	0
Node 4				-1		1	1	=	0
Node 5					-1		-1	=	0

Notice that column x_{ij} has exactly one "1" in row i and one "−1" in row j, a typical property of a network LP.

The optimal solution (obtained by TORA, file *toraEx6.3-6.txt*) is

$$z = 55, x_{13} = 1, x_{34} = 1, x_{42} = 1$$

This solution gives the shortest route from node 1 to node 2 as $1 \rightarrow 3 \rightarrow 4 \rightarrow 2$, and the associated distance is $z = 55$ (miles).

Remarks. In the given LP, node 5 constraint indicates that $x_{35} = x_{45} = 0$. The size of the LP can be reduces by deleting the columns x_{35} and x_{45} (which automatically deletes node 5 constraint).

PROBLEM SET 6.3D

1. In Example 6.3-6, use LP to determine the shortest routes between the following pairs of nodes:
   *(a) Node 1 to node 5.
   (b) Node 1 to node 4.

Solver Moment

Figure 6.25 provides the Excel Solver spreadsheet for finding the shortest route between *start* node N1 and *end* node N2 of Example 6.3-6 (file *solverEx6.3-6.xls*). The input data of the model is the distance matrix in cells B3:E6. Node N1 has no column because it has no incoming arcs, and node N5 has no row because it has no outgoing arcs. A blank cell represents a nonexisting route segment (i.e., infinite length arc). (We will see shortly how the blank cell provision is recognized in the spreadsheet formulas.) Nodes N1 and N2 are designated as the *start* and *end* nodes by entering 1 in F3 and B7, respectively. These designations can be changed as desired. For example, to find the shortest route from node N2 to node N4, enter 1 in each of F4 and D7.

As explained in the LP of Example 6.3-6, the constraints of the problem are of the general form:

$$(\text{Net output flow}) - (\text{Net input flow}) = 0$$

This definition is adapted to the spreadsheet layout by incorporating the external unit flow directly in *Net output flow* and *Net input flow* of the equation—that is,

$$\left[\left(\begin{array}{c}\textit{Out-}\text{arcs flow from Ni}\\\text{to all other nodes}\end{array}\right) - \left(\begin{array}{c}\text{External }\textit{in}\text{-flow}\\\text{into Ni}\end{array}\right)\right] - \left[\left(\begin{array}{c}\textit{In-}\text{arcs flow into Ni from}\\\text{all other nodes}\end{array}\right) - \left(\begin{array}{c}\text{External }\textit{out}\text{-flow}\\\text{from Ni}\end{array}\right)\right] = 0$$

In the spreadsheet, B3:E6 designate the *input distance* matrix, B9:E12 designate the *solution* cells, F3:F6 designate the (external) *output* unit-flow, and B7:E7 designate the (external) *input* unit-flow. Thus,

	A	B	C	D	E	F	G	H
1				Solver Shortest-Route Model (Example 6.3-6)				
2	distance	N2	N3	N4	N5		Range	Cells
3	N1	100	30			1	distance	B3:E6
4	N2		20				solution	B9:E12
5	N3			10	60		netFlow	H9:H13
6	N4	15			50		totalDist	G14
7		1						
8	solution	N2	N3	N4	N5	outFlow	inFlow	netFlow
9	N1	0	1	0	0	4.6E-12	0	4.6E-12
10	N2	0	0	0	0	0	5E-12	-5E-12
11	N3	0	0	1	0	1	1	0
12	N4	1	0	0	0	1	1	0
13	N5					0	0	0
14		5E-12	1	1	0	totalDist=	55	

Solver Parameters

Set Target Cell: [totalDist
Equal To: ○ Max ◉ Min
By Changing Cells:
[solution
Subject to the Constraints:
netFlow = 0
solution >= 0

Cell	Formula	Copy to
B8	= B2	C8:E8
A9	= A3	A10:A12
F9	= SUMIF(B3:E3,">0",B9:E9)-F3	F10:F12
B14	= SUMIF(B3:B6,">0",B9:B12)-B7	C14:E14
G10	= OFFSET(A$14,0,ROW(A1))	G11:G13
H9	= F9-G9	H10:H13
G14	= SUMPRODUCT(distance,solution)	

FIGURE 6.25

Excel Solver solution of the shortest route between nodes 1 and 2 in Example 6.3-6 (file *solverEx6.3-6.xls*)

Node N1 equation: $[\text{SUM}(B9:E9) - F3] - [0 - 0] = 0$

Node N2 equation: $[\text{SUM}(B10:E10) - F4] - [\text{SUM}(B9:B12) - B7] = 0$

Node N3 equation: $[\text{SUM}(B11:E11) - F5] - [\text{SUM}(C9:C12) - C7] = 0$

Node N4 equation: $[\text{SUM}(B12:E12) - F6] - [\text{SUM}(D9:D12) - D7] = 0$

Node N5 equation: $[0 - 0] - [\text{SUM}(E9:E12) - E7] = 0$

The assumption of this spreadsheet is that blank cells in the distance matrix B3:E6 represent blocked routes. We can use SUMIF, in place of SUM, to automatically account for this condition.[3] The following two instructions show how the modified formulas are entered in the spreadsheet.

1. Enter = SUMIF(B3:E3,">0",B9:E9)-F3 in cell F9 and copy it in cells F10:F12.
2. Enter = SUMIF(B3:B6,">0",B9:B12)-B7 in cell B14 and copy it in cells C14:E14.

The remainder of the spreadsheet formulas are entered as follows:

1. Enter = OFFSET(A$14,0,ROW(A1)) in cell G10 and copy it in cells G11:G13 to transpose the input flow to column G.
2. Enter 0 in each of G9 and F13 to indicate that N1 has no *in*-arcs or external *out*-unit flow and N5 has no *out*-arcs or external *in*-unit flow.
3. Enter = F9-G9 in cell H9 and copy it in cells H10:H13 to compute the net flow.
4. For the objective function, enter in cell G14 =SUMPRODUCT(B3:E6,B9:E12) or, equivalently, =SUMPRODUCT(distance,solution).

The spreadsheet is now ready for the application of Solver as shown in Figure 6.25. Cells B9:E12 represent the model solution. If cell (Ni, Nj) = 1, then leg (Ni, Nj) is on the shortest route. The output in Figure 6.25 yields the solution (N1 − N3 = 1, N3 − N4 = 1, and N4 − N2 = 1). The optimal route is $1 \rightarrow 3 \rightarrow 4 \rightarrow 2$, with a total distance of 55 miles.[4]

Remarks. In most textbooks, the network is defined by its explicit arcs as (node i, node j, distance), a cumbersome modeling representation particularly when the number of arcs is large. Our model is driven by the compact distance matrix (B3:E6) and its external flows (E3:E6 and B7:E7). It may be argued, however, that our model could deal with a much larger number of variables. For instance, Example 6.3-6 has 7 arcs and hence 7 variables, as opposed to $4 \times 4 = 16$ variables in our formulation. Keep in mind that, by using SUMIF, the flow constraints are *exactly the same* as in other presentations. This means that the additional 9 variables appear only in the objective function and with zero coefficients (blank entries in B3:E6). As a result, *pre-solvers* in commercial software will spot this "oddity" and automatically exclude the additional variables from the objective function prior to solving the problem, thus rendering the *same model* as in other presentations.

---

[3]The idea is that the spreadsheet treats a blank cell as a zero value. If a problem happens to have a zero distance between two nodes, the zero distance can be replaced with a very small positive value.

[4]The solution of the model exhibits a curious occurrence: If the constraint *netFlow* = 0 is replaced with *outFlow* = *inFlow* in the **Solver Parameters** dialogue box, Solver fails to find a feasible solution, even after adjusting *precision* in the **Solver Option** box. (To reproduce this experience, *solution* cells B9:E12 must all be zero or blank.) More curious yet, if the constraints are replaced with *inFlow* = *outFlow*, the optimum is found. It is not clear why this peculiarity occurs, but the problem may be related to roundoff error.

AMPL Moment

File *amplEx6.3-6a.txt* provides the AMPL model for solving Example 6.3-6. The model is general in the sense that it can be used to find the shortest route between any two nodes in a problem of any size. Explanation of the model is given in Section C.9 on the website.

PROBLEM SET 6.3E

1. Modify *solverEx6.3-6.xls* to find the shortest route between the following pairs of nodes:
   (a) Node 1 to node 5.
   (b) Node 4 to node 3.
2. Adapt *amplEx6.3-6b.txt* for Problem 2, Set 6.3a, to find the shortest route between node 1 and node 6. The input data must be the raw probabilities. Use AMPL programming facilities to print/display the optimum transmission route and its success probability.

6.4   MAXIMAL FLOW MODEL

Consider a network of pipelines that transports crude oil from oil wells to refineries. Intermediate booster and pumping stations are installed at appropriate design distances to move the crude in the network. Each pipe segment has a finite discharge rate (or capacity) of crude flow. A pipe segment may be uni- or bidirectional, depending on its design. Figure 6.26 demonstrates a typical pipeline network. The goal is to determine the maximum flow capacity of the network.

The solution of the proposed problem requires adding a single source and a single sink using unidirectional infinite capacity arcs, as shown by dashed arcs in Figure 6.26.

For arc (i, j), the notation $(\overline{C}_{ij}, \overline{C}_{ji})$ gives the flow capacities in the two directions $i \rightarrow j$ and $j \rightarrow i$. To eliminate ambiguity, we place $\overline{C}_{ij}$ next to node i and $\overline{C}_{ji}$ next to node j, as shown in Figure 6.27.

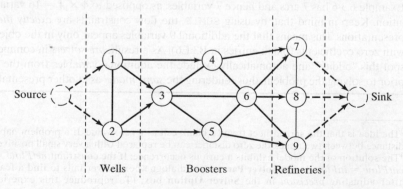

FIGURE 6.26

Capacitated network connecting wells and refineries through booster stations

6.4.1 Enumeration of Cuts

A cut defines a set of arcs whose removal from the network disrupts flow between the source and sink nodes. The **cut capacity** equals the sum of the capacities of its set of arcs. Among *all* possible cuts in the network, the cut with the *smallest capacity* is the bottleneck that determines the maximum flow in the network.

Example 6.4-1

Consider the network in Figure 6.28. The bidirectional capacities are shown on the respective arcs using the convention in Figure 6.27. For example, for arc $(3, 4)$, the flow limit is 10 units from 3 to 4 and 5 units from 4 to 3.

Figure 6.28 illustrates three cuts with the following capacities:

Cut	Associated arcs	Capacity
1	$(1, 2), (1, 3), (1, 4)$	$20 + 30 + 10 = 60$
2	$(1, 3), (1, 4), (2, 3), (2, 5)$	$30 + 10 + 40 + 30 = 110$
3	$(2, 5), (3, 5), (4, 5)$	$30 + 20 + 20 = 70$

The only information from the three cuts is that the maximum flow in the network cannot exceed 60 units. To determine the maximum flow, it is necessary to enumerate *all* the cuts, a difficult task for the general network. Thus, the need for an efficient algorithm is imperative.

PROBLEM SET 6.4A

*1. For the network in Figure 6.28, determine three additional cuts, and find their capacities.

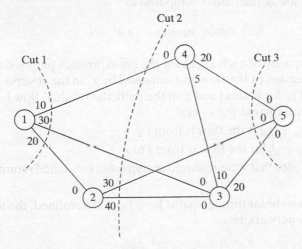

FIGURE 6.27
Arc Flows C_{ij} from $i \to j$ and C_{ji} from $j \to i$

FIGURE 6.28

Examples of cuts in flow networks

6.4.2 Maximal Flow Algorithm

The maximal flow algorithm is based on finding **breakthrough paths** with *positive* flow between the source and sink nodes. Each path commits part or all of the capacities of its arcs to the total flow in the network.

Consider arc (i, j) with the bidirectional (design) capacities $(\overline{C}_{ij}, \overline{C}_{ji})$. As portions of these capacities are committed to the flow in the arc, the **residuals** (or unused capacities) of the arc are updated. We use the notation (c_{ij}, c_{ji}) to represent the residuals.

For a node j that receives flow from node i, we attach a label $[a_j, i]$, where a_j is the flow from node i to node j.

Step 1. For all arcs (i, j), set the residual capacity equal to the design capacity—that is, $(c_{ij}, c_{ji}) = (\overline{C}_{ij}, \overline{C}_{ji})$. Let $a_1 = \infty$, and label source node 1 with $[\infty, -]$. Set $i = 1$, and go to step 2.

Step 2. Determine S_i, the set of unlabeled nodes j that can be reached directly from node i by arcs with *positive* residuals (that is, $c_{ij} > 0$ for all $j \in S_i$). If $S_i \neq \varnothing$, go to step 3. Otherwise, a partial path is dead-ended at node i. Go to step 4.

Step 3. Determine $k \in S_i$ such that

$$c_{ik} = \max_{j \varepsilon S_i}\{c_{ij}\}$$

Set $a_k = c_{ik}$ and label node k with $[a_k, i]$. If $k = n$, the sink node has been labeled, and a *breakthrough path* is found, go to step 5. Otherwise, set $i = k$, and go to step 2.

Step 4. **(Backtracking).** If $i = 1$, no breakthrough is possible; go to step 6. Otherwise, let r be the node (on the partial path) that was labeled *immediately* before current node i, and remove i from the set of nodes adjacent to r. Set $i = r$, and go to step 2.

Step 5. **(Determination of residuals).** Let $N_p = (1, k_1, k_2, \ldots, n)$ define the nodes of the pth breakthrough path from source node 1 to sink node n. Then the maximum flow along the path is computed as

$$f_p = \min\{a_1, a_{k_1}, a_{k_2}, \ldots, a_n\}$$

The residual capacity of each arc along the breakthrough path is *decreased* by f_p in the direction of the flow and *increased* by f_p in the reverse direction—that is, for nodes i and j on the path, the residual flow is changed from the current (c_{ij}, c_{ji}) to

(a) $(c_{ij} - f_p, c_{ji} + f_p)$ if the flow is from i to j

(b) $(c_{ij} + f_p, c_n - f_p)$ if the flow is from j to i

Reinstate any nodes that were removed in step 4. Set $i = 1$, and return to step 2.

Step 6. **(Solution).**

(a) Given that m breakthrough paths have been determined, the maximal flow in the network is

$$F = f_1 + f_2 + \cdots + f_m$$

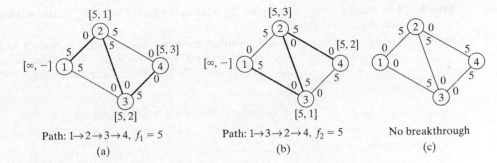

FIGURE 6.29

Use of residuals to calculate maximum flow

> **(b)** Using the (initial) *design capacities* and final *residuals* of arc (i, j), $(\overline{C}_{ij}, \overline{C}_{ji})$, and (c_{ij}, c_{ji}), respectively, the optimal flow in arc (i, j) is determined by computing $(\alpha, \beta) = (\overline{C}_{ij} - c_{ij}, \overline{C}_{ji} - c_{ji})$. If $\alpha > 0$, the optimal flow from i to j is α. Otherwise, if $\beta > 0$, the optimal flow from j to i is β. (It is impossible to have both α and β positive.)

The backtracking process of step 4 is invoked when the algorithm dead-ends at an intermediate node. The flow adjustment in step 5 can be explained via the simple flow network in Figure 6.29. Network (a) gives the first breakthrough path $N_1 = \{1, 2, 3, 4\}$ with its maximum flow $f_1 = 5$. Thus, the residuals of each of arcs $(1, 2)$, $(2, 3)$, and $(3, 4)$ are changed from $(5, 0)$ to $(0, 5)$, per step 5. Network (b) now gives the second breakthrough path $N_2 = \{1, 3, 2, 4\}$ with $f_2 = 5$. After making the necessary flow adjustments, we get network (c), where no further breakthroughs are possible. What happened in the transition from (b) to (c) is nothing but a cancellation of a previously committed flow in the direction $2 \rightarrow 3$, in essence allowing the flow to on paths $1 \rightarrow 2 \rightarrow 4$ and $1 \rightarrow 3 \rightarrow 4$ only (maximum flow = $5 + 5 = 10$). The algorithm "remembers" that a flow from 2 to 3 has been committed previously because of the earlier adjustment of the capacity in the reverse direction (per step 5).

Example 6.4-2

Determine the maximal flow in the network of Example 6.4-1 (Figure 6.28). Figure 6.30 provides a graphical summary of the iterations of the algorithm. You will find it helpful to compare the description of the iterations with the graphical summary.

Iteration 1.   Set the initial residuals (c_{ij}, c_{ji}) equal to the initial capacities $(\overline{C}_{ij}, \overline{C}_{ji})$.

Step 1.   Set $a_1 = \infty$ and label node 1 with $[\infty, -]$. Set $i = 1$.

Step 2. $S_1 = \{2, 3, 4\}$ $(\neq \emptyset)$.

Step 3. $k = 3$, because $c_{13} = max\ \{c_{12}, c_{13}, c_{14}\} = \max\ \{20, 30, 10\} = 30$. Set $a_3 = c_{13} = 30$, and label node 3 with $[30, 1]$. Set $i = 3$, and repeat step 2.

Step 2. $S_3 = (4, 5)$.

Step 3. $k = 5$ and $a_5 = c_{35} = max\{10, 20\} = 20$. Label node 5 with [20, 3]. Breakthrough is achieved. Go to step 5.

Step 5. The breakthrough path is determined from the labels starting at node 5 and moving backward to node 1—that is, $(5) \rightarrow [20, 3] \rightarrow (3) \rightarrow [30, 1] \rightarrow (1)$. Thus, $N_1 = \{1, 3, 5\}$ and $f_1 = min\{a_1, a_3, a_5\} = \{\infty, 30, 20\} = 20$. The residual capacities along path N_1 are

$$(c_{13}, c_{31}) = (30 - 20, 0 + 20) = (10, 20)$$

$$(c_{35}, c_{53}) = (20 - 20, 0 + 20) = (0, 20)$$

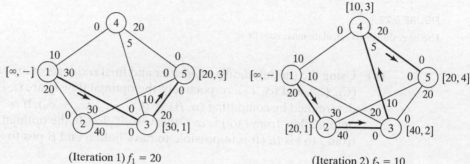

(Iteration 1) $f_1 = 20$ (Iteration 2) $f_2 = 10$

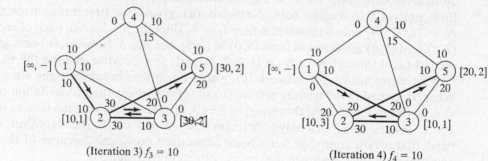

(Iteration 3) $f_3 = 10$ (Iteration 4) $f_4 = 10$

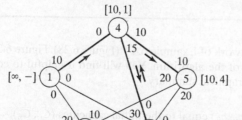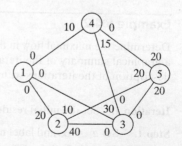

(Iteration 5) $f_5 = 10$ (Iteration 6) No breakthrough

FIGURE 6.30

Iterations of the maximum flow algorithm of Example 6.4-2

Iteration 2.

Step 1. Set $a_1 = \infty$, and label node 1 with $[\infty, -]$. Set $i = 1$.

Step 2. $S_1 = \{2, 3, 4\}$.

Step 3. $k = 2$ and $a_2 = c_{12} = max\ \{20, 10, 10\} = 20$. Set $i = 2$, and repeat step 2.

Step 2. $S_2 = \{3, 5\}$.

Step 3. $k = 3$ and $a_3 = c_{23} = 40$. Label node 3 with $[40, 2]$. Set $i = 3$, and repeat step 2.

Step 2. $S_3 = \{4\}$ (note that $c_{35} = 0$—hence, node 5 cannot be included in S_3).

Step 3. $k = 4$ and $a_4 = c_{34} = 10$. Label node 4 with $[10, 3]$. Set $i = 4$, and repeat step 2.

Step 2. $S_4 = \{5\}$ (note that nodes 1 and 3 are already labeled—hence, they cannot be included in S_4).

Step 3. $k = 5$ and $a_5 = c_{45} = 20$. Label node 5 with $[20, 4]$. Breakthrough has been achieved. Go to step 5.

Step 5. $N_2 = \{1, 2, 3, 4, 5\}$ and $f_2 = min\ \{\infty, 20, 40, 10, 20\} = 10$. The residuals along the path of N_2 are

$$(c_{12}, c_{21}) = (20 - 10, 0 + 10) = (10, 10)$$

$$(c_{23}, c_{32}) = (40 - 10, 0 + 10) = (30, 10)$$

$$(c_{34}, c_{43}) = (10 - 10, 5 + 10) = (0, 15)$$

$$(c_{45}, c_{54}) = (20 - 10, 0 + 10) = (10, 10)$$

Iteration 3.

Step 1. Set $a_1 = \infty$ and label node 1 with $[\infty, -]$. Set $i = 1$.

Step 2. $S_1 = \{2, 3, 4\}$.

Step 3. $k = 2$ and $a_2 = c_{12} = max\ \{10, 10, 10\} = 10$. (Though ties are broken arbitrarily, TORA always selects the tied node with the smallest index. We will use this convention throughout the example.) Label node 2 with $[10, 1]$. Set $i = 2$, and repeat step 2.

Step 2. $S_2 = \{3, 5\}$.

Step 3. $k = 3$ and $a_3 = c_{23} = 30$. Label node 3 with $[30, 2]$. Set $i = 3$, and repeat step 2.

Step 2. $S_3 = \varnothing$ (because $c_{34} = c_{35} = 0$). Go to step 4 to backtrack.

Step 4. *Backtracking.* The label $[30, 2]$ at node 3 gives the immediately preceding node $r = 2$. Remove node 3 from further consideration *in this iteration* by crossing it out. Set $i = r = 2$, and repeat step 2.

Step 2. $S_2 = \{5\}$ (note that node 3 has been removed in the backtracking step).

Step 3. $k = 5$ and $a_5 = c_{25} = 30$. Label node 5 with $[30, 2]$. Breakthrough has been achieved; go to step 5.

Step 5. $N_3 = \{1, 2, 5\}$ and $c_5 = min\ \{\infty, 10, 30\} = 10$. The residuals along the path of N_3 are

$$(c_{12}, c_{21}) = (10 - 10, 10 + 10) = (0, 20)$$

$$(c_{25}, c_{52}) = (30 - 10, 0 + 10) = (20, 10)$$

Iteration 4.

This iteration yields $N_4 = \{1, 3, 2, 5\}$ with $f_4 = 10$ (verify!).

Iteration 5.

This iteration yields $N_5 = \{1, 4, 5\}$ with $f_5 = 10$ (verify!).

Iteration 6.

All the arcs out of node 1 have zero residuals. Hence, no further breakthroughs are possible. We turn to step 6 to determine the solution.

Step 6.   Maximal flow in the network is $F = f_1 + f_2 + \ldots + f_5 = 20 + 10 + 10 + 10 + 10 = 60$ units. The flow in the individual arcs is computed by subtracting the last residuals (c_{ij}, c_{ji}) in iteration 6 from the design capacities $(\overline{C}_{ij}, \overline{C}_{ji})$, as the following table shows.

Arc	$(\overline{C}_{ij}, \overline{C}_{ji}) - (c_{ij}, c_{ji})_6$	Flow amount	Direction
$(1, 2)$	$(20, 0) - (0, 20) = (20, -20)$	20	$1 \rightarrow 2$
$(1, 3)$	$(30, 0) - (0, 30) = (30, -30)$	30	$1 \rightarrow 3$
$(1, 4)$	$(10, 0) - (0, 10) = (10, -10)$	10	$1 \rightarrow 4$
$(2, 3)$	$(40, 0) - (40, 0) = (0, 0)$	0	—
$(2, 5)$	$(30, 0) - (10, 20) = (20, -20)$	20	$2 \rightarrow 5$
$(3, 4)$	$(10, 5) - (0, 15) = (10, -10)$	10	$3 \rightarrow 4$
$(3, 5)$	$(20, 0) - (0, 20) = (20, -20)$	20	$3 \rightarrow 5$
$(4, 3)$	$(5, 10) - (15, 0) = (-10, 10)$	0	—
$(4, 5)$	$(20, 0) - (0, 20) = (20, -20)$	20	$4 \rightarrow 5$

TORA Moment

You can use TORA to solve the maximal flow model in an automated mode or one iteration at a time. From the SOLVE/MODIFY menu, select Solve Problem. After specifying the output format, go to the output screen and select either Maximum Flows or Iterations. File *toraEx6.4-2.txt* provides TORA's data for Example 6.4-2.

PROBLEM SET 6.4B

*1. In Example 6.4-2,
   (a) Determine the surplus capacities for all the arcs.
   (b) Determine the amount of flow through nodes 2, 3, and 4.
   (c) Can the network flow be increased by increasing the capacities in the directions $3 \rightarrow 5$ and $4 \rightarrow 5$?

2. Determine the maximal flow and the optimum flow in each arc for the network in Figure 6.31.

3. Three refineries send a gasoline product to two distribution terminals through a pipeline network. Any demand that cannot be satisfied through the network is acquired

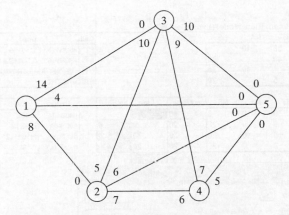

FIGURE 6.31

Network for Problem 2, Set 6.4b

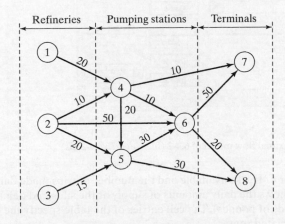

FIGURE 6.32

Network for Problem 3, Set 6.4b

from other sources. The pipeline network is served by three pumping stations, as shown in Figure 6.32. The product flows in the network in the direction shown by the arrows. The capacity of each pipe segment (shown directly on the arcs) is in million bbl per day. Determine the following:

(a) The daily production at each refinery that matches the maximum capacity of the network.

(b) The daily demand at each terminal that matches the maximum capacity of the network.

(c) The daily capacity of each pump that matches the maximum capacity of the network.

4. Suppose that the maximum daily capacity of pump 6 in the network of Figure 6.33 is limited to 50 million bbl per day. Remodel the network to include this restriction. Then determine the maximum capacity of the network.

5. Chicken feed is transported by trucks from three silos to four farms. Some of the silos cannot ship directly to some of the farms. The capacities of the other routes are

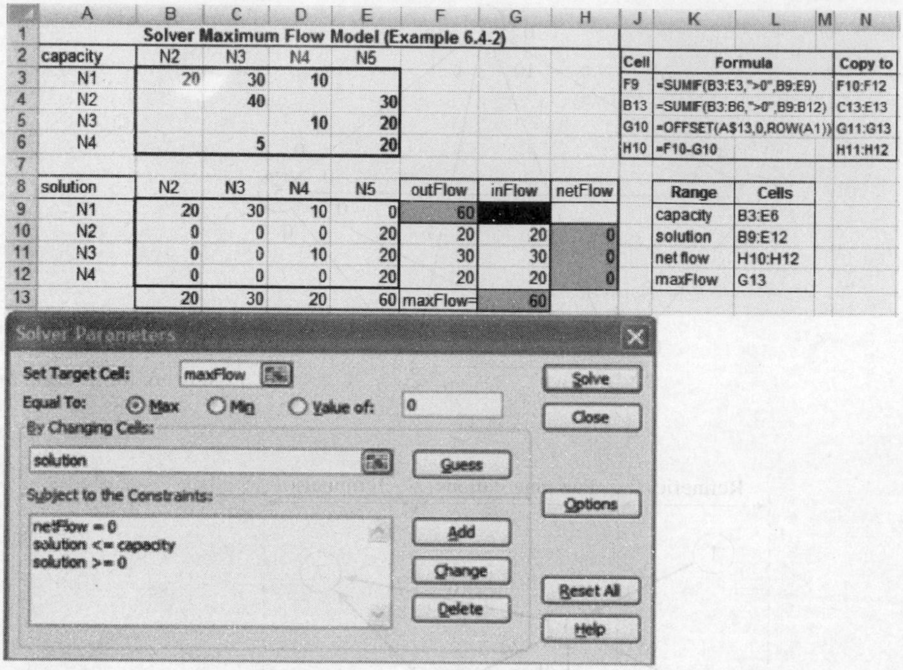

	A	B	C	D	E	F	G	H	J	K	L	M	N
1		Solver Maximum Flow Model (Example 6.4-2)											
2	capacity	N2	N3	N4	N5				Cell	Formula			Copy to
3	N1	20	30	10					F9	=SUMIF(B3:E3,">0",B9:E9)			F10:F12
4	N2		40		30				B13	=SUMIF(B3:B6,">0",B9:B12)			C13:E13
5	N3			10	20				G10	=OFFSET(A$13,0,ROW(A1))			G11:G13
6	N4		5		20				H10	=F10-G10			H11:H12
7													
8	solution	N2	N3	N4	N5	outFlow	inFlow	netFlow		Range	Cells		
9	N1	20	30	10	0	60				capacity	B3:E6		
10	N2	0	0	0	20	20	20	0		solution	B9:E12		
11	N3	0	0	10	20	30	30	0		net flow	H10:H12		
12	N4	0	0	0	20	20	20	0		maxFlow	G13		
13		20	30	20	60	maxFlow=	60						

Solver Parameters

Set Target Cell: maxFlow

Equal To: ⦿ Max ○ Min ○ Value of: 0

By Changing Cells:
solution

Subject to the Constraints:
netFlow = 0
solution <= capacity
solution >= 0

[Solve] [Close] [Guess] [Options] [Add] [Change] [Reset All] [Delete] [Help]

FIGURE 6.33

Excel Solver solution of the maximal flow model of 6.4-2 (file *solverEx6.4-2.xls*)

limited by the number of trucks available and the number of trips made daily. The following table shows the daily amounts of supply at the silos and demand at the farms (in thousands of pounds). The cell entries of the table specify the daily capacities of the associated routes.

			Farm			
		1	2	3	4	
	1	30	5	0	40	20
Silo	2	0	0	5	90	20
	3	100	40	30	40	200
		200	10	60	20	

(a) Determine the schedule that satisfies the most demand.

(b) Will the proposed schedule satisfy all the demand at the farms?

6. In Problem 5, suppose that transshipping is allowed between silos 1 and 2 and silos 2 and 3. Suppose also that transshipping is allowed between farms 1 and 2, 2 and 3, and 3 and 4. The maximum two-way daily capacity on the proposed transshipping routes is 50 (thousand) lb. What is the effect of transshipping on the unsatisfied demands at the farms?

*7. A parent has five (teenage) children and five household chores to assign to them. Past experience has shown that forcing chores on a child is counterproductive. With this in mind, the children are asked to list their preferences among the five chores, as the following table shows:

Child	Preferred chore
Rif	1, 3, 4, or 5
Mai	1
Ben	1 or 2
Kim	1, 2, or 5
Ken	2, 5

The parent's modest goal now is to finish as many chores as possible while abiding by the children's preferences. Determine the maximum number of chores that can be completed and the assignment of chores to children.

8. Four factories are engaged in the production of four types of toys. The following table lists the toys that can be produced by each factory.

Factory	Toys productions mix
1	1, 2, 3
2	2, 3
3	1, 3, 4
4	1, 3, 4

All toys require approximately the same per-unit labor and material. The daily capacities of the four factories are 250, 180, 300, and 200 toys, respectively. The daily demands for the four toys are 200, 150, 350, and 100 units, respectively. Determine the factories' production schedules that will most satisfy the demands for the four toys.

9. The academic council at the U of A is seeking representation from among six students who are affiliated with four honor societies. The academic council representation includes three areas: mathematics, art, and engineering. At most two students in each area can be on the council. The following table shows the membership of the six students in the four honor societies:

Society	Affiliated students
1	1, 2, 3, 4
2	1, 3, 6
3	2, 3, 4, 5
4	1, 2, 4, 6

The students who are skilled in the areas of mathematics, art, and engineering are shown in the following table:

Area	Skilled students
Mathematics	1, 2, 3, 4
Art	1, 3, 4, 5
Engineering	1, 4, 5, 6

A student who is skilled in more than one area must be assigned exclusively to one area only. Can all four honor societies be represented on the council?

10. *Maximal/minimal flow in networks with lower bounds.* The maximal flow algorithm given in this section assumes that all the arcs have zero lower bounds. In some models, the lower bounds may be strictly positive, and we may be interested in finding the maximal or minimal flow in the network (see case 6-3 in Appendix E). The presence of the lower bound poses difficulty because the network may not have a feasible flow at all. The objective of this exercise is to show that any maximal and minimal flow model with positive lower bounds can be solved using two steps.

Step 1.   Find an initial feasible solution for the network with positive lower bounds.

Step 2.   Using the feasible solution in step 1, find the maximal or minimal flow in the original network.

(a) Show that an arc (i, j) with flow limited by $l_{ij} \leq x_{ij} \leq u_{ij}$ can be represented equivalently by a *sink* with demand l_{ij} at node i and a *source* with supply l_{ij} at node j with flow limited by $0 \leq x_{ij} \leq u_{ij} - l_{ij}$.

(b) Show that finding a feasible solution for the original network is equivalent to finding the maximal flow x'_{ij} in the network after (1) modifying the bounds on x_{ij} to $0 \leq x'_{ij} \leq u_{ij} - l_{ij}$, (2) "lumping" all the resulting sources into one supersource with outgoing arc capacities l_{ij}, (3) "lumping" all the resulting sinks into one supersink with incoming arc capacities l_{ij}, and (4) connecting the terminal node t to the source node s in the original network by a return infinite-capacity arc. A feasible solution exists if the maximal flow in the new network equals the sum of the lower bounds in the original network. Apply the procedure to the following network and find a feasible flow solution:

Arc (i, j)	(l_{ij}, u_{ij})
(1, 2)	(5, 20)
(1, 3)	(0, 15)
(2, 3)	(4, 10)
(2, 4)	(3, 15)
(3, 4)	(0, 20)

(c) Use the feasible solution for the network in (b) together with the maximal flow algorithm to determine the *minimal* flow in the original network. (*Hint:* First compute the residue network given the initial feasible solution. Next, determine the maximum flow *from the end node to the start node*. This is equivalent to finding the maximum flow that should be canceled from the start node to the end node. Now, combining the feasible and maximal flow solutions yields the minimal flow in the original network.)

(d) Use the feasible solution for the network in (b) together with the *maximal* flow model to determine the maximal flow in the original network. (*Hint:* As in part (c), start with the residue network. Next apply the breakthrough algorithm to the resulting residue network exactly as in the regular maximal flow model.)

6.4.3   Linear Programming Formulation of Maximal Flow Mode

Define x_{ij} as the amount of flow in arc (i, j) with capacity C_{ij}. The objective is to determine x_{ij} for all i and j that maximizes the flow between start node s and terminal node t subject to flow restrictions (input flow = output flow) at all but nodes s and t.

Example 6.4-3

In the maximal flow model of Figure 6.30 (Example 6.4-2), $s = 1$ and $t = 5$. The following table summarizes the associated LP with two different, but equivalent, objective functions depending on whether we maximize the output from start node 1 ($= z_1$) or the input to terminal node 5 ($= z_2$).

	x_{12}	x_{13}	x_{14}	x_{23}	x_{25}	x_{34}	x_{35}	x_{43}	x_{45}	
Maximize $z_1 =$	1	1	1							
Maximize $z_2 =$					1		1		1	
Node 2	1			-1	-1					$= 0$
Node 3		1		1		-1	-1	1		$= 0$
Node 4			1			1		-1	-1	$= 0$
Capacity	20	30	10	40	30	10	20	5	20	

The optimal solution using either objective function is

$$x_{12} = 20, x_{13} = 30, x_{14} = 10, x_{25} = 20, x_{34} = 10, x_{35} = 20, x_{45} = 20$$

The associated maximum flow is $z_1 = z_2 = 60$.

Solver Moment

Figure 6.33 gives the Excel Solver model for the maximum flow model of Example 6.4-2 (file *solverEx6.4-2.xls*). The general idea is similar to that of the shortest-route model, detailed following Example 6.3-6. The main differences include the following: (1) there are no flow equations for the start node 1 and end node 5, and (2) the objective is to maximize the total outflow at start node 1 (F9) or, equivalently, the total inflow at terminal node 5 (G13). File *solverEx6.4-2.xls* uses G13 as the target cell. Try executing the model with G13 replacing F9.

AMPL Moment

File *amplEx6.4-2.txt* provides the AMPL model for the maximal flow problem between any two nodes in the network of Example 6.4-2. The model is applicable to any number of nodes. Explanation of the model is detailed in Section C.9 on the website.

PROBLEM SET 6.4C

1. Model each of the following problems as a linear program, then solve using Solver or AMPL.
   (a) Problem 2, Set 6.4b.
   (b) Problem 5, Set 6.4b.
   (c) Problem 9, Set 6.4b.

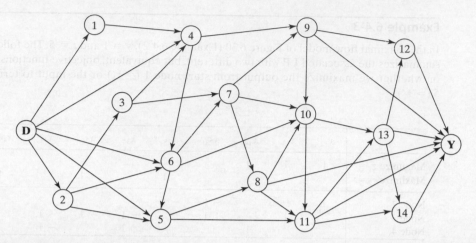

FIGURE 6.34

Network for Problem 2, Set 6.4c

2. Jim lives in Denver, Colorado, and likes to spend his annual vacation in Yellowstone National Park in Wyoming. Being a nature lover, Jim tries to drive a different scenic route each year. After consulting the appropriate maps, Jim has represented his preferred routes between Denver (D) and Yellowstone (Y) by the network in Figure 6.34. Nodes 1 through 14 represent intermediate cities. Although driving distance is not an issue, Jim's stipulation is that selected routes between D and Y do not include any common cities. Determine (using AMPL or Solver) all the distinct routes available to Jim. (*Hint*: Modify the maximal flow LP model to determine the maximum number of unique paths between *D* and *Y*.)

3. (Guéret and Associates, 2002, Section 12.1) A military telecommunication system connecting 9 sites is given in Figure 6.35. Sites 4 and 7 must continue to communicate

FIGURE 6.35

Network for Problem 3, Set 6.4c

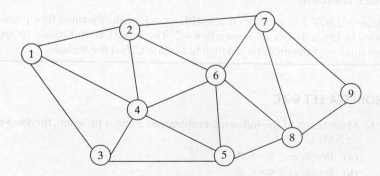

even if as many as three other sites are destroyed by enemy actions. Does the present communication network meet this requirement? Use AMPL and Solver to work out the problem.

6.5   CPM AND PERT

CPM (Critical Path Method) and PERT (Program Evaluation and Review Technique) are network-based methods designed to assist in the planning, scheduling, and control of projects. A project is defined as a collection of interrelated activities with each activity consuming time and resources. The objective of CPM and PERT is to devise analytic tools for scheduling the activities. Figure 6.36 summarizes the steps of the techniques. First, we define the activities of the project, their precedence relationships, and their time requirements. Next, the precedence relationships among the activities are modeled as a network. The third step involves specific computations for developing the time schedule. During the actual execution phase, execution of the activities may not proceed as planned, in the sense that some of the activities may be expedited or delayed. When this happens, the schedule is updated to reflect the realities on the ground. This is the reason for including a feedback loop in Figure 6.36.

The two techniques, CPM and PERT, were developed independently. They differ in that CPM assumes deterministic activity durations and PERT assumes probabilistic durations.

6.5.1   Network Representation

Each activity is represented by an arc pointing in the direction of progress in the project. The nodes of the network establish the precedence relationships among the different activities. Three rules are available for constructing the network.

Rule 1.   *Each activity is represented by one, and only one, arc.*

Rule 2.   *Each activity must be identified by two distinct end nodes.*

Figure 6.37 shows how a **dummy activity** can be used to provide unique representation of two concurrent activities, A and B. By definition, a (dashed) dummy activity

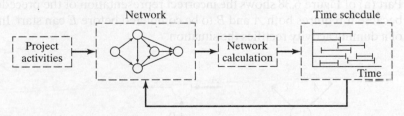

FIGURE 6.36

Phases for project planning with CPM-PERT

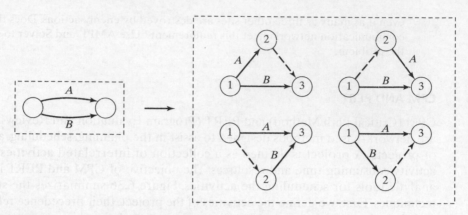

FIGURE 6.37

Use of dummy activity to produce unique representation of concurrent activities

consumes no time or resources. Inserting a dummy activity in one of the four ways shown in Figure 6.37 maintains the concurrence of A and B and provides unique end nodes for the two activities (to satisfy rule 2).

Rule 3.   *To maintain the correct precedence relationships, the following questions must be answered as each activity is added to the network:*

    (a)   *What activities immediately precede the current activity?*

    (b)   *What activities immediately follow the current activity?*

    (c)   *What activities are concurrent with the current activity?*

The answers to these questions may require the use of dummy activities to ensure correct precedence among the activities. For example, consider the following segment of a project:

1. Activity C starts immediately after activities A and B have been completed.

2. Activity E can start after activity B is completed.

Part (a) of Figure 6.38 shows the incorrect representation of the precedence relationship because it requires both A and B to be completed before E can start. In part (b), the use of a dummy activity rectifies the situation.

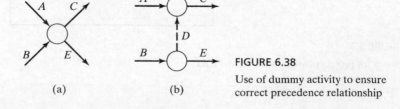

(a)   (b)

FIGURE 6.38

Use of dummy activity to ensure correct precedence relationship

Example 6.5-1

A publisher has a contract with an author to publish a textbook. The author submits a hard copy and a computer file of the manuscript. The (simplified) activities associated with the production of the textbook are summarized in the following table.

Activity	Predecessor(s)	Duration (weeks)
A: Manuscript proofreading by editor	—	3
B: Sample pages preparation	—	2
C: Book cover design	—	4
D: Artwork preparation	—	3
E: Author's approval of edited manuscript and sample pages	A, B	2
F: Book formatting	E	4
G: Author's review of formatted pages	F	2
H: Author's review of artwork	D	1
I: Production of printing plates	G, H	2
J: Book production and binding	C, I	4

Figure 6.39 provides the project network. Dummy activity (2, 3) produces unique end nodes for concurrent activities A and B. It is convenient to number the nodes in ascending order pointing toward the direction of progress in the project.

PROBLEM SET 6.5A

1. Construct the project network comprised of activities A to M with the following precedence relationships:

   (a) A, B, and C, the first activities of the project, can be executed concurrently.

   (b) A and B precede D.

   (c) B precedes E, F, and H.

   (d) F and C precede G and M.

   (e) E and H precede I and J.

   (f) C, D, F, and J precede K.

   (g) K and M precedes L.

   (h) I, G, and L are the terminal activities of the project.

FIGURE 6.39

Project network for Example 6.5-1

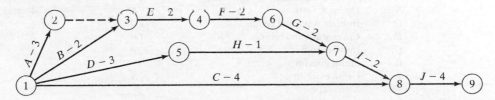

2. Construct the project network comprised of activities A to P that satisfies the following precedence relationships:

   (a) A, B, and C, the first activities of the project, can be executed concurrently.

   (b) D, E, and F follow A.

   (c) I and G follow both B and D.

   (d) H follows both C and G.

   (e) K and L follow I.

   (f) J succeeds both E and H.

   (g) M and N succeed F, but cannot start until both E and H are completed.

   (h) O succeeds M and I.

   (i) P succeeds J, L, and O.

   (j) K, N, and P are the terminal activities of the project.

*3. The footings of a building can be completed in four consecutive sections. The activities for each section include (1) digging, (2) placing steel, and (3) pouring concrete. The digging of one section cannot start until that of the preceding section has been completed. The same restriction applies to pouring concrete. Develop the project network.

4. In Problem 3, suppose that 10% of the plumbing work can be started simultaneously with the digging of the first section but before any concrete is poured. After each section of the footings is completed, an additional 5% of the plumbing can be started provided that the preceding 5% portion is complete. The remaining plumbing can be completed at the end of the project. Construct the project network.

5. An opinion survey involves designing and printing questionnaires, hiring and training personnel, selecting participants, mailing questionnaires, and analyzing the data. Construct the project network, stating all assumptions.

6. The activities in the following table describe the construction of a new house. Construct the associated project network.

	Activity	Predecessor(s)	Duration (days)
A:	Clear site	—	1
B:	Bring utilities to site	—	2
C:	Excavate	A	1
D:	Pour foundation	C	2
E:	Outside plumbing	B, C	6
F:	Frame house	D	10
G:	Do electric wiring	F	3
H:	Lay floor	G	1
I:	Lay roof	F	1
J:	Inside plumbing	E, H	5
K:	Shingling	I	2
L:	Outside sheathing insulation	F, J	1
M:	Install windows and outside doors	F	2
N:	Do brick work	L, M	4
O:	Insulate walls and ceiling	G, J	2
P:	Cover walls and ceiling	O	2
Q:	Insulate roof	I, P	1
R:	Finish interior	P	7
S:	Finish exterior	I, N	7
T:	Landscape	S	3

7. A company is in the process of preparing a budget for launching a new product. The following table provides the associated activities and their durations. Construct the project network.

	Activity	Predecessor(s)	Duration (days)
A:	Forecast sales volume	—	10
B:	Study competitive market	—	7
C:	Design item and facilities	A	5
D:	Prepare production schedule	C	3
E:	Estimate cost of production	D	2
F:	Set sales price	B, E	1
G:	Prepare budget	E, F	14

8. The activities involved in a candlelight choir service are listed in the following table. Construct the project network.

	Activity	Predecessor(s)	Duration (days)
A:	Select music	—	2
B:	Learn music	A	14
C:	Make copies and buy books	A	14
D:	Tryouts	B, C	3
E:	Rehearsals	D	70
F:	Rent candelabra	D	14
G:	Decorate candelabra	F	1
H:	Set up decorations	D	1
I:	Order choir robe stoles	D	7
J:	Check out public address system	D	7
K:	Select music tracks	J	14
L:	Set up public address system	K	1
M:	Final rehearsal	E, G, L	1
N:	Choir party	H, L, M	1
O:	Final program	I, N	1

9. The widening of a road section requires relocating ("reconductoring") 1700 feet of 13.8-kV overhead primary line. The following table summarizes the activities of the project. Construct the associated project network.

	Activity	Predecessor(s)	Duration (days)
A:	Job review	—	1
B:	Advise customers of temporary outage	A	$\frac{1}{2}$
C:	Requisition stores	A	1
D:	Scout job	A	$\frac{1}{2}$
E:	Secure poles and material	C, D	3
F:	Distribute poles	E	$3\frac{1}{2}$
G:	Pole location coordination	D	$\frac{1}{2}$
H:	Re-stake	G	$\frac{1}{2}$
I:	Dig holes	H	3

	Activity	Predecessor(s)	Duration (days)
J:	Frame and set poles	F, I	4
K:	Cover old conductors	F, I	1
L:	Pull new conductors	J, K	2
M:	Install remaining material	L	2
N:	Sag conductor	L	2
O:	Trim trees	D	2
P:	De-energize and switch lines	B, M, N, O	$\frac{1}{10}$
Q:	Energize and switch new line	P	$\frac{1}{2}$
R:	Clean up	Q	1
S:	Remove old conductor	Q	1
T:	Remove old poles	S	2
U:	Return material to stores	R, T	2

10. The following table gives the activities for buying a new car. Construct the project network.

	Activity	Predecessor(s)	Duration (days)
A:	Conduct feasibility study	—	3
B:	Find potential buyer for present car	A	14
C:	List possible models	A	1
D:	Research all possible models	C	3
E:	Conduct interview with mechanic	C	1
F:	Collect dealer propaganda	C	2
G:	Compile pertinent data	D, E, F	1
H:	Choose top three models	G	1
I:	Test-drive all three choices	H	3
J:	Gather warranty and financing data	H	2
K:	Choose one car	I, J	2
L:	Choose dealer	K	2
M:	Search for desired color and options	L	4
N:	Test-drive chosen model once again	L	1
O:	Purchase new car	B, M, N	3

6.5.2 Critical Path Method (CPM) Computations

The end result in CPM is a time schedule for the project (see Figure 6.36). To achieve this goal, special computations are carried out to produce the following information:

1. Total duration needed to complete the project.

2. Classification of the activities of the project as *critical* and *noncritical*.

An activity is **critical** if its start and finish times are predetermined (fixed). A activity is **noncritical** if it can be scheduled in a time span greater than its duration, permitting flexible start and finish times (within limits). A delay in the start time of a critical activity definitely causes a delay in the completion of the entire project, whereas a delay in a noncritical activity may not affect the completion date of the project.

To carry out the necessary computations, we define an **event** as a point in time at which activities are completed and succeeding ones are started. In terms of the network, an event corresponds to a node. Let

$\square_j$ = Earliest occurrence time of event j

Δ_j = Latest occurrence time of event j

D_{ij} = Duration of activity (i, j)

All event occurrence times are measured from the start time of the project. The span $(\square_i, \Delta_j)$ defines the time period during which activity (i, j), of duration D_{ij}, is scheduled. If activity (i, j) is critical, then $D_{ij} = \Delta_j - \square_i$. Otherwise, $D_{ij} < \Delta_j - \square_i$ for noncritical activity (i, j).

The critical path calculations involve two passes: The **forward pass** determines the *earliest* occurrence times of the events, and the **backward pass** calculates their *latest* occurrence times.

Forward Pass (earliest occurrence times, $\square$).   The computations start at node 1 and advance recursively to node n.

Initial Step.   Set $\square_1 = 0$ to indicate that the project starts at time 0.

General Step j.   Given that nodes $p, q, \ldots,$ and v are linked *directly* to node j by incoming activities $(p, j), (q, j), \ldots,$ and (v, j) and that the earliest occurrence times of events (nodes) $p, q, \ldots,$ and v have already been computed, then the earliest occurrence time of event j is computed as

$$\square_j = \max \{\square_p + D_{pj}, \square_q + D_{qj}, \cdots, \square_v + D_{vj}\}$$

The forward pass is complete when $\square_n$ at node n has been computed. By definition, $\square_j$ is the longest path (duration) to node j.

Backward Pass (latest occurrence times, Δ).   The backward pass computations start at node n and ends at node 1.

Initial Step.   Set $\Delta_n = \square_n$ to indicate that latest occurrences of the last node equals the duration of the project.

General Step j.   Given that nodes $p, q, \ldots,$ and v are linked *directly* to node j by *outgoing* activities $(j, p), (j, q), \ldots,$ and (j, v) and that the latest occurrence times of nodes $p, q, \ldots,$ and v have already been computed, the latest occurrence time of node j is computed as

$$\Delta_j = \min \{\Delta_p - D_{jp}, \Delta_q - D_{jq}, \ldots, \Delta_v - D_{jv}\}$$

The backward pass ends with $\Delta_1 = 0$ at node 1.

Based on the preceding calculations, an activity (i, j) will be *critical* if it satisfies three conditions.

1. $\Delta_i = \square_i$

2. $\Delta_j = \square_j$

3. $\Delta_j - \square_i = D_{ij}$

The three conditions state that the earliest and latest occurrence times of end nodes i and j are equal, and the duration D_{ij} fits "snugly" in the specified time span. An activity that does not satisfy all three conditions is *noncritical*.

By definition, the critical activities of a network constitute the longest path spanning the project network from start to finish.

Example 6.5-2

Determine the critical path for the project network in Figure 6.40. All the durations are in days.

Forward Pass

Node 1. Set $\square_1 = 0$

Node 2. $\square_2 = \square_1 + D_{12} = 0 + 5 = 5$

Node 3. $\square_3 = \max \{\square_1 + D_{13}, \square_2 + D_{23}\} = \max \{0 + 6, 5 + 3\} = 8$

Node 4. $\square_4 = \square_2 + D_{24} = 5 + 8 = 13$

Node 5. $\square_5 = \max \{\square_3 + D_{35}, \square_4 + D_{45}\} = \max \{8 + 2, 13 + 0\} = 13$

Node 6. $\square_6 = \max \{\square_3 + D_{36}, \square_4 + D_{46}, \square_5 + D_{56}\}$

$\qquad = \max \{8 + 11, 13 + 1, 13 + 12\} = 25$

The computations show that the project can be completed in 25 days.

FIGURE 6.40

Forward and backward pass calculations for the project of Example 6.5-2

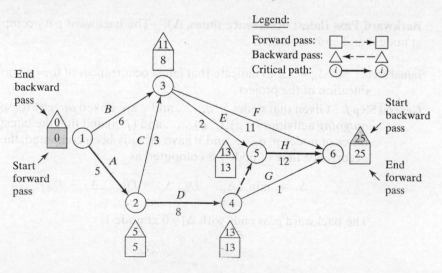

Backward Pass

Node 6. Set $\Delta_6 = \square_6 = 25$

Node 5. $\Delta_5 = \Delta_6 - D_{56} = 25 - 12 = 13$

Node 4. $\Delta_4 = \min\{\Delta_6 - D_{46}, \Delta_5 - D_{45}\} = \min\{25 - 1, 13 - 0\} = 13$

Node 3. $\Delta_3 = \min\{\Delta_6 - D_{36}, \Delta_5 - D_{35}\} = \min\{25 - 11, 13 - 2\} = 11$

Node 2. $\Delta_2 = \min\{\Delta_4 - D_{24}, \Delta_3 - D_{23}\} = \min\{13 - 8, 11 - 3\} = 5$

Node 1. $\Delta_1 = \min\{\Delta_3 - D_{13}, \Delta_2 - D_2\} = \min\{11 - 6, 5 - 5\} = 0$

Correct computations will always end with $\Delta_1 = 0$. The computations can be made directly on the network as shown in Figure 6.40.

Applying the rules for determining the critical activities, the critical path is $1 \rightarrow 2 \rightarrow 4 \rightarrow 5 \rightarrow 6$, which, as expected, spans the network from start (node 1) to finish (node 6). The sum of the durations of the critical activities $[(1, 2), (2, 4), (4, 5), \text{and } (5, 6)]$ equals the duration of the project ($= 25$ days). Observe that activity $(4, 6)$ satisfies the first two conditions for a critical activity ($\Delta_4 = \square_4 = 13$) and ($\Delta_6 = \square_6 = 25$) but not the third ($\Delta_6 - \square_4 \neq D_{46}$) Hence, the activity is noncritical.

PROBLEM SET 6.5B

*1. Determine the critical path for the project network in Figure 6.41.

2. Determine the critical path for the project networks in Figure 6.42.

3. Determine the critical path for the project in Problem 6, Set 6.5a.

4. Determine the critical path for the project in Problem 8, Set 6.5a.

5. Determine the critical path for the project in Problem 9, Set 6.5a.

6. Determine the critical path for the project in Problem 10, Set 6.5a.

6.5.3 Construction of the Time Schedule

This section shows how the information obtained from the calculations in Section 6.5.2 can be used to develop the time schedule. We recognize that for an activity (i, j), $\square_i$

FIGURE 6.41

Project networks for Problem 1, Set 6.5b

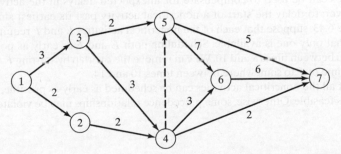

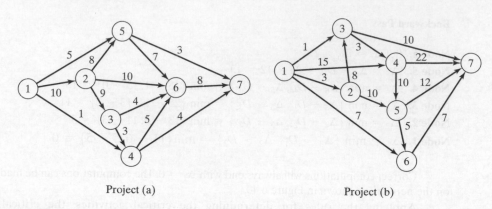

Project (a)   Project (b)

FIGURE 6.42

Project network for Problem 2, Set 6.5b

represents the *earliest start time*, and Δ_j represents the *latest completion time*. Thus, the interval $(\square_i, \Delta_j)$ delineates the (maximum) time span during which activity (i, j) can be scheduled without causing a delay in the entire project.

Construction of Preliminary Schedule.   The method for constructing a preliminary schedule is illustrated by an example.

Example 6.5-3

Determine the time schedule for the project of Example 6.5-2 (Figure 6.40).

We can get a preliminary time schedule for the different activities of the project by delineating their respective time spans as shown in Figure 6.43.

1. The critical activities (shown by solid lines) are staggered one right after the other to ensure that the project is completed within its specified 25-day duration.
2. The noncritical activities (shown by dashed lines) have permissible time spans greater than their respective durations, thus allowing slack (or "leeway") in scheduling them within their allotted time intervals.

   How do we schedule the noncritical activities within their respective spans? Normally, it is preferable to start each noncritical activity as early as possible. In this manner, remaining slack periods can be used to compensate for unexpected delays in the activity. It may be necessary, however, to delay the start of a noncritical activity past its earliest start time. For example, in Figure 6.43, suppose that each of the noncritical activities E and F requires the use of a bulldozer and that only one is available. Scheduling both E and F as early as possible requires two bulldozers between times 8 and 10. We can remove the overlap by starting E at time 8 and pushing the start time of F to somewhere between times 10 and 14.

   If all the noncritical activities can be scheduled as early as possible, the resulting schedule is always feasible. Otherwise, some precedence relationships may be violated if noncritical activities

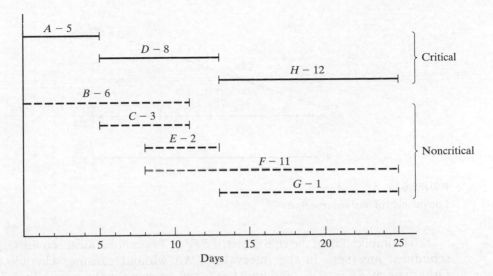

FIGURE 6.43

Preliminary schedule for the project of Example 6.5-2

are delayed past their earliest time. Take, for example, activities C and E in Figure 6.43. In the project network (Figure 6.40), though C must be completed before E, the spans of C and E in Figure 6.43 allow scheduling C between times 6 and 9, and E between times 8 and 10, which violates the requirement that C precede E. The need for a "red flag" that automatically reveals schedule conflict is thus evident. Such information is provided by computing the *floats* for the noncritical activities.

Determination of the floats. Floats are the slack times available within the allotted span of the noncritical activity. The most common types are the **total float** and the **free float**.

Figure 6.44 gives a convenient summary for computing the total float (TF_{ij}) and the free float (FF_{ij}) for an activity (i, j).

$$TF_{ij} = \Delta_j - \Box_i - D_{ij}$$
$$FF_{ij} = \Box_j - \Box_i - D_{ij}$$

By definition, $FF_{ij} \leq TF_{ij}$.

Red-Flagging Rule. *For a noncritical activity (i, j), if $FF_{ij} < TF_{ij}$, then its start can be delayed by at most FF_{ij}, relative to its earliest start time $\Box_i$, without causing schedule conflict. Any delay larger than FF_{ij} (but not more than TF_{ij}) must be coupled with an equal delay (relative to $\Box_j$) in the start time of all the activities leaving node j.*

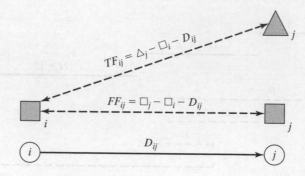

FIGURE 6.44

Computation of total and free floats

The implication of the rule is that, if $FF_{ij} = TF_{ij}$, a noncritical activity (i, j) can be scheduled anywhere in the interval $(\Box_i, \Delta_j)$ without causing schedule conflict. Otherwise, if $FF_{ij} < TF_{ij}$, activity (i, j) is red-flagged for the possibility of causing delay in the start time of the activities leaving node j.

Example 6.5-4

Compute the floats for the noncritical activities of the network in Example 6.5-2, and discuss their use in finalizing a schedule for the project.

The following table summarizes the computations of the total and free floats. For manual computations, it is more convenient to do the calculations directly on the network using the procedure in Figure 6.40.

Noncritical activity	Duration	Total float (TF)	Free float (FF)
$B(1, 3)$	6	$11 - 0 - 6 = 5$	$8 - 0 - 6 = 2$
$C(2, 3)$	3	$11 - 5 - 3 = 3$	$8 - 5 - 3 = 0$
$E(3, 5)$	2	$13 - 8 - 2 = 3$	$13 - 8 - 2 = 3$
$F(3, 6)$	11	$25 - 8 - 11 = 6$	$25 - 8 - 11 = 6$
$G(4, 6)$	1	$25 - 13 - 1 = 11$	$25 - 13 - 1 = 11$

The computations red-flag activities B and C because their $FF < TF$. The remaining activities $(E, F,$ and $G)$ have $FF = TF$ and hence can be scheduled anywhere between their earliest start and latest completion times.

To investigate the significance of red-flagged activities, consider activity B, with $TF = 5$ days and $FF = 2$ days. This activity can start any time between 0 and 2 (its FF). On the other hand, starting B past time 2 up to time 5 (its TF), the start times of the immediately succeeding activities E and F must be pushed forward relative to their earliest start time $(= 8)$ by at least an equal delay period.

As for red-flagged activity C, its zero FF means that *any* delay in starting C past its earliest start time $(= 5)$ must be coupled with at least an equal delay in the start time of its successor activities E and F.

TORA Moment

TORA provides useful tutorial tools for CPM calculations and for constructing the time schedule. To use these tools, select Project Planning $\Rightarrow$ CPM − Critical Path Method from Main Menu. In the output screen, you have the option to select CPM Calculations to produce step-by-step computations of the forward pass, backward pass, and the floats or CPM Bar Chart to construct and experiment with the time schedule.

File *toraEx6.5-2.txt* provides TORA's data for Example 6.5-2. If you elect to generate the output using the Next Step option, TORA will guide you through the details of the forward and backward pass calculations.

Figure 6.45 provides TORA schedule produced by CPM Bar Chart option for the project of Example 6.5-2. The default bar chart automatically schedules all noncritical activities as

FIGURE 6.45

TORA bar chart output for Example 6.5-2 (file *toraEx6.5-2.txt*)

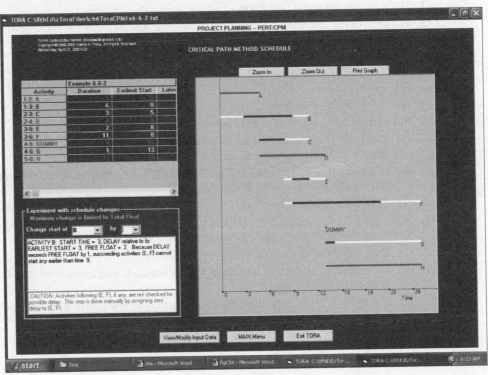

early as possible. You can study the impact of delaying the start time of a noncritical activity by using the self-explanatory drop-down lists on the left of the screen. The impact of a delay of a noncritical activity will be shown directly on the bar chart together with an explanation. For example, if you delay the start of activity B by more than 2 time units, the succeeding activities E and F will be delayed by an amount equal to the difference between the delay and free float of activity B. Specifically, given that the free float for B is 2 time units, if B is delayed by 3 time units, then the start of E and F must be delayed by at least $3 - 2 = 1$ time unit. This situation is demonstrated in Figure 6.45.

AMPL Moment

File *amplEx6.52.txt* provides the AMPL model for the CPM. The model is driven by the data of Example 6.5-2. This AMPL model is a unique application because it is not an optimization problem. The details of the model are given in Appendix C.9 on the website.

PROBLEM SET 6.5C

1. Given an activity (i, j) with duration D_{ij} and its earliest start time $\square_i$ and its latest completion time Δ_j, determine the earliest completion and the latest start times of (i, j).

2. What are the total and free floats of a critical activity? Explain.

*3. For each of the following activities, determine the maximum delay in the starting time relative to its earliest start time that will allow all the immediately succeeding activities to be scheduled anywhere between their earliest and latest completion times.
   (a) $TF = 20, FF = 20, D = 4$
   (b) $TF = 8, FF = 3, D = 4$
   (c) $TF = 5, FF = 0, D = 3$

4. In Example 6.5-4, use the floats to answer the following:
   (a) If activity B is started at time 1, and activity C is started at time 5, determine the earliest start times for E and F.
   (b) If activity B is started at time 3, and activity C is started at time 7, determine the earliest start times for E and F.
   (c) How is the scheduling of other activities impacted if activity B starts at time 6?

*5. In the project of Example 6.5-2 (Figure 6.42), assume that the durations of activities B and F are changed from 6 and 11 days to 20 and 25 days, respectively.
   (a) Determine the critical path.
   (b) Determine the total and free floats for the network, and identify the red-flagged activities.
   (c) If activity A is started at time 5, determine the earliest possible start times for activities $C, D, E,$ and G.
   (d) If activities $F, G,$ and H require the same equipment, determine the minimum number of units needed of this equipment.

6. Compute the floats and identify the red-flagged activities for the projects (a) and (b) in Figure 6.44, then develop the time schedules under the following conditions:

Project (a)

(i) Activity $(1,5)$ cannot start any earlier than time 14.

(ii) Activities $(5,6)$ and $(5,7)$ use the same equipment, of which only one unit is available.

(iii) All other activities start as early as possible.

Project (b)

(i) Activity $(1,3)$ must be scheduled at its earliest start time while accounting for the requirement that $(1,2), (1,3)$, and $(1,6)$ use a special piece of equipment, of which only 1 unit is available.

(ii) All other activities start as early as possible.

7. *(Job shop scheduling)* Three jobs, J1, J2, and J3, are processed on 3 machines, M1, M2, and M3, according to the following sequences (processing times are show in parentheses):

> J1: M3(3) – M1(4) – M2(6)
> J2: M2(1) – M3(5) – M2(9)
> J3: M3(8) – M2(8) – M1(7)

The order in which the jobs are processed on the different machines is predetermined as:

> M1: J1 – J2 – J3
> M2: J2 – J3 – J1
> M3: J3 – J1 – J2

(a) Represent the problem as a CPM network for which the critical path determines the makespan of all three jobs.

(b) Use the critical path calculations to develop the scheduling of the jobs (Gantt chart), assuming that each operation is scheduled at its earliest start time.

6.5.4   Linear Programming Formulation of CPM

The CPM model seeks the *longest* path between the start and finish nodes of the project network. Its formulation as an LP is thus similar to the LP of the shortest-route model (Section 6.3.3). The only difference is that the objective function is maximized instead of minimized.

Define

$$x_{ij} = \text{Amount of flow in activity } (i,j), \text{ for all defined } i \text{ and } j$$

$$D_{ij} = \text{Duration of activity } (i,j), \text{ for all defined } i \text{ and } j$$

Thus, the objective function of the linear program becomes

$$\text{Maximize } z = \sum_{\substack{\text{all defined} \\ \text{activities } (i,j)}} D_{ij}x_{ij}$$

For each node, there is one constraint that represents the conservation of flow:

$$\text{Total input flow} = \text{Total output flow}$$

All the variables, x_{ij}, are nonnegative.

Example 6.5-5

The LP formulation of the project of Example 6.5-2 (Figure 6.40) is given below. Note that nodes 1 and 6 are the start and finish nodes, respectively.

	A	B	C	D	E	F	Dummy	G	H	
	x_{12}	x_{13}	x_{23}	x_{24}	x_{35}	x_{36}	x_{45}	x_{46}	x_{56}	
Maximize $z =$	6	6	3	8	2	11	0	1	12	
Node 1	-1	-1								$= -1$
Node 2	1		-1	-1						$= 0$
Node 3		1	1		-1	-1				$= 0$
Node 4				1			-1	-1		$= 0$
Node 5					1		1		-1	$= 0$
Node 6						1		1	1	$= 1$

The optimum solution is

$$z = 25, \; x_{12}(A) = 1, \; x_{24}(D) = 1, \; x_{45}(\text{Dummy}) = 1, \; x_{56}(H) = 1, \text{ and all others } = 0$$

The solution defines the critical path as $A \to D \to$ Dummy $\to H$, and the project duration is 25 days, but it does not provide the data needed to construct the CPM chart.

PROBLEM SET 6.5D

1. Use LP to determine the critical path for the project network in Figure 6.43.
2. Use LP to determine the critical path for the project networks in Figure 6.44.

6.5.5   PERT Networks

PERT differs from CPM in that it assumes probabilistic duration times based on three estimates:

1. **Optimistic time**, a, which occurs when execution goes extremely well.
2. **Most likely time**, m, which occurs when execution is done under normal conditions.
3. **Pessimistic time**, b, which occurs when execution goes extremely poorly.

The most likely time, m, falls in the range (a, b).

Based on the estimates, the average duration time, $\overline{D}$, and variance, v, are approximated as

$$\overline{D} = \frac{a + 4m + b}{6}$$

$$v = \left(\frac{b - a}{6}\right)^2$$

CPM calculations given in Sections 6.5.2 and 6.5.3 may be applied directly, with $\overline{D}$, replacing the single estimate D.

Given the random variable e_j representing the earliest occurrence time of node, the probability that j will occur by a scheduled time, S_j, can be estimated in the following manner: Assume that all the activities in the network are statistically independent, first compute the mean, $E\{e_j\}$, and variance, $\text{var}\{e_j\}$. If there is only one path from the start node to node j, then the mean is the sum of expected durations, $\overline{D}$, for all the activities along this path and the variance is the sum of the variances, v, of the same activities. If more than one path leads to node j, then it is necessary to determine the statistical distribution of the duration of the longest path, a rather difficult problem because it involves determining the distribution of the maximum of at least two random variables. A simplifying assumption calls for selecting the path to node j having the longest *average* duration. If two or more paths have the same mean, the one with the largest variance is selected because it reflects the most uncertainty and, hence, leads to more conservative estimate of probabilities.

Given the mean and variance of the path to node j, $E\{e_j\}$ and $\text{var}\{e_j\}$, the probability that node j occurs by time S_j is approximated by the standard normal distribution, z (see Section 14.4.4)—that is,

$$P\{e_j \le S_j\} = P\left\{\frac{e_j - E\{e_j\}}{\sqrt{\text{var}\{e_j\}}} \le \frac{S_j - E\{e_j\}}{\sqrt{\text{var}\{e_j\}}}\right\} = P\{z \le K_j\}$$

Justification for the use of the normal distribution is that e_j is the sum of independent random variables. According to the *central limit theorem* (see Section 14.4.4), e_j is approximately normally distributed.

Example 6.5-6

Consider the project of Example 6.5-2. To avoid repeating the critical path calculations, the values of a, m, and b in the table below are selected to yield $\overline{D}_{ij} = D_{ij}$ for all i and j in Example 6.5-2.

Activity	$i-j$	(a,m,b)	Activity	$i-j$	(a,m,b)
A	1–2	(3, 5, 7)	E	3–5	(1, 2, 3)
B	1–3	(4, 6, 8)	F	3–6	(9, 11, 13)
C	2–3	(1, 3, 5)	G	4–6	(1, 1, 1)
D	2–4	(5, 8, 11)	H	5–6	(10, 12, 14)

The mean $\overline{D}_{ij}$ and variance v_{ij} for the different activities are given in the following table. Note that a dummy activity with $(a,m,b) = (0,0,0)$ has zero mean and variance.

Activity	$i-j$	$\overline{D}_{ij}$	v_{ij}	Activity	$i-j$	$\overline{D}_{ij}$	v_{ij}
A	1–2	5	.444	E	3–5	2	.111
B	1–3	6	.444	F	3–6	11	.444
C	2–3	3	.444	G	4–6	1	.000
D	2–4	8	1.000	H	5–6	12	.444

The next table gives the longest path from node 1 to the different nodes, together with their associated mean and standard deviation.

Node	Longest path based on mean durations	Path mean	Path standard deviation
2	1–2	5.00	0.67
3	1–2–3	8.00	0.94
4	1–2–4	13.00	1.20
5	1–2–4–5	13.00	1.20
6	1–2–4–5–6	25.00	1.37

The following table computes the probability that each node is realized by time S_j (specified by the analyst).

Node j	Longest path	Path mean	Path standard deviation	S_j	K_j	$P\{z \le K_j\}$
2	1–2	5.00	0.67	5.00	0	.5000
3	1–2–3	8.00	0.94	11.00	3.19	.9993
4	1–2–4	13.00	1.20	12.00	−.83	.2033
5	1–2–4–5	13.00	1.20	14.00	.83	.7967
6	1–2–4–5–6	25.00	1.37	26.00	.73	.7673

TORA Moment

TORA provides a module for carrying out PERT calculations. To use this module, select Project Planning ⇒ PERT − Program Evaluation and Review Technique from Main Menu. In the output screen, you have the option to select Activity Mean/Var to compute the mean and variance for each activity or PERT Calculations to compute the mean and variance of the longest path to each node in the network. File *toraEx6.5-6.txt* provides TORA's data for Example 6.5-6.

PROBLEM SET 6.5E

1. Consider Problem 2, Set 6.5b. The estimates (a, m, b) are listed below. Determine the probabilities that the different nodes of the project are realized without delay.

Project (a)				Project (b)			
Activity	(a, m, b)	Activity	(a, m, b)	Activity	(a, m, b)	Activity	(a, m, b)
1-2	(5, 6, 8)	3-6	(3, 4, 5)	1-2	(1, 3, 4)	3-7	(12, 13, 14)
1-4	(1, 3, 4)	4-6	(4, 8, 10)	1-3	(5, 7, 8)	4-5	(10, 12, 15)
1-5	(2, 4, 5)	4-7	(5, 6, 8)	1-4	(6, 7, 9)	4-7	(8, 10, 12)
2-3	(4, 5, 6)	5-6	(9, 10,15)	1-6	(1, 2, 3)	5-6	(7, 8, 11)
2-5	(7, 8, 10)	5-7	(4, 6, 8)	2-3	(3, 4, 5)	5-7	(2, 4, 8)
2-6	(8, 9, 13)	6-7	(3, 4, 5)	2-5	(7, 8, 9)	6-7	(5, 6, 7)
3-4	(5, 9, 19)			3-4	(10, 15, 20)		

BIBLIOGRAPHY

Ahuja, R., T. Magnati, and J. Orlin, *Network Flows: Theory, Algorithms, and Applications*, Prentice Hall, Upper Saddle River, NJ, 1993.

Bazaraa, M., J. Jarvis, and H. Sherali, *Linear Programming and Network Flow*, 4th ed., Wiley, New York, 2009.

Charnes, A., and W. Cooper, "Some Network Characterization for Mathematical Programming and Accounting Applications to Planning and Control," *The Accounting Review*, Vol. 42, No. 3, pp. 24–52, 1967.

Evans, J., and E. Minieka, *Optimization Algorithms for Networks and Graphs*, 2nd ed., Marcel Dekker, New York, 1992.

Guéret, C., C. Prins, and M. Sevaux, *Applications of Optimization with Xpress-MP*, translated and revised by Susanne Heipke, Dash Optimization Ltd., London, 2002.

Glover, F., D. Klingman, and N. Phillips, *Network Models and Their Applications in Practice*, Wiley, New York, 1992.

Robinson, E., L. Gao, and S. Muggenborg, "Designing an Integrated Distribution System at DowBrands, Inc.," *Interfaces*, Vol. 23, No. 3, pp. 107–117, 1993.

CHAPTER 7

Advanced Linear Programming

Real-Life Application—Optimal Ship Routing and Personnel Assignment for Naval Recruitment in Thailand

Thailand Navy recruits are drafted four times a year. A draftee reports to 1 of 34 local centers and is then transported by bus to one of four navy branch bases. From there, recruits are transported to the main naval base by ship. The docking facilities at the branch bases may restrict the type of ship that can visit each base. Branch bases have limited capacities but, as a whole, the four bases have sufficient capacity to accommodate all the draftees. During the summer of 1983, a total of 2929 draftees were transported from the drafting centers to the four branch bases and eventually to the main base. The problem deals with determining the optimal schedule for transporting the draftees, first from the drafting centers to the branch bases and then from the branch bases to the main base. The study uses a combination of linear and integer programming. The details are given in Case 5, Chapter 26, on the website.

7.1 SIMPLEX METHOD FUNDAMENTALS

In linear programming, the feasible solution space forms a **convex set** if the line segment joining any two *distinct* feasible points also falls in the set. An **extreme point** of the convex set is a feasible point that cannot lie on a line segment joining any two *distinct* feasible points in the set. Actually, extreme points are the same as corner points, as used in Chapters 2, 3, and 4.

Figure 7.1 illustrates two sets. Set (a) is convex (with six extreme points), and set (b) is not.

The graphical LP solution given in Section 2.3 demonstrates that the optimum solution is always associated with a feasible extreme (corner) point of the solution space. This result makes sense intuitively, because every feasible point in the LP solution space can be determined as a function of its feasible extreme points. For

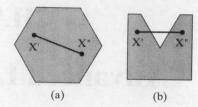

FIGURE 7.1

Examples of a convex and a nonconvex set   (a)   (b)

example, in convex set (a) of Figure 7.1, a **convex combination** of the extreme points, $X_1, X_2, X_3, X_4, X_5,$ and $X_6,$ identifies any feasible point X as

$$X = \alpha_1 X_1 + \alpha_2 X_2 + \alpha_3 X_3 + \alpha_4 X_4 + \alpha_5 X_5 + \alpha_6 X_6$$

$$\alpha_1 + \alpha_2 + \alpha_3 + \alpha_4 + \alpha_5 + \alpha_6 = 1$$

$$\alpha_i \geq 0, i = 1, 2, \ldots, 6$$

This observation shows that a finite number of extreme points completely define the infinite number of points in the solution space. This result is the crux of the simplex method.

Example 7.1-1

Show that the following set is convex:

$$C = \{(x_1, x_2) | x_1 \leq 2, x_2 \leq 3, x_1 \geq 0, x_2 \geq 0\}$$

Let $X_1 = \{x_1', x_2'\}$ and $X_2 = \{x_1'', x_2''\}$ be any two distinct points in C. If C is convex, then $X = (x_1, x_2) = \alpha_1 X_1 + \alpha_2 X_2, \alpha_1 + \alpha_2 = 1, \alpha_1, \alpha_2 \geq 0,$ must also be in C. To show that this is true, we need to show that all the constraints of C are satisfied by the line segment X—that is,

$$\left.\begin{array}{l} x_1 = \alpha_1 x_1' + \alpha_2 x_1'' \leq \alpha_1(2) + \alpha_2(2) = 2 \\ x_2 = \alpha_1 x_2' + \alpha_2 x_2'' \leq \alpha_1(3) + \alpha_2(3) = 3 \end{array}\right\} \Rightarrow x_1 \leq 2, x_2 \leq 3$$

Additionally, the nonnegativity conditions are satisfied because α_1 and α_2 are nonnegative.

PROBLEM SET 7.1a

1. Show that the set $Q = \{x_1, x_2 | x_1 - x_2 \leq 3, x_1 \geq 0, x_2 \geq 0\}$ is convex. Is the nonnegativity condition essential for the proof?

*2. Show that the set $Q = \{x_1, x_2 | x_1 \geq 1 \text{ or } x_2 \geq 2\}$ is not convex.

3. Determine graphically the extreme points of the following convex set:

$$Q = \{x_1, x_2 | x_1 + x_2 \leq 3, x_1 \geq 0, x_2 \geq 0\}$$

Show that the entire feasible solution space can be determined as a convex combination of its extreme points. Hence conclude that any convex (bounded) solution space is totally defined once its extreme points are known.

4. In the solution space in Figure 7.2 (drawn to scale), express the interior point $(3, 1)$ as a convex combination of the extreme points $A, B, C,$ and D by determining the weights associated with each extreme point.

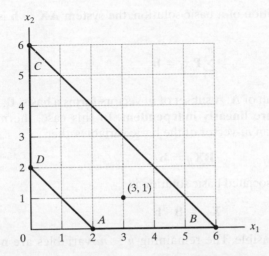

FIGURE 7.2

Solution space for Problem 4, Set 7.1a

7.1.1 From Extreme Points to Basic Solutions

It is convenient to express the general LP problem in equation form (see Section 3.1) using matrix notation.[1] Define $\mathbf{X}$ as an n-vector representing the variables, $\mathbf{A}$ as an $(m \times n)$-matrix representing the constraint coefficients, $\mathbf{b}$ as a column vector representing the right-hand side, and $\mathbf{C}$ as an n-vector representing the objective-function coefficients. The LP is then written as

$$\text{Maximize or minimize } z = \mathbf{CX}$$

subject to

$$\mathbf{AX} = \mathbf{b}$$

$$\mathbf{X} \geq \mathbf{0}$$

Using the format of Chapter 3, the rightmost m elements of $\mathbf{X}$ represent the starting basic variables. Hence, the rightmost m columns of $\mathbf{A}$ always form an identity matrix $\mathbf{I}$.

A **basic solution** of $\mathbf{AX} = \mathbf{b}$ is determined by setting $n - m$ variables equal to zero, and then solving the resulting m equations in the remaining m unknowns, *provided that the resulting solution is unique.* Given this definition, the theory of linear programming establishes the following result between the geometric definition of extreme points and the algebraic definition of basic solutions:

$$\text{Extreme points of } \{\mathbf{X} \mid \mathbf{AX} = \mathbf{b}\} \Leftrightarrow \text{Basic solutions of } \mathbf{AX} = \mathbf{b}$$

The relationship means that the extreme points of the LP solution space are defined by the basic solutions of $\mathbf{AX} = \mathbf{b}$, and vice versa. Thus, the basic solutions of $\mathbf{AX} = \mathbf{b}$ provide all the information needed to determine the optimum solution of the LP problem. Furthermore, the nonnegativity restriction, $\mathbf{X} \geq \mathbf{0}$, limit the search for the optimum to the *feasible* basic solutions only.

---

[1] A review of matrix algebra is given in Appendix D on the website.

To formalize the definition of a basic solution, the system $\mathbf{AX} = \mathbf{b}$ is written in vector form as

$$\sum_{j=1}^{n} \mathbf{P}_j x_j = \mathbf{b}$$

The vector $\mathbf{P}_j$ is the jth column of $\mathbf{A}$. A subset of m vectors forms a **basis**, $\mathbf{B}$, if, and only if, the selected m vectors are **linearly independent**. In this case, the matrix $\mathbf{B}$ is **nonsingular**. Defining $\mathbf{X}_B$ as an m-vector of the basic variables, then

$$\mathbf{BX}_B = \mathbf{b}$$

Using the inverse $\mathbf{B}^{-1}$, the associated basic solution is

$$\mathbf{X}_B = \mathbf{B}^{-1}\mathbf{b}$$

If $\mathbf{B}^{-1}\mathbf{b} \geq \mathbf{0}$, then $\mathbf{X}_B$ is feasible. The remaining $n - m$ variables are **nonbasic** at zero level.

The previous result shows that in a system of m equations and n unknowns, the *maximum* number of (feasible and infeasible) basic solutions is $\binom{n}{m} = \frac{n!}{m!(n - m)!}$.

Example 7.1-2

Determine all the basic feasible and infeasible solutions of the following system of equations.

$$\begin{pmatrix} 1 & 3 & -1 \\ 2 & -2 & -2 \end{pmatrix} \begin{pmatrix} x_1 \\ x_2 \\ x_3 \end{pmatrix} = \begin{pmatrix} 4 \\ 2 \end{pmatrix}$$

The following table summarizes the results. The inverse of $\mathbf{B}$ is determined by one of the methods in Section D.2.7 on the website.

B	$BX_B = b$	Solution	Type
$(\mathbf{P}_1, \mathbf{P}_2)$	$\begin{pmatrix} 1 & 3 \\ 2 & -2 \end{pmatrix}\begin{pmatrix} x_1 \\ x_2 \end{pmatrix} = \begin{pmatrix} 4 \\ 2 \end{pmatrix}$	$\begin{pmatrix} x_1 \\ x_2 \end{pmatrix} = \begin{pmatrix} \frac{1}{4} & \frac{3}{8} \\ \frac{1}{4} & -\frac{1}{8} \end{pmatrix}\begin{pmatrix} 4 \\ 2 \end{pmatrix} = \begin{pmatrix} \frac{7}{4} \\ \frac{3}{4} \end{pmatrix}$	Feasible
$(\mathbf{P}_1, \mathbf{P}_3)$	(Not a basis because P_1 and P_3 are dependent)		
$(\mathbf{P}_2, \mathbf{P}_3)$	$\begin{pmatrix} 3 & -1 \\ -2 & -2 \end{pmatrix}\begin{pmatrix} x_2 \\ x_3 \end{pmatrix} = \begin{pmatrix} 4 \\ 2 \end{pmatrix}$	$\begin{pmatrix} x_2 \\ x_3 \end{pmatrix} = \begin{pmatrix} \frac{1}{4} & -\frac{1}{8} \\ -\frac{1}{4} & -\frac{3}{8} \end{pmatrix}\begin{pmatrix} 4 \\ 2 \end{pmatrix} = \begin{pmatrix} \frac{3}{4} \\ -\frac{7}{4} \end{pmatrix}$	Infeasible

We can also investigate the problem by expressing it in vector form as follows:

$$\begin{pmatrix} 1 \\ 2 \end{pmatrix}x_1 + \begin{pmatrix} 3 \\ -2 \end{pmatrix}x_2 + \begin{pmatrix} -1 \\ -2 \end{pmatrix}x_3 = \begin{pmatrix} 4 \\ 2 \end{pmatrix}$$

The two-dimensional vectors $\mathbf{P}_1, \mathbf{P}_2, \mathbf{P}_3$, and $\mathbf{b}$ can be represented generically as $(a_1, a_2)^T$. Figure 7.3 graphs these vectors on the (a_1, a_2)-plane. For example, for $\mathbf{b} = (4, 2)^T$, $a_1 = 4$, and $a_2 = 2$.

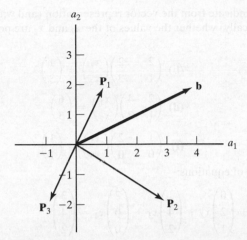

FIGURE 7.3

Vector representation of LP solution space

Because we are dealing with two equations ($m = 2$), a basis includes exactly two vectors, selected from among P_1, P_2, and P_3. The matrices (P_1, P_2) and (P_2, P_3) form bases because their associated vectors are independent. On the other hand, the vectors of the matrix (P_1, P_3) are dependent, and hence the matrix is not a basis.

Algebraically, a (square) matrix forms a basis if its determinant is not zero (see Section D.2.5 on the website). The following computations show that the combinations (P_1, P_2) and (P_2, P_3) are bases, and the combination (P_1, P_3) is not.

$$\det(P_1, P_2) = \det\begin{pmatrix} 1 & 3 \\ 2 & -2 \end{pmatrix} = (1 \times -2) - (2 \times 3) = -8 \neq 0$$

$$\det(P_2, P_3) = \det\begin{pmatrix} 3 & -1 \\ -2 & -2 \end{pmatrix} = (3 \times -2) - (-1 \times -2) = -8 \neq 0$$

$$\det(P_1, P_3) = \det\begin{pmatrix} 1 & -1 \\ 2 & -2 \end{pmatrix} = (1 \times -2) - (-1 \times 2) = 0$$

PROBLEM SET 7.1B

1. In the following sets of equations, (a) and (b) have unique (basic) solutions, (c) has an infinite number of solutions, and (d) has no solution. Show how these results can be verified using graphical vector representation. From this exercise, state the general conditions for vector dependence/independence that lead to unique solution, infinity of solutions, and no solution.

   (a) $x_1 + 3x_2 = 2$

          $3x_1 + x_2 = 3$

   (b) $2x_1 + 3x_2 = 1$

          $2x_1 - x_2 = 2$

   (c) $2x_1 + 6x_2 = 4$

          $x_1 + 3x_2 = 2$

   (d) $2x_1 - 4x_2 = 2$

          $-x_1 + 2x_2 = 1$

2. Use vectors to determine graphically the type of solution for each of the sets of equations below: unique solution, an infinite number of solutions, or no solution. For

the cases of unique solutions, indicate from the vector representation (and without solving the equations algebraically) whether the values of the x_1 and x_2 are positive, zero, or negative.

(a) $\begin{pmatrix} 5 & 4 \\ 1 & -3 \end{pmatrix}\begin{pmatrix} x_1 \\ x_2 \end{pmatrix} = \begin{pmatrix} 2 \\ 2 \end{pmatrix}$ *(b) $\begin{pmatrix} 2 & -2 \\ 1 & 3 \end{pmatrix}\begin{pmatrix} x_1 \\ x_2 \end{pmatrix} = \begin{pmatrix} 1 \\ 3 \end{pmatrix}$

(c) $\begin{pmatrix} 2 & 4 \\ 1 & 3 \end{pmatrix}\begin{pmatrix} x_1 \\ x_2 \end{pmatrix} = \begin{pmatrix} -4 \\ -2 \end{pmatrix}$ *(d) $\begin{pmatrix} 2 & 4 \\ 1 & 2 \end{pmatrix}\begin{pmatrix} x_1 \\ x_2 \end{pmatrix} = \begin{pmatrix} 6 \\ 3 \end{pmatrix}$

(e) $\begin{pmatrix} -2 & 4 \\ 1 & -2 \end{pmatrix}\begin{pmatrix} x_1 \\ x_2 \end{pmatrix} = \begin{pmatrix} 4 \\ 2 \end{pmatrix}$ *(f) $\begin{pmatrix} 1 & -2 \\ 0 & 0 \end{pmatrix}\begin{pmatrix} x_1 \\ x_2 \end{pmatrix} = \begin{pmatrix} 1 \\ 1 \end{pmatrix}$

3. Consider the following system of equations:

$$\begin{pmatrix} 1 \\ 2 \\ 3 \end{pmatrix}x_1 + \begin{pmatrix} 0 \\ 2 \\ 1 \end{pmatrix}x_2 + \begin{pmatrix} 1 \\ 4 \\ 2 \end{pmatrix}x_3 + \begin{pmatrix} 2 \\ 0 \\ 0 \end{pmatrix}x_4 = \begin{pmatrix} 3 \\ 4 \\ 2 \end{pmatrix}$$

Determine if any of the following combinations forms a basis.

*(a) $(\mathbf{P}_1, \mathbf{P}_2, \mathbf{P}_3)$
(b) $(\mathbf{P}_1, \mathbf{P}_3, \mathbf{P}_4)$
(c) $(\mathbf{P}_2, \mathbf{P}_3, \mathbf{P}_4)$
*(d) $(\mathbf{P}_1, \mathbf{P}_2, \mathbf{P}_3, \mathbf{P}_4)$

4. True or False?

(a) The system $\mathbf{BX} = \mathbf{b}$ has a unique solution even if $\mathbf{B}$ is singular.
(b) The system $\mathbf{BX} = \mathbf{b}$ has no solution if $\mathbf{B}$ is singular and $\mathbf{b}$ is independent of $\mathbf{B}$.
(c) The system $\mathbf{BX} = \mathbf{b}$ has an infinity of solutions if $\mathbf{B}$ is singular and $\mathbf{b}$ is dependent.

7.1.2   Generalized Simplex Tableau in Matrix Form

This section develops the general simplex tableau in matrix form. This representation is the basis for subsequent developments in the chapter.

Consider the LP in equation form:

$$\text{Maximize } z = \mathbf{CX}, \text{ subject to } \mathbf{AX} = \mathbf{b}, \mathbf{X} \geq \mathbf{0}$$

Equivalently, the problem can be written as

$$\begin{pmatrix} 1 & -\mathbf{C} \\ 0 & \mathbf{A} \end{pmatrix}\begin{pmatrix} z \\ \mathbf{X} \end{pmatrix} = \begin{pmatrix} 0 \\ \mathbf{b} \end{pmatrix}$$

Suppose that $\mathbf{B}$ is a feasible basis of the system $\mathbf{AX} = \mathbf{b}, \mathbf{X} \geq \mathbf{0}$, and let $\mathbf{X}_B$ be the corresponding vector of basic variables and $\mathbf{C}_B$ its associated objective vector. Given that all the nonbasic variables are zero, the solution is then computed as

$$\begin{pmatrix} z \\ \mathbf{X}_B \end{pmatrix} = \begin{pmatrix} 1 & -\mathbf{C}_B \\ 0 & \mathbf{B} \end{pmatrix}^{-1}\begin{pmatrix} 0 \\ \mathbf{b} \end{pmatrix} = \begin{pmatrix} 1 & \mathbf{C}_B\mathbf{B}^{-1} \\ 0 & \mathbf{B}^{-1} \end{pmatrix}\begin{pmatrix} 0 \\ \mathbf{b} \end{pmatrix} = \begin{pmatrix} \mathbf{C}_B\mathbf{B}^{-1}\mathbf{b} \\ \mathbf{B}^{-1}\mathbf{b} \end{pmatrix}$$

(Inversion of partitioned matrices is given in Section D.2.7. on the website)

The complete simplex tableau in matrix form can be derived from the original equations as

$$\begin{pmatrix} 1 & C_B B^{-1} \\ 0 & B^{-1} \end{pmatrix} \begin{pmatrix} 1 & -C \\ 0 & A \end{pmatrix} \begin{pmatrix} z \\ X \end{pmatrix} = \begin{pmatrix} 1 & C_B B^{-1} \\ 0 & B^{-1} \end{pmatrix} \begin{pmatrix} 0 \\ b \end{pmatrix}$$

Matrix manipulations then yield the following equations:

$$\begin{pmatrix} 1 & C_B B^{-1} A - C \\ 0 & B^{-1} A \end{pmatrix} \begin{pmatrix} z \\ X \end{pmatrix} = \begin{pmatrix} C_B B^{-1} b \\ B^{-1} b \end{pmatrix}$$

Given the jth vector P_j of A, the simplex tableau column associated with variable x_j can be written as

Basic	x_j	Solution
z	$C_B B^{-1} P_j - c_j$	$C_B B^{-1} b$
X_B	$B^{-1} P_j$	$B^{-1} b$

In fact, the tableau above is the same one used in Chapter 3 (see Problem 5 of Set 7.1c). It also includes all the primal–dual relationships developed in Section 4.2.4. An important property of this tableau is that the inverse, B^{-1}, is the only element that changes with a new iteration—meaning that the *entire* tableau can be generated from the original data once the inverse B^{-1} is known. In this regard, computational roundoff error in any tableau can be controlled by controlling the accuracy of B^{-1}. This result is one of the main reasons for the development of the revised simplex method in Section 7.2.

Example 7.1-3

Consider the following LP:

$$\text{Maximize } z = x_1 + 4x_2 + 7x_3 + 5x_4$$

subject to

$$2x_1 + x_2 + 2x_3 + 4x_4 = 10$$

$$3x_1 - x_2 - 2x_3 + 6x_4 = 5$$

$$x_1, x_2, x_3, x_4 \geq 0$$

Generate the simplex tableau associated with the basis $B = (P_1, P_2)$.
   Given $B = (P_1, P_2)$, then $X_B = (x_1, x_2)^T$ and $C_B = (1, 4)$. Thus,

$$B^{-1} = \begin{pmatrix} 2 & 1 \\ 3 & -1 \end{pmatrix}^{-1} = \begin{pmatrix} \frac{1}{5} & \frac{1}{5} \\ \frac{3}{5} & -\frac{2}{5} \end{pmatrix}$$

We then get

$$X_B = \begin{pmatrix} x_1 \\ x_2 \end{pmatrix} = B^{-1} b = \begin{pmatrix} \frac{1}{5} & \frac{1}{5} \\ \frac{3}{5} & -\frac{2}{5} \end{pmatrix} \begin{pmatrix} 10 \\ 5 \end{pmatrix} = \begin{pmatrix} 3 \\ 4 \end{pmatrix}$$

To compute the constraint columns in the body of the tableau, we have

$$\mathbf{B}^{-1}(\mathbf{P}_1, \mathbf{P}_2, \mathbf{P}_3, \mathbf{P}_4) = \begin{pmatrix} \frac{1}{5} & \frac{1}{5} \\ \frac{3}{5} & -\frac{2}{5} \end{pmatrix} \begin{pmatrix} 2 & 1 & 2 & 4 \\ 3 & -1 & -2 & 6 \end{pmatrix} = \begin{pmatrix} 1 & 0 & 0 & 2 \\ 0 & 1 & 2 & 0 \end{pmatrix}$$

Next, we compute the objective row as

$$\mathbf{C}_B(\mathbf{B}^{-1}(\mathbf{P}_1, \mathbf{P}_2, \mathbf{P}_2, \mathbf{P}_4)) - \mathbf{C} = (1, 4) \begin{pmatrix} 1 & 0 & 0 & 2 \\ 0 & 1 & 2 & 0 \end{pmatrix} - (1, 4, 7, 5) = (0, 0, 1, -3)$$

Finally, we compute the value of the objective function as

$$z = \mathbf{C}_B \mathbf{B}^{-1} \mathbf{b} = \mathbf{C}_B \mathbf{X}_B = (1, 4) \begin{pmatrix} 3 \\ 4 \end{pmatrix} = 19$$

Thus, the entire tableau can be summarized as follows.

Basic	x_1	x_2	x_3	x_4	Solution
z	0	0	1	-3	19
x_1	1	0	0	2	3
x_2	0	1	2	0	4

PROBLEM SET 7.1C

*1. In Example 7.1-3, consider $\mathbf{B} = (\mathbf{P}_3, \mathbf{P}_4)$. Show that the corresponding basic solution is feasible, then generate the corresponding simplex tableau.

2. Consider the following LP:

$$\text{Maximize } z = 5x_1 + 12x_2 + 4x_3$$

subject to

$$x_1 + 2x_2 + x_3 + x_4 = 10$$
$$2x_1 - 2x_2 - x_3 \quad\quad = 2$$
$$x_1, x_2, x_3, x_4 \geq 0$$

Check if each of the following matrices forms a (feasible or infeasible) basis: $(\mathbf{P}_1, \mathbf{P}_3)$, $(\mathbf{P}_1, \mathbf{P}_4)$, $(\mathbf{P}_2, \mathbf{P}_3)$, $(\mathbf{P}_3, \mathbf{P}_4)$.

3. In the following LP, compute the entire simplex tableau associated with $\mathbf{X}_B = (x_1, x_2, x_5)^T$.

$$\text{Minimize } z = 2x_1 + x_2$$

subject to

$$3x_1 + x_2 - x_3 \quad\quad\quad = 2$$
$$4x_1 + 3x_2 \quad - x_4 \quad\quad = 4$$
$$x_1 + 2x_2 \quad\quad\quad + x_5 = 2$$
$$x_1, x_2, x_3, x_4, x_5 \geq 0$$

*4. The following is an optimal LP tableau:

Basic	x_1	x_2	x_3	x_4	x_5	Solution
z	0	0	0	3	2	?
x_3	0	0	1	1	−1	2
x_2	0	1	0	1	0	6
x_1	1	0	0	−1	1	2

The variables x_3, x_4, and x_5 are slacks in the original problem. Use matrix manipulations to reconstruct the original LP, and then compute the optimum objective value.

5. In the matrix simplex tableau, suppose that the $\mathbf{X} = (\mathbf{X}_I, \mathbf{X}_{II})^T$, where $\mathbf{X}_{II}$ corresponds to a typical *starting* basic solution (consisting of slack and/or artificial variables) with $\mathbf{B} = \mathbf{1}$, and let $\mathbf{C} = (\mathbf{C}_I, \mathbf{C}_{II})$ and $\mathbf{A} = (\mathbf{D}, \mathbf{I})$ be the corresponding partitions of $\mathbf{C}$ and $\mathbf{A}$, respectively. Show that the matrix simplex tableau reduces to the same form used in Chapter 3—namely,

Basic	$\mathbf{X}_I$	$\mathbf{X}_{II}$	Solution
z	$\mathbf{C}_B\mathbf{B}^{-1}\mathbf{D} - \mathbf{C}_I$	$\mathbf{C}_B\mathbf{B}^{-1}\mathbf{D} - \mathbf{C}_{II}$	$\mathbf{C}_B\mathbf{B}^{-1}\mathbf{b}$
$\mathbf{X}_B$	$\mathbf{B}^{-1}\mathbf{D}$	$\mathbf{B}^{-1}$	$\mathbf{B}^{-1}\mathbf{b}$

7.2 REVISED SIMPLEX METHOD

Section 7.1.1 shows that the optimum solution of a linear program is always associated with a basic (feasible) solution. The simplex method search moves from a feasible basis, $\mathbf{B}$, to a better (actually, no-worse) basis, $\mathbf{B}_{\text{next}}$, until the optimum basis is reached.

The iterative steps of the *revised* simplex method are *exactly the same* as in the *tableau* simplex method presented in Chapter 3. The main difference is that the computations in the revised method are based on matrix manipulations rather than on row operations. Because the entire simplex tableau can be computed from the *original* data and the current inverse (see Section 7.1.2), controlling the accuracy of computing $\mathbf{B}^{-1}$ can mitigate machine roundoff error. In the tableau simplex method of Chapter 3, generating a new tableau from the immediately preceding one tends to propagate roundoff error.

7.2.1 Development of the Optimality and Feasibility conditions

The general LP problem can be written as

$$\text{Maximize or minimize } z = \sum_{j=1}^{n} c_j x_j \text{ subject to } \sum_{j=1}^{n} P_j x_j = \mathbf{b}, \; x_j \geq 0, j = 1, 2, \ldots, n$$

Given the basic vector $\mathbf{X}_B$, its basis $\mathbf{B}$, and its objective vector $\mathbf{C}_B$, the general simplex tableau developed in Section 7.1.2 shows that any simplex iteration can be represented by the following equations:

$$z + \sum_{j=1}^{n} (z_j - c_j)x_j = \mathbf{C}_B\mathbf{B}^{-1}\mathbf{b}$$

$$(\mathbf{X}_B)_i + \sum_{j=1}^{n} (\mathbf{B}^{-1}\mathbf{P}_j)_i x_j = (\mathbf{B}^{-1}\mathbf{b})_i$$

The **reduced cost** of x_j as defined in Section 4.3.2, is computed as

$$z_j - c_j = \mathbf{C}_B\mathbf{B}^{-1}\mathbf{P}_j - c_j$$

The notation $(\mathbf{V})_i$ represents element i of the vector $\mathbf{V}$.

Optimality Condition. The z-equation shows that, in the case of maximization, an increase in nonbasic x_j above its current zero value can improve the value of z (relative to its current value, $\mathbf{C}_B\mathbf{B}^{-1}\mathbf{b}$) only if $z_j - c_j < 0$. For minimization, the condition is $z_j - c_j > 0$. Thus, the **entering vector** is selected as the nonbasic vector with the *most* negative (*most* positive) $z_j - c_j$ in case of maximization (minimization).

Feasibility Condition. Given the entering vector $\mathbf{P}_j$ as determined by the optimality condition, the constraint equations reduce to

$$(\mathbf{X}_B)_i = (\mathbf{B}^{-1}\mathbf{b})_i - (\mathbf{B}^{-1}\mathbf{P}_j)_i x_j$$

(Recall that the remaining $n - 1$ nonbasic variables are zero.) The idea is to (attempt to) increase x_j above zero level, replacing one of the current basic variables. The extent to which x_j is increased is dictated by the requirement that all $(\mathbf{X}_B)_i$ remain nonnegative—namely,

$$(\mathbf{X}_B)_i = (\mathbf{B}^{-1}\mathbf{b})_i - (\mathbf{B}^{-1}\mathbf{P}_j)_i x_j \geq \mathbf{0}$$

If $(\mathbf{B}^{-1}\mathbf{P}_j)_i > 0$ for at least one i, the nonnegativity condition, $(\mathbf{X}_B)_i \geq \mathbf{0}$ all i, sets the limit on the maximum increase in the value of the entering variable x_j—namely,

$$x_j = \min_i \left\{ \frac{(\mathbf{B}^{-1}\mathbf{b})_i}{(\mathbf{B}^{-1}\mathbf{P}_j)_i} \,\middle|\, (\mathbf{B}^{-1}\mathbf{P}_j)_i > 0 \right\}$$

Suppose that $(\mathbf{X}_B)_k$ is the basic variable that corresponds to the minimum ratio. It then follows that $\mathbf{P}_k$ must be the **leaving vector**, and its associated (basic) variable must become nonbasic (at zero level) in the next simplex iteration.

PROBLEM SET 7.2A

*1. Consider the following LP:

$$\text{Maximize } z = c_1x_1 + c_2x_2 + c_3x_3 + c_4x_4$$

subject to

$$\mathbf{P}_1x_1 + \mathbf{P}_2x_2 + \mathbf{P}_3x_3 + \mathbf{P}_4x_4 = \mathbf{b}$$

$$x_1, x_2, x_3, x_4 \geq 0$$

The vectors $\mathbf{P}_1, \mathbf{P}_2, \mathbf{P}_3$, and $\mathbf{P}_4$ are shown in Figure 7.4. Assume that the basis $\mathbf{B}$ of the current iteration is comprised of $\mathbf{P}_2$ and $\mathbf{P}_3$.

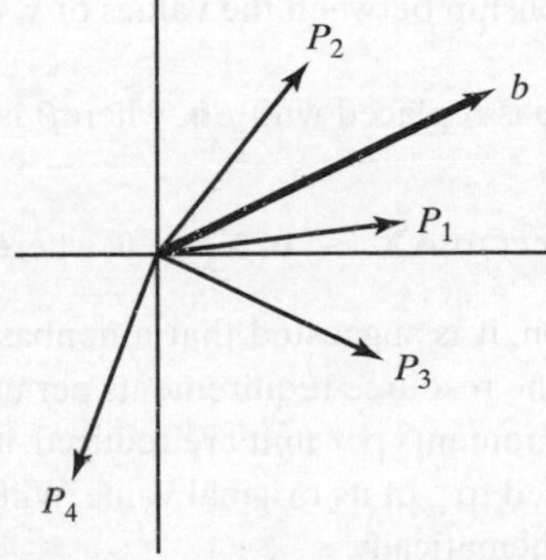

FIGURE 7.4

Vector representation of Problem 1, Set 7.2a

(a) If the vector $\mathbf{P}_1$ enters the basis, which of the current two basic vectors must leave in order for the resulting basic solution to be feasible?

(b) Can the vector $\mathbf{P}_4$ be part of a feasible basis?

*2. Prove that, in any simplex iteration, $z_j - c_j = 0$ for all the associated *basic* variables.

3. Prove that if $z_j - c_j > 0$ (<0) for all the nonbasic variables x_j of a maximization (minimization) LP problem, then the optimum is unique. Else, if $z_j - c_j$ equals zero for a nonbasic x_j, then the problem has an alternative optimum solution.

4. In an all-slack starting basic solution, show using the matrix form of the tableau that the mechanical procedure used in Section 3.3 in which the objective equation is set as

$$z - \sum_{j=1}^{n} c_j x_j = 0$$

automatically computes the proper $z_j - c_j$ for all the variables in the starting tableau.

5. Using the matrix form of the simplex tableau, show that in an all-artificial starting basic solution, the procedure in Section 3.4.1 that substitutes out the artificial variables in the objective function (using the constraint equations) actually computes the $z_j - c_j$ for all the variables in the starting tableau.

6. Consider an LP in which the variable x_k is unrestricted in sign. Prove that by substituting $x_k = x_k^- - x_k^+$, where x_k^- and x_k^+ are nonnegative, it is impossible that the two variables replace one another in an alternative optimum solution.

7. Consider the implementation of the feasibility condition of the simplex method. Specify the mathematical conditions for encountering a degenerate solution (at least one basic variable $=0$) for the first time? For continuing to obtain a degenerate solution in the next iteration? For removing degeneracy in the next iteration?

*8. Consider the general LP in equation form with m equations and n unknowns. Determine the maximum number of *adjacent* extreme points that can be reached from a nondegenerate extreme point (all basic variable are > 0) of the solution space.

9. In applying the feasibility condition of the simplex method, suppose that $x_k = 0$ is a basic variable and that x_j is the entering variable with $(\mathbf{B}^{-1}\mathbf{P}_j)_k \neq 0$. Prove that the resulting basic solution remains feasible even if $(\mathbf{B}^{-1}\mathbf{P}_j)_k$ is negative.

*10. What are the relationships between extreme points and basic solutions under degeneracy and nondegeneracy. What is the maximum number of iterations that can be performed at a given extreme point assuming no cycling?

*11. Consider the LP, maximize $z = \mathbf{CX}$ subject to $\mathbf{AX} \leq \mathbf{b}$, $\mathbf{X} \geq \mathbf{0}$, where $\mathbf{b} \geq \mathbf{0}$. Suppose that the entering vector $\mathbf{P}_j$ is such that at least one element of $\mathbf{B}^{-1}\mathbf{P}_j$ is positive.

(a) If $\mathbf{P}_j$ is replaced with $\alpha\mathbf{P}_j$, where α is a positive scalar, and provided x_j remains the entering variable, find the relationship between the values of x_j corresponding to $\mathbf{P}_j$ and $\alpha\mathbf{P}_j$.

(b) Answer Part (a) if, additionally, $\mathbf{b}$ is replaced with $\beta\mathbf{b}$, where β is a positive scalar.

12. Consider the LP

$$\text{Maximize } z = \mathbf{CX} \text{ subject to } \mathbf{AX} \leq \mathbf{b}, \mathbf{X} \geq \mathbf{0}, \text{ where } \mathbf{b} \geq \mathbf{0}$$

After obtaining the optimum solution, it is suggested that a nonbasic variable x_j can be made basic (profitable) by reducing the resource requirements per unit of x_j to $\frac{1}{q}$ of their original values, $q > 1$. Since the requirements per unit are reduced, it is expected that the profit per unit of x_j will also be reduced to $\frac{1}{q}$ of its original value. Will these changes make x_j a profitable variable? Explain mathematically.

13. Consider the LP

$$\text{Maximize } z = \mathbf{CX} \text{ subject to } (\mathbf{A}, \mathbf{I}) \mathbf{X} = \mathbf{b}, \mathbf{X} \geq \mathbf{0}$$

Define $\mathbf{X}_B$ as the current basic vector with $\mathbf{B}$ as its associated basis and $\mathbf{C}_B$ as its vector of objective coefficients. Show that if $\mathbf{C}_B$ is replaced with the new coefficients $\mathbf{D}_B$, the values of $z_j - c_j$ for the basic vector $\mathbf{X}_B$ will remain equal to zero. What is the significance of this result?

7.2.2 Revised Simplex Algorithm

Step 0. Construct a starting basic feasible solution, and let $\mathbf{B}$ and $\mathbf{C}_B$ be its associated basis and objective coefficients vector, respectively.

Step 1. Compute the inverse $\mathbf{B}^{-1}$ of the basis $\mathbf{B}$ by using an appropriate inversion method.[2]

Step 2. For each *nonbasic* vector $\mathbf{P}_j$, compute

$$z_j - c_j = \mathbf{C}_B \mathbf{B}^{-1}\mathbf{P}_j - c_j$$

If $z_j - c_j \geq 0$ in maximization (≤ 0 in minimization) for all nonbasic vectors, stop; the optimal solution is $\mathbf{X}_B = \mathbf{B}^{-1}\mathbf{b}$, $z = \mathbf{C}_B\mathbf{X}_B$.

Else, determine the *entering* vector $\mathbf{P}_j$ having the most negative (positive) $z_j - c_j$ in case of maximization (minimization) among all nonbasic vectors.

Step 3. Compute $\mathbf{B}^{-1}\mathbf{P}_j$. If all the elements of $\mathbf{B}^{-1}\mathbf{P}_j$ are negative or zero, stop; the solution is unbounded. Else, use the ratio test to determine the *leaving* vector $\mathbf{P}_j$.

Step 4. Form the next basis by replacing the *leaving* vector $\mathbf{P}_i$ with the entering vector $\mathbf{P}_j$ in the current basis $\mathbf{B}$. Go to step 1 to start a new iteration.

---

[2]In most LP presentations, including the first six editions of this book, the *product form* method for inverting a basis (see Section D.2.7 on the website) is integrated in the revised simplex algorithm because the *product form* lends itself readily to the revised simplex computations—namely successive bases differ in exactly one column. This detail has been removed from this presentation because it makes the algorithm appear more complex than it really is. Moreover, the *product form* is rarely used in the development of commercial LP codes, because it is not designed for automatic computations where machine roundoff error is a serious issue. Instead, some advanced numerical analysis method, such as the *LU decomposition* method, is used to compute the inverse. (Incidentally, TORA matrix inversion is based on LU decomposition.)

Example 7.2-1

The Reddy Mikks model (Section 2.1) is solved by the revised simplex algorithm. The same model was solved by the tableau method in Section 3.3.2. A comparison shows that the two method are one and the same.

The equation form of the Reddy Mikks model can be expressed in matrix form as

$$\text{maximize } z = (5, 4, 0, 0, 0, 0) (x_1, x_2, x_3, x_4, x_5, x_6)^T$$

subject to

$$\begin{pmatrix} 6 & 4 & 1 & 0 & 0 & 0 \\ 1 & 2 & 0 & 1 & 0 & 0 \\ -1 & 1 & 0 & 0 & 1 & 0 \\ 0 & 1 & 0 & 0 & 0 & 1 \end{pmatrix} \begin{pmatrix} x_1 \\ x_2 \\ x_3 \\ x_4 \\ x_5 \\ x_6 \end{pmatrix} = \begin{pmatrix} 24 \\ 6 \\ 1 \\ 2 \end{pmatrix}$$

$$x_1, x_2, \ldots, x_6 \geq 0$$

The notation $\mathbf{C} = (c_1, c_2, \ldots, c_6)$ represents the objective-function coefficients, and $(\mathbf{P}_1, \mathbf{P}_2, \ldots,$ and $\mathbf{P}_6)$ represent the columns vectors of the constraint equations. The right-hand side of the constraints is the vector $\mathbf{b}$.

In the computations below, we will give the algebraic formula for each step and its final numeric answer, without detailing the calculations. You will find it instructive to fill in the gaps in each step.

Iteration 0

$$\mathbf{X}_{B_0} = (x_3, x_4, x_5, x_6), \ \mathbf{C}_{B_0} = (0, 0, 0, 0)$$
$$\mathbf{B}_0 = (\mathbf{P}_3, \mathbf{P}_4, \mathbf{P}_5, \mathbf{P}_6) = \mathbf{I}, \ \mathbf{B}_0^{-1} = \mathbf{I}$$

Thus,

$$\mathbf{X}_{B_0} = \mathbf{B}_0^{-1}\mathbf{b} = (24, 6, 1, 2)^T, \ z = \mathbf{C}_{B_0}\mathbf{X}_{B_0} = 0$$

Optimality computations:

$$\mathbf{C}_{B_0}\mathbf{B}_0^{-1} = (0, 0, 0, 0)$$
$$\{z_j - c_j\}_{j=1,2} = \mathbf{C}_{B_0}\mathbf{B}_0^{-1}(\mathbf{P}_1, \mathbf{P}_2) - (c_1, c_2) = (-5, -4)$$

Thus, $\mathbf{P}_1$ is the entering vector.

Feasibility computations:

$$\mathbf{X}_{B_0} = (x_3, x_4, x_5, x_6)^T = (24, 6, 1, 2)^T$$
$$\mathbf{B}_0^{-1}\mathbf{P}_1 = (6, 1, -1, 0)^T$$

Hence,

$$x_1 = \min\left\{\frac{24}{6}, \frac{6}{1}, -, -\right\} = \min\{4, 6, -, -\} = 4$$

and $\mathbf{P}_3$ becomes the leaving vector.

The results given above can be summarized in the familiar simplex tableau format, essentially demonstrating that the two methods are the same.

Basic	x_1	x_2	x_3	x_4	x_5	x_6	Solution
z	-5	-4	0	0	0	0	0
x_3	6						24
x_4	1						6
x_5	-1						1
x_6	0						2

Iteration 1

$$\mathbf{X}_{B_1} = (x_1, x_4, x_5, x_6), \ \mathbf{C}_{B_1} = (5, 0, 0, 0)$$

$$\mathbf{B}_1 = (\mathbf{P}_1, \mathbf{P}_4, \mathbf{P}_5, \mathbf{P}_6)$$

$$= \begin{pmatrix} 6 & 0 & 0 & 0 \\ 1 & 1 & 0 & 0 \\ -1 & 0 & 1 & 0 \\ 0 & 0 & 0 & 1 \end{pmatrix}$$

By using an appropriate inversion method (see Section D.2.7 on the website), then

$$\mathbf{B}_1^{-1} = \begin{pmatrix} \frac{1}{6} & 0 & 0 & 0 \\ -\frac{1}{6} & 1 & 0 & 0 \\ \frac{1}{6} & 0 & 1 & 0 \\ 0 & 0 & 0 & 1 \end{pmatrix}$$

Thus,

$$\mathbf{X}_{B_1} = \mathbf{B}_1^{-1}\mathbf{b} = (4, 2, 5, 2)^T, z = \mathbf{C}_{B_1}\mathbf{X}_{B_1} = 20$$

Optimality computations:

$$\mathbf{C}_{B_1}\mathbf{B}_1^{-1} = (\tfrac{5}{6}, 0, 0, 0)$$

$$\{z_j - c_j\}_{j=2,3} = \mathbf{C}_{B_1}\mathbf{B}_1^{-1}(\mathbf{P}_2, \mathbf{P}_3) - (c_2, c_3) = (-\tfrac{2}{3}, \tfrac{5}{6})$$

Thus, $\mathbf{P}_2$ is the entering vector.

Feasibility computations:

$$\mathbf{X}_{B_1} = (x_1, x_4, x_5, x_6)^T = (4, 2, 5, 2)^T$$

$$\mathbf{B}_1^{-1}\mathbf{P}_2 = (\tfrac{2}{3}, \tfrac{4}{3}, \tfrac{5}{3}, 1)^T$$

Hence,

$$x_2 = \min\left\{ \frac{4}{\frac{2}{3}}, \frac{2}{\frac{4}{3}}, \frac{5}{\frac{5}{3}}, \frac{2}{1} \right\} = \min\left\{ 6, \tfrac{3}{2}, 3, 2 \right\} = \tfrac{3}{2}$$

The vector $\mathbf{P}_4$ leaves the basis. (You will find it helpful to summarize these results in the simplex tableau format as we did in iteration 0.)

Iteration 2

$$\mathbf{X}_{B_2} = (x_1, x_2, x_5, x_6)^T,\ \mathbf{C}_{B_2} = (5, 4, 0, 0)$$

$$\mathbf{B}_2 = (\mathbf{P}_1, \mathbf{P}_2, \mathbf{P}_5, \mathbf{P}_6)$$

$$= \begin{pmatrix} 6 & 4 & 0 & 0 \\ 1 & 2 & 0 & 0 \\ -1 & 1 & 1 & 0 \\ 0 & 1 & 0 & 1 \end{pmatrix}$$

Hence,

$$\mathbf{B}_2^{-1} = \begin{pmatrix} \frac{1}{4} & -\frac{1}{2} & 0 & 0 \\ -\frac{1}{8} & \frac{3}{4} & 0 & 0 \\ \frac{3}{8} & -\frac{5}{4} & 1 & 0 \\ \frac{1}{8} & -\frac{3}{4} & 0 & 1 \end{pmatrix}$$

Thus,

$$\mathbf{X}_{B_2} = \mathbf{B}_2^{-1}\mathbf{b} = (3, \tfrac{3}{2}, \tfrac{5}{2}, \tfrac{1}{2})^T, z = \mathbf{C}_{B_2}\mathbf{X}_{B_2} = 21$$

Optimality computations:

$$\mathbf{C}_{B_2}\mathbf{B}_2^{-1} = (\tfrac{3}{4}, \tfrac{1}{2}, 0, 0)$$

$$\{z_j - c_j\}_{j=3,4} = \mathbf{C}_{B_2}\mathbf{B}_2^{-1}(\mathbf{P}_3, \mathbf{P}_4) - (c_3, c_4) = (\tfrac{3}{4}, \tfrac{1}{2})$$

Thus, $\mathbf{X}_{B_2}$ is optimal, and the computations end.

Summary of optimal solution:

$$x_1 = 3, x_2 = 1.5, z = 21$$

PROBLEM SET 7.2B

1. In Example 7.2-1, summarize the data of iteration 1 in the tableau format of Section 3.3.
2. Solve the following LPs by the revised simplex method:
   (a) Maximize $z = 6x_1 - 2x_2 + 3x_3$
       subject to

   $$2x_1 - x_2 + 2x_3 \le 2$$
   $$x_1 \qquad + 4x_3 \le 4$$
   $$x_1, x_2, x_3 \ge 0$$

   *(b) Maximize $z = 2x_1 + x_2 + 2x_3$
       subject to

   $$4x_1 + 3x_2 + 8x_3 \le 12$$
   $$4x_1 + x_2 + 12x_3 \le 8$$
   $$4x_1 - x_2 + 3x_3 \le 8$$
   $$x_1, x_2, x_3 \ge 0$$

(c) Minimize $z = 2x_1 + x_2$
subject to

$$3x_1 + x_2 = 3$$
$$4x_1 + 3x_2 \geq 6$$
$$x_1 + 2x_2 \leq 3$$
$$x_1, x_2 \geq 0$$

(d) Minimize $z = 5x_1 - 4x_2 + 6x_3 + 8x_4$
subject to

$$x_1 + 7x_2 + 3x_3 + 7x_4 \leq 46$$
$$3x_1 - x_2 + x_3 + 2x_4 \leq 20$$
$$2x_1 + 3x_2 - x_3 + x_4 \geq 18$$
$$x_1, x_2, x_3, x_4 \geq 0$$

3. Solve the LP given below by the revised simplex method given the starting basic feasible vector $\mathbf{X}_{B_0} = (x_2, x_4, x_5)^T$.

$$\text{Minimize } z = 7x_2 + 11x_3 - 10x_4 + 26x_6$$

subject to

$$x_2 - x_3 + x_5 + x_6 = 3$$
$$x_2 - x_3 + x_4 + 3x_6 = 4$$
$$x_1 + x_2 - 3x_3 + x_4 + x_5 = 6$$
$$x_1, x_2, x_3, x_4, x_5, x_6 \geq 0$$

4. Solve the following using the two-phase revised simplex method:
   (a) Problem 2(c).
   (b) Problem 2(d).
   (c) Problem 3 (ignore the given starting $\mathbf{X}_{B_0}$).

5. *Revised Dual Simplex Method.* The steps of the revised dual simplex method (using matrix manipulations) can be summarized as follows:

   Step 0. Let $\mathbf{B}_0 = \mathbf{I}$ be the starting basis for which at least one of the elements of $\mathbf{X}_{B_0}$ is negative (infeasible).

   Step 1. Compute $\mathbf{X}_B = \mathbf{B}^{-1}\mathbf{b}$, the current values of the basic variables. Select the leaving variable x_r as the one having the most negative value. If all the elements of $\mathbf{X}_B$ are nonnegative, stop; the current solution is feasible (and optimal).

   Step 2. (a) Compute $z_j - c_j = \mathbf{C}_B\mathbf{B}^{-1}\mathbf{P}_j - c_j$ for all the nonbasic variables x_j.

   (b) For all the nonbasic variables x_j, compute the constraint coefficients $(\mathbf{B}^{-1}\mathbf{P}_j)_r$ associated with the row of the leaving variable x_r.

   (c) The entering variable is associated with

   $$\theta = \min_i \left\{ \left| \frac{z_j - c_j}{(\mathbf{B}^{-1}\mathbf{P}_j)_r} \right|, (\mathbf{B}^{-1}\mathbf{P}_j)_r < 0 \right\}$$

   If all $(\mathbf{B}^{-1}\mathbf{P}_j)_r \geq 0$, no feasible solution exists.

Step 3.   Obtain the new basis by interchanging the entering and leaving vectors (P_j and P_r). Compute the new inverse and go to step 1.

Apply the method to the following problem:

$$\text{Minimize } z = 3x_1 + 2x_2$$

subject to

$$3x_1 + x_2 \geq 3$$
$$4x_1 + 3x_2 \geq 6$$
$$x_1 + 2x_2 \leq 3$$
$$x_1, x_2 \geq 0$$

7.3   BOUNDED-VARIABLES ALGORITHM

In LP models, variables may have explicit upper and lower bounds. For example, in production facilities, lower and upper bounds can represent the minimum and maximum demands for certain products. Bounded variables also arise prominently in solving integer programs by the branch-and-bound algorithm (see Section 9.3.1).

The bounded algorithm is efficient computationally because it accounts *implicitly* for the bounds. We consider the lower bounds first because their treatment is simple. Given $X \geq L$, substitute $X = L + X'$, $X' \geq 0$ throughout, and solve the problem in terms of X' (whose lower bound now equals zero). The original X is then determined by back-substitution, $X = X' + L \geq 0$.

Next, consider the upper-bounding constraints, $X \leq U$. The idea of direct substitution (i.e., $X = U - X''$, $X'' \geq 0$) is not correct because back-substitution, $X = U - X''$, does not ensure that X will remain nonnegative. A different procedure is thus needed.

Define the upper bounded LP model as

$$\text{Maximize } z = \left\{ CX | (A, I) X = b, 0 \leq X \leq U \right\}$$

The bounded algorithm uses only the main constraints $(A, I)X = b, X \geq 0$. It accounts for the upper bounds, $X \leq U$, implicitly by modifying the feasibility condition.

Let $X_B = B^{-1}b$ be a current basic feasible solution of $(A, I)X = b, X \geq 0$, and assume that P_j is the entering vector (as determined by the regular optimality condition). Then, *given that all the nonbasic variables are zero*, the constraint equation of the ith basic variable is

$$(X_B)_i = (B^{-1}b)_i - (B^{-1}P_j)_i x_j$$

When the entering variable x_j increases above zero level, $(X_B)_i$ will *increase or decrease* depending on whether $(B^{-1}P_j)_i$ is negative or positive, respectively. Thus, in determining the value of the entering vector P_j, three conditions must be satisfied:

1. The basic variable remains nonnegative—that is, $(X_B)_i \geq 0$.
2. The basic variable $(X_B)_i$ does not exceed its upper bound—that is, $(X_B)_i \leq (U_B)_i$, where U_B comprises the elements of U corresponding to X_B.

3. The entering variable x_j cannot assume a value larger than its upper bound—that is, $x_j \leq u_j$, where u_j is the jth element of $\mathbf{U}$.

The first condition $(\mathbf{X}_B)_i \geq 0$ is the same as in the regular simplex method. It yields

$$x_j \leq \theta_1 = \min_i \left\{ \frac{(\mathbf{B}^{-1}\mathbf{b})_i}{(\mathbf{B}^{-1}\mathbf{P}_j)_i} \,\middle|\, (\mathbf{B}^{-1}\mathbf{P}_j)_i > 0 \right\}$$

The second condition $(\mathbf{X}_B)_i \leq (\mathbf{U}_B)_i$ specifies that

$$\left(\mathbf{B}^{-1}\mathbf{b}\right)_i - \left(\mathbf{B}^{-1}\mathbf{P}_j\right)_i x_j \leq \left(\mathbf{U}_B\right)_i$$

It is satisfied if

$$x_j \leq \theta_2 = \min_i \left\{ \frac{(\mathbf{B}^{-1}\mathbf{b})_i - (\mathbf{U}_B)_i}{(\mathbf{B}^{-1}\mathbf{P}_j)_i} \,\middle|\, \mathbf{B}^{-1}\mathbf{P}_{ji} < 0 \right\}$$

Combining the three restrictions, x_j enters the solution at the level that satisfies all three conditions—that is,

$$x_j = \min \{\theta_1, \theta_2, u_j\}$$

The change of basis for the next iteration depends on whether x_j enters the solution at level θ_1, θ_2, or u_j. Assuming that $(\mathbf{X}_B)_r$ is the leaving variable, then we have the following rules:

1. $x_j = \theta_1$: $(\mathbf{X}_B)_r$ leaves the basic solution (becomes nonbasic) at level zero. The new iteration is generated using the regular simplex method with x_j and $(\mathbf{X}_B)_r$ as the entering and the leaving variables, respectively.

2. $x_j = \theta_2$: $(\mathbf{X}_B)_r$ becomes nonbasic *at its upper bound*. The new iteration is generated as in the case of $x_j = \theta_1$, with one modification that accounts for the fact that $(\mathbf{X}_B)_r$ will be nonbasic at *upper bound*. Because the values of θ_1 and θ_2 require *all nonbasic variables to be at zero level* (convince yourself that this is the case!), the new nonbasic $(\mathbf{X}_B)_r$ at upper bound is converted to a nonbasic variable at zero level. This is achieved by using the substitution $(\mathbf{X}_B)_r = (\mathbf{U}_B)_r - (\mathbf{X}_B')_r$, where $(\mathbf{X}_B')_r \geq 0$. It is immaterial whether the substitution is made before or after the new basis is computed.

3. $x_j = u_j$: The basic vector $\mathbf{X}_B$ remains unchanged because $x_j = u_j$ stops short of forcing any of the current basic variables to reach its lower ($= 0$) or upper bound. This means that x_j will remain nonbasic *but at upper bound. The only change needed in the tableau is to use the substitution $x_j = u_j - x_j'$ to ensure that all* nonbasic variables are at zero level.

A tie among θ_1, θ_2, and u_j may be broken arbitrarily. However, it is preferable, where possible, to implement the rule for $x_j = u_j$ because it entails less computation.

The substitution $x_j = u_j - x'_j$ will change the original c_j, P_j, and b to $c'_j = -c_j$, $P'_j = -P_j$, and b to $b' = b - u_j P_j$. This means that if the revised simplex method is used, all the computations (e.g., B^{-1}, X_B, and $z_j = c_j$) should be based on the changed values of C, A, and b at each iteration (see Problem 5, Set 7.3a, for further details).

Example 7.3-1

Solve the following LP model by the upper-bounding algorithm.[3]

$$\text{Maximize } z = 3x_1 + 5y + 2x_3$$

subject to

$$x_1 + y + 2x_3 \le 14$$

$$2x_1 + 4y + 3x_3 \le 43$$

$$0 \le x_1 \le 4, 7 \le y \le 10, 0 \le x_3 \le 3$$

The lower bound on y is accounted for using the substitution $y = x_2 + 7$, where $0 \le x_2 \le 10 - 7 = 3$.

To avoid being "sidetracked" by the computational details, we will not use the revised simplex method to carry out the computations. Instead, we will use the compact tableau form. Problems 5, 6, and 7, Set 7.3a, address the revised version of the algorithm.

Iteration 0

Basic	x_1	x_2	x_3	x_4	x_5	Solution
z	-3	-5	-2	0	0	35
x_4	1	1	2	1	0	7
x_5	2	4	3	0	1	15

We have $B = B^{-1} = I$ and $X_B = (x_4, x_5)^T = B^{-1}b = (7, 15)^T$. Given that x_2 is the entering variable ($z_2 - c_2 = -5$), we get

$$B^{-1}P_2 = (1, 4)^T$$

which yields

$$\theta_1 = \min \left\{ \frac{7}{1}, \frac{15}{4} \right\} = 3.75, \text{ corresponding to } x_5$$

$$\theta_2 = \infty \text{ (because all the elements of } B^{-1}P_2 > 0)$$

Next, given the upper bound on the entering variable, $x_2 \le 3$, it follows that

$$x_2 = \min \{3.75, \infty, 3\} = 3$$

---

[3]You can use TORA's Linear Programming ⇒ Solve problem ⇒ Algebraic ⇒ Iterations ⇒ Bounded simplex to produce the associated simplex iterations (file *toraEx7.3-1.txt*).

Because $x_2 = u_2$, $\mathbf{X}_B$ remains unchanged, and x_2 becomes nonbasic *at its upper bound*. The substitution $x_2 = 3 - x_2'$ yields the following new tableau:

Basic	x_1	x_2'	x_3	x_4	x_5	Solution
z	-3	5	-2	0	0	50
x_4	1	-1	2	1	0	4
x_5	2	-4	3	0	1	3

The substitution changes the original right-hand side vector from $\mathbf{b} = (7, 15)^T$ to $\mathbf{b}' = (4, 3)^T$. Thus, $\mathbf{b}'$ replaces $\mathbf{b}$ in future iterations.

Iteration 1

The entering variable is x_1. The basic vector $\mathbf{X}_B$ and $\mathbf{B}^{-1}(=\mathbf{I})$ are the same as in iteration 0. Next, given $\mathbf{B}^{-1}\mathbf{P}_1 = (1, 2)^T$,

$$\theta_1 = \min \left\{ \frac{4}{1}, \frac{3}{2} \right\} = 1.5, \text{ corresponding to basic } x_5$$

$$\theta_2 = \infty \text{ (because } \mathbf{B}^{-1}\mathbf{P}_1 > 0)$$

Thus,

$$x_1 = \min \{1.5, \infty, 4\} = 1.5$$

Because $x_1 = \theta_1$, the entering variable x_1 becomes basic, and the leaving variable x_5 becomes nonbasic at zero level, which yields

Basic	x_1	x_2'	x_3	x_4	x_5	Solution
z	0	-1	$\frac{5}{2}$	0	$\frac{3}{2}$	$\frac{109}{2}$
x_4	0	1	$\frac{1}{2}$	1	$-\frac{1}{2}$	$\frac{5}{2}$
x_1	1	-2	$\frac{3}{2}$	0	$\frac{1}{2}$	$\frac{3}{2}$

Iteration 2

The new inverse is

$$\mathbf{B}^{-1} = \begin{pmatrix} 1 & -\frac{1}{2} \\ 0 & \frac{1}{2} \end{pmatrix}$$

Now, $\mathbf{X}_B = (x_4, x_1)^T = \mathbf{B}^{-1}\mathbf{b}' = \left(\frac{5}{2}, \frac{3}{2} \right)^T$, where $\mathbf{b}' = (4, 3)^T$ as computed at the end of iteration 0. We select x_2' as the entering variable, and, noting that $\mathbf{P}_2' = -\mathbf{P}_2$, we get

$$\mathbf{B}^{-1}\mathbf{P}_2' = (1, -2)^T$$

Thus,

$$\theta_1 = \min \left\{ \frac{\frac{5}{2}}{1}, - \right\} = 2.5, \text{ corresponding to basic } x_4$$

$$\theta_2 = \min \left\{ -, \frac{\frac{3}{2} - 4}{-2} \right\} = 1.25, \text{ corresponding to basic } x_1$$

We then have

$$x_2' = \min\{2.5, 1.25, 3\} = 1.25$$

Because $x_2' = \theta_1, x_1$ becomes nonbasic at upper bound resulting in the substitution $x_1 = 4 - x_1'$. The new tableau is

Basic	x_1'	x_2'	x_3	x_4	x_5	Solution
z	0	-1	$\frac{5}{2}$	0	$\frac{3}{2}$	$\frac{109}{2}$
x_4	0	1	$\frac{1}{2}$	1	$-\frac{1}{2}$	$\frac{5}{2}$
x_1'	-1	-2	$\frac{3}{2}$	0	$\frac{1}{2}$	$-\frac{5}{2}$

Next, the entering variable x_2' becomes basic and the leaving variable x_1' becomes nonbasic, which yields

Basic	x_1'	x_2'	x_3	x_4	x_5	Solution
z	$\frac{1}{2}$	0	$\frac{7}{4}$	0	$\frac{5}{4}$	$\frac{223}{4}$
x_4	$-\frac{1}{2}$	0	$\frac{5}{4}$	1	$-\frac{1}{4}$	$\frac{5}{4}$
x_2'	$\frac{1}{2}$	1	$-\frac{3}{4}$	0	$-\frac{1}{4}$	$\frac{5}{4}$

The last tableau is feasible and optimal. Note that the last two steps could have been reversed—meaning that we could first make x_2' basic and then apply the substitution $x_1 = 4 - x_1'$ (try it!). The sequence presented here involves less computation, however.

The optimal values of x_1, x_2, and x_3 are obtained by back-substitution as $x_1 = u_1 - x_1' = 4 - 0 = 4, x_2 = u_2 - x_2' = 3 - \frac{5}{4} = \frac{7}{4}$, and $x_3 = 0$. Finally, we get $y = l_2 + x_2 = 7 + \frac{7}{4} = \frac{35}{4}$. The associated optimal value of the objective function is $\frac{223}{4}$.

PROBLEM SET 7.3A

1. Consider the following linear program:

$$\text{Maximize } z = 2x_1 + x_2$$

subject to

$$x_1 + x_2 \leq 3$$

$$0 \leq x_1 \leq 2, 0 \leq x_2 \leq 2$$

   (a) Solve the problem graphically, and trace the sequence of extreme points leading to the optimal solution. (You may use TORA.)

   (b) Solve the problem by the upper-bounding algorithm, and show that the method produces the same sequence of extreme points as in the graphical optimal solution (you may use TORA to generate the iterations).

   (c) How does the upper-bounding algorithm recognize the extreme points?

*2. Solve the following problem by the bounded algorithm:

$$\text{Maximize } z = 6x_1 + 2x_2 + 8x_3 + 4x_4 + 2x_5 + 10x_6$$

subject to

$$8x_1 + x_2 + 8x_3 + 2x_4 + 2x_5 + 4x_6 \leq 13$$

$$0 \leq x_j \leq 1, j = 1, 2, \ldots, 6$$

3. Solve the following problems by the bounded algorithm:
   (a) Minimize $z = 6x_1 - 2x_2 - 3x_3$
      subject to

$$2x_1 + 4x_2 + 2x_3 \leq 8$$

$$x_1 - 2x_2 + 3x_3 \leq 7$$

$$0 \leq x_1 \leq 2, 0 \leq x_2 \leq 2, 0 \leq x_3 \leq 1$$

   (b) Maximize $z = 3x_1 + 5x_2 + 2x_3$
      subject to

$$x_1 + 2x_2 + 2x_3 \leq 10$$

$$2x_1 + 4x_2 + 3x_3 \leq 15$$

$$0 \leq x_1 \leq 4, 0 \leq x_2 \leq 3, 0 \leq x_3 \leq 3$$

4. In the following problems, some of the variables have positive lower bounds. Use the bounded algorithm to solve these problems.
   (a) Maximize $z = 3x_1 + 2x_2 - 2x_3$
      subject to

$$2x_1 + x_2 + x_3 \leq 8$$

$$x_1 + 2x_2 - x_3 \geq 3$$

$$1 \leq x_1 \leq 3, 0 \leq x_2 \leq 3, 2 \leq x_3$$

   (b) Maximize $z = x_1 + 2x_2$
      subject to

$$-x_1 + 2x_2 \geq 0$$

$$3x_1 + 2x_2 \leq 10$$

$$-x_1 + x_2 \leq 1$$

$$1 \leq x_1 \leq 3, 0 \leq x_2 \leq 1$$

   (c) Maximize $z = 4x_1 + 2x_2 + 6x_3$
      subject to

$$4x_1 - x_2 \qquad \leq 9$$

$$-x_1 + x_2 + 2x_3 \leq 8$$

$$-3x_1 + x_2 + 4x_3 \leq 12$$

$$1 \leq x_1 \leq 3, 0 \leq x_2 \leq 5, 0 \leq x_3 \leq 2$$

5. Consider the matrix definition of the bounded-variables problem. Suppose that the vector $\mathbf{X}$ is partitioned into $(\mathbf{X}_z, \mathbf{X}_u)$, where $\mathbf{X}_u$ represents the basic *and* nonbasic variables that

will be substituted at upper bound during the course of the algorithm. The problem may thus be written as

$$\begin{pmatrix} 1 & -\mathbf{C}_z & -\mathbf{C}_u \\ 0 & \mathbf{D}_z & \mathbf{D}_u \end{pmatrix}\begin{pmatrix} z \\ \mathbf{X}_z \\ \mathbf{X}_u \end{pmatrix} = \begin{pmatrix} 0 \\ \mathbf{b} \end{pmatrix}$$

Using $\mathbf{X}_u = \mathbf{U}_u - \mathbf{X}'_u$ where $\mathbf{U}_u$ is a subset of $\mathbf{U}$ representing the upper bounds for $\mathbf{X}_u$, let $\mathbf{B}$ (and $\mathbf{X}_B$) be the basis of the current simplex iteration after $\mathbf{X}_u$ has been substituted out. Show that the associated general simplex tableau is given as

Basic	$\mathbf{X}_z^T$	$\mathbf{X}_u'^T$	Solution
z	$\mathbf{C}_B\mathbf{B}^{-1}\mathbf{D}_z - \mathbf{C}_z$	$-\mathbf{C}_B\mathbf{B}^{-1}\mathbf{D}_u + \mathbf{C}_u$	$\mathbf{C}_u\mathbf{B}^{-1}\mathbf{B}^{-1}(\mathbf{b} - \mathbf{D}_u\mathbf{U}_u) + \mathbf{C}_u\mathbf{U}_u$
$\mathbf{X}_B$	$\mathbf{B}^{-1}\mathbf{D}_z$	$-\mathbf{B}^{-1}\mathbf{D}_u$	$\mathbf{B}^{-1}(\mathbf{b} - \mathbf{D}_u\mathbf{U}_u)$

6. In Example 7.3-1, do the following:
   (a) In iteration 1, verify that $\mathbf{X}_B = (x_4, x_1)^T = \left(\frac{5}{2}, \frac{3}{2}\right)^T$ by using matrix manipulation.
   (b) In iteration 2, show how $\mathbf{B}^{-1}$ can be computed from the original data of the problem. Then verify the given values of basic x_4 and x'_2 using matrix manipulation.

7. Solve part (a) of Problem 3 using the revised simplex (matrix) version for upper-bounded variables.

8. *Bounded Dual Simplex Algorithm.* The dual simplex algorithm (Section 4.4.1) can be modified to accommodate the bounded variables as follows. Given the upper bound constraint $x_j \leq u_j$ for all j (if u_j is infinite, replace it with a sufficiently large upper bound M), the LP problem is converted to a dual feasible (i.e., primal optimal) form by using the substitution $x_j = u_j - x'_j$, where necessary.

   Step 1. If any of the current basic variables $(\mathbf{X}_B)_i$ exceeds its upper bound, use the substitution $(\mathbf{X}_B)_i = (\mathbf{U}_B)_i - (\mathbf{X}_B)'_i$. Go to step 2.

   Step 2. If all the basic variables are feasible, stop. Otherwise, select the leaving variable x_r as the basic variable having the most negative value. Go to step 3.

   Step 3. Select the entering variable using the optimality condition of the regular dual simplex method (Section 4.4.1). Go to step 4.

   Step 4. Perform a change of basis. Go to step 1.

   Apply the given algorithm to the following problems:

   (a) Minimize $z = -3x_1 - 2x_2 + 2x_3$
   subject to

$$2x_1 + x_2 + x_3 \leq 8$$
$$-x_1 + 2x_2 + x_3 \geq 13$$
$$0 \leq x_1 \leq 2, 0 \leq x_2 \leq 3, 0 \leq x_3 \leq 1$$

   (b) Maximize $z = x_1 + 5x_2 - 2x_3$
   subject to

$$4x_1 + 2x_2 + 2x_3 \leq 26$$
$$x_1 + 3x_2 + 4x_3 \geq 17$$
$$0 \leq x_1 \leq 2, 0 \leq x_2 \leq 3, x_3 \geq 0$$

7.4   DUALITY

This section presents a rigorous treatment of duality. The presentation also lays the foundation for the development of parametric programming.

7.4.1   Matrix Definition of the Dual Problem

Suppose that the primal problem in equation form with m constraints and n variables is defined as

$$\text{Maximize } z = \mathbf{CX}$$

subject to

$$\mathbf{AX} = \mathbf{b}$$
$$\mathbf{X} \geq \mathbf{0}$$

Define the dual variables vector $\mathbf{Y} = (y_1, y_2, \ldots, y_m)$. The rules in Table 4.1 produce the following dual problem:

$$\text{Minimize } w = \mathbf{Yb}$$

subject to

$$\mathbf{YA} \geq \mathbf{C}$$
$$\mathbf{Y} \text{ unrestricted}$$

(Some of the constraints in $\mathbf{YA} \geq \mathbf{C}$ may override unrestricted $\mathbf{Y}$.)

PROBLEM SET 7.4A

1. Prove that the dual of the dual is the primal.
*2. Define the dual problem given the primal is min $z = \left\{ \mathbf{CX} \mid \mathbf{AX} \geq \mathbf{b}, \mathbf{X} \geq \mathbf{0} \right\}$.

7.4.2   Optimal Dual Solution

This section establishes relationships between the primal and dual problems and shows how the optimal dual solution can be determined from the optimal primal solution. Let $\mathbf{B}$ be the current *optimal* primal basis, and define $\mathbf{C}_B$ as the objective-function coefficients associated with the optimal vector $\mathbf{X}_B$.

Theorem 7.4-1   (Weak duality theory). *For any pair of* feasible *primal and dual solutions,* $(\mathbf{X}, \mathbf{Y})$, *the value of the objective function in the* minimization *problem sets an upper bound on the value of the objective function in the* maximization *problem. For the optimal pair* $(\mathbf{X}^*, \mathbf{Y}^*)$, *the two objective values are equal.*

Proof.   The feasible pair $(\mathbf{X}, \mathbf{Y})$ satisfies all the restrictions of the two problems. Premultiplying both sides of the constraints of the maximization problem with (unrestricted) $\mathbf{Y}$, we get

$$\mathbf{YAX} = \mathbf{Yb} = w \tag{1}$$

Also, for the minimization problem, postmultiplying both sides of each of the first two sets of constraints by $\mathbf{X}$ (≥ 0), we get

$$\mathbf{YAX} \geq \mathbf{CX} = z \tag{2}$$

Thus, from (1) and (2), $z \leq w$ for any *feasible* pair $(\mathbf{X}, \mathbf{Y})$.

Note that the feasibility requirement of $\mathbf{X}$ and $\mathbf{Y}$ is implied by $\mathbf{AX} = \mathbf{b}$ in (1), and $\mathbf{X} \geq \mathbf{0}$ and $\mathbf{YA} \geq \mathbf{C}$ in (2). Also, labeling the problems as primal or dual is immaterial. What is important is the sense of optimization in each problem—meaning that, for any pair of feasible solutions, the objective value in the maximization problem does not exceed the objective value in the minimization problem.

The implication of the theorem is that, given $z \leq w$ for any pair of feasible solutions, the maximum of z and the minimum of w are achieved when the two objective values are equal. A consequence of this result is that the "goodness" of any feasible primal and dual solutions relative to the optimum can be checked by comparing the difference $(w - z)$ to $\frac{z + w}{2}$. The smaller the ratio $\frac{2(w - z)}{z + w}$, the closer the two solutions are to being optimal. The given *rule of thumb* does *not* suggest that the optimal objective value is $\frac{z + w}{2}$.

Unboundedness and infeasibility. If the objective value of one of the two problems is unbounded, then the other problem must be infeasible. For if it is not, then both problems have feasible solutions, and the relationship $z \leq w$ must hold—an impossible result because unbounded objective value means $z = +\infty$ or $w = -\infty$.

If one problem is infeasible, then the other problem can be infeasible also, as the following example demonstrates (verify graphically!):

Primal. Maximize $z = \{x_1 + x_2 | x_1 - x_2 \leq -1, -x_1 + x_2 \leq -1, x_1, x_2 \geq 0\}$

Dual. Minimize $w = \{-y_1 - y_2 | y_1 - y_2 \geq 1, -y_1 + y_2 \geq 1, y_1, y_2 \geq 0\}$

Theorem 7.4-2 *Given the optimal primal basis* $\mathbf{B}$ *and its associated objective coefficient vector* $\mathbf{C}_B$, *the optimal solution of the dual problem is*

$$\mathbf{Y} = \mathbf{C}_B \mathbf{B}^{-1}$$

Proof. The proof rests on showing that $\mathbf{Y} = \mathbf{C}_B \mathbf{B}^{-1}$ is a feasible dual solution and that, per Theorem 7.4-1, $z = w$.

The feasibility of $\mathbf{Y} = \mathbf{C}_B \mathbf{B}^{-1}$ is guaranteed by the optimality of the primal, $z_j - c_j \geq 0$ for all j—that is,

$$\mathbf{C}_B \mathbf{B}^{-1} \mathbf{A} - \mathbf{C} \geq \mathbf{0}$$

(See Section 7.2.1.) Thus, $\mathbf{YA} - \mathbf{C} \geq \mathbf{0}$, which shows that $\mathbf{Y} = \mathbf{C}_B \mathbf{B}^{-1}$ satisfies the dual constraints, $\mathbf{YA} \geq \mathbf{C}$.

Next, we show that $w = z$ by noting that

$$w = \mathbf{Yb} = \mathbf{C}_B \mathbf{B}^{-1} \mathbf{b} \tag{1}$$

Similarly, given the primal solution $\mathbf{X}_B = \mathbf{B}^{-1}\mathbf{b}$, we get

$$z = \mathbf{C}_B\mathbf{X}_B = \mathbf{C}_B\mathbf{B}^{-1}\mathbf{b} \tag{2}$$

The dual variables $\mathbf{Y} = \mathbf{C}_B\mathbf{B}^{-1}$ are referred to by the standard names **dual** or **shadow prices** (see Section 4.3.1).

Motivation for the dual simplex algorithm. Given that $\mathbf{P}_j$ is the jth column of $\mathbf{A}$, we note from Theorem 7.4-2 that $z_j - c_j = \mathbf{C}_B\mathbf{B}^{-1}\mathbf{P}_j - c_j = \mathbf{YP}_j - c_j$ represents the difference between the left- and right-hand sides of the dual constraints. The maximization primal problem starts with $z_j - c_j < 0$ for at least one j, which means that the corresponding dual constraint, $\mathbf{YP}_j \geq c_j$, is not satisfied. When the primal optimal is reached, we get $z_j - c_j \geq 0$, for all j, rendering the dual solution $\mathbf{Y} = \mathbf{C}_B\mathbf{B}^{-1}$ feasible. Thus, as the primal problem seeks optimality, the dual problem seeks feasibility. This point is the basis for the development of the *dual simplex method* (Section 4.4.1) in which the iterations start (better than) optimal and infeasible and remain so until feasibility is attained at the last iteration. This is in contrast with the (primal) simplex method (Chapter 3), which remains worse than optimal but feasible until the optimal iteration is reached.

Example 7.4-1

The *optimal* basis for the following LP is $\mathbf{B} = (\mathbf{P}_1, \mathbf{P}_4)$. Write the dual, and find its optimum solution using the optimal primal basis.

$$\text{Maximize } z = 3x_1 + 5x_2$$

subject to

$$x_1 + 2x_2 + x_3 \quad\quad = 5$$
$$-x_1 + 3x_2 \quad\quad + x_4 = 2$$
$$x_1, x_2, x_3, x_4 \geq 0$$

The dual problem is

$$\text{Minimize } w = 5y_1 + 2y_2$$

subject to

$$y_1 - y_2 \geq 3$$
$$2y_1 + 3y_2 \geq 5$$
$$y_1, y_2 \geq 0$$

We have $\mathbf{X}_B = (x_1, x_4)^T$ and $\mathbf{C}_B = (3, 0)$. The optimal basis and its inverse are

$$\mathbf{B} = \begin{pmatrix} 1 & 0 \\ -1 & 1 \end{pmatrix}, \mathbf{B}^{-1} = \begin{pmatrix} 1 & 0 \\ 1 & 1 \end{pmatrix}$$

The associated primal and dual values are

$$(x_1, x_4)^T = \mathbf{B}^{-1}\mathbf{b} = (5, 7)^T$$
$$(y_1, y_2) = \mathbf{C}_B\mathbf{B}^{-1} = (3, 0)$$

Both solutions are feasible, and $z = w = 15$ (verify!). Thus, the two solutions are optimal.

PROBLEM SET 7.4B

1. Verify that the dual problem of the numeric example given at the end of Theorem 7.4-1 is correct. Then verify graphically that both the primal and dual problems have no feasible solution.

2. Consider the following LP:

$$\text{Maximize } z = 5x_1 + 3x_2 + x_3$$

subject to

$$
\begin{aligned}
2x_1 + x_2 \quad &= 1 \\
2x_2 \quad &= -5 \\
4x_1 \quad + x_3 &= 6 \\
x_1, x_2, x_3 &\geq 0
\end{aligned}
$$

(a) Write the dual.

(b) Show by inspection that the primal is infeasible.

(c) Show that the dual in (a) is unbounded.

(d) From Problems 1 and 2, develop a general conclusion regarding the relationship between infeasibility and unboundedness in the primal and dual problems.

3. Consider the following LP:

$$\text{Maximize } z = 5x_1 + 12x_2 + 4x_3$$

subject to

$$
\begin{aligned}
2x_1 - x_2 + 3x_3 \quad &= 2 \\
x_1 + 2x_2 + x_3 + x_4 &= 5 \\
x_1, x_2, x_3, x_4 &\geq 0
\end{aligned}
$$

(a) Write the dual.

(b) In each of the following cases, first verify that the given basis $\mathbf{B}$ is feasible for the primal. Next, using $\mathbf{Y} = \mathbf{C}_R\mathbf{B}^{-1}$, compute the associated dual values, and verify whether or not the primal solution is optimal.

    (i) $\mathbf{B} = (\mathbf{P}_4, \mathbf{P}_3)$ (iii) $\mathbf{B} = (\mathbf{P}_1, \mathbf{P}_2)$

    (ii) $\mathbf{B} = (\mathbf{P}_2, \mathbf{P}_3)$ (iv) $\mathbf{B} = (\mathbf{P}_1, \mathbf{P}_4)$

4. Consider the following LP:

$$\text{Maximize } z = 2x_1 + 4x_2 + 4x_3 - 3x_4$$

subject to

$$x_1 + x_2 + x_3 \qquad = 4$$
$$x_1 + 4x_2 + \qquad + x_4 = 8$$
$$x_1, x_2, x_3, x_4 \geq 0$$

(a) Write the dual problem.

(b) Verify that $\mathbf{B} = (\mathbf{P}_2, \mathbf{P}_3)$ is optimal by computing $z_j - c_j$ for all nonbasic $\mathbf{P}_j$.

(c) Find the associated optimal dual solution.

*5. An LP model includes two variables x_1 and x_2 and three constraints of the type $\leq$. The associated slacks are x_3, x_4, and x_5. Suppose that the optimal basis is $\mathbf{B} = (\mathbf{P}_1, \mathbf{P}_2, \mathbf{P}_3)$, and its inverse is

$$\mathbf{B}^{-1} = \begin{pmatrix} 0 & -1 & 1 \\ 0 & 1 & 0 \\ 1 & 1 & -1 \end{pmatrix}$$

The optimal primal and dual solutions are

$$\mathbf{X}_B = (x_1, x_2, x_3)^T = (1, 3, 1)^T$$
$$\mathbf{Y} = (y_1, y_2, y_3) = (0, 3, 2)$$

Determine the optimal value of the objective function in two ways using the primal and dual problems.

*6. Write the dual of max $z = \{\mathbf{CX}|\mathbf{AX} = \mathbf{b}, \mathbf{X} \text{ unrestricted}\}$.

7. Show that the dual of max $z = \{\mathbf{CX}|\mathbf{AX} \leq \mathbf{b}, \mathbf{0} < \mathbf{L} \leq \mathbf{X} \leq \mathbf{U}\}$ always possesses a feasible solution.

7.5 PARAMETRIC LINEAR PROGRAMMING

Parametric linear programming is an extension of the post-optimal analysis presented in Section 4.5. It investigates the effect of *predetermined* continuous variations in the objective-function coefficients and the right-hand side of the constraints on the optimum solution.

Let $\mathbf{X} = (x_1, x_2, \ldots, x_n)$ and define the LP as

$$\text{Maximize } z = \left\{ \mathbf{CX}| \sum_{j=1}^{n} \mathbf{P}_j x_j = \mathbf{b}, \mathbf{X} \geq \mathbf{0} \right\}$$

In parametric analysis, the objective function and right-hand side vectors, $\mathbf{C}$ and $\mathbf{b}$, are replaced with the parameterized functions $\mathbf{C}(t)$ and $\mathbf{b}(t)$, where t is the parameter of variation. Mathematically, t can assume any positive or negative value. In this presentation, we will assume that $t \geq 0$.

The general idea of parametric analysis is to start with the optimal solution at $t = 0$. Then, using the optimality and feasibility conditions of the simplex method, we determine the range $0 \leq t \leq t_1$ for which the solution at $t = 0$ remains optimal and feasible. In this case, t_1 is referred to as a **critical value**. The process continues by determining successive critical values and their corresponding optimal feasible solutions. Termination of post-optimal analysis occurs when, regardless of t, the last solution remains unchanged or there is indication that no feasible solution exists.

7.5.1 Parametric Changes in C

Let X_{B_i}, B_i, $C_{B_i}(t)$ be the elements that define the optimal solution associated with critical t_i (the computations start at $t_0 = 0$ with B_0 as its optimal basis). Next, the critical value t_{i+1} and its optimal basis, if one exists, are determined. Because changes in C can affect only the optimality of the problem, the current solution $X_{B_i} = B_i^{-1}b$ will remain optimal for some $t \geq t_i$ so long as the reduced cost, $z_j(t) - c_j(t)$, satisfies the following optimality condition:

$$z_j(t) - c_j(t) = C_{B_i}(t)B_i^{-1}P_j - c_j(t) \geq 0, \text{ for all } j$$

The value of t_{i+1} equals the largest $t > t_i$ that satisfies all the optimality conditions.

Note that *nothing* in the inequalities requires $C(t)$ to be linear in t. Any function $C(t)$, linear or nonlinear, is acceptable. However, with nonlinearity the numerical manipulation of the resulting inequalities can be cumbersome. (See Problem 5, Set 7.5a, for an illustration of the nonlinear case.)

Example 7.5-1

$$\text{Maximize } z = (3 - 6t)x_1 + (2 - 2t)x_2 + (5 + 5t)x_3$$

subject to

$$x_1 + 2x_2 + x_3 \leq 40$$
$$3x_1 + 2x_3 \leq 60$$
$$x_1 + 4x_2 \leq 30$$
$$x_1, x_2, x_3 \geq 0$$

We have

$$C(t) = (3 - 6t, 2 - 2t, 5 + 5t), t \geq 0$$

The variables x_4, x_5, and x_6 will be used as the slack variables associated with the three constraints.

Optimal Solution at $t = t_0 = 0$

Basic	x_1	x_2	x_3	x_4	x_5	x_6	Solution
z	4	0	0	1	2	0	160
x_2	$-\frac{1}{4}$	1	0	$\frac{1}{2}$	$-\frac{1}{4}$	0	5
x_3	$\frac{3}{2}$	0	1	0	$\frac{1}{2}$	0	30
x_6	2	0	0	-2	1	1	10

$$X_{B_0} - (x_2, x_3 x_6)^T = (5, 30, 10)^T$$

$$C_{B_0}(t) = (2 - 2t, 5 + 5t, 0)$$

$$B_0^{-1} = \begin{pmatrix} \frac{1}{2} & -\frac{1}{4} & 0 \\ 0 & \frac{1}{2} & 0 \\ -2 & 1 & 1 \end{pmatrix}$$

The optimality conditions for the current nonbasic vectors, P_1, P_4, and P_5, are

$$\left\{ C_{B_0}(t) B_0^{-1} P_j - c_j(t) \right\}_{j=1,4,5} = (4 + 14t, 1 - t, 2 + 3t) \geq 0$$

Thus, X_{B_0} remains optimal for $t \leq t_1$, where t_1 is determined from the optimality conditions as

$$\left. \begin{array}{r} 4 + 14t \geq 0 \\ 1 - t \geq 0 \\ 2 + 3t \geq 0 \end{array} \right\} \Rightarrow 0 \leq t \leq 1 \Rightarrow t_1 = 1$$

The reduced cost $z_4(t) - c_4(t) = 1 - t$ equals zero at $t = 1$ and becomes negative for $t > 1$. Thus, P_4 must enter the basis for $t > 1$. In this case, P_2 must leave the basis (see the optimal tableau at $t = 0$). The new basic solution X_{B_1} is the alternative solution obtained at $t = 1$ by letting P_4 enter the basis—that is, $X_{B_1} = (x_4, x_3, x_6)^T$ and $B_1 = (P_4, P_3, P_6)$.

Alternative Optimal Basis at $t = t_1 = 1$

$$B_1 = \begin{pmatrix} 1 & 1 & 0 \\ 0 & 2 & 0 \\ 0 & 0 & 1 \end{pmatrix}, \; B_1^{-1} = \begin{pmatrix} 1 & -\frac{1}{2} & 0 \\ 0 & \frac{1}{2} & 0 \\ 0 & 0 & 1 \end{pmatrix}$$

Thus,

$$X_{B_1} = (x_4, x_3, x_6)^T = B_1^{-1} b = (10, 30, 30)^T$$
$$C_{B_1}(t) = (0, 5 + 5t, 0)$$

The associated nonbasic vectors are P_1, P_2, and P_5, and we have

$$\left\{ C_{B_1}(t) B_1^{-1} P_j - c_j(t) \right\}_{j=1,2,5} = \left(\frac{9 + 27t}{2}, -2 + 2t, \frac{5 + 5t}{2} \right) \geq 0$$

According to these conditions, the basic solution X_{B_1} remains optimal for all $t \geq 1$. Observe that the optimality condition, $-2 + 2t \geq 0$, automatically "remembers" that X_{B_1} is optimal for a range of t that starts from the last critical value $t_1 = 1$. This will always be the case in parametric programming computations.

The optimal solution for the entire range of t is summarized in the following table (the value of z is computed by direct substitution).

t	x_1	x_2	x_3	z
$0 \leq t \leq 1$	0	5	30	$160 + 140t$
$t \geq 1$	0	0	30	$150 + 150t$

PROBLEM SET 7.5a

*1. In Example 7.5-1, suppose that t is unrestricted in sign. Determine the range of t for which X_{B_0} remains optimal.

2. Solve Example 7.5-1, assuming that the objective function is given as
   *(a) Maximize $z = (3 + 3t)x_1 + 2x_2 + (5 - 6t)x_3$
   (b) Maximize $z = (3 - 2t)x_1 + (2 + t)x_2 + (5 + 2t)x_3$
   (c) Maximize $z = (3 + t)x_1 + (2 + 2t)x_2 + (5 - t)x_3$
3. Study the variation in the optimal solution of the following parameterized LP, given $t \geq 0$.

$$\text{Minimize } z = (4 - t)x_1 + (1 - 3t)x_2 + (2 - 2t)x_3$$

subject to

$$3x_1 + x_2 + 2x_3 = 6$$
$$4x_1 + 3x_2 + 2x_3 \geq 12$$
$$x_1 + 2x_2 + 5x_3 \leq 8$$
$$x_1, x_2, x_3 \geq 0$$

4. The analysis in this section assumes that the optimal solution of the LP at $t = 0$ is obtained by the (primal) simplex method. In some problems, it may be more convenient to obtain the optimal solution by the dual simplex method (Section 4.4.1). Show how the parametric analysis can be carried out in this case, then analyze the LP of Example 4.4-1, assuming that the objective function is given as

$$\text{Minimize } z = (3 + t)x_1 + (2 + 4t)x_2 + x_3, t \geq 0$$

*5. In Example 7.5-1, suppose that the objective function is nonlinear in t ($t \geq 0$) and is defined as

$$\text{Maximize } z = (3 + 2t^2)x_1 + (2 - 2t^2)x_2 + (5 - t)x_3$$

Determine the first critical value t_1.

7.5.2 Parametric Changes in b

The parameterized right-hand side $\mathbf{b}(t)$ can affect the feasibility of the problem only. The critical values of t are thus determined from the condition

$$\mathbf{X}_B(t) = \mathbf{B}^{-1}\mathbf{b}(t) \geq \mathbf{0}$$

Example 7.5-2

$$\text{Maximize } z = 3x_1 + 2x_2 + 5x_3$$

subject to

$$x_1 + 2x_2 + x_3 \leq 40 - t$$
$$3x_1 + 2x_3 \leq 60 + 2t$$
$$x_1 + 4x_2 \leq 30 - 7t$$
$$x_1, x_2, x_3 \geq 0$$

Assume that $t \geq 0$.

At $t = t_0 = 0$, the problem is identical to that of Example 7.5-1. We thus have

$$\mathbf{X}_{B_0} = (x_2, x_3, x_6)^T = (5, 30, 10)^T$$

$$\mathbf{B}_0^{-1} = \begin{pmatrix} \frac{1}{2} & -\frac{1}{4} & 0 \\ 0 & \frac{1}{2} & 0 \\ -2 & 1 & 1 \end{pmatrix}$$

To determine the first critical value t_1, we apply the feasibility conditions $\mathbf{X}_{B_0}(t) = \mathbf{B}_0^{-1}\mathbf{b}(t) \geq 0$, which yields

$$\begin{pmatrix} x_2 \\ x_3 \\ x_6 \end{pmatrix} = \begin{pmatrix} 5 - t \\ 30 + t \\ 10 - 3t \end{pmatrix} \geq \begin{pmatrix} 0 \\ 0 \\ 0 \end{pmatrix} \Rightarrow 0 \leq t \leq \frac{10}{3} \Rightarrow t_1 = \frac{10}{3}$$

The basis $\mathbf{B}_0$ remains feasible for the range $0 \leq t \leq \frac{10}{3}$. However, the values of the basic variables x_2, x_3, and x_6 change with t.

The value of the basic variable $x_6 (= 10 - 3t)$ equals zero at $t = t_1 = \frac{10}{3}$, and will become negative for $t > \frac{10}{3}$. Thus, at $t = \frac{10}{3}$, we can determine the alternative basis $\mathbf{B}_1$ by applying the revised dual simplex method (see Problem 5, Set 7.2b, for details). The leaving variable is x_6.

Alternative Basis at $t = t_1 = \frac{10}{3}$

Given that x_6 is the leaving variable, we determine the entering variable as follows:

$$\mathbf{X}_{B_0} = (x_2, x_3, x_6)^T, \quad \mathbf{C}_{B_0} = (2, 5, 0)$$

Thus,

$$\{z_j - c_j\}_{j=1,4,5} = \{\mathbf{C}_{B_0}\mathbf{B}_0^{-1}\mathbf{P}_j - c_j\}_{j=1,4,5} = (4, 1, 2)$$

Next, for nonbasic x_j, $j = 1, 4, 5$, we compute

$$\begin{aligned} (\text{Row of } \mathbf{B}_0^{-1} \text{ associated with } x_6) \, \mathbf{P}_1, \mathbf{P}_4, \mathbf{P}_5 &= (\text{Third row of } \mathbf{B}_0^{-1}) \, (\mathbf{P}_1, \mathbf{P}_4, \mathbf{P}_5) \\ &= (-2, 1, 1) \, (\mathbf{P}_1, \mathbf{P}_4, \mathbf{P}_5) \\ &= (2, -2, 1) \end{aligned}$$

The entering variable is thus associated with

$$\theta = \min\left\{ -, \left| \frac{1}{-2} \right|, - \right\} = \frac{1}{2}$$

Thus, $\mathbf{P}_4$ is the entering vector. The alternative basic solution and its $\mathbf{B}_1$ and $\mathbf{B}_1^{-1}$ are

$$\mathbf{X}_{B_1} = (x_2, x_3, x_4)^T$$

$$\mathbf{B}_1 = (\mathbf{P}_2, \mathbf{P}_3, \mathbf{P}_4) = \begin{pmatrix} 2 & 1 & 1 \\ 0 & 2 & 0 \\ 4 & 0 & 0 \end{pmatrix}, \mathbf{B}_1^{-1} = \begin{pmatrix} 0 & 0 & \frac{1}{4} \\ 0 & \frac{1}{2} & 0 \\ 1 & -\frac{1}{2} & -\frac{1}{2} \end{pmatrix}$$

The next critical value t_2 is determined from the feasibility conditions, $\mathbf{X}_{B_1}(t) = \mathbf{B}_1^{-1}\mathbf{b}(t) \geq \mathbf{0}$, which yield

$$\begin{pmatrix} x_2 \\ x_3 \\ x_4 \end{pmatrix} = \begin{pmatrix} \frac{30 - 7t}{4} \\ 30 + t \\ \frac{-10 + 3t}{2} \end{pmatrix} \begin{pmatrix} 0 \\ 0 \\ 0 \end{pmatrix} \Rightarrow \frac{10}{3} \leq t \leq \frac{30}{7} \Rightarrow t_2 = \frac{30}{7}$$

At $t = t_2 = \frac{30}{7}$, an alternative basis can be obtained by the revised dual simplex method. The leaving variable is x_2, because it corresponds to the condition yielding the critical value t_2.

Alternative Basis at $t = t_2 = \frac{30}{7}$

Given that x_2 is the leaving variable, we determine the entering variable as follows:

$$\mathbf{X}_{B_1} = (x_2, x_3, x_4)^T, \ \mathbf{C}_{B_1} = (2, 5, 0)$$

Thus,

$$\{z_j - c_j\}_{j=1, 5, 6} = \left\{\mathbf{C}_{B_1}\mathbf{B}_1^{-1}\mathbf{P}_j - c_j\right\}_{j=1, 5, 6} = \left(5, \tfrac{5}{2}, \tfrac{1}{2}\right)$$

Next, for nonbasic $x_j, j = 1, 5$, and 6, we compute

$$(\text{Row of } \mathbf{B}_1^{-1} \text{ associated with } x_2)(\mathbf{P}_1, \mathbf{P}_5, \mathbf{P}_6) = (\text{First row of } \mathbf{B}_1^{-1})(\mathbf{P}_1, \mathbf{P}_5, \mathbf{P}_6)$$
$$= \left(0, 0, \tfrac{1}{4}\right)(\mathbf{P}_1, \mathbf{P}_5, \mathbf{P}_6)$$
$$= \left(\tfrac{1}{4}, 0, \tfrac{1}{4}\right)$$

Because all the denominator elements, $\left(\tfrac{1}{4}, 0, \tfrac{1}{4}\right)$, are ≥ 0, the problem has no feasible solution for $t > \frac{30}{7}$, and the parametric analysis ends at $t = t_2 = \frac{30}{7}$.

The optimal solution is summarized as

t	x_1	x_2	x_3	z
$0 \leq t \leq \frac{10}{3}$	0	$5 - t$	$30 + t$	$160 + 3t$
$\frac{10}{3} \leq t \leq \frac{30}{7}$	0	$\frac{30 - 7t}{4}$	$30 + t$	$165 + \frac{3}{2}t$
$t > \frac{30}{7}$	(No feasible solution exists)			

PROBLEM SET 7.5B

1. In Example 7.5-2, find the first critical value, t_1, and define the vectors of $\mathbf{B}_1$ in each of the following cases.

   *(a) $\mathbf{b}(t) = (40 + 2t, 60 - 3t, 30 + 6t)^T$

   (b) $\mathbf{b}(t) = (40 - t, 60 + 2t, 30 - 5t)^T$

*2. Study the variation in the optimal solution of the following parameterized LP, given $t \geq 0$.

$$\text{Minimize } z = 4x_1 + x_2 + 2x_3$$

subject to

$$3x_1 + x_2 + 2x_3 = 6 + 6t$$

$$4x_1 + 3x_2 + 2x_3 \geq 12 + 4t$$

$$x_1 + 2x_2 + 5x_3 \leq 8 - 2t$$

$$x_1, x_2, x_3 \geq 0$$

3. The analysis in this section assumes that the optimal LP solution at $t = 0$ is obtained by the (primal) simplex method. In some problems, it may be more convenient to obtain the optimal solution by the dual simplex method (Section 4.4.1). Show how the parametric analysis can be carried out in this case, and then analyze the LP of Example 4.4-1, assuming that $t \geq 0$ and the right-hand side vector is

$$\mathbf{b}(t) = (3 + 2t, 6 - t, 3 - 4t)^T$$

4. Solve Problem 2 assuming that the right-hand side is changed to

$$\mathbf{b}(t) = (3 + 3t^2, 6 + 2t^2, 4 - t^2)^T$$

Further assume that t can be positive, zero, or negative.

7.6   MORE LINEAR PROGRAMMING TOPICS

The following list provides additional LP topics (normally covered in specialized OR courses) can be found in Chapter 22 on the website. The reason these topics are included in the text is to maintain the number of printed pages at a reasonable level.

1. Minimum-cost capacitated flow problem, including LP formulation, and capacitated network simplex algorithm model.
2. Dantzig-Wolfe decomposition algorithm.
3. Karmarkar interior-point algorithm.

BIBLIOGRAPHY

Bazaraa, M., J. Jarvis, and H. Sherali, *Linear Programming and Network Flows*, 4th ed., Wiley, New York, 2009.

Chvàtal, V., *Linear Programming*, Freeman, San Francisco, 1983.

Nering, E., and A. Tucker, *Linear Programming and Related Problems*, Academic Press, Boston, 1992.

Saigal, R. *Linear Programming: A Modern Integrated Analysis*, Kluwer Academic Publishers, Boston, 1995.

Vanderbei, R., *Linear Programming: Foundation and Extensions*, 3rd ed., Springer, New York, 2008.

CHAPTER 8

Goal Programming

Real-Life Application—Allocation of Operating Room Time in Mount Sinai Hospital

The situation takes place in Canada, where health care insurance is mandatory and universal. Funding, which is based on a combination of premiums and taxes, is controlled by the individual provinces. Under this system, hospitals are advanced a fixed annual budget, and each province pays physicians retrospectively using a fee-for-service funding mechanism. This funding arrangement limits the availability of hospital facilities (e.g., operating rooms), which in turn curbs physicians' tendency to boost personal gain through overservice to patients. The objective of the study is to determine an equitable daily schedule for the use of available operating rooms. The problem is modeled using a combination of goal and integer programming. Case 6 in Chapter 26 on the website provides the details of the study.

8.1 A GOAL PROGRAMMING FORMULATION

The idea of goal programming is illustrated by an example.

Example 8.1-1 (Tax Planning)[1]

Fairville is a small city with a population of about 20000 residents. The annual taxation base for real estate property is $550 million. The annual taxation bases for food and drugs and for general sales are $35 million and $55 million, respectively. Annual local gasoline consumption is estimated at 7.5 million gallons. The city council wants to develop the tax rates based on four main goals:

1. Tax revenues must be at least $16 million to meet the city's financial commitments.
2. Food and drug taxes cannot exceed 10% of all taxes collected.

---

[1] This example is based on Chissman and Associates, 1989.

335

3. General sales taxes cannot exceed 20% of all taxes collected.

4. Gasoline tax cannot exceed 2 cents per gallon.

Let the variables x_p, x_f, and x_s represent the tax rates (expressed as proportions of taxation bases) for property, food and drug, and general sales and define the variable x_g as the gasoline tax in cents per gallon. The goals of the city council are then expressed as

$$550x_p + 35x_f + 55x_s + .075x_g \geq 16 \qquad \text{(Tax revenue)}$$

$$35x_f \leq .1(550x_p + 35x_f + 55x_3 + .075x_g) \qquad \text{(Food/drug tax)}$$

$$55x_s \leq .2(550x_p + 35x_f + 55x_s + .075x_g) \qquad \text{(General tax)}$$

$$x_g \leq 2 \qquad \text{(Gasoline tax)}$$

$$x_p, x_f, x_s, x_g \geq 0$$

These constraints are then simplified as

$$550x_p + 35x_f + 55x_s + .075x_g \geq 16$$

$$55x_p - 31.5x_f + 5.5x_s + .0075x_g \geq 0$$

$$110x_p + 7x_f - 44x_s + .015x_g \geq 0$$

$$x_g \leq 2$$

$$x_p, x_f, x_s, x_g \geq 0$$

Each of the inequalities of the model represents a goal that the city council aspires to satisfy. Most likely, however, the best that can be done is a compromise solution involving these conflicting goals.

The manner in which goal programming finds a compromise solution is to convert each inequality into a flexible goal in which the corresponding constraint may be violated, if necessary. In terms of the Fairville model, the flexible goals are expressed as follows:

$$550x_p + 35x_f + 55x_s + .075x_g + s_1^- - s_1^+ = 16$$

$$55x_p - 31.5x_f + 5.5x_s + .0075x_g + s_2^- - s_2^+ = 0$$

$$110x_p + 7x_f - 44x_s + .015x_g + s_3^- - s_3^+ = 0$$

$$x_g + s_4^- - s_4^+ = 2$$

$$x_p, x_f, x_s, x_g \geq 0$$

$$s_i^-, s_i^+ \geq 0, \ i = 1, 2, 3, 4$$

The nonnegative variables s_i^- and s_i^+, $i = 1, 2, 3, 4$, are **deviational variables** representing the deviations *below* and *above* the right-hand side of constraint i.

The deviational variables s_i^- and s_i^+ are by definition dependent, and hence cannot be basic variables simultaneously (per the theory of the simplex method). This means that in any simplex iteration, at most *one* of the two deviational variables can assume a positive value. If the original ith inequality is of the type $\leq$ and its $s_i^- \geq 0$, then the ith goal is satisfied; otherwise, goal i is not satisfied. In essence, the definition of s_i^- and s_i^+ allows meeting or violating the ith goal at will. This is the type of flexibility that characterizes goal programming when it seeks a compromise solution. Logically, a good compromise solution seeks to minimize the amount by which each goal is violated.

In the Fairville model, given that the first three constraints are of the type $\geq$ and the fourth constraint is of the type $\leq$, the deviational variables s_1^-, s_2^-, s_3^-, and s_4^+ (shown in the model in bold) represent the amounts by which the respective goals are violated. Thus, the compromise solution seeks to satisfy the following four objectives as much as possible:

$$\text{Minimize } G_1 = s_1^-$$

$$\text{Minimize } G_2 = s_2^-$$

$$\text{Minimize } G_3 = s_3^-$$

$$\text{Minimize } G_4 = s_4^+$$

These functions are minimized subject to the constraint equations of the model.

How can we optimize a multiobjective model with conflicting goals? Two methods have been developed for this purpose: (1) the weights method and (2) the preemptive method. Both methods are based on converting the multiple objectives into a single function. Section 8.2 provides the details.

PROBLEM SET 8.1A

*1. Formulate the Fairville tax problem, assuming that the town council is specifying an additional goal, G_5, that requires gasoline tax to equal at least 20% of the total tax bill.

2. The NW Shopping Mall conducts special events to attract potential patrons. Among the events that seem to attract teenagers, the young/middle-aged group, and senior citizens, the two most popular are band concerts and art shows. Their costs per presentation are $1500 and $3000, respectively. The total (strict) annual budget allocated to the two events is $20,000. The mall manager estimates the attendance as follows:

	Number attending per presentation		
Event	Teenagers	Young/middle age	Seniors
Band concert	200	100	0
Art Show	0	400	250

The manager has set minimum goals of 1500, 450, and 900 for the attendance of teenagers, the young/middle-aged group, and seniors, respectively. Formulate the problem as a goal programming model.

*3. Ozark University admission office is processing freshman applications for the upcoming academic year. The applications fall into three categories: in-state, out-of-state, and international. The male–female ratios for in-state and out-of-state applicants are 1:1 and 3:2, respectively. For international students, the corresponding ratio is 8:1. The American College Test (ACT) score is an important factor in accepting new students. The statistics gathered by the university indicate that the average ACT scores for in-state, out-of-state, and international students are 27, 26, and 23, respectively. The committee on admissions has established the following desirable goals for the new freshman class:

(a) The incoming class is at least 1200 freshmen.

(b) The average ACT score for all incoming students is at least 25.

(c) International students constitute at least 10% of the incoming class.

(d) The female–male ratio is at least 3:4.

(e) Out-of-state students constitute at least 20% of the incoming class.

Formulate the problem as a goal programming model.

4. Circle K farms consumes 3 tons of special feed daily. The feed—a mixture of limestone, corn, and soybean meal—must satisfy the following nutritional requirements:

Calcium.   At least 0.8% but not more than 1.2%.

Protein.   At least 22%.

Fiber.   At most 5%.

The following table gives the nutritional content of the feed ingredients.

	lb per lb of ingredient		
Ingredient	Calcium	Protein	Fiber
Limestone	.380	.00	.00
Corn	.001	.09	.02
Soybean meal	.002	.50	.08

Formulate the problem as a goal programming model, and state your opinion regarding the applicability of goal programming to this situation.

*5. Mantel produces a toy carriage, whose final assembly must include four wheels and two seats. The factory producing the parts operates three shifts a day. The following table provides the amounts produced of each part in the three shifts.

	Units produced per run	
Shift	Wheels	Seats
1	500	300
2	600	280
3	640	360

Ideally, the number of wheels produced is exactly twice that of the number of seats. However, because production rates vary from shift to shift, exact balance in production may not be possible. Mantel is interested in determining the number of production runs in each shift that minimizes the imbalance in the production of the parts. The capacity limitations restrict the number of runs to between 4 and 5 for shift 1, 10 and 20 for shift 2, and 3 and 5 for shift 3. Formulate the problem as a goal programming model.

6. Camyo Manufacturing produces four parts that require the use of a lathe and a drill press. The two machines operate 10 hours a day. The following table provides the time in minutes required by each part:

	Production time in min	
Part	*Lathe*	*Drill press*
1	5	3
2	6	2
3	4	6
4	7	4

It is desired to balance the two machines by limiting the difference between their total operation times to at most 30 minutes. The market demand for each part is at least 10 units. Additionally, the number of units of part 1 may not exceed that of part 2. Formulate the problem as a goal programming model.

7. Two products are manufactured on two sequential machines. The following table gives the machining times in minutes per unit for the two products.

	Machining time in min	
Machine	*Product 1*	*Product 2*
1	5	3
2	6	2

The daily production quotas for the two products are 80 and 60 units, respectively. Each machine runs 8 hours a day. Overtime, though not desirable, may be used if necessary to meet the production quota. Formulate the problem as a goal programming model.

8. Vista City hospital plans the short-stay assignment of surplus beds (those that are not already occupied) 4 days in advance. During the 4-day planning period, about 30, 25, and 20 patients will require 1-, 2-, or 3-day stays, respectively. Surplus beds during the same period are estimated at 20, 30, 30, and 30, respectively. Use goal programming to resolve the problem of overadmission and underadmission in the hospital.

9. The Von Trapp family is in the process of moving to a new city where both parents have accepted new jobs. In trying to find an ideal location for their new home, the Von Trapps list the following goals:

(a) It should be as close as possible to Mrs. Von Trapp's place of work (within $\frac{1}{4}$ mile).

(b) It should be as far as possible from the noise of the airport (at least 10 miles).

(c) It should be reasonably close to a shopping mall (within 1 mile).

Mr. and Mrs. Von Trapp use a landmark in the city as a reference point and locate the (x, y)-coordinates of work, airport, and shopping mall at $(1, 1)$, $(20, 15)$, and $(4, 7)$, respectively (all distances are in miles). Formulate the problem as a goal programming model. [*Note:* The resulting constraints are not linear.]

10. *Regression analysis.* In a laboratory experiment, suppose that y_i is the ith observed (independent) yield associated with the dependent observational measurements $x_{ij}, i = 1, 2, \ldots, m; j = 1, 2, \ldots, n$. It is desired to determine a linear regression fit into these data points. Let $b_j, j = 0, 1, \ldots, n$, be the regression coefficients. It is desired to determine all b_j such that the sum of the absolute deviations between the observed and the estimated yields is minimized. Formulate the problem as a goal programming model.

11. *Chebyshev Problem.* An alternative goal for the regression model in Problem 10 is to minimize over b_j the maximum of the absolute deviations. Formulate the problem as a goal programming model.

8.2   GOAL PROGRAMMING ALGORITHMS

This section presents two algorithms for solving goal programming. Both methods are based on representing the multiple goals by a single objective function. In the **weights method**, the single objective function is the weighted sum of the functions representing the goals of the problem. The **preemptive method** starts by prioritizing the goals in order of importance. The model then optimizes the goals one at a time in order of priority and in a manner that does not degrade a higher-priority solution.

The proposed two methods do not generally produce the same solution. Neither method, however, is superior to the other, because the two techniques entail distinct decision-making preferences.

8.2.1   The Weights Method

Suppose that the goal programming model has n goals and that the ith goal is given as

$$\text{Minimize } G_i, i = 1, 2, \ldots, n$$

The combined objective function used in the weights method is then defined as

$$\text{Minimize } z = w_1 G_1 + w_2 G_2 + \cdots + w_n G_n$$

The parameters $w_i, i = 1, 2, \ldots, n$, are positive weights that reflect the decision maker's preferences regarding the relative importance of each goal. For example, $w_i = 1$, for all i, signifies that all goals are of equal importance. The determination of the specific values of these weights is subjective. Indeed, the apparently sophisticated analytic procedures developed in the literature (see, e.g., Cohon, 1978) are still rooted in subjective assessments.

Example 8.2-1

TopAd, a new advertising agency with 10 employees, has received a contract to promote a new product. The agency can advertise by radio and television. The following table gives the number of people reached daily by each type of advertisement and the cost and labor requirements.

	Radio	Television
Exposure (in millions of persons)/min	4	8
Cost (in thousands of dollars)/min	8	24
Assigned employees/min	1	2

The contract prohibits TopAd from using more than 6 minutes of radio advertisement. Additionally, radio and television advertisements need to reach at least 45 million people. TopAd has a budget goal of $100,000 for the project. How many minutes of radio and television advertisement should TopAd use?

Let x_1 and x_2 be the minutes allocated to radio and television advertisements. The goal programming formulation for the problem is given as

$$\text{Minimize } G_1 = s_1^- \text{ (Satisfy exposure goal)}$$

$$\text{Minimize } G_2 = s_2^+ \text{ (Satisfy budget goal)}$$

subject to

$$
\begin{aligned}
4x_1 + 8x_2 + s_1^- - s_1^+ &= 45 \text{ (Exposure goal)} \\
8x_1 + 24x_2 \qquad\qquad + s_2^- - s_2^+ &= 100 \text{ (Budget goal)} \\
x_1 + 2x_2 \qquad\qquad\qquad &\leq 10 \text{ (Personnel limit)} \\
x_1 \qquad\qquad\qquad\qquad &\leq 6 \text{ (Radio limit)}
\end{aligned}
$$

$$x_1, x_2, s_1^-, s_1^+, s_2^-, s_2^+ \geq 0$$

TopAd's management estimates that the exposure goal is twice as important as the budget goal. The combined objective function thus becomes

$$\text{Minimize } z = 2G_1 + G_2 = 2s_1^- + s_2^+$$

The optimum solution is $z = 10$, $x_1 = 5$ minutes, $x_2 = 2.5$ minutes, $s_1^- = 5$ million persons, $s_1^- = 0$, and $s_2^- = 0$.

The fact that the optimum value of z is not zero indicates that at least one of the goals is not met. Specifically, $s_1^- = 5$ means that the exposure goal (of at least 45 million persons) is missed by 5 million individuals. Conversely, the budget goal (of not exceeding $100,000) is not violated, because $s_2^+ = 0$.

Remarks. Goal programming seeks only an *efficient*, rather than optimum, solution to the problem. For example, the solution $x_1 = 6$ and $x_2 = 2$ yields the same exposure ($4 \times 6 + 8 \times 2 = 40$ million persons) but costs less ($8 \times 6 + 24 \times 2 = \$96,000$). In essence, what goal programming does is to find a solution that *satisfies* the goals of the model without regard to optimization. The failure to find the optimum solution raises doubts about the viability of goal programming as an optimizing technique (see Example 8.2-3 for further discussion).

PROBLEM SET 8.2A

*1. Consider Problem 1, Set 8.1a dealing with the Fairville tax situation. Solve the problem, assuming that all five goals have the same weight. Does the solution satisfy all the goals?

2. In Problem 2, Set 8.1a, suppose that the goal of attracting young/middle-aged people is twice as important as for either of the other two categories (teens and seniors). Find the associated solution, and check if all the goals have been met.

3. In the Ozark University admission situation described in Problem 3, Set 8.1a, suppose that the limit on the size of the incoming freshmen class must be met, but the remaining requirements can be treated as flexible goals. Further, assume that the ACT score goal is twice as important as any of the remaining goals.

    (a) Solve the problem, and specify whether or not all the goals are satisfied.

    (b) If, in addition, the size of the incoming class can be treated as a flexible goal that is twice as important as the ACT goal, how would this change affect the solution?

*4. In the Circle K model of Problem 4, Set 8.1a, is it possible to satisfy all the nutritional requirements?

5. In Problem 5, Set 8.1a, determine the solution, and specify whether or not the daily production of wheels and seats can be balanced.

6. In Problem 6, Set 8.1a, suppose that the market demand goal is twice as important as that of balancing the two machines, and that no overtime is allowed. Solve the problem, and determine if the goals are met.

*7. In Problem 7, Set 8.1a, suppose that production strives to meet the quota for the two products, using overtime if necessary. Find a solution to the problem, and specify the amount of overtime, if any, needed to meet the production quota.

8. In the Vista City Hospital of Problem 8, Set 8.1a, suppose that only the bed limits represent flexible goals and that all the goals have equal weights. Can all the goals be met?

9. The Malco Company has compiled the following table from the files of five of its employees to study the impact on income of three factors: age, education (expressed in number of college years completed), and experience (expressed in number of years in the business).

Age (year)	Education (year)	Experience (year)	Annual income ($)
30	4	5	40,000
39	5	10	48,000
44	2	14	38,000
48	0	18	36,000
37	3	9	41,000

    Use the goal programming formulation in Problem 10, Set 8.1a, to fit the data into the linear equation $y = b_0 + b_1x_1 + b_2x_2 + b_3x_3$.

10. Solve Problem 9 using the Chebyshev method proposed in Problem 11, Set 8.1a.

8.2.2   The Preemptive Method

In the preemptive method, the decision maker ranks the goals of the problem in order of importance. Given an n-goal situation, the objectives of the problem are written as

$$\text{Minimize } G_1 = \rho_1 \text{(Highest priority)}$$

$$\vdots$$

$$\text{Minimize } G_n = \rho_n \text{(Lowest priority)}$$

The variable ρ_i is the component of the deviational variables, s_i^- or s_i^+, representing goal i. For example, in the TopAd model (Example 8.2-1), $\rho_1 = s_1^-$ and $\rho_2 = s_2^+$.

The solution procedure starts with optimizing the highest priority, G_1, and terminates with optimizing the lowest, G_n. The preemptive method is designed such that *a lower-priority solution never degrades a higher-priority solution.*

The literature on goal programming presents a "special" simplex method that guarantees the nondegradation of higher-priority solutions. The method uses the **column-dropping rule** that calls for eliminating a *nonbasic* variable x_j with nonzero reduced cost ($z_j - c_j \neq 0$) from the optimal tableau of goal G_k prior to solving the problem of goal G_{k+1}. The rule recognizes that such nonbasic variables, if elevated above zero level in the optimization of succeeding goals, may degrade (but never improve) the quality of a higher-priority goal. The procedure requires including the objective functions of all the goals in the simplex tableau of the model.

The proposed *column-dropping* modification needlessly complicates goal programming. In this presentation, we show that the same results can be achieved in a more straightforward manner using the following steps:

Step 0.   Identify the goals of the model and rank them in order of priority:
$$G_1 = \rho_1 > G_2 = \rho_2 > \cdots > G_n = \rho_n$$

Set $i = 1$.

General Step   Solve LP$_i$ that minimizes G_i, and let $\rho_i = \rho_i^*$ define the corresponding optimum value of the deviational variable ρ_i. If $i = n$, stop; LP$_n$ solves the n-goal program. Otherwise, add the constraint $\rho_i = \rho_i^*$ to the constraints of the G_i-problem to ensure that the value of ρ_i is not degraded in future problems. Set $i = i + 1$, and repeat step i.

The successive addition of the special constraints $\rho_i = \rho_i^*$ may not be as "elegant" theoretically as the *column-dropping rule*. Nevertheless, it achieves the exact same result. More importantly, it is easier to implement and to understand.

Remarks.   Some may argue that the *column-dropping rule* offers computational advantage because the rule makes the problem successively smaller by removing variables, whereas our procedure makes the problem larger by adding new constraints. Considering the nature of the additional constraints ($\rho_i = \rho_i^*$), we can modify the simplex algorithm to implement the additional constraint implicitly by substituting out $\rho_i = \rho_i^*$. The substitution (affecting only the constraint in which ρ_i appears) reduces the number of variables as the algorithm moves from one goal to the next. Alternatively, we can use the bounded simplex method of Section 7.4.2 by replacing $\rho_i = \rho_i^*$ with $\rho_i \leq \rho_i^*$, in which case the additional constraints are accounted for implicitly. In this regard, the *column-dropping rule*, theoretical appeal aside, does not appear to offer a particular computational advantage.

For the sake of completeness, Example 8.2-3 will illustrate how the *column-dropping rule* works.

Example 8.2-2

The problem of Example 8.2-1 is solved by the preemptive method. Assume that the exposure goal has a higher priority.

Step 0. $G_1 > G_2$

$$G_1: \text{Minimize } s_1^- \text{ (Satisfy exposure goal)}$$

$$G_2: \text{Minimize } s_2^+ \text{ (Satisfy budget goal)}$$

Step 1. Solve LP$_1$.

$$\text{Minimize } G_1 = s_1^-$$

subject to

$$
\begin{aligned}
4x_1 + 8x_2 + s_1^- - s_1^+ &= 45 \text{ (Exposure goal)} \\
8x_1 + 24x_2 \qquad\qquad + s_2^- - s_2^+ &= 100 \text{ (Budget goal)} \\
x_1 + 2x_2 \qquad\qquad &\le 10 \text{ (Personnel limit)} \\
x_1 \qquad\qquad\qquad &\le 6 \text{ (Radio limit)}
\end{aligned}
$$

$$x_1, x_2, s_1^-, s_1^+, s_2^-, s_2^+ \ge 0$$

The optimum solution (determined by TORA) is $x_1 = 5$ minutes, $x_2 = 2.5$ minutes, $s_1^- = 5$ million people, with the remaining variables equal to zero. The solution shows that the exposure goal, G_1, is violated by 5 million persons. The additional constraint to be added to the G_2-problem is $s_1^- = 5$ (or, equivalently, $s_1^- \le 5$).

Step 2. The objective function of LP$_2$ is

$$\text{Minimize } G_2 = s_2^+$$

The constraints are the same as in step 1 *plus* the additional constraint $s_1^- = 5$. (TORA's MODIFY option can be used conveniently to represent the new constraint by assigning 5 to both the lower and upper bounds of s_1^-.)

In general, the additional constraint $s_1^- = 5$ can also be accounted for by substituting out s_1^- in the first constraint. The result is that the right-hand side of the exposure goal constraint will be changed from 45 to 40, thus reducing LP$_2$ to

$$\text{Minimize } G_2 = s_2^+$$

subject to

$$
\begin{aligned}
4x_1 + 8x_2 - s_1^+ &= 40 \text{ (Exposure goal)} \\
8x_1 + 24x_2 \qquad + s_2^- - s_2^+ &= 100 \text{ (Budget goal)} \\
x_1 + 2x_2 \qquad &\le 10 \text{ (Personnel limit)} \\
x_1 \qquad\qquad &\le 6 \text{ (Radio limit)}
\end{aligned}
$$

$$x_1, x_2, s_1^+, s_2^-, s_2^+ \ge 0$$

The new formulation is one variable less than the one in LP_1, which is the general idea advanced by the *column-dropping rule*.

Actually, the optimization of LP_2 is not necessary in this problem, because the optimum solution to problem G_1 already yields $s_2^+ = 0$; that is, it is already optimum for LP_2. Such computational-saving opportunities should be taken advantage of whenever they arise during the course of implementing the preemptive method.

Example 8.2-3 (Column-Dropping Rule)

In this example, we show that a better solution for the problem of Examples 8.2-1 and 8.2-2 can be obtained if the preemptive method is used to *optimize* objectives rather than to *satisfy* goals. Later on, the same example is solved using the *column-dropping rule*.

The goals of Example 8.2-1 can be restated as

Priority 1: Maximize exposure (P_1)

Priority 2: Minimize cost (P_2)

Mathematically, the two objectives are given as

$$\text{Maximize } P_1 = 4x_1 + 8x_2 \quad \text{(Exposure)}$$
$$\text{Minimize } P_2 = 8x_1 + 24x_2 \quad \text{(Cost)}$$

The specific goal limits for exposure and cost (=45 and 100) in Examples 8.2-1 and 8.2-2 are removed, because we will allow the simplex method to determine these limits optimally.

The new problem can thus be stated as

$$\text{Maximize } P_1 = 4x_1 + 8x_2$$
$$\text{Minimize } P_2 = 8x_1 + 24x_2$$

subject to

$$x_1 + 2x_2 \leq 10$$
$$x_1 \qquad \leq 6$$
$$x_1, x_2 \geq 0$$

We first solve the problem using the procedure introduced in Example 8.2-2.

Step 1. Solve LP_1.

$$\text{Maximize } P_1 = 4x_1 + 8x_2$$

subject to

$$x_1 + 2x_2 \leq 10$$
$$x_1 \qquad \leq 6$$
$$x_1, x_2 \geq 0$$

The optimum solution (obtained by TORA) is $x_1 = 0$, $x_2 = 5$ with $P_1 = 40$, which shows that the most exposure we can get is 40 million persons.

Step 2.   Add the constraint $4x_1 + 8x_2 \geq 40$ to ensure that goal G_1 is not degraded. Thus, we solve LP_2 as

$$\text{Minimize } P_2 = 8x_1 + 24x_2$$

subject to

$$x_1 + 2x_2 \leq 10$$

$$x_1 \qquad \leq 6$$

$$4x_1 + 8x_2 \geq 40 \text{ (additional constraint)}$$

$$x_1, x_2 \geq 0$$

The optimum solution of LP_2 is $P_2 = \$96{,}000$, $x_1 = 6$ minutes, and $x_2 = 2$ minutes. It yields the same exposure ($P_1 = 40$ million people) but at a smaller cost than the one in Example 8.2-2, where we seek to satisfy rather than optimize the goals.

The same problem is solved now by using the *column-dropping rule*. The rule calls for carrying the objective rows associated with all the goals in the simplex tableau, as we will show below.

LP$_1$ (Exposure Maximization).   The LP_1 simplex tableau carries both objective rows P_1 and P_2. The optimality condition applies to the P_1-objective row only. The P_2-row plays a passive role in LP_1 but must be updated (using the simplex row operations) with the rest of the simplex tableau in preparation for the optimization of LP_2.

LP_1 is solved in two iterations as follows:

Iteration	Basic	x_1	x_2	s_1	s_2	Solution
1	P_1	-4	-8	0	0	0
	P_2	-8	-24	0	0	0
	s_1	1	2	1	0	10
	s_2	1	0	0	1	6
2	P_1	0	0	4	0	40
	P_2	4	0	12	0	120
	x_2	$\frac{1}{2}$	1	$\frac{1}{2}$	0	5
	s_2	1	0	0	1	6

The last tableau yields the optimal solution $x_1 = 0$, $x_2 = 5$, and $P_1 = 40$.

The *column-dropping rule* calls for eliminating any *nonbasic* variable x_j with $z_j - c_j \neq 0$ from the optimum tableau of LP_1 before LP_2 is optimized. The reason is that these variables, if left unchecked, could become positive in lower-priority optimization problems, which can degrade the quality of higher-priority solutions.

LP$_2$ (Cost Minimization).   The column-dropping rule eliminates s_1 (with $z_j - c_j = 4$ in LP_1). We can see from the P_2-row that if s_1 is not eliminated, it will be the entering variable at the start of the P_2-iterations and will yield the optimum solution $x_1 = x_2 = 0$, which will degrade the optimum objective value of the P_1-problem from $P_1 = 40$ to $P_1 = 0$. (Try it!)

The P_2-problem is of the minimization type. Following the elimination of s_1, the variable x_1 with $z_j - c_j = 4(> 0)$ can improve the value of P_2. The following table shows the LP_2 iterations. The P_1-row has been deleted because it serves no purpose in the optimization of LP_2.

Iteration	Basic	x_1	x_2	s_1	s_2	Solution
1	P_1					40
	P_2	4	0		0	120
	x_2	$\frac{1}{2}$	1		0	5
	s_2	1	0		1	6
2	P_1					40
	P_2	0	0		-4	96
	x_2	0	1		$-\frac{1}{2}$	2
	x_1	1	0		1	6

The optimum solution $(x_1 = 6, x_2 = 2)$ with a total exposure of $P_1 = 40$ and a total cost of $P_2 = 96$ is the same as obtained earlier.

AMPL Moment

AMPL lends itself readily to applying the idea presented in Example 8.2-2, where simple constraints are added to ensure that higher-priority solutions are not degraded. File *amplEx8.1-1.txt* provides a generic AMPL code that allows the application of the preemptive method. The model must be implemented interactively as explained in Section C.9 on the website.

PROBLEM SET 8.2B[2]

1. In Example 8.2-2, suppose that the budget goal is increased to $150,000. The exposure goal remains unchanged at 45 million persons. Show how the preemptive method will reach a solution.

*2. Solve Problem 1, Set 8.1a, using the following priority ordering for the goals:
$G_1 > G_2 > G_3 > G_4 > G_5$.

3. Consider Problem 2, Set 8.1a, which deals with the presentation of band concerts and art shows at the NW Mall. Suppose that the goals set for teens, the young/middle-aged group, and seniors are referred to as $G_1, G_2,$ and G_3, respectively. Solve the problem for each of the following priority orders:

(a) $G_1 > G_2 > G_3$

(b) $G_3 > G_2 > G_1$

---

[2]You may find it computationally convenient to use interactive AMPL to solve the problems of this set.

Show that the satisfaction of the goals (or lack of it) can be a function of the priority order.

4. Solve the Ozark University model (Problem 3, Set 8.1a) using the preemptive method, assuming that the goals are prioritized in the same order given in the problem.

BIBLIOGRAPHY

Chissman, J, T. Fey, G. Reeves, H. Lewis, and R. Weinstein, "A Multiobjective Linear Programming Methodology for Public Sector Tax Planning," *Interfaces*, Vol. 19, No. 5, pp. 13–22, 1989.

Cohon, T. L., *Multiobjective Programming and Planning*, Academic Press, New York, 1978.

Ignizio, J. P., and T. M. Cavalier, *Linear Programming,* Prentice-Hall, Upper Saddle River, NJ, 1994.

Steuer, R. E., *Multiple Criteria Optimization: Theory, Computations, and Application*, Wiley, New York, 1986.

CHAPTER 9

Integer Linear Programming

Real-Life Application—Optimizing Trailer Payloads at PFG Building Glass

PFG uses specially equipped (fifth-wheel) trailers to deliver packs of sheets of flat glass to customers. The packs vary in both size and weight, and a single trailer load may include different packs, depending on received orders. Government regulations set maximum limits on axle weights, and the actual positioning of the packs on the trailer is crucial in determining these weights. The problem deals with determining the optimal loading of the packs on the trailer bed to satisfy axle-weight limits. The problem is solved as an integer program. Case 7 in Chapter 26 on the website provides the details of the study.

9.1 ILLUSTRATIVE APPLICATIONS

Integer linear program (ILP) applications generally fall into two categories: *direct* and *transformed*. In the *direct* category, the nature of the situation precludes assigning fractional values to the variables of the model. For example, the problem may involve determining whether or not a project is undertaken (binary variable) or finding the optimal number of machines needed to perform a task (general integer variable). In the *transformed* category, auxiliary integer variables are used to convert analytically intractable situations into models that can be solved by available optimization algorithms. For example, in sequencing two jobs, A and B, on a single machine, job A may precede job B or vice versa. The "or" nature of the constraints is what makes the problem analytically intractable, because all mathematical programming algorithms deal with "and" constraints only. Section 9.1.4 shows how auxiliary binary variables are used to transform the "or" constraints into "and" constraints without altering the nature of the model.

349

For convenience, a problem is defined as a **pure** integer program when *all* the variables are integer. Else, it is a **mixed** integer program (MIP) involving a mixture of integer and continuous variables.

9.1.1   Capital Budgeting

Decisions about whether or not to undertake a project is usually made under limited-budget considerations and preset priorities. The next example deals with one of these situations.

Example 9.1-1   (Project Selection)

Five projects are being evaluated over a 3-year planning horizon. The following table gives the expected returns for each project and the associated yearly expenditures.

Project	Expenditures ($ million)/year			Returns ($ million)
	1	*2*	*3*	
1	5	1	8	20
2	4	7	10	40
3	3	9	2	20
4	7	4	1	15
5	8	6	10	30
Available funds ($ million)	25	25	25	

Which projects should be selected over the 3-year horizon?

The problem reduces to a "yes-no" decision for each project. Define the binary variable x_j as

$$x_j = \begin{cases} 1, & \text{if project } j \text{ is selected} \\ 0, & \text{if project } j \text{ is not selected} \end{cases}$$

The ILP model is

$$\text{Maximize } z = 20x_1 + 40x_2 + 20x_3 + 15x_4 + 30x_5$$

subject to

$$5x_1 + 4x_2 + 3x_3 + 7x_4 + 8x_5 \leq 25$$

$$x_1 + 7x_2 + 9x_3 + 4x_4 + 6x_5 \leq 25$$

$$8x_1 + 10x_2 + 2x_3 + x_4 + 10x_5 \leq 25$$

$$x_1, x_2, x_3, x_4, x_5 = (0,1)$$

The optimum integer solution (obtained by AMPL, Solver, or TORA)[1] is $x_1 = x_2 = x_3 = x_4 = 1, x_5 = 0$, with $z = 95$ ($ million). The solution excludes project 5 from the product mix.

---

[1]To use TORA, select Integer Programming from Main Menu. After entering the problem data, go to output screen, and select Automated B&B to obtain the optimum solution. Solver use is the same as in LP except that the targeted variables must be declared integer. The integer option (*int* or *bin*) is available in the **Solver Parameters** dialogue box when you add a new constraint. AMPL implementation for integer programming is the same as in linear programming, except that some or all the variables are declared integers by adding the key word `integer` (or `binary`) in the definition statement of the targeted variables. For example, the statement `var x{J}>=0, integer;` declares x_j as nonnegative integer for all $j \in J$. If x_j is binary, the statement is changed to `var x{J} binary;`. For execution, the statement `option solver cplex;` must precede `solve;`.

Remarks. It is interesting to compare the continuous LP solution with the ILP solution. The LP optimum, obtained by replacing $x_j = (0, 1)$ with $0 \le x_j \le 1$ for all j, yields $x_1 = .5789$, $x_2 = x_3 = x_4 = 1$, $x_5 = .7368$, and $z = 108.68$ ($ million). The solution is meaningless because binary x_1 and x_5 assume fractional values. We may *round* the solution to the closest integer, which yields $x_1 = x_5 = 1$. However, the resulting solution violates the constraints. Moreover, the concept of *rounding* is meaningless here because x_j represents a "yes-no" decision.

PROBLEM SET 9.1A[2]

1. Modify and solve the capital budgeting model of Example 9.1-1 to account for the following additional restrictions:

   (a) Project 4 must be selected if either project 1 or project 3 is selected.

   (b) Projects 2 and 4 are mutually exclusive.

2. Five items are to be loaded in a vessel. The weight w_i, volume v_i, and value r_i for item i are tabulated below.

Item i	Unit weight, w_i (tons)	Unit volume, vi (yd^3)	Unit worth, r_i ($100)
1	5	1	4
2	8	8	7
3	3	6	6
4	2	5	5
5	7	4	4

   The maximum allowable cargo weight and volume are 210 tons and 198 yd^3, respectively. Formulate the ILP model, and find the most valuable cargo.

*3. Suppose that you have 7 full wine bottles, 7 half-full, and 7 empty. You would like to divide the 21 bottles among three individuals so that each will receive exactly 7. Additionally, each individual must receive the same quantity of wine. Express the problem as ILP constraints, and find a solution. (*Hint*: Use a dummy objective function in which all the objective coefficients are zeros.)

4. An eccentric sheikh left a will to distribute a herd of camels among his three children: Tarek receives at least one-half of the herd, Sharif gets at least one third, and Maisa gets at least one-seventh. The remainder goes to charity. The will does not specify the size of the herd except to say that it is an odd number of camels and that the named charity receives exactly one camel. Use ILP to determine how many camels the sheikh left in the estate and how many each child got.

5. The three children of a farm couple are sent to the market to sell 90 apples. Karen, the oldest, carries 50 apples; Bill, the middle one, carries 30; and John, the youngest, carries only 10. The parents have stipulated five rules: (a) The selling price is either $1 for 7 apples or $3 for 1 apple, or a combination of the two prices. (b) Each child may exercise one or both options of the selling price. (c) Each of the three children must return with exactly the same amount of money. (d) Each child's income must be in whole dollars (no cents allowed). (e) The amount received by each child must be the largest possible

---

[2]Problems 3 to 6 are adapted from Malba Tahan, *El Hombre que Calculaba*, Editorial Limusa, Mexico City, pp. 39–182, 1994. Problems 13 to 16 are adapted from puzzles compiled in http://www.chlond.demon.co.uk/puzzles/puzzles1.html.

under the stipulated conditions. Given that the three kids are able to sell all they have, use ILP to show how they can satisfy the parents' conditions.

*6. Once upon a time, there was a captain of a merchant ship who wanted to reward three crew members for their valiant effort in saving the ship's cargo during an unexpected storm in the high seas. The captain put aside a certain sum of money in the purser's office and instructed the first officer to distribute it equally among the three mariners after the ship had reached shore. One night, one of the sailors, unbeknown to the others, went to the purser's office and decided to claim (an equitable) one-third of the money in advance. After he had divided the money into three equal shares, an extra coin remained, which the mariner decided to keep (in addition to one-third of the money). The next night, the second mariner got the same idea and, repeating the same three-way division with what was left, ended up keeping an extra coin as well. The third night, the third mariner also took a third of what was left, plus an extra coin that could not be divided. When the ship reached shore, the first officer divided what was left of the money equally among the three mariners, again to be left with an extra coin. To simplify things, the first officer put the extra coin aside and gave the three mariners their allotted equal shares. How much money was in the safe to start with? Formulate the problem as an ILP, and find the solution. (*Hint*: The problem has a countably infinite number of integer solutions. For convenience, assume that we are interested in determining the smallest sum of money that satisfies the problem conditions. Then, boosting the resulting sum by 1, add it as a lower bound and obtain the next smallest sum. Continuing in this manner, a general solution pattern will emerge.)

7. *Weber (1990)*. You have the following three-letter words: AFT, FAR, TVA, ADV, JOE, FIN, OSF, and KEN. Suppose that we assign numeric values to the alphabet starting with $A = 1$ and ending with $Z = 26$. Each word is scored by adding numeric codes of its three letters. For example, AFT has a score of $1 + 6 + 20 = 27$. You are to select five of the given eight words that yield the maximum total score. Simultaneously, the selected five words must satisfy the following conditions:

$$\begin{pmatrix} \text{sum of letter 1} \\ \text{scores} \end{pmatrix} < \begin{pmatrix} \text{sum of letter 2} \\ \text{scores} \end{pmatrix} < \begin{pmatrix} \text{sum of letter 3} \\ \text{scores} \end{pmatrix}$$

Formulate the problem as an ILP, and find the optimum solution.

8. Solve Problem 7 given that, in addition to the total sum being the largest, the sum of column 1 and the sum of column 2 will be the largest as well. Find the optimum solution.

9. *Weber (1990)*. Consider the following two groups of words:

Group 1	Group 2
AREA	ERST
FORT	FOOT
HOPE	HEAT
SPAR	PAST
THAT	PROF
TREE	STOP

All the words in groups 1 and 2 can be formed from the nine letters A, E, F, H, O, P, R, S, and T. Develop a model to assign a unique numeric value from 1 through 9 to these letters such that the difference between the total scores of the two groups will be as small as possible. [*Note*: The score for a word is the sum of the numeric values assigned to its individual letters.]

*10. The Record-a-Song Company has contracted with a rising star to record eight songs. The sizes in MB of the different songs are 8, 10, 8, 7, 9, 6, 7, and 12, respectively. Record-a-Song uses two CDs for the recording. Each CD has a capacity of 40 MB. The company would like to distribute the songs between the two CDs such that the used space on each CDs is about the same. Formulate the problem as an ILP, and find the optimum solution.

11. In Problem 10, suppose that the nature of the melodies dictates that songs 3 and 4 cannot be recorded on the same CD. Formulate the problem as an ILP. Would it be possible to use a 30 MB CDs to record the eight songs? If not, use ILP to determine the minimum CD capacity needed to make the recording.

*12. *Graves and Associates (1993).* Ulern University uses a mathematical model that optimizes student preferences taking into account the limitation of classroom and faculty resources. To demonstrate the application of the model, consider the simplified case of 10 students who are required to select two courses out of six offered electives. The table below gives scores that represent each student's preference for individual courses, with a score of 100 being the highest. For simplicity, it is assumed that the preference score for a two-course selection is the sum of the individual score. Course capacity is the maximum number of students allowed to take the class.

Student	Preference score for course					
	1	2	3	4	5	6
1	20	40	50	30	90	100
2	90	100	80	70	10	40
3	25	40	30	80	95	90
4	80	50	60	80	30	40
5	75	60	90	100	50	40
6	60	40	90	10	80	80
7	45	40	70	60	55	60
8	30	100	40	70	90	55
9	80	60	100	70	65	80
10	40	60	80	100	90	10
Course capacity	6	8	5	5	6	5

Formulate the problem as an ILP and find the optimum solution.

13. You have three currency denominations with 11 coins each. The *total* worth (of all 11 coins) is 12 bits for denomination 1, 14 bits for denomination 2, and 20 bits for denomination 3. You need to buy one 30-bit item. Use ILP to determine the smallest number of coins of the three denominations needed to make the purchase.

14. You have a 4×4 grid and a total of 10 tokens. Use ILP to place the tokens on the grid such that each row and each column will have an even number of tokens.

15. A street vendor selling electronic gadgets was robbed of all his possessions. When reporting the matter to the police, the vendor did not know the number of gadgets he had but stated that when dividing the total in lots of size 2, 3, 4, 5, or 6, there was always one gadget left over. On the other hand, there was no remainder when the total was divided into lots of size 7. Use ILP to determine the total number of gadgets the vendor had.

16. Given $i = 1, 2, \ldots, n$, formulate a general ILP model (for any n) to determine the smallest number y that, when divided by the integer amount $2 + i$, will always produce a remainder equal to i; that is, $y \bmod (2 + i) = i$.

17. A widely-circulated puzzle requires assigning a single *distinct* digit (0 through 9) to each letter in the equation SEND + MORE = MONEY. Formulate the problem as an integer program, and find the solution. (*Hint*: This is an assignment model with side conditions.)

18. The world-renowned Japanese logic puzzle, Sudoku, deals with a 9×9 grid subdivided into 9 nonoverlapping 3×3 subgrids. The puzzle calls for assigning the numerical digits 1 through 9 to the cells of the grid such that each row, each column, and each subgrid contain distinct digits. Some of the cells may be fixed in advance.

   Formulate the problem as an integer program, and find the solution for the instance given below.

6		1		4		5		
		8	3		5	6		
2						7		
8			4		7			6
		6				3		
7			9	1				4
5								2
		7	2		6	9		
	4		5		8		7	

[*Hint*: Let $x_{ijk} = 1$ if digit k is placed in cell (i, j), $i, j, k = 1, 2, \ldots, n, n = 9$. If you use AMPL, keep in mind that for $n = 9$, the resulting number of variables will exceed the capacity of student AMPL. If you do not have access to the full AMPL version, you can develop a general model for $n = 4$ or 9, and then solve it for the simpler (almost trivial) case of a 4×4 grid with a 2×2 subgrid.]

9.1.2   Set-Covering Problem

In this class of problems, overlapping services are offered by a number of installations to a number of facilities. The objective is to determine the minimum number of installations that will *cover* (i.e., satisfy the service needs of) each facility. For example, water treatment plants can be constructed at various locations, with each plant serving groups of cities. The overlapping occurs when more than one plant can serve a given city.

Example 9.1-2   (Installing Security Telephones)

To promote on-campus safety, the U of A Public Safety Department is in the process of installing emergency telephones at selected locations. The department wants to install the minimum number of telephones that serve each of the campus main streets. Figure 9.1 maps the campus principal streets. It is logical to maximize the utility of the telephones by placing them at street intersections. In this manner, a single unit can serve at least two streets.

Define

$$x_j = \begin{cases} 1, \text{ a telephone is installed in location } j, j = 1, 2, \ldots, 8 \\ 0, \text{ otherwise} \end{cases}$$

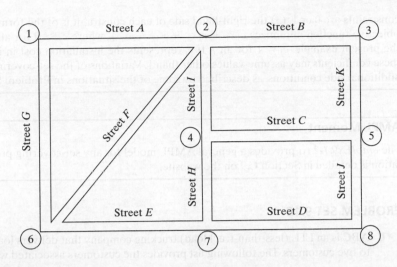

FIGURE 9.1

Street map of the U of A campus

The constraints of the problem require installing at least one telephone on each of the 11 streets $(A$ to $K)$. Thus, the model is

$$\text{Minimize } z = x_1 + x_2 + x_3 + x_4 + x_5 + x_6 + x_7 + x_8$$

subject to

$$
\begin{array}{llll}
x_1 + x_2 & & \geq 1 & (\text{Street } A) \\
x_2 + x_3 & & \geq 1 & (\text{Street } B) \\
x_4 + x_5 & & \geq 1 & (\text{Street } C) \\
x_7 + x_8 \geq 1 & (\text{Street } D) \\
x_6 + x_7 & & \geq 1 & (\text{Street } E) \\
x_2 \qquad + x_6 & & \geq 1 & (\text{Street } F) \\
x_1 \qquad + x_6 & & \geq 1 & (\text{Street } G) \\
x_4 \qquad + x_7 & & \geq 1 & (\text{Street } H) \\
x_2 \quad + x_4 & & \geq 1 & (\text{Street } I) \\
x_5 \qquad + x_8 \geq 1 & (\text{Street } J) \\
x_3 \quad + x_5 & & \geq 1 & (\text{Street } K) \\
\end{array}
$$

$$x_j = (0, 1), j = 1, 2, \ldots, 8$$

The optimum solution of the problem requires installing four telephones at intersections 1, 2, 5, and 7.

Remarks. In the strict sense, set-covering problems are characterized by the following criteria: (1) The variables $x_j, j = 1, 2, \ldots, n$, are binary, (2) the left-hand-side coefficients of the constraints are 0 or 1, (3) the right-hand side of each constraint is of the form (≥ 1), and (4) the objective function minimizes $c_1 x_1 + c_2 x_2 + \cdots + c_n x_n$, where $c_j > 0$ for all $j = 1, 2, \ldots, n$. In the present example, $c_j = 1$ for all j. If c_j represents the installation cost in intersection j, then these coefficients may assume values other than 1. Variations of the set-covering problem include additional side conditions, as described by some of the situations in Problem Set 9.1b.

AMPL Moment

File *amplEx9.1-2.txt* provides a general AMPL model for any set-covering problem. The formulation is detailed in Section C.9 on the website.

PROBLEM SET 9.1B

*1. ABC is an LTL (less-than-truckload) trucking company that delivers loads on a daily basis to five customers. The following list provides the customers associated with each route:

Route	Customers served on the route
1	3, 2, 4
2	5, 3, 4
3	2, 5, 1, 3
4	2, 3, 5
5	1, 4, 2
6	1, 3, 5

The segments of each route are dictated by the capacity of the truck delivering the loads. For example, on route 1, the capacity of the truck is sufficient to deliver the loads to customers 3, 2, and 4 only. The following table lists distances (in miles) among the truck terminal (ABC) and the customers.

		Miles from i to j				
i	j	ABC	1	2	3	4	5
ABC		0	10	12	16	9	8
1		10	0	32	8	17	10
2		12	32	0	14	21	20
3		16	8	14	0	15	18
4		9	17	21	15	0	11
5		8	10	20	18	11	0

The objective is to determine the least distance needed to make the daily deliveries to all five customers. Though the solution may result in a customer being served by more than one route, the implementation phase will use only one such route. Formulate the problem as an ILP, and find the optimum solution.

*2. The U of A is in the process of forming a committee to handle students' grievances. The administration wants the committee to include at least one female, one male, one student, one administrator, and one faculty member. Ten individuals (identified, for simplicity, by the letters *a* to *j*) have been nominated. The mix of these individuals in the different categories is given as follows:

Category	Individuals
Females	a, b, c, d, e
Males	f, g, h, i, j
Students	a, b, c, j
Administrators	e, f
Faculty	d, g, h, i

The U of A wants to form the smallest committee with representation from each of the five categories. Formulate the problem as an ILP, and find the optimum solution.

3. Washington County includes six towns that need emergency ambulance service. Because of the proximity of some of the towns, a single station may serve more than one community. The stipulation is that the station must be within 18 minutes of driving time from the towns it serves. The following table gives the driving times in minutes among the six towns.

i \ j	1	2	3	4	5	6
1	0	19	23	18	20	25
2	19	0	22	13	22	11
3	23	22	0	60	17	20
4	18	13	60	0	55	17
5	20	22	17	55	0	12
6	25	11	20	17	12	0

Time in minutes from i to j

Formulate an ILP whose solution will produce the smallest number of stations and their locations. Find the optimum solution.

4. The great treasures of King Tut are on display in the Giza Museum in Cairo. The layout of the museum is shown in Figure 9.2, with the different rooms joined by open doors. A guard standing at a door can watch two adjoining rooms. The museum's security policy requires guard presence in every room. Formulate the problem as an ILP to determine the smallest number of guards.

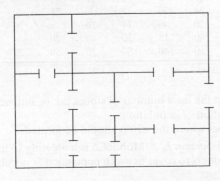

FIGURE 9.2

Museum Layout for Problem 4, Set 9.1c

5. Bill has just completed his exams for the academic year and wants to celebrate by seeing every movie showing in theaters in his town and in six other neighboring cities. If he travels to another town, he will stay there until he has seen all the movies he wants. The following table provides the information about the movie offerings and the round-trip distance to the neighboring town.

Theater location	Movies offerings	Round-trip miles	Cost per show ($)
In-town	1, 3	0	7.95
City A	1, 6, 8	25	5.50
City B	2, 5, 7	30	5.00
City C	1, 8, 9	28	7.00
City D	2, 4, 7	40	4.95
City E	1, 3, 5, 10	35	5.25
City F	4, 5, 6, 9	32	6.75

The cost of driving is 75 cents per mile. Bill wishes to determine the towns he needs to visit to see all the movies while minimizing his total cost.

6. Walmark Stores is in the process of expansion in western United States. During next year, Walmark is planning to construct new stores that will serve 10 geographically dispersed communities. Past experience indicates that a community must be within 25 miles of a store to attract customers. In addition, the population of a community plays an important role in where a store is located, in the sense that bigger communities generate more participating customers. The following table provides the populations as well as the distances (in miles) between the communities:

	Miles from community i to community j										
j \ i	1	2	3	4	5	6	7	8	9	10	Population
1		20	40	35	17	24	50	58	33	12	10,000
2	20		23	68	40	30	20	19	70	40	15,000
3	40	23		36	70	22	45	30	21	80	28,000
4	35	68	36		70	80	24	20	40	10	30,000
5	17	40	70	70		23	70	40	13	40	40,000
6	24	30	22	80	23		12	14	50	50	30,000
7	50	20	45	24	70	12		26	40	30	20,000
8	58	19	30	20	40	14	26		20	50	15,000
9	33	70	21	40	13	50	40	20		22	60,000
10	12	40	80	10	40	50	30	50	22		12,000

The idea is to construct the least number of stores, taking into account the distance restriction and the concentration of populations

Specify the communities where the stores should be located.

*7. *Guéret and Associates (2002), Section 12.6.* MobileCo is budgeting 15 million dollars to construct as many as 7 transmitters to cover as much population as possible in 15 contiguous geographical communities. The communities covered by each transmitter and the budgeted construction costs are given below.

Transmitter	Covered communities	Cost (million $)
1	1, 2	3.60
2	2, 3, 5	2.30
3	1, 7, 9, 10	4.10
4	4, 6, 8, 9	3.15
5	6, 7, 9, 11	2.80
6	5, 7, 10, 12, 14	2.65
7	12, 13, 14, 15	3.10

The following table provides the populations of the different communities:

Community	1	2	3	4	5	6	7	8	9	10
Population (in 1000s)	10	15	28	30	40	30	20	15	60	12

Which of the proposed transmitters should be constructed?

8. *Gavernini and Associates (2004).* Modern electric networks use automated electric utility meter reading in place of the more costly manual meter reading. In the automated system, meters from several customers are linked wirelessly to a single receiver. The meter sends monthly signals to a designated receiver to report the customer's consumption of electricity. The data are then channeled to a central computer to generate the utility bills. The objective is to determine the smallest number of receivers needed to serve a given number of meters. In real life, the problem encompasses thousands of meters and receivers. This problem deals with 10 meters and 8 possible locations for receivers, with the following configurations:

Receiver	1	2	3	4	5	6	7	8
Meters	1, 2, 3	2, 3, 9	5, 6, 7	7, 9, 10	3, 6, 8	1, 4, 7, 9	4, 5, 9	1, 4, 8

9. Solve Problem 8 if, additionally, each receiver can handle at most 4 meters and receiver 8 can handle meters 1, 4, 8, and 10.

9.1.3 Fixed-Charge Problem

The fixed-charge problem deals with situations in which the economic activity incurs two types of costs: a fixed cost needed to initiate the activity and a variable cost proportional to the level of the activity. For example, the initial tooling of a machine prior to starting production incurs a fixed setup cost regardless of how many units are manufactured. Once the setup is done, the cost of labor and material is proportional to the amount produced. Given that F is the fixed charge, c is the variable unit cost, and x is the level of production, the cost function is expressed as

$$C(x) = \begin{cases} F + cx, \text{ if } x > 0 \\ 0, \text{ otherwise} \end{cases}$$

The function $C(x)$ is intractable analytically because it involves a discontinuity at $x = 0$. The next example shows how auxiliary binary variables are used to render the model analytically tractable.

Example 9.1-3 (Choosing a Telephone Company)

I have been approached by three telephone companies to subscribe to their long-distance service in the United States. MaBell will charge a flat $16 per month plus $.25 a minute. PaBell will charge $25 a month but will reduce the per-minute cost to $.21. As for BabyBell, the flat monthly charge is $18, and the cost per minute is $.22. I usually make an average of 200 minutes of long-distance calls a month. Assuming that I do not pay the flat monthly fee unless I make calls and that I can apportion my calls among all three companies as I please, how should I use the three companies to minimize my monthly telephone bill?

This problem can be solved readily without ILP. Nevertheless, it is instructive to formulate it as an integer program.

Define

$$x_1 = \text{MaBell long-distance minutes per month}$$
$$x_2 = \text{PaBell long-distance minutes per month}$$
$$x_3 = \text{BabyBell long-distance minutes per month}$$
$$y_1 = 1 \text{ if } x_1 > 0 \text{ and } 0 \text{ if } x_1 = 0$$
$$y_2 = 1 \text{ if } x_2 > 0 \text{ and } 0 \text{ if } x_2 = 0$$
$$y_3 = 1 \text{ if } x_3 > 0 \text{ and } 0 \text{ if } x_3 = 0$$

We can ensure that y_j equals 1 when x_j is positive by using the constraint

$$x_j \leq My_j, j = 1, 2, 3$$

The value of M should be selected sufficiently large so as not to restrict the variable x_j artificially. Because I make about 200 minutes of calls a month, then $x_j \leq 200$ for all j, and it is safe to select $M = 200$.

The complete model is

$$\text{Minimize } z = .25x_1 + .21x_2 + .22x_3 + 16y_1 + 25y_2 + 18y_3$$

subject to

$$x_1 + x_2 + x_3 = 200$$
$$x_1 \leq 200y_1$$
$$x_2 \leq 200y_2$$
$$x_3 \leq 200y_3$$
$$x_1, x_2, x_3 \geq 0$$
$$y_1, y_2, y_3 = (0, 1)$$

The formulation shows that the jth monthly flat fee will be part of the objective function z only if $y_j = 1$, which can happen only if $x_j > 0$ (per the last three constraints of the model).

If $x_j = 0$ at the optimum, then the minimization of z, together with the fact that the objective coefficient of y_j is positive, forces y_j to equal zero, as desired.[3]

The optimum solution yields $x_3 = 200$, $y_3 = 1$, and all the remaining variables equal to zero, which shows that BabyBell should be selected as my long-distance carrier. Remember that the information conveyed by $y_3 = 1$ is redundant because the same result is implied by $x_3 > 0$ (= 200). Actually, the main reason for using y_1, y_2, and y_3 is to account for the monthly flat fee. In effect, the three binary variables convert an ill-behaved (nonlinear) model into an analytically tractable formulation. This conversion has resulted in introducing the integer (binary) variables in an otherwise continuous problem.

PROBLEM SET 9.1C

1. Leatherco is contracted to manufacture batches of pants, vests, and jackets. Each product requires a special setup of the machines needed in the manufacturing processes. The following table provides the pertinent data regarding the use of raw material (leather) and labor time together with cost and revenue estimates. Current supply of leather is estimated at 3800 ft², and available labor time is limited to 2850 hours.

	Pants	Vests	Jackets
Leather material per unit (ft²)	5.5	3.5	7.5
Labor time per unit (hr)	4.5	3.5	5.5
Production cost per unit ($)	30	20	80
Equipment setup cost per batch ($)	110	90	140
Price per unit ($)	60	40	120
Minimum number of units needed	100	150	200

Determine the optimum number of units that Leatherco must manufacture of each product.

*2. Jobco is planning to produce at least 2000 widgets on three machines. The minimum lot size on any machine is 600 widgets. The following table gives the pertinent data of the situation.

Machine	Setup cost ($)	Production cost/unit ($)	Capacity (units)
1	300	2	650
2	100	10	850
3	200	5	1250

Formulate the problem as an ILP, and find the optimum solution.

---

[3]For generalization, the condition $y_i = 0$ if $x_i = 0$ can be replaced with the compound condition $y_i = 1$ if $x_i > 0$ and 0 if $x_i = 0$ to make it independent of the sense of optimization (maximization or minimization). The result is achieved by replacing the constraint $x_i \le My_i$ with $\dfrac{x_i}{M} \le y_i \le x_i$.

*3. Oilco is considering two potential drilling sites for reaching four targets (possible oil wells). The following table provides the preparation costs at each of the two sites and the cost of drilling from site i to target j ($i = 1, 2; j = 1, 2, 3, 4$).

Site	Drilling cost ($ million) to target				Preparation cost ($ million)
	1	2	3	4	
1	2	1	8	5	5
2	4	6	3	1	6

Formulate the problem as an ILP, and find the optimum solution.

4. Three industrial sites are considered for locating manufacturing plants. The plants send their supplies to three customers. The supply at the plants, the demand at the customers, and the unit transportation cost from the plants to the customers are given in the following table.

Plant \ Customer	Unit transportations cost ($)			Supply
	1	2	3	
1	10	15	12	1800
2	17	14	20	1400
3	15	10	11	1300
Demand	1200	1700	1600	

In addition to the transportation costs, fixed costs are incurred at the rate of $12,000, $11,000, and $12,000 for plants 1, 2, and 3, respectively. Formulate the problem as an ILP, and find the optimum solution.

5. Repeat Problem 4 assuming that the demands at each of customers 2 and 3 are changed to 800.

6. *Liberatore and Miller (1985).* A manufacturing facility uses two production lines to produce three products over the next 6 months. Backlogged demand is not allowed. However, a product may be overstocked to meet demand in later months. The following table provides the data associated with the demand, production, and storage of the three products.

Product	Demand in period						Unit holding cost ($)/month	Initial inventory
	1	2	3	4	5	6		
1	50	30	40	60	20	45	.50	55
2	40	60	50	30	30	55	.35	75
3	30	40	20	70	40	30	.45	60

There is a fixed cost for switching a line from one product to another. The following tables give the switching cost, the production rates, and the unit production cost for each line:

	Line switching cost ($)		
	Product 1	Product 2	Product 3
Line 1	200	180	300
Line 2	250	200	174

	Production rate (units/month)			Unit production cost ($)		
	Product 1	Product 2	Product 3	Product 1	Product 2	Product 3
Line 1	40	60	80	10	8	15
Line 2	90	70	60	12	6	10

Develop a model for determining the optimal production schedule.

7. *Jarvis and Associates (1978).* Seven cities are being considered as potential locations for the construction of at most four wastewater treatment plants. The table below provides the data for the situation. Missing links indicate that a pipeline cannot be constructed.

		Cost ($) of pipeline construction between cities per 1000 gal/hr capacity						
	To	1	2	3	4	5	6	7
From								
1			100		200		50	
2					120		150	
3		400					120	90
4				120		120		
5			200				100	200
6				110	180			70
7		200			150			
Cost ($ million) of plant construction		1.00	1.20	2.00	1.60	1.80	.90	1.40
Population (1000s)		50	100	45	90	75	60	30

The capacity of a pipeline (in gallons per hour) is a direct function of the amount of wastewater generated, which is a function of the populations. Approximately 500 gallons per 1000 residents are discharged in the sewer system per hour. The maximum plant capacity is 100,000 gal/hr. Determine the optimal location and capacity of the plants.

8. *Brown and Associates (1987).* A company uses four special tank trucks to deliver four different gasoline products to customers. Each tank has five compartments with different capacities: 500, 750, 1200, 1500, and 1750 gallons. The daily demands for the four products are estimated at 10, 15, 12, and 8 thousand gallons. Any quantities that cannot be delivered by the company's four trucks must be subcontracted at the additional costs of 5, 12, 8, and 10 cents per gallon for products 1, 2, 3, and 4, respectively. Develop the optimal daily loading schedule for the four trucks that will minimize the additional cost of subcontracting.

9. A household uses at least 3000 minutes of long-distance telephone calls monthly and can choose to use the services of any of three companies: A, B, and C. Company A charges a fixed monthly fee of $10 and 5 cents per minute for the first 1000 minutes and 4 cents per minute for all additional minutes. Company B's monthly fee is $20 with a flat 4 cents per minute. Company C's monthly charge is $25 with 5 cents per minute for the first 1000 minutes and 3.5 cents per minute beyond that limit. Which company should be selected to minimize the total monthly charge?

*10. *Barnett (1987).* Professor Yataha needs to schedule six round-trips between Boston and Washington, D.C. The route is served by three airlines: Eastern, US Air, and Continental, and there is no penalty for the purchase of one-way tickets. Each airline offers bonus miles for frequent fliers. Eastern gives 1500 miles per (one-way) ticket plus 5000 extra miles if the number of tickets in a month reaches 3 and another 5000 miles if the number exceeds 5. US Air gives 1800 miles per trip plus 12,000 extra for each 6 tickets. Continental gives 2000 miles plus 7500 extra for each 5 tickets. Professor Yataha wishes to allocate the 16 one-way tickets among the three airlines to maximize the total number of bonus miles earned.

9.1.4   Either-Or and If-Then Constraints

In the fixed-charge problem (Section 9.1.3), auxiliary binary variables are used to handle the discontinuity in the objective cost function. This section deals with models in which constraints are not satisfied simultaneously (either-or) or are dependent (if-then), again using auxiliary binary variables. The transformation uses a mathematical trick to present the special constraint as "and" constraints.

Example 9.1-4   (Job Sequencing Model)

Jobco uses a single machine to process three jobs. Both the processing time and the due date (in days) for each job are given in the following table. The due dates are measured from zero, the assumed start time of the first job.

Job	Processing time (day)	Due date (day)	Late penalty ($/day)
1	5	25	19
2	20	22	12
3	15	35	34

The objective of the problem is to determine the job sequence that minimizes the late penalty for processing all three jobs.

Define

$$x_j = \text{Start date in days for job } j \text{ (measured from time zero)}$$

$$y_{ij} = \begin{cases} 1, & \text{if } i \text{ precedes } j \\ 0, & \text{if } j \text{ precedes } i \end{cases}$$

The problem has two types of constraints: the noninterference constraints (guaranteeing that no two jobs are processed concurrently) and the due-date constraints. Consider the noninterference constraints first.

Two jobs i and j with processing time p_i and p_j will not be processed concurrently if (depending on whether which job is processed first)

$$x_i \geq x_j + p_j \text{ or } x_j \geq x_i + p_i$$

For M sufficiently large, the "or" constraints are converted to "and" constraints by using

$$M y_{ij} + (x_i - x_j) \geq p_j \text{ and } M(1 - y_{ij}) + (x_j - x_i) \geq p_i$$

The conversion guarantees that only one of the two constraints can be active at any one time. If $y_{ij} = 0$, the first constraint is active, and the second is redundant (because its left-hand side will include M, which is much larger than p_i). If $y_{ij} = 1$, the first constraint is redundant, and the second is active.

Next, given that d_j is the due date for job j, the job is late if $x_j + p_j > d_j$. We can use two nonnegative variables, s_j^- and s_j^+ to determine the status of a completed job j with regard to its due date—namely, the due date constraint can be written as

$$x_j + p_j + s_j^- - s_j^+ = d_j$$

Job j is ahead of schedule if $s_j^- > 0$, and late if $s_j^+ > 0$. The late-penalty cost is thus proportional to s_j^+.

The model for the given problem is

$$\text{Minimize } z = 19s_1^+ + 12s_2^+ + 34s_3^+$$

subject to

$$
\begin{aligned}
x_1 - x_2 \quad + M y_{12} & \geq 20 \\
-x_1 + x_2 \quad - M y_{12} & \geq 5 - M \\
x_1 \quad - x_3 + M y_{13} & \geq 15 \\
-x_1 \quad + x_3 - M y_{13} & \geq 5 - M \\
x_2 - x_3 \quad + M y_{23} & \geq 15 \\
- x_2 + x_3 \quad - M y_{23} & \geq 20 - M \\
x_1 \quad + s_1^- - s_1^+ & = 25 - 5 \\
x_2 \quad + s_2^- - s_2^+ & = 22 - 20 \\
x_3 \quad + s_3^- - s_3^+ & = 35 - 15 \\
x_1, x_2, x_3, s_1^-, s_1^+, s_2^-, s_2^+, s_3^-, s_3^+ & \geq 0 \\
y_{12}, y_{13}, y_{23} & = (0, 1)
\end{aligned}
$$

The resulting model is a *mixed* ILP.

To solve the model, we choose $M = 100$, a value that is larger than the sum of the processing times for all three activities. The optimal solution is $x_1 = 20$, $x_2 = 0$, and $x_3 = 25$, This means that job 2 starts at time 0, job 1 starts at time 20, and job 3 starts at time 25, thus yielding the optimal processing sequence $2 : 1 : 3$. The solution calls for completing job 2 at time $0 + 20 = 20$, job 1 at time $= 20 + 5 = 25$, and job 3 at $25 + 15 = 40$ days. Job 3 is delayed by $40 - 35 = 5$ days past its due date at a cost of $5 \times \$34 = \$170$.

AMPL Moment

File *amplEx9.1-4.txt* provides the AMPL model for the problem of Example 9.1-4. The model is explained in Section C.9 on the website.

Example 9.1-5 (Job Sequencing Model Revisited)

In Example 9.1-4, suppose that we have the following additional condition: If job i precedes job j, then job k must precede job m. Mathematically, the **if-then** condition is written as

$$\text{if } x_i + p_i \leq x_j, \text{ then } x_k + p_k \leq x_m$$

Given ε (>0) is infinitesimally small and M sufficiently large, this condition is equivalent to the following two simultaneous constraints:

$$x_j - (x_i + p_i) \leq M(1 - w) - \varepsilon$$
$$(x_k + p_k) - x_m \leq Mw$$
$$w = (0, 1)$$

If $x_i + p_i \leq x_j$, then $x_j - (x_i + p_i) \geq 0$, which requires $w = 0$, and the second constraint becomes $x_k + p_k \leq x_m$, as desired. Else, w may assume the value 0 or 1, in which case the second constraint may or may not be satisfied, depending on other conditions in the model.

PROBLEM SET 9.1D

*1. A game board has 3×3 equal squares. You are required to fill each square with a number between 1 and 9 such that the sum of the numbers in each row, each column, and each diagonal equals 15. Additionally, the numbers in all the squares must be distinct. Use ILP to determine the assignment of numbers to squares.

2. A machine is used to produce two interchangeable products. The daily capacity of the machine can produce at most 20 units of product 1 and 40 units of product 2. Alternatively, the machine can be adjusted to produce at most 45 units of product 1 and 25 units of product 2 daily. Market analysis shows that the maximum daily demand for the two products combined is 50 units. Given that the unit profits for the two respective products are $10 and $12, which of the two machine settings should be selected? Formulate the problem as an ILP, and find the optimum. [*Note*: This two-dimensional problem can be solved by inspecting the graphical solution space. This is not the case for the n-dimensional problem.]

*3. Gapco manufactures three products, whose daily labor and raw material requirements are given in the following table.

Product	Required daily labor (hr/unit)	Required daily raw material (lb/unit)
1	3	4
2	4	3
3	5	6

The profits per unit of the three products are $20, $25, and $18, respectively. Gapco has two options for locating its plant. The two locations differ primarily in the availability of labor and raw material, as shown in the following table:

Location	Available daily labor (hr)	Available daily raw material (lb)
1	150	150
2	135	180

Formulate the problem as an ILP, and determine the optimum location of the plant.

4. Jobco Shop has 10 outstanding jobs to be processed on a single machine. The following table provides processing times and due dates. All times are in days, and due time is measured from time 0:

Job	Processing time (day)	Due time (day)
1	10	20
2	3	98
3	13	100
4	15	34
5	9	50
6	22	44
7	17	32
8	30	60
9	12	80
10	16	150

If job 4 precedes job 3, then job 9 must precede job 7. The objective is to process all 10 jobs in the shortest possible time. Formulate the model as an ILP, and determine the optimum solution by modifying the AMPL file *amplEx9.1-4.txt*.

5. In Problem 4, suppose that job 4 cannot be processed until job 3 has been completed. Also, machine settings for jobs 7 and 8 necessitate processing them one right after the other (i.e., job 7 immediately succeeds or precedes 8). Jobco's objective is to process all ten jobs with the smallest sum of due-time violations. Formulate the model mathematically, and determine the optimum solution.

6. Jaco owns a plant in which three products are manufactured. The labor and raw material requirements for the three products are given in the following table.

Product	Required daily labor (hr/unit)	Required daily raw material (lb/unit)
1	3	4
2	4	3
3	5	6
Daily availability	100	100

The profit per unit for the three products are $25, $30, and $45, respectively. If product 2 is to be manufactured at all, then its production level must be at least 12 units daily. Formulate the problem as a mixed ILP, and find the optimal mix.

7. UPak is a subsidiary of an LTL transportation company. Customers bring their shipments to the UPak terminal to be loaded on the trailer and can rent space up to 36 ft. The customer pays for the exact linear space (in foot increments) the shipment occupies. No partial shipment is allowed, in the sense that a shipment requiring no more than 36 ft must be loaded on one trailer. A movable barrier, called bulkhead, is installed to separate shipments. The per-foot fee UPak collects depends on the destination of the shipment. The following table provides the outstanding orders UPak needs to process.

Order	1	2	3	4	5	6	7	8	9	10
Size (ft)	5	11	22	15	7	9	18	14	10	12
Rate ($)	120	93	70	85	125	104	98	130	140	65

The terminal currently has two trailers ready to be loaded. Determine the priority orders that will maximize the total income from the two trailers. (*Hint:* A formulation using binary x_{ij} to represent load i on trailer j is straightforward. However, you are challenged to define x_{ij} as *feet* assigned to load i in trailer j. Then use *if-then* constraint to prevent partial load shipping.)

8. *N queens problem.* In the game of chess, queens attack by moving horizontally, vertically, or diagonally. It is desired to place N queens on an $(N \times N)$-grid so that no queen can "take" any other queen. Formulate the problem as an integer program, and solve with AMPL (or any other software) for $N = 4, 5, 6$, and 8. [*Hint:* Formulations 1: Let $x_{ij} = 1$ if a queen is placed in square (i, j), and zero otherwise. The constraints of the problem are of the type "if $x_{ij} > 0$, then no other queen can be placed in row i, column j, or diagonal(s) from square (i, j)." Formulations 2: Let R_i = row associated with column i in which queen i is placed on the grid. The constraints prevent diagonal placements of queens.]

9. A manufacturing process uses four interchangeable raw materials. The raw materials differ in properties, which leads to different output units per unit of raw material. They also differ in cost and lot sizes. The following table summarizes the data of the situation:

	Material 1	Material 2	Material 3	Material 4	Material 5
Lot size (units)	100	160	80	310	50
Product units per unit of raw material	3	2	5	1	4
Cost per unit of raw material ($)	30	80	200	10	120

A raw material, if used, must be in the indicated lots only (e.g., Material 1 can be bought either as a lot of size 100 units or none at all). The number of output units must be at least 950. Formulate a model to determine the raw materials that should be used at minimum cost.

10. Show how the nonconvex shaded solution spaces in Figure 9.3 can be represented by a set of simultaneous constraints. Find the optimum solution that maximizes $z = 2x_1 + 3x_2$ subject to the solution space given in (a).

11. Given the binary variables x_1, x_2, x_3, x_4, and x_5, if $x_1 = 1$ and $x_2 = 0$, then $x_3 = 1, x_4 = 1$, and $x_5 = 1$. Formulate the condition as simultaneous constraints.

FIGURE 9.3

Solution Spaces for Problem 10, Set 9.1d

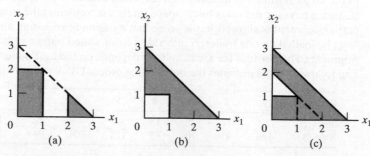

(a)　　　　(b)　　　　(c)

*12. Suppose that product zw occurs in a constraint, where z and w are binary variables. Show how this term can be linearized.

13. Consider the binary variable $y_i, i = 1, 2, \ldots, n$. Express the following condition as a set of simultaneous ILP constraints: If $i = k$, then $y_k = 1$, and all the remaining variables equal zero.

14. Suppose that it is required that *any* k out of the following m constraints must be active:

$$g_i(x_1, x_2, \ldots, x_n) \le b_i, \ i = 1, 2, \ldots, m$$

Show how this condition may be represented.

15. In the following constraint, the right-hand side may assume one of values, $b_1, b_2, \ldots,$ and b_m.

$$g(x_1, x_2, \ldots, x_n \le (b_1, b_2, \ldots, \text{ or } b_m)$$

Show how this condition is represented.

16. Consider the following objective function

$$\text{Minimize } z = \min\{2x_1 + x_2, 4x_1 - 3x_2 | x_1 \ge 1, x_2 \ge 0\}$$

Use auxiliary binary variables to convert the objective function z into an analytically manageable format that eliminates the min function.

17. Give the binary variables $y_1, y_2, \ldots, y_n$, such that if $x_i = 1$, then x_{i-1} or x_{i+1} must equal 1, $i = 1, 2, \ldots, n$, where y_0 and y_{n+1} define the variable y_n.

9.2   INTEGER PROGRAMMING ALGORITHMS

The ILP algorithms are based on exploiting the tremendous computational success of LP. The strategy of these algorithms involves three steps.

Step 1. Relax the solution space of the ILP by deleting the integer restriction on all integer variables and replacing any binary variable y with the continuous range $0 \le y \le 1$. The result of the relaxation is a regular LP.

Step 2. Solve the LP, and identify its continuous optimum.

Step 3. Starting from the continuous optimum point, add special constraints that iteratively modify the LP solution space in a manner that eventually renders an optimum extreme point satisfying the integer requirements.

Two general methods have been developed for generating the special constraints in step 3.

1. Branch-and-bound (B&B) method
2. Cutting-plane method

Neither method is consistently effective computationally. However, experience shows that the B&B method is far more successful than the cutting-plane method.

9.2.1   Branch-and-Bound (B&B) Algorithm[4]

The first B&B algorithm was developed in 1960 by A. Land and G. Doig for the general mixed and pure ILP problem. Later, in 1965, E. Balas developed the **additive algorithm** for solving ILPs with pure binary (zero or one) variables.[5] The additive algorithm's computations were so simple (mainly addition and subtraction) that it was initially hailed as a possible breakthrough in the solution of general ILP. Unfortunately, it failed to produce the desired computational advantages. Moreover, the algorithm, which initially appeared unrelated to the B&B technique, was shown to be but a special case of the general Land and Doig algorithm.

This section presents the general Land–Doig B&B algorithm only. A numeric example is used to provide the details.

Example 9.2-1

$$\text{Maximize } z = 5x_1 + 4x_2$$

subject to

$$x_1 + x_2 \leq 5$$

$$10x_1 + 6x_2 \leq 45$$

$$x_1, x_2 \text{ nonnegative integer}$$

The lattice points (dots) in Figure 9.4 define the ILP solution space. The associated continuous LP1 problem at node 1 (shaded area) is defined from ILP by removing the integer restrictions. The optimum solution of LP1 is $x_1 = 3.75$, $x_2 = 1.25$, and $z = 23.75$.

Because the optimum LP1 solution does not satisfy the integer restrictions, the solution space is subdivided in a systematic manner that eventually locates the ILP optimum. First, B&B selects an integer variable whose optimum value at LP1 is not integer. In this example, both x_1 and x_2 qualify. Selecting $x_1(= 3.75)$ arbitrarily, the region $3 < x_1 < 4$ of the LP1 solution space contains no integer values of x_1, and thus it can be deleted. This is equivalent to replacing the original LP1 with two new LPs:

$$\text{LP2 space} = \text{LP1 space} + (x_1 \leq 3)$$

$$\text{LP3 space} = \text{LP1 space} + (x_1 \geq 4)$$

Figure 9.5 depicts the LP2 and LP3 spaces. The two spaces combined contain the same feasible integer points as the original ILP—meaning that no information is lost when LP1 is replaced with LP2 and LP3.

---

[4]TORA integer programming module is equipped with a facility for generating the B&B tree interactively. To use this facility, select User-guided B&B in the output screen of the integer programming module. The resulting screen provides all the information needed to create the B&B tree.

[5]A general ILP can be expressed in terms of binary (0–1) variables as follows. Given an integer variable x with a finite upper bound u (i.e., $0 \leq x \leq u$), then

$$x = 2^0 y_0 + 2^1 y_1 + 2^2 y_2 + \cdots + 2^k y_k$$

The variables $y_0, y_1, \ldots,$ and y_k are binary, and the index k is the smallest integer satisfying $2^{k+1} - 1 \geq u$.

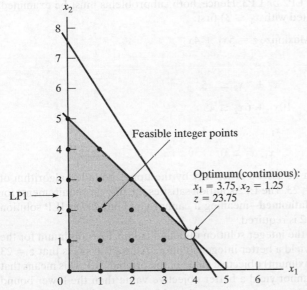

FIGURE 9.4

Solution space for ILP (lattice points) and LP1 (shaded area) of Example 9.2-1 (LP1)

In the figure: "Feasible integer points", "Optimum(continuous): $x_1 = 3.75, x_2 = 1.25$ $z = 23.75$", "LP1".

If we intelligently impose sequential constraints that exclude the integer-free regions (e.g., $3 < x_1 < 4$ in LP1), we will be reducing the continuous solution space of LP1 into a number of LP subproblems whose optimum extreme points satisfy the integer restrictions. The best of these subproblems is the optimum solution of ILP.

The new restrictions, $x_1 \le 3$ and $x_1 \ge 4$, are mutually exclusive, so that LP2 and LP3 at nodes 2 and 3 must be dealt with as separate LPs, as Figure 9.6 shows. This dichotomization gives rise to the concept of **branching** in the B&B algorithm. In this case, x_1 is called the **branching variable.**

FIGURE 9.5

Solution Spaces of LP2 and LP3 for Example 9.2-1

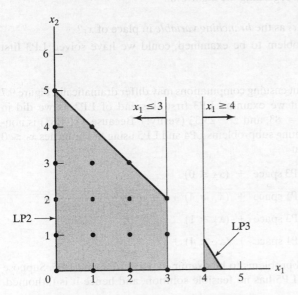

In the figure: "$x_1 \le 3$", "$x_1 \ge 4$", "LP2", "LP3".

The optimum ILP lies in *either* LP2 *or* LP3. Hence, both subproblems must be examined. We arbitrarily examine LP2 (associated with $x_1 \le 3$) first:

$$\text{Maximize } z = 5x_1 + 4x_2$$

subject to

$$x_1 + x_2 \le 5$$
$$10x_1 + 6x_2 \le 45$$
$$x_1 \le 3$$
$$x_1, x_2 \ge 0$$

The solution of LP2 (which can be solved efficiently by the upper-bounded algorithm of Section 7.3) is $x_1 = 3, x_2 = 2$, and $z = 23$. The LP2 solution satisfies the integer requirements for x_1 and x_2. Hence, LP2 is said to be **fathomed**—meaning it cannot yield any *better* ILP solution and no further branching from node 2 is required.

We cannot say at this point that the integer solution obtained from LP2 is optimum for the original problem, because LP3 may yield a better integer solution. All we can say is that $z = 23$ is a **lower bound** on the optimum (maximum) objective value of the original ILP. This means that any unexamined subproblem that cannot yield a better objective value than the lower bound must be discarded as nonpromising. If an unexamined subproblem produces a better integer solution, then the lower bound must be updated accordingly.

Given the lower bound $z = 23$, we examine LP3 (the only remaining unexamined subproblem at this point). Because optimum $z = 23.75$ at LP1 *and all the coefficients of the objective function happen to be integers,* it is impossible that LP3 can produce a better integer solution (with $z > 23$). As a result, we discard LP3 and conclude that it has been *fathomed.*

The B&B algorithm is now complete because both LP2 and LP3 have been examined and fathomed, the first for producing an integer solution and the second for failing to produce a *better* integer solution. We thus conclude that the optimum ILP solution is the one associated with the lower bound—namely, $x_1 = 3, x_2 = 2$, and $z = 23$.

Two questions remain unanswered regarding the algorithm:

1. At LP1, could we have selected x_2 as the *branching variable* in place of x_1?
2. When selecting the next subproblem to be examined, could we have solved LP3 first instead of LP2?

The answer to both questions is "yes," but ensuing computations may differ dramatically. Figure 9.7 demonstrates this point. Suppose that we examine LP3 first (instead of LP2 as we did in Figure 9.6). The solution is $x_1 = 4, x_2 = .83$, and $z = 23.33$ (verify!). Because $x_2 (=.83)$ is non-integer, LP3 is examined further by creating subproblems LP4 and LP5 using the branches $x_2 \le 0$ and $x_2 \ge 1$, respectively. This means that

$$\text{LP4 space} = \text{LP3 space} + (x_2 \le 0)$$
$$= \text{LP1 space} + (x_1 \ge 4) + (x_2 \le 0)$$
$$\text{LP5 space} = \text{LP3 space} + (x_2 \ge 1)$$
$$= \text{LP1 space} + (x_1 \ge 4) + (x_2 \ge 1)$$

We now have three "dangling" subproblems to be examined: LP2, LP4, and LP5. Suppose that we arbitrarily examine LP5 first. LP5 has no feasible solution, and hence it is fathomed.

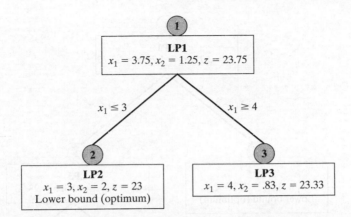

FIGURE 9.6
Using branching variable x_1 to create LP2 and LP3 for Example 9.2-1

Next, let us examine LP4. The optimum solution is $x_1 = 4.5$, $x_2 = 0$, and $z = 22.5$. The non-integer value of x_1 leads to the two branches $x_1 \leq 4$ and $x_1 \geq 5$ and the creation of subproblems LP6 and LP7 from LP4.

$$\text{LP6 space} = \text{LP1 space} + (x_1 \geq 4) + (x_2 \leq 0) + (x_1 \leq 4)$$

$$\text{LP7 space} = \text{LP1 space} + (x_1 \geq 4) + (x_2 \leq 0) + (x_1 \geq 5)$$

Now, subproblems LP2, LP6, and LP7 remain unexamined. Selecting LP7 for examination, the problem is fathomed because it has no feasible solution. Next, we select LP6. The problem yields the first integer solution ($x_1 = 4$, $x_2 = 0$, $z = 20$), and, thus provide the first lower bound ($= 20$) on the optimum ILP objective value. We are now left with subproblem LP2, and it yields a better integer solution ($x_1 = 3$, $x_2 = 2$, $z = 23$). Thus, the lower bound is updated from $z = 20$ to $z = 23$. At this point, *all* the subproblems have been fathomed (examined), and the optimum solution is the one associated with the most up-to-date lower bound—namely, $x_1 = 3$, $x_2 = 2$, and $z = 23$.

The solution sequence in Figure 9.7 (LP1 → LP3 → LP5 → LP4 → LP7 → LP6 → LP2) is a worst-case scenario that, nevertheless, may well occur in practice. In Figure 9.6, we were lucky to "stumble" upon a good lower bound at the very first subproblem (LP2), and that in turn allowed us to fathom LP3 without further examination. In essence, we completed the procedure by solving a total of two LPs. In Figure 9.7, the story is different; we solved seven LPs to terminate the B&B algorithm.

Remarks. The example points to a principal weakness in the B&B algorithm: Given multiple choices, how do we select the next subproblem and its branching variable? Although there are heuristics for enhancing the ability of B&B to "foresee" which branch can lead to an improved ILP solution (see Taha, 1975, pp. 154–171), solid theory with consistent results does not exist, and herein lies the difficulty that plagues computations in ILP. Indeed, Problem 7, Set 9.2a, demonstrates the bizarre behavior of the B&B algorithm in investigating over 25,000 LPs before optimality is verified, even though the problem is quite small (16 binary variables and 1 constraint). Unfortunately, to date, and after decades of research coupled with tremendous advances in computers, available ILP codes are not totally reliable. Nevertheless, available commercial solvers (e.g., CPLEX and XPESS) are successful in solving very large problems.

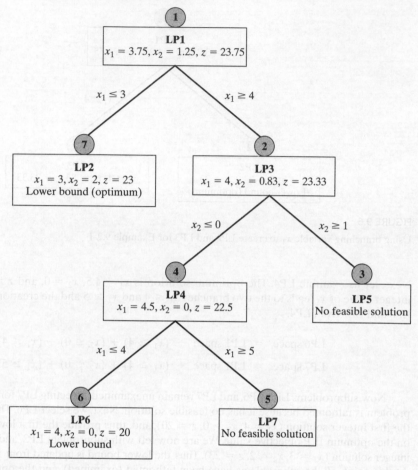

FIGURE 9.7

Alternative B&B tree for Example 9.2-1

AMPL Moment

AMPL can be used interactively to generate the B&B search tree. The following table shows the sequence of commands needed to generate the tree of Example 9.2-1 (Figure 9.7) starting with the continuous LP1. AMPL model (file *amplEx9.2-1.txt*) has two variables x1 and x2 and two constraints c0 and c1. You will find it helpful to synchronize the AMPL commands with the branches in Figure 9.7.

AMPL command	Result
ampl: `model amplEx9.2-1.txt;solve;display x1,x2;`	LP1 ($x_1 = 3.75, x_2 = 1.25$)
ampl: `c2:x1>=4;solve;display x1,x2;`	LP3 ($x_1 = 4, x_2 = .83$)
ampl: `c3:x2>=1;solve;display x1,x2;`	LP5 (no solution)
ampl: `drop c3;c4:x2<=0;solve;display x1,x2;`	LP4 ($x_1 = 4.5, x_2 = 0$)
ampl: `c5:x1>=5;solve;display x1,x2;`	LP7 (no solution)
ampl: `drop c5;c6:x1<=4;solve;display x1,x2;`	LP6 ($x_1 = 4, x_2 = 0$)
ampl: `drop c2;drop c4;drop c6;c7:x1<=3; solve; display x1,x2;`	LP2 ($x_1 = 3, x_2 = 2$)

Solver Moment

Solver can be used to obtain the solution of the different subproblems by using the add/change/delete options in the **Solver Parameters** dialogue box.

Summary of the B&B Algorithm.   Assume a maximization problem. Set an initial lower bound $z = -\infty$ on the optimum objective value of ILP and set $i = 0$.[6]

Step 1.   (*Fathoming/bounding*). Select LPi, the next subproblem to be examined. Solve LPi, and attempt to fathom it using one of three conditions:

   (a) The optimal z-value of LPi cannot yield a better objective value than the current lower bound.

   (b) LPi yields a better feasible integer solution than the current lower bound.

   (c) LPi has no feasible solution.

   Two cases will arise.

   (a) If LPi is fathomed and a better solution is found, update the lower bound. If all subproblems have been fathomed, stop; the lower bound gives the optimum solution (if no finite lower bound exists, the problem has no feasible solution). Else, set $i = i + 1$, and repeat step 1.

   (b) If LPi is not fathomed, go to step 2 for branching.

Step 2.   (*Branching*). Select one of the integer variables x_j, whose optimum value x_j^* in the LPi solution is not integer. Create the two LP subproblems that correspond to

$$x_j \le [x_j^*] \text{ and } x_j \ge [x_j^*] + 1$$

Set $i = i + 1$, and go to step 1.

The B&B algorithm can be extended to mixed problems (in which only some of the variables are integer). A continuous variable is never selected as a branching variable. A feasible subproblem provides a new bound on the objective value if the values of the discrete variables are integers with an improved objective value.

PROBLEM SET 9.2a[7]

   1. Solve the ILP of Example 9.2-1 by the B&B algorithm starting with x_2 as the branching variable. Start the procedure by solving the subproblem associated with $x_2 \le [x_2^*]$.

   2. Develop the B&B tree for each of the following problems. For convenience, always select x_1 as the branching variable at node 0.

   *(a)** Maximize $z = 3x_1 + 2x_2$

   subject to

$$2x_1 + 5x_2 \le 18$$
$$4x_1 + 2x_2 \le 18$$
$$x_1, x_2 \ge 0 \text{ and integer}$$

---

[6]For minimization problems, replace the lower bound with an initial upper bound $z = +\infty$.
[7]In this set, you may solve the subproblems interactively with AMPL or Solver or by using TORA's MODIFY option for the upper and lower bounds.

(b) Maximize $z = 2x_1 + 3x_2$

subject to

$$7x_1 + 5x_2 \le 36$$
$$4x_1 + 9x_2 \le 35$$
$$x_1, x_2 \ge 0 \text{ and integer}$$

(c) Maximize $z = 2x_1 + 2x_2$

subject to

$$2x_1 + 5x_2 \le 27$$
$$6x_1 + 5x_2 \le 16$$
$$x_1, x_2 \ge 0 \text{ and integer}$$

(d) Minimize $z = 5x_1 + 4x_2$

subject to

$$3x_1 + 2x_2 \ge 5$$
$$2x_1 + 3x_2 \ge 7$$
$$x_1, x_2 \ge 0 \text{ and integer}$$

(e) Maximize $z = 5x_1 + 7x_2$

subject to

$$2x_1 + x_2 \le 13$$
$$5x_1 + 9x_2 \le 41$$
$$x_1, x_2 \ge 0 \text{ and integer}$$

*3. Repeat Problem 2, assuming that x_1 is continuous.

4. Show graphically that the following ILP has no feasible solution, and then verify the result using B&B.

$$\text{Maximize } z = 3x_1 + 2x_2$$

subject to

$$10x_1 + 9x_2 \le 8$$
$$8x_1 + 6x_2 \ge 1$$
$$x_1, x_2 \ge 0 \text{ and integer}$$

5. Solve the following problems by B&B.

$$\text{Maximize } z = 18x_1 + 14x_2 + 8x_3 + 4x_4$$

subject to

$$15x_1 + 12x_2 + 7x_3 + 4x_4 + x_5 \le 37$$
$$x_1, x_2, x_3, x_4, x_5 = (0, 1)$$

6. Convert the following problem into a mixed ILP, and find the optimum solution.

$$\text{Maximize } z = x_1 + 2x_2 + 5x_3$$

subject to

$$|-x_1 + 10x_2 - 3x_3| \geq 15$$
$$2x_1 + x_2 + x_3 \leq 10$$
$$x_1, x_2, x_3 \geq 0$$

7. *TORA/Solver/AMPL Experiment.* The following problem is designed to demonstrate the bizarre behavior of the B&B algorithm even for small problems. In particular, note how many subproblems are examined before the optimum is found and how many are needed to verify optimality.

$$\text{Minimize } y$$

subject to

$$2(x_1 + x_2 + \cdots + x_{15}) + y = 15$$

All variables are $(0, 1)$

   (a) Use TORA's automated option to show that although the optimum is found after only 9 subproblems, over 25,000 subproblems are examined before optimality is confirmed.
   (b) Show that Solver exhibits an experience similar to TORA's. [*Note:* In Solver, you can watch the change in the number of generated branches (subproblems) at the bottom of the spreadsheet.]
   (c) Solve the problem with AMPL, and show that the solution is obtained instantly with 0 MIP simplex iterations and 0 B&B nodes. The reason for this superior performance can only be attributed to the presolve steps performed by AMPL and/or the CPLEX solver.

8. *TORA Experiment.* Consider the following ILP:

$$\text{Maximize } z = 18x_1 + 14x_2 + 8x_3$$

subject to

$$15x_1 + 12x_2 + 7x_3 \leq 43$$
$$x_1, x_2, x_3 \text{ nonnegative integers}$$

Use TORA's B&B user-guided option to generate the search tree with and without activating the objective value bound. What is the impact of activating the objective-value bound on the number of generated subproblems? For consistency, always select the branching variable as the one with the lowest index and investigate all the subproblems in a current row from left to right before moving to the next row.

*9. *TORA Experiment.* Reconsider the preceding Problem 8. Convert the problem into an equivalent 0-1 ILP, then solve it with TORA's automated option. Compare the size of the search trees in the two problems.

10. *AMPL Experiment.* In the following 0-1 ILP, use interactive AMPL to generate the associated search tree. In each case, show how the z-bound is used to fathom subproblems.

$$\text{Maximize } z = 3x_1 + 2x_2 - 5x_3 - 2x_4 + 3x_5$$

subject to

$$x_1 + x_2 + x_3 + 2x_4 + x_5 \leq 4$$
$$7x_1 \qquad + 3x_3 - 4x_4 + 3x_5 \leq 8$$
$$11x_1 - 6x_2 \qquad + 3x_4 - 3x_5 \geq 3$$
$$x_1, x_2, x_3, x_4, x_5 = (0, 1)$$

9.2.2 Cutting-Plane Algorithm

As in the B&B algorithm, the cutting-plane algorithm also starts at the continuous optimum LP solution. Special constraints (called **cuts**) are added to the solution space in a manner that renders an integer optimum extreme point. In Example 9.2-2, we first demonstrate graphically how cuts are used to produce an integer solution and then implement the idea algebraically.

Example 9.2-2

Consider the following ILP.

$$\text{Maximize } z = 7x_1 + 10x_2$$

subject to

$$-x_1 + 3x_2 \leq 6$$
$$7x_1 + x_2 \leq 35$$
$$x_1, x_2 \geq 0 \text{ and integer}$$

Figure 9.8 gives an example of two such cuts. Initially, we start with the continuous LP optimum $z = 66\frac{1}{2}$, $x_1 = 4\frac{1}{2}$, $x_2 = 3\frac{1}{2}$. Next, we add cut I, which produces the (continuous) LP optimum solution $z = 62$, $x_1 = 4\frac{4}{7}$, $x_2 = 3$. Then, we add cut II, which (together with cut I and the original constraints) produces the integer LP optimum $z = 58$, $x_1 = 4$, $x_2 = 3$.

FIGURE 9.8

Illustration of the use of cuts in ILP

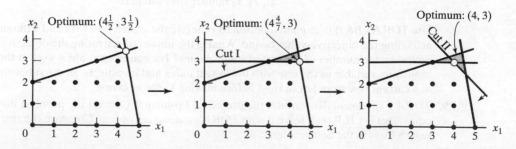

The added cuts do not eliminate any of the original feasible integer points, but must pass through at least one feasible or infeasible integer point. These are basic requirements of any cut.

It is purely accidental that a 2-variable problem used exactly 2 cuts to reach the optimum integer solution. In general, the number of cuts, though finite, cannot be determined based on the size of the problem, in the sense that a smaller problem may require more cuts than a larger problem.

Next, we use the same example to show how the cuts are constructed and implemented algebraically. Given the slacks x_3 and x_4 for constraints 1 and 2, the optimum LP tableau is given as

Basic	x_1	x_2	x_3	x_4	Solution
z	0	0	$\frac{63}{22}$	$\frac{31}{22}$	$66\frac{1}{2}$
x_2	0	1	$\frac{7}{22}$	$\frac{1}{22}$	$3\frac{1}{2}$
x_1	1	0	$-\frac{1}{22}$	$\frac{3}{22}$	$4\frac{1}{2}$

The optimum continuous solution is $z = 66\frac{1}{2}$, $x_1 = 4\frac{1}{2}$, $x_2 = 3\frac{1}{2}$, $x_3 = 0$, $x_4 = 0$. The cut is developed under the assumption that *all* the variables, *including all the slacks*, are integers. Note also that because all the original objective coefficients are integers in this example, the value of z also is integer.

The information in the optimum tableau can be written explicitly as

$$z + \tfrac{63}{22} x_3 + \tfrac{31}{22} x_4 = 66\tfrac{1}{2} \qquad \text{(z-equation)}$$

$$x_2 + \tfrac{7}{22} x_3 + \tfrac{1}{22} x_4 = 3\tfrac{1}{2} \qquad \text{(x_2-equation)}$$

$$x_1 - \tfrac{1}{22} x_3 + \tfrac{3}{22} x_4 = 4\tfrac{1}{2} \qquad \text{(x_1-equation)}$$

A constraint equation can be used as a **source row** for generating a cut, provided its right-hand side is fractional. Also, the z-equation can be used as a source row in this example because z happens to be integer. We will demonstrate how a cut is generated from each of these source rows, starting with the z-equation.

First, we factor out all the noninteger coefficients of the equation into an integer value and a *positive* fractional component. For example,

$$\tfrac{5}{2} = \left(2 + \tfrac{1}{2}\right)$$

$$-\tfrac{7}{3} = \left(-3 + \tfrac{2}{3}\right)$$

The factoring of the z-equation yields

$$z + \left(2 + \tfrac{19}{22}\right)x_3 + \left(1 + \tfrac{9}{22}\right)x_4 = \left(66 + \tfrac{1}{2}\right)$$

Moving all the integer components to the left-hand side and all the fractional components to the right-hand side, we get

$$z + 2x_3 + 1x_4 - 66 = -\tfrac{19}{22} x_3 - \tfrac{9}{22} x_4 + \tfrac{1}{2} \qquad (1)$$

Because x_3 and x_4 are nonnegative and all the fractions are positive by construction, the right-hand side must satisfy the following inequality:

$$-\tfrac{19}{22} x_3 - \tfrac{9}{22} x_4 + \tfrac{1}{2} \le \tfrac{1}{2} \qquad (2)$$

Now, because the left-hand side in Equation (1), $z + 2x_3 + 1x_4 - 66$, is an integer value by construction, the right-hand side, $-\frac{19}{22}x_3 - \frac{19}{22}x_4 + \frac{1}{2}$, must also be integer. It then follows that (2) can be replaced with the inequality:

$$-\tfrac{19}{22}x_3 - \tfrac{9}{22}x_4 + \tfrac{1}{2} \leq 0$$

This result is justified because an *integer* value less than a positive fraction must necessarily be ≤ 0.

The last inequality is the desired cut, and it represents a *necessary* (but not sufficient) condition for obtaining an integer solution. It is also referred to as the **fractional cut** because all its coefficients are fractions.

Because $x_3 = x_4 = 0$ in the optimum continuous LP tableau given above, the current continuous solution violates the cut (because it yields $\frac{1}{2} \leq 0$). Thus, if we add this cut to the optimum tableau, the resulting optimum extreme point moves the solution toward satisfying the integer restrictions.

Before showing how a cut is implemented in the optimal tableau, we will demonstrate how cuts can also be constructed from the constraint equations. Consider the x_1-row:

$$x_1 - \tfrac{1}{22}x_3 + \tfrac{3}{22}x_4 = 4\tfrac{1}{2}$$

Factoring out the equation, we get

$$x_1 + \left(-1 + \tfrac{21}{22}\right)x_3 + \left(0 + \tfrac{3}{22}\right)x_4 = \left(4 + \tfrac{1}{2}\right)$$

The associated cut is

$$-\tfrac{21}{22}x_2 - \tfrac{3}{22}x_4 + \tfrac{1}{2} \leq 0$$

Similarly, the x_2-equation

$$x_2 + \tfrac{7}{22}x_3 + \tfrac{1}{22}x_4 = 3\tfrac{1}{2}$$

is factored as

$$x_2 + \left(0 + \tfrac{7}{22}\right)x_3 + \left(0 + \tfrac{1}{22}\right)x_4 = 3 + \tfrac{1}{2}$$

Hence, the associated cut is

$$-\tfrac{7}{22}x_3 - \tfrac{1}{22}x_4 + \tfrac{1}{2} \leq 0$$

Any one of three cuts given above can be used in the first iteration of the cutting-plane algorithm. It is not necessary to generate all three cuts before selecting one.

Arbitrarily selecting the cut generated from the x_2-row, we can write it in equation form as

$$-\tfrac{7}{22}x_3 - \tfrac{1}{22}x_4 + s_1 = -\tfrac{1}{2}, \; s_1 \geq 0 \qquad \text{(Cut I)}$$

This constraint is added to the LP optimum tableau as follows:

Basic	x_1	x_2	x_3	x_4	s_1	Solution
z	0	0	$\frac{63}{22}$	$\frac{31}{22}$	0	$66\frac{1}{2}$
x_2	0	1	$\frac{7}{22}$	$\frac{1}{22}$	0	$3\frac{1}{2}$
x_1	1	0	$-\frac{1}{22}$	$\frac{3}{22}$	0	$4\frac{1}{2}$
s_1	0	0	$-\frac{7}{22}$	$-\frac{1}{22}$	1	$-\frac{1}{2}$

The tableau is optimal but infeasible. We apply the dual simplex method (Section 4.4.1) to recover feasibility, which yields

Basic	x_1	x_2	x_3	x_4	s_1	Solution
z	0	0	0	1	9	62
x_2	0	1	0	0	1	3
x_1	1	0	0	$\frac{1}{7}$	$-\frac{1}{7}$	$4\frac{4}{7}$
x_3	0	0	1	$\frac{1}{7}$	$-\frac{22}{7}$	$1\frac{4}{7}$

The last solution is still noninteger in x_1 and x_3, and we arbitrarily select x_1 as the next source row—that is,

$$x_1 + (0 + \tfrac{1}{7})x_4 + (-1 + \tfrac{6}{7})s_1 = 4 + \tfrac{4}{7}$$

The associated cut is

$$-\tfrac{1}{7}x_4 - \tfrac{6}{7}s_1 + s_2 = -\tfrac{4}{7}, \ s_2 \geq 0 \quad \text{(Cut II)}$$

Adding cut II to the previous optimal tableau, we get

Basic	x_1	x_2	x_3	x_4	s_1	s_2	Solution
z	0	0	0	1	9	0	62
x_2	0	1	0	0	1	0	3
x_1	1	0	0	$\frac{1}{7}$	$-\frac{1}{7}$	0	$4\frac{4}{7}$
x_3	0	0	1	$\frac{1}{7}$	$-\frac{22}{7}$	0	$1\frac{4}{7}$
s_2	0	0	0	$-\frac{1}{7}$	$-\frac{6}{7}$	1	$-\frac{4}{7}$

The dual simplex method yields the following tableau:

Basic	x_1	x_2	x_3	x_4	s_1	s_2	Solution
z	0	0	0	0	3	7	58
x_2	0	1	0	0	1	0	3
x_1	1	0	0	0	-1	1	4
x_3	0	0	1	0	-4	1	1
x_4	0	0	0	1	6	-7	4

The optimum solution ($x_1 = 4, x_2 = 3, z = 58$) is all integer. It is not accidental that all the coefficients of the last tableau are integers also, a consequence of using the fractional cut.

Remarks. It is important to point out that the fractional cut assumes that *all* the variables, *including slack and surplus*, are integer. This means that the cut deals with pure integer problems only. The importance of this assumption is illustrated by an example.

Consider the constraint

$$x_1 + \tfrac{1}{3}x_2 \leq \tfrac{13}{2}$$

$$x_1, x_2 \geq 0 \text{ and integer}$$

From the standpoint of solving the associated ILP, the constraint is treated as an equation by using the nonnegative slack s_1—that is,

$$x_1 + \tfrac{1}{3}x_2 + s_1 = \tfrac{13}{2}$$

The application of the fractional cut assumes that the constraint has a feasible *integer* solution in all x_1, x_2, and s_1. However, the given equation will have a feasible integer solution in x_1 and x_2 only if s_1 *is noninteger.* This means that the cutting-plane algorithm will conclude, through the applications of the dual simplex, that the problem has no feasible (integer) solution, even though the variables of concern, x_1 and x_2, can assume feasible integer values.

There are two ways to remedy this situation.

1. Multiply the entire constraint by a proper constant to remove all the fractions. For example, multiplying the constraint above by 6, we get

$$6x_1 + 2x_2 \le 39$$

Any integer solution of x_1 and x_2 automatically yields integer slack. However, this type of conversion may produce excessively large integer coefficients in some cases, and this in turn may lead to computational roundoff errors on the computer.

2. Use a special cut, called the **mixed cut,** which allows only a subset of variables to assume integer values, with all the other variables (including slack and surplus) remaining continuous. The details of this cut will not be presented in this chapter (see Taha, 1975, pp. 198–202).

PROBLEM SET 9.2B

1. In Example 9.2-2, show graphically whether or not each of the following constraints can form a legitimate cut:

   *(a) $x_1 + 2x_2 \le 10$

   (b) $2x_1 + x_2 \le 10$

   (c) $3x_2 \le 10$

   (d) $3x_1 + x_2 \le 15$

2. In Example 9.2-2, show graphically how the following two (legitimate) cuts can lead to the optimum integer solution:

   $$x_1 + 2x_2 \le 10 \quad \text{(Cut I)}$$
   $$3x_1 + x_2 \le 15 \quad \text{(Cut II)}$$

3. Express cuts I and II of Example 9.2-2 in terms of x_1 and x_2, and show that they are the same ones used graphically in Figure 9.8.

4. In Example 9.2-2, derive cut II from the x_3-row. Use the new cut to complete the solution of the example.

5. Show that, even though the following problem has a feasible integer solution in x_1 and x_2, the fractional cut would not yield a feasible solution unless all the fractions in the constraint were eliminated.

$$\text{Maximize } z = x_1 + 2x_2$$

subject to

$$x_1 + \tfrac{1}{2}x_2 \leq \tfrac{13}{4}$$

$$x_1, x_2 \geq 0 \text{ and integer}$$

6. Solve the following problems by the fractional cut, and compare the true optimum integer solution with the solution obtained by rounding the continuous optimum.

(a) Maximize $z = 4x_1 + 6x_2 + 2x_3$

subject to

$$4x_1 - 4x_2 \qquad \leq 5$$

$$-x_1 + 6x_2 \qquad \leq 5$$

$$-x_1 + x_2 + x_3 \leq 5$$

$$x_1, x_2, x_3 \geq 0 \text{ and integer}$$

(b) Maximize $z = 3x_1 + x_2 + 3x_3$

subject to

$$-x_1 + 2x_2 + x_3 \leq 4$$

$$4x_2 - 3x_3 \leq 2$$

$$x_1 - 3x_2 + 2x_3 \leq 3$$

$$x_1, x_2, x_3 \geq 0 \text{ and integer}$$

BIBLIOGRAPHY

Barnett, A., "Misapplication Review: High Road to Glory," *Interfaces*, Vol. 17, No. 5, pp. 51–54, 1987.

Chen, D.-S., R. Batson, and Y. Dang, *Applied Integer Programming: Modeling and Solutions*, Wiley, New York, 2010.

Gavernini, S., C. Clark, and G. Pataki, "Schlumberger Optimizes Receiver Location for Automated Meter Reading," *Interfaces*, Vol. 34, No. 3, pp. 208–214, 2004.

Graves, R., L. Schrage, and J. Sankaran, "An Auction Method for Course Registration," *Interfaces*, Vol. 23, No. 5, pp. 81–97, 1993.

Guéret, C., C. Prins, and M. Sevaux, *Applications of Optimization with Xpress-MP*, Dash Optimization, London, 2002.

Jarvis, J., R. Rardin, V. Unger, R. Moore, and C. Schimpler, "Optimal design of Regional Wastewater Systems: A Fixed Charge Network Flow Model," *Operations Research*, Vol. 26, No. 4, pp. 538–550, 1978.

Lee, J., *A First Course in Combinatorial Optimization*, Cambridge University Press, 2004.

Liberatore, M., and T. Miller, "A Hierarchical Production Planning System," *Interfaces*, Vol. 15, No. 4, pp. 1–11, 1985.

Nemhauser, G., and L. Wolsey, *Integer and Combinatorial Optimization*, Wiley, New York, 1988.

Schrijver, A. *Theory of Linear and Integer Programming*, Wiley, New York, 1998.

Taha, H., *Integer Programming: Theory, Applications, and Computations*, Academic Press, Orlando, FL, 1975.

Weber, G., "Puzzle contests in MS/OR Education," *Interfaces*, Vol. 20, No. 2, pp. 72–76, 1990.

Wolsey, L., *Integer Programming*, Wiley, New York, 1998.

CHAPTER 10

Heuristic Programming

Real-Life Application: FedEx Generates Bid Lines Using Simulated Annealing

FedEx delivers millions of items throughout the world daily using a fleet of more than 500 aircraft and more than 3000 pilots. Bid lines (round-trips), starting and ending at one of nine crew domiciles (or hubs), must satisfy numerous Federal Aviation Administration and FedEx regulations and, to the extent possible, personal preferences based on pilots' seniority. The main objective is to minimize the required number of bid lines (i.e., required manning). The complexity of the constraints precludes the implementation of an integer programming model. Instead, a simulated annealing heuristic is used to solve the problem.

Source: Camplell, K., B. Durfee, and G. Hines, "FedEx Bid Lines Using Simulated Annealing," *Interfaces*, Vol. 27, No. 2, 1997, pp. 1–16.

10.1 INTRODUCTION

Heuristics are designed to find good approximate solutions to difficult combinatorial problems that otherwise cannot be solved by available optimization algorithms. A heuristic is a direct search technique that uses favorable rules of thumb to locate improved solutions. The advantage of heuristics is that they usually find (good) solutions quickly. The disadvantage is that the quality of the solution (relative to the optimum) is generally unknown.

Early generations of heuristics are based on the *greedy search* rule that mandate making improvement in the value of the objective function with each search move. The search ends at a local optimum where no further improvements are possible.

In the 1980s, a new generation of metaheuristics sought to improve the quality of the heuristic solutions by allowing the search to escape entrapment at local optima. The realized advantage comes at the expense of increased computations.

Section 10.2 deals with the greedy heuristic. Section 10.3 presents three prominent metaheuristics: Tabu, simulated annealing, and genetic. Section 10.4 applies metaheuristics to the general integer programming problem. The chapter concludes in Section 10.5 with a brief discussion of the related constrained-based search known as constraint programming.

10.2   GREEDY (LOCAL SEARCH) HEURISTICS

The main ideas of the greedy heuristic are explained via a single variable problem. Define the optimization problem with a solution space S as

$$\text{Minimize } z = F(x), x \in S$$

The iterative process of a greedy heuristic starts from a (random) feasible point and then attempts to move to a better solution point in the **neighborhood** of the current solution point. Specifically, at iteration k, given the solution point x_k, the heuristic examines all the feasible points in the neighborhood $N(x_k)$ in search of a better solution. The search ends when no further improvements are possible.

The definition of $N(x_k)$ is important in the design of the heuristic. For example, for integer x, $N(x_k) = \{x_k - 1, x_k + 1\}$ defines the *immediate* neighborhood of x_k. Alternatively, an *expanded* neighborhood can to include additional neighboring solution points. The first definition involves less local search computations but could impair the quality of the final solution. The second definition (expanded neighborhood) requires more local search computations, but could lead to improvement in the quality of the solution.

Sections 10.2.1 and 10.2.2 apply the greedy heuristic to discrete and continuous single variables. Extension of the heuristic to multiple variables is discussed at the end of Section 10.2.2.

10.2.1   Discrete Variable Heuristic

This section presents two examples that use the greedy heuristic for estimating the optimum of a single discrete-variable function. The first example uses the immediate neighborhood and the second one expands the domain to include more solution points.

Example 10.2-1

Consider the function $F(x)$ given in Figure 10.1 and define the optimization problem as

$$\text{Minimize } F(x), x \in S = \{1, 2, \ldots, 8\}$$

The function has a local minimum at $x = 3(B)$ and a global minimum at $x = 7(D)$.

Table 10.1 provides the iterations of the heuristic using immediate neighborhood, $N(x_k) = \{x_k - 1, x_k + 1\}$. The random number $R = .1002$ selects the starting point $x = 1$ from among all the feasible points $x = 1, 2, \ldots,$ and 8. At iteration 1, $N(1) = \{2\}$ because $x = 0$ is infeasible. The search ends at iteration 3 because $F(x) > F(x^* = 3)$ for all $x \in N(3)$. This means that the search stops at the *local minimum* $x^* = 3$ with $F(x^*) = 50$.

Table 10.1 shows that the greedy search stops at a local minimum ($x = 3$ in Figure 10.1). We can improve the quality of the solution in two ways:

1. Repeat the heuristic using random starting points.
2. Expand the size of the neighborhood to allow reaching more feasible solution points.

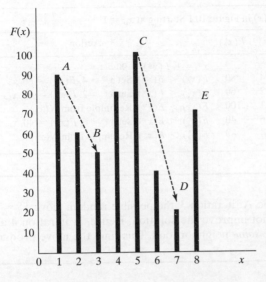

FIGURE 10.1

Function $F(x)$, $x \in S = \{1, 2, \ldots, 8\}$, with local minimum at $x = 3$ and global minimum at $x = 7$

TABLE 10.1   Greedy Heuristic Applied to $F(x)$ in Figure 10.1 Starting at $x_0 = 1$ with $N(x_k) = \{x_k - 1, x_k + 1\}$

Iteration k	x_k	$N(x_k)$	$F(x_k - 1)$	$F(x_k + 1)$	Action
(Start)0	1				Set $x^* = 1, F(x^*) = 90$, and $x_{k+1} = 1$
1	1	{2}		60	$F(x_k + 1) < F(x^*)$: Set $x^* = 2, F(x^*) = 60, x_{k+1} = 2$
2	2	{1, 3}	90	50	$F(x_k + 1) < F(x^*)$: Set $x^* = 3, F(x^*) = 50, x_{k+1} = 3$
(End)3	3	{2, 4}	60	80	$F(x_k - 1)$ and $F(x_k + 1) > F(x^*)$: Local minimum reached, stop

Search result: $x^* = 3, F(x^*) = 50$, occurs at iteration 2

The application of the first idea is straightforward and requires no further explanation.

Expanded neighborhood search can be based on evaluating *all* the neighborhood points, a strategy that increases the computational burden. Alternatively, we can determine the next search move by random selection from the neighborhood. Specifically, at iteration k, the next move, x_{k+1}, is selected from $N(x_k)$ with probability $1/m$, where m is the number of elements in the neighborhood set. Sampling from the same neighborhood is repeated, if necessary, until an improved solution is found, or until a specified number of iterations has been reached. The random selection rule describes what is known as a *random-walk heuristic*.

Example 10.2-2 (Random-Walk Heuristic)

This example applies once again to $F(x)$ in Figure 10.1. We arbitrarily define the expanded neighborhood set $N(x_k)$ as $\{1, 2, \ldots, x_k - 1, x_k + 1, \ldots, 8\}$. The search continues for five iterations starting at $x_0 = 1$. Denote x'_k [selected from $N(x_k)$] as a *possible* next move. It is accepted as the new search move only if it improves the solution. If it does not, a new random selection from $N(x_k)$ is attempted.

Table 10.2 details the application of the random-walk heuristic. In contrast with immediate-neighborhood heuristic in Example 10.2-1, the random-walk heuristic produces the solution $x = 7$ and $F(x) = 40$ at iteration 4, which accidently happens to be better than the one obtained in Example 10.2-1.

TABLE 10.2   Random Walk Heuristic Applied to $F(x)$ in Figure 10.1 Starting at $x_0 = 1$

Iteration k	x_k	$F(x_k)$	$N(x_k)$	R_k	x'_k	$F(x'_k)$	Action
(Start)0	1	90					$x^* = 1, F(x^*) = 90$
1	1	90	{2, 3, 4, 5, 6, 7, 8}	.4128	4	80	$F(x'_k) < F(x^*)$: Set $x^* = 4, F(x^*) = 80, x_{k+1} = 4$
2	4	80	{1, 2, 3, 5, 6, 7, 8}	.2039	2	60	$F(x'_k) < F(x^*)$: Set $x^* = 2, F(x^*) = 60, x_{k+1} = 2$
3	2	60	{1, 3, 4, 5, 6, 7, 8}	.0861	1	100	$F(x'_k) > F(x^*)$: Resample from $N(x_k)$
4	2	60	{1, 3, 4, 5, 6, 7, 8}	.5839	6	40	$F(x'_k) < F(x^*)$: Set $x^* = 6, F(x^*) = 40, x_{k+1} = 6$
(End)5	6	40	{1, 2, 3, 4, 5, 7, 8}	.5712	4	80	$F(x'_k) > F(x^*)$: Resample from $N(x_k)$

Best solution: $x = 6, F(x) = 40$, occurs at iteration 4

Note the behavior of the heuristic. At iteration 3, the possible random move $x'_k = 1$ from $N(x_3 = 2) = \{1, 3, 4, 5, 6, 7, 8\}$ does not improve the solution. Hence, at iteration 4 another random move is attempted from the *same* neighborhood. This time the move produces the superior solution $x^* = 6$.

10.2.2 Continuous Variable Heuristic

The optimization problem is defined as

$$\text{Minimize } F(x), L \leq x \leq U$$

The continuous random-walk heuristic differs from that of the discrete case (Example 10.2-2) in the definition of the (continuous) neighborhood and the selection of the next move from the neighborhood. The domain $L \leq x \leq U$ defines the continuous neighborhood of x_k at any iteration k (a subset of this domain is also acceptable).

The next move, x_{k+1}, is computed as a random (positive or negative) displacement above or below x_k. There are two ways to achieve this result:

1. The displacement is based on a uniform distribution in the range $\left(-\frac{U-L}{2}, \frac{U-L}{2}\right)$. Given R is a $(0, 1)$ random number, then

$$x_{k+1} = x_k + \left(-\left(\frac{U-L}{2}\right) + R(U-L)\right)$$
$$= x_k + (R - .5)(U - L)$$

2. The displacement is based on a normal distribution with mean x_k and standard deviation $\frac{U-L}{6}$ (the estimate of the standard deviation is based on the assumption that $U - L$ approximates the 6-sigma spread of the normal distribution). Thus,

$$x_{k+1} = x_k + \left(\frac{U-L}{6}\right) N(0, 1)$$

The standard $N(0, 1)$ deviate is determined from the normal tables in Appendix A, or by using *ExcelStatTables.xls*. Excel function NORMSINV(R) may also be used.

In the two formulas given above, it may be necessary to recompute x_{k+1} more than once, using the same x_k, until x_{k+1} falls within the feasible range (L, U). Moreover, if $F(x_{k+1})$ is not an improved solution relative to $F(x^*)$, the random selection is repeated for a specified number of iterations or until an improvement is realized, whichever occurs first

Example 10.2-3

Apply the random-walk heuristic to the problem

$$\text{Minimize } F(x) = x^5 - 10x^4 + 35x^3 - 50x^2 + 24x, 0 \le x \le 4$$

Use $x = .5$ as a starting point.

Tables 10.3 and 10.4 provide 5 iterations each using uniform and normal sampling. An increase in the number of iterations usually produces better-quality solutions (relative to the true optimum). Although normal sampling produces a better-quality solution in this example, the result may not be true in general.

The two sampling procedures can be combined into a hybrid heuristic: First, we implement the uniform sampling heuristic. Then the resulting solution is used to start the normal sampling heuristic. The idea is that the normal sampling heuristic may "fine tune" the solution obtained by the uniform sampling heuristic (see next Excel moment). This idea is implemented later using Excel.

TABLE 10.3 Minimization of $F(x) = x^5 - 10x^4 + 35x^3 - 50x^2 + 24x, 0 \le x \le 4$ Using Uniform Random-Walk Heuristic with $x_0 = .5$ and $x_k' = x_k + 4(R - .5)$

Iteration	x_k	$F(x_k)$	R_k	x_k'	$F(x_k')$	Action
(Start)0	.5	3.281				Set $x^* = .5, F(x^*) = 3.281, x_{k+1} = .5$
1	.5	3.281	.4128	.151	2.602	$F(x_k') < F(x^*)$: $x^* = .1512, F(x^*) = 2.602, x_{k+1} = .151$
2	.15	2.602	.2039	−1.033		Out of range: Resample using $x_{k+1} = x_k$
3	.15	2.602	.9124	1.801	−.757	$F(x_k') < F(x^*)$: $x^* = 1.801, F(x^*) = -.757, x_{k+1} = 1.801$
4	1.8	−.757	.5712	2.086	.339	$F(x_k') > F(x^*)$: Resample using $x_{k+1} = x_k$
(End)5	1.8	−.757	.8718	3.288	−1.987	$F(x_k') < F(x^*)$: $x^* = 3.288, F(x^*) = -1.987, x_{k+1} = 3.288$

Search result: $x = 1.801, F(x) = -.757$ occurs at iteration 3 [exact global minimum: $x^* = 3.64438, F(x^*) = -3.631$]

TABLE 10.4 Minimization of $F(x) = x^5 - 10x^4 + 35x^3 - 50x^2 + 24x, 0 \le x \le 4$ Using Normal Random-Walk Heuristic with $x_0 = .5$ and $x_k' = x_k + (4/6)N(0, 1)$.

Iteration k	x_k	$F(x_k)$	R_k	$N(0, 1)$	x_k'	$F(x_k')$	Action
(Start)0	.5	3.281					Set $x^* = .5, F(x^*) = 3.281, x_{k+1} = .5$
1	.5	3.281	.412	−.2203	.353	3.631	$F(x_k') > F(x^*)$: Resample using $x_{k+1} = x_k$
2	.5	3.281	.203	−.8278	−.0519		Out of range: Resample using $x_{k+1} = x_k$
3	.5	3.281	.912	1.3557	1.404	−1.401	$F(x_h') < F(x^*)$: $x^* = 1.404, F(x^*) = -1.401,$ $x_{k+1} = 1.404$
4	1.404	−1.401	.571	.1794	1.523	−1.390	$F(x_k') > F(x^*)$: Resample using $x_{k+1} = x_k$
(End)5	1.404	−1.401	.871	1.1349	2.160	.6219	$F(x_k') > F(x^*)$: Resample using $x_{k+1} = x_k$

Search result: $x = 1.404, F(x) = -1.401$, occurs at iteration 3 [exact global minimum: $x^* = 3.64438, F(x^*) = -3.631$]

Extension of the greedy search multiple variables.   Given $\mathbf{X} = (x_1, x_2, \ldots, x_n)$ and a solution space S, the optimization problem is defined as

$$\text{Minimize } z = F(\mathbf{X}), \mathbf{X} \, \varepsilon \, S$$

The greedy search algorithm is extended to the multivariable case by targeting the variables *one at a time* in each iteration, where a target variable is selected randomly from the set $(x_1, x_2, \ldots, x_n)$. The single-variable discrete and continuous heuristics given in Sections 10.2.1 and 10.2.2 are then applied to the selected variable.

Excel Moment

Figure 10.2 is a snapshot of the Excel spreadsheet application of the continuous random-walk heuristic (file *excelContSingleVarHeuristic.xls*). Using Excel syntax, the function $F(x)$ is entered in cell D2 with cell D5 assuming the role of the variable x. The sense of optimization (max or min) is specified in cell C2. The search range is entered in cells D3 and D4. The drop-down menu in cell D5 allows the use of uniform or random sampling.

A hybrid heuristic using *uniform* and *normal* sampling in tandem can be carried out in the following manner:

1. Assign a starting point in cell H3 and the number of iterations in cell H4.
2. Select uniform sampling in cell D5, and execute the heuristic by pressing the command button in step 6.
3. Use the solution from uniform sampling (cell D6) as a new starting point in cell H3.
4. Select normal sampling in cell D5 and re-execute the heuristic.

FIGURE 10.2

Excel random-walk heuristic for finding the optimum (maximum or minimum) of a single-variable continuous function (file *excelContSingleVarHeuristic.xls*)

D2		f_x	=D5^5-10*D5^4+35*D5^3-50*D5^2+24*D5					
	A	B	C	D	E	F	G	H	I
1	Random-Walk Heuristic for Continuos Single Variable functions								
2	Step 1:	Enter F(D5) ● Max ○ Min.		2.325007					
3	Step 2a:	Enter lower bound		0	Step 4:	Enter starting point, x0		0.5	
4	Step 2b:	Enter upper bound		4	Step 5:	Enter nbr of iterations, N		5	
5	Step 3:	Select sampling method		Uniform ▾	Step 6:	Execute Heuristic			
6	Solution summary:		Best solution:	x* = 1.455886	F(x*) = -1.418696				
7	Iteration, k	xk	F(xk)	R	Uniform	x'	F(x')	x°	F(x°)
8	start	0.5	3.28125					0.5	3.28125
9	1	0.5	3.28125	0.705547512	0.82219	1.322190046	-1.2972882	1.32219	-1.297288
10	2	1.32219005	-1.297288179	0.53342402	0.1336961	1.455886126	-1.4186964	1.4558861	-1.418696
11	3	1.45588613	-1.418696404	0.579518616	0.3180745	1.77396059	-0.8470017		
12	4	1.45588613	-1.418696404	0.289562464	-0.84175	0.614135981	2.65298409		
13	5	1.45588613	-1.418696404	0.301948011	-0.792208	0.663678169	2.32500697		

PROBLEM SET 10.2A

1. Re-solve the problem of Example 10.2-1 to estimate the maximum value of $F(x)$. Repeat the calculations using $x = 7$ as a starting solution.

2. Re-solve the problem of Example 10.2-2 to estimate the maximum value of $F(x)$.

3. Re-solve the problem of Example 10.2-3 to estimate the maximum value of $F(x)$ using uniform sampling. Next, use the solution from uniform sampling as a starting solution for the application of normal sampling.

4. *Excel experiment.* Consider the following function:

$$f(x) = .01172x^6 - .3185x^5 + 3.2044x^4 - 14.6906x^3 + 29.75625x^2 - 19.10625x$$

The function has multiple maxima and minima in the range $0 \leq x \leq 10$. Use *excelContVarHeuristic.xls* to estimate the maximum and minimum of the function using uniform sampling starting at $x_0 = 5$ and then refining the solution using normal sampling in which the starting point is the solution obtained from uniform sampling.

5. Consider the problem of forming a maximum-area rectangle out of a piece of wire of length 100 inches.

   (a) Manually generate 1 iteration using uniform sample in the range $(0, 20)$, starting with a 4-inch rectangle base and using $R = .7905$. Next, use the result as a starting solution for an additional normal-sampling iteration with $R = .9620$.

   (b) *Excel experiment.* Use *excelContVarHeuristic.xls* with uniform sampling to generate 5 iterations of the continuous variable heuristic to estimate the dimensions of the rectangle. Start with a base of rectangle equal to 5 inches.

   (c) *Excel experiment.* Use *excelContVarHeuristic.xls* with normal sampling to refine the solution obtained in (a). Carry out 5 iterations.

*6. Taxation can be used as an instrument to curb the demand for cigarettes. Suppose that, for a tax rate t, the average daily consumption per smoker follows the linear function $53 - 100(t/100), 10 \leq t \leq 60$. If the tax rate is set high, demand will drop, and the tax revenue will drop as well. The goal is to determine the tax rate that maximizes the tax revenue. For the purpose of taxation, the base price per cigarette is 15 cents. Formulate the problem as a mathematical model, and use a heuristic to determine the tax rate.

7. Apply the uniform sampling heuristic to estimate the minimum solution of the following two-variable function $f(x) = 3x^2 + 2y^2 - 4xy - 2x - 3y, 0 \leq x \leq 5, 0 \leq y \leq 5$.

8. The height of a cylindrical water tank must be at least twice as much as its base diameter. Neither the diameter nor the height can exceed 10 feet. The volume of the tank must be at least 300 ft^3. The cost of the elevated structure on which the tank is installed is proportional to the area of the base. The sheet metal cost is $\$8/\text{ft}^2$, and the cost of the supporting structure is $\$15/\text{ft}^2$. Formulate the problem as a mathematical model, and develop a random-walk heuristic to estimate the diameter and height of the tank.

10.3   METAHEURISTIC

The greedy heuristics presented in Section 10.2 share a common strategy: At iteration k, the search moves to a new point $\mathbf{X}_{k+1} \in N(\mathbf{X}_k)$ only if the new point improves the value of the objective function $F(\mathbf{X})$. If no better $\mathbf{X}_{k+1}$ can be found in $N(\mathbf{X}_k)$ or if a user-specified number of iterations is reached, the solution is entrapped at a *local optimum* and the search ends.

Metaheuristics are primarily designed to escape entrapment at local optima by permitting inferior moves, if necessary. The hope is that the added search flexibility will lead to a better solution.

Unlike the greedy heuristic, which always terminates when a local optimum is reached, termination of a metaheuristic search can be based on one of the following benchmarks:

1. The number of search iterations exceeds a specified number.
2. The number of iterations since the last best solution exceeds a specified number.
3. The neighborhood associated with the current search point is either empty or cannot lead to a new viable search move.
4. The quality of the current best solution is acceptable.

This section presents three prominent search metaheuristics: Tabu, simulated annealing, and genetic. These algorithms differ primarily in the manner in which the search escapes a local optimum. Each metaheuristic is illustrated by two examples: The first, dealing with a single-variable function $F(x)$, is designed to explain the basics of the metaheuristics. The second, dealing with the more complex job-shop scheduling problem, reveals additional intricacies in the implementation of the metaheuristics. In Chapter 11, the three metaheuristics are applied to the traveling salesperson problem.

10.3.1 Tabu Search Algorithm

When search is trapped at a local optimum, tabu search (TS) selects the next (possibly inferior) search move in a manner that *temporarily* prohibits reexamining previous solutions. The main instrument for achieving this result is a **tabu list** that "remembers" previous search moves and disallows them during a specified **tenure period**. When a tabu move completes its tenure, it is removed from the tabu list and becomes available for future moves.

Example 10.3-1 (Minimization of a single-variable function)

This example details the application of TS to the minimization of the function $F(x)$ in Figure 10.1. For iteration k, let

x_k = Current trial solution

$N(x_k)$ = Neighborhood of x_k

L_k = Tabu list of inadmissible values of x at iteration k

τ = Tabu tenure period expressed in number of successive iterations

x^* = Best solution encountered during the search

In terms of the function $F(x)$ in Figure 10.1, the feasible values of x are $1, 2, \ldots$, and 8. At iteration k, the neighborhood set of x_k can be defined as $N(x_k) = \{x_k - q, \ldots, x_k - 1, x_k + 1, \ldots, x_k + q\} - L_k$, where q is an integer constant. The definition implicitly

TABLE 10.5   TS Minimization of $F(x)$ in Figure 10.1 with Tabu Tenure Period $\tau = 3$ and $N(x_k) = \{x_k - 4, \ldots, x_k - 1, x_k + 1, \ldots, x_k + 4\} - L_k$

Iteration k	R_k	x_k	$F(x_k)$	L_k	$N(x_k)$
(Start)0	.0935	1	90		$\{2, 3, 4, 5\}$
1	.4128	3	50	$\{1\}$	$\{2, 4, 5, 6, 7\}$
2	.2039	4	80	$\{1, 3\}$	$\{2, 5, 6, 7, 8\}$
3	.0861	2	60	$\{1, 3, 4\}$	$\{5, 6\}$
4	.5839	5	100	$\{3, 4, 2\}$	$\{1, 6, 7, 8\}$
(End)5	.5712	7	20	$\{4, 2, 5\}$	$\{3, 6, 8\}$

Best heuristic solution: $x = 7, F(x) = 20$, at iteration 5 (also happens to be the optimum).

excludes infeasible solution points.[1] For example, for the case where $x_k = 3, q = 4$, and $L_k = \{6\}$, $N(x_k) = \{-\cancel{1}, \cancel{2}, 1, 2, 4, 5, 6, 7\} - \{6\} = \{1, 2, 4, 5, 7\}$. The crossed-out elements are infeasible.

As explained in Section 10.2, the next search move x_{k+1} can be selected as the best among all the solutions in $N(x_k)$, or as a random element of $N(x_k)$ (random-walk selection). This example uses random selection.

Table 10.5 provides 5 iterations of the TS algorithm. The search starts at $x_0 = 1$ (selected randomly from $\{1, 2, \ldots, 8\}$, using $R = .0935$). Define the neighborhood using $q = 4$, and assume a fixed tenure period $\tau = 3$ iterations (the tenure period can be random as Problem 3 of Set 10.3a demonstrates).

To illustrate the computations, $N(x_0 = 1) = \{2, 3, 4, 5\}$. At iteration 1, $L_1 = \{1\}$ and $R_1 = .4128$ selects $x_1 = 3$ from $N(x_0)$, which yields $N(x_1) = \{1, 2, 4, 5, 6, 7\} - \{1\} = \{2, 4, 5, 6, 7\}$ and updates the tabu list at iteration 2 to $L_2 = \{1, 3\}$.

An element is dropped from the tabu list on first-in first-out basis after a tenure period of $\tau = 3$ successive iterations. For example, element $\{1\}$ stays on the tabu list during iterations 1, 2, and 3 until it is dropped at iteration 4.

Example 10.3-2   (Job Sequencing)

Consider the case of sequencing n jobs on a single machine. The processing time for job j is t_j and its due date is d_j (measured from zero). Completing job j ahead of its due date incurs a holding (storage) cost h_j per unit time. A tardy job j results in a penalty cost p_j per unit time. Table 10.6 provides the data for a 4-job problem.
Define

j_{ik} = Job j occupies sequence position i during iteration k

s_k = Job sequence used in iteration k

$N(s_k)$ = Neighborhood sequences of s_k

L_k = Tabu list at iteration k

τ = Tenure period expressed in number of successive iterations

z_k = Total cost (holding + penalty) of sequence s_k

s^* = Best sequence available during the search

z^* = Total cost associated with s^*

---

[1] Actually, a tabu element can define a next search move if it satisfies the so-called *Aspiration Level Criterion*, as will be explained following Example 10.3-2.

TABLE 10.6   Data of the Job Sequencing Problem for Example 10.3-2

Job, j	Processing time in days, T_j	Due date, d_j	Holding cost per day, h_j	Penalty cost per day, p_j
1	10	15	$3	$10
2	8	20	2	22
3	6	10	5	10
4	7	30	4	8

Possible options for determining the neighborhood, $N(s_k)$, from s_k include the following:

1. Exchange the positions of successive pairs of jobs.
2. Exchange the positions of pairs comprised of every other job.
3. Exchange the position of a job with another selected randomly from the remaining jobs.

The first definition is used in this example. To demonstrate its use, consider $s_0 = $ (1-2-3-4). The neighborhood set is $N(s_0) = \{$(**2-1**-3-4), (1-**3-2**-4), (1-2-**4-3**)$\}$, which corresponds to swapping the positions (in s_0) of jobs 1 and 2, jobs 2 and 3, and jobs 3 and 4, respectively. The selection of the next move s_1 from $N(s_0)$ can be made either randomly or based on the least-cost criterion. This example employs random selection.

Table 10.7 summarizes 5 iterations assuming a tenure period $\tau = 2$ iterations. The sequence (3-1-2-4) in iteration 2 provides the best solution with $z^* = 126$. To demonstrate cost

TABLE 10.7   TS Applied to the Job Sequencing Problem with Tenure Period $\tau = 2$ Iterations

Iteration, k	Sequence, s_k	Total cost (holding) + (penalty)	z^*	Tabu list, $L(s_k)$	R	Neighborhood, $N(s_k)^*$
(Start)0	(1-2-3-4)	$(5\times3+2\times2) + (14\times10+1\times8) = 167$	167		.5124	(**2-1**-3-4)
						(1-**3-2**-4)✓
						(1-2-**4-3**)
1	(1-**3-2**-4)	$(5\times3) + (6\times10+4\times22+1\times8) = 171$		{3-2}	.3241	(**3-1**-2-4)✓
						(1-2-3-4)
						(1-3-**4-2**)
2	(**3-1**-2-4)	$(4\times5) + (1\times10+4\times22+1\times8) = 126$	126	{3-2, 3-1}	.2952	(1-3-2-4)
						(**3-2-1**-4)✓
						(3-1-**4-2**)
3	(3-**2-1**-4)	$(4\times5+6\times2) + (9\times10+1\times8) = 130$		{3-1, 2-1}	.4241	(**2-3**-1-4)✓
						(3-1-2-4)
						(3-2-**4-1**)
4	(**2-3**-1-4)	$(12\times2) + (4\times10+9\times10+1\times8) = 162$		{2-1, 2-3}	.8912	(3-2-1-4)
						(2-1-3-4)
						(2-3-**4-1**)✓
(End)5	(2-3-**4-1**)	$(12\times2+9\times4) + (4\times10+16\times10) = 260$		{4-1, 1-3}	.0992	(**3-2**-4-1)✓
						(2-**4-3**-1)
						(2-3-**1-4**)

Best search sequence: (3-1-2-4) with cost = 126 at iteration 2

*Check mark ✓ designates the non-tabu element selected randomly from $N(s_k)$ using R.

computations in the table, the value of z for the sequence $s_2 = $ (3-1-2-4) of iteration 2 is determined in the following order:[2]

Job:	3	1	2	4
Processing time:	6	10	8	7
Due date:	10	15	20	30
Completion date:	6	16	24	31
Holding time:	4	0	0	0
Delay time:	0	1	4	1
Holding cost:	20	0	0	0
Late penalty cost:	0	10	88	8

Thus, $z = $ Holding cost + Penalty cost = $20 + (10 + 88 + 8) = \$126$.

The heuristic operates in the following manner: At iteration 1, $R = .5124$ selects the sequence $s_1 = $ (1-3-2-4) randomly from $N(s_0)$. The associated tabu list becomes $L_1 = \{3\text{-}2\}$, which means that the positions of jobs 2 and 3 cannot be swapped during the tenure period (i.e., during two successive iterations). This is the reason the sequence (1-2-3-4) in $N(s_1)$ is excluded. The same reasoning applies to the crossed-out sequences in subsequent iterations. Note that the calculations in Table 10.7 apply R to admissible (uncrossed-out) neighborhood elements only.

"Fine-Tuning" TS. The following refinements can prove effective in improving the quality of the final solution:

1. **Aspiration Criterion.** The design of TS search disallows moves that are on the tabu list. An exception occurs when a disallowed move leads to an improved solution. For example, in Table 10.7 (Example 10.3-2), the crossed-out tabu sequences in iterations 1, 2, 3, and 4 should be examined for the possibility of producing better search moves. If they do, they should be accepted as search moves.

2. **Intensification and Diversification.** Two additional strategies, called intensification and diversification, are usually applied when a string of successive iterations fails to produce improvement. Intensification calls for a more thorough examination of nearby solution points, and diversification attempts to move the search to unexplored solution regions. One way to implement these strategies is by controlling the size of the tabu list. A shorter tabu list increases the size of the allowable neighborhood set and hence intensifies the search to points that lie close to the best solution. A longer tabu list does the opposite in that it permits escape from a local optimum point by allowing the exploration of "remote" regions.

Summary of Tabu Search Algorithm

Step 0. Select a starting solution $s_0 \in S$. Initialize the tabu list $L_0 = \varnothing$, and choose a schedule for specifying the size of the tabu list. Set $k = 0$.

---

[2]For convenience, cost calculations are automated using the spreadsheet *excelJobSequencing.xls* for situations involving four and five jobs. You can modify the spreadsheet to account for other situations.

Step 1. Determine the feasible neighborhood $N(s_k)$ that excludes (inferior) members of the tabu list L_k.

Step 2. Select the next move s_{k+1} from $N(s_k)$ (or from L_k if it provides a better solution), and update the tabu list L_{k+1}.

Step 3. If a termination condition is reached, stop. Otherwise, set $k = k + 1$ and go to step 1.

PROBLEM SET 10.3A

1. Solve Example 10.2-1 to estimate the maximum solution point. Use $x_0 = 3$ and $t = 3$.

2. Consider the following function:

$$f(x) = .01172x^6 - .3185x^5 + 3.2044x^4 - 14.6906x^3 + 29.75625x^2 - 19.10625x$$

The function has multiple maxima and minima in the range $x = 1, 2, \ldots, 10$. Apply 10 TS iterations to estimate the maximum and minimum. Use $x_0 = 5$ and tabu tenure period $\tau = 2$ iterations.

3. Apply TS with $\tau = 3$ iterations to solve the 5-job sequencing problem using the data in Table 10.8.

   (*Hint:* You may find it convenient to use file *excelJobSequencing.xls* to compute the cost functions.)

4. Consider 10 Boolean variables, Bi, $i = 1, 2, \ldots, 10$. Each variable assumes the value T (true) or F (false). Next, consider the following six expressions (the notation B̲i defines *not* Bi):

   (B1 and B3 and B8) or (B4 and B10) and B6

   B2 and B̲7

   (B2 or B5) and (B1 or B4 or B6)

   (B1 and B3 or B4) or (B̲5)

   (B̲4 and B6) or B9

   B2 or B5 or B6 or (B1 and B3)

   Use TS to assign a solution to each Boolean variable that maximizes the number of true logical expressions. Carry out five TS iterations starting with solution

TABLE 10.8   Data for Problem 3, Set 10.3a

Job, j	Processing time in days, T_j	Due date, d_j	Holding cost per day, h_j	Penalty cost per day, p_j
1	10	12	$1	$15
2	12	30	3	25
3	5	9	5	17
4	7	25	4	15
5	9	40	2	20

TABLE 10.9 Data for Problem 6, Set 10.2a

			c_{ij}		
i \ j	1	2	3	4	5
1	10	15	20	9	40
2	12	17	15	20	10
3	18	14	10	35	16
4	9	12	33	28	19

$S_0 = (T, F, T, F, T, F, T, F, T, F)$ and a tabu tenure period of two iterations. (*Hint:* For convenience, file *exelSAT.xls* automates the evaluation of the Boolean expressions.)

5. Repeat Problem 4 for the following Boolean expressions:

$$\text{(B1 and B5) or (B3 and B9) and (B2 or B10)}$$

$$\text{B3 or B6 and (B7 or B9 and B10)}$$

$$\text{B4 and B7 and } \overline{B8}$$

$$\text{B2 or B3 and B4 and B5 or B8 and (B1 or B6)}$$

$$\text{(B3 and B4 and B10) or (B5 and B7) or (B9 and B10)}$$

$$\text{B1 or (B4 and B7) or B8}$$

$$\text{(B3 and B5 or B6) or (B1 or B8 and B9 or B10)}$$

6. *Warehouse allocation.* Consider the case of 4 warehouses and 5 stores. The fixed cost of opening a warehouse is 20 ($ thousand). The transportation cost, c_{ij}, of shipments between the warehouses and the stores is summarized in Table 10.9.

   (a) Formulate the problem as an ILP, and find the optimum solution (using AMPL or Solver).

   (b) Solve the problem using TS with a tabu tenure period of two iterations.

7. *Constrained minimal spanning tree, Glover (1990).* Section 6.2 presents an optimum algorithm for finding the minimal spanning tree that links all the nodes of a network (by definition, a tree contains no cycles). In a practical setting, it may be necessary to impose interdependence restrictions on the arcs (branches) of the minimal spanning tree (e.g., only one of a subset of arcs can be in the spanning tree). TS can be used to account for the additional restrictions.

   Consider the 6-arc network (a, b, c, d, e, f, g, h) in Figure 10.3 with the following additional restrictions:

   1. Only one of the two arcs, a and c, can be in the tree.
   2. If arc b is in the tree then arc d must also be in the tree.

   The application of TS to determine the constrained minimal spanning tree is achieved as follows: The unconstrained minimal spanning tree (b, c, f, g, h) of length $(2 + 3 + 1 + 6 + 4) = 16$ is used as a starting solution. The remaining arcs, a, d, and e, are designated as *free*. A neighborhood spanning tree (solution) can be generated by

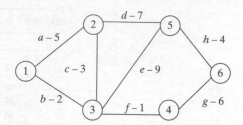

FIGURE 10.3

Network for Problem 7, Set 10.2a

adding a free arc to the current spanning tree and deleting an existing one to prevent cycles. For example, arc b or c must be deleted if free arc a is admitted in spanning tree (b, c, f, g, h) to prevent the formation of cycle a, b, c. The swapping produces two alternatives: add a and delete b, or add a and delete c. Similar alternatives can be generated when the remaining free variables, d and e, are considered. The collection of all these alternatives defines the neighborhood.

The *fitness* of an alternative includes the length of the spanning tree plus a penalty for the violation of the additional constraints given earlier. For example, given the tree (b, c, f, g, h), the alternative "add a and delete b" produces the tree (a, c, f, g, h) whose fitness is $[(5 + 3 + 1 + 6 + 4) + $ (penalty for violating the first constraint)]. Similarly, the alternative "add arc a and delete arc c" produces the tree (a, b, f, g, h) whose fitness is $[(5 + 2 + 1 + 6 + 4) + $ (penalty of violating the second constraint)]. The penalty must be sufficiently large (e.g., a multiple of the sum of the lengths of all the arcs in the network). In the present situation, the total length of the network is 37, and a penalty of 200 is appropriate. The alternative with the smallest fitness provides the next trial solution. The corresponding free variable is then augmented to the tabu list to prevent it from leaving the tree during its tenure period.

Apply five iterations to the network in Figure 10.3.

8. *Cartographic label placement, Yamamoto and Associates (2002).* Unambiguous placement of the names of cities, streets, lakes, and rivers on printed maps has long been a time-consuming manual process. With the advent of online map generation (as in Google and MapQuest), the manual process is not a viable option. A tabu heuristic can be used to automate label placement on map. This problem will deal with the case of labeling cities. The general goal is to avoid label overlapping, while accounting for label placement preferences relative to the location of the named city on the map.

Figure 10.4 provides an example of placing the names of four cities, A, B, C, and D on a map. Each city has four placement options represented by four rectangles. Priority for label placement among the four rectangles can be in any order. In Figure 10.4, we assume a counterclockwise best-to-worst order of preference for the rectangles of each city. For example, for city A, the order of labeling preference is A1-A2-A3-A4. A typical solution selects a specific rectangle for each city. For example, (A1, B2, C3, D2) is a solution for the four cities in Figure 10.4.

The "cost" of selecting a specific rectangle in a solution is the sum of two components: a numeric preference score in the range $(0, 1)$ in which zero is best, and the number of overlaps with other rectangles. Figure 10.4 gives the preference scores for the city $A(A1 = 0, A2 = .02, A3 = .03,$ and $A4 = .04)$. The same scores apply to corresponding rectangles in cities B, C, and D as well. To determine the overlaps, consider the solution (A1, B2, C3, D2). Only C3 and D2 overlap.

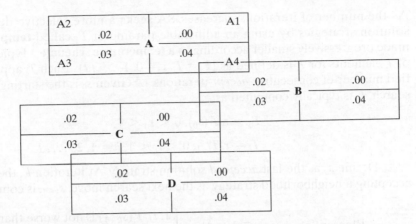

FIGURE 10.4

Label options for Problem 7, Set 10.2a

The following matrix summarizes the scores associated with solution (A1, B2, C3, D2).

	A1	B2	C3	D2
A1	.00	.00	.00	.00
B2	.00	.02	.00	.00
C3	.00	.00	.03	1.00
D2	.00	.00	1.00	.02

All diagonal entries equal the preference scores of the associated rectangle. An off-diagonal element equals 1 if the corresponding elements overlap. Else, it is zero. The cost associated with the solution (A1, B2, C3, D2) is the sum of all the entries in the matrix [=(.02 + .03 + .02) + (1 + 1) = 2.7]. The objective of the model is to find the solution that minimizes the total cost.

(a) Construct the (16 × 16) fitness table that will account for all possible label placements.

(b) Find a solution to the problem using three TS iterations with a two-iterations tabu tenure. [*Hint:* The optimum solution for this trivial problem is obvious: (A1, B1, B2, B3, and B4) with zero total fitness. To demonstrate meaningful TS iterations, however, you are required to start with the solution A1, B2, C3, D2. A neighborhood solution consists of replacing one of the rectangles of a city with another; e.g., replacing C3 with C1. In this case, city C is placed on the tabu list for the duration of the tenure period.]

10.3.2 Simulated Annealing Algorithm

Simulated annealing (SA) escapes entrapment at a local optimum by using a probability condition that accepts or rejects an inferior move (a no-worse move is always accepted). The idea of determining the acceptance probability of the next search move is explained in the following manner: Suppose the optimization problem is given as

$$\text{Maximize or minimize } z = F(s), \; s \, \varepsilon \, S$$

As the number of iterations increases, SA seeks a more selective determination of solution strategies by using an adjustable parameter T, called **temperature**, that is made progressively smaller according to a **temperature schedule**.[3] Typically, a schedule of I elements for T is defined as $\{T = T_i, i = 0, 1, \ldots, I\}$. Each T_i applies for a specified number of consecutive *accept*-iterations, t.[4] Given s_0 is the starting strategy of the search, T_i is typically computed as

$$T_0 = r_0 F(s_0), 0 < r_0 < 1,$$

$$T_i = r_i T_{i-1}, 0 < r_i < 1, i = 1, 2, \ldots, I$$

Define s_a as the last *accepted* solution strategy. At iteration k, the probability of accepting a neighborhood strategy as the next search move, s_{k+1}, is computed as

$$P\{\text{accept } s_{k+1} | s_{K+1} \in N(s_k)\} = \begin{cases} 1, & \text{if } F(s_{k+1}) \text{ is not worse than } F(s_a) \\ e^{\frac{-|F(s) - F(s_{k+1})|}{T}}, & \text{if otherwise} \end{cases}$$

The formula says that the next search move, s_{k+1}, is accepted if $F(s_{k+1})$ is not worse than $F(s_a)$. Otherwise, $F(s_{k+1})$ is an inferior solution, and s_{k+1} is accepted only if $R_k \leq e^{\frac{-|F(s_a) - F(s_{k+1})|}{T}}$, where R_k is a $(0, 1)$ random number. If s_{k+1} is rejected, a different solution strategy, chosen from $N(s_a)$, is attempted. Notice that the temperature schedule decreases the probability of acceptance as the number of iterations increases by making T_i progressively smaller.

Example 10.3-3   (Minimization of a Single Variable Function)

Table 10.10 applies five SA iterations to find the minimum of the single-variable function in Figure 10.1. The solution arbitrarily defines the neighborhood at any iteration k as $N(x_k) = \{1, 2, \ldots, 8\} - \{x_a\}$, where x_a is the solution associated with the most recent accept-iteration.

To illustrate the computations, the search arbitrarily selects $x_0 = 1$ with $t = 3$ accept-iterations and $r_0 = .5$. Thus, $N(x_0) = \{2, 3, 4, 5, 6, 7, 8\}$, $F(1) = 90$, and $T_0 = .5 F(1) = 45$. For $k = 1$, the random number $R_{11} = .4128$ selects the (possible) next-solution point $x_1 = 4$ from $N(x_0)$ with $F(4) = 80$. Because $F(x_1)$ is better than $F(x_0)$, we accept the move. At iteration 2, we set $a = 1$ with $F(x_a) = 80$. The next move $x_2 = 2$ is selected from $N(x_1) = \{1, 2, 3, 5, 6, 7, 8\}$ using $R_{12} = .2039$. The move is again accepted because it improves the solution from $F(x_1) = 80$ to $F(x_2) = 60$. This sets $a = 2$ with $F(x_a) = 60$. At iteration 3, $R_{13} = .0861$ selects $x_3 = 1$ from $N(x_2) = \{1, 3, 4, 5, 6, 7, 8\}$ with $F(x_3) = 90$. The new solution is inferior to $F(x_a) = 60$. Thus, $\Delta = |60 - 90| = 30$, and $e^{-\Delta/T} = .5134$. Given $R_{23} = .5462$, the solution $x_3 = 1$ is rejected, which requires re-sampling from the last accept-neighborhood $N(x_2)$. At iteration 4, $x_4 = 6$ is accepted because it yields an improved solution (relative to that of iteration 2). At this point, the condition $t = 3$ is satisfied, which changes the temperature to $T_1 = .5 T_0 = 22.5$ at the next iteration. At iteration 5, given $x_5 = 5$, $R_{25} (= .0197) < e^{-\Delta/T} (= .0695)$ accepts the move even though it is an inferior solution $[F(5) = 100]$.

---

[3] SA is inspired by the annealing process in metallurgy, which involves heating and controlled cooling of a material, hence the use of the term *temperature*. The use of metallurgical jargon in the description of SA is purely traditional, with no technical bearing on the development of the heuristic, save the general idea imbedded in the annealing process.

[4] Basing change in temperature on the number of *accept*-iterations is an arbitrary rule, and it can be replaced by others, such as making the change based on the total number of intervening (accept or reject) iterations.

TABLE 10.10   Minimization of $F(x)$ in Figure 10.1 Using SA Heuristic with Schedule $T_0 = .5F(x_0), T_i = .5T_{i-1}$, $i = 1, 2, 3, \ldots$ and $t = 3$ Accept-Iterations

Iteration k	R_{1k}	x_k	$F(x_k)$	a	T	$\Delta =$ |Change in F|	$e^{-\Delta/T}$	R_{2k}	Decision	$N(x_k)$
(Start)0		1	90	0	45.0					$\{2, 3, 4, 5, 6, 7, 8\}$
1	0.4128	4	80	1	45.0				Accept: $F(x_1) < F(x_0)$	$\{1, 2, 3, 5, 6, 7, 8\}$
2	0.2039	2	60	2	45.0				Accept: $F(x_2) < F(x_1)$	$\{1, 3, 4, 5, 6, 7, 8\}$
3	0.0861	1	90	2	45.0	$\|60 - 90\| = 30$	.5134	.5462	Reject: $R_{2k} > e^{-\Delta/T}$	Same as $N(x_2)$
4	0.5839	6	40	4	45.0				Accept: $F(x_4) < F(x_2)$	$\{1, 2, 3, 4, 5, 7, 8\}$
(End)5	0.5712	5	100	5	22.5	$\|40 - 100\| = 60$	.0695	.0197	Accept: $R_{2k} < e^{-\Delta/T}$	$\{1, 2, 3, 4, 6, 7, 8\}$

Search best solution: $x = 6$ with $F(6) = 40$ at iteration 4.

Example 10.3-4   (Job Sequencing)

This problem is solved in Example 10.3-2 using TS. The problem statement is repeated here for convenience. Jobs are sequenced on a single machine. Each job j has a processing time t_j and a due date d_j. If j is completed earlier than its due date, a holding cost h_j per unit time is incurred. A tardy job j results in a penalty cost p_j per unit time. Table 10.11 provides the data for a 4-job scheduling problem.
Define

s_k = Job sequence used in iteration k

$N(s_k)$ = Neighborhood sequences of s_k

T_i = Temperature schedule, $i = 12 \ldots, I$

c_k = Total cost (holding + penalty) of sequence s_k

Table 10.12 provides five SA iterations. Iteration 3 gives the best sequence. Note that when a sequence is rejected at iteration k, we reuse the neighborhood of the last *accept*-iteration to randomly select the sequence for iteration $k + 1$. This occurs at iteration 2, where the neighborhood remains the same as at iteration 1. Note also that the $t = 3$ is satisfied at iteration 4, causing temperature change from 83.5 to 41.75 at iteration 5.

Summary of Simulated Annealing Algorithm

Step 0.   Select a starting solution $s_0 \varepsilon S$. Set $k = 0, p = 0$, and $i = 0$.
Step 1.   Generate the neighborhood $N(s_k)$, and set temperature $T = T_i$.

TABLE 10.11   Data for the Job Sequencing Problem of Example 10.3-4

Job, j	Processing time in days, T_j	Due date, d_j	Holding cost per day, h_j	Penalty cost per day, p_j
1	10	15	$3	$10
2	8	20	2	22
3	6	10	5	10
4	7	30	4	8

TABLE 10.12   SA Applied to the Job Sequencing Problem with Schedule $T_0 = .5z_0$, $T_i = .5T_{i-1}$, $i = 1, 2, 3, \ldots$ and $t = 3$ Accept-Iterations

Iteration k	Sequence s_k	Total cost $c_k = $ (holding) + (penalty)	T_k	$z = \frac{\lvert\text{Change in cost}\rvert}{T_k}$	e^{-z}	R_{1k}	Decision	R_{2k}	Neighborhood, $N(s_k)$*
(Start)0	(1-2-3-4)	(5×3 + 2×2) + (14×10 +1×8) = 167	83.5					.5462	(2-1-3-4) (1-3-2-4) ✓ (1-2-4-3)
1	(1-3-2-4)	(5×3) + (6×10 + 4×22 +1×8) = 171	83.5	.0479	.9532	.5683	Accept: $R_{11} < e^{-z}$	.7431	(3-1-2-4) (1-2-3-4) (1-3-4-2) ✓
2	(1-3-4-2)	(5×3 + 7×4) + (6×10 +11×22) = 345	83.5	2.083	.1244	.3459	Reject: $R_{12} > e^{-z}$	.1932	(3-1-2-4) ✓ (1-2-3-4) (1-3-4-2)
3	(3-1-2-4)	(4 × 5) + (1 × 10 + 4 × 22 + 1 × 8) = 126	83.5				Accept: $c_3 < c_1$	.6125	(1-3-2-4) (3-2-1-4) ✓ (3-1-4-2)
4	(3-2-1-4)	(4×5 + 6×3) + (9 × 10 + 1 × 8) = 130	83.5	.0479	.9532	.6412	Accept: $R_{14} < e^{-z}$	.2234	(2-3-1-4) ✓ (3-1-2-4) (3-2-4-1)
(End)5	(2-3-1-4)	(12×2) + (4 × 10 + 9 × 10 +1 × 8) = 162	41.75	.766	.4647	.5347	Reject: $R_{15} > e^{-z}$	.8127	(2-3-1-4) (3-1-2-4) (3-2-4-1) ✓

Best search solution: (3-1-2-4) with cost 126 at iteration 3.

*Check mark ✓ indicates the sequence selected using random number R_{2k}

Step 2.   Determine the solution s_{k+1} randomly from $N(s_k)$. If s_{k+1} is not worse than the *last accepted* solution or if $R < P$ {accept s_{k+1}}, then accept s_{k+1}, set $p = p + 1$, and go to step 3. Else, reject s_{k+1}, and set $N(s_{k+1}) = N(s_k)$. Set $k = k + 1$, and go to step 1.

Step 3.   If a termination condition is reached, stop. Otherwise, set $k = k + 1$. If $p = t$, then set $i = i + 1$. Go to step 1.

PROBLEM SET 10.3B

1. Carry out five additional iterations in Example 10.3-3.
2. Solve Example 10.3-3 to estimate the maximum solution point. Use $x_0 = 2$ and $t = 3$.
3. Carry out four additional iterations of the job sequencing problem in Example 10.3-4.
4. *Timetable scheduling.* Consider a case of developing a timetable of teaching 5 classes (C) by 5 teachers (T). The teachers provide the following preferences for teaching classes (top of the list is most desired):

T1: C2 - C3 - C1 - C5

T2: C2 - C1 - C4 - C5

T3: C1 - C4 - C5 - C3

T4: C4 - C2 - C5 - C3

T5: C2 - C5 - C3 - C1

The situation is simplified to developing a one-day five-period timetable that minimizes dissatisfaction among teachers. A measure of dissatisfaction is represented by how far down the preference list a course is assigned to a teacher. For example, the measure of dissatisfaction is zero if C1 is assigned to T1 and 3 if C5 is assigned to T1. A timetable is evaluated by the sum of its individual measures.

Develop a 5-iteration SA heuristic for the problem.

5. *Map coloring problem.* The coloring problem deals with determining the least number of colors for painting the regions of a map such that no two adjacent regions will have the same color. Figure 10.5(a) provides an example of a 6-region map. The problem can be modeled as a network in which the nodes represent the regions as shown in Figure 10.5(b). An arc between two nodes signifies that the corresponding two regions are adjacent (share a common border). The map coloring problem can represent other practical situations, as Problem 6 demonstrates.

An SA heuristic can be applied to the coloring problem. The starting solution, x_0, can be determined in one of two ways:

1. Assign a unique color to each node of the network. Thus, $x_0 = (1, 2, \ldots, 6)$ for the network in Figure 10.5(b),

2. Use a greedy algorithm that starts by assigning color 1 to node 1. Next, given that nodes $1, 2, \ldots$ and $i - 1$ use the colors $1, 2, \ldots$, and $c, c \leq i - 1$, assign the *smallest* color number in the set $(1, 2, \ldots, c)$ to node i without creating *bad* arcs (those whose two end nodes use the same color). If none can be found, apply a new color $c + 1$. For the network in Figure 10.5(b), the successive steps for constructing x_0 are

$$x_0^1 = (1)$$
$$x_0^2 = (1, 2)$$
$$x_0^3 = (1, 2, 3)$$
$$x_0^4 = (1, 2, 3, 1)$$
$$x_0^5 = (1, 2, 3, 1, 4)$$
$$x_0 = x_0^6 = (1, 2, 3, 1, 4, 2)$$

The greedy algorithm uses 4 color classes: $C_1 = (1, 1), C_2 = (2, 2), C_3 = (3), C_4 = (4)$ that apply to nodes 1 and 4, nodes 2 and 6, node 3, and node 5, respectively.

FIGURE 10.5

(a) Six-region map (b) network representation for Problem 5, Set 10.3b

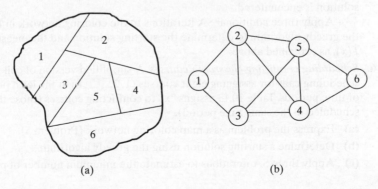

(a)   (b)

A neighborhood solution, x_{i+1}, is determined by changing the color of a random node in x_i to a random color in the same set. For example, given $x_0 = (1, 2, 3, 1, 4, 2)$ and its associated color set $c_0 = (1, 2, 3, 4)$, random selections of color 1 from c_0 and node (position) 5 from x_0 give

$$x_1 = (1, 2, 3, 1, 1, 2)$$

The new color classes of x_1 are $C_1 = (1, 1, 1)$, $C_2 = (2, 2)$, and $C_3 = (3)$ corresponding to nodes $(1, 4, 5)$, $(2, 6)$, and (3), respectively. To generate x_2 from x_1, randomly select a color from $c_1 = (1, 2, 3)$ to replace the color of a randomly selected node in x_1. If necessary, repeat the random exchange until x_2 becomes distinct from x_1.

Next, we develop a measure of performance for solution. A simple measure calls for the minimization of the number of *bad* arcs (those whose two end nodes bear the same color). A more sophisticated measure can be developed in the following manner: Solution x_1 is better than x_0 from the standpoint of reducing the number of color classes (i.e., uses less colors by increasing the size of at least one color class), but simultaneously increases the chance of creating *bad* arcs. Specifically, x_0 of the greedy algorithm has no bad arcs, and x_1 has one bad arc, 4–5. Thus, an empirical measure of performance that balances the two conflicting situations [increasing the sizes (cardinalities) of the color classes and, simultaneously, reducing the number of bad arcs] calls for *maximizing*

$$f(x) = \sum_{j=1}^{k} (|C_j|)^2 - 2\sum_{k=1}^{k} |C_j|.|A_j|$$

where

k = Number of color classes

A_j = Set of bad arcs associated with color class j

[The notation $|S|$ represents the number of elements (cardinality) of the set S.] In terms of x_0 and x_1 of the greedy algorithm, we have

$$f(x_0) = (2^2 + 2^2 + 1^2 + 1^2) - 2(2 \times 0 + 2 \times 0 + 1 \times 0 + 1 \times 0) = 10$$

$$f(x_1) = (3^2 + 2^2 + 1^2) - 2(3 \times 1 + 1 \times 0 + 2 \times 0) = 8$$

The two values show that x_1 is worse than x_0 [recall that we are maximizing $f(x)$]. Hence, per SA heuristic, we accept x_1 if $R < e^{-|f(x_0)-f(x_1)|/T}$.

Note that the generation of x_{i+1} from x_i may result in an infeasible color assignment (This point does not arise in Examples 10.3-3 and 10.3-4 because of the nature of the associated problems). In these cases, an infeasible move can be accepted using the probability condition of SA, but the best solution is updated only if a better *feasible* solution is encountered.

Apply three additional SA iterations to the coloring network in Figure 10.5(b) using the greedy algorithm to determine the starting solution and the measure of performance $f(x)$, as explained above.

6. *Scheduling conflicting classroom courses.* A simplified version of college course scheduling calls for assigning eight courses $(1, 2, \ldots, 8)$ in the least possible number of time periods. Table 10.13 assigns "x" to conflicting courses (those that cannot be scheduled in the same time period).

   (a) Express the problem as a map coloring network (Problem 5).

   (b) Determine a starting solution using the greedy algorithm.

   (c) Apply three SA iterations to estimate the minimum number of periods.

TABLE 10.13 Conflicts in Course Schedules for Problem 6, Set 10.3b

	1	2	3	4	5	6	7	8
1		x	x	x		x		
2	x				x		x	x
3	x			x		x		
4	x		x		x		x	
5		x		x		x		x
6	x		x		x		x	x
7		x		x		x		x
8		x			x	x	x	

7. Consider the well-known six-hump camelback function:

$$f(x, y) = 4x^2 - 2.1x^4 + x^6/3 + xy - 4y^2 + 4y^4, \quad -3 \leq x \leq 3, -2 \leq y \leq 2$$

The exact global minima are $(-.08984, .71266)$ and $(.08984, -.71266)$ with $f^* = -1.0316$. Apply five SA iterations to estimate the minima of $f(x, y)$. Start with $(x_0, y_0) = (2, 1)$, $T_0 = .5f(x_0, y_0)$, $T_i = .5T_{i-1}$, and $t = 3$ accept-iterations.

10.3.3 Genetic Algorithm

The genetic algorithm (GA) mimics the biological evolution process of "survival of the fittest." Each feasible solution of a problem is regarded as a **chromosome** encoded by a set of **genes**. The most common **gene codes** are **binary** $(0, 1)$ and **numeric** $(0, 1, 2, \ldots)$. For example, the chromosomes of a single variable whose feasible values are $0, 1, \ldots,$ and 8 can be represented by the binary codes (0000, 1000, 0100, 1100, 0010, 1010, 0110, 1110, and 0001). The chromosomes for a two-variable problem (x_1, x_2) with $x_1 = \{0, 1\}$ and $x_2 = \{0, 1, 2, 3\}$ can be represented by the numeric codes $(0, 0), (0, 1),$ $(0, 2), (0, 3), (1, 0), (1, 1), (1, 2),$ and $(1, 3)$. The multivariable numeric codes may also be represented as binary codes. For example, the binary code of $(x_1, x_2) = (0, 3)$ is (000, 110). There are other coding schemes, including **node code** for network models (see Beasley and Associates, 1993, Part 2).

A set of N feasible solutions is referred to as a **population** with N chromosomes. The **fitness** of a chromosome is measured in terms of an appropriate objective function. A more fit chromosome yields a better value of the objective function.

The overall idea of GA is to select two **parents** from a population. The genes of the two parents are then **crossed over** and (possibly) **mutated** (as will be explained in Example 10.3-5) to produce two **children**. The offspring replace the two weakest (least fit) chromosomes in the population, and the process of selecting new parents is repeated.

The actual implementation of GA requires additional problem-specific details. Also, the rules for selecting parents and creating children may vary. For example, the parents may be selected totally randomly from a population, or they may consist of the two fittest chromosomes. Some of these details will be provided later.

Example 10.3-5 (Minimization of a Single-Variable Function)

The GA is applied to the single variable discrete problem in Figure 10.1 with the feasible domain $X = \{1, 2, 3, 4, 5, 6, 7, 8\}$. We will arbitrarily specify a population of size $N = 4$ parents whose chromosomes are determined from X using uniform random sampling.

The random number R is applied to the uniform distribution in Table 10.14 to generate the four members ($N = 4$) of the initial population and their fitness, as shown in Table 10.15. The solution for $i = 4$ is a repeat of the solution for $i = 3$ ($x_3 = x_4$), hence the solution for $i = 4$ is discarded. The initial population is $X_0 = (8, 3, 5, 1)$, and the associated best solution is $x^* = 3$ with $F(x^*) = 50$.

Two parents can be selected from the initial population $X_0 = \{8, 3, 5, 1\}$ in a number of ways: (1) Select the two fittest members. (2) Select the fittest member and then a random one from the remaining members. (3) Select two parents randomly from X_0. In this presentation, we use the third option. Specifically, the two random numbers $R_1 = .2869$ and $R_2 = .0281$ yield $x = 3$ with $F(3) = 50$ and $x = 8$ with $F(8) = 70$.

The two children are created from the two selected parents by using **gene crossover**. There are several methods for implementing crossover.

1. **Uniform crossover.** In this rule, parents' common genes apply to both children. The remaining genes for one child are determined randomly, with the other child getting the complement gene.

2. **One-point crossover.** The genes of parents P1 and P2 are split randomly *at the same point* and then swapped; that is, P1 = (P11, $\underline{P12}$) and P2 = (P21, **P22**) yield the children chromosomes as C1 = {P11, **P22**} and C2 = {P21, $\underline{P12}$} .

3. **Multipoint crossover.** This rule extends the one-point crossover to multiple random points. For example, in a 2-point crossover, P1 = (P11, $\underline{P12}$, P13) and P2 = (P21, **P22**, P23) yield C1 = (P11, **P22**, P13) and C2 = (P21, $\underline{P12}$, P23).

This example uses the uniform crossover rule. The one-point crossover rule will be used in Example 10.3-6.

For the two parents (3, 8) generated in Table 10.15, we have

$$P1 = (1\,1\,\underline{0}\,0)$$

$$P2 = (0\,0\,\underline{0}\,1)$$

TABLE 10.14 Uniform Random Sampling from the Domain $X = \{x\} = \{1, 2, 3, 4, 5, 6, 7, 8\}$

x	1	2	3	4	5	6	7	8
Cumulative probability, $P(x)$	.125	.250	.375	.500	.625	.750	.875	1.

TABLE 10.15 Generation of the Starting Population with $N = 4$

i	R_i	x_i	Binary-coded x_i	$F(x_i)$
1	.9842	8	0001	70
2	.3025	3	1100	50
3	.5839	5	1010	100
4	.5712	5	Discard	
5	.0926	1	1000	90

In uniform crossover, the common (underlined) third gene in P1 and P2 carries over to both children. The remaining three genes are determined randomly as follows: For child 1, the gene is 1 if $0 \le R < .5$ and 0 if $.5 \le R \le 1$. The corresponding genes for child 2 are the complements of those assigned to child 1. For example, the three random numbers .2307, .7346, and .6220 show that genes 1, 2, and 4 for child 1 are 1, 0, and 0, respectively, which automatically assigns the complement genes 0, 1, and 1 to child 2. Thus

$$C1 = (1\,0\,\mathbf{0}\,0) \text{ (or } x = 1)$$

$$C2 = (01\,\mathbf{0}\,1) \text{ (or } x = 10)$$

Child 2 corresponds to an infeasible solution (recall that the feasible range is $x = 1, 2, \ldots, 8$). However, before discarding a child infeasible solution, we first apply random **mutation** (replacing one gene with another) and then check the mutated offspring for feasibility. If infeasibility persists, totally new offspring must be created (from the same parents). The process can be repeated as necessary until feasibility is achieved.

The probability of mutation is usually about .1, meaning a gene is mutated if $0 \le R < .1$. For child 1, the random number sequence .6901, .7698, .0871, .9534 shows that the third gene only is mutated from 0 to 1, yielding $C1 = (1\,0\,\mathbf{1}\,0)$ [or $x = 5$ with $F(5) = 100$]. For Child 2, the sequence .5954, .2632, .6731, .0983 mutates gene 4 and yields $C2 = (0\,1\,0\,\mathbf{0})$ [or $x = 2$ with $F(2) = 60$]. Both child chromosomes are feasible, but neither yields a better solution. Hence, the solution $x^* = 3$ of the initial population continues to be the best so far.

The least-fit parents in X_0 ($x = 5$ and $x = 1$) are now replaced with the two offspring solutions ($x = 5$ and $x = 2$). This, in effect, says that the next population is $X_1 = (8, 3, 5, 2)$. We now use X_1 to start a new iteration.

Dealing with continuous variables. The genetic coding in Example 10.3-5 assumes that the variable x is integer. The coding can be modified to include continuous variables in the following manner: Specify a finite (preferably tight) feasible range of the form $l \le x \le u$, where l and u are constants. Let v represent the numeric value of a binary string s of length n bits. The string s is then translated to a real (continuous) value by using

$$x = l + (u - l)\left(\frac{v}{2^n - 1}\right)$$

The logic of the formula is that the maximum value of an n-bit binary string is $2^0 + 2^1 + 2^2 + \cdots + 2^{n-1} = 2^n - 1$, and $\left(\frac{v}{2^n - 1}\right)$ is the proportion of the quantity $(u - l)$, which when added to the lower bound l will produce the corresponding value of x in the range (l, u). For example, given $-1 \le x \le 3$ and arbitrarily choosing $n = 5$, the binary string $(0\,0\,1\,0\,1)$ has $v = 2^2 + 2^4 = 20$, and the associated value of x is

$$x = -1 + [3 - (-1)]\left(\frac{20}{2^5 - 1}\right) = 1.580645$$

The design of the code indicates that larger values of n yield better accuracy.

The n-bit strings representing v are used in the same manner as given in Example 10.3-5. This means that children are created through crossover and mutation of the parents genes. Indeed, a multivariable situation is handled in a similar manner with each variable represented by an independent n-bit string.

Example 10.3-6   (Job Sequencing)

This problem was solved in Example 10.3-2 using TS and in Example 10.3-4 using SA. We repeat the problem statement here for convenience (a fifth job is added to render the example more viable). Jobs are sequenced on a single machine. Each job j has a processing time t_j and a due date d_j. If job j is completed earlier than its due date, a holding cost h_j per unit time is incurred. A tardy job j results in a penalty cost p_j per unit time. Table 10.16 provides the data for a 5-job scheduling problem.

Define

$\quad s_k$ = Job sequence used in iteration k

$\quad N(s_k)$ = Neighborhood sequences of s_k

$\quad z_k$ = Total cost (holding + penalty) of sequence s_k

$\quad s^*$ = Best sequence available during the search

$\quad z^*$ = Total cost associated with s^*

The first task is to develop the genetic code of the chromosomes. Although binary coding can be used in the job sequencing problem (see, e.g., Yamada and Nakano, 1997), the resulting algorithm is complex because the crossover and mutation operations may result in infeasible schedules that must be "repaired." Thus, instead of using a binary code, the nature of the problem allows representing a chromosome as a job sequence (e.g., 1-2-5-3-4).

To show how children are created, consider parents chromosomes P1 = 1-3-5-2-4 and P2 = 5-4-2-3-1. Suppose that a random 1-point crossover occurs at the third gene. The first two genes of C1(C2) are constructed by swapping the first two genes of P1(P2). The last three genes are the ones remaining from P1(P2) after excluding the first two genes—that is

$\quad$ First 2 genes of C1 = {5, 4}

$\quad$ First 2 genes of C2 = {1, 3}

$\quad$ Last 3 genes of C1 = {1, 3, 5, 2, 4} − {5, 4} = {1, 3, 2}

$\quad$ Last 3 genes of C2 = {5, 4, 2, 3, 1} − {1, 3} = {5, 4, 2}

Thus, C1 = 5-4-1-3-2 and C2 = 1-3-5-4-2.

Next, mutations of C1 and C2 are carried out in the following manner: If $R < .1$, a child chromosome is subject to mutation. Mutation is then implemented for the child by swapping two randomly selected genes (jobs). For example, the random numbers $R = .8452 (>.1)$ and $R = .0342 (<.1)$ applied to C1 and C2, respectively, indicate that only C2 is mutated. Using $R = .1924$ and $R = .8239$ to determine swapped genes in C2, the first random number selects

TABLE 10.16   Data for a Single-Machine 5-Job Sequencing Problem

Job, j	Processing time in days, T_j	Due date, d_j	Holding cost per day, h_j	Penalty cost per day, p_j
1	10	15	$3	$10
2	8	20	2	22
3	6	10	5	10
4	7	30	4	8
5	4	12	6	15

TABLE 10.17   GA Iterations Applied to the Job Sequencing Problem of Example 10.3-6

Iteration		Sequence, s	z	Explanation
0	P1	1-2-3-4-5	512	-Initial random population (P1, P2, P3, P4)
	P2	2-3-4-1-5	605	-Chosen parents are P4 (best z) and P3 (random).
	P3	4-1-5-2-3	695	-Crossover P3 and P4 starting at position 3.
	P4	3-2-1-4-5	475	
	C1	3-**2**-4-1-**5**	573	-Mutate C1 by exchanging positions 2 and 5.
	C2	**4**-1-3-2-**5**	829	-Mutate C2 by exchanging positions 1 and 5.
	mC1	3-5-4-1-2	534	
	mC2	5-1-3-2-4	367	
1	**P1**	1-2-3-4-5	512	-Worst parents P2 and P3 in iteration 0 are replaced
	P2	3-5-4-1-2	534	with their mC1 and mC2.
	P3	5-1-3-2-4	367	-Chosen parents are P3 (best z) and P1 (random).
	P4	3-2-1-4-5	475	-Crossover P1 and P3 starting at position 4.
	C1	5-**1**-**3**-2-4	367	-Mutate C1 by exchanging positions 2 and 3.
	C2	1-**2**-3-**5**-4	439	-Mutate C2 by exchanging positions 2 and 4.
	mC1	5-3-1-2-4	314	
	mC2	1-5-3-2-4	361	
2	**P1**	5-3-1-2-4	314	-Worst parents P1 and P2 in iteration 1 are replaced
	P2	1-5-3-2-4	361	with their mC1 and mC2.
	P3	5-1-3-2-4	367	-Chosen parents are P1 (best z) and P4 (random).
	P4	3-2-1-4-5	475	-Crossover P1 and P4 starting at position 3.
	C1	**3**-**2**-5-1-4	292	-Mutate C1 by exchanging positions 1 and 2.
	C2	5-3-2-1-4	222	-No mutation in C2.
	mC1	2-3-5-1-4	324	
	mC2	5-3-2-1-4	222	
3	P1	5-3-1-2-4	314	-Worst parents P3 and P4 in iteration 2 are replaced
	P2	1-5-3-2-4	361	with their mC1 and mC2.
	P3	2-3-5-1-4	324	-Chosen parents are P4 (best z) and P2 (random).
	P4	5-3-2-1-4	222	-Crossover P2 and P4 starting at position 3.
	C1	5-3-1-2-4	314	-No mutation.
	C2	1-5-3-2-4	361	-No mutation.

position 1 (job 1), and the second random number selects position 5 (job 2). Thus, C2 is mutated from 1-3-5-4-2 to 2-3-5-4-1.

Table 10.17 summarizes the calculations for iterations 0 to 3. For convenience, the cost calculations (values of z) are automated using the spreadsheet *excelJobSequencing.xls*. The best sequence is associated with P4 in iteration 3.

Summary of Genetic Algorithm

Step 0:

(a) Generate a random population X of N feasible chromosomes.

(b) For each chromosome s in the selected population, evaluate its associated fitness. Record s^* as the best solution so far available.

(c) Encode each chromosome using binary or numeric representation.

Step 1:
  (a) Select two parent chromosomes from population X.
  (b) Crossover the parents genes to create two children.
  (c) Mutate the children genes randomly.
  (d) If resulting solutions are infeasible, repeat step 1 until feasibility is achieved. Else, replace the weakest two parents with the new children to form a new population X and update s^*. Go to step 2.

Step 2: If a termination condition has been reached, stop; s^* is the best available solution. Else, repeat step 1.

PROBLEM SET 10.3C

1. Suppose that GA is used to find the maximum of $F(x)$, $x = 0,1,\ldots,275$. Let $x = 107$ and $x = 254$ represent parents P1 and P2.
   (a) Represent P1 and P2 as binary codes.
   (b) Use uniform crossover to create C1 and C2.
   (c) Create C1 and C2 using a 1-point crossover.
   (d) Create C1 and C2 using a 2-point crossover.
   (e) In Part (b), use random numbers to mutate C1 and C2.

2. Carry out two additional iterations of Example 10.3-5.

3. Carry out an additional iteration of Example 10.3-6.

*4. You have a deck of ten cards numbered 1 to 10. You need to divide the ten cards into two piles such that the *sum* of pile 1 cards is 36 and the *product* of the pile 2 cards is also 36. Develop a GA for the problem using an initial population of 4 parents, 1-point crossover, and 1% mutation rate. Carry out 5 iterations.

5. You have a piece of wire whose length is $L = 120.3$ inches and you would like to shape it into a rectangular frame. Use the GA to determine the width and height that will yield the maximum area of the rectangle.

6. Repeat Problem 5 assuming that the wire is used to form a box with the maximum volume.

7. Consider the following problem

   $$\text{Maximize } f(x, y) = x\sin(4x) + 1.1\sin(2y), x = 0, 1, 2,\ldots, 10, y = 0, 1, 2,\ldots, 10$$

   Carry out five GA iterations to estimate the optimum solution.

8. In the game of chess, queens move horizontally, vertically, or along a $(45°)$ diagonal path. We need to position N queens in $(N \times N)$ grid so that no queen can "take" any other queen. Design a GA for the problem starting with a random population of 4 parents and using a 1-point crossover. A reasonable measure of effectiveness is the number of queens in conflict. Carry out three iterations.

10.4 APPLICATION OF METAHEURISTICS TO INTEGER LINEAR PROGRAMS

This section shows how the metaheuristics developed in Section 10.3 are applied to the following general integer linear programs (ILPs):

$$\text{Maximize } z = \sum_{j=1}^{n} c_j x_j$$

subject to

$$\sum_{j=1}^{n} a_{ij}x_j (\le, \ge, \text{or} =) b_i, i = 1, 2, \ldots, m$$

$$L_j \le x_j \le U_j, j = 1, 2, \ldots, n$$

$$x_j \text{ integer}, j = 1, 2, \ldots, n$$

The basic elements of an ILP metaheuristic include selection of the starting solution, definition of the neighborhood, and determination of the next search move.

1. **Selection of starting solution.** The metaheuristics uses the *rounded* continuous optimum solution as the starting solution.
2. **Definition of neighborhood.** It is more manageable computationally to search the variables *one at a time* by defining the neighborhood for variable x_j as

$$N(x_j) = \{(x_1, \ldots x_j - 1, \ldots, x_n), (x_1, \ldots, x_j + 1, \ldots, x_n)\}$$

For example, suppose that the current solution in a 5-variable problem is $(8, 6, 4, 0, 2)$, and assume that x_3 is targeted for change. Then

$$N(x_3) = \{(8, 6, \mathbf{3}, 0, 2), (8, 6, \mathbf{5}, 0, 2)\}$$

Infeasible solutions that violate the upper and lower bounds are excluded from the neighborhood. For example, if x_4 is designated for change and $0 \le x_4 \le \infty$, then $N(x_4) = \{(8, 6, 4, -\mathbf{1}, 2), (8, 6, 4, \mathbf{1}, 2)\} = \{(8, 6, 4, \mathbf{1}, 2)\}$ because $x_4 = 1$ is infeasible.
3. **Determination of the next search move.** The next search move is determined from a neighborhood as the solution $\mathbf{X} = (x_1, x_2, \ldots, x_n)$ with the least infeasibility.[5] The *infeasibility measure* is computed as

$$I_{\mathbf{X}} = \sum_{(\le)} \max \{0, \sum_{j=1}^{n} a_{ij}x_j - b_i\} + \sum_{(\ge)} \max \{0, b_i - \sum_{j=1}^{n} a_{ij}x_j\}$$

$$+ \sum_{(=)} \max \{0, |\sum_{j=1}^{n} a_{ij}x_j - b_i|\} + \sum_{j=1}^{n} (\max \{0, L_j - x_j\} + \max \{0, x_j - U_j\})$$

If $I_{\mathbf{X}} = 0$, then the next search move is feasible.

The remainder of the section detail the development of TS, SA, and GA ILP.[6] The ideas can be applied to any ILP and, indeed, can be extended to nonlinear programs.

---

[5]More sophisticated metaheuristics include techniques for restoring feasibility or use of Lagrangean functions to penalize feasibility violations (see, e.g., Abramson and Randall, 1999).
[6]A review of Section 10.3 is recommended before proceeding with this material.

10.4.1 ILP Tabu Algorithm

Figure 10.6 outlines the algorithmic steps of TS applied to an n-variable ILP. It makes use of the following definitions:

$$\mathbf{X} = (x_1, \ldots, x_j, \ldots, x_n)$$
$$L_j = \text{Lower bound on } x_j \text{ (default } = 0)$$
$$U_j = \text{Upper bound on } x_j \text{ (default } = \infty)$$
$$N(x_j) = \{(x_1, \ldots x_j - 1, \ldots, x_n), (x_1, \ldots, x_j + 1, \ldots, x_n)\}$$
$$\mathbf{X}_j^t(k) = \text{Solution } \mathbf{X} \text{ in which } x_j \text{ is replaced with } x_j + k \ (k = \pm 1) \text{ at iteration } t$$
$$I_j^t(k) = \text{Infeasibility measure of solution } \mathbf{X}_j^t(k)$$
$$z_j^t(k) = \text{Objective value associated with } \mathbf{X}_j^t(k)$$
$$\mathbf{X}^* = \text{Best feasible solution encountered during the search}$$
$$z^* = \text{Objective value associated with } \mathbf{X}^*$$

FIGURE 10.6

ILP Tabu metaheuristic

1. **Set X** = rounded LP solution and set $z^* = -\infty$ (maximization case)
2. **For iteration** $t = 1$ to N
3.   **Set** $I^* = \infty$, $j^* = 0$, and $k^* = 0$, $\mathbf{X}_{\text{temp}} = \mathbf{X}$
4.   **For** $j = 1$ to n
5.   **If** x_j reaches it tenure limit, then remove j from tabu list
6.   **For** $k = -1$ to 1 step 2
7.   **if** $x_j + k < L_j$ or $x_j + k > U_j$ **then next** k
8.   **Set X** = $\mathbf{X}_{\text{temp}}$
9.   **Determine** infeasibility $I_j^t(k)$ for $\mathbf{X}_j^t(k) = (x_1, \ldots, x_j + k, \ldots, x_n)$
10.   **If** $I_j^t(k) = 0$ **then**
11.   **If** $z_j^t(k) > z^*$ **then**
12.   set $j^* = j$, $k^* = k$, and $z^* = z_j^t(k)$
13.   **Else: if** j is tabu **then next** j
14.   **Else** $j^* = j$ and $k^* = k$
15.   **Else: If** j is tabu then **next** j
16.   **Else: If** $I_j^t(k) < I^*$ **then** set $I^* = I_j^t(k)$, $j^* = j$, and $k^* = k$
17.   **next** k
18.   **next** j
19.   **If** $j^* > 0$, **then** set $\mathbf{X} = (x_1, \ldots, x_{j^*} + k^*, \ldots, x_n)$ and place j^* on the tabu list
20.   **Else:** Empty the tabu list (all variables are tabu or all neighbors do not improve z)
21. **Next** t

$I* = \min \{I_j^t(k), j = 1, 2, \ldots, n; k = -1, 1\}$ encountered in iteration t

$j* = $ Index j associated with $I*$

$k* = $ Value of k ($=\pm 1$) associated with $I*$

$\tau = $ Tabu tenure period, expressed in number of iterations

The tabu list is composed of the *indices* of tabu variables.

The algorithm starts by setting **X** equal to the rounded optimum LP solution (statement 1). At iteration t, a tabu variable is allowed (per the aspiration criterion) to define the next search move if it results in an improved feasible solution (statements 11 and 12). Otherwise, a tabu variable is excluded (statement 13).

At iteration t, the search computes the associated infeasibility measure $I_j^t(k)$ and the objective value $z_j^t(k)$ for all j and k. The algorithm keeps track of the candidate for the next move by updating the indices $j*$ and $k*$ (statement 14). A better feasible solution automatically defines the next move (statements 10, 11, and 12). Otherwise, the non-tabu move with the least infeasibility measure (≥ 0) is selected (statement 16). If $j* = 0$, all neighborhood solutions are tabu and the tabu list is emptied to allow the search to continue (statement 20).

Example 10.4-1

The TS is applied to the following ILP:

$$\text{Maximize } z = 2x_1 + x_2 + 3x_3 + 2x_4$$

Subject to

$$x_1 + 2x_2 - 3x_3 - x_4 \leq 10$$

$$3x_1 - 2x_2 + x_3 - x_4 \leq 14$$

$$2x_1 + x_2 - 2x_3 + 2x_4 \leq 9$$

$$-x_1 + x_2 + x_3 \leq 10$$

$$x_1, x_2, x_3, x_4 \text{ nonnegative integers}$$

The optimum continuous solution is $x_1 = 4.625$, $x_2 = 0$, $x_3 = 14.625$, $x_4 = 14.5$ with $z = 82.125$. Its optimum integer solution (obtained by TORA) is $x_1 = 5$, $x_2 = 1$, $x_3 = 14$, $x_4 = 13$ with $z = 79$. The rounded solution is $\mathbf{X}_1 = (5, 0, 15, 14)$ or $\mathbf{X}_2 = (5, 0, 15, 15)$. The associated infeasibility measures are $I_{\mathbf{X}_1} = 83$ and $I_{\mathbf{X}_2} = 85$ (verify!). The solution $\mathbf{X}_1$ has smaller infeasibility measure. Hence, it is used to start the search.

Table 10.18 gives five iterations using a tabu tenure period $\tau = 4$ iterations. An underlined index identifies a tabu variable. For example, x_2 ($= 1$) remains on the list during iterations 1, 2, 3, and 4. The search encounters the first feasible solution at iteration 3 (which happens to be the best solution in all 5 iterations). At iteration 4, *all* the variables are tabu, and no neighborhood solution leads to a better solution. Thus, the tabu list is emptied at iteration 5 (retaining the same solution as in iteration 4, less the tabu label) to allow the search to continue. In typical large problems, it is unlikely that all the variables will be on the tabu list simultaneously.

TABLE 10.18 Tabu Search of ILP Example with Tenure Period $\tau = 4$

Iteration	x_1	x_2	x_3	x_4	I^*	z	j^*	k^*
LP optimum	4.625	0	14.625	14.5		82.125		
Search start	5	0	15	14	2	83		
1	5	1	15	14	1	84	2	1
2	5	1	15	13	2	82	4	−1
(best)3	5	1	14	13	0	79	3	−1
(all-tabu)4	4	1	14	13	1	77	1	−1
5	4	1	14	13	1	77	1	−1

Excel Moment

Figure 10.7 provides the layout of an Excel spreadsheet for TS ILP (file *excelTabu-IP-Heuristic.xls*). It allows experimentation with small-size problems (up to 10 variables). The spreadsheet presentation is basically a learning tool designed to reinforce your understanding of the details of TS. Commercial TS algorithms include additional rules for solving very large problems.

PROBLEM SET 10.4A

1. Verify the entries in iterations 1, 2, and 3 in Table 10.18.
2. Carry out 10 TS iterations for each of the following problems.
   (a) Maximize $z = 4x_1 + 6x_2 + 2x_3$
   subject to

$$4x_1 - 4x_2 \leq 5$$
$$-x_1 + 6x_2 \leq 5$$
$$-x_1 + x_2 + x_3 \leq 5$$
$$x_1, x_2, x_3 \geq 0 \text{ and integer}$$

   (b) Maximize $z = 3x_1 + x_2 + 3x_3$
   subject to

$$-x_1 + 2x_2 + x_3 \leq 4$$
$$4x_2 - 3x_3 \leq 2$$
$$x_1 - 3x_2 + 2x_3 \leq 3$$
$$x_1, x_2, x_3 \geq 0 \text{ and integer}$$

3. *Excel experiment.* Use *excelTabu-IP-heuristc.xls* to find a solution for the following problems:
   (a) Project selection problem of Example 9.1-1.
   (b) Set covering problem of Example 9.1-2.
   Compare the heuristic and exact solutions.

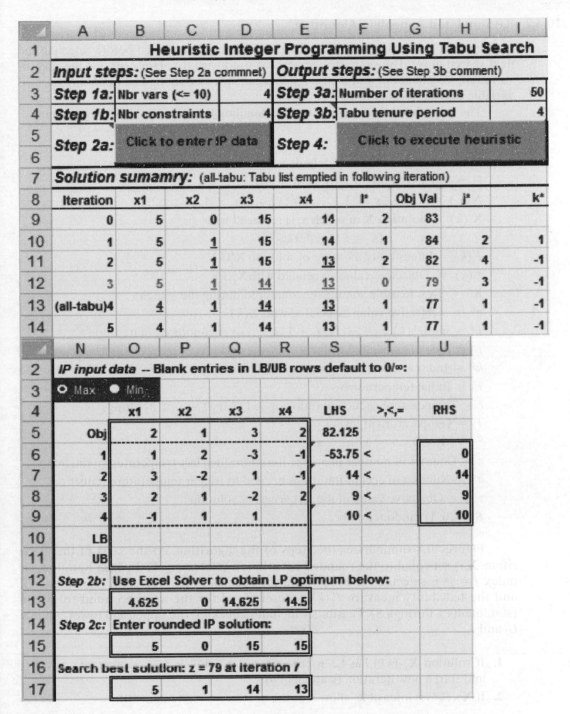

Iteration	x1	x2	x3	x4	I*	Obj Val	j*	k*
0	5	0	15	14	2	83		
1	5	1	15	14	1	84	2	1
2	5	1	15	13	2	82	4	-1
3	5	1	14	13	0	79	3	-1
(all-tabu)4	4	1	14	13	1	77	1	-1
5	4	1	14	13	1	77	1	-1

Heuristic Integer Programming Using Tabu Search

Input steps: (See Step 2a commnet) *Output steps:* (See Step 3b comment)

Step 1a: Nbr vars (<= 10) 4 *Step 3a:* Number of iterations 50

Step 1b: Nbr constraints 4 *Step 3b:* Tabu tenure period 4

Step 2a: Click to enter IP data *Step 4:* Click to execute heuristic

Solution sumamry: (all-tabu: Tabu list emptied in following iteration)

IP input data -- Blank entries in LB/UB rows default to 0/∞:

○ Max ● Min

	x1	x2	x3	x4	LHS	>,<,=	RHS
Obj	2	1	3	2	82.125		
1	1	2	-3	-1	-53.75	<	0
2	3	-2	1	-1	14	<	14
3	2	1	-2	2	9	<	9
4	-1	1	1		10	<	10
LB							
UB							

Step 2b: Use Excel Solver to obtain LP optimum below:

| 4.625 | 0 | 14.625 | 14.5 |

Step 2c: Enter rounded IP solution:

| 5 | 0 | 15 | 15 |

Search best solution: z = 79 at iteration /

| 5 | 1 | 14 | 13 |

FIGURE 10.7

Excel application of tabu search to the ILP at the start of Section 10.4 (file *excelTabu-IP-Heuristic.xls*)

10.4.2 ILP Simulated Annealing Algorithm

In Section 10.4.1 dealing with TS, *all* the variables are examined before selecting the next search move. The same strategy can be used with SA. However, for the sake of variation, we will adopt a new strategy that calls for examining one *randomly selected* variable in each iteration.

The following definitions are used in detailing the steps of the SA algorithm:

$\mathbf{X} = (x_1, \ldots, x_j, \ldots, x_n)$

$L_j = $ Lower bound on x_j (default $= 0$)

$U_j = $ Upper bound on x_j (default $= \infty$)

$N(x_j) = \{(x_1, \ldots x_j - 1, \ldots, x_n), (x_1, \ldots, x_j + 1, \ldots, x_n)\}$

$\mathbf{X}_j^i(k) = $ Solution $\mathbf{X}$ in which x_j is replaced with

$\qquad\qquad x_j + k \, (k = \pm 1)$ at iteration t

$I_j^t(k) = $ Infeasibility measure of solution $\mathbf{X}_j^t(k)$

$z_j^t(k) = $ Objective value associated with $\mathbf{X}_j^t(k)$

$\mathbf{X}^* = $ Best feasible solution encountered during the search

$z^* = $ Objective value associated with $\mathbf{X}(k)$

$I^* = \min\{I_j^t(k), k = -1, 1; j = 1, 2, \ldots, n\}$ encountered in iteration t

$j^* = $ Index j associated with I^*

$k^* = $ Index k associated with I^*

$T_0 = $ Initial temperature

$r = $ Temperature reduction ratio applied every t accept-iterations

$T_i = $ Temperature at level i

$\quad = rT_{i-1}, 0 < r < 1$

$a = $ Counter of number of accept-iteration since last temperature reduction

$a^* = $ Number of accept-iterations needed to trigger temperature reduction

$z_{\text{last}} = $ Objective value of the last *accepted* solution

$R = (0, 1)$ random number

Figure 10.8 summarizes the steps of the algorithm. At the start of the algorithm, $\mathbf{X}$ is set equal to the rounded LP solution (statement 1). In each iteration, an index $j = j^*$ is selected randomly from the variables set $\{1, 2, \ldots, n\}$ (statement 4), and the feasibility measure $I_j^t(k)$ is determined for the neighborhood solutions (statements 5 through 8). Feasibility includes checking the upper and lower bounds U_j and L_j.

1. If solution $\mathbf{X}_{j^*}^t(k^*)$ has been encountered previously (i.e., redundant), reject it and start a new iteration (statement 9).
2. If $\mathbf{X}_{j^*}^t(k^*)$ is infeasible, allow it as the next move (statement 10).

1. **Set** $a = 0$, $i = 0$, $\mathbf{X} =$ initial rounded LP solution
2. **Set** $I^* = \infty$, and $z_{\text{last}} = -\infty$ (assume maximization)
3. **For** iteration $t = 1$ to N
4.   **Select** j randomly in the range $[1, n]$ and set $j^* = j$
5.   **For** $k = -1$ to 1 step 2
6.   **Determine** $I^t_{j*}(k)$ for $\mathbf{X}^t_{j*}(k) = (x_1, \ldots, x_{j*} + k, \ldots, x_n)$
7.   **If** $I^t_{j*}(k) < I^*$ **then** $I^* = I^t_{j*}(k)$, $k^* = k$
8.   **next** k
9.   **If** $\mathbf{X}^t_{j*}(k^*)$ is redundant, **then** reject move, **next** t
10.   **If** $I^* > 0$, **then** $\mathbf{X}^t_{j*}(k^*)$ is the next move
11.   **Else: If** $z^t_{j*}(k^*) > = z_{\text{last}}$ **then**
12.   **accept** $\mathbf{X}^t_{j*}(k^*)$, set $z_{\text{last}} = z^t_{j*}(k^*)$ and $a = a + 1$
13.   **Else: If** $R \le \exp\left(-|z_{\text{last}} - z^t_{j*}(k^*)|/T_i\right)$ **then**
14.   **accept** $\mathbf{X}^t_{j*}(k^*)$, set $z_{\text{last}} = z^t_{j*}(k^*)$ and $a = a + 1$
15.   **Else** reject $\mathbf{X}^t_{j*}(k^*)$ and start a new iteration
16.   **If** $a = a^*$ **then** $a = 0$, $i = i + 1$, $T_i = rT_{i-1}$
17. **Next** t

FIGURE 10.8

ILP simulated annealing metaheuristic

    3. If $\mathbf{X}^t_{j*}(k^*)$ is a no-worse feasible solution, allow it as the next move (statement 12).

    4. If $\mathbf{X}^t_{j*}(k^*)$ is an inferior feasible solution, accept it as the next move if

$$R \le \exp\left(\frac{-|z_{\text{last}} - z^t_{j*}(k^*)|}{T}\right).$$ Otherwise, reject it (statements 13 to 15).

Prior to the start of a new iteration, the temperature T is reduced if $a = a^*$ (statement 16).

Example 10.4-2

We use the ILP defined in Example 10.4.1 starting with the rounded solution ($x_1 = 5$, $x_2 = 0$, $x_3 = 15$, $x_4 = 15$) and the initial temperature $T_0 = .75 \times$ (LP optimum objective value) $= .75(82.125) \approx 62$. Temperature reduction is triggered every $a^* = 2$ accept-iterations using a reduction ratio $r = .5$. Table 10.19 summarizes 10 iterations. At each iteration, the randomly selected variable is labeled with an underline. For example, x_1 is the random selection at iteration 1 and x_4 at iteration 2. According to the rules of the algorithm, an infeasible nonredundant solution is allowed as a move toward achieving feasibility. This occurs at iterations 1, 2, and 4. Also, a move is always generated from the most recent allowed/accepted move. For example, the move at iteration 6 is generated from the allowed move at iteration 4 because the move at iteration 5 is rejected.

    The move at iteration 3 is accepted because it is the *first* feasible solution encountered in the search. This sets $z^* = 78$ and $\mathbf{X}^* = (4, 0, 14, 14)$. At iteration 6, the *inferior* feasible solution is

TABLE 10.19   Simulated Annealing Applied to ILP of Example 10.4-1 with $T_0 = .75$ (LP Objective Value), $r = .5$, and $a^* = 2$

Iteration t	x_1	x_2	x_3	x_4	I^*	$z_{j*}^t(k^*)$	z_{last}	Temp T	$\exp\left(\dfrac{-\lvert z_{\text{last}} - z_{j*}^t(k^*)\rvert}{T}\right)$	R	Explanation
Search start	5	0	15	15	2	85	$-\infty$	62			Infeasible first trial solution
1	4	0	15	15	3	83	$-\infty$	62			Infeasible move: Allow
2	4	0	15	14	1	81	$-\infty$	62			Infeasible move: Allow
(Best)3	4	0	14	14	0	78	$-\infty$	62			First feasible move: Accept
4	4	0	13	14	1	75	78	62			Infeasible move: Allow
5	4	0	14	14	0	78	78	62			Redundant: Reject
6	4	0	13	13	0	73	78	62	0.92	0.11	$R <$ P{accept}: Accept
7	4	1	13	13	0	74	73	31			$z_{j*k*}^t > z_{\text{last}}$: Accept
8	4	1	13	12	0	72	74	31	0.94	0.93	$R <$ P{accept}: Accept
9	4	1	12	12	0	69	72	15.5	0.82	0.96	$R >$ P{accept}: Reject
10	4	0	13	12	0	71	72	15.5	0.94	0.38	$R <$ P{accept}: Accept

Best solution occurs at iteration 3

accepted because it satisfies the condition $R <$ P{accept}. At iteration 7, the feasible move is accepted because it is an improvement over last *accept*-solution (z_{last}) in iteration 6. Note that the temperature T is adjusted every 2 accept-iterations at iterations 7 and 9.

Excel Moment

Figure 10.9 gives Excel spreadsheet for SA ILP (file *excelSA-IP-Heuristic.xls*). As in TS, the application allows experimentation with small-size problems (number of variables ≤ 10). The user can study the impact of changing the data in steps 2 and 3 on the efficacy of the algorithm. One of the immediate observations about the behavior of the algorithm is that the "frequency" of rejecting feasible solutions increases with the number of iterations, a typical behavior of SA.

PROBLEM SET 10.4B

1. Carry out 5 iterations of Example 10.4-2 assuming $c_j = 1$ for all j.
2. Carry out 5 SA iterations for the following problem:

$$\text{Maximize } z = 99x_1 + 90x_2 + 58x_3 + 40x_4 + 79x_5$$
$$+ 92x_6 + 102x_7 + 74x_8 + 67x_9 + 80x_{10}$$

subject to

$$30x_1 + 8x_2 + 6x_3 + 5x_4 + 20x_5 + 12x_6 + 25x_7 + 24x_8 + 32x_9 + 29x_{10} \leq 100$$

All variables are binary

3. *Excel experiment,* Use file *excels-IP-Heuristic.xls* to find a solution for the following ILP:

$$\text{Minimize } z = x_1 + x_2 + x_3 + x_4 + x_5 + x_6 + x_7$$

	A	B	C	D	E	F	G	H
1						**Heuristic ILP Using Simulated Annealir**		
2	**Input steps:** (See Step 2a commnet)				**Output steps:** (See Steps 3b & 4 comm			
3	**Step 1a:** Nbr of vars (≤ 10)			4	**Step 3a:** Nbr of iterations			100
4	**Step 1b:** Nbr of constraints			4	**Step 3b:** Initial temp, T0			-0.75
5	**Step 2a:**	Click to enter IP data			**Step 4:**	Click to execute heuristic		
6								
7	**Solution sumamry:**				Search ended at iteration		100	
8	Iteration	x1	x2	x3	x4	Obj Val	Decision	I*
9	0	5	0	15	15	85	infeas	0
10	1	5	0	14	15	82	infeas	3
11	2	5	0	15	15	85	redun't	0
12	3	5	0	14	14	80	infeas	2
13	4	4	0	14	14	78	accept	0
14	5	4	0	14	13	76	accept	0

	N	O	P	Q	R	S	T	U
2	**IP input data** -- Blank entries in LB/UB rows default to 0/∞:							
3	○ Max ● M in							
4		x1	x2	x3	x4	MHS	>,<,=	RHS
5	Obj	2	1	3	2	82.125		
6	1	1	2	-3	-1	-53.75	<=	10
7	2	3	-2	1	-1	14	<=	14
8	3	2	1	-2	2	9	<=	9
9	4	-1	1	1		10	<=	10
10	LB							
11	UB							
12	**Step 2b:** Use Excel Solver to obtain LP optimum below:							
13		4.625	0	14.625	14.5			
14	**Step 2c:** Enter rounded IP solution:							
15		5	0	15	15			
16	Search best solution: z = 79 at iteration 9							
17		5	1	14	13			

FIGURE 10.9

Excel application of simulated annealing to the ILP of Example 10.4-1 (file *excelSA-IP-Heuristic.xls*)

subject to

$$x_1 \qquad\qquad + x_4 + x_5 + x_6 + x_7 \geq 20$$
$$x_1 + x_2 \qquad\qquad + x_5 + x_6 + x_7 \geq 12$$
$$x_1 + x_2 + x_3 \qquad\qquad + x_6 + x_7 \geq 14$$
$$x_1 + x_2 + x_3 + x_4 \qquad\qquad + x_7 \geq 17$$
$$x_1 + x_2 + x_3 + x_4 + x_5 \qquad\qquad \geq 18$$
$$x_2 + x_3 + x_4 + x_5 + x_6 \qquad\qquad \geq 19$$
$$x_3 + x_4 + x_5 + x_6 + x_7 \geq 14$$

All variables are binary

10.4.3 ILP Genetic Algorithm

In Section 10.2.3, binary coding is used in the development of the GA. The same idea can be applied to ILP. For example, in a 3-variable problem, the solution $(x_1, x_2, x_3) = (100, 24, 60)$ can be represented by the binary code in Table 10.20. In general, the number of binary bits is adjusted to represent the maximum value of any of the variables.

A convenient way to represent the ILP variables is to use numeric coding. In this case, the rounded LP solution in an n-variable problem is represented as $\bar{\mathbf{X}} = (\bar{x}_1, \bar{x}_2, \ldots, \bar{x}_n)$. The initial population chromosomes can be generated randomly from the range $(\bar{x}_j - q\bar{x}_j, \bar{x}_j + q\bar{x}_j), 0 < q < 1$. The resulting limits of the range are adjusted – if the bounds $L_j \leq x_j \leq U_j, j = 1, 2, \ldots, n$ are tighter. A convenient way to determine the genes is to sample from the *continuous* search range and then approximate the result to an integer value.

Table 10.21 demonstrates the idea of generating a population of three parent chromosomes starting with the solution $(x_1, x_2, x_3) = (100, 1, 60)$ with bounds

---

TABLE 10.20 Binary Coding of $(x_1, x_2, x_3) = (100, 24, 60)$

$x_1 = 100$	$x_2 = 24$	$x_3 = 60$
0010011	0001100	0011110

TABLE 10.21 Random Generation of Initial Population of 3 Parents Starting with Solution $(x_1, x_2, x_3) = (100, 1, 60)$

	x_1	x_2	x_3
Starting value	100	8	60
$L_j \leq x_j \leq U_j$	$0 \leq x_1 \leq 99$	$0 \leq x_2 \leq \infty$	$50 \leq x_3 \leq \infty$
$(x_j - qx_j, x_j + qx_j), q = .2$	(80, 120)	(6.4, 9.6)	(48, 72)
Adjusted search ranges	(80, 99)	(6, 10)	(50, 72)
Parent 1	92	7	58
Parent 2	81	9	70
Parent 3	90	8	62

$0 \le x_1 \le 99, 0 \le x_2 \le \infty, 50 \le x_3 \le \infty$, and using $q = .2$. The genes of each parent are determined randomly from the respective (adjusted) ranges.

Suppose that parents 1 and 2 in Table 10.21 are selected to create the two children based on a one-point crossover at x_3. This means that gene 3 is swapped between parents 1 and 2 to provide the child chromosomes as

$$\text{Child 1: } (92, 7, \underline{70})$$

$$\text{Child 2: } (81, 9, \underline{58})$$

(It is immaterial which chromosome is designated as child 1 or child 2.)

Mutation is applied according to a specified (small) probability. Suppose that gene 1 of child 1 is mutated from the original value of 92 to the new random value of 89 selected from the search range (80, 99). The mutated chromosome of child 1 thus becomes $(89, 7, 70)$.

Figure 10.10 outlines the algorithmic steps for the application of GA to an n-variable ILP. It makes use of the following definitions:

$\mathbf{X} = (\underline{x}_1, \dots, \underline{x}_j, \dots, \underline{x}_n)$

q = Neighborhood search ratio (< 1)

$\mathbf{X}^*$ = Best feasible solution encountered during the search

z^* = Objective value associated with $\mathbf{X}^*$

I_i = Infeasibility associated with chromosome i

I^* = Smallest infeasibility associated with the current population

i^* = Chromosome with the best objective value or the smallest infeasibility in the current population

i^{**} = Chromosome with the worst infeasibility in the current population

i^{***} = Chromosome with the next-worst infeasibility relative to i^{**}

P = Population size

c = Number of crossovers

p = Mutation probability

The metaheuristic starts with a population of P chromosomes (statement 3). The population is then examined for the best feasible solution (statements 5 to 8). Such a solution, if it exists, identifies Parent 1. If no feasible solution exists, the chromosome with the smallest infeasibility is used instead to identify Parent 1(statement 9). Parent 2 is then determined randomly from the remaining chromosomes (after excluding that of Parent 1) (statement 11). Child 1 and Child 2 are created from Parent 1 and Parent 2 (using crossovers or some other method) with random mutation (statement 12). Next, Child 1 and Child 2 replace chromosomes i^{**} and i^{***} having the two *worst* infeasibilities (statement 13 to 16).

1. **Set X** = initial rounded LP solution, $z^* = -\infty$ (assume maximization)
2. **Compute** the search ranges using q
3. **Create** initial population of size P randomly using the search ranges
4. **For** iteration = I to N
5.   **For** $i = 1$ to P
6.   **Determine** infeasibility I_i associated with chromosome i
7.   **If** $I_i = 0$ **then**
8.   **If** $z_j > z^*$ **then** set $I^* = 0$, $z^* = z_i$ and $\mathbf{X}^* = \mathbf{X}_i$
9.   **Else: If** $I_j < I^*$ **then** set $I^* = I_i$ and $i^* = i$
10.   **Next** i
11.   **Set** i^* as Parent 1 and randomly select parent 2 from $\{1, 2, \ldots, P\} - \{i^*\}$
12.   **Create** Children 1 and 2 from parents 1 and 2 using c crossovers
13.   **Mutate** child genes with probability p
13.   **For** $i = 1$ to P
14.   **Determine** infeasibility I_i for chromosome i
15.   **Identify** i^{**} and i^{***} with the two worst infeasibilities
16.   **Next** i
17.   **If** i^{**} and i^{***} have zero infeasibility **then**
18.   **Set** i^{**} and i^{***} to correspond to the two *worst* objective values
19.   **Replace** i^{**} and i^{***} with Child 1 and Child 2, respectively
20. **Next** t

FIGURE 10.10
ILP genetic metaheuristic

Example 10.4-3

For the ILP in Example 10.4-1, Table 10.22 provides a starting population of 10 chromosomes generated randomly from the rounded LP solution $(5, 0, 15, 15)$.

The search ranges, based on $q = .2$, are given at the bottom of the table. All ten chromosomes happen to be infeasible. Chromosome 5 is chosen as Parent 1 because it has the smallest infeasibility. Chromosome 2 is selected randomly from the remaining chromosomes to represent Parent 2. Thus,

$$\text{Parent 1: } (4, 0, 15, 16)$$

$$\text{Parent 2: } (5, 0, 15, 17)$$

With a single crossover ($c = 1$), the partition (selected randomly) occurs at variable 4. Thus, the children are created by exchanging gene 4 (shown in bold) as:

$$\text{Child 1: } (4, 0, 15, \mathbf{17})$$

$$\text{Child 2: } (5, 0, 15, \mathbf{16})$$

TABLE 10.22 Starting Population of Size $p = 10$ Generated from the Rounded LP Solution $(5, 0, 15, 15)$ with $q = .2, c = 1$ Crossover, and Mutation Probability .1

Chromosome	x_1	x_2	x_3	x_4	I	z
1	4	1	16	15	3	87
(Parent 2) 2	5	0	15	17	5	89
3	6	1	17	12	9	88
4	4	0	12	14	3	72
(Parent 1) 5	4	0	15	16	2	85
6	5	1	12	13	4	73
7	6	0	14	13	6	80
8	6	1	15	12	5	82
9	6	0	15	15	7	87
10	4	0	12	16	7	76
Child 1	4	0	15	<u>14</u>	1	81
Child 2	5	0	15	16	3	87
Search ranges	(4, 6)	(0, 1)	(12, 18)	(12, 18)		

Next, we apply mutation to each child. The probability of mutation of .1 calls for mutating a gene (to a new value in the search range) if $R < .1$. As shown in the table, only (underlined) gene 4 of child 1 is mutated from 17 to 14.

In the next iteration, child 1 and child 2 replace two parents in the current population. Parent 3 has the highest infeasibility $(= 9)$, hence $i^{**} = 3$. There is a tie between parents 9 and 10 for the next-worst infeasibility. The tie is broken in favor of the chromosome with the worse objective value (87 for parent 9 versus 76 for parent 10), which yields $i^{***} = 10$. Hence, Parent 3 and Parent 10 are replaced by Child 1 and Child 2, respectively. The new population is now ready for a new iteration.

Excel Moment

Figure 10.11 shows an Excel implementation of GA (file *excelGA-IP-Heuristic.xls*). You can step through the iterations one at a time or execute all the iterations automatically. In the former case, *FIRST Iteration* button initializes the computations. Each additional click of *NEXT Iteration* button generates a new iteration. This iterative design uses color codes to show how a child chromosome replaces a parent chromosome in the next iteration.

If the number of crossovers, c, in cell H4 is set equal to zero, the genes of the two children are given by the arithmetic and geometric means of the parents.

PROBLEM SET 10.4C

1. Carry out the next iteration that follows the one given in Table 10.22.
2. Carry out two iterations of Problem 2, Set 10.4b.
3. *Excel experiment.* Apply *excelIPHeuristicGA.xls* to Problem 3, Set 10.4b.

	A	B	C	D	E	F	G	H	I	J	K	L	M
1								Heuristic Integer Programming Using Genetic Search					
2	*Input steps:* See Step 2a commnet					*Output steps:* See 3a, 3b, and 4 comments			*Step 3e:*	Mutation probability, *p*			0.2
3	*Step 1a:*	Nbr of vars (≤ 10)			4	*Step 3a:*	Range ratio, *q*		0.2		FIRST Iteration	NEXT Iteration	
4	*Step 1b:*	Nbr of constraints			4	*Step 3b:*	Nbr of crossovers, c		0	*Step 4:*			
5	*Step 2a:*	Enter IP problem data				*Step 3c:*	Nbr of iterations, *N*		20		Execute ALL iteratios		
6						*Step 3d:*	Population size, *P*		10				
7	*Solution summary:* Replaced chromosomes = RED in col A. Child mutated genes = underlined GREEN											Iteration:	20
8	Chromosome	x1	x2	x3	x4	Infeas	Obj Val						
9	(Parent 1) 1	5	1	14	13	0	79						
10	2	5	1	14	13	0	79						
11	3	5	1	14	13	0	79						
12	4	5	1	14	13	0	79						
13	5	5	1	17	11	8	84						
14	6	5	1	14	13	0	79						
15	(Parent 2) 7	5	1	14	13	0	79						
16	8	5	1	13	12	0	74						
17	9	5	1	13	12	0	74						
18	10	5	1	13	12	0	74						
19	Child 1	5	1	15	12	3	80						
20	Child 2	5	1	14	15	4	83						

	N	O	P	Q	R	S	T	U
2	*IP input data* -- Blank entries in LB/UB rows default to 0/∞:							
3	● Max ● Min							
4		x1	x2	x3	x4	LHS	>,<,=	RHS
5	Obj	2	1	3	2	82.125		
6	1	1	2	-3	-1	-53.75	<=	10
7	2	3	-2	1	-1	14	<=	14
8	3	2	1	-2	2	9	<=	9
9	4	-1	1	1	0	10	<=	10
10	LB							
11	UB							
12	*Step 2b:* Use Excel Solver to obtain LP optimum below:							
13		4.625	0	14.625	14.5			
14	*Step 2c:* Enter rounded IP solution:							
15		5	0	15	14			
16	Search best solution: z = 79 at iteration 3							
17		5	1	14	13			

FIGURE 10.11

Excel application of genetic metaheuristic to the ILP at the start of Section 10.4 (file *excelGA-IP-Heuristic.xls*)

10.5   INTRODUCTION TO CONSTRAINT PROGRAMMING (CP)[7]

Suppose that we want to determine the values of the variables x, y, and z that satisfy the following requirements:

$$x \in \{1, 2, \ldots, 8\}$$
$$y \in \{1, 2, \ldots, 10\}$$
$$z \in \{1, 2, \ldots, 10\}$$
$$x \neq 7, y \neq 2, x - y = 3z$$

One way to solve the problem is to enumerate all 800 combinations, which is computationally inefficient. Constraint programming solves the problem by producing tighter domains for the variables and then applying an "intelligent" search tree to find the feasible solutions.

The constraints $x \neq 7$ and $y \neq 2$ reduces the domains of x and y to

$$\text{Domain of } x: x \in \{1, 2, 3, 4, 5, 6, 8\}$$
$$\text{Domain of } y: y \in \{1, 3, 4, 5, 6, 7, 8, 9, 10\}$$

Next, the constraint $x - y = 3z$ requires the minimum value of x to be 4, which occurs when $y = z = 1$. The maximum value of y is 5, which occurs when $x = 8$ and $z = 1$. Next, $\max(x - y) = 7$, which occurs when $x = 8$ and $y = 1$ and produces $\max(z) = 2$. This so-called **constraint propagation** results in the following feasible, but tight, domains:

$$x \in \{4, 5, 6, 8\}$$
$$y \in \{1, 3, 4, 5\}$$
$$z \in \{1, 2\}$$

The use of constraint propagation reduces the number of combinations from 800 to 32. Although the new problem is more manageable computationally, we can do better by using the search tree in Figure 10.12. We will select z to initiate the search because it has the smallest domain, giving rise to the two branches only: $z = 1$ and $z = 2$. Branch $z = 1$ implies that $x - y = 3$, which is satisfied for $(x = 4, y = 1)$, $(x = 6, y = 3)$, and $(x = 8, y = 5)$, resulting in three solutions in Figure 10.12. For $z = 2$, the resulting condition $x - y = 6$ is impossible to satisfy for the given domains. This completes the search tree. The computational advantage here is that we only need to investigate 4 out the possible 32 combinations.

---

[7]The material in this section is based in part on information presented in http://www.mozart-oz.org/documentation/fdt/node1.html.

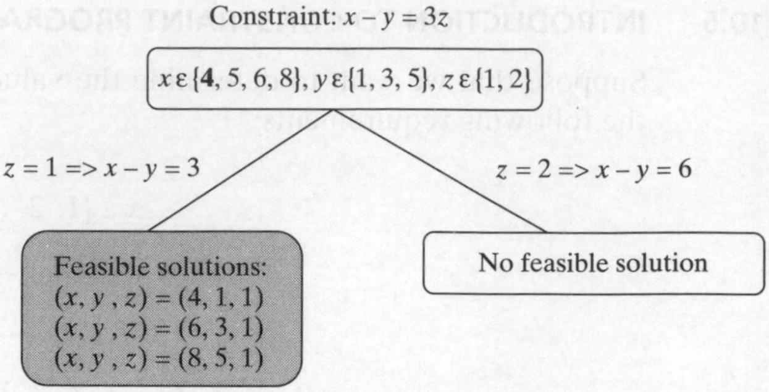

Constraint: $x - y = 3z$

$$x \varepsilon \{4, 5, 6, 8\}, y \varepsilon \{1, 3, 5\}, z \varepsilon \{1, 2\}$$

$z = 1 \Rightarrow x - y = 3$ $z = 2 \Rightarrow x - y = 6$

Feasible solutions:
$(x, y, z) = (4, 1, 1)$
$(x, y, z) = (6, 3, 1)$
$(x, y, z) = (8, 5, 1)$

No feasible solution

FIGURE 10.12

Construction of search tree for CP example

```
1 var int x in 1..8;
2 var int y in 1..10;
3 var int z in 1..10;
4 solve{
5 x<>7;
6 y<>2;
7 x-y=3*z;
8 };
```

FIGURE 10.13

ILOG OPL code for the CP example

The example above provides the gist of what CP does. It is basically an efficient search process that is based on describing the problem in terms of the domains for the variables and a set of constraints. To facilitate the search, special computer languages have been developed that allow restricting the values of the variables within their domains to satisfy the constraints. As an illustration, Figure 10.13 codes the problem in ILOG OPL. The code directly describes the problem in terms of variable domains and constraints. All domain reductions are carried out automatically by the language processor using intelligent procedures.

As the example demonstrates, CP is not an optimization technique in the sense used in mathematical programming. However, the fact that CP can be used to determine feasible solutions can enhance the efficiency of mathematical programming algorithms. In particular, CP can be imbedded within the B&B algorithm for the MIP problem.

PROBLEM SET 10.5A

1. Construct the search tree in Figure 10.12 using the variable x to initiate the search. Compare the resulting amount of computations with that in Figure 10.12.

2. Repeat Problem 1 using the variable y.

BIBLIOGRAPHY

Abramson, D., and M. Randall, "A Simulated Annealing Code for General Integer Linear Program," *Annals of Operations Research,* Vol. 86, 1999, pp. 3–21.

Glover, F., "Tabu Search – Part I," *ORSA Journal on Computing*, Vol. 1, 1989, pp. 190–206.

Glover, F., "Tabu Search – Part II," *ORSA Journal on Computing*, Vol. 2, 1990, pp. 4–32.

Hertz, A. and D. de Werra, "The Tabu Search Metaheuristic: How We Used It," *Annals of Mathematics and Artificial Intelligence*, Vol. 1, 1991, pp. 111–121.

Kirkpatrick, S., C. D. Gelatt Jr. and M. P. Vecchi, "Optimization by Simulated Annealing," *Science*, Vol. 220, 1983, pp. 671–680.

Michalewicz, Z., and D. B. Fogel. *How to Solve It: Modern Heuristics*. Springer-Verlag. 2000.

Yamada, T. and R. Nakano, Genetic algorithm for job-shop scheduling problems, *Proceeding of Modern Heuristic for Decision Support, UNICOM Seminar (March 18–19),* London, 1997, pp. 67–81.

Yamamoto, M., Câmara, G., Lorena, L., "Tabu Search Heuristic for Point-Feature Cartographic Label Placement," *GeoInformatica*, Vol. 6, No. 1, 2002, pp. 77–90.

CHAPTER 11

Traveling Salesperson Problem (TSP)

Real-Life Application

The Australian Defence Sciences and Technology Organisation employs synthetic aperture radar mounted on an aircraft to obtain high-resolution images of up to 20 rectangular swaths of land. Originally, flight path covering a sequence of swaths was done visually using a time-consuming and usually suboptimal mapping software. Subsequently, a TSP-based software was developed to plan missions with up to 20 swaths. The new software can plan a mission in less than 20 seconds, compared with one hour using the visual process. Additionally, the average mission length is 15 percent less than the one obtained manually.

Source: D. Panton and A. Elbers, "Mission Planning for Synthetic Aperture Radar Surveillance," *Interfaces*, Vol. 29, No. 2, 1999, pp. 73–88.

11.1 EXAMPLE APPLICATIONS OF TSP

Classically, the TSP problem deals with finding the shortest (closed) tour in an n-city situation, where each city is visited exactly once before returning back to the starting point. The associated TSP model is defined by two pieces of data:

1. The number of cities, n.
2. The distances d_{ij} between cities i and j ($d_{ij} = \infty$ if cities i and j are not linked).

The maximum number of tours in an n-city situation is $(n - 1)!$

In reality, TSP applications extend beyond the classical definition of visiting cities. The *real life application* given at the start of this chapter describes mission planning for synthetic aperture radar surveillance. This section summarizes five other applications that show how the classical TSP model ("cities" connected by "routes") can be adapted to represent other situations. Additional applications are given in Problem Set 11.2a.

1. *Sequencing paint products in a production facility.* A company produces batches of different paints using the same production facility. When a sequence of colors is completed, a new cycle is started in the same order. Color sequencing affects the preparation (setup) time between successive batches. The goal is to select the sequence that minimizes the total preparation time per cycle.

The TSP model for this situation regards a paint color as a city and the setup time between two colors as a distance.

2. *Integrated circuit board.* Holes in identical circuit boards are drilled to mount electronic components. The boards are fed sequentially under a moving drill. The goal is to determine the sequence that completes drilling all the holes in a board in the shortest time possible.

In the TSP model, the holes represent the cities, and the displacements between the holes represent the distances.

3. *Protein clustering.* Proteins are clustered using a numeric measure of similarity based on protein-to-protein interaction. Clustering information is used to predict unknown protein functions. The best cluster is the one that maximizes the sum of the measures of similarity between adjacent proteins.

In the TSP model, each protein takes the place of a city. The measure of similarity s_{ij} between protein i and protein j can be converted to a "distance" measure by realizing that

$$\max \left\{ \sum_{i,j \text{ in tour}} s_{ij} \right\} \equiv \min \left\{ -\sum_{i,j \text{ in tour}} s_{ij} \right\}$$

The distances can be represented as $-s_{ij}$ or $M - s_{ij}$, where M is a constant greater than the largest s_{ij}, for all i and j.

4. *Celestial objects imaging.* The US space agency NASA uses satellites for imaging celestial objects. The amount of fuel needed to reposition the satellites depends on the sequence in which the objects are imaged. The goal is to determine the optimal imaging sequence that minimizes fuel consumption.

In the TSP model, a celestial object is regarded as a city. The distance translates to the fuel consumption between two successive objects.

5. *Mona Lisa TSP art.* This intriguing application "creates" Leonardo da Vinci's Mona Lisa using a continuous line drawing. The general idea is to approximate the original painting by using computer graphics to cluster dots on a graph. The dots are then connected sequentially by piecewise-linear segments (see Bosch and Herman, 2004).

In the TSP model, the dots represent cities, and their relative locations on the graph provide the distance matrix.

PROBLEM SET 11.1A

Note: In each of the following instances, describe the data elements (cities and distances) needed to model the problem as a TSP.

1. Seers Service Center schedules its daily repair visits to customers. The jobs are categorized and grouped and each group assigned to a repairperson. At the end of the assignment, the repairperson reports back to the service center.

2. A baseball fan wishes to visit eight major league parks in (1) Portland, (2) San Francisco, (3) Los Angeles, (4) Phoenix, (5) Denver, (6) St. Luis, (7) Chicago, and (8) Miami before returning home in Seattle. Each visit lasts about one week. The goal is to spend the least money on airfare.

*3. A tourist in New York City wants to visit 8 tourist sites using local transportation. The tour starts and ends at a centrally located hotel. The tourist wants to spend the least money on transportation.

4. A manager has *m* employees working on *n* projects. An employee may work on more than one project, which results in overlap of the assignments. Currently, the manager meets with each employee individually once a week. To reduce the total meeting time for all employees, the manager wants to hold group meetings involving shared projects. The objective is to reduce the traffic (number of employees) in and out of the meeting room.

5. Meals-on-Wheels is a charity service that prepares meals in its central kitchen for delivery to people who qualify for the service. Ideally, all meals should be delivered within 20 minutes from the time they leave the kitchen. This means that the return time from the last location to the kitchen is not a factor in determining the sequence of deliveries.

6. *DNA sequencing.* In genetic engineering, a collection of DNA strings, each of a specified length, is concatenated to form one universal string. The genes of individual DNA strings may overlap. The amount of overlaps between two successive strings is measurable in length units. The length of the universal string is the sum of the lengths of the individual strings less the overlaps. The goal is to concatenate the individual strings in a manner that minimizes the length of the universal string.

7. *Automatic guided vehicle.* An AGV makes a round-trip, starting and ending at the mailroom, to deliver mail to departments on the factory floor. The AGV moves along horizontal and vertical aisles. The goal is to minimize the length of the round-trip.

11.2 TSP MATHEMATICAL MODEL

As stated in Section 11.1, a TSP model is defined by the number of cities n and the distance matrix $\|d_{ij}\|$. The definition of a tour disallows linking a city to itself by assigning a very high penalty to the diagonal elements of the distance matrix. A TSP is **symmetric** if $d_{ij} = d_{ji}$ for all i and j. Otherwise, the TSP is **asymmetric**.

Define

$$x_{ij} = \begin{cases} 1, & \text{if city } j \text{ is reached from city } i \\ 0, & \text{otherwise} \end{cases}$$

The TSP model is given as

$$\text{Minimize } z = \sum_{i=1}^{n}\sum_{j=1}^{n} d_{ij}x_{ij}, d_{ij} = \infty \text{ for all } i = j$$

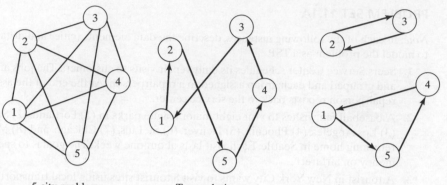

5-city problem   Tour solution   Subtour solution

$(x_{12} = x_{25} = x_{54} = x_{43} = x_{31} = 1)$ $(x_{23} = x_{32} = -1)(x_{15} = x_{54} = x_{41} = 1)$

FIGURE 11.1

A 5-city TSP example with a tour or subtour solution of the associated assignment model depending on the specific distance matrix instance

subject to

$$\sum_{j=1}^{n} x_{ij} = 1, \; i = 1, 2, \ldots, n \tag{1}$$

$$\sum_{i=1}^{n} x_{ij} = 1, \; j = 1, 2, \ldots, n \tag{2}$$

$$x_{ij} = (0, 1) \tag{3}$$

Solution forms a roundtrip city tour $\tag{4}$

Constraints (1), (2), and (3) define a regular assignment model (Section 5.4) in which $x_{ij} = 1$ if node (city) i is linked to node (city) j, and zero otherwise. If the solution of the assignment model happens to be a tour [i.e., it satisfies constraint (4)], then it is automatically optimal for the TSP. This is a rare occurrence, however, and the assignment model is likely to consist of **subtours**. Additional computations are then needed to determine the optimal tour solution.

Figure 11.1 demonstrates a 5-city TSP. The nodes represent cities, and the arcs represent two-way routes that can be distinct if the TSP is asymmetric. As explained above the assignment model can produce a tour or a subtour solution as the figure demonstrates.

Example 11.2-1

The daily production schedule at the Rainbow Company includes batches of white (W), yellow (Y), red (R), and black (B) paints. The production facility must be cleaned between successive batches. Table 11.1 summarizes the cleanup times in minutes. The objective is to determine the sequencing of colors that minimizes the total cleanup time.

TABLE 11.1 Interbatch Cleanup Times (in minutes) for the Paint Production Problem

	Interbatch cleanup (min)			
Paint	*White*	*Yellow*	*Black*	*Red*
White	∞	10	17	15
Yellow	20	∞	19	18
Black	50	44	∞	22
Red	45	40	20	∞

In the TSP model, each color represents a "city," and the clean-up time between two successive colors represents "distance." Let M be a sufficiently large penalty and define

$$x_{ij} = 1 \text{ if paint } j \text{ follows paint } i \text{ and zero otherwise}$$

The TSP model is given as

$$\text{Minimize } z = 10x_{WY} + 17x_{WB} + 15x_{WR} + 20x_{YW} + 19x_{YB} + 18x_{YR} + 50x_{BW} + 44x_{BY}$$
$$+ 22x_{BR} + 45x_{RW} + 40x_{RY} + 20x_{RB} + M(x_{WW} + x_{YY} + x_{BB} + x_{RR})$$

subject to

$$x_{WW} + x_{WY} + x_{WB} + x_{WR} = 1$$
$$x_{YW} + x_{YY} + x_{YB} + x_{YR} = 1$$
$$x_{BW} + x_{BY} + x_{BB} + x_{BR} = 1$$
$$x_{RW} + x_{RY} + x_{RB} + x_{RR} = 1$$
$$x_{WW} + x_{YW} + x_{BW} + x_{RW} = 1$$
$$x_{WY} + x_{YY} + x_{BY} + x_{RY} = 1$$
$$x_{WB} + x_{YB} + x_{BB} + x_{RB} = 1$$
$$x_{WR} + x_{YR} + x_{BR} + x_{RR} = 1$$
$$x_{ij} = (0, 1) \text{ for all } i \text{ and } j$$

Solution is a tour (loop)

The use of the penalty M in the objective function is equivalent to deleting x_{WW}, x_{YY}, x_{BB}, and x_{RR} from the model. However, the deletion of these variables destroys the underlying assignment-model structure needed to solve the TSP by B&B.

TSP solution. A straightforward way to solve TSP is exhaustive enumeration. The maximum number of tours in an n-city problem is $(n - 1)!$ For the present example, exhaustive enumeration is feasible because the number of possible tours is small ($=6$). Table 11.2 lists and evaluates all six tours and shows that tour $W \rightarrow Y \rightarrow B \rightarrow R \rightarrow W$ is optimum.

Exhaustive enumeration is not practical for the general TSP. Section 11.3 thus presents two exact integer programming algorithms: branch-and-bound (B&B) and cutting plane. Both algorithms are rooted in the solution of the assignment model, with added restrictions to guarantee a tour solution. Unfortunately, as is typical with most integer programming

TABLE 11.2 Solution of the Paint Sequencing Problem by Exhaustive Enumeration

Production loop	Total cleanup time
$W \to Y \to B \to R \to W$	$10 + 19 + 22 + 45 =$ **96**
$W \to Y \to R \to B \to W$	$10 + 18 + 20 + 50 =$ 98
$W \to B \to Y \to R \to W$	$17 + 44 + 18 + 45 = 124$
$W \to B \to R \to Y \to W$	$17 + 22 + 40 + 20 =$ 99
$W \to R \to B \to Y \to W$	$15 + 20 + 44 + 20 =$ 99
$W \to R \to Y \to B \to W$	$15 + 40 + 19 + 50 = 124$

algorithms, the proposed methods are not computationally reliable. For this reason, heuristics are used to provide good (but not necessarily optimal) solutions to the problem. Three of these heuristics are presented in Section 11.4.

Interpretation of the optimum solution. The optimum production sequence $W \to Y \to B \to R \to W$ in Table 11.2 starts with the white color, followed by yellow, then black, and then red. It is really immaterial which color we use to start the production cycle because the solution is a *closed-tour*. For example, the sequences $B \to R \to W \to Y \to B$ and $Y \to B \to R \to W \to Y$ are also optimal.

Open-tour TSP. Open tours occur when a return to the starting city is not required. This case can be demonstrated in the paint problem when production is limited to exactly one batch of each color. For example, in the open-tour sequence, $B \to W \to Y \to R$, the last "city" (R) does not link back to the starting "city" (B).

The condition can be accounted for in an n-city situation by adding a fictitious city, $n + 1$, with zero distances to and from all the real cities—that is, $d_{i, n+1} = 0, i = 1, 2, \ldots, n$ and $d_{n+1, j} = 0, j = 1, 2, \ldots, n$. For the paint example, the new distance matrix becomes

$$\|d_{ij}\| = \begin{pmatrix} \infty & 10 & 17 & 15 & 0 \\ 20 & \infty & 19 & 18 & 0 \\ 50 & 44 & \infty & 22 & 0 \\ 45 & 40 & 20 & \infty & 0 \\ 0 & 0 & 0 & 0 & \infty \end{pmatrix}$$

Row 5 and column 5 represent the fictitious color.

The optimum tour is

$$W \to Y \to R \to B \to \text{Fictitious} \to W, \text{ length } = 48 \text{ minutes}$$

The solution can be read by rearranging the tour starting and terminating points with the fictitious color:

$$\text{Fictitious} \to W \to Y \to R \to B \to \text{Fictitious}$$

Removing the fictitious color, we get the following open-tour solution:

$$W \to Y \to R \to B$$

It is important to note that the open-tour optimum solution cannot be obtained from the optimum closed-tour solution $(W \to Y \to B \to R \to W)$ directly.

Lower bound on the optimum tour length. A lower bound on the optimum tour length can be useful in solving the TSP by either the exact or the heuristic algorithms. In the case of the exact algorithms, a tight lower bound restricts the feasible space and thus makes the algorithm more efficient (particularly in the case of B&B). For the heuristics, a lower bound can be used to judge the quality of the heuristic solution.

There are a number of methods for estimating a lower bound. Two of them are presented here:

1. *Assignment model.* The assignment model is a relaxation of the TSP model, and its optimum solution provides a lower bound on the optimum tour length. Indeed, if the optimum solution of the assignment model is feasible (i.e., a tour), then it is also optimum for the TSP.

   The solution of the (closed-tour) assignment model for the paint problem yields a lower bound of 72 minutes.

2. *Linear programming.* A lower bound in an n-city situation can be determined by inscribing the *largest nonoverlapping* circles around all the cities. Let $r_j, j = 1, 2, \ldots, n$, be the largest radius of a circle inscribed around city j. The optimum value of the following LP provides a lower bound:

$$\text{Maximize } z = 2(r_1 + r_2 + \ldots + r_n)$$

subject to

$$r_i + r_j \leq \min(d_{ij}, d_{ji})\ i, j = 1, 2, \ldots, n, i < j$$

The objective function recognizes that a salesperson entering the circle around city i must cover a distance of at least $2r_i$ before entering the circle domain of any other city in the network. The constraints guarantee that none of the circles overlap.

For the paint example, we have

$$\text{Maximize } z = 2(r_W + r_Y + r_B + r_R)$$

subject to

$$r_W + r_Y \leq \min(10, 20)$$

$$r_W + r_B \leq \min(17, 50)$$

$$r_W + r_R \leq \min(15, 45)$$

$$r_Y + r_B \leq \min(19, 44)$$

$$r_Y + r_R \leq \min(18, 40)$$

$$r_B + r_R \leq \min(22, 20)$$

$$r_W, r_Y, r_B, r_R \geq 0$$

The solution yields a lower bound of 60 minutes, which is not as tight as the one obtained from the assignment model ($= 72$ minutes). Actually, experimentation with the two methods suggests that the assignment model consistently yields tighter lower bounds, particularly when the TSP is asymmetric. Note that the LP will always provide a trivial zero-value lower bound for an open-tour TSP because the zero "in-out" distances of the fictitious city set a zero limit on all the radii.

AMPL Moment

The assignment and the LP models given above for estimating the lower bound can be solved using the AMPL files provided with this chapter:

`model amplAssign.txt; data amplInputData.txt; commands solutionAssign.txt; model amplLP.txt; data amplInputData.txt; commands solutionLP.txt; File amplInputData.txt` provides the TSP data of the paint problem.

PROBLEM SET 11.2A

*1. A book salesperson who lives in Basin must call once a month on four customers located in Wald, Bon, Mena, and Kiln before returning home to Basin. The following table gives the distances in miles among the different cities.

	Miles between cities				
	Basin	Wald	Bon	Mena	Kiln
Basin	0	125	225	155	215
Wald	125	0	85	115	135
Bon	225	85	0	165	190
Mena	155	115	165	0	195
Kiln	215	135	190	195	0

The objective is to minimize the total distance traveled by the salesperson.

(a) Write down the LP for computing a lower-bound estimate on the optimum tour length.

(b) Compare the lower bounds on the optimum tour length using both the assignment model and linear programming. Is the assignment model solution optimum for the TSP?

2. Seers Service Center schedules its daily repair visits to customers. The matrix $\|T_{ij}\|$ below gives the travel time (in minutes) between the service center (row 1 and column 1) and seven jobs. The jobs are assigned to one of the repairpersons during an 8-hour shift. At the end of the day, the repairperson returns to the service center to complete paperwork.

$$\|T_{ij}\| = \begin{pmatrix} 0 & 20 & 15 & 19 & 24 & 14 & 21 & 11 \\ 20 & 0 & 18 & 22 & 23 & 22 & 9 & 10 \\ 15 & 18 & 0 & 11 & 21 & 14 & 32 & 12 \\ 19 & 22 & 11 & 0 & 20 & 27 & 18 & 15 \\ 24 & 23 & 21 & 20 & 0 & 14 & 25 & 20 \\ 14 & 22 & 14 & 27 & 14 & 0 & 26 & 17 \\ 21 & 9 & 32 & 18 & 25 & 26 & 0 & 20 \\ 11 & 10 & 12 & 15 & 20 & 17 & 20 & 0 \end{pmatrix}$$

(a) Compare the lower bounds on the optimum tour length using both the assignment model and linear programming. Is the assignment model solution optimum for the TSP?

(b) Given that journeying between jobs is nonproductive and assuming a one-hour lunch break, determine the maximum productivity of the repairperson during the day.

3. A baseball fan wishes to visit eight major league parks in (1) Seattle, (2) San Francisco, (3) Los Angeles, (4) Phoenix, (5) Denver, (6) Dallas, (7) Chicago, and (8) Tampa before returning home to Seattle. The fan will use air transportation between the different cities. The matrix $\|p_{ij}\|$ below provides the price in dollars of one-way ticket between the 8 cities.

$$\|p_{ij}\| = \begin{pmatrix} 0 & 255 & 305 & 295 & 245 & 325 & 385 & 455 \\ 255 & 0 & 190 & 220 & 230 & 300 & 310 & 395 \\ 305 & 190 & 0 & 140 & 310 & 295 & 390 & 410 \\ 295 & 220 & 140 & 0 & 200 & 275 & 285 & 350 \\ 245 & 230 & 310 & 200 & 0 & 240 & 255 & 400 \\ 325 & 300 & 295 & 275 & 240 & 0 & 260 & 370 \\ 385 & 310 & 390 & 285 & 255 & 260 & 0 & 420 \\ 455 & 395 & 410 & 350 & 400 & 370 & 420 & 0 \end{pmatrix}$$

The fan has budgeted $2200 for air travel. Is this a realistic travel budget?

4. *Proteins clustering.* Proteins are clustered using an overall measure of similarity based on protein–protein interaction information. Clustering information is used to predict unknown protein functions. By definition, the best cluster maximizes the sum of the measures of similarity between adjacent proteins. Matrix $\|s_{ij}\|$ below provides the measure of similarities (expressed as a percentage) among 8 proteins.

$$\|s_{ij}\| = \begin{pmatrix} 100 & 20 & 30 & 29 & 24 & 22 & 38 & 45 \\ 20 & 100 & 10 & 22 & 0 & 15 & 31 & 0 \\ 30 & 10 & 100 & 14 & 11 & 95 & 30 & 41 \\ 29 & 22 & 14 & 100 & 20 & 27 & 28 & 50 \\ 24 & 0 & 11 & 20 & 100 & 24 & 55 & 0 \\ 22 & 15 & 95 & 27 & 24 & 100 & 26 & 37 \\ 38 & 31 & 30 & 28 & 55 & 26 & 100 & 40 \\ 45 & 0 & 41 & 50 & 0 & 37 & 40 & 100 \end{pmatrix}$$

(a) Define the distance matrix of the TSP.

(b) Determine an upper bound on the measure of similarity for the optimum protein cluster.

5. A tourist in New York City uses local transportation to visit 8 sites. The start and end and the order in which the sites are visited are unimportant. What is important is to spend the least amount of money on transportation. Matrix $\|c_{ij}\|$ below provides the fares in dollars between the different locations.

$$\|c_{ij}\| = \begin{pmatrix} 0 & 20 & 30 & 25 & 12 & 33 & 44 & 57 \\ 22 & 0 & 19 & 20 & 20 & 29 & 43 & 45 \\ 28 & 19 & 0 & 17 & 38 & 48 & 55 & 60 \\ 25 & 20 & 19 & 0 & 28 & 35 & 40 & 55 \\ 12 & 18 & 34 & 25 & 0 & 21 & 30 & 40 \\ 35 & 25 & 45 & 30 & 20 & 0 & 25 & 39 \\ 47 & 39 & 50 & 35 & 28 & 20 & 0 & 28 \\ 60 & 38 & 54 & 50 & 33 & 40 & 25 & 0 \end{pmatrix}$$

The tourist is budgeting $120 for cab cost to all eight sites. Is this a realistic expectation? (*Hint*: This is an open-tour TSP.)

*6. A manager has a total of 10 employees working on six projects. Projects are reviewed weekly with each employee. A project may employ more than one employee resulting in assignment overlaps, as the following table shows:

		Project					
		1	2	3	4	5	6
	1		x		x	x	
	2	x		x		x	
	3		x	x	x		x
	4			x	x	x	
Employee	5	x	x	x			
	6	x	x	x	x		x
	7	x	x			x	x
	8	x		x	x		
	9					x	x
	10	x	x		x	x	x

Currently, the manager meets individually once a week with each employee. Each meeting lasts about 20 minutes for a total of 3 hours and 20 minutes for all 10 employees. To reduce the total time, the manager wants to hold group meetings depending on shared projects. The objective is to schedule the meetings in a way that will reduce the traffic (number of employees) in and out of the meeting room.

(a) Define the cities and the distance matrix of the TSP.

(b) Determine a lower bound on the optimum tour length using the assignment model. Is the assignment model solution optimum for the TSP?

7. Meals-on-Wheels is a charity service that prepares meals in its central facility for delivery to people who qualify for the service. Ideally, all meals should be delivered within 20 minutes from the time they leave the kitchen. This means that the return time from the last-meal location to the kitchen is not a factor in determining the sequence of deliveries. The charity is in the process of determining the delivery route. The first pilot schedule includes seven recipients with the following travel times, $\|t_{ij}\|$ (row 1 and column 1 represent the kitchen).

$$\|t_{ij}\| = \begin{pmatrix} 0 & 10 & 12 & 5 & 17 & 9 & 13 & 7 \\ 10 & 0 & 9 & 20 & 8 & 11 & 3 & 5 \\ 12 & 9 & 0 & 14 & 4 & 10 & 1 & 16 \\ 5 & 20 & 14 & 0 & 20 & 5 & 28 & 10 \\ 17 & 8 & 4 & 20 & 0 & 21 & 4 & 9 \\ 9 & 11 & 10 & 5 & 21 & 0 & 2 & 3 \\ 13 & 3 & 1 & 28 & 4 & 2 & 0 & 2 \\ 7 & 5 & 16 & 10 & 9 & 3 & 2 & 0 \end{pmatrix}$$

(a) Compare the lower bounds on the optimum tour length using both the assignment model and linear programming. Is the assignment model solution optimum for the TSP?

(b) Based on the information in (a), is it possible to deliver the eight meals within the 20-minute time window?

8. *Integrated circuit boards.* Circuit boards (such as those used in PCs) are drilled with holes for mounting different electronic components. The boards are fed one at a time under a moving drill. The matrix $\|d_{ij}\|$ below provides the distances (in millimeters) between pairs of 6 holes of a specific circuit board.

$$\|d_{ij}\| = \begin{pmatrix} - & 1.3 & .5 & 2.6 & 4.1 & 3.2 \\ 1.3 & - & 3.5 & 4.7 & 3.0 & 5.3 \\ .5 & 3.5 & - & 3.5 & 4.6 & 6.2 \\ 2.6 & 4.7 & 3.5 & - & 3.8 & .9 \\ 4.1 & 3.0 & 4.6 & 3.8 & - & 1.9 \\ 3.2 & 5.3 & 6.2 & .9 & 1.9 & - \end{pmatrix}$$

Suppose that the drill moves at a linear speed of 9 millimeters per second and that it takes 7 second to drill hole. Determine an upper bound on the production rate (boards per hour).

9. *DNA sequencing.* In genetic engineering, a collection of DNA strings, each of length 10 feet, is concatenated to form one universal string. The genes of individual DNA strings may overlap, thus producing a universal string with length less than the sum of the individual lengths. The matrix $\|O_{ij}\|$ below provides the length in feet of overlaps for a hypothetical case of six DNA strings.

$$\|O_{ij}\| = \begin{pmatrix} - & 1 & 0 & 3 & 4 & 3 \\ 1 & - & 4 & 5 & 3 & 2 \\ 0 & 4 & - & 3 & 5 & 6 \\ 3 & 5 & 3 & - & 2 & 1 \\ 4 & 3 & 5 & 2 & - & 2 \\ 3 & 2 & 6 & 1 & 2 & - \end{pmatrix}$$

Compare the lower bounds on the optimum tour length using both the assignment model and linear programming. Is the assignment model solution optimum for the TSP?

10. The United States Space Agency, NASA, uses satellites for imaging celestial objects. The amount of fuel needed to reposition the satellites is a function of the sequence in which the objects are imaged. The matrix $\|c_{ij}\|$ below provides units of fuel consumption used to realign the satellites with the objects.

$$\|c_{ij}\| = \begin{pmatrix} - & 1.5 & 2.6 & 3.1 & 4.4 & 3.8 \\ 1.9 & - & 4.7 & 5.3 & 3.9 & 2.7 \\ 2.9 & 4.3 & - & 3.5 & 5.4 & 6.2 \\ 3.4 & 5.1 & 3.6 & - & 2.2 & 1.9 \\ 4.4 & 3.4 & 5.9 & 2.4 & - & 2.6 \\ 3.1 & 2.7 & 6.5 & 1.1 & 2.9 & - \end{pmatrix}$$

Suppose that the cost per fuel unit is $12. Estimate a lower bound on the cost of imaging all six objects.

11. *Automatic guided vehicle.* An AGV makes a round-trip (starting and ending at the mailroom) to deliver mail to 5 departments on a factory floor. Using the mailroom as the origin $(0, 0)$, the (x, y) locations of the delivery spots are $(10, 30), (10, 50), (30, 10), (40, 40)$,

and $(50, 60)$ for the five departments. All distances are in meters. The AGV moves along horizontal and vertical aisles only. The objective is to minimize the length of the round-trip.

(a) Define the cities and the distance matrix of the TSP model.

(b) Assuming that the AGV moves at a speed of 35 meters per minute, can the round-trip be made in less than 5 minutes?

12. *Wallpaper cutting, Garfinkel (1977)*. Covering the walls of a room usually requires cutting sheets of different lengths to account for doors and windows, and the like. The sheets are cut from a single roll, and their start points must be aligned to match the repeating pattern of the roll. The amount of waste thus depends on the sequence in which the sheets are cut. For the purpose of determining the waste, we can regard a single pattern as a unit length (regardless of its real measurement) and then express the length of a sheet in terms of this unit. For example, a sheet of length 9.50 patterns requires 10 consecutive patterns. If the matching of the patterns on the wall requires starting the sheet a quarter of the way down from the first pattern, then the sheet (of length 9.5 patterns) must end three quarter of the way down the tenth pattern. Thus, waste in a sheet can take place in the first and last patterns only, and its amount is always less than the length of a full pattern.

Define $0 \le s_i \le 1$ and $0 \le e_i \le 1$ be the locations of the cuts down the first and last patterns. Then for sheet i of length L_i pattern, we have

$$e_i = (s_i + L_i) \bmod (1)$$

For the example just cited, $s = .25$ and $e = (.25 + 9.5) \bmod(1) = .75$.

The waste between two sequential sheets, i and j, in which sheet i is immediately followed by sheet j, can be computed in the following manner: If $s_j \ge e_i$, the waste is $s_j - e_i$. Else, if $s_j < e_i$, then the end cut of i and the start cut of j overlap. The result is that the start cut s_j of sheet j must be made in the pattern that immediately follows the one in which the end cut e_i of sheet i has been made. In this case, the resulting waste is $1 - e_i + s_j$.

Actually, the two amounts of waste ($s_j - e_i$ and $1 - e_i + s_j$) can be expressed in one expression as

$$w_{ij} = (s_j - e_i) \bmod(1)$$

For example, given $e_1 = .8$ and $s_2 = .35$, we use the formula for $s_2 < e_1$ to get $w_{12} = 1 - .8 + .35 = .55$. The same result can be obtained using $w_{12} = (.35 - .8) \bmod(1) = (-.45) \bmod(1) = (-1 + .55) \bmod(1) = .55$.

To account for the waste resulting from the cut in the first pattern of the first sheet (node 1) and the last pattern of the last sheet (node n), a dummy sheet (node $n + 1$) is added with its $s_{n+1} = e_{n+1} = 0$. The length of a tour passing through all $n + 1$ nodes provides the total waste resulting from a specific sequence. The problem can now be modeled as an $(n + 1)$-node TSP with distance w_{ij}.

(a) Compute the matrix w_{ij} for the following set of raw data (for convenience, spreadsheet *excelWallPaper.xls* automates the computations of w_{ij}.):

Sheet, i	Pattern start cut, s_i	Sheet length, L_i
1	0	10.47
2	.342	3.82
3	.825	5.93
4	.585	8.14
5	.126	1.91
6	.435	6.32

(b) Show that the optimum solution of the associated assignment produces the optimum tour?

(c) Quantify the total waste as a percentage of the length of all sheets.

13. *Warehouse order picking, Ratliff and Rosenthal (1983).* In a rectangular warehouse, a stacker overhead crane is used to pick and deliver orders between specified locations in the warehouse. The tasks of the crane involve the following: (1) Picking a load at a location, (2) delivering a load to a location, and (3) moving unloaded to reach a picking location. Suppose that there are n orders to be picked and delivered. The goal would be to complete all the orders while minimizing the unproductive time of the crane [item (3)]. The unproductive times can be computed based on the pickup and delivery locations of the orders and the lateral and traversal speeds of the crane, among other factors. For the purpose of this situation, the crane starts on the orders from an idle state and also terminates in an idle state after all orders are completed.

For a specific pool of eight orders, the times (in minutes) to reach the locations of orders $1, 2, \ldots,$ and 8 from idle state are .1, .4, 1.1, 2.3, 1.4, 2.1, 1.9, and 1.3, respectively. The following table provides the unproductive times (in minutes) associated with the sequencing of the orders.

$$
\|t_{ij}\| =
\begin{pmatrix}
0 & 1.0 & 1.2 & .5 & 1.7 & .9 & 1.3 & .7 \\
1.1 & 0 & .9 & 2.0 & .8 & 1.1 & .3 & .5 \\
1.2 & 1.9 & 0 & 1.4 & .4 & 1.0 & 1.0 & 1.6 \\
1.5 & 2.3 & .4 & 0 & 2.0 & 1.5 & 2.8 & 1.0 \\
1.2 & 1.8 & 1.4 & 2.5 & 0 & 2.1 & .4 & .9 \\
.9 & 1.1 & 1.0 & .5 & 2.1 & 0 & .2 & .3 \\
1.3 & .8 & 1.1 & 2.2 & 1.4 & .6 & 0 & 1.2 \\
1.7 & 1.5 & 1.6 & 1.0 & 1.9 & .9 & 2.0 & 0
\end{pmatrix}
$$

(a) Define the cities and distance matrix of the TSP model.

(b) Determine a lower bound on the unproductive time during the completion of all orders.

11.3 EXACT TSP ALGORITHMS

This section presents two exact IP algorithms: B&B and cutting plane. Both algorithms guarantee optimality theoretically. The computational issue is a different story—meaning that the algorithms may fail to produce the optimum in a reasonable amount of time and, prompting the development of the heuristics in Sections 11.4 and 11.5.

11.3.1 B&B Algorithm

The idea of the B&B algorithm is to start with the optimum solution of the associated assignment problem. If the solution is a tour, the process ends. Otherwise, restrictions are imposed on the resulting solution to disallow subtours. The idea is to create branches that assign a zero value to each of the variables of one of the subtours. Normally, the subtour with the smallest number of cities is selected for branching because it creates the smallest number of branches.

If the solution of the assignment problem at any node is a tour, its objective value provides an upper bound on the optimum tour length. If it does not, further branching at the node is required. A subproblem is *fathomed* if it yields a smaller upper bound, or if there is evidence that it cannot lead to a better upper bound. The optimum tour is given at the node with the smallest upper bound.

The following example provides the details of the TSP B&B algorithm.

Example 11.3-1

Consider the following 5-city TSP distance matrix:

$$\|d_{ij}\| = \begin{pmatrix} \infty & 10 & 3 & 6 & 9 \\ 5 & \infty & 5 & 4 & 2 \\ 4 & 9 & \infty & 7 & 8 \\ 7 & 1 & 3 & \infty & 4 \\ 3 & 2 & 6 & 5 & \infty \end{pmatrix}$$

The associated assignment is solved using AMPL, TORA, or Excel. The solution is

$$z = 15, (x_{13} = x_{31} = 1), (x_{25} = x_{54} = x_{42} = 1), \text{ all others } = 0$$

It consists of two subtours, 1-3-1 and 2-5-4-2, and constitutes the starting node of the B&B search tree, as shown at node 1 in Figure 11.2.

In the present example, we will use an arbitrary tour, 1-2-3-4-5-1, to determine the initial upper bound—namely, $10 + 5 + 7 + 4 + 3 = 29$ units. Alternatively, the heuristics in Sections 11.4 and 11.5 may be used to yield improved (smaller) upper bounds. The estimated upper bound means that the *optimum* tour length cannot exceed 29. Future B&B nodes seek smaller upper bounds, if any exists.

FIGURE 11.2

B&B solution of the TSP problem of Example 11.3-1

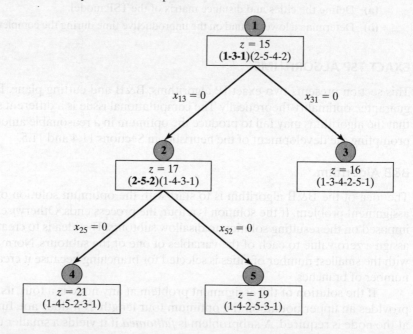

At node 1 of the B&B tree, the smaller subtour 1-3-1 creates branch $x_{13} = 0$ leading to node 2 and $x_{31} = 0$ leading to node 3. The associated assignment problems at nodes 2 and 3 are created from the problem at node 1 by setting $d_{13} = \infty$ and $d_{31} = \infty$, respectively.

At this point, we can examine either node 2 or node 3, and we arbitrarily choose to explore node 2. Its assignment solution is 2-5-2 and 1-4-3-1 with $z = 17$. Because the solution is not a tour, we select the smaller subtour 2-5-2 for branching: branch $x_{25} = 0$ leads to node 4, and branch $x_{52} = 0$ leads to node 5.

We now have three unexplored subproblems: nodes 3, 4, and 5. We arbitrarily examine the subproblem at node 4, setting $d_{25} = \infty$ in the distance matrix at node 2. The resulting solution, tour 1-4-5-2-3-1, yields the smaller upper bound $z = 21$.

The two subproblems at nodes 3 and 5 remain unexplored. Arbitrarily selecting subproblem 5, we set $d_{52} = \infty$ in the distance matrix at node 2. The result is tour 1-4-2-5-3-1 with the smaller upper bound $z = 19$. Subproblem 3 is the only one that remains unexplored. Substituting $d_{31} = \infty$ in the distance matrix at node 1, we get yet a better tour solution: 1-3-4-2-5-1 with the smaller upper bound $z = 16$.

All the nodes in the tree have been examined, thus completing the B&B search. The optimal tour is the one associated with the smallest upper bound: 1-3-4-2-5-1 with length 16 units.

Remarks.   The solution of Example 11.3-1 reveals two points:

1. The search sequence $1 \rightarrow 2 \rightarrow 4 \rightarrow 5 \rightarrow 3$ was selected deliberately to demonstrate a worst-case scenario in the B&B algorithm, in the sense that it requires exploring 5 nodes. Had we explored node 3 ($x_{31} = 0$) prior to node 2 ($x_{13} = 0$), we would have encountered the upper bound $z = 16$ units, and concluded that branching at node 2, with $z = 17$, cannot lead to a better solution, thus eliminating the need to explore nodes 4 and 5.

   Generally, there are no exact rules for selecting the best search sequence, save some rules of thumb. For example, at a given node we can start with the branch having the *largest* d_{ij} among all the created branches. The hope is that the elimination of the largest tour leg would lead to a tour with a smaller length. In Example 11.3-1, this rule would have given priority to node 3 over node 2 because $d_{31}(=4)$ is larger than $d_{13}(=3)$, as desired. Another rule calls for sequencing the exploration of the nodes horizontally (rather vertically), that is, breadth before depth. The idea is that nodes closer to the starting node are more likely to produce tighter upper bounds because the number of additional constraints (of the type $x_{ij} = 0$) is smaller. This rule also would have produced the computationally efficient search $1 \rightarrow 2 \rightarrow 3$.

2. The heuristics in Sections 11.4 and 11.5 can enhance the computational efficiency of the B&B algorithm by providing a "tight" upper bound. For example, the nearest-neighbor heuristic in Section 11.4.1 yields the tour 1-3-4-2-5-1 with length $z = 16$. This tight upper bound would have immediately eliminated the need to explore node 2 (the distance matrix is all integer, thus no better solution can be found at node 2).

AMPL Moment

Interactive AMPL commands are ideal for the implementation of the TSP B&B algorithm using the general assignment model file *amplAssign.txt*. The data of the problem is given in file *Ex11.3-1.txt*. The file *solutionAssign.txt* solves and displays the solution. The following table summarizes the AMPL commands needed to create the B&B tree in Figure 11.2 (Example 11.3-1) interactively:

AMPL commands	Result
ampl: `model amplAssign.txt; data Ex11.3-1.txt;` `commands solutionAssign.txt;`	Node 1 solution
ampl: `fix x[1,3]:= 0; commands` `solutionAssign.txt;`	Node 2 solution
ampl: `fix x[2,5]:= 0; commands` `solutionAssign.txt;`	Node 4 solution
ampl: `unfix x[2,5]; fix x[5,2]:= 0; commands` `solutionAssign.txt;`	Node 5 solution
ampl: `unfix x[5,2]; unfix x[1,3]; fix x[3,1]:= 0;` `commands solutionAssign.txt;`	Node 3 solution

TORA Moment

TORA can also be used to generate the B&B tree. Start with the assignment model at node 1. The branch condition $x_{ij} = 0$ is effected by using Solve/Modify Input Data to change the upper bound on x_{ij} to zero.

PROBLEM SET 11.3A

1. Solve Example 11.3-1 using subtour 2-5-4-2 to start the branching process at node 1, using the following sequences for exploring the nodes.
   (a) Explore all the subproblems horizontally from left to right in each tier before proceeding to the next tier.
   (b) Follow each path vertically from node 1, always selecting the leftmost branch, until the path ends at a fathomed node.
2. Solve Problem 1, Set 11.2a, by B&B.
*3. Solve Problem 6, Set 11.2a, by B&B.
4. Solve Problem 8, Set 11.2a, by B&B.
5. *AMPL experiment.* Use AMPL files *amplAssign.txt* and *solutionAssign.txt* to solve Problem 5, Set 11.2a, by B&B.

11.3.2 Cutting-Plane Algorithm

In the cutting-plane algorithm, a set of constraints is added to the assignment problem to exclude subtour solutions. Define a continuous variable $u_j (\geq 0)$ for city $j = 2, 3, \ldots,$ and n. The desired additional constraints (cutting planes) are

$$u_i - u_j + nx_{ij} \leq n - 1, \ i = 2, 3, \ldots, n; \ j = 2, 3, \ldots, n; \ i \neq j$$

The addition of these cuts to the assignment model produces a mixed integer linear program with binary x_{ij} and continuous u_j.

Example 11.3-2

Consider the following distance matrix of a 4-city TSP problem.

$$\|d_{ij}\| = \begin{pmatrix} - & 13 & 21 & 26 \\ 10 & - & 29 & 20 \\ 30 & 20 & - & 5 \\ 12 & 30 & 7 & - \end{pmatrix}$$

The complete mixed integer problem consists of the assignment model and the additional constraints in Table 11.3. All $x_{ij} = (0, 1)$ and all $u_j \geq 0$.

The optimum solution is $u_2 = 0$, $u_3 = 2$, $u_4 = 3$, $x_{12} = x_{23} = x_{34} = x_{41} = 1$. The corresponding tour is 1-2-3-4-1 with length 59. The solution satisfies all the additional constraints (verify!).

To demonstrate that the given optimum solution cannot satisfy a subtour solution, consider the subtour (1-2-1, 3-4-3), or $x_{12} = x_{21} = 1$, $x_{34} = x_{43} = 1$. The optimum values $u_2 = 0, u_3 = 2$, and $u_4 = 3$ together with $x_{43} = 1$ do not satisfy constraint 6, $4x_{43} + u_4 - u_3 \leq 3$, in Table 11.3. (Convince yourself that the same conclusion is true for other subtour solutions, such as (3-2-3, 1-4-1))

TABLE 11.3   Cuts for Excluding Subtours in the Assignment Model of Example 11.3-2

No.	x_{11}	x_{12}	x_{13}	x_{14}	x_{21}	x_{22}	x_{23}	x_{24}	x_{31}	x_{32}	x_{33}	x_{34}	x_{41}	x_{42}	x_{43}	x_{44}	u_2	u_3	u_4	
1							4										1	−1		≤3
2								4									1		−1	≤3
3										4							−1	1		≤3
4												4						1	−1	≤3
5														4			−1		1	≤3
6															4			−1	1	≤3

The disadvantage of the cutting-plane model is that the size of the resulting mixed integer linear program grows exponentially with the number of cities, making the model computationally intractable. When this happens, the only recourse is to use either the B&B algorithm one of the heuristics in Sections 11.4 and 11.5.

AMPL Moment

A general AMPL model of the cutting-plane algorithm is given in file *amplCut.txt*. The 4-city TSP of Example 11.3-2 uses the following AMPL commands:

```
model amplCut.txt; data Ex11.3-2.txt; commands SolutionCut.txt;
```

The output is presented in the following convenient format:

```
Optimal tour length = 59.00
Optimal tour: 1- 2- 3- 4- 1
```

PROBLEM SET 11.3B

1. Write down the cuts associated with the following TSP:

$$\|d_{ij}\| = \begin{pmatrix} \infty & 43 & 21 & 20 & 10 \\ 12 & \infty & 9 & 22 & 30 \\ 20 & 10 & \infty & 5 & 13 \\ 14 & 30 & 42 & \infty & 20 \\ 44 & 7 & 9 & 10 & \infty \end{pmatrix}$$

2. *AMPL experiment.* Use AMPL to solve the following TSP problem by the cutting-plane algorithm.

   (a) Problem 2, Set 11.2a.

   (b) Problem 3, Set 11.2a.

   (c) Problem 11, Set 11.2a.

3. *AMPL experiment.* In the circuit board model of Problem 8, Set 11.2a, the input data are usually given in terms of the (x, y)-coordinates of the holes rather than the distance between the respective holes. Specifically, consider the following (x, y) coordinates for a 9-hole board:

Hole	(x, y) in mm
1	$(1, 2)$
2	$(4, 2)$
3	$(3, 7)$
4	$(5, 3)$
5	$(8, 4)$
6	$(7, 5)$
7	$(3, 4)$
8	$(6, 1)$
9	$(5, 6)$

The drill always traverses the shortest distance between two successive holes.

   (a) Modify the data file to determine the optimum drilling tour using the $(x-y)$ coordinates.

   (b) Determine the production rate in boards per hour given that the drill moving speed is 9 mm/sec and the drilling time per hole is .7 sec.

11.4   LOCAL SEARCH HEURISTICS

This section presents two local search heuristics for TSP: *nearest-neighbor* and *reversal*. Local search heuristics terminate at a local optimum. One way to improve the quality of the solution is to repeat the search using randomly generated starting tours. Another option is to use metaheutistics, whose basic idea is to escape entrapment at a local optimum. The metaheuristics will be covered in Section 11.5.

11.4.1 Nearest-Neighbor Heuristic

As the name suggests, a TSP solution can be found by starting with a city (node) and then connecting it to the closest unlinked city (break ties arbitrarily). The just-added city is then linked to its nearest unlinked city. The process continues until a tour is formed.

Example 11.4-1

The matrix below summarizes the distances in miles in a 5-city TSP.

$$\|d_{ij}\| = \begin{pmatrix} \infty & 120 & 220 & 150 & 210 \\ 120 & \infty & 100 & 110 & 130 \\ 220 & 80 & \infty & 160 & 185 \\ 150 & \infty & 160 & \infty & 190 \\ 210 & 130 & 185 & \infty & \infty \end{pmatrix}$$

The heuristic can start from any of the five cities. Each starting city may lead to a different tour. Table 11.4 provides the steps of the heuristic starting at city 3. (Distances for previously selected cities are replaced with $-$).

TABLE 11.4   Steps of the Nearest-Neighbor Heuristic for Solving the TSP of Example 11.4-1

Step	Action	Tour construction
1	Start at city 3	3
2	City 2 is closest to city 3 ($d_{32} = \min\{220, \mathbf{80}, \infty, 160, 185\}$)	3-2
3	City 4 is closest to city 2 ($d_{24} = \min\{120, \infty, -, \mathbf{110}, 130\}$)	3-2-4
4	City 1 is closest to city 4 ($d_{41} = \min\{\mathbf{150}, \infty, -, -, 190\}$)	3-2-4-1
5	City 5 is closest to city 1 ($d_{15} = \min\{\infty, -, -, -, \mathbf{210}\}$)	3-2-4-1-5
6	Add city 3 to complete the tour	3-2-4-1-5-3

The resulting tour, 3-2-4-1-5-3, has a total length of $80 + 110 + 150 + 210 + 185 = 735$ miles. Observe that the quality of the solution depends on the selection of the starting city. For example, starting from city 1, the resulting tour is 1-2-3-4-5-1 with length 780 miles (try it!). A better solution may thus be found by repeating the heuristic starting with different cities.

11.4.2 Reversal Heuristic

In an n-city TSP, the reversal heuristic attempts to improve a current tour by reversing the order of nodes of an *open* subtour (a subtour is open if it is missing exactly one leg). For example, consider tour 1-3-5-2-4-1 in Figure 11.3. Reversal of open subtour 3-5-2 produces the new tour 1-2-5-3-4-1 by deleting legs 1-3 and 2-4 and adding legs 1-2 and 3-4, as Figure 11.3 shows. The smallest number of reversed subtour is 2 (e.g., 3-5 or 5-2). The largest number is $n - 2$ if the distance matrix is symmetric and $n - 1$ if it is asymmetric.[1] The heuristic scans all reversals in search for a better tour.

---

[1] In a symmetric distance matrix, the $(n - 1)$-city subtour reversal does not produce a different tour. For example, reversing 2-4-5-3 in the tour 1-2-4-5-3-1 yields the identical tour 1-3-5-4-2-1 when the distance matrix is symmetric ($d_{ij} = d_{ji}$, for all i and j). This may not be true in the asymmetric case because legs i-j and j-i may not be equal.

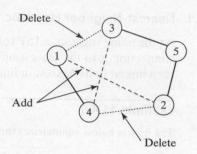

FIGURE 11.3

Subtour reversal 3-5-2 in tour 1-3-5-2-4-1 produces tour 1-2-5-3-4-1 by deleting legs 1-3 and 2-4 and adding legs 1-2 and 3-4

The length of the starting tour in the reversal heuristic need not be finite (i.e., it could have missing legs). Indeed, starting with a finite-length tour does not appear to offer a particular advantage regarding the quality of the final solution (see Problem 2, Set 11.4a, for an illustration).

Example 11.4-2

Consider the TSP of Example 11.4-1. The (self-explanatory) reversal steps are carried out in Table 11.5 starting with an arbitrary tour 1-4-3-5-2-1 of length 745 miles.

TABLE 11.5 Application of the Reversal Heuristic to the TSP of Example 11.4-1.

Type	Reversal	Tour	Length
Start	—	(1-4-3-5-2-1)	745
Two-at-a-time reversal	4-3	1-3-4-5-2-1	820
	3-5	(1-4-5-3-2-1)	**725**
	5-2	1-4-3-2-5-1	730
Three-at-a-time reversal	4-3-5	1-5-3-4-2-1	∞
	3-5-2	1-4-2-5-3-1	∞
Four-at-a-time reversal	4-3-5-2	1-2-5-3-4-1	745

The four-at-a-time reversal is investigated because the distance matrix is asymmetric. Also, none of the reversals can include the home city of the initial tour (=1 in this example) as this will not yield a feasible tour. For example, the reversal 1-4 leads to 4-1-3-5-2-1, which is not a tour.

The solution determined by the reversal heuristic is a function of the starting tour. For example, if we start with 2-3-4-1-5-2 with length 750 miles, the heuristic produces a different tour: 2-5-1-4-3-2 with length 730 miles (verify!). For this reason, the quality of the solution can be improved if the heuristic is repeated with different starting tours.

Excel Moment

Figure 11.4 provides a general Excel spreadsheet (file *excelReversalTSP.xls*) using the rules given above (a subset of the model provides the nearest-neighbor solution—see options 1 and 4 given below). The distance matrix may be entered manually, or it may be populated randomly

Traveling Salesperson Nearest-Neighbor + Subtour Reversal Heuristics

Input steps: (See comment in cell A4) | Output steps: (See comment in cell E3) | Check here if symmerical | Density | 0.8

Step 1: Number of cities = 5 | Step 3: Select option: all | Click to populate DISTANCE matrix randomly

Step 2: Click to enter input data | Step 4: Click to execute heuristic

	1	2	3	4	5
1		64	2	41	99
2			74	36	95
3	65	11		44	
4	50		38		51
5	52		91	45	

Initial tour (Use only if TOUR option is selected):

Search best tour:
Tour length: 152
Tour: 1-3-2-4-5-1

Solution sumamry:

Initial	Tour	Length
1	1-3-2-4-5-1	152
2	2-4-3-1-5-2	infinity
3	3-2-4-1-5-3	287
4	4-3-2-5-1-4	237
5	5-4-3-2-1-5	infinity
Reversals		
3-2	1-2-3-4-5-1	285
2-4	1-3-4-2-5-1	infinity
1-5	1-3-2-5-4-1	203
3-2-4	1-4-2-3-5-1	infinity
2-4-5	1-3-5-4-2-1	infinity
3-2-4-5	1-5-4-2-3-1	infinity

FIGURE 11.4

Execution of the TSP heuristic using Excel spreadsheet (file *excelReversalTSP.xls*)

(symmetric or asymmetric) with specified density. The heuristic automatically checks for matrix symmetry and adjusts the maximum reversal level accordingly. It also automates four options for the *starting* tour:

1. Option *all* applies the nearest-neighbor heuristic using each of the cities as a starting point. The best amongst the resulting tours is then used to start the reversal heuristic.
2. Option *tour* allows the use of a specific starting tour.
3. Option *random* generates a random starting tour.
4. Option *specific city number* applies the nearest-neighbor heuristic starting at the designated city.

PROBLEM SET 11.4A

1. In Table 11.5 of Example 11.4-2, specify the deleted and added legs associated with each of the two-at-a-time reversals.
2. In Table 11.5 of Example 11.4-2, use the infinite-length disconnected tour 3-2-5-4-1-3 (i.e., a tour missing at least one leg) as a starting tour to demonstrate that the subtour reversal heuristic can still lead to a solution that is just as good as when the heuristic starts with a connected tour.
3. Apply the reversal heuristic to the following problems starting with best nearest-neighbor tour:
   (a) The paint sequencing problem of Example 11.1-1.
   (b) Problem 1 of Set 11.2a.
   (c) Problem 4 of Set 11.2a.
   (d) Problem 5 of Set 11.2a.
4. *Excel–AMPL Experiment.* The matrix below provides the distances among 10 cities (all missing entries $= \infty$). (For convenience, file *Prob11.4a-4.txt* gives the distance matrix in AMPL format.)

	1	2	3	4	5	6	7	8	9	10
1		100	2	11	80	5	39	95		28
2	17		42	33	21	59	46		79	29
3		63		57	92		55		68	52
4	36	27	25		40	49	48	63	16	
5	51	11	46	60		22	11	13	54	55
6		20	46	15	93		76	47	21	10
7	17		45	88	28	26		33	30	49
8	35	49	87	76		55	64			93
9	35	48	100	3	55		41			73
10		50	70	43	82	43	23	49	89	

Use file *excelReversalTSP.xls* to implement the following situations:

(a) Use the nearest-neighbor heuristic to determine the associated tour starting at node 1.

(b) Determine the tour using the reversal heuristic starting with the tour 4-5-3-2-6-7-8-10-9-1-4-5.

(c) Determine the tour using the reversal heuristic starting with the best nearest-neighbor tour.

(d) Compare the quality of the solutions in parts (a), (b), and (c) with the exact optimum solution obtained by AMPL.

11.5   METAHEURISTICS

The drawback of the local search heuristics in Section 11.4 is possible entrapment at a local optimum. Metaheuristics, as explained in Chapter 10, are designed to alleviate this problem. This section details the application of tabu, simulated annealing, and genetic search to TSP. It is recommended that you review related material in chapter 10 before proceeding with the rest of this chapter.

11.5.1   TSP Tabu Algorithm

As explained in Section 10.3.1, tabu search escapes entrapment at local optima by permitting inferior search moves. A **tabu list** prevents repeating previously encountered solutions during a specified number of successive iterations, called **tenure period**. A tabu move can be accepted if it leads to an improved solution. For the TSP model, the elements of the tabu search are defined as follows:

1. **Starting tour.** Four options are available: (a) a specific tour, (b) a specific starting city for a tour constructed by the nearest-neighbor heuristic (Section 11.4.1), (c) the best among all tours constructed by the nearest-neighbor heuristic using each of cities $1, 2, \ldots,$ and n as a starting point, and (d) a random tour.

2. **Subtour reversal.** Two added tour legs replace two deleted ones to produce a new tour (see Section 11.4.2 for details).

3. **Neighborhood at iteration i.** All tours (including infeasible ones with infinite length) generated by applying subtour reversals to tour i.

4. **Tabu move.** A reversal tour is tabu if *both* of its deleted legs are on the tabu list.

5. **Next move at iteration i.** Identify the shortest tour in neighborhood i, and select it as the next move if it is non-tabu, or if it is tabu but yields a better solution. Else, exclude the shortest (tabu) tour and repeat the test with the next shortest neighborhood tour.

6. **Tabu tenure period τ at iteration i.** The tenure period is the (random or deterministic) number of successive iterations a tabu element stays on the tabu list.

7. **Changes in tabu list at iteration i.** Reversal legs defining tour i from tour $i - 1$ are added to the list. Tour legs completing tenure (those that entered the list at iteration $i - \tau + 1$) are deleted from the list.

Example 11.5-1

We will use the distance matrix of Example 11.4-1 to demonstrate the application of the tabu metaheuristic.

$$\|d_{ij}\| = \begin{pmatrix} \infty & 120 & 220 & 150 & 210 \\ 120 & \infty & 100 & 110 & 130 \\ 220 & 80 & \infty & 160 & 185 \\ 150 & \infty & 160 & \infty & 190 \\ 210 & 130 & 185 & \infty & \infty \end{pmatrix}$$

Assume a tabu tenure $\tau = 2$ iterations and use 1-2-3-4-5-1 of length 780 as the starting tour.

Table 11.6 provides five iterations. In iterations 1, 2, and 3, the shortest tours are non-tabu. In iteration 4, the shortest tour, 1-4-3-5-2-1 of length 745, is tabu because the reversal requires deleting legs 4-5 and 3-2, and both are on the tabu list. Since the (tabu) tour is not better than the best recorded solution (tour 1-4-5-3-2-1 of length 725 in iteration 3), the next shortest tour, 1-4-5-2-3-1 of length 790, which happens to be non-tabu, defines the next move.

In iteration 5, the two tours 1-4-5-3-2-1 (length = 725) and 1-4-3-2-5-1 (length = 730) are tabu (and neither provides a better tour). The next best tour in the neighborhood, 1-4-2-5-3-1 (of infinite length), is non-tabu and hence represents the next move. Note that only one deleted leg (4-5) in the selected tour 1-4-2-5-3-1 appears on the tabu list, which is not sufficient to declare the tour tabu because *both* deleted legs must be on the list. Note also that the top tour 1-5-4-2-3-1 (of infinite length) is not selected because it is missing two legs, compared with one missing leg in the selected tour, 1-4-2-5-3-1.

Excel Moment

Figure 11.5 presents the Excel spreadsheet (file *excelTabuTSP*.xls) for applying tabu search to the TSP model. To facilitate experimentation, symmetric or asymmetric TSPs can be generated randomly. Also, the initial tour can be specified either deterministically or randomly. The on/off buttons (row 6 of the spreadsheet) reveal/suppress the details of the iterations, including changes in the tabu list.

TABLE 11.6 Tabu Heuristic Solution of Example 11.5-1 with Tenure Period $\tau = 2$ Iterations

Iteration	Reversal	Tour	Length	Delete	Add	Tabu list ($t = 2$)
0	—	1-2-3-4-5-1	780			—
1	2-3	1-3-2-4-5-1	810			
	3-4	1-2-4-3-5-1	785			
	4-5	1-2-3-5-4-1	∞			
	2-3-4	**1-4-3-2-5-1**	**730**	1-2, 5-1	*1-4, 2-5*	*1-4, 2-5*
	3-4-5	1-2-5-4-3-1	∞			
	2-3-4-5	1-5-4-3-2-1	∞			
2	4-3	1-3-4-2-5-1	∞			
	3-2	1-4-2-3-5-1	∞			
	2-5	**1-4-3-5-2-1**	**745**	3-2, 5-1	*3-5, 2-1*	*1-4, 2-5, 3-5, 2-1*
	4-3-2	1-2-3-4-5-1	780			
	3-2-5	1-4-5-2-3-1	790			
	4-3-2-5	1-5-2-3-4-1	750			
3	4-3	1-3-4-5-2-1	820			
	3-5	**1-4-5-3-2-1**	**725**	4-3, 5-2	*4-5, 3-2*	*3-5, 2-1, 4-5, 3-2*
	5-2	1-4-3-2-5-1	730			
	4-3-5	1-5-3-4-2-1	∞			
	3-5-2	1-4-2-5-3-1	∞			
	4-3-5-2	1-2-5-3-4-1	745			
4	4-5	1-5-4-3-2-1	∞			
	5-3	1-4-3-5-2-1	745	4-5, 3-2	—	Tabu
	3-2	**1-4-5-2-3-1**	**790**	5-3, 2-1	*5-2, 3-1*	*4-5, 3-2, 5-2, 3-1*
	4-5-3	1-3-5-4-2-1	∞			
	5-3-2	1-4-2-3-5-1	∞			
	4-5-3-2	1-2-3-5-4-1	∞			
5	4-5	1-5-4-2-3-1	∞			
	5-2	**1-4-2-5-3-1**	∞	4-5, 2-3	*4-2, 5-3*	*5-2, 3-1, 4-2, 5-3*
	2-3	1-4-5-3-2-1	725	5-2, 3-1	—	Tabu
	4-5-2	1-2-5-4-3-1	∞			
	5-2-3	1-4-3-2-5-1	730	4-5, 3-1	—	Tabu
	4-5-2-3	1-3-2-5-4-1	∞			

PROBLEM SET 11.5A

1. Carry out three more iterations of Example 11.5-1.
2. Apply tabu to the following problems starting with best nearest-neighbor tour:
   (a) The paint sequencing problem of Example 11.1-1.
   (b) Problem 1 of Set 11.2a.
   (c) Problem 4 of Set 11.2a.
   (d) Problem 5 of Set 11.2a.

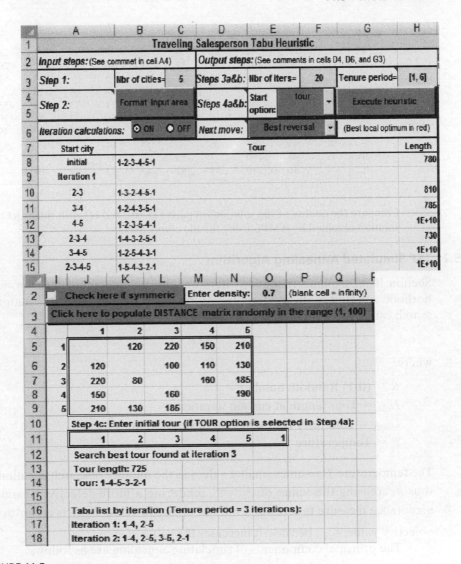

FIGURE 11.5

TSP tabu metaheuristic using Excel spreadsheet (file *excelTabuTSP.xls*)

3. *Excel–AMPL Experiment.* The matrix below provides the distances among 10 cities (all missing entries $= \infty$). (For convenience, file *prob11.5a-4.txt* gives the distance data in AMPL format.)

Use file *ExcelTabuTSP.xls* starting with the following:

(a) A random tour.

(b) Tour 4-5-3-2-6-7-8-10-9-1-4.

(c) The best nearest-neighbor tour.

	1	2	3	4	5	6	7	8	9	10
1		100	2	11	80	5	39	95		28
2	17		42	33	21	59	46		79	29
3		63		57	92		55		68	52
4	36	27	25		40	49	48	63	16	
5	51	11	46	60		22	11	13	54	55
6		20	46	15	93		76	47	21	10
7	17		45	88	28	26		33	30	49
8	35	49	87	76		55	64			93
9	35	48	100	3	55		41			73
10		50	70	43	82	43	23	49	89	

Compare the quality of the solutions in parts (a), (b), and (c) with the exact optimum solution obtained by AMPL using the file *amplCut.txt*.

11.5.2 TSP Simulated Annealing Algorithm

Section 10.3.2 explains that at any iteration in simulated annealing, a *no-worse* neighborhood solution is always accepted as the next move. If no such solution exists, the search can move to an inferior neighborhood solution conditionally if

$$R < e^{\left(\frac{L_{cur} - L_{next}}{T}\right)}$$

where

$R = (0,1)$ Random number

L_{cur} = Tour length at current iteration

L_{next} = (Inferior) Tour length at next iteration ($> L_{cur}$)

T = Temperature

The temperature T assumes smaller values as the number of search iterations increases, thus decreasing the value of $e^{\left(\frac{L_{cur} - L_{next}}{T}\right)}$, rendering a more selective search. Also, the acceptance measure favors moves whose objective value, L_{next}, is closer to the current objective value, L_{cur}, because it increases the value of $e^{\left(\frac{L_{cur} - L_{next}}{T}\right)}$.

The principal components of simulating annealing are as follows:

1. **Starting tour.** Four options are available: (a) A specific tour, (b) a specific starting city for a tour constructed by the nearest-neighbor heuristic (Section 11.4.1), (c) the best among all tours constructed by the nearest-neighbor heuristic using each of cities 1, 2, . . . , and n as a starting point, and (d) a random tour.

2. **Subtour reversal.** Two added tour legs replace two deleted legs to produce a new tour (see Section11.4.2 for details).

3. **Temperature schedule.** $\{T_k, k = 0, 1, \ldots\}, T_0$ = starting temperature, $T_k = r_k T_{k-1}$, $0 < r_k < 1, k = 1, 2, \ldots$, with the change from one temperature to the next taking place every t accept-iterations.

4. **Neighborhood at iteration i.** All tours (including infeasible ones with infinite length) generated from applying subtour reversals (Section 11.4.2) to tour i.

5. **Next move at iteration** i. Select the subtour reversal that is *no worse* than the current best tour; else, scan tours in neighborhood i in ascending order of tour length until a move is accepted (using the probability measure).

Example 11.5-2

We will use the distance matrix of Example 11.4-1 to demonstrate the application of simulated annealing metaheuristic.

$$\|d_{ij}\| = \begin{pmatrix} \infty & 120 & 220 & 150 & 210 \\ 120 & \infty & 100 & 110 & 13 \\ 220 & 80 & \infty & 160 & 185 \\ 150 & \infty & 160 & \infty & 190 \\ 210 & 130 & 185 & \infty & \infty \end{pmatrix}$$

Assume the temperature schedule $T_k = .5T_{k-1}$ with $T_0 = 50$. A change fom T_{k-1} to T_k takes place every two accept-iterations. The example starts with the infeasible (infinite length) tour 3-2-5-4-1-3.

Table 11.7 details the computations for three iterations. The best reversal move 5-4-1 in iteration 1 is accepted because it yields a better tour length ($L_{next} = 725$ versus $L_{cur} = \infty$). This means that tour 3-2-1-4-5-3 is the best solution available so far. Iteration 2 produces inferior

---

TABLE 11.7 Simulated Annealing Solution of Example 11.5-2 with $T_k = .5T_{k-1}$, $T_0 = 50$, and Change from T_{k-1} to T_k Taking Place Every Two Accept-Iterations

Iteration	Reversal	Tour	Length	L_{cur}	L_{next}	T	$p = e^{\left(\frac{L_{cur}-L_{next}}{T}\right)}$	R	Decision
0	—	3-2-5-4-1-3	∞	∞		50	—	—	—
1	2-5	3-5-2-4-1-3	795			50			
	5-4	3-2-4-5-1-3	810			50			
	4-1	3-2-5-1-4-3	730			50			
	2-5-4	3-4-5-2-1-3	820			50			
	5-4-1	**3-2-1-4-5-3**	**725**	∞	725	50	—		Accept move, $L_{next} < L_{cur}$
	2-5-4-1	3-1-4-5-2-3	790			50			
						50			
2	2-1	3-1-2-4-5-3	825			50			
	1-4	3-2-4-1-5-3	735	725	735	50	.8187	.8536	Reject move, $R > p$
	4-5	3-2-1-5-4-3	∞			50			
	2-1-4	**3-4-1-2-5-3**	**745**	725	745	50	.6703	.3701	Accept move, $R < p$
	1-4-5	3-2-5-4-1-3	∞			50			
	2-1-4-5	3-5-4-1-2-3	∞			50			
			∞						
3	4-1	3-1-4-2-5-3	∞			25			
	1-2	3-4-2-1-5-3	∞			25			
	2-5	3-4-1-5-2-3	750			25			
	4-1-2	**3-2-1-4-5-3**	**725**	745	725	25			Accept move, $L_{next} < L_{cur}$
	1-2-5	3-4-5-2-1-3	820			25			
	4-1-2-5	3-5-2-1-4-3	745			25			

moves, meaning that the previous move, 5-4-1 in iteration 1, is a local minimum. Hence, we scan all the tours in iteration 2 in ascending order of tour length until a tour is accepted (if all tours are rejected, either the scan is repeated using a new round of random numbers or the search ends). Move 1-4 with a tour length of 735 is rejected because $R = .8536$ is larger than $p = e^{(\frac{725-735}{50})} = .8187$. The next-in-order move, 2-1-4, with tour length of 745 is accepted because $R = .3701$ is less than $p = e^{(\frac{725-745}{50})} = .6703$.

At iteration 3, two accept-iterations have been realized at iterations 1 and 2. Hence, the temperature is changed from 50 to $.5(50) = 25$. The iterative process then continues until a terminating condition takes place.

Excel Moment

Figure 11.6 provides a snapshot of simulated annealing application to TSP (file *excel SimulatedAnnealingTSP.xls*). The spreadsheet follows the general layout of the tabu spreadsheet in Figure 11.5.

FIGURE 11.6

TSP simulated annealing metaheuristic using Excel spreadsheet (file *excelSimulatedAnnealingTSP.xls*)

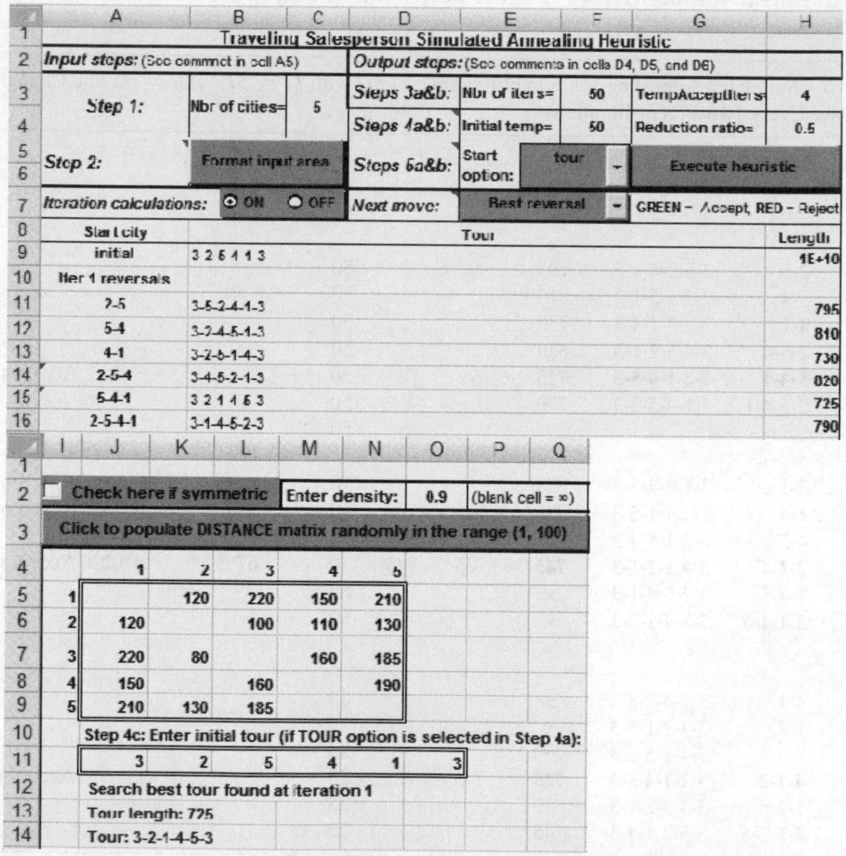

	A	B	C	D	E	F	G	H
1	Traveling Salesperson Simulated Annealing Heuristic							
2	Input steps: (See comment in cell A5)			Output steps: (See comments in cells D4, D5, and D6)				
3	Step 1:	Nbr of cities=	5	Steps 3a&b:	Nbr of iters=	50	TempAcceptIters=	4
4				Steps 4a&b:	Initial temp=	50	Reduction ratio=	0.5
5–6	Step 2:	Format input area		Steps 5a&b:	Start option:	tour	Execute heuristic	
7	Iteration calculations:	ON	OFF	Next move:	Best reversal		GREEN – Accept, RED – Reject	
8	Start city				Tour			Length
9	initial	3 2 5 4 1 3						1E+10
10	Iter 1 reversals							
11	2-5	3-5-2-4-1-3						795
12	5-4	3-2-4-5-1-3						810
13	4-1	3-2-5-1-4-3						730
14	2-5-4	3-4-5-2-1-3						820
15	5-4-1	3 2 1 4 5 3						725
16	2-5-4-1	3-1-4-5-2-3						790

	I	J	K	L	M	N	O	P	Q
1									
2	Check here if symmetric				Enter density:	0.9	(blank cell = ∞)		
3	Click to populate DISTANCE matrix randomly in the range (1, 100)								
4			1	2	3	4	5		
5		1		120	220	150	210		
6		2	120		100	110	130		
7		3	220	80		160	185		
8		4	150		160		190		
9		5	210	130	185				
10		Step 4c: Enter initial tour (if TOUR option is selected in Step 4a):							
11		3	2	5	4	1	3		
12		Search best tour found at iteration 1							
13		Tour length: 725							
14		Tour: 3-2-1-4-5-3							

PROBLEM SET 11.5B

1. Carry out three more iterations of Example 11.5-2.
2. Apply simulated annealing to the following problems starting with best nearest-neighbor tour:
   (a) The paint sequencing problem of Example 11.1-1.
   (b) Problem 1 of Set 11.2a.
   (c) Problem 4 of Set 11.2a.
   (d) Problem 5 of Set 11.2a.
3. *Excel–AMPL Experiment.* The matrix below provides the distances among 10 cities (all missing entries $= \infty$). (For convenience, file *prob11.5b-3.txt* gives the distance data in AMPL format.)

	1	2	3	4	5	6	7	8	9	10
1		100	2	11	80	5	39	95		28
2	17		42	33	21	59	46		79	29
3		63		57	92		55		68	52
4	36	27	25		40	49	48	63	16	
5	51	11	46	60		22	11	13	54	55
6		20	46	15	93		76	47	21	10
7	17		45	88	28	26		33	30	49
8	35	49	87	76		55	64			93
9	35	48	100	3	55		41			73
10		50	70	43	82	43	23	49	89	

Use file *excelSimulatedAnnealingTSP.xls* starting with the following:
   (a) A random tour.
   (b) Tour 4-5-3-2-6-7-8-10-9-1-4.
   (c) The best nearest-neighbor tour.

Compare the quality of the solutions in parts (a), (b), and (c) with the exact optimum solution obtained by AMPL.

11.5.3 TSP Genetic Algorithm

In the genetic metaheuristic introduced in Section 10.3.3, two parents are selected from a population to create two children. The children then become parents themselves replacing the two least-fit (in terms of tour length) parents in the population. The process of creating children and of retiring parents is repeated until a termination condition is reached.

The following is a description of the main elements of the genetic metaheuristic as it applies to the TSP.

1. Gene coding. The coding can be binary or numeric. The literature presents heuristics based on both types of coding. This presentation adopts the direct numeric tour code (e.g., 1-2-5-4-3-1).

2. Initial population. The first step is to identify the sets of outgoing nodes from each node in the network that can be reached *by a finite* tour leg. Starting from a specific (home) node, a tour is constructed by adding in the rightmost position a unique *non*redundant node selected from among all the outgoing nodes of the last-added node.

TABLE 11.8 Steps for Creating Children C1 and C2 from Parents P1 and P2 Using Order Crossover

Step	Action	Example (assume $n = 7$ nodes)
0	Select P1 and P2 from population.	P1 = 1-2-**5-4-3**-7-6 (link back to node 1)
		P2 = 5-4-**2-6-3**-1-7 (link back to tour 5)
1	Randomly select two crossover points, c_1 and c_2 with $c_1 < c_2$.	$R = .4425$ yields $c_1 = \text{int}(7 \times .3425) + 1 = 3$
		$R = .7123$ yields $c_2 = \text{int}(7 \times .7123) + 1 = 5$
2	Swap positions $(c_1, c_1 + 1, \ldots, c_2)$ in P1 and P2 to partially form C2 and C1, respectively.	C1 = ?-?-**2-6-3**-?-?
		C2 = ?-?-**5-4-3**-?-?
3	Create list L1(L2) by rearranging the elements of P1(P2) in the clockwise order $c_2 + 1, c_2 + 2, \ldots, n, 1, 2, \ldots, c_2$.	L1 = (7, 6, 1, 2, 5, 4, 3)
		L2 = (1, 7, 5, 4, 2, 6, 3)
4	From L1 (L2), create L1′ (L2′) by deleting the nodes already assigned to C1(2) in step 2 while preserving the order in L1 and L2.	L1′ = L1 − (2, 6, 3) = (7, 1, **5, 4**)
		L2′ = L2 − (5, 4, 3) = (1, 7, **2, 6**)
5	Assign the elements of L1′ (L2′) to the missing elements in C1(C2) in the order $c_2 + 1, c_2 + 2, \ldots, n, 1, 2, \ldots, c_1 - 1$.	C1 = **5-4**-2-6-3-7-1 (link back to node 5)
		C2 = **2-6**-5-4-3-1-7 (link back to node 2)

If a point is reached where no unique outgoing node exists, the entire process is repeated until a finite-length tour is found.

The requirement stipulating that outgoing nodes be reached by finite links guarantees that the constructed tour is feasible (has a finite length). Unlike tabu and simulated annealing where a new search move can be infeasible, infeasible parent tours may never lead to the creation of feasible child tours. This result is particularly true when the distance matrix is sparse.

3. Child creation. The process starts by selecting two parents, P1 and P2, whose genes are swapped to create two children, C1 and C2. We will assume that P1 represents the best parent (in terms of tour length) and P2 the next best. There are numerous ways for gene swapping [see Larrañaga et al. (1999) for a list of 25 such procedures]. In this presentation, we will use the **ordered crossover** procedure, whose steps are explained in Table 11.8.

The proposed procedure for creating children may lead to infeasible tours (with missing legs). If this happens, the procedure should be repeated as necessary until off-spring feasibility is realized.

4. Mutation. Mutation in child genes takes place with a small probability of about .1, interchanging the nodes of two randomly selected positions in the tour (excluding those of the home node). Random selection may be repeated to secure two distinct positions.

Example 11.5-3

We will use the TSP of Example 11.4-1 to demonstrate the application of the genetic heuristic.

$$\|d_{ij}\| = \begin{pmatrix} \infty & 120 & 220 & 150 & 210 \\ 120 & \infty & 100 & 110 & 130 \\ 220 & 80 & \infty & 160 & 185 \\ 150 & \infty & 160 & \infty & 190 \\ 210 & 130 & 185 & \infty & \infty \end{pmatrix}$$

The list of outgoing nodes can be determined from the distance matrix as

Node i	Outgoing nodes
1	$\{2, 3, 4, 5\}$
2	$\{1, 3, 4, 5\}$
3	$\{1, 2, 4, 5\}$
4	$\{1, 3, 5\}$
5	$\{1, 2, 3\}$

Table 11.9 provides the details of iterations 1, 2, and 11. Iteration 11 provides the best solution (which also happens to be optimum). The intervening iterations were omitted to conserve space.

We demonstrate the determination of initial population (6 parents) in iteration 1 by considering parent 1. Starting with home node 1, node 4 is selected randomly from the outgoing node set $\{2, 3, 4, 5\}$. Next, the outgoing nodes from node 4 are $\{1, 3, 5\} - \{1\}$ because $\{1\}$ is already in the partial tour. Selecting node 5 randomly yields the partial tour 1-4-5. The process is repeated until the full tour 1-4-5-2-3-1 is constructed. Keep in mind that if the construction of the tour is dead-ended (no new nodes can be added), then the entire process must be repeated anew. For example, tour construction cannot continue past partial tour 1-2-3-5 because there is no link from node 5 to (the only remaining) outgoing node 4.

TABLE 11.9   Genetic Algorithm Applied to TSP of Example 11.4-3

Iteration	Member	Tour	Crossovers	Length
1	1	1-4-5-2-3-1		790
	2	3-2-4-5-1-3		810
	3	1-2-4-5-3-1		825
	(Parent 2) 4	2-5-**3-4-1**-2		745
	5	3-4-5-1-2-3		780
	(Parent 1) 6	1-5-**3-2-4**-1		735
	Child 1	5-2-**3-4-1**-5	3 and 5	750
	Child 2	5-1-**3-2-4**-5		810
2	1	1-4-5-2-3-1		790
	2	5-1-3-2-4-5		810
	3	5-2-3-4-1-5		750
	(Parent 2) 4	2-5-3-**4-1**-2		745
	5	3-4-5-1-2-3		780
	(Parent 1) 6	1-5-3-**2-4**-1		735
	Child 1	5-3-2-**4-1**-5	4 and 5	735
	Child 2	5-3-1-2-4-5		825
...	...	...	...	...
11	(Parent 2) 1	1-5-**3-2**-4-1		735
	2	5 3 2 4 1-5		735
	3	5-3-2-4-1-5		735
	4	5-3-2-4-1-5		735
	(Parent 1) 5	4-5-**3-2**-1-4		725
	6	5-3-2-4-1-5		735
	Child 1	4-5-3-2-1-4	3 and 4	725
	Child 2	1-5-3-2-4-1		735

In iteration 1, P1 = 1-5-**3**-**2**-4 and P2 = 2-5-**3**-**4**-**1** because they are the two fittest parents (note that the definitions of P1 and P2 do not include the last elements 1 and 2, respectively). Using the (randomly generated) crossover points $c_1 = 3$ and $c_2 = 5$, we get partial C1 = ?-?-**3**-**4**-**1** and C2 = ?-?-**3**-**2**-**4**. Next, L1' = {1, 5, 3, 2, 4} − {3, 4, 1} = {5, 2}, which yields C1 = 5-2-**3**-**4**-**1**. Similarly, L2' = {2, 5, **3**, **4**, **1**} − {3, 2, 4} = {5, 1}, which yields C2 = 5-1-**3**-**2**-**4**. Children C1 and C2 now replace the least-fit parents 2 and 3 corresponding to the worst (longest) tour lengths (810 and 825) to yield the new population to be used in iteration 2 (it is immaterial which child replaces which of the two worst parents).

For small problems, the iterations may "saturate" rather quickly, in the sense that the children become indistinguishable from the parents they replace, as iteration 11 demonstrates. The only recourse in this case is to restart a new execution cycle that allows the use of a new (randomized) starting condition.

Excel Moment

Figure 11.7 provides a general Excel-based model for experimenting with the genetic metaheuristic (file *excelGeneticTSP.xls*). The model can be executed one iteration at a time or it can be automated until a termination condition is reached. The randomization of the starting conditions provides different stating conditions each time the execution button is pressed.

FIGURE 11.7

TSP genetic metaheuristic using Excel spreadsheet (file *excelGeneticTSP.xls*)

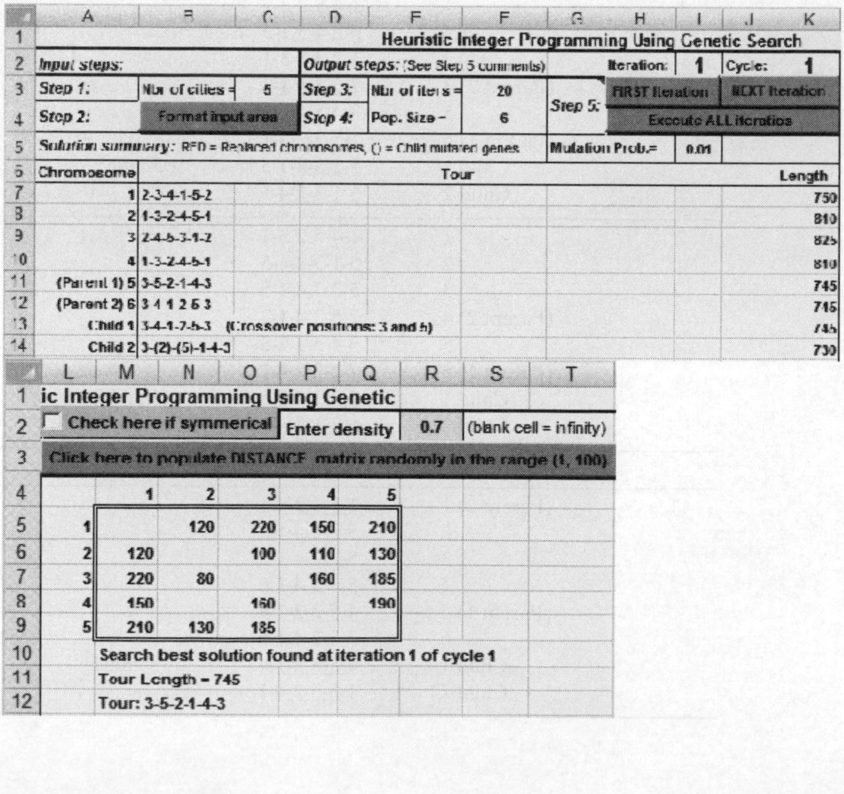

PROBLEM SET 11.5C

1. Carry out iterations 3 and 4 in Example 11.5-3.
2. Apply the genetic metaheuristic to the following problems starting with best nearest-neighbor tour:
   (a) The paint sequencing problem of Example 11.1-1.
   (b) Problem 1 of Set 11.2a.
   (c) Problem 4 of Set 11.2a.
   (d) Problem 5 of Set 11.2a.
3. *Excel–AMPL Experiment.* The matrix below provides the distances among 10 cities (all missing entries = ∞). (For convenience, file *prob11.5c-3.txt* gives the distance data in AMPL format.)

	1	2	3	4	5	6	7	8	9	10
1		100	2	11	80	5	39	95		28
2	17		42	33	21	59	46		79	29
3		63		57	92		55		68	52
4	36	27	25		40	49	48	63	16	
5	51	11	46	60		22	11	13	54	55
6		20	46	15	93		76	47	21	10
7	17		45	88	28	26		33	30	49
8	35	49	87	76		55	64			93
9	35	48	100	3	55		41			73
10		50	70	43	82	43	23	49	89	

Use file *excelGeneticTSP.xls* starting with the following:

(a) A random tour.

(b) Tour 4-5-3-2-6-7-8-10-9-1-4-5.

(c) The best nearest-neighbor tour.

Compare the quality of the solutions in parts (a), (b), and (c) with the exact optimum solution obtained by AMPL.

BIBLIOGRAPHY

Bosch, R. and A. Herman, "Continuous Line Drawings via the Traveling Salesman Problem," *Operations Research Letters*, Vol. 32, pp. 302–303, 2004.

Garfinkel, R. S., "Minimizing Wallpaper Waste. Part I: A Class of Travelling Salesman Problems," *Operations Research*, Vol. 25, pp. 741–751, 1977.

Gilmore, P. C., and Gomory, R. E., "Sequencing a One State-Variable Machine: A Solvable Case of the Travelling Salesman Problem," *Operations Research*, Vol. 12, pp. 655–679, 1964.

Laporte, G., "The Traveling Salesman Problem: An Overview of Exact and Approximate aAlgorithms," *European Journal of Operational Research*, Vol. 59, No. 2, pp. 231–247, 1992.

Larrañaga, P., C. Kuijpers, R. Murga, I. Inza, and S. Dizdarevich, "Genetic Algorithms for the Travelling Salesman Problem: A Review of Representations and Operators," *Artificial Intelligence Review*, No. 13, pp. 129–170, 1999.

Lenstra, J., and Rinnooy Kan, A., "Some Simple Applications of the Traveling Salesman Problem," *Operational Research Quarterly*, Vol. 26, No. 4, pp. 7171–733, 1975.

Ratliff, H., and Rosenthal, A. "Order-picking in a Rectangular Warehouse: A Solvable Case of the Traveling Salesman Problem," *Operations Research*, Vol. 31, pp. 507–521, 1983.

Yamada, Y. and R. Nakano "Genetic Algorithms for Job-Shop Scheduling Problems," *Proceedings of Modern Heuristic for Decision Support*, UNICOM seminar, London, 18–19 March 1997, pp. 67–81.

CHAPTER 12

Deterministic Dynamic Programming

Real-Life Application—Optimization of Crosscutting and Log Allocation at Weyerhaeuser

Mature trees are harvested and crosscut into logs to manufacture different end products (construction lumber, plywood, wafer boards, or paper). Log specifications (e.g., length and end diameters) differ depending on the mill where the logs are processed. With harvested trees measuring up to 100 feet in length, the number of crosscut combinations meeting mill requirements can be large, and the manner in which a tree is disassembled into logs can affect revenues. The objective is to determine the crosscut combinations that maximize the total revenue. The study uses dynamic programming to optimize the process. The proposed system was first implemented in 1978 with an annual increase in profit of at least $7 million. Case 8 in Chapter 26 on the website provides the details of the study.

12.1 RECURSIVE NATURE OF DYNAMIC PROGRAMMING (DP) COMPUTATIONS

The main idea of DP is to decompose the problem into (more manageable) subproblems. Computations are then carried out recursively where the optimum solution of one subproblem is used as an input to the next subproblem. The optimum solution for the entire problem is at hand when the last subproblem is solved. The manner in which the recursive computations are carried out depends on how the original problem is decomposed. In particular, the subproblems are normally linked by common constraints. The feasibility of these common constraints is maintained at all iterations.

Example 12.1-1 (Shortest-Route Problem)

Suppose that we want to select the shortest highway route between two cities. The network in Figure 12.1 provides the possible routes between the starting city at node 1 and the destination city at node 7. The routes pass through intermediate cities designated by nodes 2 to 6.

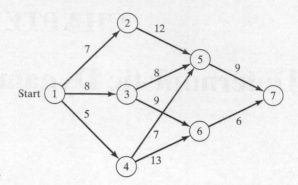

FIGURE 12.1

Route network for Example 12.1-1

We can solve this problem by enumerating all the routes between nodes 1 and 7 (there are five such routes). However, exhaustive enumeration is computationally intractable in large networks.

To solve the problem by DP, first decompose it into **stages** as delineated by the vertical dashed lines in Figure 12.2. Next, carry out the computations for each stage separately.

The general idea for determining the shortest route is to compute the shortest (cumulative) distances to all the terminal nodes of a stage and then use these distances as input data to the immediately succeeding stage. Starting from node 1, stage 1 reaches three end nodes (2, 3, and 4), and its computations are simple.

Stage 1 Summary.

Shortest distance from node 1 to node 2 = 7 miles (*from node* 1)

Shortest distance from node 1 to node 3 = 8 miles (*from node* 1)

Shortest distance from node 1 to node 4 = 5 miles (*from node* 1)

FIGURE 12.2

Decomposition of the shortest-route problem into stages

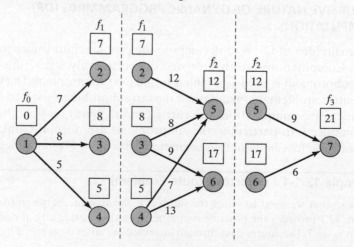

Next, stage 2 has two end nodes, 5 and 6. Figure 12.2 shows that node 5 can be reached from nodes 2, 3, and 4 via routes (2, 5), (3, 5), and (4, 5). This information, together with the summary results (shortest distances) in stage 1, determines the shortest (cumulative) distance to node 5 as

$$\begin{pmatrix} \text{Shortest distance} \\ \text{to node 5} \end{pmatrix} = \min_{i=2,3,4} \left\{ \begin{pmatrix} \text{Shortest distance} \\ \text{to node } i \end{pmatrix} + \begin{pmatrix} \text{Distance from} \\ \text{node } i \text{ to node 5} \end{pmatrix} \right\}$$

$$= \min \left\{ \begin{matrix} 7 + 12 = 19 \\ 8 + 8 = 16 \\ 5 + 7 = 12 \end{matrix} \right\} = 12 \,(from\ node\ 4)$$

Node 6 can be reached from nodes 3 and 4 only. Thus

$$\begin{pmatrix} \text{Shortest distance} \\ \text{to node 6} \end{pmatrix} = \min_{i=3,4} \left\{ \begin{pmatrix} \text{Shortest distance} \\ \text{to node } i \end{pmatrix} + \begin{pmatrix} \text{Distance from} \\ \text{node } i \text{ to node 6} \end{pmatrix} \right\}$$

$$= \min \left\{ \begin{matrix} 8 + 9 = 17 \\ 5 + 13 = 18 \end{matrix} \right\} = 17 \,(from\ node\ 3)$$

Stage 2 Summary.

Shortest distance from node 1 to node 5 $= 12$ miles $(from\ node\ 4)$

Shortest distance from node 1 to node 6 $= 17$ miles $(from\ node\ 3)$

The last step is to consider stage 3. The destination node 7 can be reached from either node 5 or 6. Using the summary results *from stage 2* and the distances from nodes 5 and 6 to node 7, we get

$$\begin{pmatrix} \text{Shortest distance} \\ \text{to node 7} \end{pmatrix} = \min_{i=5,6} \left\{ \begin{pmatrix} \text{Shortest distance} \\ \text{to node } i \end{pmatrix} + \begin{pmatrix} \text{Distance from} \\ \text{node } i \text{ to node 7} \end{pmatrix} \right\}$$

$$= \min \left\{ \begin{matrix} 12 + 9 = 21 \\ 17 + 6 = 23 \end{matrix} \right\} = 21 \,(from\ node\ 5)$$

Stage 3 Summary.

Shortest distance from node 1 to node 7 $= 21$ miles $(from\ node\ 5)$

Stage 3 summary shows that the shortest distance between nodes 1 and 7 is 21 miles. To determine the optimal route, start at stage 3 summary, where node 7 links to node 5; stage 2 summary links node 4 to node 5; and stage 1 summary links node 4 to node 1. Thus, the shortest route is $1 \rightarrow 4 \rightarrow 5 \rightarrow 7$.

The example reveals the basic properties of DP computations:

1. The computations at each stage are a function of the feasible routes of that stage, and only that stage.

2. A current stage is linked to the *immediately preceding* stage only (without regard to earlier stages) based on the shortest-distance summary of the immediately preceding stage.

Recursive equation. This section shows how the recursive computations in Example 12.1-1 can be expressed mathematically. Let $f_i(x_i)$ be the shortest distance to node x_i at stage i, and define $d(x_{i-1}, x_i)$ as the distance from node x_{i-1} to node x_i. The DP recursive equation is defined as

$$f_0(x_0 = 1) = 0$$

$$f_i(x_i) = \min_{\substack{\text{all feasible} \\ (x_{i-1}, x_i) \text{ routes}}} \{d(x_{i-1}, x_i) + f_{i-1}(x_{i-1})\}, i = 1, 2, 3$$

All distances are measured from 0 by setting $f_0(x_0 = 1) = 0$. The main recursive equation expresses the shortest distance $f_i(x_i)$ at stage i as a function of the next node, x_i. In DP terminology, x_i is referred to as the **state** at stage i. The *state* links successive *stages* in a manner that permits making optimal feasible decisions at a future stage independently of the decisions already made in all preceding stages.

The definition of the *state* leads to the following unifying framework for DP.

Principle of optimality. Future decisions for all *future* stages constitute an optimal policy regardless of the policy adopted in all *preceding* stages.

The implementation of the principle of optimality is evident in the computations in Example 12.1-1. In stage 3, the recursive computations at node 7 use the shortest distance to nodes 5 and 6 (i.e., the states of stage 2) without concern about how nodes 5 and 6 are reached from the starting node 1.

The principle of optimality does not address the details of how a subproblem is optimized. The reason is the generic nature of the subproblem. It can be linear or nonlinear, and the number of alternative can be finite or infinite. All the principle of optimality does is "break down" the original problem into more computationally tractable subproblems.

PROBLEM SET 12.1A

*1. Solve Example 12.1-1, assuming the following routes are used:

$$d(1, 2) = 5, d(1, 3) = 9, d(1, 4) = 8$$

$$d(2, 5) = 10, d(2, 6) = 17$$

$$d(3, 5) = 4, d(3, 6) = 10$$

$$d(4, 5) = 9, d(4, 6) = 9$$

$$d(5, 7) = 19$$

$$d(6, 7) = 9$$

2. I am an avid hiker. Last summer, my friend G. Don and I went on a 5-day hike-and-camp trip in the beautiful White Mountains in New Hampshire. We decided to limit our hiking to an area comprising three well-known peaks: Mounts Washington, Jefferson, and Adams. Mount Washington has a 6-mile base-to-peak trail. The corresponding base-to-peak trails for Mounts Jefferson and Adams are 4 and 5 miles, respectively. The trails joining the bases of the three mountains are 3 miles between Mounts Washington and Jefferson, 2 miles between Mounts Jefferson and Adams, and 5 miles between Mounts Adams and

Washington. We started on the first day at the base of Mount Washington and returned to the same spot at the end of 5 days. Our goal was to hike as many miles as we could. We also decided to climb exactly one mountain each day and to camp at the base of the mountain we would be climbing the next day. Additionally, we decided that the same mountain could not be visited in any two consecutive days. Use DP to schedule the 5-day hike.

12.2 FORWARD AND BACKWARD RECURSION

Example 12.1-1 uses **forward recursion** in which the computations proceed from stage 1 to stage 3. The same example can be solved by **backward recursion**, starting at stage 3 and ending at stage 1.

Naturally, both the forward and backward recursions yield the same optimum. Although the forward procedure appears more logical, DP literature mostly uses backward recursion. The reason for this preference is that, in general, backward recursion can be more efficient computationally.

We will demonstrate the use of backward recursion by applying it to Example 12.1-1. The demonstration will also provide the opportunity to present the DP computations in a compact tabular form.

Example 12.2-1

The backward recursive equation for Example 12.2-1 is

$$f_4(x_4 = 7) = 0$$

$$f_i(x_i) = \min_{\substack{\text{all feasible} \\ \text{routes } (x_i, x_{i+1})}} \{d(x_i, x_{i+1}) + f_{i+1}(x_{i+1})\}, i = 1, 2, 3$$

The order of computations is $f_3 \rightarrow f_2 \rightarrow f_1$.

Stage 3. Node 7 ($x_4 = 7$) is connected to nodes 5 and 6 ($x_3 = 5$ and 6) with exactly one route each. The following table summarizes stage 3 computations:

	$d(x_3, x_4)$	Optimum solution	
x_3	$x_4 = 7$	$f_3(x_3)$	x_4^*
5	9	9	7
6	6	6	7

Stage 2. Route (2, 6) does not exist. Given $f_3(x_3)$ from stage 3, we can compare the feasible alternatives as the following table shows:

	$d(x_2, x_3) + f_3(x_3)$		Optimum solution	
x_2	$x_3 = 5$	$x_3 = 6$	$f_2(x_2)$	x_3^*
2	12 + 9 = 21	—	21	5
3	8 + 9 = 17	9 + 6 = 15	15	6
4	7 + 9 = 16	13 + 6 = 19	16	5

The optimum solution of stage 2 reads as follows: For cities 2 and 4, the shortest routes pass through city 5, and for city 3, the shortest route passes through city 6.

Stage 1. From node 1 we have three alternative routes: $(1, 2)$, $(1, 3)$, and $(1, 4)$. Using $f_2(x_2)$ from stage 2, we get

	$d(x_1, x_2) + f_2(x_2)$			Optimum solution	
x_1	$x_2 = 2$	$x_2 = 3$	$x_2 = 4$	$f_1(x_1)$	x_2^*
1	$7 + 21 = 28$	$8 + 15 = 23$	$5 + 16 = 21$	21	4

Stage 1 solution links city 1 to city 4. Next, stage 2 solution links city 4 to city 5. Finally, stage 3 solution connects city 5 to city 7. The optimum route is $1 \rightarrow 4 \rightarrow 5 \rightarrow 7$, and the associated distance is 21 miles.

PROBLEM SET 12.2A

1. For Problem 1, Set 12.1a, develop the backward recursive equation, and use it to find the optimum solution.
2. For Problem 2, Set 12.1a, develop the backward recursive equation, and use it to find the optimum solution.
*3. For the network in Figure 12.3, it is desired to determine the shortest route between cities 1 to 7. Define the stages and the states using backward recursion, and then solve the problem.

12.3 SELECTED DP APPLICATIONS

This section presents four applications, each with a new idea in the implementation of DP. All the examples use the *backward* recursive equation because of its prevalence in the literature.

FIGURE 12.3

Network for Problem 3, Set 12.2a

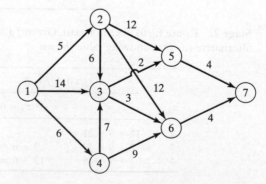

As you study each application, pay special attention to the three basic elements of the DP model:

1. Definition of the *stages*
2. Definition of the *alternatives* at each stage
3. Definition of the *states* for each stage

Of the three elements, the definition of the *state* is usually the most subtle. The applications presented here show that the definition of the state varies depending on the situation being modeled. Nevertheless, as you investigate each application, you will find it helpful to consider the following questions:

1. What relationships bind the stages together?
2. What information is needed to make feasible decisions at the current stage without regard to how the decisions made at the preceding stages have been reached?

You can enhance your understanding of the concept of the *state* by questioning the validity of the way it is defined here. Try another definition that may appear "more logical" to you, and use it in the recursive computations. You will soon discover that the definitions presented here are correct. Meanwhile, the associated mental process should give you a better understanding of the role of *states* in the development of DP recursive equation.

12.3.1 Knapsack/Fly-Away Kit/Cargo-Loading Model

The knapsack model classically deals with determining the most valuable items a combat soldier carries in a backpack. The problem represents a general resource allocation model in which limited resources are used by a number of economic activities. The objective is to maximize the total return.[1]

The (backward) recursive equation is developed for the general problem of allocating n items to a knapsack with weight capacity W. Let m_i be the number of units of item i in the knapsack, and define r_i and w_i as the unit revenue and weight of item i. The general problem can be represented as

$$\text{Maximize } z = r_1 m_1 + r_2 m_2 + \cdots + r_n m_n$$

subject to

$$w_1 m_1 + w_2 m_2 + \cdots + w_n m_n \leq W$$

$$m_1, m_2, \ldots, m_n \text{ nonnegative integers}$$

The three elements of the model are

---

[1]The *knapsack* problem is also known in the literature as the *fly-away kit* problem (determination of the most valuable items a jet pilot takes on board) and the *cargo-loading* problem (determination of the most valuable items to be loaded on a navy ship). It appears that the three names were coined to ensure equal representation of three branches of the armed forces: Army, Air Force, and Navy!

1. *Stage i* is represented by item $i, i = 1, 2, \ldots, n$.

2. The *alternatives* at stage i are the number of units of item i, $m_i = 0, 1, \ldots, \left[\frac{W}{w_i}\right]$, where $\left[\frac{W}{w_i}\right]$ is the largest integer less than or equal to $\frac{W}{w_i}$. This definition allows the solution to allocate none, some, or all of the resource W to any of the m items. The return for m_i is $r_i m_i$.

3. The *state* at stage i is represented by x_i, the total weight assigned to stages (items) $i, i + 1, \ldots$, and n. This definition recognizes that the weight limit is the only constraint that binds all n stages.[2]

Define

$$f_i(x_i) = \text{maximum return for stages } i, i + 1, \text{ and } n, \text{ given state } x_i$$

The most convenient way to construct the recursive equation is a two-step procedure:

Step 1.   Express $f_i(x_i)$ as a function of $f_i(x_{i+1})$ as follows:

$$f_{n+1}(x_{n+1}) \equiv 0$$

$$f_i(x_i) = \min_{\substack{m_i = 0, 1, \ldots, \left[\frac{W}{w_i}\right] \\ x_i \leq W}} \{r_i m_i + f_{i+1}(x_{i+1})\}, i = 1, 2, \ldots, n$$

Step 2.   Express x_{i+1} as a function of x_i to ensure consistency with the left-hand side of the recursive equation. By definition, $x_i - x_{i+1} = w_i m_i$ represents the weight used at stage i. Thus, $x_{i+1} = x_i - w_i m_i$, and the proper recursive equation is given as

$$f_i(x_i) = \max_{\substack{m_i = 0, 1, \ldots, \left[\frac{W}{w_i}\right] \\ x_i \leq W}} \{r_i m_i + f_{i+1}(x_i - w_i m_i)\}, i = 1, 2, \ldots, n$$

Example 12.3-1

A 4-ton vessel can be loaded with one or more of three items. The following table gives the unit weight, w_i, in tons and the unit revenue in thousands of dollars, r_i, for item i. The goal is to determine the number of units of each item that will maximize the total return.

Item i	w_i	r_i
1	2	31
2	3	47
3	1	14

Because the unit weight w_i and the maximum weight W are integers, the state x_i assumes integer values only.

Stage 3.   The exact weight to be allocated to stage 3 (item 3) is not known in advance but can assume one of the values $0, 1, \ldots$, and 4 (because $W = 4$ tons and $w_3 = 1$ ton). A value of m_3

---

[2]The definition of the state can be multidimensional. For example, the volume of the knapsack may pose another restriction. In general, a multidimensional state implies more complex stage calculations. See Section 12.4.

is feasible only if $w_3 m_3 \leq x_3$. Thus, all the infeasible values (with $w_3 m_3 > x_3$) are excluded. The revenue for item 3 is $14 m_3$. Thus, the recursive equation for stage 3 is

$$f_3(x_3) = \max_{m_3 = 0, 1, \ldots, 4} \{14 m_3\}$$

The following tableau summarizes the computations for stage 3:

			$14 m_3$			Optimum solution	
x_3	$m_3 = 0$	$m_3 = 1$	$m_3 = 2$	$m_3 = 3$	$m_3 = 4$	$f_3(x_3)$	m_3^*
0	0	—	—	—	—	0	0
1	0	14	—	—	—	14	1
2	0	14	28	—	—	28	2
3	0	14	28	42	—	42	3
4	0	14	28	42	56	56	4

Stage 2. $\max \{m_2\} = \left[\frac{4}{3} \right] = 1$, or $m_3 = 0, 1, f_2(x_2) = \max_{m_3 = 0, 1} \{47 m_2 + f_3(x_2 - 3 m_2)\}$

	$47 m_2 + f_3(x_2 - 3 m_2)$		Optimum solution	
x_2	$m_2 = 0$	$m_2 = 1$	$f_2(x_2)$	m_2^*
0	0 + 0 = 0	—	0	0
1	0 + 14 = 14	—	14	0
2	0 + 28 = 28	—	28	0
3	0 + 42 = 42	47 + 0 = 47	47	1
4	0 + 56 = 56	47 + 14 = 61	61	1

Stage 1. $\max \{m_1\} = \left[\frac{4}{2} \right] = 2$ or $m_1 = 0, 1, 2, f_1(x_1) = \max_{m_3 = 0, 1, 2} \{31 m_2 + f_2(x_1 - 2 m_1)\}$

	$31 m_1 + f_2(x_1 - 2 m_1)$			Optimum solution	
x_1	$m_1 = 0$	$m_1 = 1$	$m_1 = 2$	$f_1(x_1)$	m_1^*
0	0 + 0 = 0	—	—	0	0
1	0 + 14 = 14	—	—	14	0
2	0 + 28 = 28	31 + 0 = 31	—	31	1
3	0 + 47 = 47	31 + 14 = 45	—	47	0
4	0 + 61 = 61	31 + 28 = 59	62 + 0 = 62	62	2

The optimum solution is determined in the following manner: Given $W = 4$ tons, from stage 1, $x_1 = 4$ gives the optimum alternative $m_1^* = 2$—meaning that 2 units of item 1 will be loaded on the vessel. This allocation leaves $x_2 = x_1 - 2 m_2^* = 4 - 2 \times 2 = 0$ for stages 2 and 3. From stage 2, $x_2 = 0$ yields $m_2^* = 0$, which leaves $x_3 = x_2 - 3 m_2 = 0 - 3 \times 0 = 0$ units for stage 3. Next, from stage 3, $x_3 = 0$ gives $m_3^* = 0$. Thus, the complete optimal solution is $m_1^* = 2$, $m_2^* = 0$, and $m_3^* = 0$. The associated return is $f_1(4) = \$62,000$.

In the table for stage 1, we actually need to compute the row for $x_1 = 4$ only, because this is the last stage to be considered. However, the computations for $x_1 = 0, 1, 2$, and 3 are included to allow carrying out sensitivity analysis. For example, what happens if the vessel capacity is 3 tons in place of 4 tons? The new optimum solution can be determined as

$$(x_1 = 3) \rightarrow (m_1^* = 0) \rightarrow (x_2 = 3) \rightarrow (m_2^* = 1) \rightarrow (x_3 = 0) \rightarrow (m_3^* = 0)$$

Thus the optimum is $(m_1^*, m_2^*, m_3^*) = (0, 1, 0)$, and the optimum revenue is $f_1(3) = \$47{,}000$.

Excel Moment

The nature of DP computations makes it impossible to develop a general computer code that can handle all DP problems. Perhaps this explains the persistent absence of commercial DP software.

In this section, we present an Excel-based algorithm for handling a subclass of DP problems: the single-constraint knapsack problem (file *excelKnapsack.xls*). The algorithm is not data specific and can handle problems in which an alternative can assume values in the range 0 to 10.

Figure 12.4 shows the starting screen of the knapsack (backward) DP model. The screen is divided into two sections: The right section (columns Q:V) summarizes the output solution. In the left section (columns A:P), the input data for the current stage appear in rows 3, 4, and 6. Stage computations start at row 7. (Columns H:N are hidden to conserve space). The input data symbols are self-explanatory. To fit the spreadsheet conveniently on one screen, the maximum feasible value for alternative m_i at stage i is 10 (cells D6:N6).

Figure 12.5 shows the stage computations generated by the algorithm for Example 12.3-1. The computations are carried out one stage at a time, and the user provides the basic data that drive each stage.

Starting with stage 3, and using the notation and data in Example 12.3-1, the input cells are updated as the following list shows:

Cell(s)	Data
D3	Number of stages, $N = 3$
G3	Resource limit, $W = 4$
C4	Current stage $= 3$
E4	$w_3 = 1$
G4	$r_3 = 14$
D6:H6	$m_3 = (0, 1, 2, 3, 4)$

FIGURE 12.4

Excel starting screen of the general DP knapsack model (file *excelKnapsack.xls*)

	A	B	C	D	E	F	G	O	P	Q	R	S	T	U	V
1					Dynamic Programming (Backward) Knapsack Model										
2				Input Data and Stage Calculations							Ouput Solution Summary				
3		Number of stages,N=			Res. limit, W=					x	f	m	x	f	m
4	Current stage=			w=		r=									
5	Are m values correct?							Stage							
6			m=					Optimum							
7			r*m=					Solution							
8			w*m=					f	m						
9															
10															

Stage 3:

Dynamic Programming (Backward) Knapsack Model

Input Data and Stage Calculations | Ouput Solution Summary

A	B	C	D	E	F	G	H	O	P
Number of stages,N=		3	Res. limit, W=		4				
Current stage=		3	w3=	1		r3=	14		
Are m3 values correct?			yes	yes	yes	yes	yes	Stage	
		m3=	0	1	2	3	4	Optimum	
Stage4		r3*m3=	0	14	28	42	56	Solution	
	f4	w3*m3=	0	1	2	3	4	f3	m3
0	x3= 0	0	0	1111111	1111111	1111111	1111111	0	0
	x3= 1	0	14	1111111	1111111	1111111		14	1
	x3= 2	0	14	28	111111	1111111		28	2
	x3= 3	0	14	28	42	1111111		42	3
	x3= 4	0	14	28	42	56		56	4

Ouput Solution Summary:

Stage 3		
x	f	m
0	0	0
1	14	1
2	28	2
3	42	3
4	56	4

Stage 2:

Dynamic Programming (Backward) Knapsack Model

Input Data and Stage Calculations | Ouput Solution Summary

A	B	C	D	E	F	G	H	O	P
Number of stages,N=		3	Res. limit, W=		4				
Current stage=		2	w2=	3		r2=	47		
Are m2 values correct?			yes	yes	delete	delete	delete	Stage	
		m2=	0	1	2	3	4	Optimum	
Stage3		r2*m2=	0	47				Solution	
	f3	w2*m2=	0	3				f2	m2
0	x2= 0	0	0	1111111				0	0
14	x2= 1	14	1111111					14	0
28	x2= 2	28	1111111					28	0
42	x2= 3	42	47					47	1
56	x2= 4	56	61					61	1

Ouput Solution Summary:

Stage 3			Stage 2		
x	f	m	x	f	m
0	0	0	0	0	0
1	14	1	1	14	0
2	28	2	2	28	0
3	42	3	3	47	1
4	56	4	4	61	1

Stage 1:

Dynamic Programming (Backward) Knapsack Model

Input Data and Stage Calculations | Ouput Solution Summary

A	B	C	D	E	F	G	H	O	P
Number of stages,N=		3	Res. limit, W=		4				
Current stage=		1	w1=	2		r1=	31		
Are m1 values correct?			yes	yes	yes	delete	delete	Stage	
		m1=	0	1	2	3	4	Optimum	
Stage2		r1*m1=	0	31	62			Solution	
	f2	w1*m1=	0	2	4			f1	m1
0	x1= 0	0	1111111	1111111				0	0
14	x1= 1	14	1111111	1111111				14	0
28	x1= 2	28	31	1111111				31	1
47	x1= 3	47	45	1111111				47	0
61	x1= 4	61	59	62				62	2

Ouput Solution Summary:

Stage 2		
x	f	m
0	0	0
1	14	0
2	28	0
3	47	1
4	61	1

Stage 1		
x	f	m
0	0	0
1	14	0
2	31	1
3	47	0
4	62	2

FIGURE 12.5

Excel DP model for the knapsack problem of Example 12.3-1 (file *excelKnapsack.xls*)

Note that the feasible values of m_3 are $0, 1, \ldots,$ and 4 $\left(= \left[\frac{W}{w_3} \right] = \left[\frac{4}{1} \right] \right)$, as in Example 12.3-1. The spreadsheet automatically checks the validity of the values the user enters and issues self-explanatory messages in row 5: "yes," "no," and "delete."

As stage 3 data are entered and verified, the spreadsheet "comes alive" and generates all the necessary computations of the stage (columns B through P) automatically. The value -1111111 is used to indicate that the corresponding entry is not feasible. The optimum solution (f_3, m_3) for the stage is given in columns O and P. Column A provides the values of f_4, which equal 0 for all x_3 because the computations start at stage 3 (you can leave A9:A13 blank or enter zeros).

Now that stage 3 calculations are complete, take the following steps to create a *permanent* record of the optimal solution of the current stage and to prepare the spreadsheet for next stage:

Step 1.   Copy the x_3-values, C9:C13, and paste them in Q5:Q9 in the optimum solution summary section. Next, copy the (f_3, m_3)-values, O9:P13, and paste them in R5:S9. Remember that you need to paste values only, which requires selecting *Paste Special* from Edit menu and *Values* from the dialogue box.

Step 2.   Copy the f_3-values in R5:R9, and paste them in A9:A13 (you do *not* need *Paste Special* in this step).

Step 3.   Change cell C4 to 2, and enter the new values of w_2, r_2, and m_2 for stage 2.

Step 2 places $f_{i+1}(x_i - w_i m_i)$ in column A in preparation for calculating $f_i(x_i)$ at stage i (see the recursive formula for the knapsack problem in Example 12.3-1). A similar procedure is repeated for stage 1. When stage 1 is complete, the solution summary can be used to read the optimum solution, as was explained in Example 12.3-1. Note that the organization of the output solution summary area (columns Q:V) is free formatted, and you can organize its contents in any manner you desire.

PROBLEM SET 12.3A[3]

1. In Example 12.3-1, determine the optimum solution, assuming that the maximum weight capacity of the vessel is 2 tons, Repeat the question for a weight capacity of 5 tons.
2. Solve the cargo-loading problem of Example 12.3-1 for each of the following sets of data:
   *(a) $w_1 = 4, r_1 = 70, w_2 = 1, r_2 = 20, w_3 = 2, r_3 = 40, W = 6$
   (b) $w_1 = 1, r_1 = 15, w_2 = 2, r_2 = 30, w_3 = 3, r_3 = 40, W = 4$
3. In the cargo-loading model of Example 12.3-1, suppose that the revenue per item includes a constant amount that is realized only if the item is chosen, as the following table shows:

Item	Revenue
1	$\begin{cases} -5 + 31m_1, & \text{if } m_1 > 0 \\ 0, & \text{otherwise} \end{cases}$
2	$\begin{cases} -15 + 47m_2, & \text{if } m_2 > 0 \\ 0, & \text{otherwise} \end{cases}$
3	$\begin{cases} -4 + 14m_3, & \text{if } m_3 > 0 \\ 0, & \text{otherwise} \end{cases}$

Find the optimal solution using DP. (*Hint*: You can use the Excel file *excelSetupKnapsack.xls* to check your calculations.)

4. A wilderness hiker must pack three items: food, first-aid kits, and clothes. The backpack has a capacity of $3\,\text{ft}^3$. Each unit of food takes $1\,\text{ft}^3$. A first-aid kit occupies $1/4\,\text{ft}^3$, and each piece of cloth takes about $1/2\,\text{ft}^3$. The hiker assigns the priority weights 3, 4, and 5 to food, first aid, and clothes, respectively, which means that clothes are the most valuable of

---

[3]In this Problem Set, you are encouraged where applicable to verify hand computations using the template *excelKnapsack.xls*.

the three items. From experience, the hiker must take at least one unit of each item and no more than two first-aid kits. How many of each item should the hiker take?

*5. A student must select 10 electives from four different departments, with at least one course from each department. The 10 courses are allocated to the four departments in a manner that maximizes "knowledge." The student measures knowledge on a 100-point scale and comes up with the following chart:

	Number of courses						
Department	1	2	3	4	5	6	≥ 7
I	25	50	60	80	100	100	100
II	20	70	90	100	100	100	100
III	40	60	80	100	100	100	100
IV	10	20	30	40	50	60	70

How should the student select the courses?

6. I have a small backyard garden that measures 10×20 feet. This spring I plan to plant three types of vegetables: tomatoes, green beans, and corn. The garden is organized in 10-foot rows. The corn and tomatoes rows are 2 feet wide, and the beans rows are 3 feet wide. I like tomatoes the most and beans the least, and on a scale of 1 to 10, I would assign 10 to tomatoes, 7 to corn, and 3 to beans. Regardless of my preferences, my wife insists that I plant at least one row of green beans and no more than two rows of tomatoes. How many rows of each vegetable should I plant?

*7. Habitat for Humanity is a wonderful (U.S.-based) international charity organization that builds homes for needy families using volunteer labor and donates building materials. An eligible family can choose from three home sizes: 1000, 1100, and 1200 ft². Each size requires a certain number of labor volunteers. The Fayetteville, Arkansas, chapter has received five applications for the upcoming 6 months. The committee in charge assigns a score to each application based on several factors. A higher score signifies higher need. For the next 6 months, the chapter can count on a maximum of 23 volunteers. The following data summarize the scores for the applications and the required number of volunteers. Which applications should the committee approve?

Application	House size (ft²)	Score	Number of volunteers
1	1200	78	7
2	1000	64	4
3	1100	68	6
4	1000	62	5
5	1200	85	8

8. Sheriff Bassam is up for reelection in Washington county. The funds available for the campaign are about $10,000. Although the reelection committee would like to launch the campaign in all five precincts of the county, limited funds dictate otherwise. The table given below lists the voting population and the amount of funds needed to launch an effective campaign in each precinct. A precinct can receive either all its allotted funds or none. How should the funds be allocated?

Precinct	Population	Required funds ($)
1	3100	3500
2	2600	2500
3	3500	4000
4	2800	3000
5	2400	2000

9. An electronic device consists of three components. The three components are in series so that the failure of one component causes the failure of the device. The reliability (probability of no failure) of the device can be improved by installing one or two standby units in each component. The table listed below charts the reliability, r, and the cost, c. The total capital available for the construction of the device is $10,000. How should the device be constructed? (*Hint:* The objective is to maximize the reliability, $r_1 r_2 r_3$, of the device. This means that the decomposition of the objective function is multiplicative rather than additive.)

Number of parallel units	Component 1		Component 2		Component 3	
	r_1	$c_1(\$)$	r_2	$c_2(\$)$	r_3	$c_3(\$)$
1	.6	1000	.7	3000	.5	2000
2	.8	2000	.8	5000	.7	4000
3	.9	3000	.9	6000	.9	5000

10. Solve the following model by DP:

$$\text{Maximize } z = \prod_{i=1}^{n} y_i$$

subject to

$$y_1 + y_2 + \cdots + y_n = c$$

$$y_j \geq 0, \; j = 1, 2, \ldots, n$$

(*Hint:* This problem is similar to Problem 9, except that the variables, y_j, are continuous.)

11. Solve the following problem by DP:

$$\text{Minimize } z = y_1^2 + y_2^2 + \cdots + y_n^2$$

subject to

$$\prod_{i=1}^{n} y_i = c$$

$$y_i > 0, i = 1, 2, \ldots, n$$

12. Solve the following problem by DP:

$$\text{Maximize } z = (y_1 + 2)^2 + y_2 y_3 + (y_4 - 5)^2$$

subject to

$$y_1 + y_2 + y_3 + y_4 \leq 5$$

$$y_i \geq 0 \text{ and integer, } i = 1, 2, 3, 4$$

13. Solve the following problem by DP:

$$\text{Minimize } z = \max \{f(y_1), f(y_2), \ldots, f(y_n)\}$$

subject to

$$y_1 + y_2 + \cdots + y_n = c$$

$$y_i \geq 0, i = 1, 2, \ldots, n$$

Provide the solution for the special case of $n = 3, c = 10$, and $f(y_1) = y_1 + 5$, $f(y_2) = 5y_2 + 3$, and $f(y_3) = y_3 - 2$.

12.3.2 Workforce Size Model

Labor needs in construction projects can be met through hiring and firing of workers. Both activities incur cost. The goal is to minimize the total cost of labor needed for the project.

Assume that duration of the project is n weeks and that the minimum labor force required in week i is b_i workers. The model assumes that additional cost is incurred if a week's workforce exceeds the minimum requirement or if additional hiring takes place in a week. For simplicity, no cost is incurred when firing takes place.

The cost of maintaining a workforce x_i larger than the minimum b_i in week i incurs excess cost $C_1(x_i - b_i)$. If $x_i > x_{i-1}$, hiring occurs at the additional cost of $C_2(x_i - x_{i-1})$.

The elements of the DP model are defined as follows:

1. *Stage i* is represented by week i, $i = 1, 2, \ldots, n$.
2. The *alternatives* at stage i are x_i, the number of laborers in week i.
3. The *state* at stage i is x_{i-1}, the number of laborers available in week $i - 1$.

The DP recursive equation is given as

$$f_{n+1}(x_n) \equiv 0$$

$$f_i(x_{i-1}) = \min_{x_i \geq b_i} \{C_1(x_i - b_i) + C_2(x_i - x_{i-1}) + f_{i+1}(x_i)\}, i = 1, 2, \ldots, n$$

The computations start at stage n and terminate at stage 1.

Example 12.3-2

A contractor estimates that the size of the workforce needed over the next 5 weeks is 5, 7, 8, 4, and 6 workers, respectively. Excess labor kept on the force will cost \$300 per worker per week, and new hiring in any week will incur a fixed cost of \$400 plus \$200 per worker per week.

The data of the problem are

$$b_1 = 5, b_2 = 7, b_3 = 8, b_4 = 4, b_5 = 6$$

$$C_1(x_i - b_i) = 3(x_i - b_i), x_i > b_i, i = 1, 2, \ldots, 5$$

$$C_2(x_i - x_{i-1}) = 4 + 2(x_i - x_{i-1}), x_i > x_{i-1}, i = 1, 2, \ldots, 5$$

The cost functions C_1 and C_2 are in hundreds of dollars.

Stage 5. $(b_5 = 6)$

x_4	$C_1(x_5 - 6) + C_2(x_5 - x_4)$ $x_5 = 6$	Optimum solution $f_5(x_4)$	x_5^*
4	$3(0) + 4 + 2(2) = 8$	8	6
5	$3(0) + 4 + 2(1) = 6$	6	6
6	$3(0) + 0 \quad\quad = 0$	0	6

Stage 4. $(b_4 = 4)$

x_3	$C_1(x_4 - 4) + C_2(x_4 - x_3) + f_5(x_4)$ $x_4 = 4$	$x_4 = 5$	$x_4 = 6$	Optimum solution $f_4(x_3)$	x_4^*
8	$3(0) + 0 + 8 = 8$	$3(1) + 0 + 6 = 9$	$3(2) + 0 + 0 = 6$	6	6

Stage 3. $(b_3 = 8)$

x_2	$C_1(x_3 - 8) + C_2(x_3 - x_2) + f_4(x_3)$ $x_3 = 8$	Optimum solution $f_3(x_2)$	x_6^*
7	$3(0) + 4 + 2(1) + 6 = 12$	12	8
8	$3(0) + 0 \quad\quad + 6 = 6$	6	8

Stage 2. $(b_2 = 7)$

x_1	$C_1(x_2 - 7) + C_2(x_3 - x_2) + f_3(x_2)$ $x_2 = 7$	$x_2 = 8$	Optimum solution $f_2(x_1)$	x_2^*
5	$3(0) + 4 + 2(2) + 12 = 20$	$3(1) + 4 + 2(3) + 6 = 19$	19	8
6	$3(0) + 4 + 2(1) + 12 = 18$	$3(1) + 4 + 2(2) + 6 = 17$	17	8
7	$3(0) + 0 \quad\quad + 12 = 12$	$3(1) + 4 + 2(1) + 6 = 15$	12	7
8	$3(0) + 0 \quad\quad + 12 = 12$	$3(1) + 0 \quad\quad + 6 = 9$	9	8

Stage 1.   ($b_1 = 5$)

	$C_1(x_1 - 5) + C_2(x_1 - x_0) + f_2(x_1)$				Optimum solution	
x_0	$x_1 = 5$	$x_1 = 6$	$x_1 = 7$	$x_1 = 8$	$f_1(x_0)$	x_1^*
0	$3(0) + 4 + 2(5)$ $+ 19 = 33$	$3(1) + 4 + 2(6)$ $+ 17 = 36$	$3(2) + 4 + 2(7)$ $+ 12 = 36$	$3(2) + 4 + 2(8)$ $+ 9 = 35$	33	5

The optimum solution is determined as

$$x_0 = 0 \rightarrow x_1^* = 5 \rightarrow x_2^* = 8 \rightarrow x_3^* = 8 \rightarrow x_4^* = 6 \rightarrow x_5^* = 6$$

The solution can be translated to the following plan:

Week i	Minimum labor force (b_i)	Actual labor force (x_i)	Decision	Cost
1	5	5	Hire 5 workers	$4 + 2 \times 5 = 14$
2	7	8	Hire 3 workers	$4 + 2 \times 3 + 1 \times 3 = 13$
3	8	8	No change	0
4	4	6	Fire 2 workers	$3 \times 2 = 6$
5	6	6	No change	0

The total cost is $f_1(0) = \$3300$.

PROBLEM SET 12.3B

1. Solve Example 12.3.2 for each of the following minimum labor requirements:
   *(a) $b_1 = 6, b_2 = 5, b_3 = 3, b_4 = 6, b_5 = 8$
   (b) $b_1 = 6, b_2 = 4, b_3 = 7, b_4 = 8, b_5 = 2$

2. In Example 12.3-2, if a severance pay of \$100 is incurred for each fired worker, determine the optimum solution.

*3. Luxor Travel arranges 1-week tours to southern Egypt. The agency provides 7, 4, 7, and 8 rental cars over the next 4 weeks. Luxor Travel subcontracts with a local car dealer to supply rental needs. The dealer charges a rental fee of \$220 per car per week, plus a flat fee of \$500 for any rental transaction. Luxor, however, may elect to keep the rentals for an additional week and simply continue to pay the rent. What is the best way for Luxor Travel to handle the rental situation?

4. GECO is contracted for the next 4 years to supply aircraft engines at the rate of four engines a year. Available production capacity and production costs vary from year to year. GECO can produce five engines in year 1, six in year 2, three in year 3, and five in year 4. The corresponding production costs per engine over the next 4 years are \$200,000, \$330,000, \$350,000, and \$420,000, respectively. GECO can elect to produce more than it needs in a certain year, in which case the engines must be properly stored until shipment date. The storage cost per engine also varies from year to year, and is estimated to be \$20,000 for year 1, \$30,000 for year 2, \$40,000 for year 3, and \$50,000 for year 4. Currently, at the start of year 1, GECO has one engine ready for shipping. Develop an optimal production plan for GECO.

12.3.3 Equipment Replacement Model

Machines that stay longer in service incur higher maintenance cost and may be replaced after a number of years in operation. The situation deals with determining the most economical age of a machine.

Suppose that the machine replacement problem spans n years. At the *start* of each year, a machine is either kept in service an extra year or replaced with a new one. Let $r(t)$, $c(t)$, and $s(t)$ represent the yearly revenue, operating cost, and salvage value, respectively, of a t-year-old machine. The cost of acquiring a new machine in any year is I.

The elements of the DP model are as follows:

1. *Stage i* is represented by year i, $i = 1, 2, \ldots, n$.
2. The *alternatives* at stage (year) i are keep (K) or replace (R) the machine at the *start* of year i.
3. The *state* at stage i is the age of the machine at the start of year i.

Given that the machine is t years old at the *start* of year i, define

$$f_i(t) = \text{maximum net income for years } i, i + 1, \ldots, \text{and } n$$

The recursive equation is

$$f_n(t) = \max \begin{cases} r(t) - c(t) + s(t + 1), & \text{if KEEP} \\ r(0) + s(t) + s(1) - I - c(0), & \text{if REPLACE} \end{cases}$$

$$f_i(t) = \max \begin{cases} r(t) - c(t) + f_{i+1}(t + 1), & \text{if KEEP} \\ r(0) + s(t) - I - c(0) + f_{i+1}(1), & \text{if REPLACE} \end{cases}, i = 1, 2, \ldots, n-1$$

Example 12.3-3

A company needs to determine the optimal replacement policy for a current 3-year-old machine over the next 4 years ($n = 4$). A 6-year-old machine must be replaced. The cost of a new machine is $100,000. The following table gives the data of the problem.

Age, t (yr)	Revenue, $r(t)$ ($)	Operating cost, $c(t)$ ($)	Salvage value, $s(t)$ ($)
0	20,000	200	—
1	19,000	600	80,000
2	18,500	1200	60,000
3	17,200	1500	50,000
4	15,500	1700	30,000
5	14,000	1800	10,000
6	12,200	2200	5000

The determination of the feasible values for the age of the machine at each stage is somewhat tricky. Figure 12.6 summarizes the network representing the problem. At the *start* of year 1, we have a 3-year-old machine. We can either replace it (R) or keep it (K) for another year. If replacement occurs, the new machine will be 1 year old at the start of year 2; otherwise, the kept

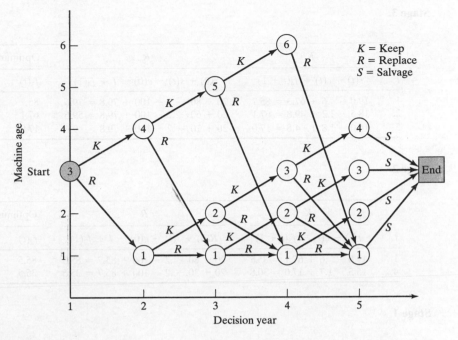

FIGURE 12.6

Representation of machine age as a function of decision year in Example 12.3-3

machine will be 4 years old. The same logic applies at the start of years 2 to 4. If a 1-year-old machine is replaced at the start of years 2, 3, and 4, its replacement will be 1 year old at the start of the following year. Also, at the start of year 4, a 6-year-old machine must be replaced, and at the end of year 4 (end of the planning horizon), we salvage (S) the machine.

The network shows that at the start of year 2, the possible ages of the machine are 1 and 4 years. For the start of year 3, the possible ages are 1, 2, and 5 years, and for the start of year 4, the possible ages are 1, 2, 3, and 6 years. The network also assumes that the machine will be salvaged at the start of year 5 regardless of age.

The solution of the network in Figure 12.6 is equivalent to finding the longest route (i.e., maximum revenue) from the start of year 1 to the end of year 4. We will use the tabular form to solve the problem. All values are in thousands of dollars. Note that if a machine is replaced in year 4 (i.e., end of the planning horizon), its revenue will include the salvage value, $s(t)$, of the *replaced* machine and the salvage value, $s(1)$, of the *replacement* machine. Also, if in year 4 a machine of age t is kept, its salvage value will be $s(t + 1)$.

Stage 4.

	K	R	Optimum solution	
t	$r(t) + s(t + 1) - c(t)$	$r(0) + s(t) + s(1) - c(0) - I$	$f_4(t)$	Decision
1	$19.0 + 60 - .6 = 78.4$	$20 + 80 + 80 - .2 - 100 = 79.8$	79.8	R
2	$18.5 + 50 - 1.2 = 67.3$	$20 + 60 + 80 - .2 - 100 = 59.8$	67.3	K
3	$17.2 + 30 - 1.5 = 45.7$	$20 + 50 + 80 - .2 - 100 = 49.8$	49.8	R
6	(Must replace)	$20 + 5 + 80 - .2 - 100 = 4.8$	4.8	R

Stage 3.

	K	R	Optimum solution	
t	$r(t) - c(t) + f_4(t + 1)$	$r(0) + s(t) - c(0) - I + f_4(1)$	$f_3(t)$	Decision
1	$19.0 - .6 + 67.3 = 85.7$	$20 + 80 - .2 - 100 + 79.8 = 79.6$	85.7	K
2	$18.5 - 1.2 + 49.8 = 67.1$	$20 + 60 - .2 - 100 + 79.8 = 59.6$	67.1	K
5	$14.0 - 1.8 + 4.8 = 17.0$	$20 + 10 - .2 - 100 + 79.8 = 9.6$	17.0	R

Stage 2.

	K	R	Optimum solution	
t	$r(t) - c(t) + f_3(t + 1)$	$R(0) + s(t) - c(0) - I + f_3(1)$	$f_2(t)$	Decision
1	$19.0 - .6 + 67.1 = 85.5$	$20 + 80 - .2 - 100 + 85.7 = 85.5$	85.5	K or R
4	$15.5 - 1.7 + 17.0 = 30.8$	$20 + 30 - .2 - 100 + 85.7 = 35.5$	35.5	R

Stage 1.

	K	R	Optimum solution	
t	$r(t) - c(t) + f_2(t + 1)$	$R(0) + s(t) - c(0) - I + f_2(1)$	$f_1(t)$	Decision
3	$17.2 - 1.5 + 35.5 = 51.2$	$20 + 50 - .2 - 100 + 85.5 = 55.3$	55.3	R

Figure 12.7 summarizes the optimal solution. At the start of year 1, given $t = 3$, the optimal decision is to replace the machine. Thus, the new machine will be 1 year old at the start of year 2, and $t = 1$ at the start of year 2 calls for either keeping or replacing the machine. If it is replaced, the new machine will be 1 year old at the start of year 3; otherwise, the kept machine will be 2 years old. The process is continued in this manner until year 4 is reached.

The alternative optimal policies starting in year 1 are (R, K, K, R) and (R, R, K, K). The total cost is \$55,300.

FIGURE 12.7

Solution of Example 12.3-3

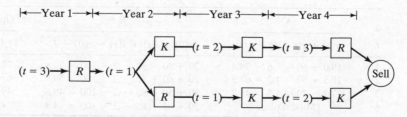

PROBLEM SET 12.3C

1. In each of the following cases, develop the network, and find the optimal solution for the model in Example 12.3-3:

    (a) The machine is 2 years old at the start of year 1.

    (b) The machine is 1 year old at the start of year 1.

    (c) The machine is bought new at the start of year 1.

*2. My son, age 13, has a lawn-mowing business with 10 customers. For each customer, he cuts the grass 3 times a year, which earns him $50 for each mowing. He has just paid $200 for a new mower. The maintenance and operating cost of the mower is $120 for the first year in service and increases by 20% a year thereafter. A 1-year-old mower has a resale value of $150, which decreases by 10% a year thereafter. My son, who plans to keep his business until he is 16, thinks that it is more economical to buy a new mower every 2 years. He bases his decision on the fact that the price of a new mower will increase only by 10% a year. Is his decision justified?

3. Circle Farms wants to develop a replacement policy for its 2-year-old tractor over the next 5 years. A tractor must be kept in service for at least 3 years, but must be disposed of after 5 years. The current purchase price of a tractor is $40,000 and increases by 10% a year. The salvage value of a 1-year-old tractor is $30,000 and decreases by 10% a year. The current annual operating cost of the tractor is $1300 but is expected to increase by 10% a year.

    (a) Formulate the problem as a shortest-route problem.

    (b) Develop the associated recursive equation.

    (c) Determine the optimal replacement policy of the tractor over the next 5 years.

4. Consider the equipment replacement problem over a period of n years. A new piece of equipment costs c dollars, and its resale value after t years in operation is $s(t) = n - t$ for $n > t$ and zero otherwise. The annual revenue is a function of the age t and is given by $r(t) = n^2 - t^2$ for $n > t$ and zero otherwise.

    (a) Formulate the problem as a DP model.

    (b) Find the optimal replacement policy given that $c = \$10,000, n = 5$, and the equipment is 2 years old.

5. Solve Problem 4, assuming that the equipment is 1 year old and that $n = 4$, $c = \$6000$, and $r(t) = \frac{n}{1+t}$.

12.3.4 Investment Model

Suppose that you want to invest the amounts $P_1, P_2, \ldots, P_n$ at the start of each of the next n years. You have two investment opportunities in two banks: First Bank pays an interest rate r_1, and Second Bank pays r_2, both compounded annually. To encourage deposits, both banks pay bonuses on new investments in the form of a percentage of the amount invested. The respective bonus percentages for First Bank and Second Bank are q_{i1} and q_{i2} for year i. Bonuses are paid at the end of the year in which the investment is made and may be reinvested in either bank in the immediately succeeding year. This means that only bonuses and fresh new money may be invested in either bank. However, once an investment is deposited, it must remain in the bank until the end of year n.

The elements of the DP model are as follows:

1. *Stage i* is represented by year i, $i = 1, 2, \ldots, n$.
2. The *alternatives* at stage i are I_i and $\bar{I}_i$, the amounts invested in First Bank and Second Bank, respectively.
3. The *state*, x_i, at stage i is the amount of capital available for investment at the start of year i.

We note that $\bar{I}_i = x_i - I_i$ by definition. Thus

$$x_1 = P_1$$

$$x_i = P_i + q_{i-1,1}I_{i-1} + q_{i-1,2}(x_{i-1} - I_{i-1})$$

$$= P_i + (q_{i-1,1} - q_{i-1,2})I_{i-1} + q_{i-1,2}x_{i-1}, i = 2, 3, \ldots, n$$

The reinvestment amount x_i includes only new money plus any bonus from investments made in year $i - 1$.

Define

$$f_i(x_i) = \text{optimal value of the investments for years } i, i + 1, \ldots, \text{and } n, \text{ given } x_i$$

Next, define s_i as the accumulated sum at the end of year n, given that I_i and $(x_i - I_i)$ are the investments made in year i in First Bank and Second Bank, respectively. Letting $\alpha_k = (1 + r_k)$, $k = 1, 2$, the problem can be stated as

$$\text{Maximize } z = s_1 + s_2 + \cdots + s_n$$

where

$$s_i = I_i\alpha_1^{n+1-i} + (x_i - I_i)\alpha_2^{n+1-i}$$

$$= (\alpha_1^{n+1-i} - \alpha_2^{n+1-i})I_i + \alpha_2^{n+1-i}x_i, i = 1, 2, \ldots, n - 1$$

$$s_n = (\alpha_1 + q_{n1} - \alpha_2 - q_{n2})I_n + (\alpha_2 + q_{n2})x_n$$

The terms q_{n1} and q_{n2} in s_n are added because the bonuses for year n are part of the final accumulated sum of money from the investment.

The backward DP recursive equation is thus given as

$$f_{n+1}(x_{n+1}) \equiv 0$$

$$f_i(x_i) = \max_{0 \le I_i \le x_i} \{s_i + f_{i+1}(x_{i+1})\}, i = 1, 2, \ldots, n - 1$$

As given previously, x_{i+1} is defined in terms of x_i.

Example 12.3-4

Suppose that you want to invest $4000 now and $2000 at the start of years 2 to 4. The interest rate offered by First Bank is 8% compounded annually, and the bonuses over the next 4 years are 1.8%, 1.7%, 2.1%, and 2.5%, respectively. The annual interest rate offered by Second Bank is .2% lower than that of First Bank, but its bonus is .5% higher. The objective is to maximize the accumulated capital at the end of 4 years.

Using the notation introduced previously, we have

$$P_1 = \$4,000, P_2 = P_3 = P_4 = \$2000$$

$$\alpha_1 = (1 + .08) = 1.08$$

$$\alpha_2 = (1 + .078) = 1.078$$

$$q_{11} = .018, q_{21} = .017, q_{31} = .021, q_{41} = .025$$

$$q_{12} = .023, q_{22} = .022, q_{32} = .026, q_{42} = .030$$

Stage 4.

$$f_4(x_4) = \max_{0 \le I_4 \le x_4} \{s_4\}$$

where

$$s_4 = (\alpha_1 + q_{41} - \alpha_2 - q_{42})I_4 + (\alpha_2 + q_{42})x_4 = -.003I_4 + 1.108x_4$$

The function s_4 is linear in I_4 in the range $0 \le I_4 \le x_4$, and its maximum occurs at $I_4 = 0$ because of the negative coefficient of I_4. Thus, the optimum solution for stage 5 can be summarized as

	Optimum solution	
State	$f_4(x_4)$	I_4^*
x_4	$1.108x_4$	0

Stage 3.

$$f_3(x_3) = \max_{0 \le I_3 \le x_3} \{s_3 + f_4(x_4)\}$$

where

$$s_3 = (1.08^2 - 1.078^2)I_3 + 1.078^2 x_3 = .00432I_3 + 1.1621x_3$$

$$x_4 = 2000 - .005I_3 + .026x_3$$

Thus,

$$f_3(x_3) = \max_{0 \le I_3 \le x_3} \{.00432I_3 + 1.1621x_3 + 1.108(2000 - .005I_3 + 0.026x_3\}$$

$$= \max_{0 \le I_3 \le x_3} \{2216 - .00122I_3 + 1.1909x_3\}$$

	Optimum solution	
State	$f_3(x_3)$	I_3^*
x_3	$2216 + 1.1909x_3$	0

Stage 2.

$$f_2(x_2) = \max_{0 \le I_2 \le x_2} \{s_2 + f_3(x_3)\}$$

where

$$s_2 = (1.08^3 - 1.078^3)I_2 + 1.078^3 x_2 = .006985 I_2 + 1.25273 x_2$$

$$x_3 = 2000 - .005 I_2 + .022 x_2$$

Thus,

$$f_2(x_2) = \max_{0 \le I_2 \le x_2} \{.006985 I_2 + 1.25273 x_2 + 2216 + 1.1909(2000 - .005 I_2 + .022 x_2)\}$$

$$= \max_{0 \le I_2 \le x_2} \{4597.8 + .0010305 I_2 + 1.27893 x_2\}$$

	Optimum solution	
State	$f_2(x_2)$	I_2^*
x_2	$4597.8 + 1.27996 x_2$	x_2

Stage 1.

$$f_1(x_1) = \max_{0 \le I_1 \le x_1} \{s_1 + f_2(x_2)\}$$

where

$$s_1 = (1.08^4 - 1.078^4)I_1 + 1.078^4 x_1 = .01005 I_2 + 1.3504 x_1$$

$$x_2 = 2000 - .005 I_1 + .023 x_1$$

Thus,

$$f_1(x_1) = \max_{0 \le I_1 \le x_1} \{.01005 I_1 + 1.3504 x_1 + 4597.8 + 1.27996(2000 - .005 I_1 + .023 x_1)\}$$

$$= \max_{0 \le I_1 \le x_1} \{7157.7 + .00365 I_1 + 1.37984 x_1\}$$

	Optimum solution	
State	$f_1(x_1)$	I_1^*
$x_1 = \$4000$	$7157.7 + 1.38349 x_1$	$\$4000$

Working backward and noting that $I_1^* = 4000$, $I_2^* = x_2$, $I_3^* = I_4^* = 0$, we get

$$x_1 = 4000$$

$$x_2 = 2000 - .005 \times 4000 + .023 \times 4000 = \$2072$$

$$x_3 = 2000 - .005 \times 2072 + .022 \times 2072 = \$2035.22$$

$$x_4 = 2000 - .005 \times 0 + .026 \times \$2035.22 = \$2052.92$$

The optimum solution is thus summarized as

Year	Optimum solution	Decision	Accumulation
1	$I_1^* = x_1$	Invest $x_1 = \$4000$ in First Bank	$s_1 = \$5441.80$
2	$I_2^* = x_2$	Invest $x_2 = \$2072$ in First Bank	$s_2 = \$2610.13$
3	$I_3^* = 0$	Invest $x_3 = \$2035.22$ in Second Bank	$s_3 = \$2365.13$
4	$I_4^* = 0$	Invest $x_4 = \$2052.92$ in Second Bank	$s_4 = \$2274.64$

Total accumulation $= f_1(x_1) = 7157.7 + 1.38349(4000) = \$12{,}691.66 \, (= s_1 + s_2 + s_3 + s_4)$

PROBLEM SET 12.3D

1. Solve Example 12.3-4, assuming that $r_1 = .085$ and $r_2 = .08$. Additionally, assume that $P_1 = \$5000$, $P_2 = \$4000$, $P_3 = \$3000$, and $P_4 = \$2000$.

2. An investor with an initial capital of \$10,000 must decide at the end of each year how much to spend and how much to invest in a savings account. Each dollar invested returns $\alpha = \$1.09$ at the end of the year. The satisfaction derived from spending \$$y$ in any one year is quantified monetarily as \$$\sqrt{y}$. Solve the problem by DP for a span of 5 years.

3. A farmer owns k sheep. At the end of each year, a decision is made as to how many to sell or keep. The profit from selling a sheep in year i is P_i. The sheep kept in year i will double in number in year $i + 1$. The farmer plans to sell out completely at the end of n years.

   *(a) Derive the general recursive equation for the problem.

   (b) Solve the problem for $n = 3$ years, $k = 2$ sheep, $p_1 = \$100$, $p_2 = \$130$, and $p_3 = \$120$.

12.3.5 Inventory Models

DP has important applications in the area of inventory control. Chapters 13 and 16 present some of these applications. The models in Chapter 13 are deterministic, and those in Chapter 16 are probabilistic. Other probabilistic DP applications are given in Chapter 24 on the website.

12.4   PROBLEM OF DIMENSIONALITY

In all the DP models presented in this chapter, the *state* at any stage is represented by a single element. For example, in the knapsack model (Section 12.3.1), the only restriction is the weight of the item. More realistically in this case, the volume of the knapsack may also be another viable restriction, in which case the *state* at any stage is said to be two-dimensional: weight and volume.

The increase in the number of state variables increases the computations at each stage. This is particularly clear in DP tabular computations because the number of rows in each tableau corresponds to all possible combinations of state variables. This computational difficulty is sometimes referred to in the literature as the **curse of dimensionality**.

The following example is chosen to demonstrate the *problem of dimensionality*. It also serves to show the relationship between linear and dynamic programming.

Example 12.4-1

Acme Manufacturing produces two products. The daily capacity of the manufacturing process is 430 minutes. Product 1 requires 2 minutes per unit, and product 2 requires 1 minute per unit. There is no limit on the amount produced of product 1, but the maximum daily demand for product 2 is 230 units. The unit profit of product 1 is $2 and that of product 2 is $5. Find the optimal solution by DP.

The problem is represented by the following linear program:

$$\text{Maximize } z = 2x_1 + 5x_2$$

subject to

$$2x_1 + x_2 \leq 430$$
$$x_2 \leq 230$$
$$x_1, x_2 \geq 0$$

The elements of the DP model are as follows:

1. *Stage i* corresponds to product $i, i = 1, 2$.
2. *Alternative* x_i is the amount of product $i, i = 1, 2$.
3. *State* (v_2, w_2) represents the amounts of resources 1 and 2 (production time and demand limits) used in stage 2.
4. *State* (v_1, w_1) represents the amounts of resources 1 and 2 (production time and demand limits) used in stages 1 *and* 2.

Stage 2. Define $f_2(v_2, w_2)$ as the maximum profit for stage 2 (product 2), given the state (v_2, w_2). Then

$$f_2(v_2, w_2) = \max_{\substack{0 \leq x_2 \leq v_2 \\ 0 \leq x_2 \leq w_2}} \{5x_2\}$$

Thus, max $\{5x_2\}$ occurs at $x_2 = \min\{v_2, w_2\}$, and the solution for stage 2 is

	Optimum solution	
State	$f_2(v_2, w_2)$	x_2
(v_2, w_2)	$5 \min\{v_2, w_2\}$	$\min\{v_2, w_2\}$

Stage 1.

$$f_1(v_1, w_1) = \max_{0 \leq 2x_1 \leq v_1} \{2x_1 + f_2(v_1 - 2x_1, w_1)\}$$

$$= \max_{0 \leq x_1 \leq v_1/2} \{2x_1 + 5\min(v_1 - 2x_1, w_1)\}$$

The optimization of stage 1 involves the solution of a (generally more difficult) minimax problem. For the present problem, we set $v_1 = 430$ and $w_1 = 230$, which gives $0 \le x_1 \le 215$. Because $\min(430 - 2x_1, 230)$ is the lower envelope of two intersecting lines (verify!), it follows that

$$\min(430 - 2x_1, 230) = \begin{cases} 230, & 0 \le x_1 \le 100 \\ 430 - 2x_1, & 100 \le x_1 \le 215 \end{cases}$$

and

$$f_1(430, 230) = \max_{0 \le x_1 \le 215} \{2x_1 + 5\min(430 - 2x_1, 230)\}$$

$$= \max_{x_1} \begin{cases} 2x_1 + 1150, & 0 \le x_1 \le 100 \\ -8x_1 + 2150, & 100 \le x_1 \le 215 \end{cases}$$

You can verify graphically that the optimum value of $f_1(430, 230)$ occurs at $x_1 = 100$. Thus, we get

State	Optimum solution	
	$f_1(v_1, w_1)$	x_1
$(430, 230)$	1350	100

To determine the optimum value of x_2, we note that

$$v_2 = v_1 - 2x_1 = 430 - 200 = 230$$

$$w_2 = w_1 - 0 = 230$$

Consequently,

$$x_2 = \min(v_2, w_2) = 230$$

The complete optimum solution is thus summarized as

$$x_1 = 100 \text{ units}, x_2 = 230 \text{ units}, z = \$1350$$

PROBLEM SET 12.4A

1. Solve the following problems by DP.
   (a) Maximize $z = 4x_1 + 14x_2$
   subject to ·

   $$2x_1 + 7x_2 \le 21$$
   $$7x_1 + 2x_2 \le 21$$
   $$x_1, x_2 \ge 0$$

   (b) Maximize $z = 8x_1 + 7x_2$
   subject to

   $$2x_1 + x_2 \le 8$$
   $$5x_1 + 2x_2 \le 15$$
   $$x_1, x_2 \ge 0 \text{ and integer}$$

(c) Maximize $z = 7x_1^2 + 6x_1 + 5x_2^2$
subject to

$$x_1 + 2x_2 \leq 10$$
$$x_1 - 3x_2 \leq 9$$
$$x_1, x_2 \geq 0$$

2. In the n-item knapsack problem of Example 12.3-1, suppose that the weight and volume limitations are W and V, respectively. Given that w_i, v_i, and r_i are the weight, value, and revenue per unit, respectively, of item i, write the DP backward recursive equation for the problem.

BIBLIOGRAPHY

Bertsekas, D., *Dynamic Programming: Deterministic and Stochastic Models*, Prentice Hall, Upper Saddle River, NJ, 1987.

Denardo, E., *Dynamic Programming Theory and Applications*, Prentice Hall, Upper Saddle River, NJ, 1982.

Dreyfus, S., and A. Law, *The Art and Theory of Dynamic Programming*, Academic Press, New York, 1977.

Sntedovich, M., *Dynamic Programming*, Marcel Dekker, New York, 1991.

CHAPTER 13

Deterministic Inventory Models

13.1 GENERAL INVENTORY MODEL

The inventory problem deals with stocking an item to meet fluctuations in demand. Keeping too much of an item on hand increases cost of capital and storage, and stocking too little adversely disrupts production and/or sales. The result is to seek an inventory level that balances the two extreme situations by minimizing an appropriate cost function. The problem reduces to controlling the inventory level by devising an **inventory policy** that answers two questions:

1. *How much* to order?
2. *When* to order?

The basis of the inventory model is the following generic cost function:

$$\begin{pmatrix} \text{Total} \\ \text{inventory} \\ \text{cost} \end{pmatrix} = \begin{pmatrix} \text{Purchasing} \\ \text{cost} \end{pmatrix} + \begin{pmatrix} \text{Setup} \\ \text{cost} \end{pmatrix} + \begin{pmatrix} \text{Holding} \\ \text{cost} \end{pmatrix} + \begin{pmatrix} \text{Shortage} \\ \text{cost} \end{pmatrix}$$

1. *Purchasing cost* is the price per unit of an inventory item. At times the item is offered at a discount if the order size exceeds a certain amount, which is a factor in deciding *how much to order.*
2. *Setup cost* represents the fixed charge incurred when an order (no matter the size) is placed.
3. *Holding cost* represents the cost of maintaining inventory in stock. It includes the interest on capital and the cost of storage, maintenance, and handling.
4. *Shortage cost* is the penalty incurred when stock is out. It includes potential loss of income, disruption in production, and the subjective cost of loss in customer's goodwill.

491

The described costs are conflicting, in the sense that an increase in one may result in the reduction of another (e.g., more frequent ordering results in higher setup cost but lower inventory holding cost). The purpose of the minimization of the total inventory cost function is to balance these conflicting costs.

An inventory system may require **periodic reviews** (e.g., ordering at the start of every week or every month). Alternatively, the system may be based on **continuous reviews**, placing a new order when the inventory level drops to a specific **reorder point**. An example of the two types occurs in retail stores. The review is *periodic* if the item is replenished every week or month. It is *continuous* if replenishment takes place whenever the inventory level dips below a certain level.

13.2   ROLE OF DEMAND IN THE DEVELOPMENT OF INVENTORY MODELS

In general, the analytic complexity of inventory models depends on whether the demand is deterministic or probabilistic. Within either category, the demand may or may not vary with time. For example, the consumption of natural gas used in heating homes is seasonal. Though the seasonal pattern repeats itself annually, a same-month consumption may vary from year to year, depending, for example, on the severity of weather.

In practical situations, the demand pattern in an inventory model may assume one of four types:

1. Deterministic and constant (static) with time.
2. Deterministic and variable (dynamic) with time.
3. Probabilistic and stationary over time.
4. Probabilistic and nonstationary over time.

This categorization assumes the availability of reliable data to forecast future demand.

In terms of the development of inventory models, the first category is the simplest analytically, and the fourth is the most complex. On the other hand, the first category is the least likely to occur in practice and the fourth is the most prevalent. In practice, the goal is to balance model simplicity and model accuracy.

How can we decide if a certain approximation of demand is acceptable? An initial "guesstimate" is based on computing the mean and standard deviation of consumption for a specific period (e.g., monthly). The coefficient of variation, $V = \frac{\text{Standard deviation}}{\text{Mean}} \times 100$, can then be used to assess the nature of demand using the following guideline:[1]

1. If the average monthly demand (taken over a number of years) is "approximately" constant and V is reasonably small ($<20\%$), then the demand may be considered deterministic and constant.

---

[1]The coefficient of variation, V, measures the relative variation or spread of the data around the mean. In general, higher values of V indicate higher uncertainty in the use of the mean as an approximation of the monthly consumption. For deterministic demand, $V = 0$, because the associated standard deviation is zero.

2. If the average monthly demand varies appreciably among the different months but *V* remains reasonably small for all months, then the demand may be considered deterministic but variable.

3. If in Case 1 *V* is high (>20%) but approximately constant, then the demand is probabilistic and stationary.

4. The remaining case is the probabilistic nonstationary demand, which occurs when the averages and coefficients of variation vary appreciably month to month.

Example 13.2-1

The data in Table 13.1 provide the monthly (January through December) consumption of natural gas in a rural residential home over a span of 10 years (1990–1999). The supplier sends a truck to fill a tank at the request of a homeowner.

From the standpoint of inventory modeling, it is reasonable to assume that each month represents a decision period for the placement of an order. The purpose of this example is to analyze the nature of the demand.

An examination of the mean and the coefficient of variation, *V*, in Table 13.1 reveals two results:

1. Average consumption is dynamic (not constant) because of the high average consumption during winter months.

2. The coefficient of variation, *V*, is reasonably small (<15%) so that the monthly demand can be considered approximately deterministic.

The conclusion is that the monthly demand is (approximately) deterministic but variable.

TABLE 13.1   Monthly (January through December) Consumption of Natural Gas

	Natural-Gas Consumption in Cubic Feet											
Year	Jan	Feb	Mar	Apr	May	Jun	Jul	Aug	Sep	Oct	Nov	Dec
1990	100	110	90	70	65	50	40	42	56	68	88	95
1991	110	125	98	80	60	53	44	45	63	77	92	99
1992	90	100	88	79	56	57	38	39	60	70	82	90
1993	121	130	95	90	70	58	41	44	70	80	95	100
1994	109	119	99	75	68	55	43	41	65	79	88	94
1995	130	122	100	85	73	58	42	43	64	75	80	101
1996	115	100	103	90	76	55	45	40	67	78	98	97
1997	130	115	100	95	80	60	49	48	64	85	96	105
1998	125	100	94	86	79	59	46	39	69	90	100	110
1999	87	80	78	75	69	48	39	41	50	70	88	93
Mean	111.7	110	95	82.5	69.6	55.3	42.7	42.2	62.8	77.2	90.7	98
Std Dev	15.54	15.2	7.5	7.99	7.82	3.95	3.4	2.86	6.09	6.91	6.67	6
V(%)	13.91	13.8	7.9	9.68	11.24	7.13	7.96	6.78	9.69	8.95	7.35	6.1

13.3   STATIC ECONOMIC-ORDER-QUANTITY (EOQ) MODELS

This section presents three variations of the economic-order-quantity (EOQ) model with static (constant) demand. These models are simple analytically.

13.3.1 Classical EOQ Model

The simplest of the inventory models involves constant-rate demand with instantaneous order replenishment and no shortage. Define

$$y = \text{Order quantity (number of units)}$$
$$D = \text{Demand rate (units per unit time)}$$
$$t_0 = \text{Ordering cycle length (time units)}$$

The inventory level follows the pattern depicted in Figure 13.1. When the inventory reaches zero level, an order of size y units is received instantaneously. The stock is depleted uniformly at a constant demand rate, D. The ordering cycle for this pattern is

$$t_0 = \frac{y}{D} \text{ time units}$$

The cost model requires two cost parameters.

$$K = \text{Setup cost associated with the placement of an order (dollars per order)}$$
$$h = \text{Holding cost (dollars per inventory unit per unit time)}$$

Given that the average inventory level is $\frac{y}{2}$, the total cost *per unit time* (TCU) is

$$TCU(y) = \text{Setup cost per unit time} + \text{Holding cost per unit time}$$

$$= \frac{\text{Setup cost} + \text{Holding cost per cycle } t_0}{t_0}$$

$$= \frac{K + h\left(\frac{y}{2}\right)t_0}{t_0}$$

$$= \frac{K}{\left(\frac{y}{D}\right)} + h\left(\frac{y}{2}\right)$$

FIGURE 13.1

Inventory pattern in the classical EOQ model

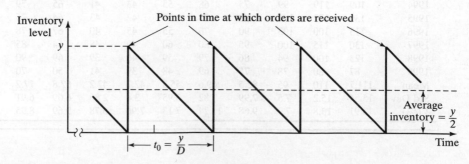

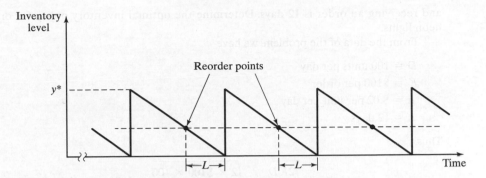

FIGURE 13.2

Reorder point in the classic EOQ model

The optimum value of the order quantity y is determined by minimizing $\text{TCU}(y)$. Assuming y is continuous, a necessary condition for optimality is

$$\frac{d\,\text{TCU}(y)}{dy} = -\frac{KD}{y^2} + \frac{h}{2} = 0$$

The condition is also sufficient because $\text{TCU}(y)$ is convex.

The solution of the equation yields the EOQ y^* as

$$y^* = \sqrt{\frac{2KD}{h}}$$

Thus, the optimum inventory policy for the proposed model is

$$\text{Order } y^* = \sqrt{\tfrac{2KD}{h}} \text{ units every } t_0^* = \tfrac{y^*}{D} \text{ time units}$$

Actually, a new order need not be received at the instant it is ordered. Instead, a positive **lead time**, L, may occur between the placement and the receipt of an order as Figure 13.2 demonstrates. In this case, the **reorder point** occurs when the inventory level drops to LD units.

Figure 13.2 assumes that the lead time L is less than the cycle length t_0^*, which may not be the case in general. In such cases, we define the **effective lead time** as

$$L_e = L - nt_0^*$$

The parameter n is the largest integer value not exceeding $\frac{L}{t_0^*}$. The formula recognizes that after n cycles the actual interval between the placement and the receipt of two successive orders is L_e. Thus, the reorder point occurs at L_eD units, and the inventory policy can be restated as

Order the quantity y^* whenever the inventory level drops to L_eD units.

Example 13.3-1

Neon lights on the U of A campus are replaced at the rate of 100 units per day. The physical plant orders the neon lights periodically. It costs $100 to initiate a purchase order. A neon light kept in storage is estimated to cost about $.02 per day. The lead time between placing and receiving an order is 12 days. Determine the optimal inventory policy for ordering the neon lights.

From the data of the problem, we have

D = 100 units per day
K = $100 per order
h = $.02 per unit per day
L = 12 days

Thus,

$$y^* = \sqrt{\frac{2KD}{h}} = \sqrt{\frac{2 \times \$100 \times 100}{.02}} = 1000 \text{ neon lights}$$

The associated cycle length is

$$t_0^* = \frac{y^*}{D} = \frac{1000}{100} = 10 \text{ days}$$

Because the lead time L (=12 days) exceeds the cycle length t_0^* (=10 days), we must compute L_e. The number of integer cycles included in L is

$$n = \left(\text{largest integer} \leq \frac{L}{t_0^*}\right) = \left(\text{largest integer} \leq \frac{12}{10}\right) = 1$$

Thus,

$$L_e = L - nt_0^* = 12 - 1 \times 10 = 2 \text{ days}$$

The reorder point thus occurs when the inventory level drops to

$$L_e D = 2 \times 100 = 200 \text{ neon lights}$$

The inventory policy is

Order 1000 units whenever the inventory level drops to 200 units.

The daily inventory cost associated with the proposed policy is

$$\text{TCU}(y) = \frac{K}{\left(\frac{y}{D}\right)} + h\left(\frac{y}{2}\right)$$

$$= \frac{\$100}{\left(\frac{1000}{100}\right)} + \$.02\left(\frac{1000}{2}\right) = \$20 \text{ per day}$$

Excel Moment

File *exelEOQ.xls* is designed to carry out the computations for the general EOQ with shortage and simultaneous production–consumption operation, as stated in Problem 10, Set 13.3a. It also solves the price-breaks situation presented in Section 13.3.2. To use the template with the special case of Example 13.3-1, enter −1 in cells C3:C5, C8, and C10 to indicate that the corresponding data are not applicable, as shown in Figure 13.3.

B	C	D
General Economic Order Quantity (EOQ)		
Input data: (Enter -1 in column C if data element does not apply)		
Item cost, c1 =	-1	
Qty discount limit, q =	-1	
Item cost, c2 =	-1	
Setup cost, K =	100	
Demand rate, D =	100	
Production rate, a =	-1	
Unit holding cost, h =	0.02	
Unit penalty cost, p =	-1	
Lead time, L =	12	
Model output results:		
Order qty, y* =	1000.00	
Shortage qty, w* =	0.00	
Reorder point, R =	200.00	
TCU(y*) =	20.00	
Purchase/prod. Cost =	0.00	
Setup cost/unit time =	10.00	
Holding cost /unit time =	10.00	
shortage cost/unit time =	0.00	
Optimal inventory policy: Order 1000.00 units when level drops to 200.00 units		
Model intermediate calculations:		
ym =	1000.00	
TCU1(ym)=	Not applicable	
Q-equation:	Not applicable	
Q =	Not applicable	
cycle length, t0 =	10.00	
Optimization zone =	Not applicable	
Effectice lead time, Le =	2.00	

FIGURE 13.3

Excel solution of Example 13.3-1 (file *excelEOQ.xls*)

PROBLEM SET 13.3A

1. In each of the following cases, no shortage is allowed, and the lead time between placing and receiving an order is 35 days. Determine the optimal inventory policy and the associated cost per day.

   (a) $K = \$120, h = \$.04, D = 25$ units per day

   (b) $K = \$80, h = \$.03, D = 35$ units per day

   (c) $K = \$100, h = \$.02, D = 50$ units per day

   (d) $K = \$110, h = \$.03, D = 25$ units per day

*2. McBurger orders ground meat at the start of each week to cover the week's demand of 300 lb. The fixed cost per order is $20. It costs about $.03 per lb per day to refrigerate and store the meat.

   (a) Determine the inventory cost per week of the present ordering policy.

   (b) Determine the optimal inventory policy that McBurger should use, assuming zero lead time between the placement and receipt of an order.

3. A company stocks an item that is consumed at the rate of 50 units per day. It costs the company $25 each time an order is placed. An inventory unit held in stock for a week will cost $.36.

   (a) Determine the optimum inventory policy, assuming a lead time of 2 week.

   (b) Determine the optimum number of orders per year (based on 365 days per year).

*4. Two inventory policies have been suggested by the purchasing department of a company:

   Policy 1. Order 150 units. The reorder point is 50 units, and the time between placing and receiving an order is 10 days.

   Policy 2. Order 200 units. The reorder point is 75 units, and the time between placing and receiving an order is 15 days.

   The setup cost per order is $20, and the holding cost per unit inventory per day is $.02.

   (a) Which of the two policies should the company adopt?

   (b) If you were in charge of devising an inventory policy for the company, what would you recommend assuming that the supplier requires a lead time of 22 days?

5. Walmark Store compresses and palletizes empty merchandise cartons for recycling. The store generates five pallets a day. The cost of storing a pallet in the store's back lot is $.10 per day. The company that moves the pallets to the recycling center charges a flat fee of $100 for the rental of its loading equipment plus a variable transportation cost of $3 per pallet. Graph the change in number of pallets with time, and devise an optimal policy for hauling the pallets to the recycling center.

6. A hotel uses an external laundry service to provide clean towels. The hotel generates 600 soiled towels a day. The laundry service picks up the soiled towels and replaces them with clean ones at regular intervals. There is a fixed charge of $81 per pickup and delivery service, in addition to the variable cost of $.60 per towel. It costs the hotel $.02 a day to store a soiled towel and $.01 per day to store a clean one. How often should the hotel use the pickup and delivery service? (*Hint*: There are two types of inventory items in this situation. As the level of the soiled towels increases, that of clean towels decreases at an equal rate.)

7. *Lewis (1996).* An employee of a multinational company is on loan from the United States to the company's subsidiary in Europe. During the year, the employee's financial obligations in the United States (e.g., mortgage and insurance premium payments) amount to $12,000, distributed evenly over the months of the year. The employee can meet these obligations by depositing the entire sum in a U.S. bank prior to departure for Europe. However, at present the interest rate in the United States is quite low (about 1.5% per year) in comparison with the interest rate in Europe (6.5% per year). The cost of sending funds from overseas is $50 per transaction. Determine an optimal policy for transferring funds from Europe to the United States, and discuss the practical implementation of the solution. State all the assumptions.

8. Consider the inventory situation in which the stock is replenished uniformly (rather than instantaneously) at the rate a. Consumption occurs at the constant rate D. Because consumption also occurs during the replenishment period, it is necessary that $a > D$. The setup cost is K per order, and the holding cost is h per unit per unit time. If y is the order size and no shortage is allowed, show that

   (a) The maximum inventory level is $y\left(1 - \frac{D}{a}\right)$.

   (b) The total cost per unit time given y is

   $$\text{TCU}(y) = \frac{KD}{y} + \frac{h}{2}\left(1 - \frac{D}{a}\right)y$$

(c) The economic order quantity is

$$y^* = \sqrt{\frac{2KD}{h\left(1 - \frac{D}{a}\right)}}, D < a$$

(d) Show that the EOQ under instantaneous replenishment can be derived from the formula in (c).

9. A company can produce an item or buy it from a contractor. If it is produced, it will cost $20 each time the machines are set up. The production rate is 100 units per day. If it is bought from a contractor, it will cost $15 each time an order is placed. The cost of maintaining the item in stock, whether bought or produced, is $.02 per unit per day. The company's usage of the item is estimated at 26,000 units annually. Assuming that no shortage is allowed, should the company buy or produce?

10. In Problem 8, suppose that shortage is allowed at a penalty cost of p per unit per unit time.

(a) If w is the maximum shortage during the inventory cycle, show that

$$\text{TCU}(y, w) = \frac{KD}{y} + \frac{h\{y\left(1 - \frac{D}{a}\right) - w\}^2 + pw^2}{2\left(1 - \frac{D}{a}\right)y}$$

$$y^* = \sqrt{\frac{2KD(p + h)}{ph\left(1 - \frac{D}{a}\right)}}$$

$$w^* = \sqrt{\frac{2KDh\left(1 - \frac{D}{a}\right)}{p(p + h)}}$$

(b) Show that the EOQ results in Section 13.3.1 can be derived from the general formulas in (a).

13.3.2 EOQ with Price Breaks

This model is the same as in Section 13.3.1, except that the inventory item may be purchased at a discount if the size of the order, y, exceeds a given limit, q. Mathematically, the unit purchasing price, c, is given as

$$c = \begin{Bmatrix} c_1, \text{ if } y \le q \\ c_2, \text{ if } y > q \end{Bmatrix}, c_1 > c_2$$

Hence,

$$\text{Purchasing cost per unit time} = \begin{cases} \dfrac{c_1 y}{t_0} = \dfrac{c_1 y}{\left(\frac{y}{D}\right)} = Dc_1, y \le q \\ \dfrac{c_2 y}{t_0} = \dfrac{c_2 y}{\left(\frac{y}{D}\right)} = Dc_2, y > q \end{cases}$$

Using the notation in Section 13.3.1, the total cost per unit time is

$$\text{TCU}(y) = \begin{cases} TCU_1(y) = Dc_1 + \dfrac{KD}{y} + \dfrac{h}{2}y, y \le q \\ TCU_2(y) = Dc_2 + \dfrac{KD}{y} + \dfrac{h}{2}y, y > q \end{cases}$$

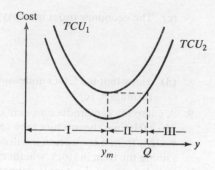

FIGURE 13.4

Inventory cost function with price breaks

The functions TCU_1 and TCU_2 are graphed in Figure 13.4. Because the two functions differ only by a constant amount, their minima must coincide at

$$y_m = \sqrt{\frac{2KD}{h}}$$

The determination of the optimum order quantity y^* depends on where the price breakpoint, q, lies with respect to zones I, II, and III, delineated in Figure 13.4 by the ranges $(0, y_m)$, (y_m, Q), and (Q, ∞), respectively. The value of $Q(>y_m)$ is determined from the equation

$$TCU_2(Q) = TCU_1(y_m)$$

or

$$c_2 D + \frac{KD}{Q} + \frac{hQ}{2} = TCU_1(y_m)$$

which simplifies to

$$Q^2 + \left(\frac{2(c_2 D - TCU_1(y_m))}{h} \right) Q + \frac{2KD}{h} = 0$$

Figure 13.5 shows that the desired optimum quantity y^* is

$$y^* = \begin{cases} y_m, \text{ if } q \text{ is in zones I or III} \\ q, \text{ if } q \text{ is in zone II} \end{cases}$$

The steps for determining y^* are

Step 1. Determine $y_m = \sqrt{\dfrac{2KD}{h}}$. If q is in zone I, then $y^* = y_m$. Otherwise, go to step 2.

Step 2. Determine $Q(>y_m)$ from the Q-equation

$$Q^2 + \left(\frac{2(c_2 D - TCU_1(y_m))}{h} \right) Q + \frac{2KD}{h} = 0$$

Define zones II and III. If q is in zone II, $y^* = q$. Otherwise, q is in zone III, and $y^* = y_m$.

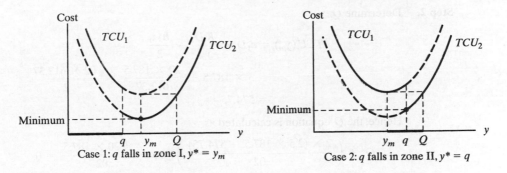

FIGURE 13.5

Optimum solution of the inventory problems with price breaks

Example 13.3-2

LubeCar specializes in fast automobile oil change. The garage buys car oil in bulk at $3 per gallon discounted to $2.50 per gallon if the order quantity is more than 1000 gallons. The garage services approximately 150 cars per day, and each oil change takes 1.25 gallons. LubeCar stores bulk oil at the cost of $.02 per gallon per day. Also, the cost of placing an order is $20. There is a 2-day lead time for delivery. Determine the optimal inventory policy.

The consumption of oil per day is

$$D = 150 \text{ cars per day} \times 1.25 \text{ gallons per car} = 187.5 \text{ gallons per day}$$

We also have

$h = \$.02$ per gallon per day

$K = \$20$ per order

$L = 2$ days

$c_1 = \$3$ per gallon

$c_2 = \$2.50$ per gallon

$q - 1000$ gallons

Step 1.   Compute

$$y_m = \sqrt{\frac{2KD}{h}} = \sqrt{\frac{2 \times 20 \times 187.5}{.02}} = 612.37 \text{ gallons}$$

Because $q = 1000$ is larger than $y_m = 612.37$, we move to step 2.

Step 2.   Determine Q.

$$TCU_1(y_m) = c_1 D + \frac{KD}{y_m} + \frac{hy_m}{2}$$

$$= 3 \times 187.5 + \frac{20 \times 187.5}{612.37} + \frac{.02 \times 612.37}{2}$$

$$= 574.75$$

Hence, the Q-equation is calculated as

$$Q^2 + \left(\frac{2 \times (2.5 \times 187.5 - 574.75)}{.02} \right) Q + \frac{2 \times 20 \times 187.5}{.02} = 0$$

or

$$Q^2 - 10,599.74Q + 375,000 = 0$$

The solution $Q = 10,564.25$ ($> y_m$) defines the zones as

$$\text{Zone I} = (0, 612.37)$$
$$\text{Zone II} = (612.37, 10,564.25)$$
$$\text{Zone III} = (10,564.25, \infty)$$

Now, $q(=1000)$ falls in zone II, which yields the optimal order quantity $y^* = q = 1000$ gallons.

Given a 2-day lead time, the reorder point is $2D = 2 \times 187.5 = 375$ gallons. Thus, the optimal inventory policy is "*Order 1000 gallons when the inventory level drops to 375 gallons.*"

Excel Moment

File *excelEOQ.xls* solves the discount price situation as a special case of template in Figure 13.3. Enter applicable data in the input data section C3:C11. The output gives the optimal inventory policy as well as all the intermediate calculations of the model.

PROBLEM SET 13.3B

1. Consider the hotel laundry service situation in Problem 6, Set 13.3a. The normal charge for washing a soiled towel is $.60, but the laundry service will charge only $.45 if the hotel delivers the towels in lots of at least 2600. Should the hotel take advantage of the discount?

*2. An item is consumed at the rate of 30 items per day. The holding cost per unit per day is $.05, and the setup cost is $100. Suppose that no shortage is allowed and that the purchasing cost per unit is $10 for any quantity not exceeding 500 units and $8 otherwise. The lead time is 21 days. Determine the optimal inventory policy.

3. An item sells for $30 a unit, but a 10% discount is offered for lots of 200 units or more. A company uses this item at the rate of 20 units per day. The setup cost for ordering a lot is $50, and the holding cost per unit per day is $.30. The lead time is 15 days. Should the company take advantage of the discount?

*4. In Problem 3, determine the range on the price discount percentage that, when offered for lots of size 150 units or more, will not result in any financial advantage to the company.

5. In the inventory model discussed in this section, suppose that the holding cost per unit per unit time is h_1 for quantities below q and h_2 otherwise, $h_1 > h_2$. Show how the economic lot size is determined.

13.3.3   Multi-Item EOQ with Storage Limitation

This model deals with multiple items whose individual inventory fluctuations follow the pattern as in Figure 13.1 (no shortage allowed). The difference is that the items compete for a limited storage space.

Define for item $i, i = 1, 2, \ldots, n$,

D_i = Demand rate

K_i = Setup cost

h_i = Unit holding cost per unit time

y_i = Order quantity

a_i = Storage area requirement per inventory unit

A = Maximum available storage area for all n items

Under the assumption of no shortage, the mathematical model representing the inventory situation is given as

$$\text{Minimize TCU}(y_1, y_2, \ldots, y_n) = \sum_{i=1}^{n} \left(\frac{K_i D_i}{y_i} + \frac{h_i y_i}{2} \right)$$

subject to

$$\sum_{i=1}^{n} a_i y_i \leq A$$

$$y_i > 0, i = 1, 2, \ldots, n$$

To solve the problem, we try the unconstrained solution first:

$$y_i^* = \sqrt{\frac{2K_i D_i}{h_i}}, i = 1, 2, \ldots, n$$

If the solution satisfies the constraint, then the process ends. Otherwise, the constraint is binding and must be activated.

In previous editions of this book, we used the (rather involved) Lagrangean algorithm and trial-and-error calculations to find the constrained optimum solution. With the availability of powerful packages (such as AMPL and Solver), the problem can be solved directly as a nonlinear program, as will be demonstrated in the following example.

Example 13.3-3

The following data describe three inventory items.

Item i	K_i ($)	D_i (units per day)	h_i($)	a_1 (ft^2)
1	10	2	.30	1
2	5	4	.10	1
3	15	4	.20	1
		Total available storage area = 25 ft^2		

The unconstrained optimum values, $y_i^* = \sqrt{\frac{2K_iD_i}{h_i}}, i = 1, 2, 3$, are 11.55, 20.00, and 24.49 units, respectively, which violate the storage constraint $y_1 + y_2 + y_3 \leq 25$. The constrained problem can be solved as a nonlinear program using Solver or AMPL as explained below.

The optimum solution is $y_1^* = 6.34$ units, $y_2^* = 7.09$ units, $y_3^* = 11.57$ units, and cost = $13.62/day.

Solver Moment

Figure 13.6 shows how Solver can be used to solve Example 13.3-3 as a nonlinear program (file *solverConstrEOQ.xls*). Details of the formulas used in the template and of the Solver parameters are shown in the figure. As with most nonlinear programs, initial solution values must be given (in this template, $y_1 = y_2 = y_3 = 1$ in row 9). A *nonzero* initial value is mandatory because the objective function includes division by y_i. Indeed, it may be a good idea to replace K_iD_i/y_i with $K_iD_i/(y_i + \Delta)$, where Δ is a very small positive value, to avoid division by zero during the iterations. In general, different initial values may be needed before a (local optimum) solution is found. In this example, the resulting solution is the global optimum because the objective function and the constraints are well behaved (convex objective function and convex solution space).

AMPL Moment

The AMPL nonlinear model for the general multi-item EOQ with storage limitation (file *amplConstrEOQ.txt*) is explained in Figure C.17 in Appendix C on the website.

FIGURE 13.6

Solver template for Example 13.3-3 (file *solverConstrEOQ.xls*)

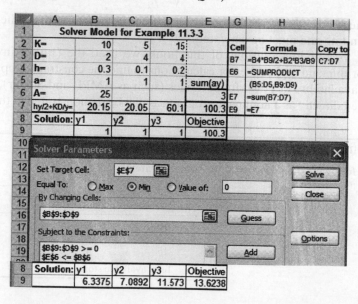

PROBLEM SET 13.3C[2]

*1. The following data describe five inventory items.

Item i	K_i ($)	D_i (units per day)	h_i ($)	a_i (ft^2)
1	35	22	0.35	1.0
2	28	34	0.15	0.8
3	30	14	0.28	1.1
4	25	21	0.30	0.5
5	20	26	0.42	1.2
Total available storage area $= 22$ ft^2				

Determine the optimal order quantities.

2. Solve the model of Example 13.3-3, assuming that we require the sum of the average inventories for all the items to be less than 25 units.

3. In Problem 2, assume that the only restriction is a limit of $1000 on the amount of capital that can be invested in inventory. The purchase costs per unit of items 1, 2, and 3 are $100, $55, and $100, respectively. Determine the optimum solution.

*4. The following data describe four inventory items.

Item i	K_i ($)	D_i (units per day)	h_i ($)
1	100	10	.1
2	50	20	.2
3	90	5	.2
4	20	10	.1

The company wishes to determine the economic order quantity for each of the four items such that the total number of orders per 365-day year is at most 150. Formulate the problem as a nonlinear program, and find the optimum solution.

13.4 DYNAMIC EOQ MODELS

These models differ from those in Section 13.3 in two respects:

1. The inventory level is reviewed periodically over a finite number of equal periods.
2. The demand per period, though deterministic, is dynamic, in that it varies from one period to the next.

A situation in which dynamic deterministic demand occurs is **materials requirement planning** (MRP). The idea of MRP is described by an example. Suppose that the quarterly demands over the next year for two final models, $M1$ and $M2$, of a given product are 100 and 150 units, respectively. Deliveries of the quarterly lots are made at the end of each quarter. The production lead time is 2 months for $M1$ and 1 month for $M2$.

---

[2]You will find files *solverConstrEOQ.xls* and *amplConstrEOQ.txt* useful in solving the problems of this set.

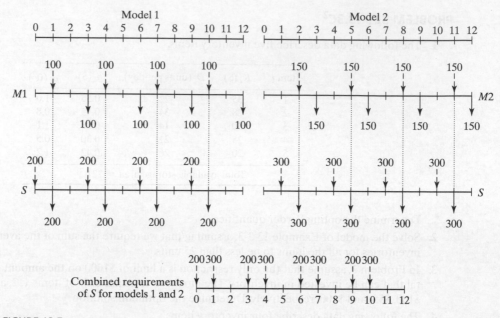

FIGURE 13.7

Example of dynamic demand generated by MRP

Each unit of $M1$ and $M2$ uses 2 units of a subassembly S. The lead time for the production of S is 1 month.

Figure 13.7 depicts the production schedules for $M1$ and $M2$. The schedules start with the quarterly demand for the two models (shown by solid arrows) occurring at the end of months 3, 6, 9, and 12. Given the lead times for $M1$ and $M2$, the dashed arrows show the planned starts of each production lot.

To start the production of the two models on time, the delivery of subassembly S must coincide with the occurrence of the dashed $M1$ and $M2$ arrows. This information is shown by the solid arrows in the S-chart, where the resulting S-demand is 2 units per unit of $M1$ or $M2$. Using a lead time of 1 month, the dashed arrows on the S-chart give the production schedules for S. From these two schedules, the combined demand for S corresponding to $M1$ and $M2$ can then be determined as shown at the bottom of Figure 13.7. The resulting *variable but known* demand for S is typical of the situation where dynamic EOQ applies.

Two models are presented in this section. The first model assumes no setup (ordering) cost, and the second one does. This seemingly "small" variation makes a difference in the complexity of the model.

PROBLEM SET 13.4A

1. In Figure 13.7, determine the combined requirements for subassembly S in each of the following cases:
   *(a) Lead time for $M1$ is only one period.
   (b) Lead time for $M1$ is three periods.

13.4.1 No-Setup EOQ Model

This model involves a planning horizon of n equal periods. Each period has a limited production capacity with one or more production levels (e.g., regular time and overtime represent two production levels). A current period may produce more than its immediate demand to satisfy the need in later periods, in which case an inventory holding cost takes place.

The general assumptions of the model are

1. No setup cost is incurred in any period.
2. No shortage is allowed.
3. The unit production cost function in any period either is constant or has increasing (convex) marginal costs.
4. The unit holding cost in any period is constant.

The absence of shortage signifies that delayed production in future periods cannot fill the demand in a current period. This assumption requires the cumulative production capacity for periods $1, 2, \ldots,$ and i to equal at least the cumulative demand for the same periods.

Figure 13.8 illustrates the unit production cost function with increasing margins. For example, regular time and overtime production correspond to two levels where the unit production cost during overtime exceeds that regular time.

The n-period problem can be formulated as a transportation model (see Chapter 5) with kn sources and n destinations, where k is the number of production levels per period (e.g., $k = 2$ if each period uses regular time and overtime). The production capacity of each of the kn production-level sources equals the supply amounts. The demand amounts are specified by each period's demand. The unit "transportation" cost from a source to a destination is the sum of the applicable production and holding costs per unit. The solution of the problem as a transportation model determines the minimum-cost production amounts in each production level.

The resulting transportation model can be solved without using the familiar transportation technique presented in Chapter 5. The validity of the new solution algorithm rests on the special assumptions of no shortage and a convex production-cost function.

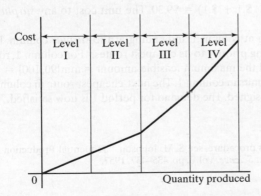

FIGURE 13.8

Convex unit production cost function

Example 13.4-1

Metalco produces draft deflectors for use in home fireplaces during the months of December to March. The demand starts slow, peaks in the middle of the season, and tapers off toward the end. Because of the popularity of the product, Metalco may use overtime to satisfy the demand. The following table provides the production capacities and the demands for the four winter months.

Month	Capacity		Demand (units)
	Regular (units)	*Overtime (units)*	
1	90	50	100
2	100	60	190
3	120	80	210
4	110	70	160

Unit production cost in any period is $6 during regular time and $9 during overtime. Holding cost per unit per month is $.10.

To ensure that the model has a feasible solution when shortage is not allowed, each month's cumulative supply cannot be smaller than its cumulative demand, as the following table shows.

Month	Cumulative supply	Cumulative demand
1	90 + 50 = 140	100
2	140 + 100 + 60 = 300	100 + 190 = 290
3	300 + 120 + 80 = 500	290 + 210 = 500
4	500 + 110 + 70 = 680	500 + 160 = 660

Table 13.2 summarizes the model and its solution. The symbols R_i and O_i represent regular and overtime production levels in period i, $i = 1, 2, 3, 4$. Because cumulative supply at period 4 exceeds cumulative demand, a dummy surplus destination is added to balance the model as shown in Table 13.2. All the "transportation" routes from a previous to a current period are blocked because no shortage is allowed.

The unit "transportation" cost is the sum of applicable production and holding costs. For example, unit cost from R_1 to period 1 equals unit production cost only (=$6), whereas unit cost from O_1 to period 4 equals unit production cost in O_1 plus unit holding cost from period 1 to period 4—that is, $9 + ($.1 + $.1 + $.1) = $9.30. The unit cost to any *surplus* destination is zero.

The model is solved starting at column 1 and ending at the *surplus* column. For each column, the demand is satisfied giving priority to its cheapest routes.[3] For column 1, route $(R_1, 1)$ is the cheapest and is thus assigned the maximum feasible amount = min{90,100} = 90 units. This assignment leaves 10 unsatisfied units in column 1. The next-cheapest route in column 1 is $(O_1, 1)$, to which 10 (=min{50,10}) are assigned. The demand for period 1 is now satisfied.

---

[3]For a proof of the optimality of this procedure, see S. M. Johnson, "Sequential Production Planning over Time at Minimum Cost," *Management Science*, Vol. 3, pp. 435–437, 1957.

TABLE 13.2 Solution of Example 13.4-1

	1	2	3	4	Surplus	Supply
R_1	6 **90**	6.1	6.2	6.3	0	90
O_1	9 **10**	9.1 **30**	9.2 **10**	9.3	0	$50 \to 40 \to 10$
R_2	(shaded)	6 **100**	6.1	6.2	0	100
O_2	(shaded)	9 **60**	9.1	9.2	0	60
R_3	(shaded)	(shaded)	6 **120**	6.1	0	120
O_3	(shaded)	(shaded)	9 **80**	9.1	0	80
R_4	(shaded)	(shaded)	(shaded)	6 **110**	0	110
O_4	(shaded)	(shaded)	(shaded)	9 **50**	0 **20**	$70 \to 20$
Demand	100 ↓ 10	190 ↓ 90 ↓ 30	210 ↓ 90 ↓ 10	160 ↓ 50	20	

Next, we move to column 2. The assignments in this column occur in the following order: 100 units to $(R_2, 2)$, 60 units to $(O_2, 2)$, and 30 units to $(O_1, 2)$. The unit costs of these assignments are \$6, \$9, and \$9.10, respectively. We did not use the route $(R_1, 2)$, whose unit cost is \$6.10, because all the supply of R_1 has been assigned to period 1 already.

Continuing in the same manner, we satisfy the demands of column 3 and then column 4. The optimum solution (shown in boldface in Table 13.2) is summarized as follows:

Period	Production Schedule
Regular 1	Produce 90 units for period 1.
Overtime 1	Produce 50 units: 10 units for period 1, 30 for 2, and 10 for 3.
Regular 2	Produce 100 units for period 2.
Overtime 2	Produce 60 units for period 2.
Regular 3	Produce 120 units for period 3.
Overtime 3	Produce 80 units for period 3.
Regular 4	Produce 110 units for period 4.
Overtime 4	Produce 50 units for period 4, with 20 units of idle capacity.

The associated total cost is $90 \times \$6 + 10 \times \$9 + 30 \times \$9.10 + 100 \times \$6 + 60 \times \$9 + 10 \times \$9.20 + 120 \times \$6 + 80 \times \$9 + 110 \times \$6 + 50 \times \$9 = \$4685$.

PROBLEM SET 13.4B

1. Solve Example 13.4-1, assuming that the unit production and holding costs are as given in the following table.

Period i	Regular time unit cost ($)	Overtime unit cost ($)	Unit holding cost ($) to period $i + 1$
1	5.00	7.50	.10
2	3.00	4.50	.15
3	4.00	6.00	.12
4	1.00	1.50	.20

2. An item is manufactured to meet known demand for four periods according to the following data:

	Unit production cost ($) for period			
Production range (units)	1	2	3	4
1–3	1	2	2	3
4–11	1	4	5	4
12–15	2	4	7	5
16–25	5	6	10	7
Unit holding cost to next period ($)	.30	.35	.20	.25
Total demand (units)	11	4	17	29

   (a) Find the optimal solution, indicating the number of units to be produced in each period.

   (b) Suppose that 30 additional units are needed in period 4. Where should they be produced?

*3. The demand for a product over the next five periods may be filled from regular production, overtime production, or subcontracting. Subcontracting may be used only if the overtime capacity has been used. The following table gives the supply, demand, and cost data of the situation.

	Production capacity (units)			
Period	Regular time	Overtime	Subcontracting	Demand
1	100	50	30	153
2	40	60	80	200
3	90	80	70	150
4	60	50	20	200
5	70	50	100	203

   The unit production costs for the three levels in each period are $4, $6, and $7, respectively. The unit holding cost per period is $.50. Determine the optimal solution.

13.4.2 Setup EOQ Model

In this situation, no shortage is allowed, and a setup cost is incurred each time a new production lot is started. Two solution methods will be presented: an exact dynamic programming algorithm and a heuristic.

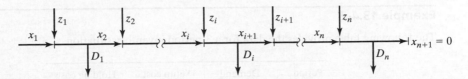

FIGURE 13.9

Elements of the dynamic inventory model with setup cost

Figure 13.9 summarizes the inventory situation schematically. The symbols shown in the figure are defined for period $i, i = 1, 2, \ldots, n$, as

z_i = Amount ordered

D_i = Demand for period i

x_i = Inventory at the start of period i

The cost elements of the situation are defined as

K_i = Setup cost in period i

h_i = Unit inventory holding cost from period i to $i + 1$

The associated production cost function for period i is

$$C_i(z_i) = \begin{cases} 0, & z_i = 0 \\ K_i + C_i(z_i), & z_i > 0 \end{cases}$$

The function $c_i(z_i)$ is the marginal production cost function, given z_i.

General dynamic programming algorithm. In the absence of shortage, the inventory model is based on minimizing the sum of production and holding costs for all n periods. For simplicity, we will assume that the holding cost for period i is based on end-of-period inventory, defined as

$$x_{i+1} = x_i + z_i - D_i$$

For the forward recursive equation, the *state* at *stage* (period) i is defined as x_{i+1}, the end-of-period inventory level. In the extreme case, the remaining inventory, x_{i+1}, can satisfy the demand for all the remaining periods—that is,

$$0 \leq x_{i+1} \leq D_{i+1} + \ldots + D_n$$

Let $f_i(x_{i+1})$ be the minimum inventory cost for periods $1, 2, \ldots,$ and i given the end-of-period inventory x_{i+1}. The forward recursive equation is

$$f_1(x_2) = \min_{z_1 = D_1 + x_2 - x_1} \{C_1(z_1) + h_1 x_2\}$$

$$f_i(x_{i+1}) = \min_{0 \leq z_i \leq D_i + x_{i+1}} \{C_i(z_i) + h_i x_{i+1} + f_{i-1}(x_{i+1} + D_i - z_i)\}, i = 2, 3, \ldots, n$$

Note that for period 1, z_1 exactly equals $D_1 + x_2 - x_1$. For $i > 1$, z_i can be zero because D_i can be satisfied from the production in preceding periods.

Example 13.4-2

The following table provides the data for a 3-period inventory situation.

Period i	Demand D_i (units)	Setup cost K_i (\$)	Holding cost h_i (\$)
1	3	3	1
2	2	7	3
3	4	6	2

The demand occurs in discrete units, and the starting inventory is $x_1 = 1$ unit. The unit production cost, $c_i(z_i)$, is \$10 for the first 3 units and \$20 for each additional unit—that is,

$$c_i(z_i) = \begin{cases} 10z_i, & 0 \le z_i \le 3 \\ 30 + 20(z_i - 3), & z_i \ge 4 \end{cases}$$

Determine the optimal inventory policy.

Period 1: $D_1 = 3, 0 \le x_2 \le 2 + 4 = 6, z_1 = x_2 + D_1 - x_1 = x_2 + 2$

					$C_1(z_1) + h_1 x_2$					
		$z_1 = 2$	3	4	5	6	7	8	Optimal solution	
x_2	$h_1 x_2$	$C_1(z_1) = 23$	33	53	73	93	113	133	$f_1(x_2)$	z_1^*
0	0	23							23	2
1	1		34						34	3
2	2			55					55	4
3	3				76				76	5
4	4					97			97	6
5	5						118		118	7
6	6							139	139	8

Note that because $x_1 = 1$, the smallest value of z_1 is $D_1 - x_1 = 3 - 1 = 2$.

Period 2: $D_2 = 2, 0 \le x_3 \le 4, 0 \le z_2 \le D_2 + x_3 = x_3 + 2$

				$C_2(z_2) + h_2 x_3 + f_1(x_3 + D_2 - z_2)$				Optimal solution	
		$z_2 = 0$	1	2	3	4	5	6	
x_3	$h_2 x_3$	$C_2(z_2) = 0$	17	27	37	57	77	97	$f_2(x_3)$	z_2^*
0	0	0 + 55 = 55	17 + 34 = 51	27 + 23 = 50					50	2
1	3	3 + 76 = 79	20 + 55 = 75	30 + 34 = 64	40 + 23 = 63				63	3
2	6	6 + 97 = 103	23 + 76 = 99	33 + 55 = 88	43 + 34 = 77	63 + 23 = 86			77	3
3	9	9 + 118 = 127	26 + 97 = 123	36 + 76 = 112	46 + 55 = 101	66 + 34 = 100	86 + 23 = 109		100	4
4	12	12 + 139 = 151	29 + 118 = 147	39 + 97 = 136	49 + 76 = 125	69 + 55 = 124	89 + 34 = 123	109 + 23 = 132	123	5

Period 3: $D_3 = 4, x_4 = 0, 0 \le z_3 \le D_3 + x_4 = 4$

		$C_3(z_3) + h_3x_4 + f_2(x_4 + D_3 - z_3)$					Optimal solution	
		$z_3 = 0$	1	2	3	4		
x_4	h_3x_4	$C_3(z_3) = 0$	16	26	36	56	$f_3(x_4)$	z_3^*
0	0	$0 + 123$ $= 123$	$16 + 100$ $= 116$	$26 + 77$ $= 103$	$36 + 63$ $= 99$	$56 + 50$ $= 106$	99	3

The optimum solution is read in the following manner:

$$(x_4 = 0) \to \boxed{z_3 = 3} \to (x_3 = 0 + 4 - 3 = 1) \to \boxed{z_2 = 3}$$

$$\to (x_2 = 1 + 2 - 3 = 0) \to \boxed{z_1 = 2}$$

Thus, the optimum solution is $z_1^* = 2, z_2^* = 3$, and $z_3^* = 3$, with a total cost of $99.

Excel Moment

Template *excelDPInv.xls* is designed to solve the general DP inventory problem with up to 10 periods. The design of the spreadsheet is similar to that of *excelKnapsack.xls* given in Section 12.3.1, where the computations are carried out one stage a time and user input is needed to link successive stages.

Figure 13.10 shows the application of *excelDPInv.xls* to Example 13.4-2. The input data are entered for each stage. The computations start with period 1. Note how the cost function $c_i(z_i)$ is entered in row 3: (G3 = 10, H3 = 20, I3 = 3) means that the unit cost is $10 for the first three items and $20 for additional items. Note also that the amount entered for D_1 must be the net after the initial inventory has been written off ($=3 - x_1 = 3 - 1 = 2$). Additionally, you need to create the feasible values of the variable z_1. The spreadsheet automatically checks if the entered values are correct, and issues self-explanatory messages in row 6 (yes, no, or delete).

Once all input data have been entered, the optimum values of f_i and z_i for the stage are given in columns S and T. Next, a permanent record for period 1 solution (x_1, f_1, z_1), is created in the optimum solution summary section of the spreadsheet, as Figure 13.10 shows. This requires copying D9:D15 and S9:T15 and then pasting them using *paste special + values* (you may need to review the proper procedure for creating the permanent record given in conjunction with *excelKnapsack.xls* in Section 12.3.1).

Next, to prepare for stage 2, copy f_1 from the permanent record and paste it in column A as shown in Figure 13.10. All that is needed now is to update the input data for period 2. The process is repeated for period 3.

PROBLEM SET 13.4C

*1. Consider Example 13.4-2.

(a) Will $x_4 = 0$ in the optimum solution?

(b) For each of the following two cases, determine the feasible ranges for z_1, z_2, z_3, x_1, x_2, and x_3. (You will find it helpful to represent each situation as in Figure 13.10.)

Period 1:

	B	C	D	E	F	G	H	I	J	K	S	T	U	V	W	X	Y	Z
1		General (Forward) Dynamic Programming Inventory Model																
2 I	Number of periods, N=	3	Current period=	1									Optimum solution				
3 N	K1= 3	h1= 1	c1(z1)=	10	20	3									Summary		
4 P	Period 1	2	3											x f z		x f z	
5 U	D(1 to 3)= 2	2	4											Period 1			
6 T	Are z1 values correct?		yes	yes	yes	yes	yes	yes	yes	Optimum			0 23 2				
7	Period 0	z1=	2	3	4	5	6	7	8	Period1			1 34 3				
8	f 0	C1(z1)=	23	33	53	73	93	113	133	f1 z1			2 55 4				
9 S	x2= 0	23	1111111	1111111	1111111	1111111	1111111	1111111	23 2			3 76 5					
10 T	x2= 1	1111111	34	1111111	1111111	1111111	1111111	1111111	34 3			4 97 6					
11 A	x2= 2	1111111	1111111	55	1111111	1111111	1111111	1111111	55 4			5 118 7					
12 G	x2= 3	1111111	1111111	1111111	76	1111111	1111111	1111111	76 5			6 139 8					
13 E	x2= 4	1111111	1111111	1111111	1111111	97	1111111	1111111	97 6								
14	x2= 5	1111111	1111111	1111111	1111111	1111111	118	1111111	118 7								
15 C	x2= 6	1111111	1111111	1111111	1111111	1111111	1111111	139	139 8								

Period 2:

	B	C	D	E	F	G	H	I	J	K	S	T	U	V	W	X	Y	Z
1		General (Forward) Dynamic Programming Inventory Model																
2 I	Number of periods, N=	3	Current period=	2									Optimum solution				
3 N	K2= 7	h2= 3	c2(z2)=	10	20	3									Summary		
4 P	Period 1	2	3											x f z		x f z	
5 U	D(1 to 3)= 2	2	4											Period 1		Period 2	
6 T	Are z2 values correct?		yes	yes	yes	yes	yes	yes	yes	Optimum			0 23 2		0 50 2	
7	Period 1	z2=	0	1	2	3	4	5	6	Period2			1 34 3		1 63 3	
8	f 1	C2(z2)=	0	17	27	37	57	77	97	f2 z2			2 55 4		2 77 3	
9 S	23	x3= 0	55	51	50	1111111	1111111	1111111	1111111	50 2			3 76 5		3 100 4	
10 T	34	x3= 1	79	75	64	63	1111111	1111111	1111111	63 3			4 97 6		4 123 5	
11 A	55	x3= 2	103	99	88	77	86	1111111	1111111	77 3			5 118 7		Period 3	
12 G	76	x3= 3	127	123	112	101	100	109	1111111	100 4			6 139 8			
13 E	97	x3= 4	151	147	136	125	124	123	132	123 5						
14	118															
15 C	139															

Period 3:

	B	C	D	E	F	G	H	I	J	K	S	T	U	V	W	X	Y	Z
1		General (Forward) Dynamic Programming Inventory Model																
2 I	Number of periods, N=	3	Current period=	3									Optimum solution				
3 N	K3= 6	h3= 2	c3(z3)=	10	20	3									Summary		
4 P	Period 1	2	3											x f z		x f z	
5 U	D(1 to 3)= 2	2	4											Period 1		Period 2	
6 T	Are z3 values correct?		yes	yes	yes	yes	yes			Optimum			0 23 2		0 50 2	
7	Period 2	z3=	0	1	2	3	4			Period3			1 34 3		1 63 3	
8	f 2	C3(z3)=	0	16	26	36	56			f3 z3			2 55 4		2 77 3	
9 S	50	x4= 0	123	116	103	99	106			99 3			3 76 5		3 100 4	
10 T	63												4 97 6		4 123 5	
11 A	77												5 118 7		Period 3	
12 G	100												6 139 8		0 99 3	

FIGURE 13.10

Excel DP solution of Example 13.4-2 (file *excelDPInv.xls*)

(i) $x_1 = 3$ and all the remaining data are the same.

(ii) $x_1 = 0, D_1 = 5, D_2 = 4$, and $D_3 = 5$.

2. *(a) Find the optimal solution for the following 4-period inventory model.

Period i	Demand D_i (units)	Setup cost K_i ($)	Holding cost h_i ($)
1	5	5	1
2	2	7	1
3	3	9	1
4	3	7	1

The unit production cost is $1 each for the first 6 units and $2 each for additional units.

(b) Verify the computations using *excelDPInv.xls*.

3. Suppose that the inventory-holding cost is based on the *average* inventory during the period. Develop the corresponding forward recursive equation.

4. Develop the backward recursive equation for the model, and then use it to solve Example 13.4-2.

5. Develop the backward recursive equation for the model, assuming that the inventory-holding cost is based on the *average* inventory in the period.

Dynamic programming algorithm with constant or decreasing marginal costs. The general DP given above is applicable with any cost function. This generalization dictates that the state x_i and the alternatives z_i at stage i assume values in increments of 1, which could result in large tableaus when the demand amounts are large.

A special case of the general DP model holds promise in reducing the volume of computations. In this special situation, both the unit production and the unit holding costs are *nonincreasing* (concave) functions of the production quantity and the inventory level, respectively. This situation typically occurs when the unit cost function is constant or when quantity discount is allowed.

Under the given conditions, it can be proved that[4]

1. Given zero initial inventory ($x_1 = 0$), it is optimal to satisfy the demand in any period i either from new production or from entering inventory, but never from both—that is, $z_i x_i = 0$. (For the case with positive initial inventory, $x_1 > 0$, the amount can be written off from the demands of the successive periods until it is exhausted.)

2. The optimal production quantity, z_i, for period i must either be zero or it must satisfy the exact demand for one or more contiguous succeeding periods.

Example 13.4-3

A 4-period inventory model operates with the following data:

Period i	Demand D_i (units)	Setup cost K_i($)
1	76	98
2	26	114
3	90	185
4	67	70

The initial inventory x_1 is 15 units, the unit production cost is $2, and the unit holding cost per period is $1 for all the periods. (For simplicity, the unit production and holding costs are the same for all the periods.)

The solution is determined by the forward algorithm given previously, except that the values of x_{i+1} and z_i now assume "lump" sums rather than in increments of one. Because $x_1 = 15$, the demand for the first period is adjusted to $76 - 15 = 61$ units.

---

[4]See H. Wagner and T. Whitin, "Dynamic Version of the Economic Lot Size Model," *Management Science*, Vol. 5, pp. 89–96, 1958. The optimality proof imposes the restrictive assumption of constant and identical cost functions for all the periods. The assumption was later relaxed by A. Veinott Jr. to allow different concave cost functions.

Period 1. $D_1 = 61$

		$C_1(z_1) + h_1x_2$				Optimal solution	
		$z_1 = 61$	87	177	244		
x_2	h_1x_2	$C_1(z_1) = 220$	272	452	586	$f_1(x_2)$	z_1^*
0	0	220				220	61
26	26		298			298	87
116	116			568		568	177
183	183				769	769	244
Order in 1 for		1	1, 2	1, 2, 3	1, 2, 3, 4		

Period 2. $D_2 = 26$

		$C_2(z_2) + h_2x_3 + f_1(x_3 + D_2 - z_2)$				Optimal solution	
		$z_2 = 0$	26	116	183		
x_3	h_2x_3	$C_2(z_2) = 0$	166	346	480	$f_2(x_3)$	z_2^*
0	0	$0 + 298$ $= 298$	$166 + 220$ $= 386$			298	0
90	90	$90 + 568$ $= 658$		$436 + 220$ $= 656$		656	116
157	157	$157 + 769$ $= 926$			$637 + 220$ $= 857$	857	183
Order in 2 for		—	2	2, 3	2, 3, 4		

Period 3. $D_3 = 90$

		$C_3(z_3) + h_3x_4 + f_2(x_4 + D_3 - z_3)$			Optimal solution	
		$z_3 = 0$	90	157		
x_4	h_3x_4	$C_3(z_3) = 0$	365	499	$f_3(x_4)$	z_3^*
0	0	$0 + 656 = 656$	$365 + 298 = 663$		656	0
67	67	$67 + 857 = 924$		$566 + 298 = 864$	864	157
Order in 3 for		—	3	3, 4		

Period 4. $D_4 = 67$

		$C_4(z_4) + h_4x_5 + f_3(x_5 + D_4 - z_4)$		Optimal solution	
		$z_4 = 0$	67		
x_5	h_4x_5	$C_4(z_4) = 0$	204	$f_4(x_5)$	z_4^*
0	0	$0 + 864 = 864$	$204 + 656 = 860$	860	67
Order in 4 for		—	4		

The optimal policy is determined from the tableaus as follows:

$$(x_5 = 0) \rightarrow \boxed{z_4 = 67} \rightarrow (x_4 = 0) \rightarrow \boxed{z_3 = 0}$$

$$\rightarrow (x_3 = 90) \rightarrow \boxed{z_2 = 116} \rightarrow (x_2 = 0) \rightarrow \boxed{z_1 = 61}$$

This gives $z_1^* = 61, z_2^* = 116, z_3^* = 0$, and $z_4^* = 67$, at a total cost of \$860.

Excel Moment

Template *excelWagnerWhitin.xls* is similar to that of the general model *excelDPInv.xls*. The only difference is that lump sums are used for the state x and alternative z. Also, for simplicity, the new spreadsheet does not allow for quantity discount. The template is limited to a maximum of 10 periods. Remember to use *paste special* + *values* when creating the output solution summary (columns Q:V).

PROBLEM SET 13.4D

*1. Solve Example 13.4-3, assuming that the initial inventory is 80 units. You may use *excelWagnerWhitin.xls* to check your calculations.

2. Solve the following 10-period deterministic inventory model. Assume an initial inventory of 50 units.

Period i	Demand D_i (units)	Unit production cost (\$)	Unit holding cost (\$)	Setup cost (\$)
1	150	6	1	100
2	100	6	1	100
3	20	4	2	100
4	40	4	1	200
5	70	6	2	200
6	90	8	3	200
7	130	4	1	300
8	180	4	4	300
9	140	2	2	300
10	50	6	1	300

3. Find the optimal inventory policy for the following 5-period model. The unit production cost is \$10 for all periods. The unit holding cost is \$1 per period.

Period i	Demand D_i (units)	Setup cost K_1 (\$)
1	50	80
2	70	70
3	100	60
4	30	80
5	60	60

4. Find the optimal inventory policy for the following 6-period inventory situation: The unit production cost is $2 for all the periods.

Period i	D_i (units)	K_i ($)	h_i ($)
1	10	20	1
2	15	17	1
3	7	10	1
4	20	18	3
5	13	5	1
6	25	50	1

Silver-Meal heuristic. This heuristic is valid only when the unit production cost is constant and identical for all the periods. For this reason, it balances only the setup and holding costs.

The heuristic identifies the successive future periods whose demand can be filled from the production of the current period. The objective is to minimize the associated setup and holding costs per period.

Suppose that we produce in period i for periods $i, i + 1, \ldots$, and $t, i \le t$, and define $TC(i, t)$ as the associated setup and holding costs for the same periods. Using the same notation of the DP models, we have

$$
TC(i, t) = \begin{cases} K_i, & t = i \\ K_i + h_i D_{i+1} + (h_i + h_{i+1})D_{i+2} + \cdots + \left(\sum_{k=i}^{t-1} h_k\right)D_t, & t > i \end{cases}
$$

Next, define $TCU(i,t)$ as the associated cost per period—that is,

$$
TCU(i,t) = \frac{TC(i,t)}{t - i + 1}
$$

Given a current period i, the heuristic determines t^* that minimizes $TCU(i, t)$.

The function $TC(i, t)$ can be computed recursively as

$$
TC(i, i) = K_i
$$

$$
TC(i,t) = TC(i, t - 1) + \left(\sum_{k=i}^{t-1} h_k\right)D_t, t = i + 1, i + 2, \ldots, n
$$

Step 0. Set $i = 1$.

Step 1. Determine the local minimum t^* that satisfies the following two conditions:

$$
TCU(i, t^* - 1) \ge TCU(i, t^*)
$$

$$
TCU(i, t^* + 1) \ge TCU(i, t^*)
$$

The heuristic calls for ordering the amount $(D_i + D_{i+1} + \cdots + D_{t^*})$ in period i for periods $i, i + 1, \ldots$, and t^*.

Step 2. Set $i = t^* + 1$. If $i > n$, stop; the entire planning horizon has been covered. Otherwise, go to step 1.

Example 13.4-4

Find the optimal inventory policy for the following 6-period inventory situation:

Period i	D_i (units)	K_i ($)	h_i ($)
1	10	20	1
2	15	17	1
3	7	10	1
4	20	18	3
5	13	5	1
6	25	50	1

The unit production cost is $2 for all the periods.

Iteration 1 ($i = 1, K_1 = \$20$) The function $\text{TC}(1, t)$ is computed recursively in t. For example, given $\text{TC}(1,1) = \$20$, $\text{TC}(1,2) = \text{TC}(1,1) + h_1 D_2 = 20 + 1 \times 15 = \$35$.

Period t	D_i	$\text{TC}(1, t)$	$\text{TCU}(1, t)$
1	10	$20	$\frac{20}{1} = \$20.00$
2	15	$20 + 1 \times 15 = \$35$	$\frac{35}{2} = \$17.50$
3	7	$35 + (1+1) \times 7 = \$94$	$\frac{49}{3} = \boxed{\$16.33}$
4	20	$49 + (1+1+1) \times 20 = \$109$	$\frac{109}{4} = \$27.25$

The local minimum occurs at $t^* = 3$, which calls for ordering $10 + 15 + 7 = 32$ units in period 1 for periods 1 to 3. Set $i = t^* + 1 = 3 + 1 = 4$.

Iteration 2 ($i = 4, K_4 = \$18$).

Period t	D_i	$\text{TC}(4, t)$	$\text{TCU}(4, t)$
4	20	$18	$\frac{18}{1} = \boxed{\$18.00}$
5	13	$18 + 3 \times 13 = \$57$	$\frac{57}{2} = \$28.50$

The calculations show that $t^* = 4$, which calls for ordering 20 units in period 4 for period 4. Set $i = 4 + 1 = 5$.

Iteration 3 ($i = 5, K_5 = \$5$)

Period t	D_r	$\text{TC}(5, t)$	$\text{TCU}(5, t)$
5	13	$5	$\frac{5}{1} = \boxed{\$5}$
6	25	$5 + 1 \times 25 = \$30$	$\frac{30}{2} = \$15$

The minimum occurs at $t^* = 5$, which requires ordering 13 units in period 5 for period 5. Next, we set $i = 5 + 1 = 6$. However, because $i = 6$ is the last period of the planning horizon, we must order 25 unit in period 6 for period 6.

Remarks. The following table compares the heuristic and the exact DP solution. We have deleted the unit production cost in the dynamic programming model because it is not included in the heuristic computations.

Period	Heuristic		Dynamic programming	
	Units produced	Cost ($)	Units produced	Cost ($)
1	32	49	10	20
2	0	0	22	24
3	0	0	0	0
4	20	18	20	18
5	13	5	38	30
6	25	50	0	0
Total	90	122	90	92

The heuristic production schedule costs about 32% more than that of the DP solution ($122 vs. $92). The "inadequate" performance of the heuristic may be attributed to the nature of the data, as the problem may lie in the extreme setup cost values for periods 5 and 6. Nevertheless, the example shows that the heuristic does not have the capability to "look ahead" for better scheduling opportunities. For example, ordering in period 5 for periods 5 and 6 (instead of ordering for each period separately) can save $25, which will bring the total heuristic cost down to $97.

Excel Moment

Excel template *excelSilverMeal.xls* is designed to carry out all the iterative computations and provide the final solution. The procedure starts with entering the data needed to drive the calculations, including N, K, h, and D for all the periods (these entries are highlighted in turquoise in the spreadsheet). The user must then initiate each iteration manually until all the periods have been covered.

Figure 13.11 shows the application of the Excel heuristic to Example 13.4-4. The first iteration is initiated by entering the value 1 in cell J11, signaling that iteration 1 starts at period 1. The spreadsheet will then generate as many rows as the number of periods, N (=6 in this example). The period number will be listed in ascending order in cells K11:K16. Now, examine TCU in column P (highlighted in turquoise) and locate the period that corresponds to the local minimum at $t = 3$ with TCU = $16.33. This means that the next iteration will start at period 4. Now, skip a blank row, and enter the value 4 in J18. This action, which produces the calculations for iteration 2, shows that its local minimum will be at period 4 (TCU = $18.00) and signals the start of iteration 3 at period 5. Again, entering 5 in J22, the local minimum for iteration 3 occurs at node 5. Next, entering the value 6 in J25 produces the terminating iteration of the problem. The spreadsheet will automatically update the associated optimal policy and its total cost, as shown in Figure 13.11.

	Silver-Meal Heuristic Inventory Model						
Input data:							
Number of periods, N =	6	<<Maximum 14 periods					
Period t=	1	2	3	4	5	6	
Setup cost, K_t =	20	17	10	18	5	50	
Holding cost, h_t =	1	1	1	3	1	1	
Demand, D_t =	10	15	7	20	13	25	

Solution complete	Model calculations: *(Clear Column J man...*				Optimum solution (Total cost = $122.00):	
Start Iteration at Period	**Period**	D_t	$\sum D_i$	$\sum h_i$	**TC**	**TCU**	
1	1	10	10	0.00	20.00	20.00	
	2	15	25	1.00	35.00	17.50	
	3	7	32	2.00	49.00	16.33	
	4	20	52	3.00	109.00	27.25	
	5	13	65	6.00	187.00	37.40	
	6	25	90	7.00	362.00	60.33	Order 32 in period 1 for periods 1 to 3, cost = $49.00
4	4	20	20	0.00	18.00	18.00	
	5	13	33	3.00	57.00	28.50	
	6	25	58	4.00	157.00	52.33	Order 20 in period 4 for periods 4 to 4, cost = $18.00
5	5	13	13	0.00	5.00	5.00	
	6	25	38	1.00	30.00	15.00	Order 13 in period 5 for periods 5 to 5, cost = $5.00
6	6	25	25	0.00	50.00	50.00	Order 25 in period 6 for periods 6 to 6, cost = $50.00

FIGURE 13.11

Excel solution of Example 13.4-4 using Silver-Meal heuristic (file *ExcelSilverMeal.xls*)

PROBLEM SET 13.4E

*1. The demand for fishing poles is at its minimum during the month of December and reaches its maximum during the month of April. Fishing Hole, Inc., estimates the December demand at 50 poles. It increases by 10 poles a month until it reaches 90 in April. Thereafter, the demand decreases by 5 poles a month. The setup cost for a production lot is $250, except during the peak demand months of February to April, where it increases to $300. The production cost per pole is approximately constant at $15 throughout the year, and the holding cost per pole per month is $1. Fishing Hole is developing next year's (January through December) production plan. How should it schedule its production facilities?

2. A small publisher reprints a novel to satisfy the demand over the next 12 months. The demand estimates for the successive months are 100, 120, 50, 70, 90, 105, 115, 95, 80, 85, 100, and 110. The setup cost for reprinting the book is $200.00, and the holding cost per book per month is $1.20. Determine the optimal reprint schedule.

BIBLIOGRAPHY

Bishop, J., "Experience with a Successful System for Forecasting and Inventory Control," *Operations Research*, Vol. 22, No. 6, pp. 1224–1231, 1974.

Edwards, J., H. Wagner, and W. Wood, "Blue Bell Trims Its Inventory," *Interfaces*, Vol. 15, No. 1, pp. 34–52, 1985.

Lewis, T., "Personal Operations Research: Practicing OR on Ourselves," *Interfaces*, Vol. 26, No. 5, pp. 34–41, 1996.

Nahmias, S., *Production and Operations Analysis*, 5th ed., Irwin, Homewood, IL, 2005.

Silver, E., D. Pyke, and R. Peterson, *Decision Systems for Inventory Management and Production Control*, 3rd ed., Wiley, New York, 1998.

Tersine, R., *Principles of Inventory and Materials Management*, 3rd ed., North Holland, New York, 1988.

Waters, C., *Inventory Control and Management*, Wiley, New York, 1992.

CHAPTER 14

Review of Basic Probability

14.1 LAWS OF PROBABILITY

Probability deals with random outcomes of an **experiment**. The conjunction of all the outcomes is the **sample space**, and a subset of the sample space is an **event**. As an illustration, the experiment of rolling a (6-faced) die produces the sample space $\{1, 2, 3, 4, 5, 6\}$. The subset $\{1, 3, 5\}$ defines the event of turning up odd values.

An experiment may deal with a continuous sample space as well. For example, the time between failures of an electronic component may assume any nonnegative value.

If an event E occurs m times in an n-trial experiment, then the probability of realizing the event E is defined as

$$P\{E\} = \lim_{n \to \infty} \frac{m}{n}$$

The definition says that when the experiment is repeated an infinite number of times ($n \to \infty$), the probability of realizing an event is $\frac{m}{n}$. For example, the longer a fair coin is flipped, the closer will be the estimate of $P\{\text{head}\}$ (or $P\{\text{tail}\}$) to the theoretical value of 0.5.

By definition,

$$0 \leq P\{E\} \leq 1$$

An event E is impossible if $P\{E\} = 0$, and certain if $P\{E\} = 1$. For example, in a 6-faced die experiment, rolling a seven is impossible, but rolling a number in the range 1 to 6 is certain.

PROBLEM SET 14.1A

*1. In a survey conducted in the State of Arkansas high schools to study the correlation between senior year scores in mathematics and enrollment in engineering colleges,

523

400 out of 1000 surveyed seniors have studied mathematics. Engineering enrollment shows that, of the 1000 seniors, 150 students have studied mathematics and 29 have not. Determine the probabilities of the following events:

   (a) A student who studied mathematics is (is not) enrolled in engineering.

   (b) A student neither studied mathematics nor enrolled in engineering.

   (c) A student is not studying engineering.

*2. Consider a random gathering of n persons. Determine the smallest n such that it is more likely that two persons or more have the same birthday. (*Hint*: Assume no leap years and that all days of the year are equally likely to be a person's birthday.)

*3. Answer Problem 2 assuming that two or more persons share your birthday.

14.1.1   Addition Law of Probability

The **union** of two events E and F is $E + F$ or $E \cup F$, and their **intersection** is EF or $E \cap F$. The events E and F are **mutually exclusive** if the occurrence of one event precludes the occurrence of the other, or $P\{EF\} = 0$. Based on these definitions, the addition law of probability can be stated as

$$P\{E + F\} = \begin{cases} P\{E\} + P\{F\}, & E \text{ and } F \text{ mutually exclusive} \\ P\{E\} + P\{F\} - P\{EF\}, & \text{otherwise} \end{cases}$$

Example 14.1-1

Consider the experiment of rolling a die. The sample space of the experiment is $\{1, 2, 3, 4, 5, 6\}$. For a fair die, we have

$$P\{1\} = P\{2\} = P\{3\} = P\{4\} = P\{5\} = P\{6\} = \tfrac{1}{6}$$

Define

$$E = \{1, 2, 3, \text{ or } 4\}$$

$$F = \{3, 4, \text{ or } 5\}$$

The event $EF = \{3 \text{ or } 4\}$ because the outcomes 3 and 4 are common between E and F. Thus,

$$P\{E\} = P\{1\} + P\{2\} + P\{3\} + P\{4\} = \tfrac{1}{6} + \tfrac{1}{6} + \tfrac{1}{6} + \tfrac{1}{6} = \tfrac{2}{3}$$

$$P\{F\} = P\{3\} + P\{4\} + P\{5\} = \tfrac{1}{2}$$

$$P\{EF\} = P\{3\} + P\{4\} = \tfrac{1}{3}$$

$$P\{E + F\} = P\{E\} + P\{F\} - P\{EF\} = \tfrac{2}{3} + \tfrac{1}{2} - \tfrac{1}{3} = \tfrac{5}{6}$$

Intuitively, the result makes sense because $P\{E + F\} = P\{1, 2, 3, 4, 5\} = \tfrac{5}{6}$.

PROBLEM SET 14.1B

   1. A fair 6-faced die is tossed twice. Letting E and F represent the outcomes of the two tosses, compute the following probabilities:

   (a) The sum of E and F is 10.

   (b) The sum of E and F is even.

(c) The sum of E and F is odd and greater than 3.

(d) E is odd less than 6, and F is even greater than 1.

(e) E is greater than 2, and F is less than 4.

(f) E is 4, and the sum of E and F is even.

2. Two dice are rolled independently, and the two numbers that turn up are recorded. Determine the following:

(a) The probability that the two numbers are odd with values less than 5.

(b) The probability that the sum of the two numbers is 10.

(c) The probability that the two numbers differ by at least 3.

3. You can toss a fair coin up to 7 times. You will win $100 if three tails appear before a head is encountered. What are your chances of winning?

*4. Ann, Jim, John, and Nancy are scheduled to compete in a racquetball tournament. Ann is twice as likely to beat Jim, and Jim is at the same level as John. Nancy's past winning record against John is one out of three. Determine the following:

(a) The probability that Jim will win the tournament.

(b) The probability that a woman will win the tournament.

(c) The probability that no woman will win.

14.1.2 Conditional Law of Probability

Given the two events E and F with $P\{F\} > 0$, the conditional probability of E given F is computed as

$$P\{E|F\} = \frac{P\{EF\}}{P\{F\}}, \quad P\{F\} > 0$$

If E is a subset of F, then $P\{EF\} = P\{E\}$. The two events are *independent* if, and only if,

$$P\{E|F\} = P\{E\}$$

In this case, the conditional probability law reduces to

$$P\{EF\} = P\{E\}\, P\{F\}$$

Example 14.1-2

You are playing a game in which another person is rolling a die. You cannot see the die, but you are given information about the outcomes. Your job is to predict the outcome of each roll. Determine the probability that the outcome is 6, given that you are told that the roll has turned up an even number.

Let $E = \{6\}$, and define $F = \{2, 4, \text{or } 6\}$ Thus,

$$P\{E|F\} = \frac{P\{EF\}}{P\{F\}} = \frac{P\{E\}}{P\{F\}} = \left(\frac{1/6}{1/2}\right) = \tfrac{1}{3}$$

Note that $P\{EF\} = P\{E\}$ because E is a subset of F.

PROBLEM SET 14.1C

1. In Example 14.1-2, suppose that you are told that the outcome is less than 6.

   (a) Determine the probability of getting an even number.

   (b) Determine the probability of getting an odd number larger than one.

2. The stock of WalMark Stores, Inc., trades on the New York Stock Exchange under the symbol WMS. Historically, the price of WMS goes upward with the Dow 65% of the time and goes downward with the Dow 20% of the time. There is also a 10% chance that WMS will go up when the Dow goes down and 5% that it will go down when the Dow goes up.

   (a) Determine the probability that WMS will go up regardless of the Dow.

   (b) Find the probability that WMS goes up given that the Dow is up.

   (c) What is the probability WMS goes down given that Dow is down?

*3. Graduating high school seniors with an ACT score of at least 26 can seek admission in two universities, A and B. The probability of being accepted in A is .4 and in B .25. The chance of being accepted in both universities is only 15%.

   (a) Determine the probability that the student is accepted in B given that A has granted admission as well.

   (b) What is the probability that admission will be granted in A given that the student was accepted in B?

4. Prove that if the probability $P\{A|B\} = P\{A\}$, then A and B must be independent.

5. *Bayes' theorem.*[1] Given the two events A and B, show that

$$P\{A|B\} = \frac{P\{B|A\}P\{A\}}{P\{B\}}, \quad P\{B\} > 0$$

6. A retailer receives 70% of its batteries from Factory A and 30% from Factory B. The percentages of defectives produced by A and B are known to be 3% and 5%, respectively. A customer has just bought a battery randomly from the retailer.

   (a) What is the probability that the battery is defective?

   (b) If a battery is defective, what is the probability that it came from Factory A? (*Hint*: Use Bayes' theorem in Problem 5.)

*7. Statistics show that 70% of all men have some form of prostate cancer. The PSA test will show positive 90% of the time for afflicted men and 10% of the time for healthy men. What is the probability that a man who tested positive does have prostate cancer?

14.2   RANDOM VARIABLES AND PROBABILITY DISTRIBUTIONS

The outcomes of an experiment can be naturally numeric (e.g., rolling a die) or can be represented by numeric code (e.g., flipping a coin, with the outcome head/tail coded as 0/1). The numeric representation of the outcomes defines what is known as a **random variable**.

A random variable, x, may be **discrete** (as in die rolling) or **continuous** (as in time-to-failure of an equipment). Each continuous or discrete random variable x is

---

[1]Section 15.2.2 provides more details about Bayes' theorem.

quantified by a **probability density function (pdf)**, $f(x)$ or $p(x)$, satisfying the following conditions:

Characteristic	Random variable, x	
	Discrete	*Continuous*
Applicability range	$x = a, a + 1, \ldots, b$	$a \le x \le b$
Conditions for the pdf	$p(x) \ge 0, \displaystyle\sum_{x=a}^{b} p(x) = 1$	$f(x) \ge 0, \displaystyle\int_a^b f(x)dx = 1$

An important probability measure is the **cumulative distribution function (CDF)**, defined as

$$p\{x \le X\} = \begin{cases} P(X) = \displaystyle\sum_{x=a}^{X} p(x), & x \text{ discrete} \\ F(X) = \int_a^X f(x)dx, & x \text{ continuous} \end{cases}$$

Example 14.2-1

Consider the experiment of rolling a fair die represented by the random variable $x = \{1, 2, 3, 4, 5, 6\}$. The associated pdf and CDF are

$$p(x) = \frac{1}{6}, x = 1, 2, \ldots, 6$$

$$P(X) = \frac{X}{6}, X = 1, 2, \ldots, 6$$

Figure 14.1 graphs the two functions. The pdf $p(x)$ is a **uniform discrete function** because all the values of the random variables occur with equal probabilities.

The continuous counterpart of uniform $p(x)$ is illustrated by the following experiment. A needle of length l is pivoted in the center of a circle with diameter l. After marking an

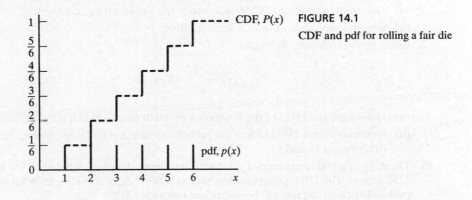

FIGURE 14.1

CDF and pdf for rolling a fair die

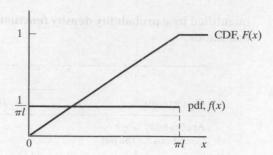

FIGURE 14.2

CDF and pdf for spinning a needle

arbitrary reference point on the circumference, the needle is spun clockwise, and the circumference distance, x, from where the pointer stops to the marked point is measured. Because any stopping point on the circumference is equally likely to occur, the distribution of x is uniform in the range $0 \le x \le \pi l$ with the following pdf:

$$f(x) = \frac{1}{\pi l}, 0 \le x \le \pi l$$

The associated CDF, $F(X)$, is computed as

$$F(X) = P\{x \le X\} = \int_0^X f(x)dx = \int_0^X \frac{1}{\pi l} dx = \frac{X}{\pi l}, 0 \le X \le \pi l$$

Figure 14.2 graphs the two functions.

PROBLEM SET 14.2A

1. The number of units, x, needed of an item is discrete from 1 to 6. The probability, $p(x)$, is directly proportional to the number of units needed. The constant of proportionality is K.

   (a) Determine the pdf and CDF of x, and graph the resulting functions.

   (b) Find the probability that x is an even value.

2. Consider the following function:

$$f(x) = \frac{k}{x^2}, 10 \le x \le 20$$

   *(a) Determine the value of the constant k that will render $f(x)$ a pdf.

   (b) Determine the CDF, and find the probability that x is (i) larger than 12 and (ii) between 13 and 15.

*3. The daily demand for unleaded gasoline is uniformly distributed between 750 and 1250 gallons. The 1100-gallon gasoline tank is refilled daily at midnight. What is the probability that the tank will be empty just before a refill?

14.3 EXPECTATION OF A RANDOM VARIABLE

Given a real function $h(x)$ of a random variable x, the **expected value** of $h(x)$ is computed as

$$E\{h(x)\} = \begin{cases} \sum_{x=a}^{b} h(x)p(x), & x \text{ discrete} \\ \int_a^b h(x)f(x)dx, & x \text{ continuous} \end{cases}$$

Example 14.3-1

During the first week of each month, I pay all my bills and answer a few letters. I usually buy 20 first-class mail stamps each month for this purpose. The number of stamps I actually use varies randomly between 10 and 24, with equal probabilities. Determine the average number of stamps left (i.e., average surplus) per month.

The pdf of the number of stamps used is

$$p(x) = \tfrac{1}{15}, \; x = 10, 11, \ldots, 24.$$

The number of stamps left is

$$h(x) = \begin{cases} 20-x, & x = 10, 11, \ldots, 19 \\ 0, & \text{otherwise} \end{cases}$$

Thus,

$$E\{h(x)\} = \tfrac{1}{15}[(20 - 10) + (20 - 11) + (20 - 12) + \ldots + (20 - 19)] + \tfrac{5}{15}(0) = 3\tfrac{2}{3}$$

The product $\tfrac{5}{15}(0)$ accounts for the outcome of being left with no stamps, which corresponds to the probability of using at least 20 stamps—that is,

$$P\{x \geq 20\} = p(20) + p(21) + p(22) + p(23) + p(24) = 5(\tfrac{1}{15}) = \tfrac{5}{15}$$

PROBLEM SET 14.3A

1. In Example 14.3-1, compute the average shortage of stamps per month. (*Hint:* Shortage can occur if I need more than 20 stamps.)

2. The results of Example 14.3-1 and of Problem 1 show *positive* averages for *both* the surplus and shortage of stamps. Are these results inconsistent? Explain.

*3. The owner of a newspaper stand receives 50 copies of *Al Ahram* newspaper every morning. The number of copies sold, x, varies randomly according to the following probability distribution:

$$p(x) = \begin{cases} \tfrac{1}{45}, & x = 35, 36, \ldots, 49 \\ \tfrac{1}{30}, & x = 50, 51, \ldots, 59 \\ \tfrac{1}{33}, & x = 60, 61, \ldots, 70 \end{cases}$$

   (a) Determine the probability that the owner will sell out completely.
   (b) Determine the expected number of unsold copies per day.
   (c) A single copy costs 50 cents and sells for $1.00. Determine the expected net income per day.

14.3.1 Mean and Variance (Standard Deviation) of a Random Variable

The **mean value** $E\{x\}$ is measure of the central tendency (or weighted sum) of the random variable x. The **variance** var$\{x\}$ is a measure of the dispersion or deviation of x around its mean value. Its square root is known as the **standard deviation** of x, stdDev$\{x\}$. A larger standard deviation implies higher uncertainty.

The formulas for the mean and variance can be derived from the general definition of $E\{h(x)\}$ in Section 14.3 by substituting $h(x) = x$ to obtain $E\{x\}$ and by substituting $h(x) = (x - E\{x\})^2$ to obtain var$\{x\}$—that is

$$E(x) = \begin{cases} \sum_{x=a}^{b} x p(x), & x \text{ discrete} \\ \int_a^b x f(x) dx, & x \text{ continuous} \end{cases}$$

$$\text{var}\{x\} = \begin{cases} \sum_{x=a}^{b} (x - E\{x\})^2 p(x), & x \text{ discrete} \\ \int_a^b (x - E\{x\})^2 f(x) dx, & x \text{ continuous} \end{cases}$$

$$\text{stdDev}\{x\} = \sqrt{\text{var}\{x\}}$$

Example 14.3-2

We compute the mean and variance for each of the two experiments in Example 14.2-1.

Case 1 (Die Rolling).   The pdf is $p(x) = \frac{1}{6}, x = 1, 2, \ldots, 6$. Thus,

$$E\{x\} = 1\left(\tfrac{1}{6}\right) + 2\left(\tfrac{1}{6}\right) + 3\left(\tfrac{1}{6}\right) + 4\left(\tfrac{1}{6}\right) + 5\left(\tfrac{1}{6}\right) + 6\left(\tfrac{1}{6}\right) = 3.5$$

$$\text{var}\{x\} = \left(\tfrac{1}{6}\right)\big\{(1 - 3.5)^2 + (2 - 3.5)^2 + (3 - 3.5)^2 + (4 - 3.5)^2$$
$$+ (5 - 3.5)^2 + (6 - 3.5)^2\big\} = 2.917$$

$$\text{stdDev}(x) = \sqrt{2.917} = 1.708$$

Case 2 (Needle Spinning).   Suppose that the length of the needle is 1 inch. Then,

$$f(x) = \frac{1}{3.14}, \quad 0 \le x \le 3.14$$

The mean and variance are

$$E(x) = \int_0^{3.14} x\left(\tfrac{1}{3.14}\right) dx = 1.57 \text{ inch}$$

$$\text{var}(x) = \int_0^{3.14} (x - 1.57)^2 \left(\tfrac{1}{3.14}\right) dx = .822 \text{ inch}^2$$

$$\text{stdDev}(x) = \sqrt{.822} = .906 \text{ inch}$$

Excel Moment

Template *excelStatTables.xls* computes the mean, standard deviation, probabilities, and percentiles for 16 common pdfs, including the discrete and continuous uniform distributions. The use of the spreadsheet is self-explanatory.

PROBLEM SET 14.3B

*1. Compute the mean and variance of the random variable defined in Problem 1, Set 14.2a.

2. Compute the mean and variance of the random variable in Problem 2, Set 14.2a.

3. Show that the mean and variance of a uniform random variable $x, a \leq x \leq b$, are

$$E\{x\} = \frac{b + a}{2}$$

$$\text{var}\{x\} = \frac{(b - a)^2}{12}$$

4. Given the pdf $f(x), a \leq x \leq b$, prove that

$$\text{var}\{x\} = E\{x^2\} - (E\{x\})^2$$

5. Given the pdf $f(x), a \leq x \leq b$, and $y = cx + d$, where c and d are constants, prove that

$$E\{y\} = cE\{x\} + d$$

$$\text{var}\{y\} = c^2 \, \text{var}\{x\}$$

14.3.2 Joint Random Variables

Consider the two continuous random variables x_1 and x_2, where $a_1 \leq x_1 \leq b_1$ and $a_2 \leq x_2 \leq b_2$. Define $f(x_1, x_2)$ as the **joint pdf** of x_1 and x_2 and $f_1(x_1)$ and $f_2(x_2)$ as their respective **marginal pdfs**. Then

$$f(x_1, x_2) \geq 0, a_1 \leq x_1 \leq b_1, a_2 \leq x_2 \leq b_2$$

$$\int_{a_1}^{b_1} dx_1 \int_{a_2}^{b_2} dx_2 f(x_1, x_2) = 1$$

$$f_1(x_1) = \int_{a_2}^{b_2} f(x_1, x_2) \, dx_2$$

$$f_2(x_2) = \int_{a_1}^{b_1} f(x_1, x_2) \, dx_1$$

$$f(x_1, x_2) = f_1(x_1)f_2(x_2), \text{if } x_1 \text{ and } x_2 \text{ are independent}$$

The same formulas apply to discrete pdfs, replacing integration with summation.

For the special case $y = c_1x_1 + c_2x_2$, where the random variables x_1 and x_2 are jointly distributed according to the pdf $f(x_1, x_2)$, we can prove that

$$E\{c_1x_1 + c_2x_2\} = c_1E\{x_1\} + c_2E\{x_2\}$$
$$\text{var}\{c_1x_1 + c_2x_2\} = c_1^2\text{var}\{x_1\} + c_2^2\text{var}\{x_2\} + 2c_1c_2\text{cov}\{x_1, x_2\}$$

where

$$\text{cov}\{x_1, x_2\} = E\{(x_1 - E\{x_1\})(x_2 - E\{x_2\})\}$$
$$= E(x_1x_2 - x_1E\{x_2\} - x_2E\{x_1\} + E\{x_1\}E\{x_2\})$$
$$= E\{x_1x_2\} - E\{x_1\}E\{x_2\}$$

If x_1 and x_2 are *independent*, then $E\{x_1x_2\} = E\{x_1\}E\{x_2\}$ and $\text{cov}\{x_1, x_2\} = 0$. The converse is not true, in the sense that two *dependent* variables may have zero covariance.

Example 14.3-3

A lot includes four defective (D) items and six good (G) ones. One item is selected randomly and tested. Next, a second item is selected from the remaining nine items and tested. Let x_1 and x_2 represent the outcomes of the first and second selections.

(a)   Determine the joint and marginal pdfs of x_1 and x_2.

(b)   Suppose that a good item nets a revenue of \$5 and a defective item results in a loss of \$6. Determine the mean and variance of revenue following the testing of two items.

Let $p(x_1, x_2)$ be the joint pdf of x_1 and x_2, and define $p_1(x_1)$ and $p_2(x_2)$ as the respective marginal pdfs. First, we determine $p_1(x_1)$ as

$$p_1(G) = \tfrac{6}{10} = .6, \; p_1(D) = \tfrac{4}{10} = .4$$

Next, we know that the second outcome x_2 depends on the first outcome x_1. Hence, to determine $p_2(x_2)$, we first determine the joint pdf $p(x_1, x_2)$ (using the formula $P\{AB\} = P\{A|B\}P\{B\}$ in Section 14.1.2), from which we can determine the marginal distribution $p_2(x_2)$. Thus,

$$P\{x_2 = G|x_1 = G\} = \tfrac{5}{9}$$
$$P\{x_2 = G|x_1 = B\} = \tfrac{6}{9}$$
$$P\{x_2 = B|x_1 = G\} = \tfrac{4}{9}$$
$$P\{x_2 = B|x_1 = B\} = \tfrac{3}{9}$$

Next,

$$p\{x_2 = G, x_1 = G\} = \tfrac{5}{9} \times \tfrac{6}{10} = \tfrac{5}{15}$$
$$p\{x_2 = G, x_1 = B\} = \tfrac{6}{9} \times \tfrac{4}{10} = \tfrac{4}{15}$$
$$p\{x_2 = B, x_1 = G\} = \tfrac{4}{9} \times \tfrac{6}{10} = \tfrac{4}{15}$$
$$p\{x_2 = B, x_1 = B\} = \tfrac{3}{9} \times \tfrac{4}{10} = \tfrac{2}{15}$$

The expected revenue can be determined from the joint distribution by recognizing that G produces \$5 and B yields $-\$6$. Thus,

$$\text{Expected revenue} = (5 + 5)\tfrac{5}{15} + (5 - 6)\tfrac{4}{15} + (-6 + 5)\tfrac{4}{15} + (-6 - 6)\tfrac{2}{15} = \$1.20$$

The same result can be determined by recognizing that the expected revenue for both selections equals the sum of the expected revenue for each individual selection (even though the two variables are *not* independent). These computations require determining the marginal distributions, $p_1(x_1)$ and $p_2(x_2)$.

A convenient way to determine the marginal distributions is to present the joint distribution, $p(x_1, x_2)$, as a table and then add the respective columns and rows to determine $p(x_1)$ and $p(x_2)$, respectively. Thus,

	$x_2 = G$	$x_2 = B$	$p_1(x_1)$
$x_1 = G$	$\tfrac{5}{15}$	$\tfrac{4}{15}$	$\tfrac{9}{15} = .6$
$x_1 = B$	$\tfrac{4}{15}$	$\tfrac{2}{15}$	$\tfrac{6}{15} = .4$
$p_2(x_2)$	$\tfrac{9}{15} = .6$	$\tfrac{6}{15} = .4$	

Now, the expected revenue is determined from the marginal distributions as

$$\text{Expected revenue} = \text{Selection 1 expected revenue} + \text{Selection 2 expected revenue}$$

$$= (5 \times .6 - 6 \times .4) + (5 \times .6 - 6 \times .4) = \$1.20$$

To compute the variance of the total revenue, we note that

$$\text{var\{revenue\}} = \text{var\{revenue 1\}} + \text{var\{revenue 2\}} + 2\,\text{cov\{revenue 1, revenue 2\}}$$

Because $p_1(x_1) = p_2(x_2)$, $\text{var\{revenue 1\}} = \text{var\{revenue 2\}}$. To compute the variance, we use the following formula (see Problem 4, Set 14.3b)

$$\text{var\{}x\} = E\{x^2\} - (E\{x\})^2$$

Thus,

$$\text{var\{revenue 1\}} = [5^2 \times .6 + (-6)^2 \times .4] - .6^2 = 29.04$$

Next, to compute the covariance, we use the formula

$$\text{cov\{}x_1, x_2\} = E\{x_1 x_2\} - E\{x_1\}E\{x_2\}$$

The term $E\{x_1 x_2\}$ can be computed from the joint pdf of x_1 and x_2 as

$$\text{Convariance} = [(5 \times 5)(\tfrac{5}{15}) + (5 \times -6)(\tfrac{4}{15}) + (-6 \times 5)(\tfrac{4}{15})$$

$$+ (-6 \times -6)(\tfrac{2}{15})] - .6 \times .6 = -3.23$$

Thus,

$$\text{Variance} = 29.04 + 29.04 + 2(-3.23) = 51.62$$

PROBLEM SET 14.3C

1. The joint pdf of x_1 and x_2 is

	$x_2 = 3$	$x_2 = 5$	$x_2 = 7$
$x_1 = 1$	.2	0	.2
$x_1 = 2$	0	.2	0
$x_1 = 3$	.2	0	.2

$p(x_1, x_2) = $

*(a) Find the marginal pdfs $p_1(x_1)$ and $p_2(x_2)$.
*(b) Are x_1 and x_2 independent?
(c) Compute $E\{x_1 + x_2\}$.
(d) Compute $cov\{x_1, x_2\}$.
(e) Compute $var\{5x_1 - 6x_2\}$.

14.4   FOUR COMMON PROBABILITY DISTRIBUTIONS

In Sections 14.2 and 14.3, we discussed the (discrete and continuous) uniform distribution. This section presents four additional pdfs that are encountered often in operations research studies: discrete binomial and Poisson, and continuous exponential and normal.

14.4.1 Binomial Distribution

A manufacturer produces an item in lots of n items each. The fraction of defective items, p, in each lot is estimated from historical data. We are interested in determining the pdf of the number of defectives in a lot.

There are $C_x^n = \frac{n!}{x!(n-x)!}$ distinct combinations of x defectives in a lot of size n, and the probability of realizing each combination is $p^x(1 - p)^{n-x}$. Thus, from the addition law (Section 14.1.1), the probability of k defectives in a lot of n items is

$$P\{x = k\} = C_k^n p^k(1 - p)^{n-k}, \ k = 0, 1, 2, \ldots, n$$

This is the binomial distribution with parameters n and p. Its mean and variance are

$$E\{x\} = np$$
$$var\{x\} = np(1 - p)$$

Example 14.4-1

John Doe's daily chores require making 10 round trips by car between two towns. Once through with all 10 trips, Mr. Doe can take the rest of the day off, a good enough motivation to drive above the speed limit. Experience shows that there is a 40% chance of getting a speeding fine on any round trip.

(a) What is the probability that the day will end without a speeding ticket?

(b) If each speeding ticket costs $80, what is the average daily fine?

The probability of getting a ticket on any one trip is $p = .4$. Thus, the probability of not getting a ticket in any one day is

$$P\{x = 0\} = C_0^{10}(.4)^0(.6)^{10} = .006$$

This means that there is less than 1% chance of finishing the day without a fine.

The average fine per day is

$$\text{Average fine} = \$80\, E\{x\} = \$80\,(np) = 80 \times 10 \times .4 = \$320$$

Remarks. $P\{x = 0\}$ can be computed using *excelStatTables.xls*. Enter 10 in F7, .4 in G7, and 0 in J7. The answer, $P\{x = 0\} = .006047$, is given in M7.

PROBLEM SET 14.4A

*1. A fair die is rolled 10 times. What is the probability that the rolled die will not show an even number?

2. Suppose that four fair coins are tossed independently. What is the probability that exactly one of the coins will be different from the remaining three?

*3. A fortune-teller claims to predict whether people will amass financial wealth in their lifetime by examining their handwriting. To verify this claim, 10 millionaires and 10 university professors were asked to provide samples of their handwriting. The samples are then paired, one millionaire and one professor, and presented to the fortune teller. We say that the claim is true if the fortune teller makes at least eight correct predictions. What is the probability that the claim is a "fluke"?

4. In a gambling casino, you play the game of selecting a number from 1 to 6 before the operator rolls 3 fair dice simultaneously. The casino pays you as many dollars as the number of dice that match your selection. If there is no match, you pay the casino only $1. Determine your long-run expected payoff.

5. Suppose that you throw 2 fair dice simultaneously. If there is a match, you receive 50 cents. Otherwise, you pay 10 cents. Determine the expected payoff of the game.

6. Prove the formulas for the mean and variance of the binomial distribution.

14.4.2 Poisson Distribution

Customers arrive at a bank or a grocery store in a "totally random" fashion—meaning that arrival times cannot be predicted in advance. The pdf describing the *number* of arrivals during a specified time period is the Poisson distribution.

Let x be the number of events (e.g., arrivals) that take place during a specified time period (e.g., a minute or an hour). Given that λ is a known constant, the Poisson pdf is defined as

$$P\{x = k\} = \frac{\lambda^k e^{-\lambda}}{k!}, \quad k = 0, 1, 2, \dots$$

The mean and variance of the Poisson are

$$E\{x\} = \lambda$$
$$\text{var}\{x\} = \lambda$$

The formula for the mean reveals that λ must represent the rate at which events occur.

The Poisson distribution figures prominently in the study of queues (see Chapter 18).

Example 14.4-2

Repair jobs arrive at a small-engine repair shop randomly at the rate of 10 per day.

(a)   What is the average number of jobs that are received daily at the shop?

(b)   What is the probability that no jobs will arrive during any 1 hour, assuming that the shop is open 8 hours a day?

The average number of jobs received per day equals $\lambda = 10$ jobs per day. To compute the probability of no arrivals per *hour*, we need to compute the arrival rate per hour—namely, $\lambda_{\text{hour}} = \frac{10}{8} = 1.25$ jobs per hour. Thus

$$P\{\text{no arrivals per hour}\} = \frac{(\lambda_{\text{hour}})^0 e^{-\lambda_{\text{hour}}}}{0!}$$
$$= \frac{1.25^0 e^{-1.25}}{0!} = .2865$$

Remark. The probability above can be computed with *excelStatTables.xls*. Enter 1.25 in F16 and 0 in J16. The answer, .286505, appears in M16.

PROBLEM SET 14.4B

*1.   Customers arrive at a service facility according to a Poisson distribution at the rate of 4 per minute. What is the probability that at least one customer will arrive in any given 30-second interval?

2.   The Poisson distribution with parameter λ approximates the binomial distribution with parameters (n, p) when $n \to \infty$, $p \to 0$, and $np \to \lambda$. Demonstrate this result for the situation where a manufactured lot is known to contain 1% defective items. If a sample of 10 items is taken from the lot, compute the probability of at most one defective item in a sample, first by using the (exact) binomial distribution and then by using the (approximate) Poisson distribution. Show that the approximation will not be acceptable if the value of p is increased to, say, 0.5.

*3.   Customers arrive randomly at a checkout counter at the average rate of 10 per hour.

(a)   Determine the probability that the counter is idle.

(b)   What is the probability that at least one person is in line awaiting service?

4.   Prove the formulas for the mean and variance of the Poisson distribution.

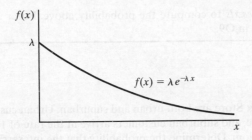

FIGURE 14.3

Probability density function of the exponential distribution

14.4.3 Negative Exponential Distribution

If the *number* of arrivals at a service facility during a specified time period follows the Poisson distribution (Section 14.4.2), then, automatically, the distribution of the *interarrival time* (i.e., between successive arrivals) is the negative exponential (or, simply, exponential) distribution. Specifically, given λ is the rate of occurrence of Poisson arrivals, then the distribution of interarrival time, x, is

$$f(x) = \lambda e^{-\lambda x}, x > 0$$

Figure 14.3 graphs $f(x)$.

The mean and variance of the exponential distribution are

$$E\{x\} = \frac{1}{\lambda}$$

$$\text{var}\{x\} = \frac{1}{\lambda}$$

The mean $E\{x\}$ is consistent with the definition of λ. If λ is the *rate* at which events occur, then $\frac{1}{\lambda}$ is the average time interval between successive events.

Example 14.4-3

Cars arrive randomly at a gas station. The average interarrival time is 2 minutes. Determine the probability that the interarrival time does not exceed 1 minute.

The determination of the desired probability is the same as computing the CDF of x—namely,

$$P\{x \leq A\} = \int_0^A \lambda e^{-\lambda x} dx$$

$$= -e^{-\lambda x}\big|_0^A$$

$$= 1 - e^{-\lambda A}$$

The arrival rate for the example is $\lambda = \frac{1}{2}$ arrival per minute. Substituting $A = 1$, the desired probability is

$$P\{x \leq 1\} = 1 - e^{-(\frac{1}{2})(1)} = .3934$$

PROBLEM SET 14.4C

*1. Customers shopping at Walmark Store are both urban and suburban. Urban customers arrive at the rate of 5 per minute, and suburban customers arrive at the rate of 10 per minute. Arrivals are totally random. Determine the probability that the interarrival time for all customers is less than 8 seconds.

2. Prove the formulas for the mean and variance of the exponential distribution.

14.4.4   Normal Distribution

The normal distribution describes many random phenomena in everyday life, such as test scores and weights and heights of individuals. The pdf of the normal distribution is

$$f(x) = \frac{1}{\sqrt{2\pi\sigma^2}} e^{-\frac{1}{2}\left(\frac{x-\mu}{\sigma}\right)^2}, \quad -\infty < x < \infty$$

The mean and variance are

$$E\{x\} = \mu$$

$$\text{var}\{x\} = \sigma^2$$

The notation $N(\mu, \sigma)$ is usually used to represent a normal distribution with mean μ and standard deviation σ.

Figure 14.4 graphs the normal pdf. The function is always symmetrical around the mean μ.

An important property of the normal random variable is that it approximates the distribution of the average of a sample taken from *any* distribution. This remarkable result is based on the following theorem:

Central Limit Theorem. *Let $x_1, x_2, \ldots,$ and x_n be independent and identically distributed random variables, each with mean μ and standard deviation σ, and define*

$$s_n = x_1 + x_2 + \cdots + x_n$$

FIGURE 14.4

Probability density function of the
normal random variable

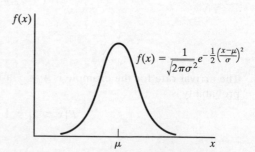

$$f(x) = \frac{1}{\sqrt{2\pi\sigma^2}} e^{-\frac{1}{2}\left(\frac{x-\mu}{\sigma}\right)^2}$$

The distribution of s_n is asymptotically normal with mean $n\mu$ and variance $n\sigma^2$, regardless of the original distribution of $x_1, x_2, \ldots,$ and x_n.

A special case of the central limit theorem deals with the distribution of the *average* of a sample of size n (drawn from *any* distribution). The average is asymptotically normal with mean μ and variance $\frac{\sigma^2}{n}$. This result has important applications in statistical quality control.

The CDF of the normal random variable cannot be determined in a closed form. Table A.1 in Appendix A give the probabilities for $N(0, 1)$, the **standard normal distribution** with mean zero and standard deviation 1. A general normal random variable x with mean μ and standard deviation σ can be converted to a standard normal z using the transformation

$$z = \frac{x - \mu}{\sigma}$$

Over 99% of the area under any normal density function is enclosed in the range $\mu - 3\sigma \leq x \leq \mu + 3\sigma$, also known as the **6-sigma limits**.

Example 14.4-4

The inside diameter of a cylinder has the specification $1 \pm .03$ cm. The output of the machining process producing the cylinder follows a normal distribution with mean 1 cm and standard deviation .1 cm. Determine the percentage of production that will meet the specifications.

Defining x as the inside parameter of the cylinder, the probability that a cylinder will meet specifications is

$$P\{1 - .03 \leq x \leq 1 + .03\} = P\{.97 \leq x \leq 1.03\}$$

This probability is computed using the standard normal (Table A.1 in Appendix A). Given $\mu = 1$ and $\sigma = .1$, we have

$$P\{.97 \leq x \leq 1.03\} = P\{\tfrac{.97 - 1}{.1} \leq z \leq \tfrac{1.03 - 1}{.1}\}$$
$$= P\{-.3 \leq z \leq .3\}$$
$$= P\{z \leq .3\} - P\{z \leq -.3\}$$
$$= P\{z \leq .3\} - P\{z \geq .3\}$$
$$= P\{z \leq .3\} - [1 - P\{z \leq .3\}]$$
$$= 2P\{z \leq .3\} - 1$$
$$= 2 \times .6179 - 1$$
$$= .2358$$

Notice that $P\{z \leq -.3\} = 1 - P\{z \leq .3\}$ because of the symmetry of the pdf, as shown in Figure 14.5. The cumulative probability $P\{z \leq .3\}(= .6179)$ is obtained from the standard normal table (Table A.1 in Appendix A) as the entry designated with row $z = 0.3$ and column $z = 0.00$.

Remark. $P\{.97 \leq x \leq 1.03\}$ can be computed directly from *excelStatTables.xls*. Enter 1 in F15, .1 in G15, .97 in J15, and 1.03 in K15. The answer $(= .235823)$ appears in Q15.

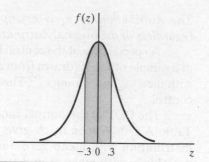

FIGURE 14.5

Calculation of $P\{-.3 \le z \le .3\}$ in a standard normal distribution

PROBLEM SET 14.4D

1. The college of engineering at U of A requires a minimum ACT score of 27. The test scores among high school seniors in a given school district are normally distributed with mean 23 and standard deviation 4.

    (a) Determine the percentage of high school seniors who are potential engineering recruits.

    (b) If U of A does not accept any student with an ACT score less than 17, what percentage of students will not be eligible for admission at U of A?

*2. The weights of individuals who seek a helicopter ride in an amusement park have a mean of 180 lb and a standard deviation of 15 lb. The helicopter can carry five persons but has a maximum weight capacity of 1000 1b. What is the probability that the helicopter will not take off with five persons aboard? (*Hint*: Apply the central limit theorem.)

3. The inside diameter of a cylinder is normally distributed with a mean of 1 cm and a standard deviation of .01 cm. A solid rod is assembled inside each cylinder. The diameter of the rod is also normally distributed with a mean of .99 cm and a standard deviation of .01 cm. Determine the percentage of rod–cylinder pairs that will not fit in an assembly. (*Hint*: The difference between two normal random variables is also normal.)

14.5   EMPIRICAL DISTRIBUTIONS

The preceding sections have dealt with the pdfs and CDFs of five common distributions—uniform, binomial, Poisson, exponential, and normal. How are these distributions recognized in practice?

The basis for identifying any pdf is the raw data we collect about the situation under study. This section shows how sampled data can be converted into a pdf.

Step 1.   Summarize the raw data in the form of an appropriate frequency histogram to determine the associated empirical pdf.

Step 2.   Use the *goodness-of-fit test* to test if the resulting empirical pdf is sampled from a known theoretical pdf.

Frequency histogram.   A frequency histogram is constructed from raw data by dividing the range of the data (minimum value to maximum value) into nonoverlapping bins. The frequency in each bin is the tally of all the raw data values that fall within the bin's designated boundaries.

Example 14.5-1

The following data represent the service time (in minutes) in a service facility for a sample of 60 customers.

.7	.4	3.4	4.8	2.0	1.0	5.5	6.2	1.2	4.4
1.5	2.4	3.4	6.4	3.7	4.8	2.5	5.5	.3	8.7
2.7	.4	2.2	2.4	.5	1.7	9.3	8.0	4.7	5.9
.7	1.6	5.2	.6	.9	3.9	3.3	.2	.2	4.9
9.6	1.9	9.1	1.3	10.6	3.0	.3	2.9	2.9	4.8
8.7	2.4	7.2	1.5	7.9	11.7	6.3	3.8	6.9	5.3

The minimum and maximum values of the data are .2 and 11.7, respectively. This means that the sample is covered by the range (0, 12). We arbitrarily divide the range (0, 12) into 12 bins, each of width 1 minute. The proper selection of the bin width is crucial in revealing the shape of the empirical distribution. Although there are no hard rules for determining the optimal bin width, a general rule of thumb is to use from 10 to 20 bins. In practice, it may be necessary to try different bin widths before deciding on an acceptable histogram.

The following table summarizes the histogram information for the given sample. The relative-frequency column, f_i, is computed by dividing the entries of the observed-frequency column, o_i, into the total number of observations ($n = 60$). For example, $f_1 = \frac{11}{60} = .1833$. The cumulative-frequency column, F_i, is generated by summing the values of f_i recursively. For example, $F_1 = f_1 = .1833$ and $F_2 = F_1 + f_2 = .1833 + .1333 = .3166$.

i	Bin interval	Observations tally	Observed frequency, o_i	Relative frequency, f_i	Cumulative relative frequency, F_i
1	(0, 1)	⦀⦀ ⦀⦀ ⦀	11	.1833	.1833
2	(1, 2)	⦀⦀ ⦀⦀⦀	8	.1333	.3166
3	(2, 3)	⦀⦀ ⦀⦀⦀⦀	9	.1500	.4666
4	(3, 4)	⦀⦀ ⦀⦀	7	.1167	.5833
5	(4, 5)	⦀⦀ ⦀	6	.1000	.6833
6	(5, 6)	⦀⦀	5	.0833	.7666
7	(6, 7)	⦀⦀⦀⦀	4	.0667	.8333
8	(7, 8)	⦀⦀	2	.0333	.8666
9	(8, 9)	⦀⦀⦀	3	.0500	.9166
10	(9, 10)	⦀⦀⦀	3	.0500	.9666
11	(10, 11)	⦀	1	.0167	.9833
12	(11, 12)	⦀	1	.0167	1.0000
Totals			60	1.0000	

The values of f_i and F_i provide a "discretized" version of the pdf and the CDF for the service time. We can convert the resulting CDF into a piecewise-continuous function by joining the resulting points with linear segments. Figure 14.6 provides the empirical pdf and CDF for the example. The CDF, as given by the histogram, is defined at midpoints of the bins.

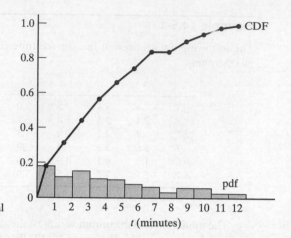

FIGURE 14.6

Piecewise-linear CDF of an empirical
distribution

We can now estimate the mean, $\bar{t}$, and variance, s_t^2, of the empirical distribution. Let N be the number of bins in the histogram, and define $\bar{t}_i$ as the midpoint of bin i, then

$$\bar{t} = \sum_{i=1}^{N} f_i \bar{t}_i$$

$$s_t^2 = \sum_{i=1}^{N} f_i (\bar{t}_i - \bar{t})^2$$

Applying these formulas to the present example, we get

$$\bar{t} = .1833 \times .5 + .133 \times 1.5 + \cdots + 11.5 \times .0167 = 3.934 \text{ minutes}$$

$$s_t^2 = .1883 \times (.5 - 3.934)^2 + .1333 \times (1.5 - 3.934)^2 + \cdots$$
$$+ .0167 \times (11.5 - 3.934)^2 = 8.646 \text{ minutes}^2$$

Excel Moment

Histograms can be constructed conveniently using Excel. Select Data Analysis ⇒ Histogram, then enter the pertinent data in the dialogue box.

The *Histogram* tool in Excel does not produce the mean and standard deviation directly as part of the output.[2] You may use Excel template *excelMeanVar.xls* to calculate the sample mean, variance, maximum, and minimum. Also, Excel allows the use of *histogram* tool.

---

[2]*Data Analysis* in Excel does provide a separate tool called *Descriptive Statistics*, which can be used to compute the mean and variance (as well as volumes of other statistics you may never use!).

Goodness-of-fit test. The goodness-of-fit test evaluates whether the sample used in determining the empirical distribution is drawn from a specific theoretical distribution. An initial evaluation of the data can be made by comparing the empirical CDF with the CDF of the assumed theoretical distribution. If the two CDFs do not deviate "excessively," then it is likely that the sample is drawn from the proposed theoretical distribution. This initial "hunch" can be supported further by applying the goodness-of-fit test. The following example provides the details of the proposed procedure.

Example 14.5-2

This example tests the data of Example 14.5-1 for a hypothesized exponential distribution. The first task is to specify the function that defines the theoretical distribution. From Example 14.5-1, $\bar{t} = 3.934$ minutes. Hence, $\lambda = \frac{1}{3.934} = .2542$ service per minute for the hypothesized exponential distribution (see Section 14.4.3), and the associated pdf and CDF are given as

$$f(t) = .2542e^{-.2542t}, t > 0$$

$$F(T) = \int_0^T f(t)\,dt = 1 - e^{-.2542T}, T > 0$$

We can use the CDF, $F(T)$, to compute the theoretical CDF for $T = .5, 1.5, \ldots,$ and 11.5, and then compare them graphically with empirical value $F_i, i = 1, 2, \ldots, 12$, as computed in Example 14.5-1 as shown in Figure 14.7. A cursory examination of the two graphs suggests that the exponential distribution may indeed provide a reasonable fit for the observed data.

The next step is to implement a goodness-of-fit test. Two such tests exist: (1) the **Kolmogrov-Smirnov** test, and (2) the **chi-square** test. We will limit this presentation to the chi-square test.

FIGURE 14.7

Comparison of the empirical CDF and theoretical exponential CDF

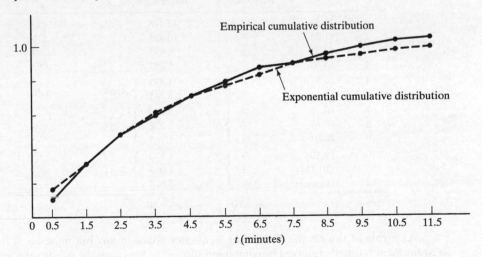

Empirical cumulative distribution

Exponential cumulative distribution

t (minutes)

The chi-square test is based on a measurement of the deviation between the empirical and theoretical frequencies. Specifically, for bin i, the theoretical frequency n_i corresponding to the observed frequency o_i is computed as

$$n_i = n \int_{I_{i-1}}^{I_i} f(t)dt$$

$$= n(F(I_i) - F(I_{i-1}))$$

$$= 60(e^{-.2542I_{i-1}} - e^{-.2542I_i})$$

Next, assuming N bins, a measure of the deviation between the empirical and observed frequencies is computed as

$$\chi^2 = \sum_{i=1}^{N} \frac{(o_i - n_i)^2}{n_i}$$

The measure χ^2 is asymptotically a chi-square pdf with $N - k - 1$ degrees of freedom, where k is the number of parameters estimated from the raw data and used for defining the theoretical distribution.

The null hypothesis for the test stating that the observed sample is drawn from the theoretical distribution $f(t)$ is accepted if

$$H: \text{Accept } f(t) \text{ if } \chi^2 < \chi^2_{N-k-1,1-\alpha}$$

The critical value $\chi^2_{N-k-1,1-\alpha}$ is obtained from chi-square tables (see Table A.3, Appendix A) corresponding to $N - k - 1$ degrees of freedom and a significance level α.

The computations of the test are shown in the following table:

i	Bin	Observed frequency, o_i	Theoretical frequency, n_i	$\dfrac{(o_i - n_i)^2}{n_i}$
1	$(0,1)$	11	13.448	.453
2	$(1,2)$	8	10.435	.570
3	$(2,3)$	9	8.095	.100
4	$(3,4)$	7	6.281	.083
5	$(4,5)$	6 ⎫ 11	4.873 ⎫ 8.654	.636
6	$(5,6)$	5 ⎭	3.781 ⎭	
7	$(6,7)$	4 ⎫	2.933 ⎫	
8	$(7,8)$	2 ⎬ 9	2.276 ⎬ 6.975	.588
9	$(8,9)$	3 ⎭	1.766 ⎭	
10	$(9,10)$	3 ⎫	1.370 ⎫	
11	$(10,11)$	1 ⎬ 5	1.063 ⎬ 6.111	.202
12	$(11,\infty)$	1 ⎭	3.678 ⎭	
Totals		$n = 60$	$n = 60$	χ^2-value = 2.623

As a rule of thumb, the *theoretical* frequency count in any bin must be at least 5. This requirement is usually resolved by combining successive bins until the rule is satisfied, as shown in the table. The resulting number of bins becomes $N = 7$. Because we are estimating one parameter from the observed data (namely, λ), the degrees of freedom for the chi-square is

$7 - 1 - 1 = 5$. If we assume a significance level $\alpha = .05$, we get the critical value $\chi^2_{5,.05} = 11.07$ (use Table A.3 in Appendix A, or, in *excelStatTables.xls*, enter 5 in F8 and .05 in L8, and get the answer in R8). Because the χ^2-value($=2.623$) is less than the critical value, we accept the hypothesis that the sample is drawn from an exponential pdf.

PROBLEM SET 14.5A

1. The following data represent the interarrival time (in minutes) at a service facility:

4.3	3.4	.9	.7	5.8	3.4	2.7	7.8
4.4	.8	4.4	1.9	3.4	3.1	5.1	1.4
.1	4.1	4.9	4.8	15.9	6.7	2.1	2.3
2.5	3.3	3.8	6.1	2.8	5.9	2.1	2.8
3.4	3.1	.4	2.7	.9	2.9	4.5	3.8
6.1	3.4	1.1	4.2	2.9	4.6	7.2	5.1
2.6	.9	4.9	2.4	4.1	5.1	11.5	2.6
.1	10.3	4.3	5.1	4.3	1.1	4.1	6.7
2.2	2.9	5.2	8.2	1.1	3.3	2.1	7.3
3.5	3.1	7.9	.9	5.1	6.2	5.8	1.4
.5	4.5	6.4	1.2	2.1	10.7	3.2	2.3
3.3	3.3	7.1	6.9	3.1	1.6	2.1	1.9

(a) Use Excel to develop three histograms for the data based on bin widths of .5, 1, and 1.5 minutes, respectively.

(b) Compare graphically the cumulative distribution of the empirical CDF and that of a corresponding exponential distribution.

(c) Test the hypothesis that the given sample is drawn from an exponential distribution. Use a 95% confidence level.

(d) Which of the three histograms is "best" for the purpose of testing the null hypothesis?

2. The following data represent the period (in seconds) needed to transmit a message.

25.8	67.3	35.2	36.4	58.7
47.9	94.8	61.3	59.3	93.4
17.8	34.7	56.4	22.1	48.1
48.2	35.8	65.3	30.1	72.5
5.8	70.9	88.9	76.4	17.3
77.4	66.1	23.9	23.8	36.8
5.6	36.4	93.5	36.4	76.7
89.3	39.2	78.7	51.9	63.6
89.5	58.6	12.8	28.6	82.7
38.7	71.3	21.1	35.9	29.2

Use Excel to construct a suitable histogram. Test the hypothesis that these data are drawn from a uniform distribution at a 95% confidence level, given the following additional information about the theoretical uniform distribution:

(a) The range of the distribution is between 0 and 100.

(b) The range of the distribution is estimated from the sample data.

(c) The maximum limit on the range of the distribution is 100, but the minimum limit must be estimated from the sample data.

3. An automatic device is used to count the volume of traffic at a busy intersection. The arrival time is recorded and translated into an absolute time starting from zero. The following table provides the arrival times (in minutes) for the first 60 cars. Use Excel to construct a suitable histogram. Test the hypothesis that the interarrival time is exponential using a 95% confidence level.

Arrival	Arrival time (min)	Arrival	Arrival time (min)	Arrival	Arrival time (min)	Arrival	Arrival time (min)
1	5.2	16	67.6	31	132.7	46	227.8
2	6.7	17	69.3	32	142.3	47	233.5
3	9.1	18	78.6	33	145.2	48	239.8
4	12.5	19	86.6	34	154.3	49	243.6
5	18.9	20	91.3	35	155.6	50	250.5
6	22.6	21	97.2	36	166.2	51	255.8
7	27.4	22	97.9	37	169.2	52	256.5
8	29.9	23	111.5	38	169.5	53	256.9
9	35.4	24	116.7	39	172.4	54	270.3
10	35.7	25	117.3	40	175.3	55	275.1
11	44.4	26	118.2	41	180.1	56	277.1
12	47.1	27	124.1	42	188.8	57	278.1
13	47.5	28	1127.4	43	201.2	58	283.6
14	49.7	29	127.6	44	218.4	59	299.8
15	67.1	30	127.8	45	219.9	60	300.0

BIBLIOGRAPHY

Feller, W., *An Introduction to Probability Theory and Its Applications*, 2nd ed., Vols. 1 and 2, Wiley, New York, 1967.

Paulos, J. A., *Innumeracy: Mathematical Illiteracy and Its Consequences*, Hill and Wang, New York, 1988.

Papoulis, A., *Probability and Statistics*, Prentice Hall, Upper Saddle River, NJ, 1990.

Ross, S., *Introduction to Probability Models*, 5th ed., Academic Press, New York, 1993.

CHAPTER 15

Decision Analysis and Games

Real-Life Application—Layout Planning of a Computer Integrated Manufacturing (CIM) Facility

The engineering college in an academic institution wants to establish a computer integrated manufacturing (CIM) laboratory in a vacated building. The new lab will serve as a teaching and research facility and as industry center of technical excellence. Recommendations solicited from the faculty regarding a layout plan for the new laboratory providing the ideal and absolute minimum square footage for each unit are compiled. The study uses both AHP (analytic hierarchy process) and goal programming to reach a satisfactory compromise solution that meets the needs for teaching, research, and service to industry. The details of the study are given in Case 9, Chapter 26, on the website.

15.1 DECISION MAKING UNDER CERTAINTY—ANALYTIC HIERARCHY PROCESS (AHP)

The LP models presented in Chapters 2 through 9 are examples of decision making under certainty (all the data are known with certainty). AHP is designed for situations in which ideas, feelings, and emotions affecting the decision process are quantified to provide a numeric scale for prioritizing the alternatives.

Example 15.1-1 (Overall Idea of AHP)

Martin Hans, a bright high school senior, has received full academic scholarships from three institutions: U of A, U of B, and U of C. Martin bases his choice on two criteria: location and academic reputation. To him, academic reputation is five times as important as location, which assigns a weight of approximately 83% to reputation and 17% to location. He then uses a

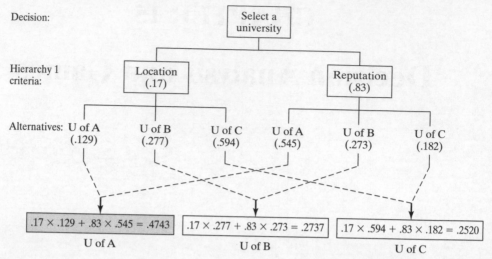

FIGURE 15.1

Summary of AHP calculations for Example 15.1-1

systematic process (which will be detailed later) to rank the three universities from the standpoint of location and reputation, as the following table shows:

| Criterion | Percent weight estimates for | | |
	U of A	U of B	U of C
Location	12.9	27.7	59.4
Reputation	54.5	27.3	18.2

The structure of the decision problem is summarized in Figure 15.1. The problem involves a single hierarchy (level) with two criteria (location and reputation) and three decision alternatives (U of A, U of B, and U of C).

The ranking of each university is based on the following *composite* weights:

$$U \text{ of } A = .17 \times .129 + .83 \times .545 = \mathbf{.4743}$$

$$U \text{ of } B = .17 \times .277 + .83 \times .273 = .2737$$

$$U \text{ of } C = .17 \times .594 + .83 \times .182 = .2520$$

Based on these calculations, Martin chooses U of A because it has the highest composite weight.

Remarks. The general structure of AHP may include several hierarchies of criteria. Suppose in Example 15.1-1 that Martin's twin sister, Jane, was also accepted with full scholarship to the three universities. The parents insist that the two siblings attend the same university. Figure 15.2 summarizes the decision problem, which now involves two hierarchies. The values p and q at the first hierarchy are the relative weights representing Martin's and Jane's opinions (presumably equal). The weights (p_1, p_2)

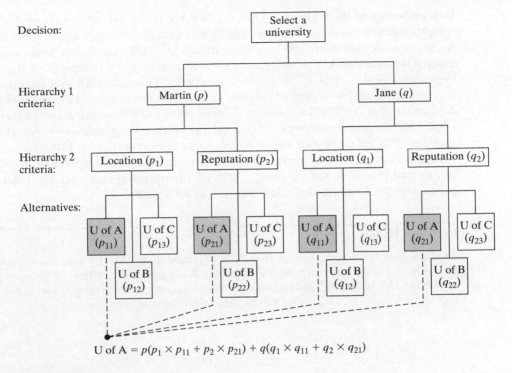

FIGURE 15.2
Embellishment of the decision problem of Example 15.1-1

and (q_1, q_2) at the second hierarchy, respectively, represent Martin's and Jane's preferences regarding location and reputation of each university. The remainder of the decision-making chart can be interpreted similarly. Note that $p + q = 1$, $p_1 + p_2 = 1$, $q_1 + q_2 = 1$, $p_{11} + p_{12} + p_{13} = 1$, $p_{21} + p_{22} + p_{23} = 1$, $q_{11} + q_{12} + q_{13} = 1$, and $q_{21} + q_{22} + q_{23} = 1$. The bottom of Figure 15.2 demonstrates how the U of A composite weight is computed.

PROBLEM SET 15.1A

*1. Suppose that the following weights are specified for the situation of Martin and Jane (Figure 15.2):

$$p = .5, q = .5$$

$$p_1 = .4, p_2 = .6$$

$$p_{11} = .129, p_{12} = .277, p_{13} = .594$$

$$p_{21} = .545, p_{22} = .273, p_{23} = .182$$

$$q_1 = .6, q_2 = .4$$

$$q_{11} = .2, q_{12} = .3, q_{13} = .5$$

$$q_{21} = .5, q_{22} = .2, q_{23} = .3$$

Based on this information, rank the three universities.

Determination of the weights. The crux of AHP is the determination of the relative weights (such as those used in Example 15.1-1) to rank the alternatives. Assuming that we are dealing with n criteria at a given hierarchy, AHP establishes a pairwise $n \times n$ **comparison matrix, A,** that quantifies the decision maker's judgment of the relative importance of the criteria. The pairwise comparison is made such that the criterion in row $i(i = 1, 2, \ldots, n)$ is ranked relative to every other criterion. Letting a_{ij} define the element (i, j) of $\mathbf{A}$, AHP uses a numeric scale from 1 to 9 in which $a_{ij} = 1$ signifies that i and j are of *equal importance*, $a_{ij} = 5$ indicates that i is *strongly more important* than j, and $a_{ij} = 9$ indicates that i is *extremely more important* than j. Other intermediate values between 1 and 9 are interpreted correspondingly. **Consistency** in judgment means that if $a_{ij} = k$, then $a_{ji} = \frac{1}{k}$. Also, all the diagonal elements a_{ii} of $\mathbf{A}$ equal 1, because these elements rank each criterion against itself.

Example 15.1-2

To show how the comparison matrix $\mathbf{A}$ is determined for Martin's decision problem of Example 15.1-1, we start with the top hierarchy dealing with the criteria of location (L) and reputation (R). In Martin's judgment, R is *strongly more important* than L, and hence $a_{21} = 5$ and, automatically, $a_{12} = \frac{1}{5}$, thus yielding the following comparison matrix:

$$
\mathbf{A} = \begin{array}{c} L \\ R \end{array}\!\!\begin{pmatrix} \overset{L}{1} & \overset{R}{\frac{1}{5}} \\ 5 & 1 \end{pmatrix}
$$

The relative weights of R and L can be determined by normalizing $\mathbf{A}$ to create a new matrix $\mathbf{N}$. The process requires dividing the individual elements of each column by the column sum. Thus, we divide the elements of columns 1 by 6 (1 + 5) and those of column 2 by 1.2 ($= \frac{1}{5} + 1$). The desired relative weights, w_R and w_L, are then computed as row averages:

$$
\mathbf{N} = \begin{array}{c} L \\ R \end{array}\!\!\begin{pmatrix} \overset{L}{.17} & \overset{R}{.17} \\ .83 & .83 \end{pmatrix} \quad \begin{array}{l} \text{Row averages} \\ w_L = \frac{.17 + .17}{2} = .17 \\ w_R = \frac{.83 + .83}{2} = .83 \end{array}
$$

The computations yield $w_L = .17$ and $w_R = .83$, the weights we used in Figure 15.1. The columns of $\mathbf{N}$ are equal, an indication that the decision maker is exhibiting consistent judgment in specifying the entries of the comparison matrix $\mathbf{A}$. Consistency is always guaranteed in 2×2 comparison matrices but not in higher-order matrices (as we explain shortly).

Martin's preferences regarding the relative importance of the three universities from the standpoint of the two criteria L and R are summarized in the following comparison matrices:

$$
\mathbf{A}_L = \begin{array}{c} A \\ B \\ C \end{array}\!\!\begin{pmatrix} \overset{A}{1} & \overset{B}{\frac{1}{2}} & \overset{C}{\frac{1}{5}} \\ 2 & 1 & \frac{1}{2} \\ 5 & 2 & 1 \end{pmatrix}, \quad \mathbf{A}_R = \begin{array}{c} A \\ B \\ C \end{array}\!\!\begin{pmatrix} \overset{A}{1} & \overset{B}{2} & \overset{C}{3} \\ \frac{1}{2} & 1 & \frac{3}{2} \\ \frac{1}{3} & \frac{2}{3} & 1 \end{pmatrix}
$$

Next, we have

$$
\mathbf{A}_L\text{-column sum} = (8, 3.5, 1.7)
$$

$$
\mathbf{A}_R\text{-column sum} = (1.83, 3.67, 5.5)
$$

The normalized matrices are determined by dividing each column-entry by its respective column-sum—namely,

$$
\mathbf{N}_L = \begin{matrix} A \\ B \\ C \end{matrix} \begin{pmatrix} .125 & .143 & .118 \\ .250 & .286 & .294 \\ .625 & .571 & .588 \end{pmatrix}
$$

with column headers $A \quad B \quad C$ and Row averages

$$w_{LA} = \tfrac{.125 + .143 + .118}{3} = .129$$
$$w_{LB} = \tfrac{.250 + .286 + .294}{3} = .277$$
$$w_{LC} = \tfrac{.625 + .571 + .588}{3} = .594$$

$$
\mathbf{N}_R = \begin{matrix} A \\ B \\ C \end{matrix} \begin{pmatrix} .545 & .545 & .545 \\ .273 & .273 & .273 \\ .182 & .182 & .182 \end{pmatrix}
$$

with column headers $A \quad B \quad C$ and Row averages

$$w_{RA} = \tfrac{.545 + .545 + .545}{3} = .545$$
$$w_{RB} = \tfrac{.273 + .273 + .273}{3} = .273$$
$$w_{RC} = \tfrac{.182 + .182 + .182}{3} = .182$$

The values of w_{LA}, w_{LB}, and w_{LC} (= .129, .277, and .594) provide the respective location weights for U of A, U of B, and U of C, respectively. Similarly, the values of w_{RA}, w_{RB}, and w_{RC} (= .545, .273, .182) give the relative weights regarding academic reputation of the three universities. These are the values used in Figure 15.1.

Consistency of the comparison matrix. In Example 15.1-2, all the columns of the normalized matrices $\mathbf{N}$ and $\mathbf{N}_R$ are identical, and those of $\mathbf{N}_L$ are not. This means that $\mathbf{A}$ and $\mathbf{A}_R$ are *consistent* and $\mathbf{A}_L$ is not.

Consistency implies rational judgment on the part of the decision maker. Mathematically, we say that a comparison matrix $\mathbf{A}$ is consistent if

$$a_{ij}a_{jk} = a_{ik}, \text{ for all } i, j, \text{ and } k$$

For example, in matrix $\mathbf{A}_R$ of Example 15.1-2, $a_{13} = 3$ and $a_{12}a_{23} = 2 \times \frac{3}{2} = 3$. This property requires all the columns (and rows) of $\mathbf{A}_R$ to be linearly dependent. In particular, the columns of any 2×2 comparison matrix, such as $\mathbf{A}$, are by definition dependent, and hence a 2×2 matrix is always consistent.

It is unusual for higher-order comparison matrices to be always consistent, and a degree of inconsistency is expected. To decide what level of inconsistency is "tolerable," we need to develop a quantifiable measure of consistency for the comparison matrix $\mathbf{A}$. We have seen in Example 15.1-2 that a consistent $\mathbf{A}$ produces a normalized matrix $\mathbf{N}$ in which all the columns are identical—that is,

$$
\mathbf{N} = \begin{pmatrix} w_1 & w_1 & \cdots & w_1 \\ w_2 & w_2 & \cdots & w_2 \\ \vdots & \vdots & \vdots & \vdots \\ w_n & w_n & \cdots & w_n \end{pmatrix}
$$

The original comparison matrix $\mathbf{A}$ can be determined from $\mathbf{N}$ by a reverse process that divides the elements of column i by w_i—that is,

$$
\mathbf{A} = \begin{pmatrix}
1 & \frac{w_1}{w_2} & \cdots & \frac{w_1}{w_n} \\
\frac{w_2}{w_1} & 1 & \cdots & \frac{w_2}{w_n} \\
\vdots & \vdots & \vdots & \vdots \\
\frac{w_n}{w_1} & \frac{w_n}{w_2} & \cdots & 1
\end{pmatrix}
$$

Post-multiplying $\mathbf{A}$ by $\mathbf{w} = (w_1, w_2, \ldots, w_n)^T$, we get

$$
\begin{pmatrix}
1 & \frac{w_1}{w_2} & \cdots & \frac{w_1}{w_n} \\
\frac{w_2}{w_1} & 1 & \cdots & \frac{w_2}{w_n} \\
\vdots & \vdots & \vdots & \vdots \\
\frac{w_n}{w_1} & \frac{w_n}{w_2} & \cdots & 1
\end{pmatrix}
\begin{pmatrix}
w_1 \\ w_2 \\ \vdots \\ w_n
\end{pmatrix}
=
\begin{pmatrix}
nw_1 \\ nw_2 \\ \vdots \\ nw_n
\end{pmatrix}
= n
\begin{pmatrix}
w_1 \\ w_2 \\ \vdots \\ w_n
\end{pmatrix}
$$

Hence, $\mathbf{A}$ is consistent if,

$$
\mathbf{Aw} = n\mathbf{w}
$$

For the case where $\mathbf{A}$ is not consistent, the relative weight, w_i, is approximated by the average of the n elements of row i in the normalized matrix $\mathbf{N}$ (see Example 15.1-2). Letting $\overline{\mathbf{w}}$ be the vector of computed averages, it can be shown that

$$
\mathbf{A}\overline{\mathbf{w}} = n_{\max}\overline{\mathbf{w}}, \, n_{\max} \geq n
$$

In this case, the closer $n_{\max}$ is to n, the more consistent is the comparison matrix $\mathbf{A}$. Based on this observation, AHP computes the **consistency ratio** as

$$
CR = \frac{CI}{RI}
$$

where

$$
CI = \text{Consistency index of } \mathbf{A}
$$

$$
= \frac{n_{\max} - n}{n - 1}
$$

$$
RI = \text{Random consistency of } \mathbf{A}
$$

$$
= \frac{1.98(n - 2)}{n}
$$

The random consistency index, RI, is determined empirically as the average CI of a large sample of randomly generated comparison matrices, $\mathbf{A}$.

If $CR \leq .1$, the level of inconsistency is acceptable. Otherwise, the inconsistency is high, and the decision maker may need to revise the estimates of the elements a_{ij} to realize better consistency.

The value of $n_{\max}$ is computed from $\mathbf{A}\overline{\mathbf{w}} = n_{\max}\overline{\mathbf{w}}$ by noting that the ith equation is

$$
\sum_{j=1}^{n} a_{ij}\overline{w}_j = n_{\max}\overline{w}_i, \, i = 1, 2, \ldots, n
$$

Given $\sum_{i=1}^{n} \overline{w}_i = 1$, we get

$$\sum_{i=1}^{n}\left(\sum_{j=1}^{n} a_{ij}\overline{w}_j\right) = n_{\max}\sum_{i=1}^{n}\overline{w}_i = n_{\max}$$

This means that the value of $n_{\max}$ equals the sum of the elements of the column vector $\mathbf{A}\overline{\mathbf{w}}$.

Example 15.1-3

In Example 15.1-2, the matrix $\mathbf{A}_L$ is inconsistent because the columns of its $\mathbf{N}_L$ are not identical. To test the consistency of $\mathbf{N}_L$, we start by computing $n_{\max}$. From Example 15.1-2, we have

$$\overline{w}_1 = .129, \overline{w}_2 = .277, \overline{w}_3 = .594$$

Thus,

$$\mathbf{A}_L\overline{\mathbf{w}} = \begin{pmatrix} 1 & \frac{1}{2} & \frac{1}{5} \\ 2 & 1 & \frac{1}{2} \\ 5 & 2 & 1 \end{pmatrix}\begin{pmatrix} .129 \\ .277 \\ .594 \end{pmatrix} = \begin{pmatrix} 0.3863 \\ 0.8320 \\ 1.7930 \end{pmatrix}$$

$$n_{\max} = .3863 + .8320 + 1.7930 = 3.0113$$

Now, for $n = 3$,

$$CI = \frac{n_{\max} - n}{n - 1} = \frac{3.0113 - 3}{3 - 1} = .00565$$

$$RI = \frac{1.98(n - 2)}{n} = \frac{1.98 \times 1}{3} = .66$$

$$CR = \frac{CI}{RI} = \frac{.00565}{.66} = .00856$$

Because $CR < .1$, the level of inconsistency in $\mathbf{A}_L$ is acceptable.

Excel Moment

Template *excelAHP.xls* is driven by user input and can handle comparison matrices of size 8×8 or less. Figure 15.3 demonstrates the application of the model to Example 15.1-2 (columns F:I and rows 10:13 are hidden to conserve space). The comparison matrices of the problem are entered *one at a time* in the (top) input data section of the spreadsheet. The order in which the comparison matrices are entered is unimportant, though it makes more sense to consider them in their natural hierarchal order.

The output (bottom) section of the spreadsheet provides the associated normalized matrix and its consistency ratio, CR.[1] The weights, w, are copied from column J and pasted into the solution summary area (the right section of the spreadsheet). Remember to use Paste Special $\Rightarrow$ Values when performing this step to guarantee a permanent record. The process is repeated until all the weights for all the comparison matrices have been stored in the solution summary area starting at column K.

---

[1]The more accurate results of the spreadsheet differ from those in Examples 15.1-2 and 15.1-3 because of manual roundoff approximation.

	A	B	C	D	E	J	K	L	M	N
1				AHP-Analytic Hierarchy Process						
2		Input: Comparison matrix						Solution summary		
3	Matrix name:	AL						A		
4	Matrix size=	3					R	0.83333		
5	Matrix data:	UA	UB	UC			L	0.16667		
6	UA	1	0.5	0.2				AR		AL
7	UB	2	1	0.5			UA	0.54545	UA	0.1285
8	UC	5	2	1			UB	0.27273	UB	0.27661
9							UC	0.18182	UC	0.59489
14	Col sum	8	3.5	1.7						
15		Output: Normalized martix								
16		nMax=	3.00746	CR=	0.0056					
17		UA	UB	UC		Weight		Final ranking		
18	UA	0.12500	0.14286	0.11765		0.12850		UA= 0.47596		
19	UB	0.25000	0.28571	0.23412		0.27661		UB= 0.27337		
20	UC	0.62500	0.57143	0.58824		0.59489		UC= 0.25066		

FIGURE 15.3

Excel solution of Example 15.1-2 (file *excelAHP.xls*)

In Figure 15.3, the final ranking is given in cells (K18:K20). The formula in cell K18 is

$$= \$L\$4*\$L7 + \$L\$5*\$N7$$

This formula provides the composite weight for alternative UA and is copied in cells K19 and K20 to evaluate alternatives UB and UC. Note from the formula in K18 that cell reference to the alternative UA must be *column*-fixed (namely, $L7 and $N7), whereas *all* other references must be *row-and-column*-fixed (namely, $L$4 and $L$5). The validity of the copied formulas requires stacking the (column-fixed) *alternative* weights of each matrix in a *single* column (no intervening empty cells). In Figure 15.3, the A_R-weights are in column L and the A_L-weights are in column N. There are no restrictions on the placement of the A-weights because they are row- and column-fixed in the formula.

You can embellish the formula in K18 to capture the names of the alternatives by using

$$= \$K7\&" = "\&TEXT(\$L\$4*\$L7 + \$L\$5*\$ N7,"\#\#\#\# 0.00000")$$

The procedure for evaluating alternatives can be extended to any number of hierarchy levels. Once you develop the formula correctly for the first alternative, the same formula is copied to the remaining cells. Remember that *all* cell references in the formula must be row-and-column-fixed, except for references to the alternatives, which must be column-fixed only. Problem 1, Set 15.1b, asks you to develop the formula for a 3-level problem.

PROBLEM SET 15.1B[2]

1. Consider the two-hierarchal data of Problem 1, Set 15.1a. Copy the weights in a logical order into the solution summary section of the spreadsheet *excelAHP.xls*, then develop

---

[2]Spreadsheet *excelAHP.xls* should prove helpful in verifying your calculations.

the formula for evaluating the first alternative, UA, and copy it to evaluate the remaining two alternatives.

*2. The personnel department at C&H has narrowed the search for a new hire to three candidates: Steve (S), Jane (J), and Maisa (M). The final selection is based on three criteria: personal interview (I), experience (E), and references (R). The department uses matrix $\mathbf{A}$ (given below) to establish the preferences among the three criteria. After interviewing the three candidates and compiling the data regarding their experiences and references, the matrices $\mathbf{A}_I$, $\mathbf{A}_E$, and $\mathbf{A}_R$ are constructed. Which of the three candidates should be hired? Assess the consistency of the data.

$$\mathbf{A} = \begin{array}{c} \\ I \\ E \\ R \end{array}\begin{array}{c} \begin{array}{ccc} I & E & R \end{array} \\ \left(\begin{array}{ccc} 1 & 2 & \frac{1}{4} \\ \frac{1}{2} & 1 & \frac{1}{5} \\ 4 & 5 & 1 \end{array} \right) \end{array} \qquad \mathbf{A}_I = \begin{array}{c} \\ S \\ J \\ M \end{array}\begin{array}{c} \begin{array}{ccc} S & J & M \end{array} \\ \left(\begin{array}{ccc} 1 & 3 & 4 \\ \frac{1}{3} & 1 & \frac{1}{5} \\ \frac{1}{4} & 5 & 1 \end{array} \right) \end{array}$$

$$\mathbf{A}_E = \begin{array}{c} \\ S \\ J \\ M \end{array}\begin{array}{c} \begin{array}{ccc} S & J & M \end{array} \\ \left(\begin{array}{ccc} 1 & \frac{1}{3} & 2 \\ 3 & 1 & \frac{1}{2} \\ \frac{1}{2} & 2 & 1 \end{array} \right) \end{array} \qquad \mathbf{A}_R = \begin{array}{c} \\ S \\ J \\ M \end{array}\begin{array}{c} \begin{array}{ccc} S & J & M \end{array} \\ \left(\begin{array}{ccc} 1 & \frac{1}{2} & 1 \\ 2 & 1 & \frac{1}{2} \\ 1 & 2 & 1 \end{array} \right) \end{array}$$

3. Kevin and June Park (K and J) are in the process of buying a new house. Three houses, A, B, and C, are available. The Parks have agreed on two criteria for the selection of the house—amount of yard work (Y) and proximity to place of work (W)--and have developed the following comparison matrices. Rank the three houses in order of priority, and compute the consistency ratio for each matrix.

$$\mathbf{A} = \begin{array}{c} \\ K \\ J \end{array}\begin{array}{c} \begin{array}{cc} K & J \end{array} \\ \left(\begin{array}{cc} 1 & 2 \\ \frac{1}{2} & 1 \end{array} \right) \end{array}$$

$$\mathbf{A}_K = \begin{array}{c} \\ Y \\ W \end{array}\begin{array}{c} \begin{array}{cc} Y & W \end{array} \\ \left(\begin{array}{cc} 1 & \frac{1}{3} \\ 3 & 1 \end{array} \right) \end{array} \qquad \mathbf{A}_J = \begin{array}{c} \\ Y \\ W \end{array}\begin{array}{c} \begin{array}{cc} Y & W \end{array} \\ \left(\begin{array}{cc} 1 & 4 \\ \frac{1}{4} & 1 \end{array} \right) \end{array}$$

$$\mathbf{A}_{KY} = \begin{array}{c} \\ A \\ B \\ C \end{array}\begin{array}{c} \begin{array}{ccc} A & B & C \end{array} \\ \left(\begin{array}{ccc} 1 & 2 & 3 \\ \frac{1}{2} & 1 & 2 \\ \frac{1}{3} & \frac{1}{2} & 1 \end{array} \right) \end{array} \quad \mathbf{A}_{KW} = \begin{array}{c} \\ A \\ B \\ C \end{array}\begin{array}{c} \begin{array}{ccc} A & B & C \end{array} \\ \left(\begin{array}{ccc} 1 & 2 & \frac{1}{2} \\ \frac{1}{2} & 1 & \frac{1}{3} \\ 2 & 3 & 1 \end{array} \right) \end{array} \quad \mathbf{A}_{JY} = \begin{array}{c} \\ A \\ B \\ C \end{array}\begin{array}{c} \begin{array}{ccc} A & B & C \end{array} \\ \left(\begin{array}{ccc} 1 & 4 & 2 \\ \frac{1}{4} & 1 & 3 \\ \frac{1}{2} & \frac{1}{3} & 1 \end{array} \right) \end{array} \quad \mathbf{A}_{JW} = \begin{array}{c} \\ A \\ B \\ C \end{array}\begin{array}{c} \begin{array}{ccc} A & B & C \end{array} \\ \left(\begin{array}{ccc} 1 & \frac{1}{2} & 4 \\ \frac{1}{2} & 1 & 3 \\ \frac{1}{4} & \frac{1}{3} & 1 \end{array} \right) \end{array}$$

*4. A new author sets three criteria for selecting a publisher for an OR textbook: royalty percentage (R), marketing (M), and advance payment (A). Two publishers, H and P, have expressed interest in the book. Using the following comparison matrices, rank the two publishers and assess the consistency of the decision.

$$\mathbf{A} = \begin{array}{c} \\ R \\ M \\ A \end{array} \begin{array}{c} R \quad M \quad A \\ \begin{pmatrix} 1 & 1 & \frac{1}{4} \\ 1 & 1 & \frac{1}{5} \\ 4 & 5 & 1 \end{pmatrix} \end{array}$$

$$\mathbf{A}_R = \begin{array}{c} H \quad P \\ H \\ P \end{array} \begin{pmatrix} 1 & 2 \\ \frac{1}{2} & 1 \end{pmatrix} \quad \mathbf{A}_M = \begin{array}{c} H \quad P \\ H \\ P \end{array} \begin{pmatrix} 1 & \frac{1}{2} \\ 2 & 1 \end{pmatrix} \quad \mathbf{A}_A = \begin{array}{c} H \quad P \\ H \\ P \end{array} \begin{pmatrix} 1 & 1 \\ 1 & 1 \end{pmatrix}$$

5. A professor of political science wants to predict the outcome of a school board election. Three candidates, Ivy (I), Bahrn (B), and Smith (S), are running for one position. There are three categories of voters: left (L), center (C), and right (R). The candidates are judged based on three factors: educational experience (E), stand on issues (S), and personal character (P). The following are the comparison matrices for the first hierarchy of left, center, and right.

$$\mathbf{A} = \begin{array}{c} \\ L \\ C \\ R \end{array} \begin{array}{c} L \quad C \quad R \\ \begin{pmatrix} 1 & 2 & \frac{1}{2} \\ \frac{1}{2} & 1 & \frac{1}{5} \\ 2 & 5 & 1 \end{pmatrix} \end{array} \quad \mathbf{A}_L = \begin{array}{c} \\ E \\ S \\ P \end{array} \begin{array}{c} E \quad S \quad P \\ \begin{pmatrix} 1 & 3 & \frac{1}{2} \\ \frac{1}{3} & 1 & \frac{1}{3} \\ 2 & 3 & 1 \end{pmatrix} \end{array}$$

$$\mathbf{A}_C = \begin{array}{c} \\ E \\ S \\ P \end{array} \begin{array}{c} E \quad S \quad P \\ \begin{pmatrix} 1 & 2 & 2 \\ \frac{1}{2} & 1 & 1 \\ \frac{1}{2} & 1 & 1 \end{pmatrix} \end{array} \quad \mathbf{A}_R = \begin{array}{c} \\ E \\ S \\ P \end{array} \begin{array}{c} E \quad S \quad P \\ \begin{pmatrix} 1 & 1 & 9 \\ 1 & 1 & 8 \\ \frac{1}{9} & \frac{1}{8} & 1 \end{pmatrix} \end{array}$$

The professor generated nine more comparison matrices for the second hierarchy representing experience (E), stand on issues (S), and personal character (P). AHP was then used to reduce these matrices to the following relative weights:

Candidate	Left			Center			Right		
	E	S	P	E	S	P	E	S	P
Ivy	.1	.2	.3	.3	.5	.2	.7	.1	.3
Bahrn	.5	.4	.2	.4	.2	.4	.1	.4	.2
Smith	.4	.4	.5	.3	.3	.4	.2	.5	.5

Determine the winning candidate, and assess the consistency of the decision.

6. A school district is in dire need to reduce expenses to meet new budgetary restrictions at its elementary schools. Two options are available: Delete the physical education program (E), or delete the music program (M). The superintendent has formed a committee with equal-vote representation from the School Board (S) and the Parent–Teacher Association (P) to study the situation and make a recommendation. The committee has decided to study the issue from the standpoint of budget restriction (B) and students needs (N). The analysis produced the following comparison matrices:

$$\mathbf{A}_s = \begin{array}{c} B \\ N \end{array} \begin{array}{c} B \quad N \\ \begin{pmatrix} 1 & 4 \\ \frac{1}{4} & 1 \end{pmatrix} \end{array} \quad \mathbf{A}_P = \begin{array}{c} B \\ N \end{array} \begin{array}{c} B \quad N \\ \begin{pmatrix} 1 & \frac{1}{2} \\ 2 & 1 \end{pmatrix} \end{array}$$

$$\mathbf{A}_{SB} = \begin{array}{c} \\ E \\ M \end{array}\begin{array}{cc} E & M \\ \left(1 & \frac{1}{2} \right. \\ \left. 2 & 1 \right) \end{array} \quad \mathbf{A}_{SN} = \begin{array}{c} \\ E \\ M \end{array}\begin{array}{cc} E & M \\ \left(1 & \frac{1}{3} \right. \\ \left. 3 & 1 \right) \end{array}$$

$$\mathbf{A}_{PB} = \begin{array}{c} \\ E \\ M \end{array}\begin{array}{cc} E & M \\ \left(1 & \frac{1}{3} \right. \\ \left. 3 & 1 \right) \end{array} \quad \mathbf{A}_{PN} = \begin{array}{c} \\ E \\ M \end{array}\begin{array}{cc} E & M \\ \left(1 & 2 \right. \\ \left. \frac{1}{2} & 1 \right) \end{array}$$

Analyze the decision problem, and make a recommendation.

7. An individual is in the process of buying a car and has narrowed the choices to three models: $M1$, $M2$, and $M3$. The deciding factors include purchase price (PP), maintenance cost (MC), cost of city driving (CD), and cost of rural driving (RD). The following table provides the relevant data for 3 years of operation:

Car Model	PP($)	MC($)	CD($)	RD($)
$M1$	6,000	1800	4500	1500
$M2$	8,000	1200	2250	750
$M3$	10,000	600	1125	600

Use the cost data to develop the comparison matrices. Assess the consistency of the matrices, and determine the choice of model.

15.2 DECISION MAKING UNDER RISK

Under conditions of risk, the payoffs associated with each decision alternative are represented by probability distributions, and decision can be based on the *expected value criterion*—maximization of expected profit or the minimization of expected cost. The expected value criterion is sometimes modified to account for other situations, as will be described later in this section.

Real-Life Application—Booking Limits in Hotel Reservations

Hotel La Posada has a total of 300 guest rooms. Its clientele includes both business and leisure travelers. Room prices are discounted, mainly to leisure travelers. Business travelers, who usually are late in booking their rooms, pay full price. La Posada sets a *booking limit* on the number of discount rooms to take advantage of the full price paid by business customers. Case 10 in Chapter 26 on the website utilizes decision tree analysis to determine the booking limit.

15.2.1 Decision Tree–Based Expected Value Criterion

The expected value criterion seeks the maximization of expected (average) profit or the minimization of expected cost. The data of the problem assumes that the payoff (or cost) associated with each decision alternative is probabilistic.

Decision tree analysis. The following example considers simple decision situations with a finite number of decision alternatives and explicit payoff matrices.

Example 15.2-1

Suppose that you want to invest $10, 000 in the stock market by buying shares in one of two companies: A and B. Shares in Company A, though risky, could yield a 50% return during the next year. If the stock market conditions are not favorable (i.e., "bear" market), the stock may lose 20% of its value. Company B provides safe investments with 15% return in a "bull" market and only 5% in a "bear" market. All the publications you have consulted (and there is always a flood of them at the end of the year!) are predicting a 60% chance for a "bull" market and 40% for a "bear" market. How should you invest your money?

The decision problem is summarized in the following table.

Decision alternative	1-year return on $10, 000 investment	
	"Bull" market ($)	*"Bear" market ($)*
Company A stock	5000	−2000
Company B stock	1500	500
Probability of occurrence	.6	.4

The problem can also be represented as a **decision tree** as shown in Figure 15.4. Two types of nodes are used in the tree: A square (□) represents a *decision point*, and a circle (○) represents a *chance event*. Thus, the two branches from decision point 1 represent the two alternatives of investing in stock A or stock B. Next, the two branches emanating from chance events 2 and 3 represent the "bull" and the "bear" markets with their respective probabilities and payoffs.

From Figure 15.4, the expected 1-year returns are

$$\text{Stock } A = \$5000 \times .6 + (-2000) \times .4 = \$2200$$
$$\text{Stock } B = \$1500 \times .6 + \$500 \times .4 = \$1100$$

Stock A is chosen because it yields a higher expected return.

Remarks. In the terminology of decision theory, the probabilistic "bull" and the "bear" markets are called **states of nature**. In general, a decision problem may include n states of nature and m alternatives. If $p_j(>0)$ is the probability of occurrence for state j and a_{ij} is the payoff of alternative i, given state $j(i = 1, 2, \ldots, m; j = 1, 2, \ldots, n)$, then the expected payoff for alternative i is computed as

$$EV_i = a_{i1}p_1 + a_{i2}p_2 + \ldots + a_{in}p_n, i = 1, 2, \ldots, n$$
$$p_1 + p_2 + \ldots + p_n = 1$$

FIGURE 15.4

Decision-tree representation of the stock market problem

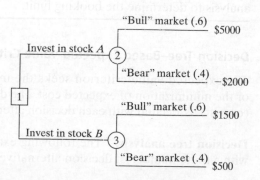

The best alternative is the one associated with $EV^* = \max_i \{EV_i\}$ in case of profit or $EV^* = \min_i \{EV_i\}$ in case of loss.

PROBLEM SET 15.2A

1. You have been invited to play the Fortune Wheel game on television. The wheel operates electronically with two buttons that produce hard (H) or soft (S) spin. The wheel itself is divided into white (W) and red (R) half-circle regions. You have been told that the wheel is designed to stop on white 40% of the time. The payoff of the game is

	W	R
H	$800	$200
S	-$2500	$2000

   Develop the associated decision tree, and determine a course of action based on the expected value criterion.

*2. Farmer McCoy can plant either corn or soybeans. The probabilities that the next harvest prices will go up, stay the same, or go down are .25, .30, and .45, respectively. If the prices go up, the corn crop will net $30, 000 and the soybeans will net $10, 000. If the prices remain unchanged, McCoy will (barely) break even. But if the prices go down, the corn and soybeans crops will sustain losses of $35, 000 and $5000, respectively.

   (a) Represent McCoy's problem as a decision tree.

   (b) Which crop should McCoy plant?

3. You have the chance to invest in three mutual funds: utility, aggressive growth, and global. The value of your investment will change depending on the market conditions. There is a 20% chance the market will go down, 45% chance it will remain moderate, and 35% chance it will perform well. The following table provides the percentage change in the investment value under the three conditions:

	Percent return on investment		
Alternative	Down market (%)	Moderate market (%)	Up market (%)
Utility	+5	+7	+8
Aggressive growth	-10	+5	+30
Global	+2	+9	+20

   (a) Represent the problem as a decision tree.

   (b) Which mutual fund should you select?

4. You have the chance to invest your money in either a 7.5% bond that sells at face value or an aggressive growth stock that pays only 1% dividend. If inflation occurs, the interest rate will go up to 8%, in which case the principal value of the bond will go down by 10%, and the stock value will go down by 20%. If recession materializes, the interest rate will go down to 6%. In this case, the principal value of the bond is expected to go up by 5%, and the stock value will increase by 20%. If the economy remains unchanged, the stock value will go up by 8%, and the bond principal value will remain the same. Economists

estimate a 10% chance of inflation and 5% of recession. You are basing your investment decision on next year's economic conditions.

(a) Represent the problem as a decision tree.

(b) Would you invest in stocks or bonds?

5. AFC is about to launch its new Wings 'N Things fast food nationally. The research department is convinced that Wings 'N Things will be a great success and wants to introduce it immediately in all AFC outlets without advertising. The marketing department sees "things" differently and wants to unleash an intensive advertising campaign. The advertising campaign will cost $120,000 and if successful will produce $950,000 revenue. If the campaign is unsuccessful (and there is a 25% chance it won't be), the revenue is estimated at only $200,000. If no advertising is used, the revenue is estimated at $400,000 with probability .7 if customers are receptive to the new product and $200,000 with probability .3 if they are not.

(a) Draw the associated decision tree.

(b) What course of action should AFC follow in launching the new product?

*6. A fair coin is flipped three successive times. You receive $1.00 for each head ($H$) that turns up and an additional $.25 for each two successive heads that appear (remember that HHH includes two sets of HH). However, you give back $1.10 for each tail that shows up. You have the options to either play or not play the game.

(a) Draw the decision tree for the game.

(b) Would you favor playing this game?

7. You have the chance to play the following game in a gambling casino. A fair die is rolled twice, leading to four outcomes: (1) both rolls show the same even number, (2) both rolls show the same odd number, (3) the two rolls show either even followed by odd or odd followed by even, and (4) all other outcomes. You are allowed to bet your money on exactly two outcomes with equal dollar amounts. For example, you can bet equal dollars on even-match (outcome 1) and odd-match (outcome 2). The payoff for each dollar you bet is $2.00 for the first outcome, $1.95 for the second and the third outcomes, and $1.50 for the fourth outcome.

(a) Draw the decision tree for the game.

(b) Which two choices would you make?

(c) Do you ever come out ahead in this game?

8. Acme Manufacturing produces lots of widget with .8%, 1%, 1.2%, and 1.4% defectives according to the respective probabilities .4, .3, .25, and .05. Three customers, A, B, and C, are contracted to receive batches with no more than .8%, 1.2%, and 1.4% defectives, respectively. If the defectives are higher than contracted, Acme is penalized $100 for each .1% increase. Supplying higher-quality batches than required costs Acme $50 for each .1% below specifications. Assume that the batches are not inspected before shipment.

(a) Draw the associated decision tree.

(b) Which of the three customers should have the highest priority to receive their order?

9. TriStar plans to open a new plant in Arkansas. The company can open a full-size plant now or a small-size plant that can be expanded 2 years later if warranted by high demand. The time horizon for the decision problem is 10 years. TriStar estimates that the probabilities for high and low demands over the next 10 years are .75 and .25, respectively. The cost of immediate construction is $5 million for a large plant and $1 million for a

small plant. The expansion cost of a small plant 2 years from now is $4.2 million. The income from the operation over the next 10 years is given in the following table:

	Annual income estimates (in $1000)	
Alternative	*High demand*	*Low demand*
Full-size plant now	1000	300
Small-size plant now	250	200
Expanded plant in 2 years	900	200

(a) Develop the associated decision tree, given that after 2 years TriStar has the option to expand or not expand the small plant.

(b) Develop a construction strategy for TriStar over the next 10 years. (For simplicity, ignore the time value of money.)

10. Rework Problem 9, assuming that decisions are made taking into account the time value of money at an annual interest rate of 10%. [*Note*: You need compound interest tables to solve this problem. You can use Excel function NPV(i, R) to compute the present value of cash flows stored in range R, given interest rate i. NPV assumes that each cash flow occurs at the end of the year.]

11. Rework Problem 9, assuming that the demand can be high, medium, and low with probabilities .7, .2, and .1, respectively. Expansion of a small plant will occur only if demand in the first 2 years is high. The following table provides estimates of the annual income. Ignore the time value of money.

	Annual income estimates (in $1000)		
Alternative	*High demand*	*Medium demand*	*Low demand*
Full-sized plant now	1000	500	300
Small-sized plant now	400	280	150
Expanded plant in 2 years	900	600	200

*12. Sunray Electric Coop uses a fleet of 20 trucks to service its electric network. The company wants to develop a preventive maintenance schedule for the fleet. The probability of a breakdown in year 1 is zero. For year 2, the breakdown probability is .03, increasing annually by .01 for years 3 through 10. Beyond year 10, the breakdown probability remains constant at .13. The maintenance cost per truck is $200 for a random breakdown and $75 for a scheduled maintenance.

(a) Develop the associated decision tree.

(b) Determine the optimal period (in months) between successive preventive maintenances.

13. Daily demands for loaves of bread at a grocery store are specified by the following probability distribution:

n	100	150	200	250	300
p_n	.20	.25	.30	.15	.10

The store buys a loaf for 55 cents and sells it for $1.20 each. Any unsold loaves at the end of the day are disposed of at 25 cents each. Assume that the stock level is restricted to one of the demand levels specified for p_n.

(a) Develop the associated decision tree.

(b) How many loaves should be stocked daily?

14. In Problem 13, suppose that the store wishes to extend the decision problem to a 2-day horizon. The alternatives for the second day depend on the demand in the first day. If demand on day 1 equals the amount stocked, the store will continue to order the same quantity for day 2; if it exceeds the amount stocked, the store can order any of the higher-level stocks; and if it is less than the amount stocked, the store can order any of the lower-level stocks. Develop the associated decision tree, and determine the optimal ordering strategy.

*15. An automatic machine produces α (thousands of) units of a product per day. As α increases, the proportion of defectives, p, goes up according to the following probability density function

$$f(p) = \begin{cases} \alpha p^{\alpha-1}, & 0 \le p \le 1 \\ 0, & \text{otherwise} \end{cases}$$

Each defective item incurs a loss of $50. A good item yields $5 profit.

(a) Develop a decision tree for this problem.

(b) Determine the value of α that maximizes the expected profit.

16. The outer diameter, d, of a cylinder is processed on an automatic machine with upper and lower tolerance limits of $d + t_U$ and $d - t_L$. The production process follows a normal distribution with mean μ and standard deviation σ. Oversized cylinders are reworked at the cost of c_1 dollars each. Undersized cylinders are salvaged at the cost of c_2 dollars each. Develop the decision tree, and determine the optimal setting d for the machine.

17. *Cohan and Associates (1984).* Modern forest management uses controlled fires to reduce fire hazards and to stimulate new forest growth. Management has the option to postpone or plan a burning. In a specific forest tract, if burning is postponed, a general administrative cost of $300 is incurred. If a controlled burning is planned, there is a 50% chance that good weather will prevail and burning will cost $3200. The results of the burning may be either successful with probability .6 or marginal with probability .4. Successful execution will result in an estimated benefit of $6000, and marginal execution will provide only $3000 in benefits. If the weather is poor, burning will be cancelled incurring a cost of $1200 and no benefit.

(a) Develop a decision tree to determine whether burning should be planned or postponed.

(b) Study the sensitivity of the solution to changes in the probability of good weather.

18. *Rappaport (1967).* A manufacturer has used linear programming to determine the optimum production mix of the various TV models it produces. Recent information received by the manufacturer indicates that there is a 40% chance that the supplier of a component used in one of the models may raise the price by $35. The manufacturer thus can either continue to use the original (optimum) product mix (A1) or use a new (optimum) mix based on the higher component price (A2). Naturally, action A1 is ideal if the price is not raised, and action A2 will also be ideal if the price is raised. The following

table provides the resulting total profit per month as a function of the action taken and the random outcome regarding the component price.

	Price increase (O1)	No price increase (O2)
Original mix (A1)	$400,000	$295,500
New mix (A2)	$372,000	$350,000

(a) Develop the associated decision tree, and determine which action should be adopted.

(b) The manufacturer can invest $1000 to obtain additional information about whether or not the price will increase. This information says that there is a 58% chance that the probability of price increase will be .9 and a 42% chance that the probability of price increase will be .3. Would you recommend the additional investment?

*19. *Aspiration Level Criterion.* Acme Manufacturing uses a chemical in one of its processes. The shelf life is 1 month, and any amount left is destroyed. The amount, x, in gallons of the chemical used by Acme is represented by the following distribution:

$$f(x) = \begin{cases} \dfrac{200}{x^2}, & 100 \leq x \leq 200 \\ 0, & \text{otherwise} \end{cases}$$

The actual consumption of the chemical occurs instantaneously at the start of the month. Acme wants to determine the level of the chemical that satisfies two conflicting criteria (or aspiration levels): The average excess quantity for the month does not exceed 20 gallons, and the average shortage quantity for the month does not exceed 40 gallons.

15.2.2 Variants of the Expected Value Criterion

This section addresses two issues relating to the expected value criterion: the determination of *posterior probabilities* based on experimentation and the use of *utility* versus actual value of money.

Posterior (Bayes') probabilities. The probabilities used in the expected value criterion are usually estimated from historical data (see Section 14.5). In some cases, the accuracy of these estimates can be enhanced by using additional experimentation. The resulting probabilities are referred to as **posterior (or Bayes') probabilities**, as opposed to the **prior probabilities** determined from raw data.

Real-Life Application—Casey's Problem: Interpreting and Evaluating a New Test

A screening test of a newborn, named Casey, reveals a C14:1 enzyme deficiency. The enzyme is required to digest a particular form of long-chain fats, and its absence could lead to severe illness or mysterious death (broadly categorized under the sudden infant death syndrome or SIDS). The test had been administered previously to approximately 13,000 newborns, and Casey was the first to test positive. Though the screening test does not in itself constitute a definitive diagnosis, the extreme rarity of the condition led her doctors to conclude that there was an 80–90% chance that she was suffering from this deficiency. Given that Casey tested positive, Bayes' posterior probability is used to assess whether or not the child has the C14:1 deficiency. The situation is detailed in Case 11, Chapter 26, on the website.

Example 15.2-2

This example demonstrates how the expected-value criterion is modified to take advantage of posterior probabilities. In Example 15.2-1, the (prior) probabilities of .6 and .4 of a "bull" and a "bear" market are determined from available financial publications. Suppose that rather than relying solely on these publications, you have decided to conduct a more "personal" investigation by consulting a friend who has done well in the stock market. The friend quantifies a "for/against" investment recommendation in the following manner: In a "bull" market, there is a 90% chance the recommendation is "for." It drops to 50% in a "bear" market. How does the additional information affect the decision?

The friend's statement provides conditional probabilities of the recommendations "for" and "against" given that the states of nature are "bull" and "bear" markets. Define

v_1 = "For" vote

v_2 = "Against" vote

m_1 = "Bull" market

m_2 = "Bear" market

Thus, the friend's statement may be written in the form of probability statements as

$$P\{v_1|m_1\} = .9, P\{v_2|m_1\} = .1$$

$$P\{v_1|m_2\} = .5, P\{v_2|m_2\} = .5$$

With this representation, the decision problem is summarized as:

1. If the friend's recommendation is "for," would you invest in stock A or in stock B?
2. If the friend's recommendation is "against," would you invest in stock A or in stock B?

The decision tree in Figure 15.5 represents the problem. Node 1 is a chance event representing the "for" and "against" possibilities. Nodes 2 and 3 are decision points for choosing between stocks A and B, given the "for" and "against" recommendations, respectively. Finally, nodes 4 to 7 are chance events representing the "bull" and "bear" markets.

To evaluate the different alternatives in Figure 15.5, it is necessary to compute the *posterior* probabilities $P\{m_i|v_j\}$ shown on the m_1- and m_2-branches of nodes 4, 5, 6, and 7. These posterior probabilities take into account the additional information provided by the friend's "for/against" recommendation and are computed according to the following general steps:

Step 1. Summarize the conditional probabilities $P\{v_j|m_i\}$ in the following tabular form:

	v_1	v_2
m_1	.9	.1
m_2	.5	.5

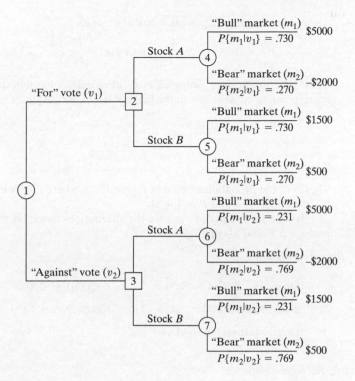

FIGURE 15.5

Decision tree for the stock market problem with posterior probabilities

Step 2.   Compute the joint probabilities as

$$P\{m_i, v_j\} = P\{v_j | m_i\} P\{m_i\}, \text{ for all } i \text{ and } j$$

Given the *prior* probabilities $P\{m_1\} = .6$ and $P\{m_2\} = .4$, the joint probabilities are determined by multiplying the first and the second rows of the table in step 1 by .6 and .4, respectively—that is,

	v_1	v_2
m_1	.54	.06
m_2	.20	.20

The sum of all the entries in the table equals 1.

Step 3.   Compute the absolute probabilities as

$$P\{v_j\} = \sum_{\text{all } i} P\{m_i, v_j\}, \text{ for all } j$$

These probabilities are the column sums in the table in step 2—that is,

$P\{v_1\}$	$P\{v_2\}$
.74	.26

Step 4.   Determine the desired posterior probabilities as

$$P\{m_i | v_j\} = \frac{P\{m_i, v_j\}}{P\{v_j\}}$$

These probabilities are computed by dividing each column in the table of step 2 by the corresponding column sum in the table of step 3, which yields

	v_1	v_2
m_1	.730	.231
m_2	.270	.769

These are the probabilities used in Figure 15.5 and are different from the prior probabilities $P\{m_1\} = .6$ and $P\{m_2\} = .4$.

We are now ready to evaluate the alternatives based on the expected payoffs for nodes 4, 5, 6, and 7—that is,

"For" Recommendation

Stock A at node 4 = $5000 \times .730 + (-2000) \times .270 \times = \mathbf{\$3110}$

Stock B at node 5 = $1500 \times .730 + 500 \times .270 = 1230$

Decision. Invest in stock A.

"Against" Recommendation

Stock A at node 6 = $5000 \times .231 + (-2000) \times .769 = -\$383$

Stock B at node 7 = $1500 \times .231 + 500 \times .769 = \mathbf{\$731}$

Decision. Invest in stock B.

The given decisions are equivalent to saying that the expected payoffs at decision nodes 2 and 3 are \$3110 and \$731, respectively (see Figure 15.5). Thus, given the probabilities $P\{v_1\} = .74$ and $P\{v_2\} = .26$ as computed in step 3, we can compute the expected payoff for the entire decision tree. (See Problem 3, Set 15.2b.)

Excel Moment

Excel file *excelBayes.xls* is designed to determine the posterior probabilities for prior probability matrices of sizes up to 10×10 (some rows and columns have been hidden to conserve space). The input data include $P\{m\}$ and $P\{v|m\}$. The spreadsheet checks input data errors and displays appropriate error messages.

PROBLEM SET 15.2B

1. Data in a community college show that 80% of new students who took calculus in high school do well, compared with 50% of those who did not take calculus. Admissions for the current academic year show that only 40% of the new students

have completed a course in calculus. What is the probability that a new student will do well in college?

*2. Elektra receives 75% of its electronic components from vendor A and the remaining 25% from vendor B. The percentage of defectives from vendors A and B are 1% and 2%, respectively. When a random sample of size 5 from a received lot is inspected, only one defective unit is found. Determine the probability that the lot is received from vendor A. From vendor B. (*Hint*: The probability distribution of defective items in a sample is binomial.)

3. In Example 15.2-2, suppose that you have the additional option of investing the original $10,000 in a safe certificate of deposit that yields 4% interest. The friend's advice applies to investing in the stock market only.

   (a) Develop the associated decision tree.

   (b) What is the optimal decision in this case? (*Hint*: Make use of $P\{v_1\}$ and $P\{v_2\}$ given in step 3 of Example 15.2-2 to determine the expected value of investing in the stock market.)

*4. You are the author of what promises to be a successful novel. You have the option to either publish the novel yourself or through a publisher. The publisher is offering you $20,000 for signing the contract. If the novel is successful, it will sell 200,000 copies. Else, it will sell 10,000 copies only. The publisher pays a $1 royalty per copy. A market survey indicates that there is a 70% chance that the novel will be successful. If you undertake publishing, you will incur an initial cost of $90,000 for printing and marketing, but each copy sold will net you $2.

   (a) Based on the given information, would you accept the publisher's offer or publish the novel yourself?

   (b) Suppose that you contract a literary agent to conduct a survey concerning the potential success of the novel. From past experience, the agent advises you that when a novel is successful, the survey will predict the wrong outcome 20% of the time. When the novel is not successful, the survey will give the correct prediction 85% of the time. How would this information affect your decision?

5. Consider Farmer McCoy's decision situation in Problem 2, Set 15.2a. The farmer has the additional option of using the land as a grazing range, in which case a payoff of $7500 is guaranteed. The farmer has also secured additional information from a broker regarding the degree of stability of future commodity prices. The broker's assessment of "favorable" and "unfavorable" is described by the following conditional probabilities:

		a_1	a_2
	s_1	.85	.15
$P\{a_j \mid s_i\} =$	s_2	.50	.50
	s_3	.15	.85

The symbols a_1 and a_2 represent the "favorable" and "unfavorable" assessments, and s_1, s_2, and s_3 represent the "up," "same," and "down" changes in future prices.

   (a) Develop the associated decision tree.

   (b) Specify the optimal decision for the problem.

6. In Problem 5, Set 15.2a, suppose that AFC management has decided to test-market its Wings 'N Things in selective locations. The outcome of the test is either "good" (a_1)

or "bad" (a_2). The test yields the following conditional probabilities with and without the advertising campaign:

$P\{a_j|v_i\}$ − With campaign $P\{a_j|w_i\}$ − No campaign

	a_1	a_2
v_1	.95	.05
v_2	.3	.7

	a_1	a_2
w_1	.8	.2
w_2	.4	.6

The symbols v_1 and v_2 represent "success" and "no success," and w_1 and w_2 represent "receptive" and "not receptive."

(a) Develop the associated decision tree.

(b) Determine the best course of action for AFC.

7. Historical data at Acme Manufacturing estimate a 5% chance that a batch of widgets will be unacceptable (bad). A bad batch has 15% defective items, and a good batch includes only 4% defective items. Letting $a = \theta_1$ and $a = \theta_2$ represent a good and a bad batch, respectively, the associated prior probabilities are given as

$$P\{a = \theta_1\} = .95 \text{ and } P\{a = \theta_2\} = .05$$

Instead of shipping batches based solely on prior probabilities, a test sample of two items is used, giving rise to three possible outcomes: (1) both items are good (z_1), (2) one item is good (z_2), and (3) both items are defective (z_3).

(a) Determine the posterior probabilities $P\{\theta_i|z_j\}, i = 1, 2; j = 1, 2, 3$.

*__(b)__ Suppose that the manufacturer ships batches to two customers, A and B. The contracts specify that the defectives for A and B should not exceed 5% and 8%, respectively. A penalty of $100 is incurred per percentage point above the maximum limit. Supplying better-quality batches than specified by the contract costs the manufacturer $50 per percentage point. Develop the associated decision tree, and determine a priority strategy for shipping the batches.

Utility Functions. In the preceding presentation, the expected value criterion is applied to situations where the payoff is *real* money. There are cases where the *utility* rather than the real value should be used in the analysis. To illustrate this point, suppose there is a 50-50 chance that a $20,000 investment will produce a profit of $40,000 or be lost. The associated expected profit is $40,000 \times .5 - 20,000 \times .5 = \$10,000$. Although there is a net expected profit, different individuals vary in interpreting the result. An investor who is willing to accept risk may undertake the investment for a 50% chance to make a $40,000 profit. Conversely, a conservative investor may not be willing to risk losing $20,000. The concept of *utility function* is devised to reflect these differences. The utility function then takes the place of real money in the decision-making model.

How is the subjective attitude toward risk quantified in the form of a utility function? In the preceding investment illustration, the best payoff is $40,000, and the worst is −$20,000. We can establish a utility scale, U, from 0 to 100 that specifies $U(-\$20,000) = 0$ and $U(\$40,000) = 100$. The value of U for investment return between −$20,000 and $40,000 can be determined in the following manner: If the decision maker is neutral (indifferent) toward risk, then U can be represented by a

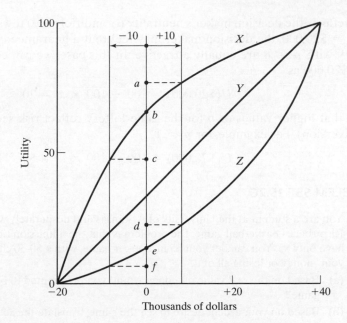

FIGURE 15.6

Utility functions for risk averse (X), neutral (Y), and risk seeker (Z) decision makers

straight line joining $(0, -\$20,000)$ and $(100, \$40,000)$. In this case, both real money and its utility lead to the same decisions. More generally, the function U can take other forms reflecting different attitudes toward risk. Figure 15.6 illustrates the cases of individuals X, Y, and Z. Individual Y is **risk neutral**, individual X is **risk averse** (or cautious), and individual Z, the opposite of X, is a **risk seeker**. The figure demonstrates that for the risk-averse X, the drop in utility bc corresponding to a loss of \$10,000 is larger than the increase ab associated with a gain of \$10,000. The opposite is true for risk seeker Z where $de > ef$. In general, an individual can be both risk averse and risk seeking, in which case the associated utility curve will follow an elongated S-shape.

Utility curves similar to the ones demonstrated in Figure 15.6 are determined by "quantifying" the decision maker's attitude toward risk for different levels of cash money. In our example, the desired range is $(-\$20,000$ to \$40,000$)$ with $U(-\$20,000) = 0$ and $U(\$40,000) = 100$. To specify the values of U for intermediate cash values (e.g., $\$10,000, \$0, \$10,000, \$20,000$, and \$30,000$), we establish a **lottery** for a cash amount x whose expected utility is

$$U(x) = pU(-20,000) + (1 - p)U(\$40,000), 0 \le p \le 1$$

$$- 0p + 100(1 \quad p)$$

$$= 100 - 100p$$

To determine $U(x)$, the decision maker must state a preference between a *guaranteed* cash amount x and the chance to play a lottery for which there is a loss of $-\$20,000$ with probability p and a profit of \$40,000 with probability $1-p$. The value of p reflects the decision maker's neutrality (or indifference) toward risk. For example, for $x = \$20,000$, the decision maker may feel that a guaranteed $20,000 cash and the lottery with $p = .8$ are equally attractive. In this case, we can compute the utility of $x = \$20,000$ as

$$U(\$20,000) = 100 - 100 \times .8 = 20$$

Note that higher values of p for the same lottery reflect risk seeking (as opposed to risk aversion). For example, for $p = .1$,

$$U(\$20,000) = 100 - 100 \times .2 = 80$$

PROBLEM SET 15.2C

*1. You are a student at the University of Arkansas and desperately want to attend the next Razorbacks basketball game. The problem is that the admission ticket costs $10, and you have only $5. You can bet your $5 in a poker game, with a 50-50 chance of either doubling your money or losing all of it.

   (a) Based on the real value of money, would you be tempted to participate in the poker game?

   (b) Based on your ardent desire to see the game, translate the actual money into a utility function.

   (c) Based on the utility function you developed in (b), would you be tempted to participate in the poker game?

*2. The Golden family has just moved to a location where earthquakes are not uncommon. They must decide whether to build their house according to the high-standard earthquake code. The construction cost using the earthquake code is $850,000; otherwise, a comparable house can be constructed for only $350,000. If an earthquake occurs (and there is a probability of .001 it might happen), a substandard home will cost $900,000 to repair. Develop the lottery associated with this situation, assuming a utility scale from 0 to 100.

3. An investment of $10,000 in a high-risk venture has a 50-50 chance over the next year of increasing to $14,000 or decreasing to $8000. Thus the net return can be either $4000 or $-\$2000$.

   (a) Assuming a risk-neutral investor and a utility scale from 0 to 100, determine the utility of $0 net return on investment and the associated indifference probability.

   (b) Suppose that two investors A and B have exhibited the following indifference probabilities:

	Indifference probability	
Net return ($)	Investor A	Investor B
-2000	1.00	1.00
-1000	0.30	0.90
0	0.20	0.80
1000	0.15	0.70
2000	0.10	0.50
3000	0.05	0.40
4000	0.00	0.00

Graph the utility functions for investors A and B, and categorize each investor as either a risk-averse person or a risk seeker.

(c) Suppose that investor A has the chance to invest in one of two ventures. Venture I can produce a net return of $2000 with probability .4 or a net loss of $1000 with probability .6. Venture II can produce a net return of $3000 with probability .6 and no return with probability .4. Based on the utility function in (b), use the expected utility criterion to determine the venture investor A should select. What is the expected monetary value associated with the selected venture? (*Hint*: Use linear interpolation of the utility function.)

(d) Repeat part (c) for investor B.

15.3 DECISION UNDER UNCERTAINTY

Decision making under uncertainty, as under risk, involves alternative actions whose payoffs depend on the (random) *states of nature*. Specifically, the payoff matrix of a decision problem with m alternative actions and n states of nature can be represented as

	s_1	s_2	$\cdots$	s_n
a_1	$v(a_1, s_1)$	$v(a_1, s_2)$	$\cdots$	$v(a_1, s_n)$
a_2	$v(a_2, s_1)$	$v(a_2, s_2)$	$\cdots$	$v(a_2, s_n)$
$\vdots$	$\vdots$	$\vdots$	$\vdots$	$\vdots$
a_m	$v(a_m, s_1)$	$v(a_m, s_2)$	$\cdots$	$v(a_m, s_n)$

The element a_i represents action i and the element s_j represents state of nature j. The payoff or outcome associated with action a_i and state s_j is $v(a_i, s_j)$.

In decision making under uncertainty, the probability distribution associated with the states $s_j, j = 1, 2, \ldots, n$, is either unknown or cannot be determined. This lack of information has led to the development of special decision criteria:

1. Laplace
2. Minimax
3. Savage
4. Hurwicz

These criteria differ in how conservative the decision maker is in the face of uncertainty.

The **Laplace** criterion is based on the **principle of insufficient reason**. Because the probability distributions are not known, there is no reason to believe that the probabilities associated with the states of nature are different. The alternatives are thus evaluated using the *liberal* assumption that all states are equally likely to occur—that is, $P\{s_1\} = P\{s_2\} = \ldots = P\{s_n\} = \frac{1}{n}$. Given that the payoff $v(a_i, s_j)$ represents gain, the best alternative is the one that yields

$$\max_{a_i} \left\{ \frac{1}{n} \sum_{j=1}^{n} v(a_i, s_j) \right\}$$

The **maximin (minimax)** criterion is based on the *conservative* attitude of making the best of the worst-possible conditions. If $v(a_i, s_j)$ is loss, then we select the action that corresponds to the following *minimax* criterion

$$\min_{a_i} \left\{ \max_{s_j} v(a_i, s_j) \right\}$$

If $v(a_i, s_j)$ is gain, we use the *maximin* criterion given by

$$\max_{a_i} \left\{ \min_{s_j} v(a_i, s_j) \right\}$$

The **Savage regret** criterion aims at "moderating" the degree of conservatism in the *minimax (maximin)* criterion by replacing the (gain or loss) payoff matrix $v(a_i, s_j)$ with a *loss* (or regret) matrix, $r(a_i, s_j)$, by using the following transformation:

$$r(a_i, s_j) = \begin{cases} v(a_i, s_j) - \min_{a_k}\{v(a_k, s_j)\}, & \text{if } v \text{ is loss} \\[2ex] \max_{a_k}\{v(a_k, s_j)\} - v(a_i, s_j), & \text{if } v \text{ is gain} \end{cases}$$

To show why the Savage criterion moderates the minimax (maximin) criterion, consider the following *loss* matrix

		s_1	s_2	Row max	
$v(a_i, s_j) =$	a_1	$11,000	$90	$11,000	
	a_2	$10,000	$10,000	**$10,000**	← Minimax

The application of the minimax criterion shows that a_2, with a definite loss of $10,000, is the preferred alternative. However, it may better to choose a_1 because there is a chance of limiting the loss to $90 only if s_2 occurs. This happens to be the case when the regret matrix is used:

		s_1	s_2	Row max	
$r(a_i, v_j) =$	a_1	$1,000	$0	**$1,000**	← Minimax
	a_2	$0	$9,910	$9,910	

The last criterion, **Hurwicz**, is designed to represent different decision-making attitudes, ranging from the most liberal (optimistic) to the most conservative (pessimistic). Define $0 \le \alpha \le 1$. The selected action must be associated with

$$\max_{a_i} \left\{ \alpha \max_{s_j} v(a_i, s_j) + (1 - \alpha)\min_{s_j} v(a_i, s_j) \right\}, \text{if } v \text{ is gain}$$

$$\min_{a_i} \left\{ \alpha \min_{s_j} v(a_i, s_j) + (1 - \alpha)\max_{s_j} v(a_i, s_j) \right\}, \text{if } v \text{ is loss}$$

The parameter α is the **index of optimism**. If $\alpha = 0$, then the criterion reduces to conservative minimax criterion, seeking the *best of the worst* conditions. If $\alpha = 1$, then the criterion is liberal because it seeks *the best of the best* conditions. The degree of optimism (or pessimism) can be adjusted by selecting a value of α between 0 and 1. In the absence of strong feeling regarding extreme optimism and extreme pessimism, $\alpha = .5$ may be a fair choice.

Example 15.3-1

National Outdoors School (NOS) is preparing a summer campsite in the heart of Alaska to train individuals in wilderness survival. NOS estimates that attendance can fall into one of four categories: 200, 250, 300, and 350 persons. The cost of the campsite will be the smallest when its size meets the demand exactly. Deviations above or below the ideal demand levels incur additional costs resulting from constructing more capacity than needed or losing income opportunities when the demand is not met. Letting a_1 to a_4 represent the sizes of the campsites (200, 250, 300, and 350 persons) and s_1 to s_4 the level of attendance, the following table summarizes the cost matrix (in thousands of dollars) for the situation.

	s_1	s_2	s_3	s_4
a_1	5	10	18	25
a_2	8	7	12	23
a_3	21	18	12	21
a_4	30	22	19	15

The problem is analyzed using all four criteria.

Laplace. Given $P\{s_j\} = \frac{1}{4}, j = 1$ to 4, the expected values for the different actions are computed as

$$E\{a_1\} = \frac{1}{4}(5 + 10 + 18 + 25) = \$14,500$$

$$E\{a_2\} = \frac{1}{4}(8 + 7 + 12 + 23) = \$12,500 \leftarrow \textbf{Optimum}$$

$$E\{a_3\} = \frac{1}{4}(21 + 18 + 12 + 21) = \$18,000$$

$$E\{a_4\} = \frac{1}{4}(30 + 22 + 19 + 15) = \$21,500$$

Minimax. The minimax criterion produces the following matrix:

	s_1	s_2	s_3	s_4	Row max
a_1	5	10	18	25	25
a_2	8	7	12	23	23
a_3	21	18	12	21	**21** $\leftarrow$ Minimax
a_4	30	22	19	15	30

Savage. The regret matrix is determined by subtracting 5, 7, 12, and 15 from columns 1 to 4, respectively. Thus,

	s_1	s_2	s_3	s_4	Row max
a_1	0	3	6	10	10
a_2	3	0	0	8	**8** ← Minimax
a_3	16	11	0	6	16
a_4	25	15	7	0	25

Hurwicz. The following table summarizes the computations.

Alternative	Row min	Row max	$\alpha(\text{Row min}) + (1 - \alpha)(\text{Row max})$
a_1	5	25	$25 - 20\alpha$
a_2	7	23	$23 - 16\alpha$
a_3	12	21	$21 - 9\alpha$
a_4	15	30	$30 - 15\alpha$

Using an appropriate α, we can determine the optimum alternative. For example, at $\alpha = .5$, either a_1 or a_2 is the optimum, and at $\alpha = .25$, a_3 is the optimum.

Excel Moment

Template *excelUncertainty.xls* can be used to automate the computations of Laplace, maximin, Savage, and Hurwicz criteria. The spreadsheet is based on the use of a *cost* matrix. To use a reward matrix, all entries must be multiplied by -1. The maximum matrix size is (10×10).

PROBLEM SET 15.3A

*1. Hank is an intelligent student and usually makes good grades, provided that he can review the course material the night before the test. For tomorrow's test, Hank is faced with a small problem: His fraternity brothers are having an all-night party in which he would like to participate. Hank has three options:

a_1 = Party all night

a_2 = Divide the night equally between studying and partying

a_3 = Study all night

Tomorrow's exam can be easy (s_1), moderate (s_2), or tough (s_3), depending on the professor's unpredictable mood. Hank anticipates the following scores:

	s_1	s_2	s_3
a_1	85	60	40
a_2	92	85	81
a_3	100	88	82

(a) Recommend a course of action for Hank (based on each of the four criteria of decisions under uncertainty).

(b) Suppose that Hank is more interested in the letter grade he will get. The dividing scores for the passing letter grades A to D are 90, 80, 70, and 60, respectively. Would this attitude toward grades call for a change in Hank's course of action?

2. For the upcoming planting season, Farmer McCoy can plant corn (a_1), wheat (a_2), or soybeans (a_3) or use the land for grazing (a_4). The payoffs associated with the different actions are influenced by the amount of rain: heavy rainfall (s_1), moderate rainfall (s_2), light rainfall (s_3), or drought (s_4). The payoff matrix (in thousands of dollars) is estimated as

	s_1	s_2	s_3	s_4
a_1	−20	60	30	−5
a_2	40	50	35	0
a_3	−50	100	45	−10
a_4	12	15	15	10

Develop a course of action for Farmer McCoy based on each of the four decisions under uncertainty criteria.

3. One of N machines must be selected for manufacturing Q units of a specific product. The minimum and maximum demands for the product are Q^* and Q^{**}, respectively. The total production cost for Q items on machine i involves a fixed cost K_i and a variable cost per unit c_i, and it is given as

$$TC_i = K_i + c_i Q$$

(a) Devise a solution for the problem under each of the four criteria of decisions under uncertainty.

(b) For $1000 \le Q \le 4000$, solve the problem for the following set of data:

Machine i	K_i ($)	C_i ($)
1	100	5
2	40	12
3	150	3
4	90	8

15.4 GAME THEORY

Game theory deals with decision situations in which two *intelligent* opponents with conflicting objectives are vying to outdo one another. Typical examples include launching advertising campaigns for competing products and planning strategies for war battles.

In a conflict, each of two **players** (opponents) has a (finite or infinite) number of alternatives or **strategies**. Associated with each pair of strategies is the **payoff** one player receives from the other. Such a situation is known as a **two-person zero-sum game**, because a gain by one player is an equal loss by the other. This means that we can represent the game in terms of the payoff to one player. Designating the two players as

A and B with m and n strategies, respectively, the game is usually presented in terms of the payoff matrix to player A as

	B_1	B_2	$\ldots$	B_n
A_1	a_{11}	a_{12}	$\cdots$	a_{1m}
A_2	a_{21}	a_{22}	$\cdots$	a_{2m}
$\vdots$	$\vdots$	$\vdots$	$\vdots$	$\vdots$
A_m	a_{m1}	a_{m1}	$\cdots$	a_{mn}

The representation indicates that if A uses strategy i and B uses strategy j, the payoff to A is a_{ij}, and the payoff to B is $-a_{ij}$.

Real-Life Application—Ordering Golfers on the Final Day of Ryder Cup Matches

On the final day of a golf tournament, two teams compete for the championship. Each team captain must submit a *slate* (an ordered list of golfers) that determines the matches. For two competing players occupying the same order in their respective slates, it is plausible to assume that there is 50-50 chance that either golfer will win the match. The win-probability increases for a higher-order golfer when matched with a lower-order player. The goal is to develop an analytical procedure that will support or refute the idea of using slates. Case 12, Chapter 26, on the website details a study based on game theory.

15.4.1 Optimal Solution of Two-Person Zero-Sum Games

Because games involve a conflict of interest, the basis for the selection of optimal strategies guarantees that neither player is tempted to seek a different strategy because a worse payoff will ensue. These solutions can be in the form of a single pure strategy or several strategies mixed randomly.

Example 15.4-1

Two companies, A and B, sell two brands of flu medicine. Company A advertises in radio (A_1), television (A_2), and newspapers (A_3). Company B, in addition to using radio (B_1), television (B_2), and newspapers (B_3), also mails brochures (B_4). Depending on the effectiveness of each advertising campaign, one company can capture a portion of the market from the other. The following matrix summarizes the percentage of the market captured or lost by company A.

	B_1	B_2	B_3	B_4	Row min
A_1	8	-2	9	-3	-3
A_2	6	**5**	6	8	**5** ← Maximin
A_3	-2	4	-9	5	-9
Column max	8	**5**	9	8	

↑
Minimax

The solution of the game is based on the principle of securing the *best of the worst* for each player. If Company A selects strategy A_1, then regardless of what B does, the worst that can happen is that A loses 3% of the market share to B. This is represented by the minimum value of the entries in row 1. Similarly, with strategy A_2, the worst outcome is for A to capture 5% from B, and for strategy A_3, the worst outcome is for A to lose 9% to B. These results are listed under *row min*. To achieve the *best* of the *worst*, Company A chooses strategy A_2 because it corresponds to the maximin value.

Next, for Company B, the given payoff matrix is for A, and B's *best of the worst* solution is based on the minimax value. The result is that Company B will select strategy B_2.

The optimal solution of the game calls for selecting strategies A_2 and B_2, which means that both companies should use television advertising. The payoff will be in favor of company A, because its market share will increase by 5%. In this case, we say that the **value of the game** is 5% and that A and B are using a **pure saddle-point** solution.

The saddle-point solution precludes the selection of a better strategy by either company. If B moves to another strategy $(B_1, B_3, \text{or } B_4)$, Company A can stay with strategy A_2, ensuring worse loss for B (6% or 8%). By the same token, A would not seek a different strategy because B can change to B_3 to realize a 9% market gain if A_1 is used and 3% if A_3 is used.

The optimal saddle-point solution of a game need not be a pure strategy. Instead, the solution may require mixing two or more strategies randomly, as the following example illustrates.

Example 15.4-2

Two players, A and B, play the coin-tossing game. Each player, unbeknownst to the other, chooses a head (H) or a tail (T). Both players would reveal their choices simultaneously. If they match $(HH \text{ or } TT)$, player A receives \$1 from B. Otherwise, A pays B \$1.

The following payoff matrix for player A gives the row-min and the column-max values corresponding to A's and B's strategies, respectively.

	B_H	B_T	Row min
A_H	1	−1	−1
A_T	−1	1	−1
Column max	1	1	

The maximin and the minimax values of the games are −\$1 and \$1, respectively, and the game does not have a pure strategy solution because the two values are not equal. Specifically, if player A selects A_H, player B can select B_T to receive \$1 from A. If this happens, A can move to strategy A_T to reverse the outcome by receiving \$1 from B. The constant temptation to switch to another strategy shows that a pure strategy solution is not acceptable. What is needed in this case is for both players to randomly mix their respective pure strategies. The optimal value of the game will then occur somewhere between the maximin and the minimax values of the game— that is,

$$\text{maximin (lower) value} \leq \text{value of the game} \leq \text{minimax (upper) value}$$

In the coin-tossing example, the value of the game must lie between −\$1 and +\$1 (see Problem 5, Set 15.4a).

PROBLEM SET 15.4A

1. In games (a) and (b) given below, the payoff is for player A. Each game has a pure strategy solution. In each case, determine the strategies that define the saddle point and the value of the game.

*(a)

	B_1	B_2	B_3	B_4
A_1	9	6	2	8
A_2	8	9	4	5
A_3	7	5	2	5

(b)

	B_1	B_2	B_3	B_4
A_1	5	-4	-5	6
A_2	-3	-4	-8	-2
A_3	6	8	-8	-9
A_4	7	3	-9	6

2. In games (a) and (b) below, the payoff is for player A. Determine the values of p and q that will make (A_2, B_2) a saddle point:

(a)

	B_1	B_2	B_3
A_1	1	q	6
A_2	p	5	10
A_3	6	2	3

(b)

	B_1	B_2	B_3
A_1	2	4	5
A_2	10	7	q
A_3	4	p	6

3. In the games below, the payoff is for player A. Specify the range for the value of the game in each case.

*(a)

	B_1	B_2	B_3	B_4
A_1	1	9	6	0
A_2	2	3	8	4
A_3	-5	-2	10	-3
A_4	7	4	-2	-5

(b)

	B_1	B_2	B_3	B_4
A_1	-1	9	6	8
A_2	-2	10	4	6
A_3	5	3	0	7
A_4		-2	8	4

(c)

	B_1	B_2	B_3
A_1	3	6	1
A_2	5	2	3
A_3	4	2	-5

(d)

	B_1	B_2	B_3	B_4
A_1	3	7	1	3
A_2	4	8	0	-6
A_3	6	-9	-2	4

4. Two companies promote two competing products. Currently, each product controls 50% of the market. Because of recent improvements in the two products, each company plans to launch an advertising campaign. If neither company advertises, equal market shares will continue. If either company launches a stronger campaign, the other company is certain to lose a proportional percentage of its customers. A survey of the market shows that 50% of potential customers can be reached through television, 30% through newspapers, and 20% through radio.

   (a) Formulate the problem as a two-person zero-sum game, and determine the advertising media for each company.

   (b) Determine a range for the value of the game. Can each company operate with a single pure strategy?

5. Let a_{ij} be the (i, j)th element of a payoff matrix with m strategies for player A and n strategies for player B. The payoff is for player A. Prove that

$$\max_i \min_j a_{ij} \leq \min_j \max_i a_{ij}$$

15.4.2 Solution of Mixed Strategy Games

Games with mixed strategies can be solved either graphically or by linear programming. The graphical solution is suitable for games with exactly two pure strategies for one or both players. Linear programming, on the hand, can solve any two-person zero-sum game. The graphical method is interesting because it explains the idea of a saddle point pictorially.

Graphical solution of games. We start with the case of $(2 \times n)$ games in which player A has two strategies, A_1 and A_2.

$$
\begin{array}{cccccc}
 & & y_1 & y_2 & \cdots & y_n \\
x_1: & A_1 & B_1 & B_2 & \cdots & B_n \\
1 - x_1: & A_2 & \boxed{\begin{array}{cccc} a_{11} & a_{12} & \cdots & a_{1m} \\ a_{21} & a_{22} & \cdots & a_{2m} \end{array}}
\end{array}
$$

Player A mixes strategies A_1 and A_2 with probabilities x_1 and $1 - x_1, 0 \leq x_1 \leq 1$. Player B mixes strategies $B_1, B_2, \ldots,$ and B_n with probabilities $y_1, y_2, \ldots,$ and $y_n, y_j \geq 0$ for $j = 1, 2, \ldots, n$, and $y_1 + y_2 + \cdots + y_n = 1$. In this case, A's expected payoff corresponding to B's jth pure strategy is

$$(a_{1j} - a_{2j})x_1 + a_{2j}, j = 1, 2, \ldots, n$$

Player A seeks the value of x_1 that maximizes the minimum expected payoffs—that is,

$$\max_{x_j} \min_j \{(a_{1j} - a_{2j})x_1 + a_{2j}\}$$

Example 15.4-3

Consider the following 2×4 game. The payoff is for player A.

$$
\begin{array}{c|cccc}
 & B_1 & B_2 & B_3 & B_4 \\
\hline
A_1 & 2 & 2 & 3 & -1 \\
A_2 & 4 & 3 & 2 & 6 \\
\end{array}
$$

The game has no pure strategy solution because the maximin and minimax values are not equal (verify!). A's expected payoffs corresponding to B's pure strategies are given as

B's pure strategy	A's expected payoff
1	$-2x_1 + 4$
2	$-x_1 + 3$
3	$x_1 + 2$
4	$-7x_1 + 6$

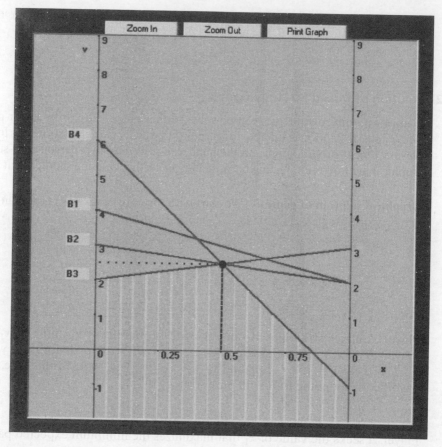

FIGURE 15.7

TORA graphical solution of the two-person zero-sum game of Example 15.4-3 (file *toraEx15.4-3.txt*)

Figure 15.7 provides TORA plot of the four straight lines associated with B's pure strategies (file *toraEx15.4-3.txt*).[3] To determine the *best of the worst* solution, the lower envelope of the four lines (delineated by vertical stripes) represents the minimum (worst) expected payoff for A regardless of B's choices. The maximum (best) of the lower envelope corresponds to the maximin solution point at $x_1^* = .5$. This point is the intersection of the lines associated with strategies B_3 and B_4. Player A's optimal solution thus calls for 50-50 mix of A_1 and A_2. The corresponding value of the game, v, is determined by substituting $x_1 = .5$ in the function of either line 3 or line 4, which gives

$$v = \begin{cases} \frac{1}{2} + 2 = \frac{5}{2}, & \text{from line 3} \\ -7\left(\frac{1}{2}\right) + 6 = \frac{5}{2}, & \text{from line 4} \end{cases}$$

Player B's optimal mix is determined by the two strategies that define the lower envelope of the graph. This means that B can mix strategies B_3 and B_4, in which case $y_1 = y_2 = 0$ and $y_4 = 1 - y_3$. As a result, B's expected payoffs corresponding to A's pure strategies are

---

[3]From Main Menu, select Zero-sum Games and enter the problem data, then select Graphical an from the SOLVE/MODIFY menu.

A's pure strategy	B's expected payoff
1	$4y_3 - 1$
2	$-4y_3 + 6$

The *best of the worst* solution for B is the minimum point on the *upper* envelope of the given two lines (you will find it instructive to graph the two lines and identify the upper envelope). This process is equivalent to solving the equation

$$4y_3 - 1 = -4y_3 + 6$$

The solution gives $y_3 = \frac{7}{8}$, which yields the value of the game as $v = 4 \times \left(\frac{7}{8}\right) - 1 = \frac{5}{2}$.

The solution of the game calls for player A to mix A_1 and A_2 with equal probabilities and for player B to mix B_3 and B_4 with probabilities $\frac{7}{8}$ and $\frac{1}{8}$. (Actually, the game has alternative solutions for B, because the maximin point in Figure 15.7 is determined by more than two lines. Any nonnegative combination of these alternative solutions is also a legitimate solution.)

Remarks. Games in which player A has m strategies and player B has only two can be treated similarly. The main difference is that we will be plotting B's expected payoff corresponding to A's pure strategies. As a result, we will be seeking the minimax, rather than the maximin, point of the *upper envelope* of the plotted lines. However, to solve the problem with TORA, it is necessary to express the payoff in terms of the player that has two strategies, multiplying the payoff matrix by -1.

PROBLEM SET 15.4B[4]

*1. Solve the coin-tossing game of Example 15.4-2 graphically.

*2. Robin travels between two cities and may use one of two routes: Route A is a fast four-lane highway, and route B is a long winding road. She has the habit of driving "superfast." The highway patrol has a limited police force. If the full force is allocated to the route driven by Robin, she is certain to receive a $100 speeding fine. If the force is split 50-50 between the two routes, there is a 50% chance of getting a $100 fine on route A, and only a 30% chance of getting the same fine on route B. Develop a strategy for both Robin and the police patrol.

3. Solve the following games graphically. The payoff is for Player A.

(a)

	B_1	B_2	B_3
A_1	2	−3	8
A_2	3	3	−6

(b)

	B_1	B_2
A_1	5	8
A_2	6	5
A_3	5	7

---

[4]TORA Zero-sum Games module can be used to verify your answer.

4. Consider the following two-person, zero-sum game:

	B_1	B_2	B_3
A_1	5	50	50
A_2	1	1	.1
A_3	10	1	10

(a) Verify that the strategies $(\frac{1}{6}, 0, \frac{5}{6})$ for A and $(\frac{49}{54}, \frac{5}{54}, 0)$ for B are optimal, and determine the value of the game.

(b) Show that the optimal value of the game equals

$$\sum_{i=1}^{3} \sum_{j=1}^{3} a_{ij} x_i y_j$$

Linear programming solution of games.   Game theory bears a strong relationship to linear programming, in the sense that any two-person zero-sum game can be expressed as a linear program, and vice versa. In fact, G. Dantzig (1963, p. 24) states that J. von Neumann, father of game theory, when first introduced to the simplex method in 1947, immediately recognized this relationship and further pinpointed and stressed the concept of *duality* in linear programming. This section explains how games are solved by linear programming.

Player A's optimal probabilities, $x_1, x_2, \ldots,$ and x_m, can be determined by solving the following maximin problem:

$$\max_{x_i}\left\{ \min\left(\sum_{i=l}^{m} a_{i1}x_i, \ \sum_{i=1}^{m} a_{i2}x_i, \ \ldots, \ \sum_{i=1}^{m} a_{in}x_i \right)\right\}$$

$$x_1 + x_2 + \cdots + x_m = 1$$

$$x_i \geq 0, \, i = 1, 2, \ldots, m$$

Let

$$v = \min\left\{ \sum_{i=1}^{m} a_{i1}x_i, \ \sum_{i=1}^{m} a_{i2}x_i, \ \ldots, \ \sum_{i=1}^{m} a_{in}x_i \right\}$$

The equation implies that

$$\sum_{i=1}^{m} a_{ij}x_i \geq v, \, j = 1, 2, \ldots, n$$

Player A's problem thus can be written as

Maximize $z = v$

subject to

$$v - \sum_{i=1}^{m} a_{ij} x_i \le 0, j = 1, 2, \ldots, n$$

$$x_1 + x_2 + \ldots + x_m = 1$$

$$x_i \ge 0, i = 1, 2, \ldots, m$$

$$v \text{ unrestricted}$$

Note that the value of the game, v, is unrestricted in sign.

Player B's optimal strategies, $y_1, y_2, \ldots,$ and $y_n,$ are determined by solving the problem

$$\min_{y_j} \left\{ \max \left(\sum_{j=1}^{n} a_{1j} y_j, \sum_{j=1}^{n} a_{2j} y_j, \ldots, \sum_{j=1}^{n} a_{mj} y_j \right) \right\}$$

$$y_1 + y_2 + \cdots + y_n = 1$$

$$y_j \ge 0, j = 1, 2, \ldots, n$$

Using a procedure similar to that of player A, B's problem reduces to

$$\text{Minimize } w = v$$

subject to

$$v - \sum_{j=1}^{n} a_{ij} y_j \ge 0, i = 1, 2, \ldots, m$$

$$y_1 + y_2 + \cdots + y_n = 1$$

$$y_j \ge 0, j = 1, 2, \ldots, n$$

$$v \text{ unrestricted}$$

The two problems optimize the same (unrestricted) variable v, the value of the game. The reason is that B's problem is the dual of A's problem (verify this claim using the definition of duality in Chapter 4). This means that the optimal solution of one problem automatically yields the optimal solution of the other.

Example 15.4-4

Solve the following game by linear programming. The value of the game, v, lies between -2 and 2.

	B_1	B_2	B_3	Row min
A_1	3	−1	−3	−3
A_2	−2	4	−1	−2
A_3	−5	−6	2	−6
Column max	3	4	2	

Player A's linear program

$$\text{Maximize } z = v$$

subject to

$$v - 3x_1 + 2x_2 + 5x_3 \leq 0$$
$$v + x_1 - 4x_2 + 6x_3 \leq 0$$
$$v + 3x_1 + x_2 - 2x_2 \leq 0$$
$$x_1 + x_2 + x_3 = 1$$
$$x_1, x_2, x_3 \geq 0$$

$$v \text{ unrestricted}$$

The optimum solution[5] is $x_1 = .39$, $x_2 = .31$, $x_3 = .29$, and $v = -0.91$.

Player B's Linear Program

$$\text{Minimize } z = v$$

subject to

$$v - 3y_1 + y_2 + 3y_3 \geq 0$$
$$v + 2y_1 - 4y_2 + y_3 \geq 0$$
$$v + 5y_1 + 6y_2 - 2y_3 \geq 0$$
$$y_1 + y_2 + y_3 = 1$$

$$v \text{ unrestricted}$$

The solution yields $y_1 = .32$, $y_2 = .08$, $y_3 = .60$, and $v = -0.91$.

PROBLEM SET 15.4C

1. On a picnic outing, 2 two-person teams are playing hide-and-seek. There are four hiding locations (A, B, C, and D), and the two members of the hiding team can hide separately in any two of the four locations. The other team can then search any two locations. The searching team gets a bonus point if they find both members of the hiding team. If they miss both, they lose a point. Otherwise, the outcome is a draw.

   *(a) Set up the problem as a two-person zero-sum game.

   (b) Determine the optimal strategy and the value of the game.

2. UA and DU are devising their strategies for the 1994 national championship men's college basketball game. Assessing the strengths of their respective "benches," each coach comes up with four strategies for rotating the players during the game. The ability of each team to score 2-pointers, 3-pointers, and free throws is key to determining the final score of the game. The following table summarizes the net points UA will score per possession as a function of the different strategies available to each team:

---

[5]TORA Zero-sum Games $\Rightarrow$ Solve $\Rightarrow$ LP-based can be used to solve any two-person zero-sum game.

$$\begin{array}{c} \quad\quad DU_1 \; DU_2 \; DU_3 \; DU_4 \end{array}$$

	DU_1	DU_2	DU_3	DU_4
UA_1	3	−2	1	4
UA_2	2	3	−5	0
UA_3	−1	2	−2	2
UA_4	−3	−5	4	1

(a) Solve the game by linear programming, and determine a strategy for the championship game.

(b) Based on the given information, which of the two teams is projected to win the championship?

(c) Suppose that the entire game will have a total of 60 possessions (30 for each team). Predict the expected number of points by which the championship will be won.

3. Colonel Blotto's army is fighting for the control of two strategic locations. Blotto has two regiments and the enemy has three. A location will fall to the army with more regiments. Otherwise, the result of the battle is a draw.

*(a) Formulate the problem as a two-person zero-sum game, and solve by linear programming.

(b) Which army will win the battle?

4. In the two-player, two-finger Morra game, each player shows one or two fingers, and simultaneously guesses the number of fingers the opponent will show. The player making the correct guess wins an amount equal to the total number of fingers shown. Otherwise, the game is a draw. Set up the problem as a two-person zero-sum game, and solve by linear programming.

BIBLIOGRAPHY

Chen, S., and C. Hwang, *Fuzzy Multiple Attribute Decision Making*, Springer-Verlag, Berlin, 1992.

Clemen, R. J., and T. Reilly, *Making Hard Decisions: An introduction to Decision Analysis*, 2nd ed., Duxbury, Pacific Grove, CA, 1996.

Cohan, D., S. Haas, D. Radloff, and R. Yancik, "Using Fire in Forest Management: Decision Making under Uncertainty," *Interfaces*, Vol. 14, No. 5, pp. 8–19, 1984.

Dantzig, G. B., *Linear Programming and Extensions*, Princeton University Press, Princeton, NJ, 1963.

Meyerson, R., *Game Theory: Analysis of Conflict*, Harvard University Press, Cambridge, MA, 1991.

Rapport, A. "Sensitivity Analysis in Decision Making," *The Accounting Review*, Vol. 42, No. 3, pp. 441–456, 1967.

Saaty, T. L., *Fundamentals of Decision Making*, RWS Publications, Pittsburgh, 1994.

CHAPTER 16

Probabilistic Inventory Models

Real-Life Application—Inventory Decisions in Dell's Supply Chain

Dell, Inc., implements a direct-sales business model in which personal computers are sold directly to customers in the United States. When an order arrives from a customer, the specifications are sent to a manufacturing plant in Austin, Texas, where the computer is built, tested, and packaged in about 8 hours. Dell carries little inventory. Its suppliers, normally located in Southeast Asia, are required to keep what is known as "revolving" inventory on hand in *revolvers* (warehouses) near the manufacturing plants. These revolvers are owned by Dell and leased to the suppliers. Dell then "pulls" parts as needed from the revolvers, and it is the suppliers' responsibility to replenish the inventory to meet Dell's demand. Although Dell does not own the inventory in the revolvers, its cost is indirectly passed on to customers through component pricing. Thus, any reduction in inventory directly benefits Dell's customers by reducing product prices. The proposed solution has resulted in an estimated $2.7 million in annual savings. Case 13 in Chapter 26 on the website details the study.

16.1 CONTINUOUS REVIEW MODELS

This section presents two models: (1) a "probabilitized" version of the deterministic EOQ (Section 13.3.1) that uses a buffer stock to account for probabilistic demand and (2) a more exact probabilistic EOQ model that includes the random demand directly in the formulation.

16.1.1 "Probabilitized" EOQ Model

Some practitioners have sought to adapt the deterministic EOQ model (Section 13.3.1) to approximate the probabilistic nature of demand. The critical period during the inventory cycle occurs between placing and receiving orders. This is the time period when

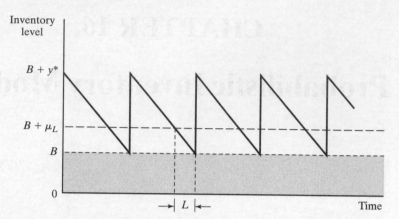

FIGURE 16.1

Buffer stock, B, imposed on the classical EOQ model

shortage (running out of stock) could occur. The idea then is to maintain a constant buffer stock that will put a cap on the probability of shortage. Intuitively, lower shortage probability entails larger buffer stock, and vice versa.

Figure 16.1 depicts the relationship between the buffer stock, B, and the parameters of the deterministic EOQ model that include the lead time, L; the average demand during lead time, μ_L; and the EOQ, y^*. Note that L is the *effective* lead time as defined in Section 13.3.1.

The main assumption of the model is that the demand per unit time is normal with mean D and standard deviation σ—that is, $N(D, \sigma)$. Under this assumption, the demand during lead time L must also be normal with mean $\mu_L = DL$ and standard deviation $\sigma_L = \sqrt{L\sigma^2}$. The formula for σ_L assumes that L is (approximated, if necessary, by) an integer value.

The size of the buffer B is determined such that the probability of shortage during L is at most α. Let x_L be the demand during lead time L, then

$$P\{x_L \geq B + \mu_L\} \leq \alpha$$

Using $N(0, 1)$, $z = \frac{x_L - \mu_L}{\sigma_L}$ (as defined in Section 14.4.4), we get

$$P\left\{z \geq \frac{B}{\sigma_L}\right\} \leq \alpha$$

Defining the parameter K_α for the standard normal distribution such that $P\{z \geq k_\alpha\} \leq \alpha$ (see Figure 16.2), it follows that

$$B \geq \sigma_L K_\alpha$$

The amount $\sigma_L K_\alpha$ provides the minimum value of B. (The value of K_α can be determined from the standard normal table in Appendix A or by using file *excelStat Tables.xls*.)

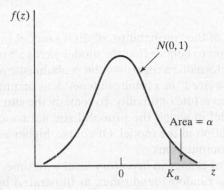

FIGURE 16.2

Probability of running out of stock,

$P\{z \geq K_\alpha\} = \alpha$

Example 16.1-1

In Example 13.3-1, dealing with determining the inventory policy of neon lights, the EOQ is 1000 units. Assume that the *daily* demand is $N(100, 10)$—that is, $D = 100$ units and standard deviation $\sigma = 10$ units. Determine the buffer size, B, using $\alpha = .05$.

From Example 13.3-1, the *effective* lead time is $L = 2$ days. Thus,

$$\mu_L = DL = 100 \times 2 = 200 \text{ units}$$

$$\sigma_L = \sqrt{\sigma^2 L} = \sqrt{10^2 \times 2} = 14.14 \text{ units}$$

Given $K_{.05} = 1.645$, the buffer size is computed as

$$B \geq 14.14 \times 1.645 \approx 23 \text{ neon lights}$$

The (buffered) optimal inventory policy calls for ordering 1000 units whenever the inventory level drops to $223\, (=B + \mu_L = 23 + 2 \times 100)$ units.

PROBLEM SET 16.1A

1. In Example 16.1-1, determine the optimal inventory policy for each of the following cases:

   *(a) Lead time = 15 days.

   (b) Lead time = 25 days.

   (c) Lead time = 9 days.

   (d) Lead time = 12 days.

2. The daily demand for a popular CD in a music store is approximately $N(200, 20)$. The cost of keeping the CD on the shelves is $.04 per disc per day. It costs the store $100 to place a new order. There is a 7-day lead time for delivery. Determine the store's optimal inventory policy given that the store wishes to limit the probability of shortage to at most .02.

3. The daily demand for camera films at a gift shop is $N(300, 5)$. The cost of holding a roll in the shop is $.02 per day, and the fixed cost of placing a replenishment order is $30. The shop's inventory policy is to order 150 rolls whenever the inventory level drops to 80 units. It simultaneously maintains a buffer of 20 rolls at all times.

   (a) Determine the probability of running out of stock.

   (b) Given the data of the situation, recommend an inventory policy for the shop given that the shortage probability cannot exceed .10.

16.1.2 Probabilistic EOQ Model

The basis for the development of the "probabilitized" EOQ model in Section 16.1.1 is "plausible," but there is no reason to believe that the model yields an optimal inventory policy. The fact that pertinent information regarding the probabilistic nature of demand is initially ignored, only to be "revived" in a totally independent manner at a later stage of the calculations, is sufficient to refute optimality. To remedy the situation, this section presents a more accurate model in which the probabilistic nature of the demand is included directly in the formulation of the model. Of course, higher accuracy comes at the expense of more complex computations.

Figure 16.3 depicts a typical change in inventory level with time. Shortage may or may not occur during (possibly random) lead times, as illustrated by cycles 1 and 2, respectively. The policy calls for ordering the quantity y whenever the amount of inventory on hand drops to level R. As in the deterministic case, the reorder level R is a function of the lead time between placing and receiving an order. The optimal values of y and R are determined by minimizing the expected sum of setup, holding, and shortage costs per unit time.

The model is based on three assumptions:

1. Unfilled demand during lead time is backlogged.
2. No more than one outstanding order is allowed.
3. The distribution of demand during lead time remains stationary with time.

To develop the total cost function per unit time, let

$f(x)$ = pdf of demand, x, during lead time
D = Expected demand per unit time
h = Holding cost per inventory unit per unit time
p = Shortage cost per inventory unit
K = Setup cost per order

FIGURE 16.3

Probabilistic inventory model with shortage

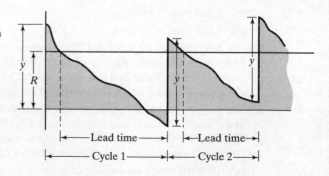

The elements of the cost function are now determined.

1. *Setup cost.* The approximate number of orders per unit time is $\frac{D}{y}$, so that the setup cost per unit time is approximately $\frac{KD}{y}$.
2. *Expected holding cost.* Given I is the average inventory level, the expected holding cost per unit time is hI. The average inventory level is computed as

$$I = \frac{(y + E\{R - x\}) + E\{R - x\}}{2} = \frac{y}{2} + R - E\{x\}$$

The formula averages the starting and ending expected inventories in a cycle— $y + E\{R - x\}$ and $E\{R - x\}$, respectively. As an approximation, the expression ignores the case where $R - E\{x\}$ may be negative.

3. *Expected shortage cost.* Shortage occurs when $x > R$. Its expected value per cycle is computed as

$$S = \int_R^\infty (x - R)f(x)dx$$

Because p is assumed to be proportional to the shortage quantity only, the expected shortage cost per cycle is pS, and, based on $\frac{D}{y}$ cycles per unit time, the shortage cost per unit time is $\frac{pS}{y/D} = \frac{pDS}{y}$.

The resulting total cost function per unit time is

$$\text{TCU}(y, R) = \frac{DK}{y} + h\left(\frac{y}{2} + R - E\{x\}\right) + \frac{pD}{y}\int_R^\infty (x - R)f(x)\,dx$$

The optimal values, y^* and R^*, are determined from

$$\frac{\partial \text{TCU}}{\partial y} = -\left(\frac{DK}{y^2}\right) + \frac{h}{2} - \frac{pDS}{y^2} = 0$$

$$\frac{\partial \text{TCU}}{\partial R} = h - \left(\frac{pD}{y}\right)\int_R^\infty f(x)dx = 0$$

These two equations yield

$$y^* = \sqrt{\frac{2D(K + pS)}{h}} \tag{1}$$

$$\int_R^\infty f(x)\,dx = \frac{hy^*}{pD} \tag{2}$$

The optimal values of y^* and R^* cannot be determined in closed forms. An iterative algorithm, developed by Hadley and Whitin (1963, pp. 169–174), is applied to

Equations (1) and (2) to find the solution. The algorithm converges in a finite number of iterations, provided a feasible solution exists.

For $R = 0$, Equations (1) and (2) yield

$$\hat{y} = \sqrt{\frac{2D(K + pE\{x\})}{h}}$$

$$\tilde{y} = \frac{PD}{h}$$

Unique optimal values of y and R exist when $\tilde{y} \geq \hat{y}$. The smallest value of y^* is $\sqrt{\frac{2KD}{h}}$, which occurs when $S = 0$.

The steps of the algorithm are

Step 0.   Use the initial solution $y_1 = y^* = \sqrt{\frac{2KD}{h}}$, and let $R_0 = 0$. Set $i = 1$, and go to step i.

Step i.   Use y_i to determine R_i from Equation (2). If $R_i \approx R_{i-1}$, stop; the optimal solution is $y^* = y_i$, and $R^* = R_i$. Otherwise, use R_i in Equation (1) to compute y_i. Set $i = i + 1$, and repeat step i.

Example 16.1-2

Electro uses resin in its manufacturing process at the rate of 1000 gallons per month. It cost Electro $100 to place an order. The holding cost per gallon per month is $2, and the shortage cost per gallon is $10. Historical data show that the demand during lead time is uniform in the range $(0, 100)$ gallons. Determine the optimal ordering policy for Electro.

Using the symbols of the model, we have

$D = 1000$ gallons per month
$K = \$100$ per order
$h = \$2$ per gallon per month
$p = \$10$ per gallon
$f(x) = \frac{1}{100}, 0 \leq x \leq 100$
$E\{x\} = 50$ gallons

First, we need to check whether the problem has a unique solution. Using the equations for $\hat{y}$ and $\tilde{y}$ we get

$$\hat{y} = \sqrt{\frac{2 \times 1000(100 + 10 \times 50)}{2}} = 774.6 \text{ gallons}$$

$$\tilde{y} = \frac{10 \times 1000}{2} = 5000 \text{ gallons}$$

Because $\tilde{y} \geq \hat{y}$, a unique solution exists for y^* and R^*.

The expression for S is computed as

$$S = \int_R^{100} (x - R) \frac{1}{100} dx = \frac{R^2}{200} - R + 50$$

Using S in Equations (1) and (2), we obtain

$$y_i = \sqrt{\frac{2 \times 1000(100 + 10S)}{2}} = \sqrt{100,000 + 10,000S} \text{ gallons} \tag{3}$$

$$\int_R^{100} \frac{1}{100} \, dx = \frac{2y_i}{10 \times 1000} \tag{4}$$

Equation (4) yields

$$R_i = 100 - \frac{y_i}{50} \tag{5}$$

We now use Equations (3) and (5) to determine the optimum solution.

Iteration 1

$$y_1 = \sqrt{\frac{2KD}{h}} = \sqrt{\frac{2 \times 1000 \times 100}{2}} = 316.23 \text{ gallons}$$

$$R_1 = 100 - \frac{316.23}{50} = 93.68 \text{ gallons}$$

Iteration 2

$$S = \frac{R_1^2}{200} - R_1 + 50 = .19971 \text{ gallons}$$

$$y_2 = \sqrt{100,000 + 10,000 \times .19971} = 319.37 \text{ gallons}$$

Hence,

$$R_2 = 100 - \frac{319.39}{50} - = 93.612$$

Iteration 3

$$S = \frac{R_2^2}{200} - R_2 + 50 = .20399 \text{ gallon}$$

$$y_3 = \sqrt{100,000 + 10,000 \times .20399} = 319.44 \text{ gallons}$$

Thus,

$$R_3 = 100 - \frac{319.44}{50} = 93.611 \text{ gallons}$$

Because $y_3 \approx y_2$ and $R_3 \approx R_2$, the optimum is $R^* \approx 93.611$ gallons, $y^* \approx 319.44$ gallons. File *excelContRev.xls* can be used to determine the solution to any degree of accuracy by specifying the tolerance $|R_{i-1} - R_i|$. The optimal inventory policy calls for ordering approximately 320 gallons whenever the inventory level drops to 94 gallons.

PROBLEM SET 16.1B

1. For the data given in Example 16.1-2, determine the following:
   (a) The approximate number of orders per month.
   (b) The expected monthly setup cost.
   (c) The expected holding cost per month.
   (d) The expected shortage cost per month.
   (e) The probability of running out of stock during lead time.
*2. Solve Example 16.1-2, assuming that the demand during lead time is uniform between 0 and 50 gallons.
*3. In Example 16.1-2, suppose that the demand during lead time is uniform between 40 and 60 gallons. Compare the solution with that obtained in Example 16.1-2, and interpret the results. (*Hint*: In both problems, $E\{x\}$ is the same, but the variance in the present problem is smaller.)
4. Find the optimal solution for Example 16.1-2, assuming that the demand during lead time is $N(100, 2)$. Assume that $D = 10,000$ gallons per month, $h = \$2$ per gallon per month, $p = \$4$ per gallon, and $K = \$20$.

16.2   SINGLE-PERIOD MODELS

This section deals with inventory items that are in stock during a single time period. At the end of the period, leftover units, if any, are disposed of, as in fashion items. Two models will be developed. The difference between the two models is whether or not a setup cost is incurred for placing an order.

The symbols used in the development of the models include

K = Setup cost per order
h = Holding cost per held unit during the period
p = Penalty cost per shortage unit during the period
$f(D)$ = pdf of demand, D, during the period
y = Order quantity
x = Inventory on hand before an order is placed.

The model determines the optimal value of y that minimizes the sum of the expected holding and shortage costs. Given optimal $y(=y^*)$, the inventory policy calls for ordering $y^* - x$ if $x < y$; otherwise, no order is placed.

16.2.1   No-Setup Model (Newsvendor Model)

This model is known in the literature as the *newsvendor* model (the original classical name is the *newsboy* model). It deals with stocking and selling newspapers and periodicals.

The assumptions of the model are

1. Demand occurs instantaneously at the start of the period immediately after the order is received.
2. No setup cost is incurred.

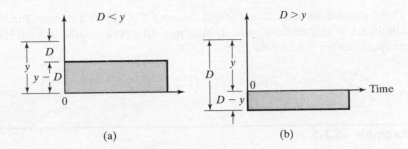

FIGURE 16.4

Holding and shortage inventory in a single-period model

Figure 16.4 demonstrates the inventory position after the demand, D, is satisfied. If $D < y$, the quantity $y - D$ is held during the period. Otherwise, a shortage amount $D - y$ will result if $D > y$.

The expected cost for the period, $E\{C(y)\}$, is expressed as

$$E\{C(y)\} = h \int_0^y (y - D)f(D)dD + p \int_y^\infty (D - y)f(D)dD$$

The function $E\{C(y)\}$ can be shown to be convex in y, thus having a unique minimum. Taking the first derivative of $E\{C(y)\}$ with respect to y and equating it to zero, we get

$$h \int_0^y f(D)\, dD - p \int_0^\infty f(D)\, dD = 0$$

or

$$hP\{D \le y\} - p(1 - P\{D \le y\}) = 0$$

or

$$P\{D \le y^*\} = \frac{p}{p + h}$$

If the demand, D, is discrete, then the associated cost function is

$$E\{C(y)\} = h \sum_{D=0}^y (y - D)f(D) + p \sum_{D=y+1}^\infty (D - y)f(D)$$

The necessary conditions for optimality are

$$E\{C(y - 1)\} \ge E\{C(y)\} \text{ and } E\{C(y + 1)\} \ge E\{C(y)\}$$

These conditions are also sufficient because $E\{C(y)\}$ is a convex function. After some algebraic manipulations, the application of these conditions yields the following inequalities for determining y^*:

$$P\{D \leq y^* - 1\} \leq \frac{p}{p + h} \leq P\{D \leq y^*\}$$

Example 16.2-1

The owner of a newsstand wants to determine the number of newspapers of *USA Now* to be stocked at the start of each day. The owner pays 30 cents for a copy and sells it for 75 cents. The sale of the newspaper typically occurs between 7:00 and 8:00 A.M. (practically, instant demand). Newspapers left at the end of the day are recycled for an income of 5 cents a copy. How many copies should the owner stock every morning, assuming that the demand for the day can be described as

(a) A normal distribution with mean 300 copies and standard deviation 20 copies.

(b) A discrete pdf, $f(D)$, defined as

D	200	220	300	320	340
$f(D)$	.1	.2	.4	.2	.1

The holding and penalty costs are not defined directly in this situation. The data of the problem indicate that each unsold copy will cost the owner $30 - 5 = 25$ cents and that the penalty for running out of stock is $75 - 30 = 45$ cents per copy. Thus, in terms of the parameters of the inventory problem, we have $h = 25$ cents per copy per day and $p = 45$ cents per copy per day.

First, we determine the critical ratio as

$$\frac{p}{p + h} = \frac{45}{45 + 25} = .643$$

Case (a). The demand D is $N(300, 20)$. We can use *excelStatTables.xls* to determine the optimum order quantity by entering 300 in F15, 20 in G15, and .643 in L15, which gives the desired answer of 307.33 newspapers in R15. Alternatively, we can use the standard normal tables in Appendix A. Define

$$z = \frac{D - 300}{20}$$

Then from the normal tables

$$P\{z \leq .366\} \approx .643$$

or

$$\frac{y^* - 300}{20} = .366$$

Thus, $y^* = 307.3$. The optimal order is approximately 308 copies.

Case (b). The demand D follows a discrete pdf, $f(D)$. First, we determine the CDF $P\{D \leq y\}$ as

y	200	220	300	320	340
$P\{D \leq y\}$	.1	.3	.7	.9	1.0

For the computed critical ratio of .643, we have

$$P(D \leq 220) \leq .643 \leq P(D \leq 300)$$

It only follows that $y^* = 300$ copies.

PROBLEM SET 16.2A

1. For the single-period model, show that for the discrete demand the optimal order quantity is determined from

$$P\{D \leq y^* - 1\} \leq \frac{p}{p+h} \leq P\{D \leq y^*\}$$

2. The demand for an item during a single period occurs instantaneously at the start of the period. The associated pdf is uniform between 15 and 20 units. Because of the difficulty in estimating the cost parameters, the order quantity is determined such that the probability of either surplus or shortage does not exceed .1. Is it possible to satisfy both conditions simultaneously?

*3. The unit holding cost in a single-period inventory situation is $1. If the order quantity is 4 units, find the permissible range of the unit penalty cost implied by the optimal conditions. Assume that the demand occurs instantaneously at the start of the period and that the pdf of demand is as follows:

D	0	1	2	3	4	5	6	7	8
$f(D)$	.05	.1	.1	.2	.25	.15	.05	.05	.05

4. The U of A Bookstore offers a program of reproducing class notes for participating professors. Professor Yataha teaches a freshmen-level class with an enrollment of between 100 and 150 students, uniformly distributed. A copy costs $10 to produce, and it sells for $25. The students purchase their books at the start of the semester. Any unsold copies of Professor Yataha's notes are shredded for recycling. In the meantime, once the bookstore runs out of copies, no additional copies are printed. If the bookstore wants to maximize its revenues, how many copies should it print?

5. QuickStop provides its customers with coffee and donuts at 6:00 A.M. each day. The convenience store buys the donuts for 7 cents apiece and sells them for 25 cents apiece until 8:00 A.M. After 8:00 A.M., the donuts sell for 5 cents apiece. The number of customers buying donuts between 6:00 and 8:00 is uniformly distributed between 30 and 50. Each customer usually orders 3 donuts with coffee. Approximately how many dozen donuts should QuickStop stock every morning to maximize revenues?

*6. Colony Shop is stocking heavy coats for next winter. Colony pays $50 for a coat and sells it for $110. At the end of the winter season, Colony offers the coats at $55 each. The demand for coats during the winter season is more than 20 but less than or equal to 30, all with equal probabilities. Because the winter season is short, the unit holding cost is negligible. Also, Colony's manager does not believe that any penalty would result from coat shortages. Determine the optimal order quantity that will maximize the revenue for Colony Shop. You may use continuous approximation.

7. For the single-period model, suppose that the item is consumed uniformly during the period (rather than instantaneously at the start of the period). Develop the associated cost model, and find the optimal order quantity.

8. Solve Example 16.2-1, assuming that the demand is continuous and uniform during the period and that the pdf of demand is uniform between 0 and 100. (*Hint*: Use of the results of Problem 7.)

16.2.2 Setup Model (*s-S* Policy)

The present model differs from the one in Section 16.2.1 in that a setup cost K is incurred. Using the same notation, the total expected cost per period is

$$E\{\overline{C}(y)\} = K + E\{C(y)\}$$

$$= K + h \int_0^y (y - D)f(D)dD + p \int_y^\infty (D - y)f(D)dD$$

As shown in Section 16.2.1, the optimum value y^* must satisfy

$$P\{y \le y^*\} = \frac{p}{p + h}$$

Because K is constant, the minimum value of $E\{\overline{C}(y)\}$ must also occur at y^*.

In Figure 16.5, $S = y^*$, and the value of $s(< S)$ is determined from the equation

$$E\{C(s)\} = E\{\overline{C}(S)\} = K + E\{C(S)\}, s < S$$

The equation yields another value $s_1 (>S)$, which is discarded.

FIGURE 16.5

(*s-S*) optimal ordering policy in a single-period model with setup cost

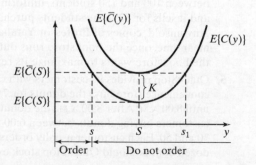

Assume that x is the amount on hand before an order is placed. How much should be ordered? This question is answered under three conditions:

1. $x < s$.
2. $s \leq x \leq S$.
3. $x > S$.

Case 1 ($x > s$). Because x is already on hand, its equivalent cost is given by $E\{C(x)\}$. If any additional amount $y - x (y > x)$ is ordered, the corresponding cost given y is $E\{\overline{C}(y)\}$, which includes the setup cost K. From Figure 16.5, we have

$$\min_{y>x} E\{\overline{C}(y)\} = E(\overline{C}(S)) < E\{C(x)\}$$

Thus, the optimal inventory policy in this case is to order $S - x$ units.

Case 2 ($s \leq x \leq S$). From Figure 16.5, we have

$$E\{C(x)\} \leq \min_{y>x} E\{\overline{C}(y)\} = E(\overline{C}(S))$$

Thus, it is *not* advantageous to order in this case and $y^* = x$.

Case 3 ($x > S$). From Figure 16.5, we have for $y > x$,

$$E\{C(x)\} < E\{\overline{C}(y)\}$$

This condition indicates that, as in case (2), it is not advantageous to place an order—that is, $y^* = x$.

The optimal inventory policy, frequently referred to as the **s-S policy**, is summarized as

$$\text{If } x < s, \text{order } S - x$$

$$\text{If } x \geq s, \text{do not order}$$

The optimality of the s-S policy is guaranteed because the associated cost function is convex.

Example 16.2-2

The daily demand for an item during a single period occurs instantaneously at the start of the period. The pdf of the demand is uniform between 0 and 10 units. The unit holding cost of the item during the period is $.50, and the unit penalty cost for running out of stock is $4.50. A fixed cost of $25 is incurred each time an order is placed. Determine the optimal inventory policy for the item.

To determine y^*, consider

$$\frac{p}{p + h} = \frac{4.5}{4.5 + .5} = .9$$

Also,

$$P\{D \leq y^*\} = \int_0^{y^*} \frac{1}{10} \, dD = \frac{y^*}{10}$$

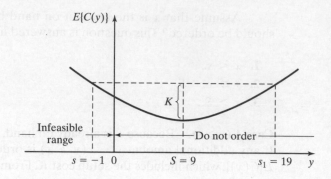

FIGURE 16.6

s-S policy applied to Example 16.2-2

Thus, $S = y^* = 9$.

The expected cost function is

$$E\{C(y)\} = .5 \int_0^y \frac{1}{10}(y - D)dD + 4.5 \int_y^{10} \frac{1}{10}(D - y)dD$$

$$= .25y^2 - 4.5y + 22.5$$

The value of s is determined by solving

$$E\{C(s)\} = K + E\{C(S)\}$$

Or

$$.25s^2 - 4.5s + 22.5 = 25 + .25S^2 - 4.5S + 22.5$$

Given $S = 9$, the preceding equation reduces to

$$s^2 - 18s - 19 = 0$$

The solution of this equation is $s = -1$ or $s = 19$. The value of $s > S$ is discarded. Because the remaining value is negative ($= -1$), s has no feasible value. As Figure 16.6 shows, the optimal inventory policy in this case calls for not ordering the item. This result usually happens when the cost function is "flat" or when the setup cost is high relative to the other costs of the model.

PROBLEM SET 16.2B

*1. Determine the optimal inventory policy for the situation in Example 16.2-2, assuming that the setup cost is $5.

2. In the single-period model in Section 16.2.1, suppose that the model maximizes profit and that a setup cost K is incurred. Given that r is the unit selling price and using the information in Section 16.2.1, develop an expression for the expected profit, and determine the optimal order quantity. Solve the problem numerically for $r = \$3$, $c = \$2, p = \$4, h = \$1$, and $K = \$10$. The demand pdf is uniform between 0 and 10.

3. Work Problem 5, Set 16.2a, assuming that there is a fixed cost of $10 associated with the delivery of donuts.

16.3   MULTIPERIOD MODEL

This section presents a multiperiod model under the assumption of no setup cost. Additionally, the model allows backlog of demand and assumes a zero-delivery lag. It further assumes that the demand D in any period is described by a stationary pdf, $f(D)$.

The multiperiod model considers the discounted value of money. If α (<1) is the discount factor per period, then an amount $\$A$ available n periods from now has a present value of $\$\alpha^n A$.

Suppose that the inventory situation encompasses n periods and that unfilled demand can be backlogged exactly one period. Define

$F_i(x_i)$ = Maximum expected profit for periods $i, i + 1, \ldots,$ and n, given that

x_i is the amount on hand before an order is placed in period i

Using the notation in Section 16.2 and assuming that c and r are the cost and revenue per unit, respectively, the inventory situation can be formulated using the following probabilistic dynamic programming model (see Chapter 24 on the website):

$$F_{n+1}(y_n - D) = 0$$

$$F_i(x_i) = \max_{y_i \geq x_i} \left\{ -c(y_i - x_i) + \int_0^{y_i} [rD - h(y_i - D)]f(D)dD \right.$$

$$+ \int_{y_i}^{\infty} [ry_i + \alpha r(D - y_i) - p(D - y_i)]f(D)dD$$

$$\left. + \alpha \int_0^{\infty} F_{i+1}(y_i - D)f(D)dD \right\}, i = 1, 2, \ldots, n$$

The value of x_i may be negative because unfilled demand is backlogged. The quantity $\alpha r(D - y_i)$ in the second integral is included because $(D - y_i)$ is the unfilled demand in period i that must be filled in period $i + 1$.

The problem can be solved recursively. For the case where the number of periods is infinite, the recursive equation reduces to

$$F(x) = \max_{y \geq x} \left\{ -c(y - x) + \int_0^y [rD - h(y - D)]f(D)dD \right.$$

$$+ \int_y^{\infty} [ry + \alpha r(D - y) - p(D - y)]f(D)dD$$

$$\left. + \alpha \int_0^{\infty} F(y - D)f(D)dD \right\}$$

where x and y are the inventory levels for each period before and after an order is received, respectively.

The optimal value of y can be determined from the following necessary condition, which also happens to be sufficient because the expected revenue function $F(x)$ is concave.

$$\frac{\partial(.)}{\partial y} = -c - h \int_0^y f(D)\,dD + \int_y^\infty [(1 - \alpha)r + p]f(D)dD$$

$$+ \alpha \int_0^\infty \frac{\partial F(y - D)}{\partial y} f(D)dD = 0$$

The value of $\frac{\partial F(y - D)}{\partial y}$ is determined as follows. If there are $\beta\,(>0)$ more units on hand at the start of the next period, the profit for the next period will increase by $c\beta$, because this much less has to be ordered. This means that

$$\frac{\partial F(y - D)}{\partial y} = c$$

The necessary condition thus becomes

$$-c - h \int_0^y f(D)\,dD + \left[(1 - \alpha)r + p\right]\left(1 - \int_0^y f(D)dD\right) + \alpha c \int_0^\infty f(D)\,dD = 0$$

The optimum inventory level y^* is thus determined from

$$\int_0^{y^*} f(D)\,dD = \frac{p + (1 - \alpha)(r - c)}{p + h + (1 - \alpha)r}$$

The optimal inventory policy for each period, given its entering inventory level x, is thus given as

$$\text{If } x < y^*, \text{order } y^* - x$$

$$\text{If } x \geq y^*, \text{do not order}$$

PROBLEM SET 16.3A

1. Consider a two-period probabilistic inventory model in which the demand is backlogged, and orders are received with zero delivery lag. The demand pdf per period is uniform between 0 and 10, and the cost parameters are given as

   Unit selling price = \$2
   Unit purchase price = \$1
   Unit holding cost per month = \$.10
   Unit penalty cost per month = \$3
   Discount factor = .8

   Find the optimal inventory policy for the two periods, assuming that the initial inventory for period 1 is zero.

*2. The pdf of the demand per period in an infinite-horizon inventory model is given as

$$f(D) = .08D, 0 \leq D \leq 5$$

The unit cost parameters are

Unit selling price $= \$10$
Unit purchase price $= \$8$
Unit holding cost per month $= \$1$
Unit penalty cost per month $= \$10$
Discount factor $= .9$

Determine the optimal inventory policy assuming zero delivery lag and that the unfilled demand is backlogged.

3. Consider the infinite-horizon inventory situation with zero delivery lag and back-logged demand. Develop the optimal inventory policy based on the minimization of cost given that

$$\text{Holding cost for } z \text{ units} = hz^2$$
$$\text{Penalty cost for } z \text{ units} = px^2$$

Show that for the special case where $h = p$, the optimal solution is independent of pdf of demand.

BIBLIOGRAPHY

Cohen, R., and F. Dunford, "Forecasting for Inventory Control: An Example of When 'Simple' Means 'Better,'" *Interfaces*, Vol. 16, No. 6, pp. 95–99, 1986.

Hadley, G., and T. Whitin, *Analysis of Inventory Systems*, Prentice Hall, Upper Saddle River, NJ, 1963.

Nahmias, S., *Production and Operations Analysis*, 5th ed., Irwin, Homewood, IL, 2005.

Silver, E., D. Pyke, and R. Peterson, *Decision Systems for Inventory Management and Production Control*, 3rd ed., Wiley, New York, 1998.

Zipken, P., *Foundations of Inventory Management*, McGraw-Hill, Boston, MA, 2000.

CHAPTER 17

Markov Chains

17.1 DEFINITION OF A MARKOV CHAIN

Let X_t be a random variable that characterizes the state of the system at discrete points in time $t = 1, 2, \ldots$. The family of random variables $\{X_t\}$ forms a **stochastic process** with a finite or infinite number of states.

Example 17.1-1 (Machine Maintenance)

The condition of a machine at the time of the monthly preventive maintenance is fair, good, or excellent. For month t, the stochastic process for this situation can be represented as follows:

$$X_t = \left\{ \begin{array}{l} 0, \text{ if the condition is poor} \\ 1, \text{ if the condition is fair} \\ 2, \text{ if the condition is good} \end{array} \right\}, \ t = 1, 2, \ldots$$

The random variable X_t is *finite* because it represents three states: poor (0), fair (1), and good (2).

Example 17.1-2 (Job Shop)

Jobs arrive randomly at a shop at the rate of 5 jobs per hour. The arrival process follows a Poisson distribution, which, theoretically, allows any number of jobs to arrive at the shop during the time interval $(0, t)$. The infinite-state process describing the number of arriving jobs is $X_t = 0, 1, 2, \ldots, t > 0$.

Markov process. A stochastic process is a Markov process if a future state depends only on the immediately preceding state. This means that given the chronological times $t_0, t_1, \ldots, t_n$, the family of random variables $\{X_{t_n}\} = \{x_1, x_2, \ldots, x_n\}$ is a Markov process if

$$P\{X_{t_n} = x_n | X_{t_{n-1}} = x_{n-1}, \ldots, X_{t_0} = x_0\} = P\{X_{t_n} = x_n | X_{t_{n-1}} = x_{n-1}\}$$

In a Markovian process with n exhaustive and mutually exclusive states, the probabilities at a specific point in time $t = 0, 1, 2, \ldots$ are defined as

$$p_{ij} = P\{X_t = j | X_{t-1} = i\}, i = 1, 2, \ldots, n, j = 1, 2, \ldots, n, t = 0, 1, 2, \ldots, T$$

This is known as the **one-step transition probability** of moving from state i at $t - 1$ to state j at t. By definition, we have

$$\sum_j p_{ij} = 1, i = 1, 2, \ldots, n$$

$$p_{ij} \geq 0, (i, j) = 1, 2, \ldots, n$$

The matrix notation is a convenient way to summarize the one-step transition probabilities:

$$\mathbf{P} = \begin{pmatrix} p_{11} & p_{12} & p_{13} & \cdots & p_{1n} \\ p_{21} & p_{22} & p_{23} & \cdots & p_{2n} \\ \vdots & \vdots & \vdots & \vdots & \vdots \\ p_{n1} & p_{n2} & p_{n3} & \cdots & p_{nn} \end{pmatrix}$$

The matrix $\mathbf{P}$ defines a **Markov chain**. It has the property that all its transition probabilities p_{ij} are stationary and independent over time. Although a Markov chain may include an infinite number of states, the presentation in this chapter is limited to finite chains only, as this is the only type needed in the text.

Example 17.1-3 (The Gardener Problem)

Every year, during the March-through-September growing season, a gardener uses a chemical test to check soil condition. Depending on the outcome of the test, productivity for the new season can be one of three states: (1) good, (2) fair, and (3) poor. Over the years, the gardener has observed that last year's soil condition impacts current year's productivity and that the situation can be described by the following Markov chain:

$$\mathbf{P} = \begin{array}{c} \textit{State of} \\ \textit{the system} \\ \textit{this year} \end{array} \begin{array}{c} 1 \\ 2 \\ 3 \end{array} \begin{pmatrix} .2 & .5 & .3 \\ 0 & .5 & .5 \\ 0 & 0 & 1 \end{pmatrix}$$

State of the system next year

$$\begin{array}{ccc} 1 & 2 & 3 \end{array}$$

The transition probabilities show that the soil condition can either deteriorate or stay the same but never improve. For example, if this year's soil condition is good (state 1), there is a 20%

chance it will not change next year, a 50% chance it will be fair (state 2), and a 30% chance it will deteriorate to a poor condition (state 3). The gardener alters the transition probabilities **P** by using organic fertilizer. In this case, the transition matrix becomes:

$$\mathbf{P}_1 = \begin{array}{c} 1 \\ 2 \\ 3 \end{array} \begin{pmatrix} \overset{1}{.30} & \overset{2}{.60} & \overset{3}{.10} \\ .10 & .60 & .30 \\ .05 & .40 & .55 \end{pmatrix}$$

The use of fertilizer can lead to improvement in soil condition.

PROBLEM SET 17.1A

1. An engineering professor acquires a new computer once every two years. The professor can choose from three models: $M1$, $M2$, and $M3$. If the present model is $M1$, the next computer can be $M2$ with probability .25, or $M3$ with probability .1. If the present model is $M2$, the probabilities of switching to $M1$ and $M3$ are .5 and .15, respectively. And, if the present model is $M3$, then the probabilities of purchasing $M1$ and $M2$ are .7 and .2, respectively. Represent the situation as a Markov chain.

*2. A police car is on patrol in a neighborhood known for its gang activities. During a patrol, there is a 60% chance of responding in time to the location where help is needed, else regular patrol will continue. Upon receiving a call, there is a 10% chance for cancellation (in which case normal patrol is resumed) and a 30% chance that the car is already responding to a previous call. When the police car arrives at the scene, there is a 10% chance that the instigators will have fled (in which case the car returns back to patrol) and a 40% chance that apprehension is made immediately. Else, the officers will search the area. If apprehension occurs, there is a 60% chance of transporting the suspects to the police station, else they are released and the car returns to patrol. Express the probabilistic activities of the police patrol in the form of transition matrix.

3. *Cyert and Associates (1963).* Bank1 offers loans which are either paid when due or are delayed. If the payment on a loan is delayed by more than 4 quarters (1 year), Bank1 considers the loan a bad debt and writes it off. The following table provides a sample of Bank1's past experience with loans.

Loan amount	Quarters late	Payment history
$20,000	0	$2000 paid, $3000 delayed by an extra quarter, $3000 delayed by 2 extra quarters, and the rest delayed by 3 extra quarters.
$50,000	1	$4000 paid, $12,000 delayed by an extra quarter, $6000 delayed by 2 extra quarters, and the rest delayed by 3 extra quarters.
$75,000	2	$7500 paid, $15,000 delayed by an extra quarter, and the rest delayed by 2 extra quarters.
$84,000	3	$42,000 paid, and the rest delayed by an extra quarter.
$200,000	4	$50,000 paid.

Express Bank1's loan situation as a Markov chain.

4. *Pliskin and Tell (1981).* Patients suffering from kidney failure can either get a transplant or undergo periodic dialysis. During any one year, 30% undergo cadaveric transplants, and 10% receive living-donor kidneys. In the year following a transplant, 30% of the

cadaveric transplants and 15% of living-donor recipients go back to dialysis. Death percentages among the two groups are 20% and 10%, respectively. Of those in the dialysis pool, 10% die, and of those who survive more than one year after a transplant, 5% die and 5% go back to dialysis. Represent the situation as a Markov chain.

17.2 ABSOLUTE AND n-STEP TRANSITION PROBABILITIES

Given the transition matrix $\mathbf{P}$ of a Markov chain and the initial probabilities vector $\mathbf{a}^{(0)} = \{a_j^{(0)}, j = 1, 2, \ldots, n\}$, the absolute probabilities $\mathbf{a}^{(n)} = \{a_j^{(n)}, j = 1, 2, \ldots, n\}$ after $n (> 0)$ transitions are computed as follows:

$$\mathbf{a}^{(1)} = \mathbf{a}^{(0)}\mathbf{P}$$

$$\mathbf{a}^{(2)} = \mathbf{a}^{(1)}\mathbf{P} = \mathbf{a}^{(0)}\mathbf{P}\mathbf{P} = \mathbf{a}^{(0)}\mathbf{P}^2$$

$$\mathbf{a}^{(3)} = \mathbf{a}^{(2)}\mathbf{P} = \mathbf{a}^{(0)}\mathbf{P}^2\mathbf{P} = \mathbf{a}^{(0)}\mathbf{P}^3$$

$$\vdots$$

$$\mathbf{a}^{(n)} = \mathbf{a}^{(0)}\mathbf{P}^n$$

The matrix $\mathbf{P}^n$ is known as the **n-step transition matrix**. From these calculations, we can see that

$$\mathbf{P}^n = \mathbf{P}^{n-1}\mathbf{P}$$

and

$$\mathbf{P}^n = \mathbf{P}^{n-m}\mathbf{P}^m, 0 < m < n$$

These are known as **Chapman-Kolomogorov** equations.

Example 17.2-1

The following transition matrix applies to the gardener problem with fertilizer (Example 17.1-3):

$$\mathbf{P} = \begin{matrix} 1 \\ 2 \\ 3 \end{matrix} \begin{pmatrix} .30 & .60 & .10 \\ .10 & .60 & .30 \\ .05 & .40 & .55 \end{pmatrix}$$

The initial condition of the soil is good—that is $\mathbf{a}^{(0)} = (1, 0, 0)$. Determine the absolute probabilities of the three states of the system after 1, 8, and 16 gardening seasons.

$$\mathbf{P}^8 = \begin{pmatrix} .30 & .60 & .10 \\ .10 & .60 & .30 \\ .05 & .40 & .55 \end{pmatrix}^8 = \begin{pmatrix} .101753 & .525514 & .372733 \\ .101702 & .525435 & .372863 \\ .101669 & .525384 & .372863 \end{pmatrix}$$

$$\mathbf{P}^{16} = \begin{pmatrix} .30 & .60 & .10 \\ .10 & .60 & .30 \\ .05 & .40 & .55 \end{pmatrix}^{16} = \begin{pmatrix} .101659 & .52454 & .372881 \\ .101659 & .52454 & .372881 \\ .101659 & .52454 & .372881 \end{pmatrix}$$

Thus, the required absolute probabilities are computed as

$$\mathbf{a}^{(1)} = (1 \quad 0 \quad 0) \begin{pmatrix} .30 & .60 & .10 \\ .10 & .60 & .30 \\ .05 & .40 & .55 \end{pmatrix} = (.30 \quad .60 \quad .1)$$

$$\mathbf{a}^{(8)} = (1 \quad 0 \quad 0) \begin{pmatrix} .101753 & .525514 & .372733 \\ .101702 & .525435 & .372863 \\ .101669 & .525384 & .372863 \end{pmatrix} = (.101753 \quad .525514 \quad .372733)$$

$$\mathbf{a}^{(16)} = (1 \quad 0 \quad 0) \begin{pmatrix} .101659 & .52454 & .372881 \\ .101659 & .52454 & .372881 \\ .101659 & .52454 & .372881 \end{pmatrix} = (.101659 \quad .52454 \quad .372881)$$

The rows of $\mathbf{P}^8$ and the vector of absolute probabilities $\mathbf{a}^{(8)}$ are almost identical. The result is more evident for $\mathbf{P}^{16}$. It demonstrates that, as the number of transitions increases, the absolute probabilities become independent of the initial $\mathbf{a}^{(0)}$. The resulting probabilities are known as the **steady-state probabilities**.

Remarks. The computations associated with Markov chains are tedious. Template *excelMarkovChains.xls* provides a general easy-to-use spreadsheet for carrying out these calculations (see *Excel moment* following Example 17.4-1).

PROBLEM SET 17.2A

1. Consider Problem 1, Set 17.1A. Determine the probability that the professor will purchase the current model in 4 years.

*2. Consider Problem 2, Set 17.1A. If the police car is currently at a call scene, determine the probability that an apprehension will take place in two patrols.

3. Consider Problem 3, Set 17.1A. Suppose that Bank1 currently has $1,000,000 worth of outstanding loans. Of these, $300,000 have just been paid, $150,000 are one quarter late, $250,000 are two quarters late, $200,000 are three quarters late, and the rest are over four quarters late. What would the picture of these loans be like after two cycles of loans?

4. Consider Problem 4, Set 17.1A.

   (a) For a patient who is currently on dialysis, what is the probability of receiving a transplant in two years?

   (b) For a patient who is currently a more-than-one-year survivor, what is the probability of surviving four more years?

5. A die-rolling game uses a 4-square grid. The squares are designated clockwise as $A, B, C,$ and D with monetary rewards of $4, $-$2, $-$6, and $9, respectively. Starting at square A, roll the die to determine the next square to move to in a clockwise direction. For example, if the die shows 2, we move to square C. The game is repeated using the last square as a starting point.

   (a) Express the problem as a Markov chain.

   (b) Determine the expected gain or loss after the die is rolled 5 time.

17.3   CLASSIFICATION OF THE STATES IN A MARKOV CHAIN

The states of a Markov chain can be classified based on the transition probability p_{ij} of **P**.

1. A state j is **absorbing** if it is certain to return to itself in one transition—that is $p_{jj} = 1$.
2. A state j is **transient** if it can reach another state but cannot be reached back from another state. Mathematically, this will happen if $\lim_{n \to \infty} p_{ij}^{(n)} = 0$, for all i.
3. A state j is **recurrent** if the probability of being revisited from other states is 1. This can happen if, and only if, the state is not transient.
4. A state j is **periodic** with period $t > 1$ if a return is possible only in $t, 2t, 3t, \ldots$ steps. This means that $p_{jj}^{(n)} = 0$ when n is not divisible by t.

Based on the given definitions, a *finite* Markov chain cannot consist of all-transient states because, by definition, the transient property requires entering other "trapping" states and never revisiting the transient state. The "trapping" state need not be a single absorbing state. For example, consider the chain

$$\mathbf{P} = \begin{pmatrix} 0 & 1 & 0 & 0 \\ 0 & 0 & 1 & 0 \\ 0 & 0 & .3 & .7 \\ 0 & 0 & .4 & .6 \end{pmatrix}$$

States 1 and 2 are transient because they cannot be reentered once the system is "trapped" in states 3 and 4. States 3 and 4, in a way playing the role of an absorbing state, constitute a **closed set**. By definition, all the states of a *closed set* must **communicate**, which means that it is possible to go from any state to every other state in the set in one or more transitions—that is, $p_{ij}^{(n)} > 0$ for all $i \neq j$ and $n \geq 1$. Notice that each of states 3 and 4 can be absorbing if $p_{33} = p_{44} = 1$. In such a case, each state forms a closed set.

A *closed* Markov chain is said to be **ergodic** if all its states are *recurrent* and **aperiodic** (not periodic). In this case, the absolute probabilities after n transitions, $\mathbf{a}^{(n)} = \mathbf{a}^{(0)}\mathbf{P}^n$, always converge uniquely to a limiting (steady-state) distribution that is independent of the initial probabilities $\mathbf{a}^{(0)}$, as will be shown in Section 17.4.

Example 17.3-1   (Absorbing and Transient States)

Consider the gardener Markov chain with no fertilizer:

$$\mathbf{P} = \begin{pmatrix} .2 & .5 & .3 \\ 0 & .5 & .5 \\ 0 & 0 & 0 \end{pmatrix}$$

States 1 and 2 are transient because they reach state 3 but can never be reached back. State 3 is absorbing because $p_{33} = 1$. These classifications can also be seen when $\lim_{n \to \infty} p_{ij}^{(n)} = 0$ is computed. For example, consider

$$\mathbf{P}^{100} = \begin{pmatrix} 0 & 0 & 1 \\ 0 & 0 & 1 \\ 0 & 0 & 1 \end{pmatrix}$$

The result shows that, in the long run, the probability of reentering transient state 1 or 2 is zero, and the probability of being "trapped" in absorbing state 3 is certain.

Example 17.3-2   (Periodic States)

We can test the periodicity of a state by computing $\mathbf{P}^n$ and observing the values of $p_{ii}^{(n)}$ for $n = 2, 3, 4, \ldots$. These values will be positive only at the corresponding period of the state. For example, consider

$$\mathbf{P} = \begin{pmatrix} 0 & .6 & .4 \\ 0 & 1 & 0 \\ .6 & .4 & 0 \end{pmatrix} \quad \mathbf{P}^2 = \begin{pmatrix} .24 & .76 & 0 \\ 0 & 1 & 0 \\ 0 & .76 & .24 \end{pmatrix}, \quad \mathbf{P}^3 = \begin{pmatrix} 0 & .904 & .0960 \\ 0 & 1 & 0 \\ .144 & .856 & 0 \end{pmatrix}$$

$$\mathbf{P}^4 = \begin{pmatrix} .0567 & .9424 & 0 \\ 0 & 1 & 0 \\ 0 & .9424 & .0576 \end{pmatrix}, \quad \mathbf{P}^5 = \begin{pmatrix} 0 & .97696 & .02304 \\ 0 & 1 & 0 \\ .03456 & .96544 & 0 \end{pmatrix}$$

The results show that p_{11} and p_{33} are positive for even values of n and zero otherwise (you can confirm this observation by computing $\mathbf{P}^n$ for $n > 5$). This means that each of states 1 and 3 has period $t = 2$.

PROBLEM SET 17.3A

1. Classify the states of the following Markov chains. If a state is periodic, determine its period:

*(a) $\begin{pmatrix} 0 & 1 & 0 \\ 0 & 0 & 1 \\ 1 & 0 & 0 \end{pmatrix}$

*(b) $\begin{pmatrix} \frac{1}{2} & \frac{1}{4} & \frac{1}{4} & 0 \\ 0 & 0 & 1 & 0 \\ \frac{1}{3} & 0 & \frac{1}{3} & \frac{1}{3} \\ 0 & 0 & 0 & 1 \end{pmatrix}$

(c) $\begin{pmatrix} 0 & 1 & 0 & 0 & 0 & 0 \\ 0 & .5 & .5 & 0 & 0 & 0 \\ 0 & .7 & .3 & 0 & 0 & 0 \\ 0 & 0 & 0 & 1 & 0 & 0 \\ 0 & 0 & 0 & 0 & .4 & .6 \\ 0 & 0 & 0 & 0 & .2 & 8 \end{pmatrix}$

(d) $\begin{pmatrix} .1 & 0 & .9 \\ .7 & .3 & 0 \\ .2 & .7 & .1 \end{pmatrix}$

2. A game involves four balls and two urns. A ball in either urn has a 50:50 chance of being transferred to the other urn. Represent the game as a Markov chain, and show that its states are periodic with period $t = 2$.

3. A museum has six rooms of equal sizes arranged in the form of a grid with three rows and two columns. Each interior wall has a door that connects adjacent rooms. Museum guards move about the rooms through the interior doors. Represent the movements of each guard in the museum as a Markov chain, and show that its states are periodic with period $t = 2$.

17.4   STEADY-STATE PROBABILITIES AND MEAN RETURN TIMES OF ERGODIC CHAINS

In an ergodic Markov chain, the steady-state probabilities are defined as

$$\pi_j = \lim_{n \to \infty} a_j^{(n)}, \quad j = 0, 1, 2, \dots$$

These probabilities, which are independent of $\{a_j^{(0)}\}$, can be determined from the equations

$$\boldsymbol{\pi} = \boldsymbol{\pi}\mathbf{P}$$

$$\sum_j \pi_j = 1$$

(One of the equations in $\boldsymbol{\pi} = \boldsymbol{\pi}\mathbf{P}$ is redundant.) What $\boldsymbol{\pi} = \boldsymbol{\pi}\mathbf{P}$ says is that the probabilities $\boldsymbol{\pi}$ remain unchanged after an additional transition, and for this reason, they represent the steady-state distribution.

A direct by-product of the steady-state probabilities is the determination of the expected number of transitions before the system returns to a state j for the first time. This is known as the **mean first return time** or the **mean recurrence time**, and it is computed in an n-state Markov chain as

$$\mu_{jj} = \frac{1}{\pi_j}, j = 1, 2, \dots, n$$

Example 17.4-1

To determine the steady-state probability distribution of the gardener problem with fertilizer (Example 17.1-3), we have

$$(\pi_1 \ \pi_2 \ \pi_3) = (\pi_1 \ \pi_2 \ \pi_3) \begin{pmatrix} .3 & .6 & .1 \\ .1 & .6 & .3 \\ .05 & .4 & .55 \end{pmatrix}$$

Or,

$$\pi_1 = .3\pi_1 + .1\pi_2 + .05\pi_3$$

$$\pi_2 = .6\pi_1 + .6\pi_2 + .4\pi_3$$

$$\pi_3 = .1\pi_1 + .3\pi_2 + .55\pi_3$$

$$\pi_1 + \pi_2 + \pi_3 = 1$$

(Any one of the first three equations is redundant). The solution is $\pi_1 = 0.1017$, $\pi_2 = 0.5254$, and $\pi_3 = 0.3729$—meaning that in the long run the soil condition will be good 10% of the time, fair 52% of the time, and poor 37% of the time.

The mean first return times are computed as

$$\mu_{11} = \frac{1}{.1017} = 9.83, \; \mu_{22} = \frac{1}{.5254} = 1.9, \; \mu_{33} = \frac{1}{.3729} = 2.68$$

This means that, on the average, it will take approximately 10 gardening seasons for the soil to return to a *good* state, 2 seasons to return to a *fair* state, and 3 seasons to return to a *poor* state. These results point to a less promising outlook for the soil condition under the proposed use of fertilizers. A more aggressive program should improve the picture. For example, consider the following transition matrix in which the probabilities of moving to a good state are higher than in the previous matrix:

$$P = \begin{pmatrix} .35 & .6 & .05 \\ .3 & .6 & .1 \\ .25 & .4 & .35 \end{pmatrix}$$

In this case, $\pi_1 = 0.31$, $\pi_2 = 0.58$, and $\pi_3 = 0.11$, which yields $\mu_{11} = 3.2$, $\mu_{22} = 1.7$, and $\mu_{33} = 8.9$, a reversal of the bleak outlook given previously.

Excel Moment

Figure 17.1 applies the general Excel template *excelMarkovChains.xls* to the gardener example. The template computes n-step, absolute, and steady-state probabilities, and mean return time for any Markov chain. The steps are self-explanatory. In step 2a, you may override the default state codes $(1, 2, 3, \dots)$ by a code of your choice, then click the button located in cell L2. The new codes will automatically transfer throughout the spreadsheet when you execute step 4.

FIGURE 17.1

Excel spreadsheet for Markov chain computations (file *excelMarkovChains.xls*)

	A	B	C	D	E	F	G	H
1				Markov	Chains			
2	Step 1:	Number of states =		3	Step 2a:	Initial probabilities:		
3	Step 2:					Codes:	1	2	3
4		Click to enter Markov chain					1	0	0
5	Step 3:	Number of transitions=		8	Step 2b:	Input Markov chain:		
6	Step 4:						1	2	3
7		Click to execute				1	0.3	0.6	0.1
8		Output Results				2	0.1	0.6	0.3
9		Absolute	Steady	Mean return		3	0.05	0.4	0.55
10	state	(8-step)	state	time		Output (8-step) transition matrix		
11	1	0.10175	0.101695	9.8333254			1	2	3
12	2	0.52551	0.525424	1.9032248		1	0.10175	0.525514	0.372733
13	3	0.37273	0.372882	2.6818168		2	0.1017	0.525435	0.372864
14						3	0.10167	0.525384	0.372947

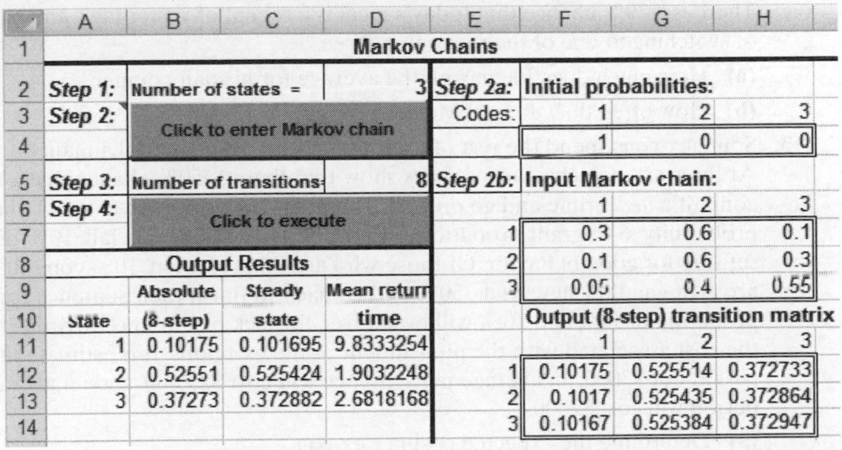

Example 17.4-2   (Cost Model)

Consider the gardener problem with fertilizer (Example 17.1-3). The garden needs two bags of fertilizer if the soil is good. The amount is increased by 25% if the soil is fair and 60% if the soil is poor. The cost of the fertilizer is $50 per bag. The gardener estimates an annual yield of $250 if no fertilizer is used and $420 if fertilizer is applied. Is it economical to use fertilizer?

Using the steady-state probabilities in Example 17.4-1, we get

$$\text{Expected annual cost of fertilizer} = 2 \times \$50 \times \pi_1 + (1.25 \times 2) \times \$50 \times \pi_2$$
$$+ (1.60 \times 2) \times \$50 \times \pi_3$$
$$= 100 \times .1017 + 125 \times .5254 + 160 \times .3729$$
$$= \$135.51$$

Differential increase in the annual value of the yield = $420 - $250 = $170
The use of fertilizer is recommended.

PROBLEM SET 17.4A

*1. On a sunny day, MiniGolf can gross $2000 in revenues. If the day is cloudy, revenues drop by 20%. A rainy day will reduce revenues by 80%. If today's weather is sunny, there is an 80% chance it will remain sunny tomorrow with no chance of rain. If it is cloudy, there is a 20% chance that tomorrow will be rainy and 30% chance it will be sunny. Rain will continue through the next day with a probability of .8, but there is a 10% chance it may be sunny.

   (a) Determine the expected daily revenues for MiniGolf.

   (b) Determine the average number of days the weather will not be sunny.

2. Joe loves to eat out in area restaurants. His favorite foods are Mexican, Italian, Chinese, and Thai. On the average, Joe pays $12.00 for a Mexican meal, $17.00 for an Italian meal, $11.00 for a Chinese meal, and $13.00 for a Thai meal. Joe's eating habits are predictable: There is a 70% chance that today's meal is a repeat of yesterday's and equal probabilities of switching to one of the remaining three.

   (a) How much does Joe pay on the average for his daily dinner?

   (b) How often does Joe eat Mexican food?

3. Some ex-cons spend the rest of their lives either free, on trial, in jail, or on probation. At the start of each year, statistics show that there is 50% chance that a free ex-con will commit a new crime and go on trial. The judge may send the ex-con to jail with probability .6 or grant probation with probability .4. Once in jail, 10% of ex-cons will be set free for good behavior. Of those who are on probation, 10% commit new crimes and are arraigned for new trials, 50% will go back to finish their sentence for violating probation orders, and 10% will be set free for lack of evidence. Taxpayers underwrite the cost associated with the punishment of the ex-felons. It is estimated that a trial will cost about $8000, an average jail sentence will cost $25,000, and an average probation period will cost $2000.

   (a) Determine the expected cost per ex-con.

   (b) How often does an ex-con return to jail? Go on trial? Be set free?

4. A store sells a special item whose daily demand can be described by the following pdf:

Daily demand, D	0	1	2	3
$P\{D\}$	.1	.3	.4	.2

The store is comparing two ordering policies: (1) Order up to 3 units every 3 days if the stock level is less than 2, else do not order. (2) Order 3 units every 3 days if the stock level is zero, else do not order. The fixed ordering cost per shipment is $300, and the cost of holding excess units per unit per day is $3. Immediate delivery is expected.

  (a) Which policy should the store adopt to minimize the total expected daily cost of ordering and holding?

  (b) For the two policies, compare the average number of days between successive inventory depletions.

*5. There are three categories of income tax filers in the United States: those who never evade taxes, those who sometimes do it, and those who always do it. An examination of audited tax returns from one year to the next shows that of those who did not evade taxes last year, 95% continue in the same category this year, 4% move to the "sometimes" category, and the remainder move to the "always" category. For those who sometimes evade taxes, 6% move to "never," 90% stay the same, and 4% move to "always." As for the "always" evaders, the respective percentages are 0%, 10%, and 90%.

  (a) Express the problem as a Markov chain.

  (b) In the long run, what would be the percentages of "never," "sometimes," and "always" tax categories?

  (c) Statistics show that a taxpayer in the "sometimes" category evades taxes on about $5000 per return and in the "always" category on about $12,000. Assuming that the taxpayer population is 70 millions and that the average income tax rate is 12%, determine the annual reduction in collected taxes due to evasion.

6. Warehouzer owns a renewable forest land for growing pine trees. Trees can fall into one of four categories depending on their age: baby (0–5 years), young (5–10 years), mature (11–15 years), and old (more than 15 years). Ten percent of baby and young trees die before reaching the next age group. For mature and old trees, 50% are harvested and only 5% die. Because of the renewal nature of the operation, all harvested and dead trees are replaced with new (baby) trees by the end of the next 5-year cycle.

  (a) Express the forest dynamics as a Markov chain.

  (b) If the forest land can hold a total of 1,000,000 trees, determine the long-run composition of the forest.

  (c) If a new tree is planted at the cost of $1.50 per tree and a harvested tree has a market value of $25, determine the average annual income from the forest operation.

7. Population dynamics is impacted by the continual movement of people who are seeking better quality of life or better employment. The city of Mobile has an inner city population, a suburban population, and a surrounding rural population. The census taken in 10-year intervals shows that 10% of the rural population move to the suburbs and 5% to the inner city. For the suburban population, 30% move to rural areas and 15% to the inner city. Inner-city population would not move into suburbs, but 20% of them move to the quiet rural life.

  (a) Express the population dynamics as a Markov chain.

  (b) If the greater Mobile area currently includes 20,000 rural residents, 100,000 suburbanites, and 30,000 inner-city inhabitants, what will the population distribution be in 10 years? In 20 years?

  (c) Determine the long-run population picture of Mobile.

8. A car rental agency has offices in Phoenix, Denver, Chicago, and Atlanta. The agency allows one- and two-way rentals so that cars rented in one location may end up in another. Statistics show that at the end of each week 70% of all rentals are two-way. As for the one-way rentals: From Phoenix, 20% go to Denver, 60% to Chicago, and the rest goes to Atlanta; from Denver, 40% go to Atlanta and 60% to Chicago; from Chicago, 50% go to Atlanta and the rest to Denver; and from Atlanta, 80% go to Chicago, 10% to Denver, and 10% to Phoenix.

   (a) Express the situation as a Markov chain.

   (b) If the agency starts the week with 100 cars in each location, what will the distribution be like in two weeks?

   (c) If each location is designed to handle a maximum of 110 cars, would there be a long-run space availability problem in any of the locations?

   (d) Determine the average number of weeks that elapse before a car is returned to its originating location.

9. A bookstore restocks a popular book to a level of 100 copies at the start of each day. The data for the last 30 days provide the following end-of-day inventory position: 1, 2, 0, 3, 2, 1, 0, 0, 3, 0, 1, 1, 3, 2, 3, 3, 2, 1, 0, 2, 0, 1, 3, 0, 0, 3, 2, 1, 2, 2.

   (a) Represent the daily inventory as a Markov chain.

   (b) Determine the steady-state probability that the bookstore will run out of books in any one day.

   (c) Determine the expected daily inventory.

   (d) Determine the average number of days between successive zero inventories.

10. In Problem 9, suppose that the daily demand can exceed supply, which gives rise to shortage (negative inventory). The end-of-day inventory level for the past 30 days is given as: 1, 2, 0, −2, 2, 2, −1, −1, 3, 0, 0, 1, −1, −2, 3, 3, −2, −1, 0, 2, 0, −1, 3, 0, 0, 3, −1, 1, 2, −2.

    (a) Express the situation as a Markov chain.

    (b) Determine the long-term probability of a surplus inventory in a day.

    (c) Determine the long-term probability of a shortage inventory in a day.

    (d) Determine the long-term probability that the daily supply meets the daily demand exactly.

    (e) If the holding cost per (end-of-day) surplus book is $15 per day and the penalty cost per shortage book is $4.00 per day, determine the expected inventory cost per day.

11. A store starts a week with at least 3 PCs. The demand per week is estimated at 0 with probability .15, 1 with probability .2, 2 with probability .35, 3 with probability .25, and 4 with probability .05. Unfilled demand is backlogged. The store's policy is to place an order for delivery at the start of the following week whenever the inventory level drops below 3 PCs. The new replenishment always brings the stock back to 5 PCs.

    (a) Express the situation as a Markov chain.

    (b) Suppose that the week starts with 4 PCs. Determine the probability that an order will be placed at the end of two weeks.

    (c) Determine the long-run probability that no order will be placed in any week.

    (d) If the fixed cost of placing an order is $200, the holding cost per PC per week is $5, and the penalty cost per shortage PC per week is $20, determine the expected inventory cost per week.

12. Solve Problem 11 assuming that the order size, when placed, is exactly 5 pieces.

13. In Problem 12, suppose that the demand for the PCs is 0, 1, 2, 3, 4, or 5 with equal probabilities. Further assume that the unfilled demand is not backlogged, but that the penalty cost is still incurred.

    (a) Express the situation as a Markov chain.

    (b) Determine the long-run probability that a shortage will take place.

    (c) If the fixed cost of placing an order is $200, the holding cost per PC per week is $5, and the penalty cost per shortage PC per week is $20, determine the expected ordering and inventory cost per week.

14. The federal government tries to boost small business activities by awarding annual grants for projects. All bids are competitive, but the chance of receiving a grant is highest if the owner has not received any during the last three years and lowest if awards were given in each of the last three years. Specifically, the probability of getting a grant if none were awarded in the last three years is .9. It decreases to .8 if one grant was awarded, .7 if two grants were awarded, and only .5 if 3 were received.

    (a) Express the situation as a Markov chain.

    (b) Determine the expected number of awards per owner per year.

15. Jim Bob has a history of receiving many fines for driving violations. Unfortunately for Jim Bob, modern technology can keep track of his previous fines. As soon as he has accumulated 4 tickets, his driving license is revoked until he completes a new driver education class, in which case he starts with a clean slate. Jim Bob is most reckless immediately after completing the driver education class and he is invariably stopped by the police with a 50-50 chance of being fined. After each new fine, he tries to be more careful, which reduces the probability of a fine by .1.

    (a) Express Jim Bob's problem as Markov chain.

    (b) What is the average number of times Jim Bob is stopped by police before his license is revoked again?

    (c) What is the probability that Jim Bob will lose his license?

    (d) If each fine costs $100, how much, on the average, does Jim Bob pay between successive suspensions of his license?

16. The daily weather in Fayettville, Arkansas, can be cloudy (C), sunny (S), rainy (R), or windy (W). Records over the past 90 days are CCSWRRWSSCCCRCSSWRCRRRR CWSSWRWWRCRRRRCWSSWRWCCSWRRWSSCCCRCSSWSSWRWWRCR RRRCWSSWRWCCSWRRWSSS. Based on these records, use a Markov chain to determine the probability that a typical day in Fayetteville will be cloudy, sunny, rainy, or windy.

17.5   FIRST PASSAGE TIME

In Section 17.4, we used the steady-state probabilities to compute μ_{jj}, the *mean first return time* for state j. In this section, we are concerned with the **mean first passage time** μ_{ij}, defined as the expected number of transitions to reach state j from state i for the first time. The calculations are rooted in the determination of the probability of *at least* one passage from state i to state j, defined as $f_{ij} = \sum_{n=1}^{\infty} f_{ij}^{(n)}$, where $f_{ij}^{(n)}$ is the probability of a first passage from state i to state j in n transitions. An expression for $f_{ij}^{(n)}$ can be determined recursively from

$$p_{ij}^{(n)} = f_{ij}^{(n)} + \sum_{k=1}^{n-1} f_{ij}^{(k)} p_{ij}^{(n-k)}, \quad n = 1, 2, \ldots$$

The transition matrix $\mathbf{P} = \|p_{ij}\|$ is assumed to have m states.

1. If $f_{ij} < 1$, it is not certain that the system will ever pass from state i to state j and $\mu_{ij} = \infty$.
2. If $f_{ij} = 1$, the Markov chain is ergodic, and the *mean first passage time* from state i to state j is computed as

$$\mu_{ij} = \sum_{n=1}^{\infty} n f_{ij}^{(n)}$$

A simpler way to determine the mean first passage time for all the states in an m-transition matrix, $\mathbf{P}$, is to use the following matrix-based formula:

$$\|\mu_{ij}\| = (\mathbf{I} - \mathbf{N}_j)^{-1}\mathbf{1}, j \neq i$$

where

$\mathbf{I} = (m-1)$-identity matrix
$\mathbf{N}_j$ = transition matrix $\mathbf{P}$ less its jth row and jth column of target state j
$\mathbf{1} = (m-1)$ column vector with all elements equal to 1

The matrix operation $(\mathbf{I} - \mathbf{N}_j)^{-1}\mathbf{1}$ essentially sums the columns of $(\mathbf{I} - \mathbf{N}_j)^{-1}$.

Example 17.5-1

Consider the gardener Markov chain with fertilizers once again.

$$\mathbf{P} = \begin{pmatrix} .30 & .60 & .10 \\ .10 & .60 & .30 \\ .05 & .40 & .55 \end{pmatrix}$$

To demonstrate the computation of the first passage time to a specific state from all others, consider the passage from states 2 and 3 (fair and poor) to state 1 (good). Thus, $j = 1$ and

$$\mathbf{N}_1 = \begin{pmatrix} .60 & .30 \\ .40 & .55 \end{pmatrix}, (\mathbf{I} - \mathbf{N}_1)^{-1} = \begin{pmatrix} .4 & -.3 \\ -.4 & .45 \end{pmatrix}^{-1} = \begin{pmatrix} 7.50 & 5.00 \\ 6.67 & 6.67 \end{pmatrix}$$

Thus,

$$\begin{pmatrix} \mu_{21} \\ \mu_{31} \end{pmatrix} = \begin{pmatrix} 7.50 & 5.00 \\ 6.67 & 6.67 \end{pmatrix}\begin{pmatrix} 1 \\ 1 \end{pmatrix} = \begin{pmatrix} 12.50 \\ 13.34 \end{pmatrix}$$

Thus, on the average, it will take 12.5 seasons to pass from fair to good soil, and 13.34 seasons to go from bad to good soil.

Similar calculations can be carried out to obtain μ_{12} and μ_{32} from $(\mathbf{I} - \mathbf{N}_2)$ and μ_{13} and μ_{23} from $(\mathbf{I} - \mathbf{N}_3)$, as shown below.

Excel Moment

Excel template *excelFirstPassTime.xls* can be used to carry out the calculations of the mean first passage times. Figure 17.2 shows the calculations associated with Example 17.5-1. Step 2 of the spreadsheet automatically initializes the transition matrix $\mathbf{P}$ to zero values per the size given in

	A	B	C	D	E	F	G	H
1	First Passage Times in Ergodic and Absorbing Markov Chains							
2	Step 1:	Number of states =		3	Step 2a:			
4	Step 2:	Click to enter Markov chain, P			Step 3:	Click to compute i- P		
5		Matrix P:						
6	Codes	1	2	3				
7	1	0.3	0.6	0.1				
8	2	0.1	0.6	0.3				
9	3	0.05	0.4	0.55				
10		Matrix I-P:						
11		1	2	3				
12	1	0.7	-0.6	-0.1				
13	2	-0.1	0.4	-0.3				
14	3	-0.05	-0.4	0.45				
15	Step 4: Perform first passage time calculations below:							
16		I-N			inv(I-N)			Mu
17	i=1	2	3		2	3		1
18	2	0.4	-0.3		7.5	5		12.5
19	3	-0.4	0.45		6.666667	6.6666667		13.33333
20								
21	i=2	1	3		1	3		2
22		0.7	-0.1	1	1.451613	0.3225806		1.774194
23		-0.05	0.45	3	0.16129	2.2580645		2.419355
24								
25	i=3	1	2		1	2		3
26	1	0.7	-0.6	1	1.818182	2.7272727		4.545455
27	2	-0.1	0.4	2	0.454545	3.1818182		3.636364

FIGURE 17.2

Excel spreadsheet calculations of first passage time of Example 17.5-1 (file *excelFirstPassTime.xls*)

step 1. In step 2a, you may override the default state codes in row 6 with a code of your choice. The code is then transferred automatically throughout the spreadsheet. After you enter the transition probabilities, step 3 creates the matrix $I - P$. Step 4 is carried out entirely by you using $I - P$ as the source for creating $I - N_j (j = 1, 2,$ and $3)$. You can do so by copying the entire $I - P$ and its state codes and pasting it in the target location and then using appropriate Excel Cut and Paste operations to rid $I - P$ of row j and column j. For example, to create $I - N_2$, first copy $I - P$ and its state codes to the selected target location. Next, highlight column 3 of the copied matrix, cut it, and paste it in column 2, thus eliminating column 2. Similarly, highlight row 3 of the resulting matrix, cut it, and then paste it in row 2, thus eliminating row 2. The created $I - N_2$ automatically carries its correct state code.

Once $I - N_j$ is created, the inverse, $(I - N_j)^{-1}$, is computed in the target location. The associated operations are demonstrated by inverting $(I - N_1)$ in Figure 17.2:

1. Enter the formula = MINVERSE(B18:C19) in E18.
2. Highlight E18:F19, the area where the inverse will reside.
3. Press F2.
4. Press CTRL + SHIFT + ENTER.

The values of the first passage times from states 2 and 3 to state 1 are then computed by summing the rows of the inverse—that is, by entering = SUM(E18:F18) in H18 and then copying H18 into H19. After creating $\mathbf{I} - \mathbf{N}$ for $i = 2$ and $i = 3$, the remaining calculations are automated by copying E18:F19 into E22:F23 and E26:F27, and copying H18:H19 into H22:H23 and H26:H27.

PROBLEM SET 17.5A

*1. A mouse maze consists of the paths shown in Figure 17.3. Intersection 1 is the maze entrance, and intersection 5 is the exit. At any intersection, the mouse has equal probabilities of selecting any of the available paths. When the mouse reaches intersection 5, the experiment is repeated by reentering the maze at intersection 1.

   (a) Express the maze as a Markov chain.

   (b) Determine the probability that, starting at intersection 1, the mouse will reach the exit after three trials.

   (c) Determine the long-run probability that the mouse will locate the exit intersection.

   (d) Determine the average number of trials needed to reach the exit point from intersection 1.

2. In Problem 1, intuitively, if more options (routes) are added to the maze, will the average number of trials needed to reach the exit point increase or decrease? Demonstrate the answer by adding a route between intersections 3 and 4.

3. Jim and Joe start a game with five tokens, three for Jim and two for Joe. A coin is tossed, and if the outcome is heads, Jim gives Joe a token, else Jim gets a token from Joe. The game ends when Jim or Joe has all the tokens. At this point, there is 30% chance that Jim and Joe will continue to play the game, again starting with three tokens for Jim and two for Joe.

   (a) Represent the game as a Markov chain.

   (b) Determine the probability that Joe will win in three coin tosses. That Jim will win in three coin tosses.

   (c) Determine the probability that a game will end in Jim's favor. Joe's favor.

   (d) Determine the average number of coin tosses needed before Jim wins. Joe wins.

4. An amateur gardener with training in botany is tinkering with cross-pollinating pink irises with red, orange, and white irises. Annual experiments show that pink can produce 60% pink and 40% white; red can produce 40% red, 50% pink, and 10% orange; orange can produce 25% orange, 50% pink, and 25% white; and white can produce 50% pink and 50% white.

   (a) Express the gardener situation as a Markov chain.

   (b) If the gardener started the cross-pollination with equal numbers of each type of iris, what would the distribution be like after 5 years? In the long run?

   (c) How many years on the average would a red iris take to produce a white bloom?

FIGURE 17.3

Mouse maze for Problem 1, Set 17.5A

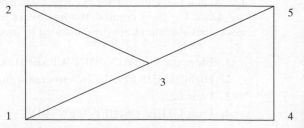

*5. Customers tend to exhibit loyalty to product brands but may be persuaded through clever marketing and advertising to switch brands. Consider the case of three brands: A, B, and C. Customer "unyielding" loyalty to a given brand is estimated at 75%, giving the competitors only a 25% margin to realize a switch. Competitors launch their advertising campaigns once a year. For brand A customers, the probabilities of switching to brands B and C are .1 and .15, respectively. Customers of brand B are likely to switch to A and C with probabilities .2 and .05, respectively. Brand C customers can switch to brands A and B with equal probabilities.

(a) Express the situation as a Markov chain.

(b) In the long run, how much market share will each brand command?

(c) How long on the average will it take for a brand A customer to switch to brand B? To brand C?

17.6 ANALYSIS OF ABSORBING STATES

In the gardener problem, without fertilizer the transition matrix is given as

$$P = \begin{pmatrix} .2 & .5 & .3 \\ 0 & .5 & .5 \\ 0 & 0 & 1 \end{pmatrix}$$

States 1 and 2 (good and fair soil conditions) are *transient*, and State 3 (poor soil condition) is *absorbing*, because once in that state the system will remain there indefinitely. A Markov chain may have more than one absorbing state. For example, an employee may remain employed with the same company until full retirement or may quit early (two absorbing states). In these types of chains, we are interested in determining the probability of reaching absorption and the expected number of transitions to absorption, given that the system starts in a specific transient state. For example, in the gardener Markov chain given above, if the soil is currently good, we will be interested in determining the average number of gardening seasons till the soil becomes poor and also the probability associated with this transition.

The analysis of Markov chains with absorbing states can be carried out conveniently using matrices. First, the Markov chain is partitioned in the following manner:

$$P = \left(\begin{array}{c|c} N & A \\ \hline 0 & 1 \end{array} \right)$$

The arrangement requires all the absorbing states to occupy the southeast corner of the new matrix. For example, consider the following transition matrix:

$$P = \begin{array}{c} \\ 1 \\ 2 \\ 3 \\ 4 \end{array} \begin{array}{cccc} 1 & 2 & 3 & 4 \\ \begin{pmatrix} .2 & .3 & .4 & .1 \\ 0 & 1 & 0 & 0 \\ .5 & .3 & 0 & .2 \\ 0 & 0 & 0 & 1 \end{pmatrix} \end{array}$$

The matrix **P** can be rearranged and partitioned as

$$
\mathbf{P^*} = \begin{array}{c} \\ 1 \\ 3 \\ 2 \\ 4 \end{array}
\begin{array}{cc} \begin{matrix} 1 & \;\; 3 & \;\; 2 & \;\; 4 \end{matrix} \\
\left(\begin{array}{cc|cc}
.2 & .4 & .3 & .1 \\
.5 & 0 & .3 & .2 \\
\hline
0 & 0 & 1 & 0 \\
0 & 0 & 0 & 1
\end{array} \right)
\end{array}
$$

In this case, we have

$$
\mathbf{N} = \begin{pmatrix} .2 & .4 \\ .5 & 0 \end{pmatrix}, \quad \mathbf{A} = \begin{pmatrix} .3 & .1 \\ .3 & .2 \end{pmatrix}, \quad \mathbf{I} = \begin{pmatrix} 1 & 0 \\ 0 & 1 \end{pmatrix}
$$

Given the definition of **A** and **N** and the unit column vector **1** (of all 1 elements), it can be shown that:

Expected time in state j starting in state i = element (i, j) of $(\mathbf{I} - \mathbf{N})^{-1}$

Expected time to absorption = $(\mathbf{I} - \mathbf{N})^{-1}\mathbf{1}$

Probability of absorption = $(\mathbf{I} - \mathbf{N})^{-1}\mathbf{A}$

Example 17.6-1[1]

A product is processed on two sequential machines, I and II. Inspection takes place after a product unit is completed on either machine. There is a 5% chance that the unit will be junked before inspection. After inspection, there is a 3% chance the unit will be junked, and a 7% chance of being returned to the same machine for reworking. Else, a unit passing inspection on both machines is good.

(a) For a part starting at machine I, determine the average number of visits to each state.

(b) If a batch of 1000 units is started on machine I, determine the average number of completed good units.

For the Markov chain, the production process has 6 states: start at I ($s1$), inspect after I ($i1$), start at II ($s2$), inspect after II ($i2$), junk after inspection I or II (J), and good after II (G). States J and G are absorbing states. The transition matrix is given as

$$
\mathbf{P} = \begin{array}{c} \\ s1 \\ i1 \\ s2 \\ i2 \\ J \\ G \end{array}
\begin{array}{c} \begin{matrix} s1 & \;\; i1 & \;\; s2 & \;\; i2 & \;\; J & \;\; G \end{matrix} \\
\left(\begin{array}{cccc|cc}
0 & .95 & 0 & 0 & .05 & 0 \\
.07 & 0 & .9 & 0 & .03 & 0 \\
0 & 0 & 0 & .95 & .05 & 0 \\
0 & 0 & .07 & 0 & .03 & .9 \\
\hline
0 & 0 & 0 & 0 & 1 & 0 \\
0 & 0 & 0 & 0 & 0 & 1
\end{array} \right)
\end{array}
$$

---

[1]Adapted from J. Shamblin and G. Stevens, *Operations Research: A Fundamental Approach*, McGraw-Hill, New York, Chapter 4, 1974.

Thus,

$$
\mathbf{N} = \begin{array}{c} s1 \\ i1 \\ s2 \\ i2 \end{array} \begin{pmatrix} \begin{array}{cccc} s1 & i1 & s2 & i2 \\ 0 & .95 & 0 & 0 \\ .07 & 0 & .9 & 0 \\ 0 & 0 & 0 & .95 \\ 0 & 0 & .07 & 0 \end{array} \end{pmatrix}, \quad \mathbf{A} = \begin{pmatrix} \begin{array}{cc} J & G \\ .05 & 0 \\ .03 & 0 \\ .05 & 0 \\ .03 & .9 \end{array} \end{pmatrix}
$$

Using the spreadsheet calculations in *excelEx17.6-1.xls* (see *Excel moment* following Example 17.5-1), we get

$$
(\mathbf{I} - \mathbf{N})^{-1} = \begin{pmatrix} 1 & -.95 & 0 & 0 \\ -.07 & 1 & -.9 & 0 \\ 0 & 0 & 0 & -.95 \\ 0 & 0 & -.07 & 1 \end{pmatrix}^{-1} = \begin{pmatrix} 1.07 & 1.02 & .98 & 0.93 \\ 0.07 & 1.07 & 1.03 & 0.98 \\ 0 & 0 & 1.07 & 1.02 \\ 0 & 0 & 0.07 & 1.07 \end{pmatrix}
$$

$$
(\mathbf{I} - \mathbf{N})^{-1}\mathbf{A} = \begin{pmatrix} 1.07 & 1.02 & .98 & 0.93 \\ 0.07 & 1.07 & 1.03 & 0.98 \\ 0 & 0 & 1.07 & 1.02 \\ 0 & 0 & 0.07 & 1.07 \end{pmatrix} \begin{pmatrix} .05 & 0 \\ .03 & 0 \\ .05 & 0 \\ .03 & .9 \end{pmatrix} = \begin{pmatrix} .16 & .84 \\ .12 & .88 \\ .08 & .92 \\ .04 & .96 \end{pmatrix}
$$

The top row of $(\mathbf{I} - \mathbf{N})^{-1}$ shows that, on the average, machine I is visited 1.07 times, inspection I is visited 1.02 times, machine II is visited .98 time, and inspection II is visited .93 time. The reason the number of visits in machine I and inspection I is greater than 1 is because of rework and reinspection. On the other hand, the corresponding values for machine II are less than 1 because some parts are junked before reaching machine II. Indeed, under perfect conditions (no parts junked and no rework), the matrix $(\mathbf{I} - \mathbf{N})^{-1}$ will show that each station is visited exactly once (try it by assigning a transition probability of 1 for all the states). Of course, the duration of stay in each state could differ. For example, if the processing times at machines I and II are 20 and 30 minutes and if the inspection times at I and II are 5 and 7 minutes, then a part starting at machine 1 will be processed (i.e., either junked or completed) in $1.07 \times 20 + 1.02 \times 5 + .98 \times 30 + .93 \times 7 = 62.41$ minutes.

To determine the number of completed parts in a starting batch of 1000 pieces, we can see from the top row of $(\mathbf{I} - \mathbf{N})^{-1}\mathbf{A}$ that

Probability of a piece being junked = .16
Probability of a piece being completed = .84

This means that $1000 \times .84 = 840$ pieces will be completed in a starting batch of 1000.

PROBLEM SET 17.6A

1. In Example 17.6-1, suppose that the labor cost for machines I and II is $25 per hour and that for inspection is only $15 per hour. Further assume that it takes 30 minutes and 20 minutes to process a piece on machines I and II, respectively. The inspection time at each of the two stations is 10 minutes. Determine the labor cost associated with a completed (good) piece.

*2. When I borrow a book from the city library, I try to return it after one week. Depending on the length of the book and my free time, there is a 30% chance that I keep it for another week. If I have had the book for two weeks, there is a 10% chance that I'll keep it for an additional week. Under no condition do I keep it for more than three weeks.

(a) Express the situation as a Markov chain.

(b) Determine the average number of weeks before returning a book to the library.

3. In Casino del Rio, a gambler can bet in whole dollars. Each bet will either gain $1 with probability .4 or lose $1 with probability .6. Starting with three dollars, the gambler will quit if all money is lost or the accumulation is doubled.

(a) Express the problem as a Markov chain.

(b) Determine the average number of bets until game ends.

(c) Determine the probability of ending the game with $6. Of losing all $3.

4. Jim must make five years worth of progress to complete his doctorate degree at ABC University. However, he enjoys the life of a student and is in no hurry to finish his degree. In any academic year, there is a 50% chance he may take the year off, and a 50% chance of pursuing the degree full time. After completing three academic years, there is a 30% chance that Jim may "bail out" and simply get a master's degree, a 20% chance of taking the next year off but continuing in the Ph.D. program, and 50% chance of attending school full time toward his doctorate.

(a) Express Jim's situation as a Markov chain.

(b) Determine the expected number of academic years before Jim's student life comes to an end.

(c) Determine the probability that Jim will end his academic journey with only a master's degree.

(d) If Jim's fellowship pays an annual stipend of $18,000 (but only when he attends school), how much will he be paid before ending up with a degree?

5. An employee who is now 55 years old plans to retire at the age of 62 but does not rule out the possibility of quitting earlier. At the end of each year, he weighs his options (and state of mind regarding work). The probability of quitting after one year is only .1 but seems to increase by approximately .01 with each additional year.

(a) Express the problem as a Markov chain.

(b) What is the probability that the employee stay with the company until planned retirement at age 62?

(c) At age 57, what is the probability the employee will call it quits?

(d) At age 58, what is the expected number of years before the employee is off the payroll?

6. In Problem 3, Set 17.1A,

(a) Determine the expected number of quarters until a debt is either repaid or lost as bad debt.

(b) Determine the probability that a new loan will be written off as bad debt. Repaid in full.

(c) If a loan is 6 months old, determine the number of quarters until its status is settled.

7. In a men's singles tennis tournament, Andre and John are playing a match for the championship. The match is won when either player wins three out of five sets. Statistics show that there is 60% chance that Andre will win any one set.

(a) Express the match as a Markov chain.

(b) On the average, how long will the match last, and what is the probability that Andre will win the championship?

(c) If the score is 1 set to 2, John's favor, what is the probability that Andre will win?

(d) In Part (c), determine the average number of sets till the match ends, and interpret the result.

*8. Students at U of A have expressed dissatisfaction with the fast pace at which the math department is teaching the one-semester Cal I. To cope with this problem, the math department is now offering Cal I in 4 modules. Students will set their individual pace for each module and, when ready, will take a test that will elevate them to the next module. The tests are given once every 4 weeks, so that a diligent student can complete all 4 modules in one semester. After a couple of years with this self-paced program, 20% of the students did not complete the first module on time. The percentages for modules 2 through 4 were 22%, 25%, and 30%, respectively.

(a) Express the problem as a Markov chain.

(b) On the average, would a student starting with module 1 at the beginning of the current semester be able to take Cal II the next semester (Cal I is a prerequisite for Cal II)?

(c) Would a student who has completed only one module last semester be able to finish Cal I by the end of the current semester?

(d) Do you recommend extending the module idea to other basic classes? Explain.

9. At U of A, promotion from assistant to associate professor requires the equivalent of five points (years) of acceptable performance. Performance reviews are conducted once a year, and the candidate is given an average rating, a good rating, or an excellent rating. An average rating is the same as probation, and the candidate gains no points toward promotion. A good rating is equivalent to gaining one point, and an excellent rating adds two points. Statistics show that in any year 10% of the candidates are rated average and 70% are rated good, and the rest are rated excellent.

(a) Express the problem as a Markov chain.

(b) Determine the average number of years until a new assistant professor is promoted.

10. *Pfifer and Carraway (2000).* A company targets its customers through direct mail advertising. During the first year, the probability that the customer will make a purchase is .5, which decreases to .4 in year 2, .3 in year 3, and .2 in years 4. If no purchases are made in four consecutive years, the customer is deleted from the mailing list. Making a purchase resets the count back to zero.

(a) Express the situation as a Markov chain.

(b) Determine the expected number of years a new customer will be on the mailing list.

(c) If a customer has not made a purchase in two years, determine the expected number of years on the mailing list.

11. An NC machine is designed to operate properly with power voltage setting between 108 and 112 volts. If the voltage falls outside this range, the machine will stop. The power regulator for the machine can detect variations in increments of one volt. Experience shows that change in voltage takes place once every 15 minutes. Within the admissible range (118 to 112 volts), voltage can go up by 1 volt, stay the same, or go down by one volt, all with equal probabilities.

(a) Express the situation as a Markov chain.

(b) Determine the probability that the machine will stop because the voltage is low. High.

(c) What should be the ideal voltage setting that will render the longest working duration for the machine?

12. Consider Problem 4, Set 17.1A, dealing with patients suffering from kidney failure. Determine the following measures:

(a) The expected number of years a patient stays on dialysis.

(b) The longevity of a patient who starts on dialysis.

(c) The life expectancy of a patient who survives 1 year or longer after a transplant.

(d) The expected number of years before an at-least-1-year transplant survivor goes back to dialysis or dies.

(e) The quality of life for those who survive a year or more after a transplant (presumably, spending fewer years on dialysis signify better quality of life).

BIBLIOGRAPHY

Bini, D., E. Harold, and J. Palacios, *Numerical Methods for Structured Markov Chains,* Oxford University Press, New York, 2005.

Cyert, R., H. Davidson, and G. Thompson, "Estimation of the Allowance for Doubtful Accounts by Markov Chains," *Management Science*, Vol. 8, No. 4, pp. 287–303, 1963.

Pfifer, P., and R. Cassaway, "Modeling Customer Relations with Markov Chains," *Journal of Interactive Marketing*, Vol. 14, No. 2, pp. 43–55, 2000.

Grimmet, G., and D. Stirzaker, *Probability and Random Processes*, 2nd ed., Oxford University Press, Oxford, England, 1992.

Pliskin, J., and E. Tell, "Using Dialysis Need-Projection Model for Health Planning in Massachusetts," *Interfaces*, Vol. 11, No. 6, pp. 84–99, 1981.

Stewart, W., *Introduction to the Numerical Solution of Markov Chains*, Princeton University Press, Princeton, NJ, 1995.

Tijms, H., *A First Course in Stochastic Models*, Wiley, New York, 2003.

CHAPTER 18

Queuing Systems

Real-Life Application—Study of an Internal Transport System in a Manufacturing Plant

Three trucks are used in a manufacturing plant to transport materials. The trucks wait in a central parking lot until requested. A truck answering a request will travel to the customer location, carry a load to its destination, and then return to the central parking lot. The principal departments using the service are production, workshop, and maintenance. Complaints about long wait for a free truck have prompted users, especially production, to request adding a fourth truck to the fleet. This is an unusual application, because queuing theory is used to show that the source of long delays is mainly logistical and that with a simple change in the operating procedure of the truck pool, a fourth truck is not needed. Case 14 in Chapter 26 on the website details the study

---

18.1 WHY STUDY QUEUES?

Waiting for service is part of daily life. We wait for service in restaurants, we queue up to board a plane, and we line up for service in post offices. And the waiting phenomenon is not an experience limited to human beings: Jobs wait to be processed on a machine, planes circle in stack before given permission to land, and cars stop at traffic lights. Eliminating waiting altogether is not a feasible option because the cost of installing and operating the service facility can be prohibitive. Our only recourse is to strike a balance between cost of offering a service and the cost of waiting experienced by customers. Queuing analysis is the vehicle for achieving this goal.

The study of queues deals with quantifying the phenomenon of waiting using representative measures of performance, such as average queue length, average waiting time in queue, and average facility utilization. The following example demonstrates how these measures can be used to design a service facility.

Example 18.1-1

McBurger is a fast-food restaurant with three service counters. The manager wants to expedite service. A study reveals the following relationship between the number of service counters and the waiting time for service:

Number of cashiers	1	2	3	4	5	6	7
Average waiting time (min)	16.2	10.3	6.9	4.8	2.9	1.9	1.3

An examination of these data shows a 7-minute average waiting time for the present 3-counter situation. Five counters would reduce waiting to about 3 minutes.

Cost-based model. The results of queuing analysis can be incorporated in a cost optimization mode that seeks the minimization of the sum of the cost of offering the service and the cost of waiting by customers. Figure 18.1 depicts a typical cost model (in dollars per unit time) where the cost of service increases with the increase in the level of service (e.g., the number of service counters). At the same time, the cost of waiting decreases with the increase in level of service.

The main obstacle in implementing cost models is the difficulty of determining the cost of waiting, particularly when waiting is experienced by human beings. This point is discussed in Section 18.9.

PROBLEM SET 18.1A

*1. Suppose that further analysis of the McBurger restaurant reveals the following additional results:

Number of cashiers	1	2	3	4	5	6	7
Idleness (%)	0	8	12	18	29	36	42

FIGURE 18.1

Cost-based queuing decision model

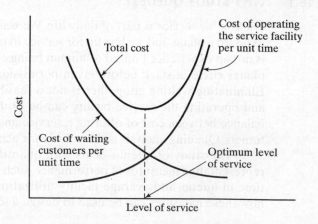

    (a) What is the productivity of the operation (expressed as the percentage of time the employees are busy) when the number of cashiers is five?

    (b) The manager wants to keep the average waiting time around 3 minutes and, simultaneously, maintain the efficiency of the facility at approximately 90%. Can the two goals be achieved? Explain.

  2. Acme Metal Jobshop is in the process of purchasing a multipurpose drill press. Two models, *A* and *B*, are available with hourly operating costs of $20 and $35, respectively. Model *A* is slower than model *B*. Queuing analysis of similar machines shows that when *A* is used, the average number of jobs in the queue is 4, which is 30% higher than the queue size in *B*. A delayed job represents lost income, which is estimated by Acme at $10 per waiting job per hour. Which model should Acme purchase?

18.2 ELEMENTS OF A QUEUING MODEL

The principal players in a queuing situation are the **customer** and the **server**. Customers arrive at a (service) **facility** from a **source**. On arrival, a customer can start service immediately or wait in a **queue** if the facility is busy. When a facility completes a service, it automatically "pulls" a waiting customer, if any, from the queue. If the queue is empty, the facility becomes idle until a new customer arrives.

From the standpoint of analyzing queues, the arrival of customers is represented by the **interarrival time** (time between successive arrivals), and the service is measured by the **service time** per customer. Generally, the interarrival and service times are probabilistic (e.g., operation of a post office) or deterministic (e.g., arrival of applicants for job interview or for a doctor's appointment).

Queue size plays a role in the analysis of queues. It may be finite (as in the buffer area between two successive machines), or, for all practical purposes, infinite (as in mail order facilities).

Queue discipline, which represents the order in which customers are selected from a queue, is an important factor in the analysis of queuing models. The most common discipline is **first-come, first-served (FCFS)**. Other disciplines include **last-come, first-served (LCFS)** and **service in random order (SIRO)**. Customers may also be selected from the queue based on some order of **priority**. For example, rush jobs in a shop are processed ahead of regular jobs.

Queuing behavior plays a role in waiting-line analysis. Customers may **jockey** from a longer queue to a shorter one to reduce waiting time, they may **balk** from joining a queue altogether because of anticipated long delay, or they may **renege** from a queue because they have been waiting too long.

The design of the service facility may include parallel servers (e.g., post office or bank operation). The servers may also be arranged in series (e.g., jobs processed on successive machines), or they may be networked (e.g., routers in a computer network).

The source from which customers are generated may be finite or infinite. A **finite source** limits the number of arriving customers (e.g., machines requesting the service of a repairperson). An **infinite source** is, for all practical purposes, forever abundant (e.g., calls arriving at a telephone exchange).

Variations in the elements of a queuing situation give rise to a variety of mathematical queuing models. This chapter provides examples of these models. Complex queuing situations that cannot be represented mathematically are usually analyzed by using simulation (see Chapter 19).

PROBLEM SET 18.2A

1. In each of the following situations, identify the customer and the server:

   *(a) Planes arriving at an airport.

   *(b) Taxi stand serving waiting passengers.

   (c) Tools checked out from a crib in a machining shop.

   (d) Letters processed in a post office.

   (e) Registration for classes in a university.

   (f) Legal court cases.

   (g) Checkout operation in a supermarket.

   *(h) Parking lot operation.

2. For each of the situations in Problem 1, identify the following: (a) nature of the calling source (finite or infinite), (b) nature of arriving customers (individually or in bulk), (c) type of the interarrival time (probabilistic or deterministic), (d) definition and type of service time, (f) queue capacity (finite or infinite), and (g) queue discipline.

3. Study the following system and identify the associated queuing situations. For each situation, define the customers, the server(s), the queue discipline, the service time, the maximum queue length, and the calling source.

   Orders for jobs are received at a workshop for processing. On receipt, the supervisor decides whether it is a rush or a regular job. Some orders require the use of one of several identical machines. The remaining orders are processed in a two-stage production line, of which two are available. In each group, one facility is assigned to handle rush jobs.

   Jobs arriving at any facility are processed in order of arrival. Completed orders are shipped on arrival from a shipping zone having a limited capacity.

   Sharpened tools for the different machines are supplied from a central tool crib. When a machine breaks down, a repairperson is summoned from the service pool to make the repair. Machines working on rush orders always receive priorities both in acquiring new tools from the crib and in receiving repair service.

4. True or False?

   (a) An impatient waiting customer may not elect to renege.

   (b) If a long waiting time is anticipated, an arriving customer may not elect to balk.

   (c) Jockeying from one queue to another is exercised in hope of reducing waiting time.

5. In each of the situations in Problem 1, discuss the possibility of the customers jockeying, balking, and reneging.

18.3 ROLE OF EXPONENTIAL DISTRIBUTION

In most queuing situations, arrivals occur *randomly*. Randomness means that the occurrence of an event (e.g., arrival of a customer or completion of a service) is not influenced by the length of time that has elapsed since the occurrence of the last event.

Random interarrival and service times are described quantitatively in queuing models by the **exponential distribution**, which is defined as

$$f(t) = \lambda e^{-\lambda t}, t > 0$$

Section 12.4.3 shows that for the exponential distribution

$$E\{t\} = \frac{1}{\lambda}$$

$$P\{t \le T\} = \int_0^T \lambda e^{-\lambda t} dt = 1 - e^{-\lambda T}$$

The definition of $E\{t\}$ shows that λ is the rate per unit time at which events (arrivals or departures) are generated.

The exponential distribution describes a *totally random* phenomenon. For example, if the time now is 8:20 A.M. and the last arrival has occurred at 8:02 A.M., the probability that the next arrival will occur by 8:29 is a function of the interval from 8:20 to 8:29 only, and it is totally independent of the length of time that has elapsed since the occurrence of the last event (8:02 to 8:20).

The totally random property of the exponential is referred to as **forgetfulness** or **lack of memory**. Given $f(t)$ is the exponential distribution of the time, t, between successive (arrival) events, if S is the interval since the occurrence of the last event, then the *forgetfulness property* implies that

$$P\{t > T + S | t > S\} = P\{t > T\}$$

To prove this result, we note that for the exponential with mean $\frac{1}{\lambda}$,

$$P\{t > Y\} = 1 - P\{t < Y\} = e^{-\lambda Y}$$

Thus,

$$P\{t > T + S | t > S\} = \frac{P\{t > T + S, t > S\}}{P\{t > S\}} = \frac{P\{t > T + S\}}{P\{t > S\}}$$

$$= \frac{e^{-\lambda(T+S)}}{e^{-\lambda S}} = e^{-\lambda T}$$

$$= P\{t > T\}$$

Example 18.3-1

A service machine always has a standby unit for immediate replacement upon failure. The time to failure of the machine (or its standby unit) is exponential and occurs every 5 hours, on the average. The machine operator claims that the machine is "in the habit" of breaking down every night around 8:30 P.M. Analyze the operator's claim.

The average failure rate of the machine is $\lambda = \frac{1}{5} = .2$ failure per hour. Thus, the exponential distribution of the time to failure is

$$f(t) = .2e^{-.2t}, t > 0$$

Regarding the operator's claim, we know offhand that it cannot be true because it conflicts with the fact that the time between breakdowns is exponential and, hence, totally random. The probability that a failure will occur by 8:30 P.M. cannot be used to support or refute the operator's claim, because the value of such probability depends on the time (relative to 8:30 P.M.) at which it is computed. For example, if the time now is 8:20 P.M., then there is a low probability that the operator's claim is right—namely,

$$p\left\{t < \tfrac{10}{60}\right\} = 1 - e^{-.2\left(\tfrac{10}{60}\right)} = .03278$$

If the time now is 1:00 P.M., then the probability that a failure will occur by 8:30 P.M. increases to approximately .777 (verify!). These two extreme values show that the operator's claim is not true.

PROBLEM SET 18.3A

1. **(a)** Explain your understanding of the relationship between the arrival rate λ and the average interarrival time. What are the units describing each variable?

   (b) In each of the following cases, determine the average arrival rate per hour, λ, and the average interarrival time in hours.

   (i) One arrival occurs every 10 minutes.

   (ii) Two arrivals occur every 6 minutes.

   (iii) Number of arrivals in a 30-minute period is 10.

   (iv) The average interval between successive arrivals is .5 hour.

   (c) In each of the following cases, determine the average service rate per hour, μ and the average service time in hours.

   (i) One service is completed every 12 minutes.

   (ii) Two departures occur every 15 minutes.

   (iii) Number of customers served in a 30-minute period is 5.

   (iv) The average service time is .3 hour.

2. In Example 18.3-1, determine the following:

   (a) The average number of failures per day, assuming the service is offered 24 hours a day, 7 days a week.

   (b) The probability of at least one failure in a 3-hour period.

   (c) The probability that the next failure will *not* occur within 4 hours.

   (d) If no failure has occurred 3 hours after the last failure, what is the probability that interfailure time is at least 5 hours?

3. The time between arrivals at the State Revenue Office is exponential with mean value .05 hour. The office opens at 8:00 A.M.

   (a) Write the exponential distribution that describes the interarrival time.

   (b) Find the probability that no customers will arrive at the office by 8:15 A.M.

   (c) It is now 8:35 A.M. The last customer entered the office at 8:26. What is the probability that the next customer will arrive before 8:38 A.M.? That the next customer will not arrive by 8:40 A.M.?

   (d) What is the average number of arriving customers between 8:10 and 8:45 A.M.?

4. Suppose that the time between breakdowns for a machine is exponential with mean 5 hours. If the machine has worked without failure during the last 4 hours, what is the probability that it will continue without failure during the next 2 hours? That it will break down during the next hour?

5. The time between arrivals at the game room in the student union is exponential, with mean 10 minutes.

   (a) What is the arrival rate per hour?

   (b) What is the probability that no students will arrive at the game room during the next 15 minutes?

   (c) What is the probability that at least one student will visit the game room during the next 20 minutes?

6. The manager of a new fast-food restaurant wants to quantify the arrival process of customers by estimating the fraction of interarrival time intervals that will be (a) less than 1 minutes, (b) between 1 and 2 minutes, and (c) more than 2 minutes. Arrivals in similar restaurants occur at the rate of 20 customers per hour. The interarrival time is exponentially distributed.

*7. Ann and Jim, two employees in a fast-food restaurant, play the following game while waiting for customers to arrive: Jim pays Ann 2 cents if the next customer does not arrive within 1 minute; otherwise, Ann pays Jim 2 cents. Determine Jim's average payoff in an 8-hour period. The interarrival time is exponential with mean 1.5 minute.

8. Suppose that in Problem 7 the rules of the game are such that Jim pays Ann 2 cents if the next customer arrives after 1.5 minutes, and Ann pays Jim an equal amount if the next arrival is within 1 minute. For arrivals within the range 1 to 1.5 minutes, the game is a draw. Determine Jim's expected payoff in an 8-hour period.

9. In Problem 7, suppose that Ann pays Jim 2 cents if the next arrival occurs within 1 minute and 3 cents if the interarrival time is between 1 and 1.5 minutes. Ann receives from Jim 5 cents if the interarrival time is between 1.5 and 2 minutes and 6 cents if it is larger than 2 minutes. Determine Ann's expected payoff in an 8-hour period.

*10. A customer arriving at a McBurger fast-food restaurant within 4 minutes of the immediately preceding customer will receive a 10% discount. If the interarrival time is between 4 and 5 minutes, the discount is 6%. If the interarrival time is longer than 5 minutes, the customer gets 2% discount. The interarrival time is exponential with mean 6 minutes.

   (a) Determine the probability that an arriving customer will receive the 10% discount.

   (b) Determine the average discount per arriving customer.

11. The time between failures of a Kencore refrigerator is known to be exponential with mean value 9000 hours (about 1 year of operation), and the company issues a 1-year warranty on the refrigerator. What are the chances that a breakdown repair will be covered by the warranty?

12. The U of A runs two bus lines on campus: red and green. The red line serves north campus, and the green line serves south campus with a transfer station linking the two lines. Green buses arrive randomly (exponential interarrival time) at the transfer station every 10 minutes. Red buses also arrive randomly every 7 minutes.

   (a) What is the probability distribution of the waiting time for a student arriving on the red line to get on the green line?

   (b) What is the probability distribution of the waiting time for a student arriving on the green line to get on the red line?

13. Prove that the mean and standard deviation of the exponential distribution are equal.

18.4 PURE BIRTH AND DEATH MODELS (RELATIONSHIP BETWEEN THE EXPONENTIAL AND POISSON DISTRIBUTIONS)

This section presents two queuing situations: the **pure birth** model in which only arrivals occur, and the **pure death** model in which departures only take place. An example of the pure birth model is the creation of birth certificates for newly born babies. The pure death model may be demonstrated by the random withdrawal of a stocked item in a store.

The exponential distribution is used to describe the interarrival time in the pure birth model and the interdeparture time in the pure death model. A by-product of the development of the two models is to show the close relationship between the exponential and the Poisson distributions, in the sense that one distribution automatically defines the other.

18.4.1 Pure Birth Model

Define

$$p_0(t) = \text{Probability of no arrivals during a period of time } t$$

Given that the interarrival time is exponential and that the arrival rate is λ customers per unit time, then

$$
\begin{aligned}
p_0(t) &= P\{\text{interarrival time} \geq t\} \\
&= 1 - P\{\text{interarrival time} \leq t\} \\
&= 1 - (1 - e^{-\lambda t}) \\
&= e^{-\lambda t}
\end{aligned}
$$

For a sufficiently small time interval $h > 0$, we have

$$p_0(h) = e^{-\lambda h} = 1 - \lambda h + \frac{(\lambda h)^2}{2!} - \cdots = 1 - \lambda h + 0(h^2)$$

The exponential distribution is based on the assumption that during $h > 0$, at most one event (arrival) can occur. Thus, as $h \to 0$,

$$p_1(h) = 1 - p_0(h) \approx \lambda h$$

This result shows that the probability of an arrival during h is directly proportional to h, with the arrival rate, λ, being the constant of proportionality.

To derive the distribution of the *number* of arrivals during a period t when the interarrival time is exponential with mean $\frac{1}{\lambda}$, define

$$p_n(t) = \text{Probability of } n \text{ arrivals during } t$$

For a sufficiently small $h > 0$,

$$p_n(t + h) \approx p_n(t)(1 - \lambda h) + p_{n-1}(t)\lambda h, \quad n > 0$$
$$p_0(t + h) \approx p_0(t)(1 - \lambda h), \quad\quad\quad\quad n = 0$$

In the first equation, n arrivals will be realized during $t + h$ if there are n arrivals during t and no arrivals during h, or $n - 1$ arrivals during t and one arrival during h. All other combinations are not allowed because, according to the exponential distribution, at most one arrival can occur during a very small period h. The product law of probability is applicable to the right-hand side of the equation because arrivals are independent. For the second equation, zero arrivals during $t + h$ can occur only if no arrivals occur during t and h.

Rearranging the terms and taking the limits as $h \to 0$ to obtain the first derivative of $p_n(t)$ with respect to t, we get

$$p'_n(t) = \lim_{h \to 0} \frac{p_n(t + h) - p_n(t)}{h} = -\lambda p_n(t) + \lambda p_{n-1}(t), \; n > 0$$

$$p'_0(t) = \lim_{h \to 0} \frac{p_0(t - h) - p_0(t)}{h} = -\lambda p_0(t), \qquad\qquad n = 0$$

The solution of the preceding difference-differential equations yields

$$p_n(t) = \frac{(\lambda t)^n e^{-\lambda t}}{n!}, \; n = 0, 1, 2, \ldots$$

This is a **Poisson distribution** with mean $E\{n|t\} = \lambda t$ arrivals during t.

The preceding result shows that if the time between arrivals is exponential with mean $\frac{1}{\lambda}$, then the number of arrivals during a specific period t is Poisson with mean λt. The converse is also true.

The following table summarizes the relationships between the exponential and the Poisson, given the arrival rate λ:

	Exponential	Poisson
Random variable	*Time* between successive arrivals, t	*Number* of arrivals, n, during a specified period T
Range	$t \geq 0$	$n = 0, 1, 2, \ldots$
Density function	$f(t) = \lambda e^{-\lambda t}, t \geq 0$	$p_n(T) = \dfrac{(\lambda T)^n e^{-\lambda T}}{n!}, n = 0, 1, 2, \ldots$
Mean value	$\dfrac{1}{\lambda}$ time units	λT arrivals during T
Cumulative probability	$P\{t \leq A\} = 1 - e^{-\lambda A}$	$p_{n \leq N}(T) = p_0(T) + p_1(T) + \cdots + p_N(T)$
$P\{$no arrivals during period $A\}$	$P\{t > A\} = e^{-\lambda A}$	$p_0(A) = e^{-\lambda A}$

Example 18.4-1

Babies are born in a large city at the rate of one birth every 12 minutes. The time between births follows an exponential distribution. Find the following:

(a) The average number of births per year.

(b) The probability that no births will occur during 1 day.

(c) The probability of issuing 50 birth certificates in 3 hours, given that 40 certificates were issued during the first 2 hours of the 3-hour period.

The birth rate per day is computed as

$$\lambda = \frac{24 \times 60}{12} = 120 \text{ births/day}$$

Thus, the number of births per year in the state is

$$\lambda t = 120 \times 365 = 43{,}800 \text{ births/year}$$

The probability of no births during 1 day is

$$p_0(1) = \frac{(120 \times 1)^0 e^{-120 \times 1}}{0!} = e^{-120} = 0$$

Another way to compute the same probability is to note that no birth in any one day is equivalent to saying that the *time between successive births* exceeds one day. We can thus use the exponential distribution to compute the desired probability as

$$P\{t > 1\} = e^{-120} = 0$$

Because the distribution of the number of births is Poisson, the probability of issuing 50 certificates in 3 hours, given that 40 certificates were issued during the first 2 hours, is equivalent to having $10 \, (=50 - 40)$ births in one $(=3 - 2)$ hour—that is,

$$p_{10}(1) = \frac{\left(\frac{60}{12} \times 1\right)^{10} e^{-5 \times 1}}{10!} = .01813$$

Excel moment

The calculations associated with the Poisson distribution and, indeed, all queuing formulas are tedious and require programming skill to secure reasonable computational accuracy. You can use Excel POISSON, POISSONDIST, and EXPONDIST functions to compute the individual and cumulative probabilities Poisson and exponential probabilities. These functions are also automated in *exceStatTables.xls*. For example, for a birth rate of 5 babies per hour, the probability of *exactly* 10 births in .5 hour is computed by entering 2.5 in F16 and 10 in J16 to obtain the answer .000216 in M16. The cumulative probability of *at most* 10 births is given in O16 (=.999938). To determine the probability of the time between births being less than or equal to 18 minutes, use the exponential distribution by entering 2.5 in F9 and .3 in J9. The answer, .527633, is found in O9.

TORA/Excel moment

You can also use TORA (file *toraEx18.4-1.txt*) or template *excelPoissonQ.xls* to determine all significant ($>10^{-5}$ in TORA and $>10^{-7}$ in Excel) Poisson probabilities automatically. In both cases, the input data are the same. For the pure birth model of Example 18.4-1, the data are as follows:

Lambda	Mu	c	System limit	Source limit
5	0	0	infinity	infinity

Note the entry under Lambda $\lambda t = 5 \times 1 = 5$ births per day. Note also that Mu = 0 identifies the model as pure birth.

PROBLEM SET 18.4A

*1. In Example 18.4-1, suppose that the clerk who enters the information from birth certificates into the computer normally waits until at least 5 certificates have accumulated. Find the probability that the clerk will be entering a new batch every hour.

2. An art collector travels to art auctions once a month on the average. Each trip is guaranteed to produce one purchase. The time between trips is exponentially distributed. Determine the following:

  (a) The probability that no purchase is made in a 2-month period.

  (b) The probability that no more than 6 purchases are made per year.

  (c) The probability that the time between successive trips will exceed 2 month.

3. In a bank operation, the arrival rate is 3 customers per minute. Determine the following:

  (a) The average number of arrivals during 10 minutes.

  (b) The probability that no arrivals will occur during the next minute.

  (c) The probability that at least one arrival will occur during the next minute.

  (d) The probability that the time between two successive arrivals is at least 2 minutes.

4. The time between arrivals at L&J restaurant is exponential with mean 5 minutes. The restaurant opens for business at 11:00 A.M. Determine the following:

  *(a) The probability of having 10 arrivals in the restaurant by 11:12 A.M., given that 8 customers arrived by 11:05 A.M.

  (b) The probability that a new customer will arrive between 11:28 and 11:33 A.M., given that the last customer arrived at 11:25 A.M.

5. The Springdale Public Library receives new books according to a Poisson distribution with mean 25 books per day. Each shelf in the stacks holds 100 books. Determine the following:

  (a) The average number of shelves that will be stacked with new books each (30-day) month.

  (b) The probability that more than 10 bookcases will be needed each month, given that a bookcase has 5 shelves.

6. The U of A runs two bus lines on campus: red and green. The red line serves north campus and the green line serves south campus with a transfer station linking the two lines. Green buses arrive randomly (according to a Poisson distribution) at the transfer station every 10 minutes. Red buses also arrive randomly every 7 minutes.

  *(a) What is the probability that two buses (red and/or green) will stop at the station during a 5-minute interval?

  (b) A student whose dormitory is located next to the station has a class in 10 minutes. Either bus will take the student to the classroom building. The ride takes 5 minutes, after which the student will walk for about 3 minutes to reach the classroom. What is the probability that the student will make it to class on time?

7. Prove that the mean and variance of the Poisson distribution during an interval t equal λt, where λ is the arrival rate.

8. Derive the Poisson distribution from the difference-differential equations of the pure birth model. Hint: The solution of the general differential equation

$$y' + a(t)y = b(t)$$

is

$$y = e^{-\int a(t)\,dt}\left\{ \int b(t)e^{\int a(t)\,dt}\,dt + \text{constant} \right\}$$

18.4.2 Pure Death Model

In the pure death model, the system starts with N customers at time 0, with no new arrivals allowed. Departures occur at the rate μ customers per unit time. To develop the difference-differential equations for the probability $p_n(t)$ of n customers *remaining* after t time units, we follow the arguments used with the pure birth model (Section 18.4.1). Thus,

$$p_N(t + h) = p_N(t)(1 - \mu h)$$

$$p_n(t + h) = p_n(t)(1 - \mu h) + p_{n+1}(t)\mu h, 0 < n < N$$

$$p_0(t + h) = p_0(t)(1) + p_1(t)\mu h$$

As $h \to 0$, we get

$$p'_N(t) = -\mu p_N(t)$$

$$p'_n(t) = -\mu p_n(t) + \mu p_{n+1}(t), 0 < n < N$$

$$p'_0(t) = \mu p_1(t)$$

The solution of these equations yields the following **truncated Poisson** distribution:

$$p_n(t) = \frac{(\mu t)^{N-n} e^{-\mu t}}{(N - n)!}, n = 1, 2, \ldots, N$$

$$p_0(t) = 1 - \sum_{n-1}^{N} p_n(t)$$

Example 18.4-2

The florist section in a grocery store stocks 18 dozen roses at the beginning of each week. On the average, the florist sells 3 dozens a day (one dozen at a time), but the actual demand follows a Poisson distribution. Whenever the stock level reaches 5 dozens, a new order of 18 new dozens is placed for delivery at the beginning of the following week. Because of the nature of the item, all roses left at the end of the week are disposed of. Determine the following:

(a) The probability of placing an order in any one day of the week.
(b) The average number of dozen roses discarded at the end of the week.

Because purchases occur at the rate of $\mu = 3$ dozens per day, the probability of placing an order by the end of day t is

$$P_{n \le 5}(t) = p_0(t) + p_1(t) + \cdots + p_5(t)$$

$$= p_0(t) + \sum_{n=1}^{5} \frac{(3t)^{18-n} e^{-3t}}{(18 - n)!}, t = 1, 2, \ldots, 7$$

The calculations of $P_{n \le 5}(t)$ are best done using *excelPoissonQ.xls* or TORA. TORA's multiple scenarios may be more convenient in this case. The associated input data for the pure death model corresponding to $t = 1, 2, \ldots,$ and 7 are Lambda = 0, Mu = $3t$, c = 1, System Limit = 18, and Source Limit = 18. Note that t must be substituted out numerically as shown in file *toraEx18.4-2.txt*.

The output is summarized as follows:

t (day)	1	2	3	4	5	6	7
μt	3	6	9	12	15	18	21
$p_{n \leq 5}(t)$	.0000	.0088	.1242	.4240	.7324	.9083	.9755

The average number of dozen roses discarded at the end of the week $(t = 7)$ is $E\{n|t = 7\}$. To calculate this value, we need $p_n(7), n = 0, 1, 2, \ldots, 18$, which can be determined using provided software. The result is

$$E\{n|t = 7\} = \sum_{n=0}^{18} n p_n(7) = .664 \approx 1 \, \text{dozen}$$

PROBLEM SET 18.4B

1. In Example 18.4-2, use *excelPoissonQ.xls* or TORA to compute $p_n(7), n = 1, 2, \ldots, 18$, and then verify manually that these probabilities yield $E\{n|t = 7\} = .664$ dozen.

2. Consider Example 18.4-2. In each of the following cases, first write the answer algebraically, and then use *excelPoissonQ.xls* or TORA to provide numerical answers.

   *(a) The probability that the stock is depleted after 3 days.

   (b) The average number of dozen roses left at the end of the second day.

   *(c) The probability that at least one dozen is purchased by the end of the fourth day, given that the last dozen was bought at the end of the third day.

   (d) The probability that the time remaining until the next purchase is at most half a day, given that the last purchase occurred a day earlier.

   (e) The probability that no purchases will occur during the first day.

   (f) The probability that no order will be placed by the end of the week.

3. The Springdale High School band is performing a benefit concert in its new 400-seat auditorium. Local businesses buy the tickets in blocks of 5 and donate them to youth organizations. Tickets go on sale to business entities for 5 hours only the day before the concert. The process of placing orders for tickets is Poisson with a mean 12 calls per hour. Any (blocks of) tickets remaining after the box office is closed are sold at a discount as "rush tickets" 1 hour before the concert starts. Determine the following:

   (a) The probability that it will be possible to buy rush tickets.

   (b) The average number of rush tickets available.

4. Each morning, the refrigerator in a small machine shop is stocked with two cases (24 cans per case) of soft drinks for use by the shop's 12 employees. The employees can quench their thirst at any time during the 8-hour work day (8:00 A.M. to 4:00 P.M.), and each employee is known to consume approximately 4 cans a day, but the process is totally random (Poisson distribution). What is the probability that an employee will not find a drink at noon (the start of the lunch period)? Just before the shop closes?

*5. A freshman student receives a bank deposit of $100 a month from home to cover incidentals. Withdrawal checks of $20 each occur randomly during the month and are spaced according to an exponential distribution with a mean value of 1 week. Determine the probability that the student will run out of incidental money before the end of the fourth week.

6. Inventory is withdrawn from a stock of 80 items according to a Poisson distribution at the rate of 5 items per day. Determine the following:

   (a) The probability that 10 items are withdrawn during the first 2 days.

   (b) The probability that no items are left at the end of 4 days.

   (c) The average number of items withdrawn over a 4-day period.

7. A machine shop has just stocked 10 spare parts for the repair of a machine. Stock replenishment that brings the stock level back to 10 pieces occurs every 7 days. The time between breakdowns is exponential with mean 1 day. Determine the probability that the machine will remain broken for 2 days because no spare parts are available.

8. Demand for an item occurs according to a Poisson distribution with mean 3 per day. The maximum stock level is 25 items, which occurs on each Monday immediately after a new order is received. The order size depends on the number of units left at the end of the week on Saturday (business is closed on Sundays). Determine the following:

   (a) *The average weekly size of the order.

   (b) *The probability of shortage at the start of business on Friday.

   (c) The probability that the weekly order size exceeds 10 units.

9. Prove that the distribution of the time between departures corresponding to the truncated Poisson in the pure death model is an exponential distribution with mean $\frac{1}{\mu}$ time units.

10. Derive the truncated Poisson distribution from the difference-differential equations of the pure death model using induction. [*Note*: See the hint in Problem 8, Set 18.4A.]

18.5   GENERAL POISSON QUEUING MODEL

This section develops a general queuing model that combines both arrivals and departures based on the Poisson assumptions—that is, the interarrival and the service times follow the exponential distribution. The model is the basis for the derivation of the specialized Poisson models in Section 18.6.

The development of the generalized model is based on the long-run or **steady-state** behavior of the queuing situation, achieved after the system has been in operation for a sufficiently long time. This type of analysis contrasts with the **transient** (or warm-up) behavior that prevails during the early operation of the system. (One reason for not discussing the transient behavior in this chapter is its analytical complexity. Another reason is that the study of most queuing situations occurs under steady-state conditions.)

The general model assumes that both the arrival and departure rates are **state dependent**—meaning that they depend on the number of customers in the service facility. For example, at a highway toll booth, attendants tend to speed up toll collection during rush hours. Another example occurs in a shop where the rate of machine breakdown decreases as the number of broken machines increases (because only working machines are capable of generating new breakdowns).

Define

n = Number of customers in the system (in-queue plus in-service)

λ_n = Arrival rate, given n customers in the system

μ_n = Departure rate, given n customers in the system

p_n = Steady-state probability of n customers in the system

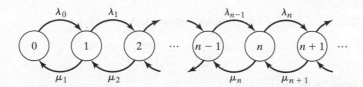

FIGURE 18.2

Poisson queues transition diagram

The general model derives p_n as a function of λ_n and μ_n. These probabilities are then used to determine the system's measures of performance, such as the average queue length, the average waiting time, and the average utilization of the facility.

The probabilities p_n are determined by using the **transition-rate diagram** in Figure 18.2. The queuing system is in state n when the number of customers in the system is n. As explained in Section 18.3, the probability of more than one event occurring during a small interval h tends to zero as $h \to 0$. This means that for $n > 0$, state n can change only to two possible states: $n - 1$ when a departure occurs at the rate μ_n, and $n + 1$ when an arrival occurs at the rate λ_n. State 0 can only change to state 1 when an arrival occurs at the rate λ_0. Notice that μ_0 is undefined because no departures can occur if the system is empty.

Under steady-state conditions, for $n > 0$, the *expected* rates of flow into and out of state n must be equal. Based on the fact that state n can be changed to states $n - 1$ and $n + 1$ only, we get

$$\begin{pmatrix} \text{Expected rate of} \\ \text{flow into state } n \end{pmatrix} = \lambda_{n-1}p_{n-1} + \mu_{n+1}p_{n+1}$$

Similarly,

$$\begin{pmatrix} \text{Expected rate of} \\ \text{flow out of state } n \end{pmatrix} = (\lambda_n + \mu_n)p_n$$

Equating the two rates, we get the following **balance equation**

$$\lambda_{n-1}p_{n-1} + \mu_{n+1}p_{n+1} = (\lambda_n + \mu_n)p_n, \; n = 1, 2, \ldots$$

From Figure 18.2, the balance equation associated with $n = 0$ is

$$\lambda_0 p_0 = \mu_1 p_1$$

The balance equations are solved recursively in terms of p_0. For $n = 0$, we have

$$p_1 = \left(\frac{\lambda_0}{\mu_1} \right) p_0$$

Next, for $n = 1$, we have

$$\lambda_0 p_0 + \mu_2 p_2 = (\lambda_1 + \mu_1)p_1$$

Substituting $p_1 = \left(\frac{\lambda_0}{\mu_0}\right) p_0$ and simplifying, we get (verify!)

$$p_2 = \left(\frac{\lambda_1 \lambda_0}{\mu_2 \mu_1}\right) p_0$$

We can show by induction that

$$p_n = \left(\frac{\lambda_{n-1} \lambda_{n-2} \cdots \lambda_0}{\mu_n \mu_{n-1} \cdots \mu_1}\right) p_0, \, n = 1, 2, \ldots$$

The value of p_0 is determined from the equation $\sum_{n=0}^{\infty} p_n = 1$

Example 18.5-1

B&K Groceries operates with three checkout counters. The manager uses the following schedule to determine the number of counters in operation, depending on the number of customers in line:

Number of customers in store	Number of counters in operation
1 to 3	1
4 to 6	2
More than 6	3

Customers arrive in the counters area according to a Poisson distribution with a mean rate of 10 customers per hour. The average checkout time per customer is exponential with mean 12 minutes. Determine the steady-state probability p_n of n customers in the checkout area.

From the information of the problem, we have

$$\lambda_n = \lambda = 10 \text{ customers per hour}, \qquad n = 0, 1, \ldots$$

$$\mu_n = \begin{cases} \frac{60}{12} = 5 \text{ customers per hour}, & n = 0, 1, 2, 3 \\ 2 \times 5 = 10 \text{ customers per hour}, & n = 4, 5, 6 \\ 3 \times 5 = 15 \text{ customers per hour}, & n = 7, 8, \ldots \end{cases}$$

Thus,

$$p_1 = \left(\tfrac{10}{5}\right) p_0 = 2 p_0$$

$$p_2 = \left(\tfrac{10}{5}\right)^2 p_0 = 4 p_0$$

$$p_3 = \left(\tfrac{10}{5}\right)^3 p_0 = 8 p_0$$

$$p_4 = \left(\tfrac{10}{5}\right)^3 \left(\tfrac{10}{10}\right) p_0 = 8 p_0$$

$$p_5 = \left(\tfrac{10}{5}\right)^3 \left(\tfrac{10}{10}\right)^2 p_0 = 8 p_0$$

$$p_6 = \left(\tfrac{10}{5}\right)^3 \left(\tfrac{10}{10}\right)^3 p_0 = 8 p_0$$

$$p_{n \geq 7} = \left(\tfrac{10}{5}\right)^3 \left(\tfrac{10}{10}\right)^3 \left(\tfrac{10}{15}\right)^{n-6} p_0 = 8 \left(\tfrac{2}{3}\right)^{n-6} p_0$$

The value of p_0 is determined from the equation

$$p_0 + p_0 \left\{ 2 + 4 + 8 + 8 + 8 + 8 + 8\left(\tfrac{2}{3}\right) + 8\left(\tfrac{2}{3}\right)^2 + 8\left(\tfrac{2}{3}\right)^3 + \cdots \right\} = 1$$

or, equivalently

$$p_0\left\{31 + 8\left(1 + \left(\tfrac{2}{3}\right) + \left(\tfrac{2}{3}\right)^2 + \cdots\right)\right\} = 1$$

Using the geometric sum series

$$\sum_{i=0}^{\infty} x^i = \frac{1}{1-x}, \; |x| < 1$$

we get

$$p_0\left\{31 + 8\left(\frac{1}{1-\tfrac{2}{3}}\right)\right\} = 1$$

Thus, $p_0 = \frac{1}{55}$.

Given p_0, we can now determine p_n for $n > 0$. For example, the probability that only one counter will be open is computed as the probability that there are at most three customers in the system:

$$p_1 + p_2 + p_3 = (2 + 4 + 8)\left(\tfrac{1}{55}\right) \approx .255$$

We can use p_n to determine measures of performance for the B&K situation. For example,

$$\begin{pmatrix}\text{Expected number} \\ \text{of idle counters}\end{pmatrix} = 3p_0 + 2(p_1 + p_2 + p_3) + 1(p_4 + p_5 + p_6)$$
$$+ 0(p_7 + p_8 + \cdots)$$
$$= 1 \text{ counter}$$

PROBLEM SET 18.5A

1. In Example 18.5-1, determine the following:
   (a) The probability distribution of the number of open counters.
   (b) The average number of busy counters.

2. In the B&K model of Example 18.5-1, suppose that the interarrival time at the checkout area is exponential with mean 8 minutes and that the checkout time per customer is also exponential with mean 12 minutes. Suppose further that B&K will add a fourth counter and that counters will open based on increments of two customers. Determine the following:
   (a) The steady-state probabilities, p_n for all n.
   (b) The probability that a fourth counter will be needed.
   (c) The average number of idle counters.

*3. In the B&K model of Example 18.5-1, suppose that all three counters are always open and that the operation is set up such that the customer will go to the first empty counter. Determine the following:
   (a) The probability that all three counters will be in use.
   (b) The probability that an arriving customer will not wait.

4. First Bank of Springdale operates a one-lane drive-in ATM machine. Cars arrive according to a Poisson distribution at the rate of 10 cars per hour. The time per car

needed to complete the ATM transaction is exponential with mean 5 minutes. The lane can accommodate a total of 6 cars. Once the lane is full, other arriving cars seek service in another branch. Determine the following:

(a) The probability that an arriving car will not be able to use the ATM machine because the lane is full.

(b) The probability that a car will not be able to use the ATM machine immediately on arrival.

(c) The average number of cars in the lane.

5. Have you ever heard someone repeat the contradictory statement, "The place is so crowded no one goes there any more"? This statement can be interpreted as saying that the opportunity for balking increases with the increase in the number of customers seeking service. A possible platform for modeling this situation is to say that the arrival rate at the system decreases as the number of customers in the system increases. More specifically, we consider the simplified case of M&M Pool Club, where customers usually arrive in pairs to "shoot pool." The normal arrival rate is 6 pairs (of people) per hour. However, once the number of pairs in the pool hall exceeds 8, the arrival rate drops to 5 pairs per hour. The arrival process is assumed to follow the Poisson distribution. Each pair shoots pool for an exponential time with mean 30 minutes. The pool hall has a total of 5 tables and can accommodate no more than 12 pairs at any one time. Determine the following:

(a) The probability that customers will begin balking.

(b) The probability that all tables are in use.

(c) The average number of tables in use.

(d) The average number of pairs waiting for a pool table to be available.

*6. A barbershop serves one customer at a time and provides three seats for waiting customers. If the place is full, customers go elsewhere. Arrivals occur according to a Poisson distribution with mean 4 per hour. The time to get a haircut is exponential with mean 15 minutes. Determine the following:

(a) The steady-state probabilities.

(b) The expected number of customers in the shop.

(c) The probability that customers will go elsewhere because the shop is full.

7. Consider a one-server queuing situation in which the arrival and service rates are given by

$$\lambda_n = 10 - n, n = 0, 1, 2, 3$$

$$\mu_n = \frac{n}{2} + 5, n = 1, 2, 3, 4$$

This situation is equivalent to reducing the arrival rate and increasing the service rate as the number in the system, n, increases.

(a) Set up the transition diagram, and determine the balance equation for the system.

(b) Determine the steady-state probabilities.

8. Consider the single queue model, where only one customer is allowed in the system. Customers who arrive and find the facility busy never return. Assume that the arrivals distribution is Poisson with mean λ per unit time and that the service time is exponential with mean $\frac{1}{\mu}$ time units.

(a) Set up the transition diagram, and determine the balance equations.

(b) Determine the steady-state probabilities.

(c) Determine the average number in the system.

9. The induction proof for deriving the general solution of the generalized model is applied as follows. Consider

$$p_k = \prod_{i=0}^{k-1}\left(\frac{\lambda_i}{\mu_{i+1}}\right)p_0,\ k = 0, 1, 2, \ldots$$

We substitute for p_{n-1} and p_{n-2} in the general difference equation involving p_n, p_{n-1}, and p_{n-2} to derive the desired expression for p_n. Verify this procedure.

18.6 SPECIALIZED POISSON QUEUES

Figure 18.3 depicts the specialized Poisson queuing situation with c parallel servers. A waiting customer is selected from the queue to start service with the first available server. The arrival rate at the system is λ customers per unit time. All parallel servers are identical, meaning that the service rate for any server is μ customers per unit time. The number of customers in the *system* is defined to include those *in service* and those waiting *in queue*.

A convenient notation for summarizing the characteristics of the queuing situation in Figure 18.3 is given by the following format:

$$(a/b/c):(d/e/f)$$

where

    a = Arrivals distribution
    b = Departures (service time) distribution
    c = Number of parallel servers (= 1, 2, ..., ∞)
    d = Queue discipline
    e = Maximum number (finite or infinite) allowed in the system
        (in-queue plus in-service)
    f = Size of the calling source (finite or infinite)

FIGURE 18.3

Schematic representation of a queuing system with c parallel servers

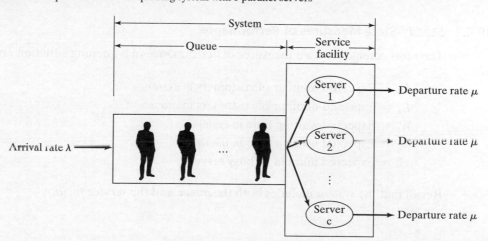

The standard notation for representing the arrivals and departures distributions (symbols *a* and *b*) is

M = Markovian (or Poisson) arrivals or departures distribution
    (or equivalently exponential interarrival or service time distribution)
D = Constant (deterministic) time
E_k = Erlang or gamma distribution of time
    (or, equivalently, the sum of independent exponential distributions)
GI = General (generic) distribution of interarrival time
G = General (generic) distribution of service time

The queue discipline notation (symbol *d*) include

$FCFS$ = First-come, first-served
$LCFS$ = Last-come, first-served
$SIRO$ = Service in random order
GD = General discipline (i.e., any type of discipline)

To illustrate the use of the notation, the model $(M/D/10):(GD/20/\infty)$ uses Poisson arrivals (or exponential interarrival time), constant service time, and 10 parallel servers. The queue discipline is GD, and there is a limit of 20 customers on the entire system. The size of the source from which customers arrive is infinite.

As a historical note, the first three elements of the notation (*a*/*b*/*c*) were devised by D.G. Kendall in 1953 and are known in the literature as the **Kendall notation**. In 1966, A.M. Lee added the symbols *d* and *e* to the notation. This author added the last element, symbol *f*, in 1968.

Before presenting the details of the specialized Poisson queues, we show how the steady-state measures of performance of the generalized queuing situation can be derived from the steady-state probabilities p_n given in Section 18.5.

18.6.1 Steady-State Measures of Performance

The most commonly used measures of performance in a queuing situation are

L_s = Expected number of customers in *system*
L_q = Expected number of customers in *queue*
W_s = Expected waiting time in *system*
W_q = Expected waiting time in *queue*
$\bar{c}$ = Expected number of busy servers

Recall that the *system* includes both the *queue* and the *service facility*.

We show now how these measures are derived (directly or indirectly) from the steady-state probability of n in the system p_n as

$$L_s = \sum_{n=1}^{\infty} n p_n$$

$$L_q = \sum_{n=c+1}^{\infty} (n - c) p_n$$

The relationship between L_s and W_s (also L_q and W_q) is known as **Little's formula**, and it is given as

$$L_s = \lambda_{\text{eff}} W_s$$

$$L_q = \lambda_{\text{eff}} W_q$$

These relationships are valid under rather general conditions. The parameter λ_{eff} is the *effective* arrival rate at the system. It equals the (nominal) arrival rate λ when all arriving customers can join the system. Otherwise, if some customers cannot join because the system is full (e.g., a parking lot), then $\lambda_{\text{eff}} < \lambda$. We will show later how λ_{eff} is determined.

A direct relationship also exists between W_s and W_q. By definition,

$$\begin{pmatrix} \text{Expected waiting} \\ \text{time in system} \end{pmatrix} = \begin{pmatrix} \text{Expected waiting} \\ \text{time in queue} \end{pmatrix} + \begin{pmatrix} \text{Expected service} \\ \text{time} \end{pmatrix}$$

This translates to

$$W_s = W_q + \frac{1}{\mu}$$

Next, we can relate L_s to L_q by multiplying both sides of the last formula by λ_{eff}, which together with Little's formula gives

$$L_s = L_q + \frac{\lambda_{\text{eff}}}{\mu}$$

The difference between the average number in the system, L_s, and the average number in the queue, L_q, must equal the average number of *busy* servers, $\bar{c}$. Thus,

$$\bar{c} = L_s - L_q = \frac{\lambda_{\text{eff}}}{\mu}$$

It follows that

$$\begin{pmatrix} \text{Facility} \\ \text{utilization} \end{pmatrix} = \frac{\bar{c}}{c}$$

Example 18.6-1

Visitors' parking at Ozark College is limited to 5 spaces only. Cars making use of this space arrive according to a Poisson distribution at the rate of 6 cars per hour. Parking time is exponentially distributed with a mean of 30 minutes. Visitors who cannot find an empty space on arrival may temporarily wait inside the lot until a parked car leaves. That temporary space can hold only 3 cars. Other cars that cannot park or find a temporary waiting space must go elsewhere. Determine the following:

(a) The probability, p_n, of n cars in the system.

(b) The effective arrival rate for cars that actually use the lot.

(c) The average number of cars in the lot.

(d) The average time a car waits for a parking space inside the lot.

(e) The average number of *occupied* parking spaces.

(f) The average utilization of the parking lot.

We note first that a parking space acts as a server, so that the system has a total of $c = 5$ parallel servers. Also, the maximum capacity of the system is $5 + 3 = 8$ cars.

The probability p_n can be determined as a special case of the generalized model in Section 18.5 using

$$\lambda_n = 6 \text{ cars/hour}, \quad n = 0, 1, 2, \ldots, 8$$

$$\mu_n = \begin{cases} n\left(\frac{60}{30}\right) = 2n \text{ cars/hour}, & n = 1, 2, 3, 4, 5 \\ 5\left(\frac{60}{30}\right) = 10 \text{ cars/hour}, & n = 6, 7, 8 \end{cases}$$

From Section 18.5, we get

$$p_n = \begin{cases} \dfrac{3^n}{n!} p_0, & n = 1, 2, 3, 4, 5 \\ \dfrac{3^n}{5!\, 5^{n-5}} p_0, & n = 6, 7, 8 \end{cases}$$

The value of p_0 is computed by substituting $p_n, n = 1, 2, \ldots, 8$, in the following equation

$$p_0 + p_1 + \cdots + p_8 = 1$$

or

$$p_0 + p_0\left(\frac{3}{1!} + \frac{3^2}{2!} + \frac{3^3}{3!} + \frac{3^4}{4!} + \frac{3^5}{5!} + \frac{3^6}{5!5} + \frac{3^7}{5!5^2} + \frac{3^8}{5!5^3} \right) = 1$$

This yields $p_0 = .04812$ (verify!). From p_0, we can now compute p_1 through p_8 as

n	1	2	3	4	5	6	7	8
p_n	.14436	.21654	.21654	.16240	.09744	.05847	.03508	.02105

The effective arrival rate λ_{eff} can be computed by observing the schematic diagram in Figure 18.4, where customers arrive from the source at the rate λ cars per hour. An arriving car may enter the parking lot at the rate λ_{eff} or it may go elsewhere at the rate λ_{lost}. This means that $\lambda = \lambda_{\text{eff}} + \lambda_{\text{lost}}$.

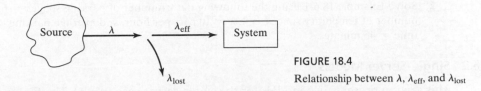

FIGURE 18.4

Relationship between λ, λ_{eff}, and λ_{lost}

A car will not be able to enter the parking lot if 8 cars are already in. This means that the proportion of cars that will *not* be able to enter the lot is p_8. Thus,

$$\lambda_{\text{lost}} = \lambda p_8 = 6 \times .02105 = .1263 \text{ cars/hour}$$

$$\lambda_{\text{eff}} = \lambda - \lambda_{\text{lost}} = 6 - .1263 = 5.8737 \text{ cars/hour}$$

The average number of cars in the lot (those waiting for or occupying a space) equals L_s, the average number in the system. We can compute L_s from p_n as

$$L_s = 0p_0 + 1p_1 + \cdots + 8p_8 = 3.1286 \text{ cars}$$

A car waiting in the temporary space is actually a car in queue. Thus, its waiting time until a space is found is W_q. To determine W_q we use

$$W_q = W_s - \frac{1}{\mu}$$

Thus,

$$W_s = \frac{L_s}{\lambda_{\text{eff}}} = \frac{3.1286}{5.8737} = .53265 \text{ hour}$$

$$W_q = .53265 - \frac{1}{2} = .03265 \text{ hour}$$

The average number of occupied parking spaces is the same as the average number of busy servers,

$$\bar{c} = L_s - L_q = \frac{\lambda_{\text{eff}}}{\mu} = \frac{5.8737}{2} = 2.9368 \text{ spaces}$$

From $\bar{c}$, we get

$$\text{Parking lot utilization} = \frac{\bar{c}}{c} = \frac{2.9368}{5} = .58736$$

PROBLEM SET 18.6A

1. In Example 18.6-1, do the following:
   *(a) Compute L_q directly using the formula $\sum_{n=c+1}^{\infty}(n - c)p_n$.
   (b) Compute W_s from L_q.
   *(c) Compute the average number of cars that will not be able to enter the parking lot during an 8-hour period.
   *(d) Show that $c - (L_s - L_q)$, the average number of empty spaces, equals
   $\sum_{n=0}^{c-1}(c - n)p_n$.

2. Solve Example 18.6-1 using the following data: number of parking spaces = 6, number of temporary spaces = 4, λ = 10 cars per hour, and average parking time = 45 minutes.

18.6.2 Single-Server Models

This section presents two models for the single server case ($c = 1$). The first model sets no limit on the maximum number in the system, and the second model assumes a finite system limit. Both models assume an infinite-capacity source. Arrivals occur at the rate λ customers per unit time and the service rate is μ customers per unit time.

The results of the two models (and indeed of all the remaining models in Section 18.6) are derived as special cases of the results of the generalized model of Section 18.5.

The extended Kendall notation will be used to characterize each situation. Because the derivations of p_n in Section 18.5 and of all the measures of performance in Section 18.6.1 are totally independent of a specific queue discipline, the symbol GD (general discipline) will be used with the notation.

($M/M/1$):($GD/\infty/\infty$).   Using the notation of the general model, we have

$$\left.\begin{array}{l} \lambda_n = \lambda \\ \mu_n = \mu \end{array}\right\}, n = 0, 1, 2, \ldots$$

Also, $\lambda_{\text{eff}} = \lambda$ and $\lambda_{\text{lost}} = 0$, because all arriving customers can join the system.

Letting $\rho = \frac{\lambda}{\mu}$, the expression for p_n in the generalized model reduces to

$$p_n = \rho^n p_0, \ n = 0, 1, 2, \ldots$$

To determine the value of p_0, we use the identity

$$p_0(1 + \rho + \rho^2 + \cdots) = 1$$

The sum of the geometric series is $\left(\frac{1}{1-\rho}\right)$, provided $\rho < 1$. Thus

$$p_0 = 1 - \rho, \ \rho < 1$$

The general formula for p_n is thus given by the following geometric distribution

$$p_n = (1 - \rho)\rho^n, \ n = 1, 2, \ldots \ (\rho < 1)$$

The mathematical derivation of p_n imposes the condition $\rho < 1$, or $\lambda < \mu$. If $\lambda \geq \mu$, the geometric series diverges, and the steady-state probabilities p_n do not exist. This result makes intuitive sense, because unless the service rate is larger than the arrival rate, queue length will continually increase and no steady state can be reached.

The measure of performance L_q can be derived in the following manner:

$$L_s = \sum_{n=0}^{\infty} n p_n = \sum_{n=0}^{\infty} n(1-\rho)\rho^n$$

$$= (1 - \rho)\rho \frac{d}{d\rho} \sum_{n=0}^{\infty} \rho^n$$

$$= (1 - \rho)\rho \frac{d}{d\rho}\left(\frac{1}{1-\rho}\right) = \frac{\rho}{1-\rho}$$

Because $\lambda_{eff} = \lambda$ for the present situation, the remaining measures of performance are computed using the relationships in Section 18.6.1. Thus,

$$W_s = \frac{L_s}{\lambda} = \frac{1}{\mu(1-\rho)} = \frac{1}{\mu - \lambda}$$

$$W_q = W_s - \frac{1}{\mu} = \frac{\rho}{\mu(1-\rho)}$$

$$L_q = \lambda W_q = \frac{\rho^2}{1-\rho}$$

$$\bar{c} = L_s - L_q = \rho$$

Example 18.6-2

Automata car wash is a one-bay facility. Cars arrive according to a Poisson distribution with a mean of 4 cars per hour and may wait in the facility's parking lot or on the street bordering the wash facility if the bay is busy. The time for washing and cleaning a car is exponential, with a mean of 10 minutes. This means that, for all practical purposes, there is no limit on the size of the system. The manager of the facility wants to determine the size of the parking lot.

For this situation, we have $\lambda = 4$ cars per hour, and $\mu = \frac{60}{10} = 6$ cars per hour. Because $\rho = \frac{\lambda}{\mu} < 1$, the system can operate under steady-state conditions. The TORA or *excelPoissonQ.xls* input for this model is

Lambda	Mu	c	System limit	Source limit
4	6	1	infinity	infinity

The output of the model is shown in Figure 18.5. The average number of cars waiting in the queue, L_q, is 1.33 cars.

Generally, using L_q as the sole basis for the determination of the number of parking spaces is not advisable, because the design should, in some sense, account for the maximum possible length of the queue. For example, it may be more plausible to design the parking lot such that an arriving car will find a parking space at least 90% of the time. To do this, let S represent the number of parking spaces. Having S parking spaces is equivalent to having $S + 1$ spaces in the *system* (queue plus wash bay). An arriving car will find a space 90% of the time if there are *at most* S cars in the system. This condition is equivalent to the following probability statement:

$$p_0 + p_1 + \cdots + p_S \geq .9$$

From Figure 18.5, *cumulative* p_n for $n = 5$ is .91221. This means that the condition is satisfied for $S \geq 5$ parking spaces.

The number of spaces S can be determined also by using the mathematical definition of p_n—that is,

$$(1 - \rho)(1 + \rho + \rho^2 + \cdots + \rho^S) \geq .9$$

The sum of the truncated geometric series is $\frac{1 - \rho^{S+1}}{1 - \rho}$, which reduces the condition to

$$(1 - \rho^{S+1}) \geq .9$$

Scenario 1: (M/M/1):(GD/infinity/infinity)

Lambda = 4.00000	Mu = 6.00000
Lambda eff = 4.00000	Rho/c = 0.66667
Ls = 2.00000	Lq = 1.33333
Ws = 0.50000	Wq = 0.33333

n	Probability pn	Cumulative Pn	n	Probability pn	Cumulative Pn
0	0.33333	0.33333	13	0.00171	0.99657
1	0.22222	0.55556	14	0.00114	0.99772
2	0.14815	0.70370	15	0.00076	0.99848
3	0.09877	0.80247	16	0.00051	0.99899
4	0.06584	0.86831	17	0.00034	0.99932
5	0.04390	0.91221	18	0.00023	0.99955
6	0.02926	0.94147	19	0.00015	0.99970
7	0.01951	0.96098	20	0.00010	0.99980
8	0.01301	0.97399	21	0.00007	0.99987
9	0.00867	0.98266	22	0.00004	0.99991
10	0.00578	0.98844	23	0.00003	0.99994
11	0.00385	0.99229	24	0.00002	0.99996
12	0.00257	0.99486	25	0.00001	0.99997

FIGURE 18.5

TORA output of Example 18.6-2 (file *toraEx18.6-2.txt*)

Simplification of the inequality yields

$$\rho^{S+1} \le .1$$

Taking the logarithms on both sides (and noting that log $(x) < 0$ for $0 < x < 1$, which reverses the direction of the inequality), we get

$$S \ge \frac{\ln (.1)}{\ln \left(\frac{4}{6}\right)} - 1 = 4.679 \approx 5$$

PROBLEM SET 18.6B

1. In Example 18.6-2, do the following.
   (a) Determine the percent utilization of the wash bay.
   (b) Determine the probability that an arriving car must wait in the parking lot prior to entering the wash bay.
   (c) If there are 6 parking spaces, determine the probability that an arriving car will find an empty parking space.
   (d) How many parking spaces should be provided so that an arriving car may find a parking space 95% of the time?

*2. John Macko is a student at Ozark U. He does odd jobs to supplement his income. Job requests come every 5 days on the average, but the time between requests is exponential. The time for completing a job is also exponential with mean 4 days.

(a) What is the probability that John will be out of jobs?

(b) If John gets about $50 a job, what is his average monthly income?

(c) If at the end of the semester, John decides to subcontract on the outstanding jobs at $40 each. How much, on the average, should he expect to pay?

3. Over the years, Detective Columbo, of the Fayetteville Police Department, has had phenomenal success in solving every single crime case. It is only a matter of time before any case is solved. Columbo admits that the time per case is "totally random," but, on the average, each investigation will take about a week and half. Crimes in peaceful Fayetteville are not very common. They occur randomly at the rate of one crime per (4-week) month. Detective Columbo is asking for an assistant to share the heavy work load. Analyze Columbo's claim, particularly from the standpoint of the following points:

(a) The average number of cases awaiting investigation.

(b) The percentage of time the detective remains busy.

(c) The average time needed to solve a case.

4. Cars arrive at the Lincoln Tunnel toll gate according to a Poisson distribution, with a mean of 90 cars per hour. The time for passing the gate is exponential with mean 38 seconds. Drivers complain of the long waiting time, and authorities are willing to reduce the average passing time to 30 seconds by installing automatic toll collecting devices, provided two conditions are satisfied: (1) the average number of waiting cars in the present system exceeds 5 and (2) the percentage of the gate idle time with the new device installed does not exceed 10%. Can the new device be justified?

*5. A fast-food restaurant has one drive-in window. Cars arrive according to a Poisson distribution at the rate of 2 cars every 5 minutes. The space in front of the window can accommodate at most 10 cars, including the one being served. Other cars can wait outside this space if necessary. The service time per customer is exponential, with a mean of 1.5 minutes. Determine the following:

(a) The probability that the facility is idle.

(b) The expected number of customers waiting to be served.

(c) The expected waiting time until a customer reaches the window to place an order.

(d) The probability that the waiting line will exceed the 10-space capacity.

6. Customers arrive at a one-window drive-in bank according to a Poisson distribution, with a mean of 10 per hour. The service time per customer is exponential, with a mean of 5 minutes. There are three spaces in front of the window, including the car being served. Other arriving cars line up outside this 3-car space.

(a) What is the probability that an arriving car can enter one of the 3-car spaces?

(b) What is the probability that an arriving car will wait outside the designated 3-car space?

(c) How long is an arriving customer expected to wait before starting service?

+(d) How many car spaces should be provided in front of the window (including the car being served) so that an arriving car can find a space there at least 90% of the time?

7. In the $(M/M/1):(GD/\infty/\infty)$, give a plausible argument as to why L_s does not equal $L_q + 1$, in general. Under what condition will the equality hold?

8. For the $(M/M/1):(GD/\infty/\infty)$, derive the expression for L_q using the basic definition $\sum_{n=2}^{\infty}(n-1)p_n$.

9. For the $(M/M/1){:}(GD/\infty/\infty)$, show that

   (a) The expected number in the queue, given that the queue is not empty, $= \frac{1}{(1-\rho)}$.

   (b) The expected waiting time in the queue for those who must wait $= (\frac{1}{\mu - \lambda})$.

$(M/M/1){:}(GD/N/\infty)$. This model differs from $(M/M/1){:}(GD/\infty/\infty)$ in that there is a limit N on the number in the *system* (maximum queue length $= N - 1$). Examples include manufacturing situations in which a machine may have a limited buffer space and a one-lane drive-in window in a fast-food restaurant. New arrivals are not allowed when the number of customers in the system reaches N. Thus,

$$\lambda_n = \begin{cases} \lambda, & n = 0, 1, \ldots, N - 1 \\ 0, & n = N, N + 1 \end{cases}$$

$$\mu_n = \mu, \quad n = 0, 1, \ldots$$

Using $\rho = \frac{\lambda}{\mu}$, the generalized model in Section 18.5 yields

$$p_n = \begin{cases} \rho^n p_0 & n \leq N \\ 0, & n > N \end{cases}$$

The value of p_0 is determined from the equation $\sum_{n=0}^{\infty} p_n = 1$, which yields

$$p_0 (1 + \rho + p^2 + \cdots + \rho^N) = 1$$

or

$$p_0 = \begin{cases} \dfrac{1 - \rho}{1 - \rho^{N+1}}, & \rho \neq 1 \\[2mm] \dfrac{1 - \rho}{1 - \rho^{N+1}}, & \rho = 1 \end{cases}$$

Thus,

$$p_n = \left\{ \begin{array}{ll} \dfrac{(1 - \rho)\rho^n}{1 - \rho^{N+1}}, & \rho \neq 1 \\[2mm] \dfrac{(1 - \rho)\rho^n}{1 - \rho^{N+1}}, & \rho = 1 \end{array} \right\}, n = 0, 1, \ldots, N$$

The value of $\rho = \frac{\lambda}{\mu}$ need *not* be less than 1 in this model, because arrivals at the system are controlled by the system limit N. This means that λ_{eff}, rather than λ, is the rate that matters in this case. Because customers will be lost when there are N in the system, then, as shown in Figure 18.4,

$$\lambda_{\text{lost}} = \lambda p_N$$

$$\lambda_{\text{eff}} = \lambda - \lambda_{\text{lost}} = \lambda(1 - p_N)$$

In this case, $\lambda_{\text{eff}} < \mu$.

The expected number of customers in the system is computed as

$$L_s = \sum_{n=1}^{N} n p_n$$

$$= \frac{1-\rho}{1-\rho^{N+1}} \sum_{n=0}^{N} n \rho^n$$

$$= \left(\frac{1-\rho}{1-\rho^{N+1}} \right) \rho \frac{d}{d\rho} \sum_{n=0}^{N} \rho^n$$

$$= \frac{(1-\rho)\rho}{1-\rho^{N+1}} \frac{d}{d\rho} \left(\frac{1-\rho^{N+1}}{1-\rho} \right)$$

$$= \frac{\rho[1-(N+1)\rho^N + N\rho^{N+1}]}{(1-\rho)(1-\rho^{N+1})}, \rho \neq 1$$

When $\rho = 1$, $L_s = \frac{N}{2}$ (verify!). We can derive W_s, W_q, and L_q from L_s using λ_{eff} as shown in Section 18.6.1.

The use of a hand calculator to compute the queuing formulas is at best cumbersome (the formulas get more complex in later models!). The use of TORA or the template *excelPoissonQ.xls* to handle these computations is recommended.

Example 18.6-4

Consider the car wash facility of Example 18.6-2. Suppose that the facility has a total of 4 parking spaces. If the parking lot is full, newly arriving cars balk to other facilities. The owner wishes to determine the impact of the limited parking space on losing customers to the competition.

In terms of the notation of the model, the limit on the system is $N = 4 + 1 = 5$. The following input data provide the output in Figure 18.6.

Lambda	Mu	c	System limit	Source limit
4	6	1	5	infinity

Because the limit on the system is $N = 5$, the proportion of lost customers is $p_5 = .04812$, which, based on a 24-hour day, is equivalent to losing the business of $(\lambda p_5) \times 24 = 4 \times .04812 \times 24 = 4.62$ cars a day. A decision regarding increasing the size of the parking lot should be based on the value of lost business.

Looking at the problem from a different angle, the expected total time in the system, W_s, is .3736 hour, or approximately 22 minutes, down from 30 minutes in Example 18.6-3, when all arriving cars are allowed to join the facility. This reduction of about 25% is secured at the expense of losing about 4.8% of all potential customers because of the limited parking space.

Scenario 1:(M/M/1):(GD/5/infinity)
___

Lambda = 4.00000   Mu = 6.00000
Lambda eff = 3.80752   Rho/c = 0.66667

Ls = 1.42256   Lq = 0.78797
Ws = 0.37362   Wq = 0.20695
___

n	Probability pn	Cumulative Pn	n	Probability pn	Cumulative Pn
0	0.36541	0.36541	3	0.10827	0.87970
1	0.24361	0.60902	4	0.07218	0.95188
2	0.16241	0.77143	5	0.04812	1.00000
___

FIGURE 18.6

TORA output of Example 18.6-4 (file *toraEx18.6-4.txt*)

PROBLEM SET 18.6C

*1. In Example 18.6-4, determine the following:

  (a) Probability that an arriving car will go into the wash bay immediately on arrival.

  (b) Expected waiting time until a service starts.

  (c) Expected number of empty parking spaces.

  (d) Probability that all parking spaces are occupied.

  (e) Percent reduction in average service time that will limit the average time in the system to about 10 minutes. (*Hint*: Use trial and error with *excelPoissonQ.xls* or TORA.)

2. Consider the car wash facility of Example 18.6-4. Determine the number of parking spaces such that the percentage of cars that cannot find a space does not exceed 3%.

3. The time barber Joe takes to give a haircut is exponential with a mean of 12 minutes. Because of his popularity, customers usually arrive (according to a Poisson distribution) at a rate much higher than Joe can handle: 6 customers per hour. Joe will really feel comfortable if the arrival rate is effectively reduced to about 4 customers per hour. To accomplish this goal, he came up with the idea of providing limited seating in the waiting area so that newly arriving customers will go elsewhere when they discover that all the seats are taken. How many seats should Joe provide to accomplish his goal?

*4. The final assembly of electric generators at Electro is produced at the Poisson rate of 10 generators per hour. The generators are then conveyed on a belt to the inspection department for final testing. The belt can hold a maximum of 7 generators. An electronic sensor will automatically stop the conveyor once it is full, preventing the final assembly department from assembling more units until a space becomes available. The time to inspect the generators is exponential, with a mean of 15 minutes.

  (a) What is the probability that the final assembly department will stop production?

  (b) What is the average number of generators on the conveyor belt?

  (c) The production engineer claims that interruptions in the assembly department can be reduced by increasing the capacity of the belt. In fact, the engineer claims that the capacity can be increased to the point where the assembly department can operate 95% of the time without interruption. Is this claim justifiable?

5. A cafeteria can seat a maximum of 50 persons. Customers arrive in a Poisson stream at the rate of 10 per hour and are served (one at a time) at the rate of 12 per hour.

   (a) What is the probability that an arriving customer will not eat in the cafeteria because it is full?

   (b) Suppose that 3 customers (with random arrival times) would like to be seated together. What is the probability that their wish can be fulfilled? (Assume that arrangements can be made to seat them together as long as three seats are available.)

6. Patients arrive at a 1-doctor clinic according to a Poisson distribution at the rate of 20 patients per hour. The waiting room does not accommodate more than 14 patients. Examination time per patient is exponential, with a mean of 8 minutes.

   (a) What is the probability that an arriving patient will not wait?

   (b) What is the probability that an arriving patient will find a seat in the room?

   (c) What is the expected total time a patient spends in the clinic?

7. The probabilities p_n of n customers in the system for an $(M/M/1):(GD/5/\infty)$ are given in the following table:

n	0	1	2	3	4	5
p_n	.399	.249	.156	.097	.061	.038

   The arrival rate λ is 5 customers per hour. The service rate μ is 8 customers per hour. Compute the following:

   *(a) Probability that an arriving customer will be able to enter the system.

   *(b) Rate at which the arriving customers will not be able to enter the system.

   (c) Expected number in the system.

   (d) Average waiting time in the queue.

8. Show that when $\rho = 1$ for $(M/M/1):(GD/N/\infty)$, the expected number in the system, L_s, equals $\frac{N}{2}$. ($Hint: 1 + 2 + \cdots + i = \frac{i(i+1)}{2}$.)

9. Show that λ_{eff} for $(M/M/1):(GD/N/\infty)$ can be computed from the formula

   $$\lambda_{\text{eff}} = \mu(L_s - L_q)$$

18.6.3 Multiple-Server Models

This section considers three queuing models with multiple parallel servers. The first two models are the multiserver versions of the models in Section 18.6.2. The third model treats the self-service case, which is equivalent to having an infinite number of parallel servers.

Real-Life Application—Telephone Sales Manpower Planning at Qantas Airways

To reduce operating costs, Qantas Airways seeks to staff its main telephone sales reservation office efficiently while providing convenient service to its customers. Traditionally, staffing needs are estimated by forecasting future telephone calls based on historical increase in business. The increase in staff numbers is then calculated based on the projected average increase in telephone calls divided by the average number of calls an operator can handle. Because the calculations are based on averages, the additional number of hired staff does not take into account the fluctuations in demand during the day. In particular, long waiting time for service during peak business hours has resulted in customer complaints and lost business. The problem deals with the determination of a plan that strikes a balance between the number of hired operators and the customer needs. The solution uses $(M/M/c)$ queuing analysis imbedded into an integer programming model. Savings from the model in the Sydney office alone were around \$173,000 in fiscal year 1975–1976. The details of the study are given in Case 15, Chapter 26, on the website.

(M/M/c):(GD/∞/∞). This model deals with c identical parallel servers. The arrival rate is λ and the service rate per server is μ. In this situation, $\lambda_{eff} = \lambda$ because there is no limit on the number in the system.

The effect of using c identical parallel servers is a proportionate increase in the facility service rate. In terms of the generalized model (Section 18.5), λ_n and μ_n are thus defined as

$$\lambda_n = \lambda, \qquad n \geq 0$$

$$\mu_n = \begin{cases} n\mu, & n < c \\ c\mu, & n \geq c \end{cases}$$

Thus,

$$p_n = \begin{cases} \dfrac{\lambda^n}{\mu(2\mu)(3\mu)\dots(n\mu)}p_0 = \dfrac{\lambda^n}{n!\,\mu^n}p_0 = \dfrac{\rho^n}{n!}p_0, & n < c \\[2ex] \dfrac{\lambda^n}{\left(\prod_{i=1}^{c}i\mu\right)(c\mu)^{n-c}}p_0 = \dfrac{\lambda^n}{c!\,c^{n-c}\mu^n}p_0 = \dfrac{\rho^n}{c!\,c^{n-c}}\,p_0, & n \geq c \end{cases}$$

Letting $\rho = \frac{\lambda}{\mu}$, and assuming $\frac{\rho}{c} < 1$, the value of p_0 is determined from $\sum_{n=0}^{\infty} p_n = 1$, which gives,

$$p_0 = \left\{ \sum_{n=0}^{c-1} \frac{\rho^n}{n!} + \frac{\rho^c}{c!} \sum_{n=c}^{\infty} \left(\frac{\rho}{c}\right)^{n-c} \right\}^{-1}$$

$$= \left\{ \sum_{n=0}^{c-1} \frac{\rho^n}{n!} + \frac{\rho^c}{c!}\left(\frac{1}{1-\frac{\rho}{c}}\right) \right\}^{-1}, \frac{\rho}{c} < 1$$

The expression for L_q can be determined as follows:

$$L_q = \sum_{n=c}^{\infty} (n - c)p_n$$

$$= \sum_{k=0}^{\infty} k p_{k+c}$$

$$= \sum_{k=0}^{\infty} k \frac{\rho^{k+c}}{c^k c!} p_0$$

$$= \frac{\rho^{c+1}}{c!c} p_0 \sum_{k=0}^{\infty} k \left(\frac{\rho}{c} \right)^{k-1}$$

$$= \frac{\rho^{c+1}}{c!c} p_0 \frac{d}{d\left(\frac{\rho}{c} \right)} \sum_{k=0}^{\infty} \left(\frac{\rho}{c} \right)^{k}$$

$$= \frac{\rho^{c+1}}{(c-1)!(c-\rho)^2} p_0$$

because $\lambda_{\text{eff}} = \lambda$, $L_s = L_q + \rho$. The measures W_s and W_q are determined by dividing L_s and L_q by λ.

Example 18.6-5

A community is served by two cab companies. Each company owns two cabs, and both share the market equally, with call arriving at each company's dispatching office at the average rate of 8 per hour. The average time per ride is 12 minutes. Calls arrive according to a Poisson distribution, and the ride time is exponential. The two companies have been bought by an investor and will be consolidated into a single dispatching office. Analyze the new owner's proposal.

From the standpoint of queuing, the cabs are the servers, and the cab ride is the service. Each company can be represented by the model $(M/M/2):(GD/\infty/\infty)$ with $\lambda = 8$ calls per hour and $\mu = \frac{60}{10} = 5$ rides per cab per hour. The consolidated model is $(M/M/4):(GD/\infty/\infty)$, with $\lambda = 2 \times 8 = 16$ calls per hour and $\mu = 5$ rides per cab per hour.

A suitable measure for comparing the two models is the average waiting time for a ride, W_q. The following table gives TORA comparative analysis input data.

Scenario	Lambda	Mu	c	System limit	Source limit
1	8	5	2	infinity	infinity
2	16	5	4	infinity	infinity

Figure 18.7 provides the output for the two scenarios. The results show that the waiting time for a ride is .356 hour (≈ 21 minutes) for the two-cab situation and .149 (≈ 9 minutes) for the consolidated situation, a remarkable reduction of more than 50% and a clear evidence that the consolidation of the two companies is warranted.

Remarks. The conclusion from the preceding analysis is that **service pools** *always* provide a more efficient mode of operation. This result is true even if the separate installations happen to be "very" busy (see Problems 2 and 10, Sct 18.6D).

FIGURE 18.7

TORA output for Example 18.6-5 (file *toraEx18.6-5.txt*)

```
Comparative analysis
```

c	Lambda	Mu	L'da eff	p0	Ls	Ws	Lq	Wq
2	8.000	5.000	8.00	0.110	4.444	0.556	2.844	0.356
4	16.000	5.000	16.00	0.027	5.586	0.349	2.386	0.149

PROBLEM SET 18.6D

1. Consider Exampl~

    (a) Show th~~ ~emarkable reduction in waiting time by more than 50% for the consolidated case is coupled with an increase in the percentage of time the servers remain busy.

    (b) Suppose that calls for cab service in the consolidated company is increased to 20 customers per hour. What is the minimum number of cabs the company should employ?

    (c) In part (b), determine the minimum number of cabs that would limit the average waiting time for a ride to less than 5 minutes.

*2. In the cab company example, suppose that the average time per ride is actually about 14.5 minutes, so that the utilization $\left(=\frac{\lambda}{\mu c}\right)$ for the 2- and 4-cab operations increases to more than 96%. Is it still worthwhile to consolidate the two companies into one? Use the average waiting time for a ride as the comparison measure.

3. Determine the minimum number of parallel servers needed in each of the following (Poisson arrival/departure) situations to guarantee that the operation of the queuing situation will be stable (i.e., the queue length will not grow indefinitely):

    (a) Customers arrive every 6 minutes and are served at the rate of 10 customers per hour.

    (b) The average interarrival time is 3 minutes, and the average service time is 6 minutes.

    (c) The arrival rate is 25 customers per hour, and the service rate per server is 30 customers per hour.

4. Customers arrive at Thrift Bank according to a Poisson distribution, with a mean of 45 customers per hour. Transactions per customer last about 5 minutes and are exponentially distributed. The bank wants to use a single-line multiple-teller operation, similar to the ones used in airports and post offices. The manager is conscious of the fact that customers may switch to other banks if they perceive that their wait in line is "excessive." For this reason, the manager wants to limit the average waiting time in the queue to no more than 3 minutes. How many tellers should the bank provide?

*5. McBurger fast-food restaurant has 3 cashiers. Customers arrive according to a Poisson distribution every 3 minutes and form one line to be served by the first available cashier. The time to fill an order is exponentially distributed with a mean of 5 minutes. The waiting room inside the restaurant is limited. However, the food is good, and customers are willing to line up outside the restaurant, if necessary. Determine the size of the waiting room inside the restaurant (excluding those at the cashiers) such that the probability that an arriving customer does not wait outside the restaurant is at least .999.

6. A small post office has two open windows. Customers arrive according to a Poisson distribution at the rate of 1 every 3 minutes. However, only 80% of them seek service at the windows. The service time per customer is exponential, with a mean of 5 minutes. All arriving customers form one line and access available windows on an FCFS basis.

    (a) What is the probability that an arriving customer will wait in line?

    (b) What is the probability that both windows are idle?

    (c) What is the average length of the waiting line?

    (d) Would it be possible to offer reasonable service with only one window? Explain.

7. U of A computer center is equipped with 4 identical mainframe computers. The number of users at any time is 25. Each user is capable of submitting a job from a terminal every 15 minutes, on the average, but the actual time between submissions is exponential. Arriving jobs will automatically go to the first available computer. The execution time per submission is exponential with mean 2 minutes. Compute the following:

    *(a) The probability that a job is not executed immediately on submission.

    (b) The average time until the output of a job is returned to the user.

    (c) The average number of jobs awaiting execution.

    (d) The percentage of time the entire computer center is idle.

  *(e) The average number of idle computers.

8. Drake Airport services rural, suburban, and transit passengers. The arrival distribution for each of the three groups is Poisson with mean rates of 15, 10, and 20 passengers per hour, respectively. The time to check in a passenger is exponential with mean 6 minutes. Determine the number of counters that should be provided at Drake under each of the following conditions:

    (a) The total average time to check a customer in is less than 15 minutes.

    (b) The percentage of idleness of the counters does not exceed 10%.

    (c) The probability that all counters are idle does not exceed .01.

9. In the United States, the use of single-line, multiple-server queues is common in post offices and in passenger check-in counters at airports. However, both grocery stores and banks (especially in smaller communities) tend to favor single-line, single-server setups, despite the fact that single-line, multiple-server queues offer a more efficient operation. Comment on this observation.

10. For the $(M/M/c){:}(GD/\infty/\infty)$ model, Morse (1958, p. 103) shows that as $\frac{\rho}{c} \to 1$,

$$L_q = \frac{\rho}{c - \rho}$$

Noting that $\frac{\rho}{c} \to 1$ means that the servers are extremely busy, use this information to show that the ratio of the average waiting time in queue in the $(M/M/c){:}(GD/\infty/\infty)$ model to that in the $(M/M/1){:}(GD/\infty/\infty)$ model approaches $\frac{1}{c}$ as $\frac{\rho}{c} \to 1$. Thus, for $c = 2$, the average waiting time can be reduced by 50%. The conclusion from this exercise is that it is always advisable to pool services regardless of how "overloaded" the servers may be.

11. In the derivation of p_n for the $(M/M/c){:}(GD/\infty/\infty)$ model, indicate which part of the derivation requires the condition $\frac{\rho}{c} < 1$. Explain verbally the meaning of the condition. What will happen if the condition is not satisfied?

12. Prove that $L_s = L_q + \bar{c}$ starting with the definition $L_q = \sum_{n=c+1}^{\infty}(n - c)p_n$, where $\bar{c}$ is the average number of busy servers. Hence, show that $\bar{c} = \frac{\lambda_{\text{eff}}}{\mu}$.

13. Show that p_n for the $(M/M/1){:}(GD/\infty/\infty)$ model can be obtained from that of the $(M/M/c){:}(GD/\infty/\infty)$ model by setting $c = 1$.

14. Show that for the $(M/M/c){:}(GD/\infty/\infty)$ model

$$L_q = \frac{c\rho}{(c-\rho)^2}\, p_c$$

15. For the $(M/M/c){:}(GD/\infty/\infty)$ model, show that

    (a) The probability that a customer is waiting is $\frac{\rho}{(c - \rho)}\, p_c$.

    (b) The average number in the queue given that it is not empty is $\frac{c}{(c - \rho)}$.

    (c) The expected waiting time in the queue for customers who must wait is $\frac{1}{\mu(c - \rho)}$.

$(M/M/c){:}(GD/N/\infty)$, $c \le N$. This model differs from $(M/M/c){:}(GD/\infty/\infty)$ in that the system limit is finite and equal to N. This means that the maximum queue size is $N - c$. The arrival and service rates are λ and μ. The effective arrival rate λ_{eff} is less than λ because of the system limit, N.

In terms of the generalized model (Section 18.5), λ_n and μ_n for the current model are defined as

$$\lambda_n = \begin{cases} \lambda, & 0 \le n \le N \\ 0, & n > N \end{cases}$$

$$\mu_n = \begin{cases} n\mu, & 0 \le n \le c \\ c\mu, & c \le n \le N \end{cases}$$

Substituting λ_n and μ_n in the general expression in Section 18.5 and noting that $\rho = \frac{\lambda}{\mu}$, we get

$$p_n = \begin{cases} \dfrac{\rho^n}{n!} p_0, & 0 \le n < c \\[3mm] \dfrac{\rho^n}{c!c^{n-c}} p_0, & c \le n \le N \end{cases}$$

where

$$p_0 = \begin{cases} \left(\displaystyle\sum_{n=0}^{c-1} \dfrac{\rho^n}{n!} + \dfrac{\rho^c \left(1 - \left(\frac{\rho}{c} \right)^{N-c+1} \right)}{c! \left(1 - \left(\frac{\rho}{c} \right) \right)} \right)^{-1}, & \dfrac{\rho}{c} \ne 1 \\[5mm] \left(\displaystyle\sum_{n=0}^{c-1} \dfrac{\rho^n}{n!} + \dfrac{\rho^c}{c!}(N - c + 1) \right)^{-1}, & \dfrac{\rho}{c} = 1 \end{cases}$$

Next, we compute L_q for the case where $\frac{\rho}{c} \ne 1$ as

$$L_q = \sum_{n=c}^{N} (n - c) p_n$$

$$= \sum_{j=0}^{N-c} j p_{j+c}$$

$$= \frac{\rho^c \rho}{c!c} p_0 \sum_{j=0}^{N-c} j \left(\frac{\rho}{c} \right)^{j-1}$$

$$= \frac{\rho^{c+1}}{cc!} p_0 \frac{d}{d\left(\frac{\rho}{c} \right)} \sum_{j=0}^{N-c} \left(\frac{\rho}{c} \right)^{j}$$

$$= \frac{\rho^{c+1}}{(c-1)!(c-\rho)^2} \left\{ 1 - \left(\frac{\rho}{c} \right)^{N-c+1} - (N - c + 1)\left(1 - \frac{\rho}{c} \right)\left(\frac{\rho}{c} \right)^{N-c} \right\} p_0$$

It can be shown that for $\frac{\rho}{c} = 1$, L_q reduces to

$$L_q = \frac{\rho^c (N - c)(N - c + 1)}{2c!} p_0, \quad \frac{\rho}{c} = 1$$

To determine W_q and hence W_s and L_s, we compute the value of λ_{eff} as

$$\lambda_{\text{lost}} = \lambda p_N$$

$$\lambda_{\text{eff}} = \lambda - \lambda_{\text{lost}} = (1 - p_N)\lambda$$

Example 18.6-6

In the consolidated cab company problem of Example 18.6-5, suppose that new funds cannot be secured to purchase additional cabs. The owner was advised that one way to reduce the waiting time is for the dispatching office to inform new customers of potential excessive delay once the waiting list reaches 6 customers. The expectation is that these customers will seek service elsewhere, which in turn will reduce the average waiting time for those on the waiting list. Assess the situation.

Limiting the waiting list to 6 customers is equivalent to setting $N = 6 + 4 = 10$ customers, leading to the model $(M/M/4):(GD/10/\infty)$ with $\lambda = 16$ customers per hour and $\mu = 5$ rides per hour. The following input data provide the results in Figure 18.8.

Lambda	Mu	c	System limit	Source limit
16	5	4	10	infinity

The average waiting time, W_q, before setting a limit on the capacity of the system is .149 hour (≈ 9 minutes) (see Figure 18.7), which is about twice the new average of .075 hour (≈ 4.5 minutes) This remarkable reduction is achieved at the expense of losing about 3.6% of potential customers ($p_{10} = .03574$). However, this result does not reflect the intangible loss of customer goodwill on the operation of the company.

PROBLEM SET 18.6E

1. In Example 18.6-6, determine the following:
   (a) The expected number of idle cabs.
   (b) The probability that a calling customer will be next to last on the list.
   (c) The limit on the waiting list if it is desired to keep the waiting time in the queue to below 3.5 minutes.

FIGURE 18.8

TORA output of Example 18.6-6 (file *toraEx18.6-6.txt*)

Scenario1: (M/M/4):(GD/10/infinity)

Lambda =	16.00000		Mu =	5.00000
Lambda eff =	15.42815		Rho/c =	0.80000
Ls =	4.23984		Lq =	1.15421
Ws =	0.27481		Wq =	0.07481

n	Probability pn	Cumulative Pn	n	Probability pn	Cumulative Pn
0	0.03121	0.03121	6	0.08726	0.79393
1	0.09986	0.13106	7	0.06981	0.86374
2	0.15977	0.29084	8	0.05584	0.91958
3	0.17043	0.46126	9	0.04468	0.96426
4	0.13634	0.59760	10	0.03574	1.00000

2. Eat & Gas convenience store operates a two-pump gas station. The lane leading to the pumps can house at most 3 cars, excluding those being serviced. Arriving cars go elsewhere if the lane is full. The distribution of arriving cars is Poisson with mean 20 per hour. The time to fill up and pay for the purchase is exponential with mean 6 minutes. Determine the following:

    (a) Percentage of cars that will seek business elsewhere.

    (b) Percentage of time both pumps are in use.

    *(c) Percent utilization of the two pumps.

    *(d) Probability that an arriving car will not start service immediately but will find an empty space in the lane.

    (e) Capacity of the lane that will ensure that, on the average, no more than 10% of the arriving cars are turned away.

    (f) Capacity of the lane that will ensure that the probability that both pumps are idle is .1 or less.

3. A small engine repair shop is run by three mechanics. Early in March of each year, people bring in their tillers and lawn mowers for service and maintenance. The shop is willing to accept all the tillers and mowers that customers bring in. However, when new customers see the floor of the shop covered with waiting jobs, they go elsewhere for more prompt service. The floor shop can house a maximum of 12 mowers or tillers, excluding those being serviced. The customers arrive at the shop every 15 minutes on the average, and it takes a mechanic an average of 40 minutes to complete each job. Both the interarrival and the service times are exponential. Determine the following:

    (a) Average number of idle mechanics.

    (b) Amount of business lost to competition per 8-hour day because of the limited capacity of the shop.

    (c) Probability that the next arriving customer will be serviced by the shop.

    (d) Probability that at least one of the mechanics will be idle.

    (e) Average number of tillers or mowers awaiting service.

    (f) A measure of the overall productivity of the shop.

4. At U of A, newly enrolled freshmen students are notorious for wanting to drive their cars to class (even though most of them are required to live on campus and can conveniently make use of the university's free transit system). During the first couple of weeks of the fall semester, traffic havoc prevails on campus as freshmen try desperately to find parking spaces. With unusual dedication, the students wait patiently in the lanes of the parking lot for someone to leave so they can park their cars. Let us consider a specific scenario: The parking lot has 30 parking spaces but can also accommodate 10 more cars in the lanes. These additional 10 cars cannot park in the lanes permanently and must await the availability of one of the 30 parking spaces. Freshman students arrive at the parking lot according to a Poisson distribution, with a mean of 20 cars per hour. The parking time per car averages about 60 minutes but actually follows an exponential distribution.

    *(a) What is the percentage of freshmen who are turned away because they cannot enter the lot?

    *(b) What is the probability that an arriving car will wait in the lanes?

    (c) What is the probability that an arriving car will occupy the only remaining parking space on the lot?

    *(d) Determine the average number of occupied parking spaces.

*(e) Determine the average number of spaces that are occupied in the lanes.

(f) Determine the number of freshmen who will not make it to class during an 8-hour period because the parking lot is totally full.

5. Verify the expression for p_0 for the $(M/M/c):(GD/N/\infty)$ model, given that $\frac{\rho}{c} \neq 1$

6. Prove the following equality for $(M/M/c):(GD/N/\infty)$:

$$\lambda_{\text{eff}} = \mu\bar{c},$$

where $\bar{c}$ is the number of busy servers.

7. Verify the expression for p_0 and L_q for $(M/M/c):(GD/N/\infty)$ when $\frac{\rho}{c} = 1$.

8. For $(M/M/c):(GD/N/\infty)$ with which $N = c$, define λ_n and μ_n in terms of the general model (Section 18.5), then show that the expression for p_n is given as

$$p_n = \frac{\rho^n}{n!} p_0, n = 1, 2, \ldots, c$$

where

$$p_0 = \left(1 + \sum_{n=1}^{c} \frac{\rho^n}{n!}\right)^{-1}$$

$(M/M/\infty):(GD/\infty \neq \infty)$—Self-Service Model. In this model, the arrival and service rates are λ and μ, respectively, and the number of servers is unlimited because the customer is also the server. A typical example is taking the written part of a driver's license test. Self-service gas stations and 24-hour ATM banks do not fall under this model because the servers in these cases are actually the gas pumps and the ATM machines.

In terms of the general model of Section 18.5, we have

$$\lambda_n = \lambda, \quad n = 0, 1, 2, \ldots$$

$$\mu_n = n\mu, \quad n = 0, 1, 2, \ldots$$

Thus,

$$p_n = \frac{\lambda^n}{n!\mu^n} p_0 = \frac{\rho^n}{n!} p_0, n = 0, 1, 2, \ldots$$

Because $\sum_{n=0}^{\infty} p_n = 1$, it follows that

$$p_0 = \frac{1}{1 + \rho + \dfrac{\rho^2}{2!} + \cdots} = \frac{1}{e^\rho} = e^{-\rho}$$

As a result,

$$p_n = \frac{e^{-\rho}\rho^n}{n!}, n = 0, 1, 2, \ldots$$

which is Poisson with mean $L_s = \rho$. As should be expected, L_q and W_q are zero because it is a self-service facility.

Example 18.6-7

An investor invests $1000 a month, on average, in a stock market security. Because the investor must wait for good "buy" opportunity, the actual time of purchase is random. The investor usually keeps the securities for about 3 years on the average but will sell at random times when a good "sell" opportunity presents itself. Although the investor is generally recognized as a shrewd stock market player, past experience indicates that about 25% of the securities decline at about 20% a year. The remaining 75% appreciate at the rate of about 12% a year. Estimate the investor's (long-run) average equity in the stock market.

This situation can be treated as $(M/M/\infty):(GD/\infty/\infty)$ because, for all practical purposes, the investor does not have to wait in line to buy or to sell securities. The average time between order placements is 1 month, which yields $\lambda = 12$ securities per year. The rate of selling securities is $\mu = \frac{1}{3}$ security per year. You can secure the model output using the following input:

Lambda	Mu	c	System limit	Source limit
12	.3333333	infinity	infinity	infinity

Given the values of λ and μ, we obtain

$$L_s = \rho = \frac{\lambda}{\mu} = 36 \text{ securities}$$

The estimate of the (long-run) average *annual* net worth of the investor is

$$(.25L_s \times \$1000)(1 - .20) + (.75L_s \times \$1000)(1 + .12) = \$63,990$$

PROBLEM SET 18.6F

1. In Example 18.6-7, compute the following:
   (a) The probability that the investor will sell out completely.
   (b) The probability that the investor will own at least 20 securities.
   (c) The probability that the investor will own between 20 and 30 securities, inclusive.
   (d) The investor's net annual equity if only 20% of the securities depreciate by 30% a year and the remaining 80% appreciate by 12% a year.

2. New drivers are required to pass written tests before they are given road driving test. These tests are usually administered by the city police department. Records at the City of Springdale show that the average number of written tests is 100 per 8-hour day. The average time needed to complete the test is about 30 minutes. However, the actual arrival of test takers and the time each spends on the test are totally random. Determine the following:
   *(a) The average number of seats the police department should provide in the test hall.
   *(b) The probability that the number of test takers will exceed the average number of seats provided in the test hall.
   (c) The probability that no tests will be administered in any one day.

3. Demonstrate (by using *excelPoissonQ.xls* or TORA) that for small $\rho = .1$, the values of $L_s, L_q, W_s, W_q,$ and p_n for the $(M/M/c):(GD/\infty/\infty)$ model can be estimated reliably using

the less cumbersome formulas of the $(M/M/\infty):(GD/\infty/\infty)$ model for c as small as 4 servers.

4. Repeat Problem 3 for large $\rho = 9$, and show that the same conclusion holds except that the value of c must be higher (at least 14). From the results of Problems 3 and 4, what general conclusion can be drawn regarding the use of $(M/M/\infty):(GD/\infty/\infty)$ to estimate the results of the $(M/M/c):(GD/\infty/\infty)$ model?

18.6.4 Machine Servicing Model—$(M/M/R):(GD/K/K)$, $R < K$

The venue for this model is a shop with K machines. When a machine breaks down, one of R repairpersons is called upon to do the repair. The rate of breakdown *per machine* is λ breakdowns per unit time, and a repairperson will service broken machines at the rate of μ machines per unit time. All breakdowns and services follow the Poisson distribution.

The source in this model is finite because only machines in working order can break down and hence can generate calls for service. Once all machines are broken, no new calls for service can occur.

Given λ, the rate of breakdown *per machine*, the rate of breakdown for the *entire shop* is proportional to the number of working machines. In terms of the queuing model, having n machines *in the system* signifies that n machines are broken, and the associated rate of breakdown for the entire shop is

$$\lambda_n = (K - n)\lambda, \, 0 \le n \le K$$

In terms of the generalized model of Section 18.5, we have

$$\lambda_n = \begin{cases} (K - n)\lambda, & 0 \le n \le K \\ 0, & n \ge K \end{cases}$$

$$\mu_n = \begin{cases} n\mu, & 0 \le n \le R \\ R\mu, & R \le n \le K \end{cases}$$

From the generalized model, we can then obtain (verify!)

$$p_n = \begin{cases} C_n^K \rho^n p_0, & 0 \le n \le R \\ C_n^K \dfrac{n! \, \rho^n}{R! \, R^{n-R}} p_0, & R \le n \le K \end{cases}$$

$$p_0 = \left(\sum_{n=0}^{R} C_n^K \rho^n + \sum_{n=R+1}^{K} C_n^K \frac{n! \, \rho^n}{R! \, R^{n-R}} \right)^{-1}$$

There is no closed form expression for L_s, and hence it must be computed using the following basic definition:

$$L_s = \sum_{n=0}^{K} n p_n$$

The value of λ_{eff} is computed as

$$\lambda_{\text{eff}} = E\{\lambda(K - n)\} = \lambda(K - L_s)$$

Using the formulas in Section 18.6.1, we can compute the remaining measures of performance W_s, W_q, and L_q.

Example 18.6-8

Toolco operates a machine shop with 22 machines. On the average, a machine breaks down every 2 hours. It takes an average of 12 minutes to complete a repair. Both the time between break-downs and the repair time are exponential. Toolco is interested in determining the number of repairpersons needed to keep the shop running "smoothly."

The situation can be analyzed by investigating the productivity of the machines as a function of the number of repairpersons, defined as

$$\left(\begin{array}{c}\text{Machines}\\\text{productivity}\end{array}\right) = \frac{\text{Available machines} - \text{Broken machines}}{\text{Available machines}} \times 100$$

$$= \frac{22 - L_s}{22} \times 100$$

The results for this situation can be obtained using the following input data: lambda = .5, mu = 5, R = 1, 2, 3, or 4, system limit = 22, and source limit = 22. Figure 18.9 provides the output. The following table gives the associated productivity as a function of the number of repairpersons.

Repairperson, R	1	2	3	4
Machines productivity (100%)	45.44	80.15	88.79	90.45
Marginal increase (100%)	—	34.71	8.64	1.66

The results show that with one repairperson, the productivity is low (=45.44%). By increasing the number of repairpersons to two, the productivity jumps by 34.71% to 80.15%. When the shop employs three repairpersons, the productivity increases only by about 8.64% to 88.79%, whereas four repairpersons will increase the productivity by a meager 1.66% to 90.45%.

Judging from these results, the use of two repairpersons is justifiable. The case for three repairpersons is not as strong as it raises the productivity by only 8.64%. Perhaps a monetary comparison between the cost of hiring a third repairperson and the income attributed to the 8.64% increase in productivity can be used to settle this point (see Section 18.10 for discussion of cost models).

FIGURE 18.9

TORA comparative analysis output for Example 18.6-8 (file *toraEx18.6-8.txt*)

```
Comparative Analysis
```

c	Lambda	Mu	L'da eff	p0	Ls	Lq	Ws	Wq
1	0.500	5.00	4.9980	0.0004	12.0040	11.0044	2.4018	2.2018
2	0.500	5.00	8.8161	0.0564	4.3677	2.6045	0.4954	0.2954
3	0.500	5.00	9.7670	0.1078	2.4660	0.5128	0.2525	0.0525
4	0.500	5.00	9.9500	0.1199	2.1001	0.1102	0.2111	0.0111

PROBLEM SET 18.6G

1. In Example 18.6-8, do the following:
   (a) Verify the values of λ_{eff} given in Figure 18.9.
   *(b) Compute the expected number of idle repairpersons, given $R = 4$.
   (c) Compute the probability that all repairpersons are idle, given $R = 3$.
   *(d) Compute the probability that the majority (more than half) of repairpersons are idle, given $R = 3$.

2. In Example 18.6-8, define and compute the productivity of the repairpersons for $R = 1, 2, 3$, and 4. Use this information in conjunction with the measure of machine productivity to decide on the number of repairpersons Toolco should hire.

3. In the computations in Figure 18.9, it may appear confusing that the average rate of machine breakdown in the shop, λ_{eff}, increases with the increase in R. Explain why the increase in λ_{eff} should be expected.

*4. An operator attends 5 automatic machines. After each machine completes a batch run, the operator must reset it before a new batch is started. The time to complete a batch run is exponential with mean 45 minutes. The setup time is also exponential with mean 8 minutes.
   (a) Determine the average number of machines that are awaiting setup or are being set up.
   (b) Compute the probability that all machines are working.
   (c) Determine the average time a machine is down.

5. Kleen All is a service company that performs a variety of odd jobs, such as yard work, tree pruning, and house painting. The company's 4 employees leave the office with the first assignment of the day. After completing an assignment, the employee calls the office requesting instruction for the next job to be performed. The time to complete an assignment is exponential, with a mean of 35 minutes. The travel time between jobs is also exponential, with a mean of 30 minutes.
   (a) Determine the average number of employees who are traveling between jobs.
   (b) Compute the probability that no employee is on the road.

*6. After a long wait, the Newborns were rewarded with quintuplets, 2 boys and 3 girls, thanks to the wonders of new medical advances. During the first 5 months, the babies' life consisted of two states: awake (and mostly crying) and asleep. According to the Newborns, the babies' "awake-asleep" activities never coincide. Instead, the whole affair is totally random. In fact, Mrs. Newborn, a statistician by profession, believes that the length of time each baby cries is exponential, with a mean of 30 minutes. The amount of sleep each baby gets also happens to be exponential, with a mean of 2 hours. Determine the following:
   (a) The average number of babies who are awake at any one time.
   (b) The probability that all babies are asleep.
   (c) The probability that the Newborns will not be happy because more babies are awake (and crying) than are asleep.

7. Verify the expression for p_n for the $(M/M/R):(GD/K/K)$ model.

8. Show that the rate of breakdown in the shop can be computed from the formula

$$\lambda_{eff} = \mu\overline{R}$$

where $\overline{R}$ is the average number of busy repairpersons.

9. Verify the following results for the special case of one repairperson ($R = 1$):

$$p_n = \frac{K!\,\rho^n}{(K - n)!}\,p_0$$

$$p_0 = \left(1 + \sum_{n=1}^{R} \frac{K!\,\rho^n}{(K - n)}\right)^{-1}$$

$$L_s = K - \frac{(1 - p_0)}{\rho}$$

18.7   (M/G/1):(GD/∞/∞)—POLLACZEK-KHINTCHINE (P-K) FORMULA

Queuing models in which arrivals and departures do not follow the Poisson distribution are complex. In general, it is advisable to use simulation as an alternative tool for analyzing these situations (see Chapter 19).

This section presents one of the few non-Poisson queues for which analytic results are available. It deals with the case in which the service time, t, is represented by any probability distribution with mean $E\{t\}$ and variance $\text{var}\{t\}$. The results of the model include the basic measures of performance L_s, L_q, W_s, and W_q, as well as p_0. The model does not provide a closed-form expression for p_n because of analytic intractability.

Let λ be the arrival rate at the single-server facility. Given $E\{t\}$ and $\text{var}\{t\}$ of the service time distribution and that $\lambda E\{t\} < 1$, it can be shown using sophisticated probability/Markov chain analysis that

$$L_s = \lambda E\{t\} + \frac{\lambda^2(E^2\{t\} + \text{var}\{t\})}{2(1 - \lambda E\{t\})},\quad \lambda E\{t\} < 1$$

The probability that the facility is empty (idle) is computed as

$$p_0 = 1 - \lambda E\{t\} = 1 - \rho$$

Given $\lambda_{\text{eff}} = \lambda$, the remaining measures of performance ($L_q, W_s,$ and W_q) can be derived from L_s, as explained in Section 18.6.1.

Template *excelPKFormula.xls* automates the calculations of this model.

Example 18.7-1

In the Automata car wash facility of Example 18.6-2, suppose that a new system is installed so that the service time for all cars is constant and equal to 10 minutes. How does the new system affect the operation of the facility?

From Example 18.6-2, $\lambda_{\text{eff}} = \lambda = 4$ cars per hour. The service time is constant so that $E\{t\} = \frac{10}{60} = \frac{1}{6}$ hour and $\text{var}\{t\} = 0$. Thus,

$$L_s = 4\left(\tfrac{1}{6}\right) + \frac{4^2\left(\left(\tfrac{1}{6}\right)^2 + 0\right)}{2\left(1 - \tfrac{4}{6}\right)} = 1.33 \text{ cars}$$

$$L_q = 1.333 - \left(\tfrac{4}{6}\right) = .667 \text{ cars}$$

$$W_s = \frac{1.333}{4} = .333 \text{ hour}$$

$$W_q = \frac{.667}{4} = .167 \text{ hour}$$

It is interesting to compare the waiting times with those of the Poisson case in Example 18.6-2, (*M/D/*1):(*GD/*∞/∞). The arrival and departure rates are the same in both cases ($\lambda = 4$ cars per hour and $\mu = \frac{1}{E\{t\}} = 6$ cars per hour). Yet, as the table given below shows, the expected waiting time is lower in the current model. The results make sense because a constant service time indicates *more certainty* in the operation of the facility.

	(*M/M/*1):(*GD/*∞/∞)	(*M/D/*1):(*GD/*∞/∞)
W_s (hr)	.500	.333
W_q (hr)	.333	.167

PROBLEM SET 18.7A

1. In Example 18.7-1, compute the percentage of time the facility is idle.
2. Solve Example 18.7-1 assuming that the service-time distribution is given as follows:
   *(a) Uniform between 8 and 20 minutes.
   (b) Normal with $\mu = 12$ minutes and $\sigma = 3$ minutes.
   (c) Discrete with values equal to 4, 8, and 12 minutes and probabilities .1, .6, and .3, respectively.
3. Layson Roofing Inc. installs shingle roofs on new and old homes in Arkansas. Prospective customers request the service randomly at the rate of 6 jobs per 30-day month and are placed on a waiting list to be processed on an FCFS basis. Homes sizes vary, but it is fairly reasonable to assume that the roof areas are uniformly distributed between 120 and 360 squares. The work crew can usually complete 60 squares a day. Determine the following:
   (a) Layson's average backlog of roofing jobs.
   (b) The average time a customer waits until a roofing job is completed.
   (c) If the work crew is increased to the point where they can complete 100 squares a day, how will this affect the average time until a job is completed?
*4. Optica makes prescription glasses according to orders received from customers. Each worker is specialized in certain types of glasses. The company has been experiencing unusual delays in the processing of bifocal and trifocal prescriptions. The worker in charge receives 30 orders per 8-hour day. The time to complete a prescription is normally distributed, with a mean of 12 minutes and a standard deviation of 3 minutes. After spending between 2 and 4 minutes, uniformly distributed, to inspect the glasses, the worker can start on a new prescription. Determine the following:
   (a) The percentage of time the worker is idle.
   (b) The average backlog of bifocal and trifocal prescriptions in Optica.
   (c) The average time until a prescription is filled.
5. A product arrives according to a Poisson distribution at the rate of one every 45 minutes. The product requires two tandem operations attended by one worker. The first operation uses a semiautomatic machine that completes its cycle in exactly 28 minutes. The second

operation makes adjustments and minor changes, and its time depends on the condition of the product when it leaves operation 1. Specifically, the time of operation 2 is uniform between 3 and 6 minutes. Because each operation requires the complete attention of the worker, a new item cannot be loaded on the semiautomatic machine until the current item has cleared operation 2.

(a) Determine the number of items awaiting processing on the semiautomatic machine.

(b) What is the percentage of time the worker will be idle?

(c) How much time is needed, on the average, for an arriving item to clear operation 2?

6. $(M/D/1):(GD/\infty/\infty)$. Show that for the case where the service time is constant, the P-K formula reduces to

$$L_s = \rho + \frac{\rho^2}{2(1-\rho)}$$

where $\mu = \frac{1}{E\{t\}}$ and $\rho = \frac{\lambda}{\mu} = \lambda E\{t\}$.

7. $(M/E_m/1):(GD/\infty/\infty)$. Given that the service time is Erlang with parameters m and μ (i.e., $E\{t\} = \frac{m}{\mu}$ and var$\{t\} = \frac{m}{\mu^2}$), show that the P-K formula reduces to

$$L_s = m\rho + \frac{m(1+m)\rho^2}{2(1-m\rho)}$$

8. Show that the P-K formula reduces to L_s of the $(M/M/1):(GD/\infty/\infty)$ when the service time is exponential with a mean of $\frac{1}{\mu}$ time units.

9. In a service facility with c parallel servers, suppose that customers arrive according to a Poisson distribution, with a mean rate of λ. Arriving customers are assigned to servers (busy or free) on a strict rotational basis.

(a) Determine the probability distribution of the interarrival time.

(b) Suppose in part (a) that arriving customers are assigned randomly to the c servers with probabilities α_i, $\alpha_i \geq 0$, $i = 1, 2, \ldots, c$, and $\alpha_1 + \alpha_2 + \cdots + \alpha_c = 1$. Determine the probability distribution of the interarrival time.

18.8 OTHER QUEUING MODELS

The preceding sections have concentrated on the Poisson queuing models. Queuing literature is rich with other types of models. In particular, queues with priority for service, network queues, and non-Poisson queues form an important body of the queuing theory literature. These models can be found in most specialized books on queuing theory.

18.9 QUEUING DECISION MODELS

The *service level* in a queuing facility is a function of the service rate, μ, and the number of parallel servers, c. This section presents two decision models for determining "suitable" service levels for queuing systems: (1) a cost model and (2) an aspiration-level model. Both models recognize that higher service levels reduce the waiting time in the system. The goal is to strike a balance between service level and waiting.

18.9.1 Cost Models

Cost models attempt to balance two conflicting costs:

1. Cost of offering the service.
2. Cost of delay in offering the service (customer waiting time).

An increase in one cost automatically causes a decrease in the other, as demonstrated earlier in Figure 18.1.

Letting x (= μ or c) represent the *service level*, the cost model can be expressed as

$$ETC(x) = EOC(x) + EWC(x)$$

where

ETC = Expected total cost *per unit time*
EOC = Expected cost of operating the facility *per unit time*
EWC = Expected cost of waiting *per unit time*

The simplest forms for EOC and EWC are the following linear functions:

$$EOC(x) = C_1 x$$

$$EWC(x) = C_2 L_s$$

where

C_1 = *Marginal* cost per unit of x per unit time
C_2 = Cost of waiting per unit time per (waiting) customer

The following two examples illustrate the use of the cost model. The first example assumes $x = \mu$, and the second assumes $x = c$.

Example 18.9-1

KeenCo Publishing is in the process of purchasing a high-speed commercial copier. Four models whose specifications are summarized below have been proposed by vendors.

Copier model	Operating cost ($/hr)	Speed (sheets/min)
1	15	30
2	20	36
3	24	50
4	27	66

Jobs arrive at KeenCo in a Poisson stream at the rate of four jobs per 24-hour day. Job size is random but averages about 10,000 sheets per job. Contracts with the customers specify a penalty cost for late delivery of $80 per jobs per day. Which copier should KeenCo purchase?

The total expected cost *per day* associated with copier i is

$$ETC_i = EOC_i + EWC_i$$
$$= C_{1i} \times 24 + C_{2i}L_{si}$$
$$= 24C_{1i} + 80L_{si}, i = 1,2,3,4$$

The values of C_{1i} are given by the data of the problem. We determine L_{si} by recognizing that, for all practical purposes, each copier can be treated as $(M/M/1):(GD/\infty/\infty)$ model. The arrival rate is $\lambda = 4$ jobs/day. The service rate μ_i associated with model i is computed as

Model i	Service rate μ_i (jobs/day)
1	4.32
2	5.18
3	7.20
4	9.50

Computation of the service rate is demonstrated for model 1.

$$\text{Average time per job} = \frac{10{,}000}{30} \times \frac{1}{60} = 5.56 \text{ hours}$$

Thus,

$$\mu_1 = \frac{24}{5.56} = 4.32 \text{ jobs/day}$$

The values of L_{si}, computed by TORA or *excePoissonQ.xls*, are given in the following table:

Model i	λ_i (Jobs/day)	μ_i (Jobs/day)	L_{si} (Jobs)
1	4	4.32	12.50
2	4	5.18	3.39
3	4	7.20	1.25
4	4	9.50	0.73

The costs for the four models are computed as follows:

Model i	EOC_i (\$)	EWC_i (\$)	ETC_i (\$)
1	360.00	1000.00	1360.00
2	480.00	271.20	751.20
3	**576.00**	**100.00**	**676.00**
4	648.00	58.40	706.40

Model 3 produces the lowest cost.

PROBLEM SET 18.9A

1. In Example 18.9-1, do the following:
   (a) Verify the values of μ_2, μ_3, and μ_4 given in the example.
   (b) Suppose that the penalty of \$48 per job per day is levied only on jobs that are *not* "in progress" at the end of the day. Which copier yields the lowest total cost per day?

*2. Metalco is in the process of hiring a repairperson for a 10-machine shop. Two candidates are under consideration. The first candidate can carry out repairs at the rate of 5 machines per hour and earns $15 an hour. The second candidate, being more skilled, receives $20 an hour and can repair 8 machines per hour. Metalco estimates that each broken machine will incur a cost of $50 an hour because of lost production. Assuming that machines break down according to a Poisson distribution with a mean of 3 per hour and that repair time is exponential, which repairperson should be hired?

3. B&K Groceries is opening a new store boasting "state-of-the-art" checkout scanners. Mr. Bih, one of the owners of B&K, has limited the choices to two scanners: Scanner A can process 15 items a minute, and the better-quality scanner B can scan 20 items a minute. The daily (10 hours) cost of operating and maintaining the scanners are $30 and $50 for models A and B, respectively. Customers who finish shopping arrive at the cashier according to a Poisson distribution at the rate of 10 customers per hour. Each customer's cart carries between 25 and 35 items, uniformly distributed. Mr. Bih estimates the average cost per waiting customer per minute to be about 20 cents. Which scanner should B&K acquire? (*Hint:* The service time per customer is not exponential. It is uniformly distributed.)

4. H&I Industry produces a special machine with different production rates (pieces per hour) to meet customer specifications. A shop owner is considering buying one of these machines and wants to decide on the most economical speed (in pieces per hour) to be ordered. From past experience, the owner estimates that orders from customers arrive at the shop according to a Poisson distribution at the rate of three orders per hour. Each order averages about 500 pieces. Contracts between the owner and the customers specify a penalty of $100 per late order per hour.

   (a) Assuming that the actual production time per order is exponential, develop a general cost model as a function of the production rate, μ.

   *(b) From the cost model in (a), determine an expression for the optimal production rate.

   *(c) Using the data given in the problem, determine the optimal production rate the owner should request from H&I.

5. Jobs arrive at a machine shop according to a Poisson distribution at the rate of 80 jobs per week. An automatic machine represents the bottleneck in the shop. It is estimated that a unit increase in the production rate of the machine will cost $250 per week. Delayed jobs normally result in lost business, which is estimated to be $500 per job per week. Determine the optimum production rate for the automatic machine.

6. Pizza Unlimited sells two franchised restaurant models. Model A has a capacity of 20 groups of customers, and model B can seat 30 groups. The monthly cost of operating model A is $12,000 and that of model B is $16,000. An investor wants to set up a buffet-style pizza restaurant and estimates that groups of customers, each occupying one table, arrive according to a Poisson distribution at a rate of 25 groups per hour. If all the tables are occupied, customers will go elsewhere. Model A will serve 26 groups per hour, and model B will serve 29 groups per hour. Because of the variation in group sizes and in the types of orders, the service time is exponential. The investor estimates that the average cost of lost business per customer group per hour is $15. A delay in serving waiting customers is estimated to cost an average of $10 per customer group per hour.

   (a) Develop an appropriate cost mode.

   (b) Assuming that the restaurant will be open for business 10 hours a day, which model would you recommend for the investor?

7. Suppose in Problem 6 that the investor can choose any desired restaurant capacity based on a specific marginal cost for each additional capacity unit requested. Derive the associated general cost model, and define all its components and terms.

8. Second Time Around sells popular used items on consignment. Its operation can be viewed as an inventory problem in which the stock is replenished and depleted randomly according to Poisson distributions with rates λ and μ items per day. Every time unit the item is out of stock, Second Time loses $\$C_1$ because of lost opportunities, and every time unit an item is held in stock, a holding cost $\$C_2$ is incurred.

   (a) Develop an expression for the expected total cost per unit time.

   (b) Determine the optimal value of $\rho = \frac{\lambda}{\mu}$. What condition must be imposed on the relative values of C_1 and C_2 in order for the solution to be consistent with the assumptions of the $(M/M/1):(GD/\infty/\infty)$ model?

Example 18.9-2

In a multiclerk tool crib facility, requests for tool exchange occur according to a Poisson distribution at the rate of 17.5 requests per hour. Each clerk can handle an average of 10 requests per hour. The cost of hiring a new clerk in the facility is $12 an hour. The cost of lost production per waiting machine per hour is approximately $50. Determine the optimal number of clerks for the facility.

   The situation corresponds to an $(M/M/c)$ model in which it is desired to determine the optimum value of c. Thus, in the general cost model presented at the start of this section, we put $x = c$, resulting in the following cost model:

$$ETC(c) = C_1 c + C_2 L_s(c)$$
$$= 12c + 50 L_s(c)$$

Note that $L_s(c)$ is a function of the number of (parallel) clerks in the crib.

   We use $(M/M/c):(GD/\infty/\infty)$ with $\lambda = 17.5$ requests per hour and $\mu = 10$ requests per hour. Steady state is reached only if $c > \frac{\lambda}{\mu}$—that is, $c \geq 2$ for the present example. The table below provides the necessary calculations for determining optimal c. The values of $L_s(c)$ (determined by *excelPoissonQ.xls* or TORA) show that the optimum number of clerks is 4.

c	$L_s(c)$ (requests)	$ETC(c)$ ($)
2	7.467	397.35
3	2.217	146.85
4	**1.842**	**140.10**
5	1.769	148.45
6	1.754	159.70

PROBLEM SET 18.9B

1. Solve Example 18.9-2, assuming that $C_1 = \$25$ and $C_2 = \$50$.

*2. Tasco Oil owns a pipeline booster unit that operates continuously. The time between breakdowns for each booster is exponential with a mean of 20 hours. The repair time is exponential with mean 3 hours. In a particular station, two repairpersons attend 10 boosters. The hourly wage for each repairperson is $18. Pipeline losses are estimated to be $30 per broken booster per hour. Tasco is studying the possibility of hiring an additional repairperson.

(a) Will there be any cost savings in hiring a third repairperson?

(b) What is the schedule loss in dollars per breakdown when the number of repairpersons on duty is two? Three?

3. A company leases a wide-area telecommunications service (WATS) telephone line for $2000 a month. The office is open 200 working hours per month. At all other times, the WATS line service is used for other purposes and is not available for company business. Access to the WATS line during business hours is extended to 100 salespersons, each of whom may need the line at any time but averages twice per 8-hour day with exponential time between calls. A salesperson will always wait for the WATS line if it is busy at an estimated inconvenience of 1 cent per minute of waiting. It is assumed that no additional needs for calls will arise while the salesperson waits for a given call. The normal cost of calls (not using the WATS line) averages about 50 cents per minute, and the duration of each call is exponential, with a mean of 6 minutes. The company is considering leasing (at the same price) a second WATS line to improve service.

(a) Is the single WATS line saving the company money over a no-WATS system? How much is the company gaining or losing per month over the no-WATS system?

(b) Should the company lease a second WATS line? How much would it gain or lose over the single WATS case by leasing an additional line?

*4. A machine shop includes 20 machines and 3 repairpersons. A working machine breaks down randomly according to a Poisson distribution. The repair time per machine is exponential with a mean of 6 minutes. A queuing analysis of the situation shows an average of 57.8 calls for repair per 8-hour day for the entire shop. Suppose that the production rate per machine is 25 units per hour and that each produced unit generates $2 in revenue. Further, assume that a repairperson is paid at the rate of $20 an hour. Compare the cost of hiring the repairpersons against the cost of lost revenue when machines are broken.

5. The necessary conditions for $ETC(c)$ (defined earlier) to assume a minimum value at $c = c^*$ are

$$ETC(c^* - 1) \geq ETC(c^*) \text{ and } ETC(c^* + 1) \geq ETC(c^*)$$

Show that these conditions reduce to

$$L_s(c^*) - L_s(c^* + 1) \leq \frac{C_1}{C_2} \leq L_s(c^* - 1) - L_s(c^*)$$

Apply the result to Example 18.9-2, and show that it yields $c^* = 4$.

18.9.2 Aspiration Level Model

The viability of the cost model depends on how well we can estimate the cost parameters. Generally, these parameters are difficult to estimate, particularly the one associated with the waiting time of customers. The aspiration level model alleviates this difficulty by working directly with the measures of performance of the queuing situation. The idea is to determine an acceptable range for the service level (μ or c) by specifying reasonable limits on conflicting measures of performance. Such limits are the **aspiration levels** the decision maker wishes to reach.

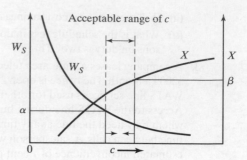

FIGURE 18.10

Application of aspiration levels in queuing decision making

The model is applied to the multiple-server model to determine an "acceptable" number of servers, c^*, taking into account two (conflicting) measures of performance:

1. The average time in the system, W_s.
2. The idleness percentage of the servers, X.

The idleness percentage can be computed as follows:

$$X = \frac{c - \bar{c}}{c} \times 100 = \frac{c - (L_s - L_q)}{c} \times 100 = \left(1 - \frac{\lambda_{\text{eff}}}{c\mu}\right) \times 100$$

(See Problem 12, Set 18.6D for the proof.)

The problem reduces to determining the number of servers c^* such that

$$W_s \leq \alpha \text{ and } X \leq \beta$$

The constants α and β are the levels of aspiration specified by the decision maker. For example, $\alpha = 3$ minutes and $\beta = 10\%$.

The solution of the problem may be determined by plotting W_s and X as a function of c, as shown in Figure 18.10. By locating α and β on the graph, we can determine an acceptable range for c^*. If the two conditions cannot be satisfied simultaneously, then one or both must be relaxed before a feasible range can be found.

Example 18.9-3

In Example 18.9-2, suppose that it is desired to determine the number of clerks such that the expected waiting time until a tool is received stays below 5 minutes. Simultaneously, the percentage of idleness should be below 20%.

Offhand, and before any calculations are made, an aspiration limit of 5 minutes on the waiting time until a tool is received (i.e., $W_s \leq 5$ minutes) is unreachable because, according to the data of the problem, the average service time alone is 6 minutes.

The following table summarizes W_s and X as a function of c:

c	2	3	4	5	6	7	8
W_s (min)	25.4	7.6	6.3	6.1	6.0	6.0	6.0
X (%)	12.5	41.7	56.3	65.0	70.8	75.0	78.0

Based on these results, we should either reduce the service time or recognize that the source of the problem is that tools are being requested at an unreasonably high rate ($\lambda = 17.5$ requests per hour). This, most likely, is the area that should be addressed. For example, we may want to investigate the reason for such high demand for tool replacement. Could it be that the design of the tool itself is faulty? Or could it be that the operators of the machines are purposely trying to disrupt production to express grievances?

PROBLEM SET 18.9C

*1. A shop uses 10 identical machines. Each machine breaks down once every 7 hours on the average. It takes half an hour on the average to repair a broken machine. Both the breakdown and repair processes follow the Poisson distribution. Determine the following:

   (a) The number of repairpersons needed such that the average number of broken machines is less than 1.

   (b) The number of repairpersons needed so that the expected delay time until repair is started is less than 10 minutes.

2. In the cost model in Section 18.9.1, it is generally difficult to estimate the cost parameter C_2 (cost of waiting). As a result, it may be helpful to compute the cost C_2 implied by the aspiration levels. Using the aspiration level model to determine c^*, we can then estimate the implied C_2 by using the following inequality:

$$L_s(c^*) - L_s(c^* + 1) \le \frac{C_1}{C_2} \le L_s(c^* - 1) - L_s(c^*)$$

(See Problem 5, Set 18.9B, for the derivation.) Apply the procedure to the problem in Example 18.9-2, assuming $c^* = 3$ and $C_1 = \$15$.

BIBLIOGRAPHY

Bose, S., *An Introduction to Queuing Systems*, Kluwer Academic Publishers, Boston, 2001.

Gross, D., and M. Harris, *Fundamentals of Queuing Theory*, 3rd ed., Wiley, New York, 1998.

Lee, A., *Applied Queuing Theory*, St. Martin's Press, New York, 1966.

Lipsky, L., *Queuing Theory, A Linear Algebraic Approach*, Macmillan, New York, 1992.

Saaty, T., *Elements of Queuing Theory with Applications*, Dover, New York, 1983.

Tanner, M., *Practical Queuing Analysis*, McGraw-Hill, New York, 1995.

CHAPTER 19

Simulation Modeling

19.1 MONTE CARLO SIMULATION

A forerunner to present-day simulation is the Monte Carlo experiment, a modeling scheme that estimates stochastic or deterministic parameters based on random sampling. Examples of Monte Carlo applications include evaluation of multiple integrals, estimation of the constant π ($\cong 3.14159$), and matrix inversion.

This section uses an example to demonstrate the Monte Carlo technique. The objective of the example is to emphasize the statistical nature of simulation.

Example 19.1-1

We will use Monte Carlo sampling to estimate the area of the following circle:

$$(x - 1)^2 + (y - 2)^2 = 25$$

The radius of the circle is $r = 5$ cm, and its center is $(x, y) = (1, 2)$.

The procedure for estimating the area requires enclosing the circle tightly in a square whose side equals the diameter of the circle, as shown in Figure 19.1. The corner points are determined from the geometry of the square.

The estimation of the area of the circle is based on a sampling experiment that gives equal chance to selecting any point in the square. If m out of n sampled points fall within the circle, then

$$\begin{pmatrix} \text{Approximate} \\ \text{area of the circle} \end{pmatrix} = \frac{m}{n} \begin{pmatrix} \text{Area of} \\ \text{the square} \end{pmatrix} = \frac{m}{n} (10 \times 10)$$

To ensure that all the points in the square are equally probable, the coordinates x and y of a point in the square are represented by the following *uniform* distributions:

$$f_1(x) = \frac{1}{10}, -4 \le x \le 6$$

$$f_2(y) = \frac{1}{10}, -3 \le y \le 7$$

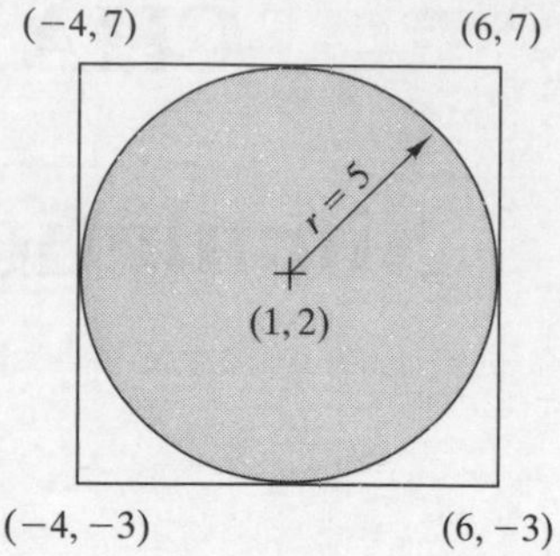

FIGURE 19.1

Monte Carlo estimation of the area of a circle

The determination of a sample (x, y) is based on the use of independent 0-1 random numbers. Table 19.1 lists a sample of such numbers which we will use in the examples in this chapter. For the purpose of general simulation, special arithmetic operations are used to generate (pseudo) 0-1 random numbers, as will be shown in Section 19.4.

A pair of 0-1 random numbers, R_1 and R_2, can be used to generate a random point (x, y) in the square by using the following formulas:

$$x = -4 + [6 - (-4)]R_1 = -4 + 10R_1$$

$$y = -3 + [7 - (-3)]R_2 = -3 + 10R_2$$

To demonstrate the application of the procedure, consider $R_1 = .0589$ and $R_2 = .6733$.

$$x = -4 + 10R_1 = -4 + 10 \times .0589 = -3.411$$

$$y = -3 + 10R_2 = -3 + 10 \times .6733 = 3.733$$

This point falls inside the circle because

$$(-3.411 - 1)^2 + (3.733 - 2)^2 = 22.46 < 25$$

Remarks.   The accuracy of the area estimate can be enhanced by using procedures from ordinary statistical experiments:

1. Increase the sample size, n.
2. Use replications, N.

TABLE 19.1   A Short List of 0-1 Random Numbers

.0589	.3529	.5869	.3455	.7900	.6307
.6733	.3646	.1281	.4871	.7698	.2346
.4799	.7676	.2867	.8111	.2871	.4220
.9486	.8931	.8216	.8912	.9534	.6991
.6139	.3919	.8261	.4291	.1394	.9745
.5933	.7876	.3866	.2302	.9025	.3428
.9341	.5199	.7125	.5954	.1605	.6037
.1782	.6358	.2108	.5423	.3567	.2569
.3473	.7472	.3575	.4208	.3070	.0546
.5644	.8954	.2926	.6975	.5513	.0305

The discussion in Example 19.1-1 poses two questions regarding the simulation experiment:

1. How large should the sample size be?
2. How many replications are needed?

There are some formulas in statistical theory for determining n and N, and they depend on the nature of the simulation experiment as well as the desired confidence level. However, as in any statistical experiment, the golden rule is that higher values of n and N mean more accurate simulation results. In the end, the sample size will depend on the cost associated with conducting the simulation experiment. Generally speaking, however, a selected sample size is considered "adequate" if it produces a relatively "small" standard deviation.

It is necessary to express the results as a confidence interval to account for the random variation in the output of the experiment. Letting $\overline{A}$ and s be the mean and variance of N replications, then, given a confidence level α, the confidence interval for the true area A is

$$\overline{A} - \frac{s}{\sqrt{N}} t_{\frac{\alpha}{2}, N-1} \leq A \leq \overline{A} + \frac{s}{\sqrt{N}} t_{\frac{\alpha}{2}, N-1}$$

The parameter $t_{\frac{\alpha}{2}, N-1}$ is determined from the t-distribution tables given a confidence level α and $N - 1$ degrees of freedom (see the t-table in Appendix A or use *excelStatTables.xls*). Note that N equals the number of replications, which is distinct from the sample size n.

Excel Moment

The computations associated with each sample in Example 19.1-1 are voluminous. Excel template *excelCircle.xls* (with VBA macros) is used to test the effect of sample size and number of replications on the accuracy of the area estimate. The input data include the circle radius, r; and its center (cx, cy); sample size, n; number of replications, N; and the confidence level α. The entry *Steps* in cell D4 allows executing several samples in the same run. For example, if $n = 30,000$ and Steps $= 3$, the template will automatically produce output for $n = 30,000, 60,000$, and $90,000$. New estimates are realized each time the command button Press to Execute Monte Carlo is clicked because Excel refreshes the seed of the random number generator.

Figure 19.2 summarizes the results for 5 replications and sample sizes of $30,000, 60,000$, and $90,000$. The exact area is 78.54 cm^2, and the Monte Carlo results show that the mean estimated areas for the three sample sizes are slightly different.

Figure 16.2 gives the 95% confidence intervals for each n. For example, the confidence interval $78.452 \leq A \leq 78.68$ corresponds to $n = 90,000$, with $N = 5$, $\overline{A} = 78.566 \text{ cm}^2$, and $s = .092 \text{ cm}$, *and* $t_{.025,4} = 2.776$. In general, to realize reasonable accuracy in the estimation of the confidence interval, the value of N should be at least 5.

PROBLEM SET 19.1A

1. In Example 19.1-1, estimate the area of the circle using the first two columns of the 0-1 random numbers in Table 19.1. (For convenience, go down each column, selecting R_1 first and then R_2.) How does this estimate compare with the ones given in Figure 19.2?

	B	C	D	E
1	Monte Carlo Estimation of the Area of a Circle			
2	Input data			
3	Nbr. Replications, N =	5	α =	0.025
4	Sample size, n =	30,000	Steps =	3
5	Radius, r =	5		
6	Center, cx =	1		
7	Center, cy =	2		
8	Output results			
9	Exact area =	78.540		
10	Press to Execute Monte Carlo			
11	Monte Carlo Calculations:			
12		n=30000	n=60000	n=90000
13	Replication 1	78.590	78.543	78.536
14	Replication 2	78.447	78.695	78.731
15	Replication 3	78.747	78.648	78.534
16	Replication 4	78.363	78.500	78.512
17	Replication 5	78.540	78.420	78.517
18				
19	Mean =	78.537	78.561	78.566
20	Std. Deviation =	0.142	0.118	0.092
21				
22	95% lower conf. limit =	78.361	78.415	78.452
23	95% upper conf. limit =	78.714	78.708	78.680

FIGURE 19.2

Excel output of Monte Carlo estimation of the area of a circle (file *excelCircle.xls*)

2. Suppose that the equation of a circle is

$$(x - 4)^2 + (y + 3)^2 = 25$$

(a) Define the corresponding distributions $f(x)$ and $f(y)$, and then show how a sample point (x, y) is determined using the $(0, 1)$ random pair (R_1, R_2).

(b) Use *excelCircle.xls* to estimate the area and the associated 95% confidence interval, given $n = 100,000$ and $N = 10$.

3. Use Monte Carlo sampling to estimate the area of the lake shown in Figure 19.3. Base the estimate on the first two columns of $(0, 1)$ random numbers in Table 19.1.

4. Consider the game in which two players, Jan and Jim, take turns in tossing a fair coin. If the outcome is heads, Jim gets $10 from Jan. Otherwise, Jan gets $10 from Jim.

*(a) How is the game simulated as a Monte Carlo experiment?

(b) Run the experiment for 5 replications of 10 tosses each. Use the first five columns of the 0-1 random numbers in Table 19.1, with each column corresponding to one replication.

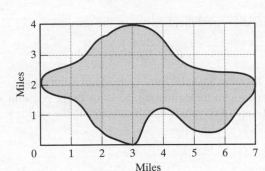

FIGURE 19.3

Lake map for Problem 3, Set 19.1A

(c) Establish a 95% confidence interval on Jan's winnings.

(d) Compare the confidence interval in (c) with Jan's expected theoretical winnings.

5. Consider the following definite integral:

$$\int_0^1 x^2 dx$$

(a) Develop the Monte Carlo experiment to estimate the value of the integral.

(b) Use the first four columns in Table 19.1 to evaluate the integral based on 4 replications of size 5 each. Compute a 95% confidence interval, and compare it with the exact value of the integral.

6. Simulate five wins or losses of the following game of craps: The player rolls two fair dice. If the outcome sum is 7 or 11, the player wins $10. Otherwise, the player records the resulting sum (called *point*) and keeps on rolling the dice until the outcome sum matches the recorded *point*, in which case the player wins $10. If a 7 is obtained prior to matching the *point*, the player loses $10.

*7. The lead time for receiving an order can be 1 or 2 days, with equal probabilities. The demand *per day* assumes the values 0, 1, and 2 with the respective probabilities of .2, .7, and .1. Use the random numbers in Table 19.1 (starting with column 1) to estimate the joint distribution of the demand and lead time. From the joint distribution, estimate the pdf of demand during lead time. (*Hint:* The demand during lead time assumes discrete values from 0 to 4.)

8. Consider the Buffon needle experiment. A horizontal plane is ruled with parallel lines spaced D cm apart. A needle of length d cm ($d < D$) is dropped randomly on the plane. The objective of the experiment is to determine the probability that either end of the needle touches or crosses one of the lines. Define

$h = $ *Perpendicular* distance from the needle center to a (parallel) line

$\theta = $ *Inclination* angle of the needle with a line

(a) Show that the needle will touch or cross a line only if

$$h \le \frac{d}{2} \sin \theta, 0 \le h \le \frac{D}{2}, 0 \le \theta \le \pi$$

(b) Design the Monte Carlo experiment, and provide an estimate of the desired probability.

(c) Use Excel to obtain 4 replications of size 10 each of the desired probability. Determine a 95% confidence interval for the estimate. Assume $D = 20$ cm and $d = 10$ cm.

(d) Prove that the theoretical probability is given by the formula

$$p = \frac{2d}{\pi D}$$

(e) Use the result in (c) together with the formula in (d) to estimate π.

9. Design a Monte Carlo experiment for estimating the value of the constant π. [*Hint*: (Area of a circle)/(Area of rectangle tightly enveloping the circle) $= \pi/4$.]

19.2 TYPES OF SIMULATION

The execution of present-day simulation is based on the idea of sampling used with the Monte Carlo method. It differs in that it deals with the study of the behavior of real systems *as a function of time*. Two distinct types of simulation models exist.

1. **Continuous models** deal with systems whose behavior changes *continuously* with time. These models usually use difference-differential equations to describe the interactions among the different elements of the system. A typical example deals with the study of world population dynamics.

2. **Discrete models** deal primarily with the study of waiting lines, with the objective of determining such measures as the average waiting time and length of the queue. These measures change only when a customer enters or leaves the system. The instants at which changes take place occur at specific discrete points in time (arrivals and departure events), giving rise to the name **discrete event simulation**.

This chapter presents the basics of discrete event simulation, including a description of the components of a simulation model, collection of simulation statistics, and the statistical aspect of the simulation experiment. The chapter also emphasizes the role of the computer and simulation languages in the execution of simulation models.

PROBLEM SET 19.2A

1. Categorize the following situations as either discrete or continuous (or a combination of both). In each case, specify the objective of developing the simulation model.

   *(a) Orders for an item arrive randomly at a warehouse. An order that cannot be filled immediately from available stock must await the arrival of new shipments.

   (b) World population is affected by the availability of natural resources, food production, environmental conditions, educational level, health care, and capital investments.

   (c) Goods arrive on pallets at a receiving bay of an automated warehouse. The pallets are loaded on a lower conveyor belt and lifted through an up-elevator to an upper conveyor that moves the pallets to corridors. The corridors are served by cranes that pick up the pallets from the conveyor and place them in storage bins.

2. Explain why you would agree or disagree with the following statement: "Most discrete event simulation models can be viewed in some form or another as queuing systems consisting of *sources* from which customers arrive, *queues* where customers may wait, and *facilities* where customers are served."

19.3 ELEMENTS OF DISCRETE EVENT SIMULATION

The ultimate goal of simulation is to estimate some desirable measures of performance that describe the behavior of the simulated system. For example, in a service facility, the associated measures of performance can include the average waiting time until a customer is served, the average length of the queue, and the average utilization of the service facility. This section shows how the statistics of the simulated system are collected based on the concept of *events*.

19.3.1 Generic Definition of Events

All discrete event simulations describe, directly or indirectly, queuing situations in which customers arrive (for service), wait in a queue (if necessary), and then receive service before leaving the service facility. As such, any discrete event simulation, regardless of the complexity of the system it describes, reduces to dealing with two basic events: arrivals and departures. The following example illustrates the use of the arrival and departure events to describe a system consisting of distinct queues.

Example 19.3-1

Metalco Jobshop receives two types of jobs: regular and rush. All jobs are processed on two consecutive machines with ample buffer areas. Rush jobs always assume nonpreemptive priority over regular jobs.

This situation consists of two tandem queues representing the two machines. At first, one may be inclined to identify the events of the situation as

$A11$: A regular job arrives at machine 1.

$A21$: A rush job arrives at machine 1.

$D11$: A regular job departs machine 1.

$D21$: A rush job departs machine 1.

$A12$: A regular job arrives at machine 2.

$A22$: A rush job arrives at machine 2.

$D12$: A regular job departs machine 2.

$D22$: A rush job departs machine 2.

In reality, there are only two events: an arrival of a (new) job at the shop and a departure of a (completed) job from a machine. First notice that events $D11$ and $A12$ are actually one and the same. The same applies to $D21$ and $A22$. Next, in discrete simulation we can use one event (arrival or departure) for both types of jobs and simply "tag" the event with an **attribute** that identifies the job type as either regular or rush. (We can think of the attribute in this case as a *personal identification descriptor*, and indeed it is.) Given this reasoning, the events of the model reduce to (1) an arrival A (at the shop) and (2) a departure D (from a machine). The actions associated with the arrival event depends on the type of arriving job (rush or regular) and the availability of a machine. Similarly, the processing of the departure event will depend on the machine and the status of waiting jobs.

Having defined the basic events of a simulation model, we show how the model is executed. Figure 19.4 gives a schematic representation of typical occurrences of events on the simulation timescale. After all the actions associated with a current event have been performed, the simulation advances by "jumping" to the next chronological event. In essence, the execution of the simulation occurs at the instants at which the events occur.

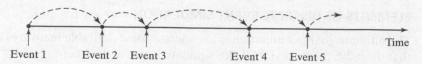

FIGURE 19.4

Example of the occurrence of simulation events on the timescale

How does the simulation determine the occurrence time of the events? The arrival events are separated by the interarrival time (the interval between successive arrivals), and the departure events are a function of the service time in the facility. These times may be deterministic (e.g., a train arriving at a station every 5 minutes) or probabilistic (e.g., the random arrival of customers at a bank). If the time between events is deterministic, the determination of their occurrence times is straightforward. If it is probabilistic, we use a special procedure to sample from the corresponding probability distribution. This point is discussed in the next section.

PROBLEM SET 19.3A

1. Identify the discrete events needed to simulate the following situation: Three types of jobs arrive from different sources. All three types are processed on a single machine, with the highest priority given to jobs from the first source followed by source 2, then source3.

2. Jobs arrive at a constant rate at a carousel conveyor system. Two service stations are spaced equally around the carousel. If the server is idle when a job arrives at the station, the job is removed from the conveyor for processing. Otherwise, the job continues to rotate on the carousel until a server becomes available. A processed job is stored in an adjacent shipping area. Identify the discrete events needed to simulate this situation.

3. Cars arrive at a two-lane, drive-in bank, where each lane can house a maximum of four cars. If the two lanes are full, arriving cars seek service elsewhere. If at any time one lane is at least two cars longer than the other, the last car in the longer lane will jockey to the last position in the shorter lane. The bank operates the drive-in facility from 8:00 A.M. to 3:00 P.M. each work day. Define the discrete events for the situation.

*4. The cafeteria at Elmdale Elementary provides a single-tray, fixed-menu lunch to all its pupils. Kids arrive at the dispensing window every 30 seconds. It takes 18 seconds to receive the lunch tray. Map the arrival–departure events on the time scale for the first five pupils.

19.3.2 Sampling from Probability Distributions

Randomness in simulation arises when the interval, t, between successive events is probabilistic. This section presents three methods for generating successive random samples $(t = t_1, t_2, \dots)$ from a probability distribution $f(t)$:

1. Inverse method.
2. Convolution method.
3. Acceptance–rejection method.

The inverse method is particularly suited for analytically tractable probability density functions, such as the exponential and the uniform. The remaining two methods deal with more complex cases, such as the normal and the Poisson. All three methods are rooted in the use of independent and identically distributed uniform 0-1 random numbers.

This section will present the first two methods only. Details of the acceptance–rejection method can be found in the bibliography.

Inverse method.   Suppose that it is desired to obtain a random sample x from the (continuous or discrete) probability density function $f(x)$. The inverse method first determines a closed-form expression of the cumulative density function $F(x) = P\{y \le x\}$, where $0 \le F(x) \le 1$, for all defined values of y.

It can be proved that the random variable $z = F(x)$ is uniformly distributed in the interval $0 \le z \le 1$. Based on this result, a random sample from $f(x)$ is determined using the following steps (F^{-1} is the inverse of F):

Step 1.   Generate a 0-1 random number, R.

Step 2.   Compute the desired sample $x = F^{-1}(R)$.

Figure 19.5 illustrates the procedures for both a continuous and a discrete random distribution.

Example 19.3-2   (Exponential Distribution)

The exponential probability density function $f(t) = \lambda e^{-\lambda t}, t > 0$ represents the interarrival time t at a facility with a mean value of $\frac{1}{\lambda}$. The cumulative density function is

$$F(t) = \int_0^t \lambda e^{-\lambda x}\, dx = 1 - e^{-\lambda t}, t > 0$$

Setting $R = F(t)$, we can solve for t as

$$t = -\left(\frac{1}{\lambda}\right) \ln (1 - R)$$

FIGURE 19.5

Sampling from a probability distribution by the inverse method

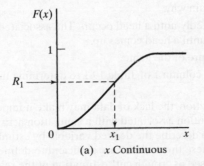

(a) x Continuous

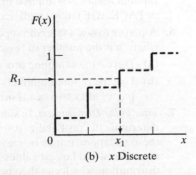

(b) x Discrete

For example, for $\lambda = 4$ customers per hour and $R = .9$, the time period until the next arrival occurs is

$$t_1 = -\left(\frac{1}{4}\right)\ln(1 - .9) = .577 \text{ hour} = 34.5 \text{ minutes}$$

Note that $\ln(1 - R)$ may be replaced with $\ln(R)$ because $1 - R$ is the complement of R.

PROBLEM SET 19.3B

*1. In Example 19.3-2, suppose that the first customer arrives at time 0. Use the first three random numbers in column 1 of Table 19.1 to generate the arrival times of the next 3 customers, and graph the resulting events on the timescale.

*2. *Uniform Distribution.* Suppose that the time needed to manufacture a part on a machine is described by the following uniform distribution:

$$f(t) = \frac{1}{b - a}, a \le t \le b$$

Determine an expression for the sample t, given the random number R.

3. Jobs are received randomly at a one-machine shop. The time between arrivals is exponential with mean 2 hours. The time needed to manufacture a job is uniform between 1.1 and 2 hours. Assuming that the first job arrives at time 0, determine the arrival and departure time for the first five jobs using the $(0, 1)$ random numbers in column 1 of Table 19.1.

4. The demand for an expensive spare part of a passenger jet is 0, 1, 2, or 3 units per month with probabilities .3, .3, .2, and .2, respectively. The airline maintenance shop starts operation with a stock of 6 units and will bring the stock level back to 6 units immediately after it drops below 5 units.

*(a) Devise the procedure for sampling demand.

(b) How many months will elapse until the first replenishment occurs? Use successive values of R from the first column in Table 19.1.

5. In a simulation situation, TV units are inspected for possible defects. There is an 70% chance that a unit will pass inspection, in which case it is sent to packaging. Otherwise, the unit is repaired. We can represent the situation symbolically in one of two ways.

goto REPAIR/.3, PACKAGE/.7

goto PACKAGE/.7, REPAIR/.3

These two representations appear equivalent. Yet, when a given sequence of $(0, 1)$ random numbers is applied to the two representations, different decisions (REPAIR or PACKAGE) may result. Explain why.

6. A player tosses a fair coin repeatedly until a head occurs. The associated payoff is 3^n, where n is the number of tosses until a head comes up.

(a) Devise the sampling procedure of the game.

(b) Use the random numbers in column 1 of Table 19.1 to determine the cumulative payoff after two heads occur.

7. *Triangular Distribution.* In simulation, the lack of data may make it impossible to determine the probability distribution associated with a simulation activity. In most of these situations, it may be easy to describe the desired variable by estimating its smallest, most likely, and largest values. These three values are sufficient to define a triangular distribution, which can then be used as "rough cut" estimation of the real distribution.

(a) Develop the formula for sampling from the following triangular distribution, whose respective parameters are a, b, and c:

$$f(x) = \begin{cases} \dfrac{2(x - a)}{(b - a)(c - a)}, & a \leq x \leq b \\[2ex] \dfrac{2(c - x)}{(c - b)(c - a)}, & b \leq x \leq c \end{cases}$$

(b) Generate three samples from a triangular distribution with parameters $(1, 3, 7)$ using the first three random numbers in column 1 of Table 19.1.

8. Consider a probability distribution that consists of a rectangle flanked on the left and right sides by two symmetrical right triangles. The respective ranges for the triangle on the left, the rectangle, and the triangle on the right are $[a, b], [b, c]$, and $[c, d]$, $a < b < c < d$. Both triangles have the same height as the rectangle.

(a) Develop a sampling procedure.

(b) Determine five samples with $(a, b, c, d) = (1, 2, 4, 6)$ using the first five random numbers in column 1 of Table 19.1.

*9. *Geometric distribution.* Show how a random sample can be obtained from the following geometric distribution:

$$f(x) = p(1 - p)^x, x = 0, 1, 2, \ldots$$

The parameter x is the number of (Bernoulli) failures until a success occurs, and p is the probability of a success, $0 < p < 1$. Generate five samples for $p = .6$, using the first five random numbers in column 1 of Table 19.1.

10. *Weibull distribution.* Show how a random sample can be obtained from the Weibull distribution with the following probability density function:

$$f(x) = \alpha \beta^{-\alpha} x^{\alpha-1} e^{-(x/\beta)^\alpha}, x > 0$$

where $\alpha > 0$ is the shape parameter, and $\beta > 0$ is the scale parameter.

Convolution method.   The basic idea of the convolution method is to express the desired sample as the statistical sum of other easy-to-sample random variables. Typical among these distributions are the Erlang and the Poisson whose samples can be obtained from the exponential distribution samples.

Example 19.3-3   (Erlang Distribution)

The m-Erlang random variable is defined as the statistical sum (convolutions) of m independent and identically distributed exponential random variables. Let y represent the m-Erlang random variable; then

$$y = y_1 + y_2 + \cdots + y_m$$

where $y_i, i = 1, 2, \ldots, m$, are independent and identically distributed exponentials with the following probability density function:

$$f(y_i) = \lambda e^{-\lambda y_i}, y_i > 0, i = 1, 2, \ldots, m$$

From Example 19.3-2, a sample from the ith exponential distribution is computed as

$$y_i = -\left(\frac{1}{\lambda}\right) \ln{(R_i)}, i = 1, 2, \dots, m$$

Thus, the m-Erlang sample is computed as

$$y = -\left(\frac{1}{\lambda}\right)\{\ln{(R_1)} + \ln{(R_2)} + \cdots + \ln{(R_m)}\}$$

$$= -\left(\frac{1}{\lambda}\right) \ln{\left(\prod_{i=1}^{m} R_i\right)}$$

To illustrate the use of the formula, suppose that $m = 3$ and $\lambda = 4$ events per hour. The first 3 random numbers in column 1 of Table 19.1 yield $R_1 R_2 R_3 = (.0589)(.6733)(.4799) = .0190$, which yields

$$y = -\left(\tfrac{1}{4}\right) \ln{(.019)} = .991 \text{ hour}$$

Example 19.3-4 (Poisson Distribution)

Section 18.4.1 shows that if the distribution of the time between the occurrences of successive events is exponential, then the distribution of the number of events per unit time is Poisson, and vice versa. We use this relationship to sample the Poisson distribution.

Assume that mean of the Poisson distribution is λ events per unit time. It follows that the time between events is exponential with mean $\frac{1}{\lambda}$ time units. This means that a Poisson sample, n, will occur during t time units if, and only if,

Period till event n occurs $\leq t <$ Period till event $n + 1$ occurs

This condition translates to

$$t_1 + t_2 + \cdots + t_n \leq t < t_1 + t_2 + \cdots + t_{n+1}, n > 0$$

$$0 \leq t < t_1, n = 0$$

The random variable t_i, $i = 1, 2, \dots, n + 1$, is a sample from the exponential distribution with mean $\frac{1}{\lambda}$. From the result in Example 19.3-3, we have

$$-\left(\frac{1}{\lambda}\right) \ln{\left(\prod_{i=1}^{n} R_i\right)} \leq t < -\left(\frac{1}{\lambda}\right) \ln{\left(\prod_{i=1}^{n+1} R_i\right)}, n > 0$$

$$0 \leq t < -\left(\frac{1}{\lambda}\right) \ln{(R_1)}, n = 0$$

These expressions reduce to

$$\prod_{i=1}^{n} R_i \geq e^{-\lambda t} > \prod_{i=1}^{n+1} R_i, n > 0$$

$$1 \geq e^{-\lambda t} > R_1, n = 0$$

To illustrate the implementation of the sampling process, suppose that $\lambda = 4$ events per hour. To obtain a sample for a period $t = .5$ hour, we first compute $e^{-\lambda t} = .1353$. The random number $R_1 = .0589$ is less than $e^{-\lambda t} = .1353$. Hence, the corresponding sample is $n = 0$.

Example 19.3-5   (Normal Distribution)

The central limit theorem (see Section 14.4.4) states that the sum (convolution) of n independent and identically distributed random variables becomes asymptotically normal as n becomes sufficiently large. We use this result to generate samples from normal distribution with mean μ and standard deviation σ.

Define

$$x = R_1 + R_2 + \ldots + R_n$$

The random variable is asymptotically normal by the central limit theorem. Given that the uniform $(0, 1)$ random number R has a mean of $\frac{1}{2}$ and a variance of $\frac{1}{12}$, it follows that the mean and variance of x are $\frac{n}{2}$ and $\frac{n}{12}$, respectively. Thus, a random sample, y, from a normal distribution $N(\mu, \sigma)$, with mean μ and standard deviation σ, can be computed from x as

$$y = \mu + \sigma \left(\frac{x - \frac{n}{2}}{\sqrt{\frac{n}{12}}} \right)$$

In practice, we take $n = 12$ for convenience, which reduces the formula to

$$y = \mu + \sigma(x - 6)$$

To illustrate the use of this method, suppose that we wish to generate a sample from $N(10, 2)$ (mean $\mu = 10$ and standard deviation $\sigma = 2$). Taking the sum of the first 12 random numbers in columns 1 and 2 of Table 19.1, we get $x = 6.1094$. Thus, $y = 10 + 2(6.1094 - 6) = 10.2188$.

Box-Muller normal sampling formula.   The disadvantage of the preceding procedure is that it requires generating 12 random numbers per normal sample, which is computationally inefficient. A more efficient procedure calls for using the transformation

$$x = \cos(2\pi R_2)\sqrt{-2\ln(R_1)}$$

Box and Muller (1958) prove that x is a standard $N(0, 1)$. Thus, $y = \mu + \sigma x$ will produce a sample from $N(\mu, \sigma)$. The new procedure is more efficient because it requires two 0-1 random numbers only. Actually, this method is even more efficient than stated, because Box and Miller prove that the given formula produces another $N(0, 1)$ sample if $\sin(2\pi R_2)$ replaces $\cos(2\pi R_2)$.

To illustrate the implementation of the Box-Muller procedure to the normal distribution $N(10, 2)$, the first two random numbers in column 1 of Table 19.1 yield the following $N(0, 1)$ samples:

$$x_1 = \cos(2\pi \times .6733)\sqrt{-2\ln(.0589)} \approx -1.103$$

$$x_2 = \sin(2\pi \times .6733)\sqrt{-2\ln(.0589)} \approx -2.109$$

Thus, the corresponding $N(10, 2)$ samples are

$$y_1 = 10 + 2(-1.103) = 7.794$$

$$y_2 = 10 + 2(-2.109) = 5.782$$

PROBLEM SET 19.3C[1]

*1. In Example 19.3-3, compute an Erlang sample, given $m = 3$ and $\lambda = 10$ events per hour.

2. In Example 19.3-4, generate three Poisson samples during a half-hour period, given that the mean of the Poisson is 9 events per hour.

3. In Example 19.4-5, generate two samples from $N(7, 2)$ by using both the convolution method and the Box-Muller method.

4. Jobs arrive at Metalco Jobshop according to a Poisson distribution, with a mean of 6 jobs per day. Received jobs are assigned to the five machining centers of the shop on a strict rotational basis. Determine one sample of the interval between the arrival of jobs at the first machine center.

5. The ACT scores for the 1994 senior class at Springdale High is normal, with a mean of 27 points and a standard deviation of 3 points. Suppose that we draw a random sample of six seniors from that class. Use the Box-Muller method to determine the mean and standard deviation of the sample.

*6. Psychology professor Yataha is conducting a learning experiment in which mice are trained to find their way around a maze. The base of the maze is square. A mouse enters the maze at one of the four corners and must find its way through the maze to exit at the same point where it entered. The design of the maze is such that the mouse must pass by each of the remaining three corner points exactly once before it exits. The multipaths of the maze connect the four corners in a strict clockwise order. Professor Yataha estimates that the time the mouse takes to reach one corner point from another is uniformly distributed between 10 and 20 seconds, depending on the path it takes. Develop a sampling procedure for the time a mouse spends in the maze.

7. In Problem 6, suppose that once a mouse makes an exit from the maze, another mouse instantly enters. Develop a sampling procedure for the number of mice that exit the maze in 5 minutes.

---

[1]For all the problems of this set, use the random numbers in Table 19.1 starting with column 1.

8. *Negative Binomial.* Show how a random sample can be determined from the negative binomial whose distribution is given as

$$f(x) = C_x^{r+x-1} p^r (1 - p)^x, x = 0, 1, 2, \ldots$$

where x is the number of failures until the rth success occurs in a sequence of independent Bernoulli trials and p is the probability of success, $0 < p < 1$. (*Hint:* The negative binomial is the convolution of r independent geometric samples. See Problem 9, Set 19.3B.)

19.4 GENERATION OF RANDOM NUMBERS

Uniform $(0, 1)$ random numbers play a key role in sampling from distributions. True 0-1 random numbers can be generated by electronic devices only. However, because simulation models are executed on the computer, the use of electronic devices to generate random numbers is much too slow for that purpose. Additionally, electronic devices are activated by laws of chance, making it impossible to duplicate the same sequence of random numbers at will. This point is important because debugging, verification, and validation of the simulation model often require duplicating the random numbers sequence.

The only feasible way for generating 0-1 random numbers for use in simulation is based on arithmetic operations. Such numbers are not truly random because the entire sequence can be generated in advance. It is thus more appropriate to refer to them as **pseudorandom numbers**.

The most common arithmetic operation for generating $(0, 1)$ random numbers is the **multiplicative congruential method**. Given the parameters u_0, b, c, and m, a pseudorandom number R_n can be generated from the formulas:

$$u_n = (bu_{n-1} + c) \bmod(m), n = 1, 2, \ldots$$

$$R_n = \frac{u_n}{m}, n = 1, 2, \ldots$$

The initial value u_0 is usually referred to as the **seed** of the generator.

Variations of the multiplicative congruential method that improve the quality of the generator can be found in Law (2007).

Example 19.4-1

Generate three random numbers based on the multiplicative congruential method using $b = 9$, $c = 5$, and $m = 12$. The seed is $u_0 = 11$.

$$u_1 = (9 \times 11 + 5) \bmod 12 = 8, R_1 = \frac{8}{12} = .6667$$

$$u_2 = (9 \times 8 + 5) \bmod 12 = 5, R_2 = \frac{5}{12} = .4167$$

$$u_3 = (9 \times 5 + 5) \bmod 12 = 2, R_3 = \frac{2}{12} = .1667$$

Excel Moment

Excel template *excelRN.xls* implements the multiplicative congruential method. Figure 19.6 generates the sequence associated with the parameters of Example 19.4-1. Notice that the cycle length is exactly 4, after which the sequence repeats itself. The point to be made here is that the selected values of u_0, b, c, and m are critical in determining the (statistical) quality of the generator and its cycle length. Thus, "casual" implementation of the congruential formula is not recommended. Instead, one must use a reliable and tested generator. All commercial computer programs are equipped with dependable random number generators.

PROBLEM SET 19.4A

*1. Use *excelRN.xls* with the following sets of parameters, and compare the results with those of Example 19.4-1:

$$b = 17, c = 111, m = 103, \text{seed} = 7$$

FIGURE 19.6

Excel random numbers output for the data of Example 19.4-1 (file *excelRN.xls*)

	A	B
1	**Multiplicative Congruential Method**	
2	**Input data(B7<=1000)**	
3	**b =**	9
4	**c =**	5
5	**u0 =**	11
6	**m =**	12
7	**How many numbers?**	10
8	**Output results**	
9	**Press to Generate Sequence**	
10	Generated random numbers:	
11	1	0.66667
12	2	0.41667
13	3	0.16667
14	4	0.91667
15	5	0.66667
16	6	0.41667
17	7	0.16667
18	8	0.91667
19	9	0.66667
20	10	0.41667

2. Find a random number generator on your computer, and use it to generate 500 zero-one random numbers. Histogram the resulting values (using the Microsoft histogram tool, see Section 12.5) and visually convince yourself that the obtained numbers reasonably follow the $(0, 1)$ uniform distribution. Actually, to test the sequence properly, you would need to apply the following tests: chi-square goodness of fit (see Section 14.6), runs test for independence, and correlation test—see Law (2007) for details.

19.5 MECHANICS OF DISCRETE SIMULATION

This section details how typical statistics are collected in a simulation model. The vehicle of explanation is a single-queue model. Section 19.5.1 uses a numeric example to detail the actions and computations that take place in a single-server queuing simulation model. Because of the tedious computations that typify the execution of a simulation model, Section 19.5.2 shows how the single-server model is modeled and executed using Excel spreadsheet.

19.5.1 Manual Simulation of a Single-Server Model

The interarrival time of customers at HairKare Barbershop is exponential with mean 15 minutes. The shop is operated by only one barber, and it takes between 10 and 15 minutes, uniformly distributed, to do a haircut. Customers are served on a first-in, first-out (FIFO) basis. The objective of the simulation is to compute the following measures of performance:

1. The average utilization of the shop.
2. The average number of waiting customers.
3. The average time a customer waits in queue.

The logic of the simulation model can be described in terms of the actions associated with the arrival and departure events of the model.

Arrival Event

1. Generate and store chronologically the occurrence time of the next arrival event (= current simulation time + interarrival time).
2. If the facility (barber) is idle
   a. Start service and declare the facility busy. Update the facility utilization statistics.
   b. Generate and store chronologically the time of the departure event for the customer (= current simulation time + service time).
3. If the facility is busy, place the customer in the queue, and update the queue statistics.

Departure Event

1. If the queue is empty, declare the facility idle. Update the facility utilization statistics.
2. If the queue is not empty
   a. Select a customer from the queue, and place it in the facility. Update the facility utilization and queue statistics.

b. Generate and store chronologically the occurrence time of the departure event for the customer (= current simulation time + service time).

From the data of the problem, the interarrival time is exponential with mean 15 minutes, and the service time is uniform between 10 and 15 minutes. Letting p and q represent random samples of interarrival and service times, then, as explained in Section 19.3.2, we get

$$p = -15 \ln(R) \text{ minutes}, 0 \le R \le 1$$
$$q = 10 + 5R \text{ minutes}, \quad 0 \le R \le 1$$

For the purpose of this example, we use R from Table 19.1, starting with column 1. We also use the symbol T to represent the simulation clock time. We further assume that the first customer arrives at $T = 0$ and that the facility starts empty.

Because the simulation computations are typically voluminous, the simulation is limited to the first 5 arrivals only. The example is designed to cover all possible situations that could arise in the course of the simulation. Later in Section 19.5.2, we introduce the template *excelSingleServer.xls* that allows experimenting with the model without the need to carry out the computations manually.

Arrival of customer 1 at $T = 0$. Generate the arrival of customer 2 at

$$T = 0 + p_1 = 0 + [-15 \ln(.0589)] = 42.48 \text{ minutes}$$

Because the facility is idle at $T = 0$, customer 1 starts service immediately. The departure time is thus computed as

$$T = 0 + q_1 = 0 + (10 + 5 \times .6733) = 13.37 \text{ minutes}$$

The *chronological* list of future events thus becomes

Time, T	Event
13.37	Departure of customer 1
42.48	Arrival of customer 2

Departure of customer 1 at $T = 13.37$. Because the queue is empty, the facility is declared idle. At the same time, we record that the facility has been busy between $T = 0$ and $T = 13.37$ minutes. The updated list of future events becomes

Time, T	Event
42.48	Arrival of customer 2

Arrival of customer 2 at $T = 42.48$. Customer 3 will arrive at

$$T = 42.48 + [-15 \ln(.4799)] = 53.49 \text{ minutes}$$

Because the facility is idle, customer 2 starts service, and the facility is declared busy. The departure time is

$$T = 42.48 + (10 + 5 \times .9486) = 57.22 \text{ minutes}$$

The list of future events is updated as

Time, T	Event
53.49	Arrival of customer 3
57.22	Departure of customer 2

Arrival of customer 3 at $T = 53.49$.   Customer 4 will arrive at

$$T = 53.49 + [-15 \ln(.6139)] = 60.81 \text{ minutes}$$

Because the facility is currently busy (until $T = 57.22$), customer 3 is placed in queue at $T = 53.49$. The updated list of future events is

Time, T	Event
57.22	Departure of customer 2
60.81	Arrival of customer 4

Departure of customer 2 at $T = 57.22$.   Customer 3 is taken out of the queue to start service. The waiting time is

$$W_3 = 57.22 - 53.49 = 3.73 \text{ minutes}$$

The departure time is

$$T = 57.22 + (10 + 5 \times .5933) = 70.19 \text{ minutes}$$

The updated list of future events is

Time, T	Event
60.81	Arrival of customer 4
70.19	Departure of customer 3

Arrival of customer 4 at $T = 60.81$.   Customer 5 will arrive at

$$T = 60.81 + [-15 \ln(.9341)] = 61.83 \text{ minutes}$$

Because the facility is busy until $T = 70.19$, customer 4 is placed in the queue. The updated list of future events is

Time, T	Event
61.83	Arrival of customer 5
70.19	Departure of customer 3

Arrival of customer 5 at $T = 61.83$.   The simulation is limited to 5 arrivals, hence customer 6 arrival is not generated. The facility is still busy, hence the customer is placed in queue at $T = 61.83$. The updated list of events is

Time, T	Event
70.19	Departure of customer 3

Departure of customer 3 at $T = 70.19$.   Customer 4 is taken out of the queue to start service. The waiting time is

$$W_4 = 70.19 - 60.81 = 9.38 \text{ minutes}$$

The departure time is

$$T = 70.19 + [10 + 5 \times .1782] = 81.08 \text{ minutes}$$

The updated list of future events is

Time, T	Event
81.08	Departure of customer 4

Departure of customer 4 at $T = 81.08$.   Customer 5 is taken out of the queue to start service. The waiting time is

$$W_5 = 81.08 - 61.83 = 19.25 \text{ minutes}$$

The departure time is

$$T = 81.08 + (10 + 5 \times .3473) = 92.82 \text{ minutes}$$

The updated list of future events is

Time, T	Event
92.82	Departure of customer 5

Departure of customer 5 at $T = 92.82$.   There are no more customers in the system (queue and facility) and the simulation ends.

Figure 19.7 summarizes the changes in the length of the queue and the utilization of the facility as a function of the simulation time.

The queue length and the facility utilization are known as **time-based** variables because their variation is a function of time. As result, their average values are computed as

$$\left(\begin{array}{c} \text{Average value of a} \\ \text{time-based variable} \end{array} \right) = \frac{\text{Area under curve}}{\text{Simulated period}}$$

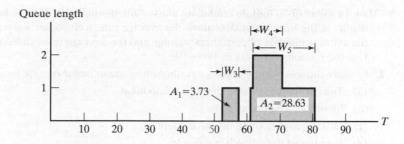

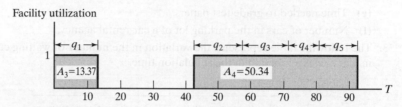

FIGURE 19.7

Changes in queue length and facility utilization as a function of simulation time, T

Implementing this formula for the data in Figure 19.7, we get

$$\begin{pmatrix} \text{Average queue} \\ \text{length} \end{pmatrix} = \frac{A_1 + A_2}{92.82} = \frac{32.36}{92.82} = .349 \text{ customer}$$

$$\begin{pmatrix} \text{Average facility} \\ \text{utilization} \end{pmatrix} = \frac{A_3 + A_4}{92.82} = \frac{63.71}{92.82} = .686 \text{ barber}$$

The average waiting time in the queue is an **observation-based** variable whose value is computed as

$$\begin{pmatrix} \text{Average value of an} \\ \text{observation-based variable} \end{pmatrix} = \frac{\text{Sum of observations}}{\text{Number of observations}}$$

Examination of Figure 19.7 reveals that the area under the queue-length curve actually equals the sum of the waiting time for the three customers who joined the queue; namely,

$$W_1 + W_2 + W_3 + W_4 + W_5 = 0 + 0 + 3.73 + 9.38 + 19.25 = 32.36 \text{ minutes}$$

The average waiting time in the queue for all customers is thus computed as

$$\overline{W}_q = \tfrac{32.36}{5} = 6.47 \text{ minutes}$$

PROBLEM SET 19.5A

1. Suppose that the barbershop in Section 19.5.1 is operated by two barbers, and customers are served on a FCFS basis. Suppose further that the time to get a haircut is uniformly distributed between 15 and 30 minutes. The interarrival time of customers is exponential,

with a mean of 10 minutes. Simulate the system manually for 75 time units. From the results of the simulation, determine the average time a customer waits in queue, the average number of customers waiting, and the average utilization of the barbers. Use the random numbers in Table 19.1.

2. Classify the following variables as either *observation based* or *time based*:

   *(a) Time-to-failure of an electronic component.

   *(b) Inventory level of an item.

   (c) Order quantity of an inventory item.

   (d) Number of defective items in a lot.

   (e) Time needed to grade test papers.

   (f) Number of cars in the parking lot of a car-rental agency.

*3. The following table represents the variation in the number of waiting customers in a queue as a function of the simulation time.

Simulation time, T (hr)	No. of waiting customers
$0 \le T \le 3$	0
$3 < T \le 4$	1
$4 < T \le 6$	2
$6 < T \le 7$	1
$7 < T \le 10$	0
$10 < T \le 12$	2
$12 < T \le 18$	3
$18 < T \le 20$	2
$20 < T \le 25$	1

Compute the following measures of performance:

   (a) The average length of the queue.

   (b) The average waiting time in the queue for those who must wait.

4. Suppose that the barbershop described at the start of Section 19.5.1 is operated by three barbers. Assume further that the utilization of the servers (barbers) is summarized as given in the following table:

Simulation time, T (hr)	No. of busy servers
$0 < T \le 10$	0
$10 < T \le 20$	1
$20 < T \le 30$	2
$30 < T \le 40$	0
$40 < T \le 60$	1
$60 < T \le 70$	2
$70 < T \le 80$	3
$80 < T \le 90$	1
$90 < T \le 100$	0

Determine the following measures of performance:

(a) The average utilization of the facility.

(b) The average busy time of the facility.

(c) The average idle time of the facility.

19.5.2 Spreadsheet-Based Simulation of the Single-Server Model

This section develops a spreadsheet-based model for the single server model. The objective of the development is to reinforce the ideas introduced in Section 19.5.1. Of course, a single-server model is a simple situation that can be modeled readily in a spreadsheet environment. Other situations require more involved modeling effort, a task that is facilitated by available simulation packages (see Section 19.7).

The presentation in Section 19.5.1 shows that the simulation model of the single-server facility requires two basic elements:

1. A chronological list of the model's events.
2. A graph that keeps track of the changes in facility utilization and queue length.

These two elements remain essential in the development of the spreadsheet-based (indeed, any computer-based) simulation model. The difference is that the implementation is realized in a manner that is compatible with the use of the computer. As in Section 19.5.1, customers are served in order of arrival (FIFO).

Figure 19.8 provides the output of *excelSingleServer.xls*. The input data allow representing the interarrival and service time in one of four ways: constant, exponential, uniform, and triangular. The triangular distribution is useful in that it can be used as a rough initial estimate of any distribution, simply by providing three estimates *a*, *b*, and *c* that represent the smallest, the most likely, and the largest values of the interarrival or

FIGURE 19.8

Excel output of a single-server simulation model (file *excelSingleServer.xls*)

	A	B	C	D	E	F	G	H	K	L	M	N	O	P	Q
1		Simulation of a Single-Server Queueing Model													
2		Nbr of arrivals =	20	<<Maximum 500											
3		Enter x in column A to select interarrival pdf:							Nbr	InterArrT	ServiceT	ArrT	DepartT	Wq	Ws
4		Constant =							1	3.73	12.83	0.00	12.83	0.00	12.83
5	x	Exponential:	λ =	0.067					2	5.37	14.71	3.73	27.56	9.10	23.82
6		Uniform:	a =		b =				3	3.86	12.21	9.09	39.75	18.45	30.66
7		Triangular:	a =		b =		c =		4	14.10	11.18	12.95	50.94	25.80	37.98
8		Enter x in column A to select service time pdf:							5	7.35	14.92	27.05	65.85	23.88	38.80
9		Constant =							6	35.70	14.22	34.41	80.07	31.45	45.67
10		Exponential:	μ =						7	0.60	14.50	70.11	94.58	9.97	24.47
11	x	Uniform:	a =	10	b =	15			8	4.25	13.35	70.71	107.93	23.87	37.22
12		Triangular:	a =		b =		c =		9	4.85	12.45	74.96	120.38	32.97	45.41
13		Output Summary							10	7.43	11.57	79.81	131.94	40.56	52.13
14		Av. facility utilization =		0.98					11	8.99	14.65	87.24	146.59	44.70	59.34
15		Percent idleness (%) =		1.96					12	49.78	12.85	96.23	159.43	50.36	63.20
16						Press F9 to			13	0.42	14.12	146.01	173.55	13.43	27.54
17		Av. queue length, Lq =		1.57		trigger a			14	8.77	13.69	146.43	187.24	27.13	40.82
18		Av. nbr in system, Ls =		2.55		new simulation			15	11.19	10.50	155.20	197.75	32.05	42.55
19		Av. queue time, Wq =		21.24		run.			16	42.82	13.78	166.38	211.53	31.36	45.14
20		Av. system time, Ws =		34.47					17	19.87	12.29	209.20	223.82	2.33	14.62
21		Sum(ServiceTime) =		264.65					18	9.25	12.95	229.07	242.03	0.00	12.95
22		Sum(Wq) =		424.80					19	13.98	12.99	238.33	255.02	3.70	16.69
23		Sum(Ws) =		669.44					20	58.46	14.88	252.31	269.90	2.71	17.59

service time. The only other information needed to drive the simulation is the length of the simulation run, which in this model is specified by the number of arrivals that can be generated in the model.

The spreadsheet calculations reserve one row for each arrival. The interarrival and service times for each arrival are generated from the input data. The first arrival is assumed to occur at $T = 0$. Because the facility starts idle, the customer starts service immediately. The spreadsheet provides sufficient information to demonstrate the internal computations given in Section 19.5.1.

Another spreadsheet was developed for simulating multiserver models (*excelMultiServer.xls*). The design of the template is based on the same ideas used in the single-server case. However, the determination of the departure time is not as straightforward and requires the use of VBA macros.

PROBLEM SET 19.5B

1. Using the input data in Section 19.5.1, run the Excel simulator for 10 arrivals and graph the changes in facility utilization and queue length as a function of the simulation time. Verify that the areas under the curves equal the sum of the service times and the sum of the waiting times, respectively.

2. Simulate the $M/M/1$ model for 500 arrivals, given the arrival rate $\lambda = 4$ customers per hour and the service rate $\mu = 6$ departures per hour. Run 5 replications (by refreshing the spreadsheet—pressing F9) and determine a 95% confidence interval for all the measures of performance of the model. Compare the results with the steady-state theoretical values of the $M/M/1$ model.

3. Television units arrive on a conveyor belt every 15 minutes for inspection at a single-operator station. Detailed data for the inspection station are not available. However, the operator estimates that it takes 10 minutes "on the average" to inspect a unit. Under worst conditions, the inspection time does not exceed 13 minutes, and for certain units, inspection time may be as low as 9 minutes.

   (a) Use the Excel simulator to simulate the inspection of 200 TV units.

   (b) Based on 5 replications, estimate the average number of units awaiting inspection and the average utilization of the inspection station.

19.6   METHODS FOR GATHERING STATISTICAL OBSERVATIONS

Simulation is a statistical experiment, and its output must be interpreted using proper statistical inference tools (e.g., confidence intervals and hypothesis testing). To accomplish this task, a simulation experiment must satisfy three conditions:

1. Observations are drawn from stationary (identical) distributions.
2. Observations are sampled from a normal population.
3. Observations are independent.

In a strict sense, the simulation experiment does not satisfy any of these conditions. Nevertheless, we can ensure that these conditions remain statistically acceptable by restricting the manner in which the observations are gathered.

First, we consider the issue of stationary distributions. Simulation output is a function of the length of the simulated period. The initial period produces erratic behavior and is usually referred to as the **transient** or **warm-up period**. When the output stabilizes, the system operates under **steady state**. Unfortunately, there is no definitive way to predict the start point of steady state in advance. In general, a longer simulation run has better chance of reaching steady state—meaning that the problem is addressed by using a sufficiently large sample size.

Next, we consider the requirement that simulation observations are drawn from a normal population. This requirement is realized by using the *central limit theorem* (see Section 14.4.4), which confirms that the distribution of the average of a sample is asymptotically normal regardless of the parent population. The central limit theorem is thus the main tool we use for satisfying the normal distribution assumption.

The third condition deals with the independence of the observations. In simulation, an observation can be based on a single independent run, or by subdividing a single run into subintervals each representing an observation. Each method has it advantages and disadvantages. The first method alleviates the question of independence but has the disadvantage of including the transient period in each observation. In the second method, the effect of the transient period is not as pronounced, but it inherently worsens the issue of independence. As will be explained subsequently in this section, a possible remedy calls for increasing the length of the simulation run.

The most common methods for collecting observations in simulation are

1. Subinterval method.
2. Replication method.
3. Regenerative (or cycles) method.

The first two methods can be readily automated in all widely used simulation languages (see Section 19.7). On the other hand, the third method, though it addresses directly the issue of independence by seeking identical starting conditions for the different observations, may be difficult to implement in practice.

Sections 19.6.1 and 19.6.2 present the first two methods. Details of the third method can be found in Law (2007).

19.6.1   Subinterval Method

Figure 19.9 illustrates the idea of the subinterval method. Suppose that the length of the simulation run is T time units. The subinterval method first truncates an initial transient period, and then subdivides the remainder of the simulation run into n equal subintervals (or batches). The average of a desired measure of performance (e.g., queue length or waiting time in queue) within each subinterval is then used to represent a single observation. Truncation of the initial transient period means that no statistical data are collected during that period.

The advantage of the subinterval method is that the effect of the transient (nonstationary) conditions is mitigated, particularly for the observations that are collected toward the end of the simulation run. The disadvantage is that successive batches with common boundary conditions are not necessarily independent. The problem can be alleviated by increasing the time base for each observation.

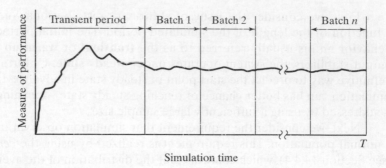

FIGURE 19.9

Collecting simulation data using the subinterval method

Example 19.6-1

Figure 19.10 shows the change in queue length in a single-queue model as a function of the simulation time. The simulation run length is $T = 35$ hours, and the length of the transient period is estimated to equal 5 hours. The time base for an observation is 6 hours, which produces $n = 5$ observation.

Let $\overline{Q}_i$ represent the average queue length in batch i. Because the queue length is a time-based variable, we have

$$\overline{Q}_i = \frac{A_i}{t}, i = 1, 2, \ldots, 5$$

where A_i is the area under the queue length curve associated with batch (observation) i, and $t(\,=6)$ is the time base per batch.

The data in Figure 19.10 produce the following observations:

Observation i	1	2	3	4	5
A_i	14	10	11	6	15
$\overline{Q}_i$	2.33	1.67	1.83	1.00	2.50
Sample mean = 1.87		Sample standard deviation = .59			

FIGURE 19.10

Change in queue length with simulation time in Example 19.6-1

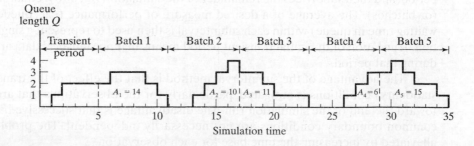

The sample mean and variance can be used to compute a confidence interval, if desired. The computation of the sample variance in Example 19.6-1 is based on the following familiar formula:

$$s = \sqrt{\frac{\sum_{i=1}^{n} x_i^2 - n\bar{x}^2}{n - 1}}$$

This formula is only an approximation of the true standard deviation because it ignores the effect of autocorrelation between the successive batches. The exact formula can be found in Law (2007).

19.6.2 Replication Method

In the replication method, each observation is represented by an independent simulation run in which the transient period is truncated, as illustrated in Figure 19.11. The computation of the observation averages for each batch is the same as in the subinterval method. The only difference is that the standard variance formula is applicable because the batches are not independent.

The advantage of the replication method is that each simulation run is driven by a distinct 0-1 random number stream, which yields statistically independent observations. The disadvantage is that each observation may be biased by the initial effect of the transient conditions. Such a problem may be alleviated by making the run length sufficiently large.

PROBLEM SET 19.6A

1. In Example 19.6-1, use the subinterval method to compute the average waiting time in the queue for those who must wait.

*2. In a simulation model, the subinterval method is used to compute batch averages. The transient period is estimated to be 100, and each batch has a time base of 100 time units as well. Using the following data, which provide the waiting times for customers as a function of the simulation time, estimate the 95% confidence interval for the mean waiting time.

FIGURE 19.11

Collecting simulation data using the replication method

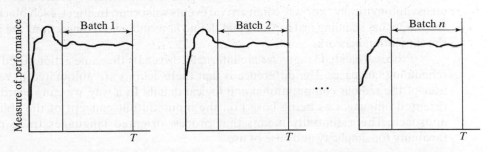

Time interval	Waiting times
0–100	10, 20, 13, 14, 8, 15, 6, 8
100–200	12, 30, 10, 14, 16
200–300	15, 17, 20, 22
300–400	10, 20, 30, 15, 25, 31
400–500	15, 17, 20, 14, 13
500–600	25, 30, 15

19.7 SIMULATION LANGUAGES

Execution of simulation models entails two distinct types of computations: (1) file manipulations that deal with the chronological storage and processing of model events and (2) arithmetic and bookkeeping computations associated with generation of random samples and collection of model statistics. The first type of computation involves extensive logic in the development of list processing, and the second type entails tedious and time-consuming calculations. The nature of these computations makes the computer an essential tool for executing simulation models, and, in turn, prompts the development of special computer simulation languages for performing these computations conveniently and efficiently.

Available discrete simulation languages fall into two broad categories:

1. Event scheduling
2. Process oriented

In event scheduling languages, the user details the actions associated with the occurrence of each event, in much the same way they are given in Example 19.5-1. The main role of the language in this case is (1) automation of sampling from distributions, (2) storage and retrieval of events in chronological order, and (3) collection of model statistics.

Process-oriented languages use blocks or nodes that can be linked together to form a network that describes the movements of **transactions** or **entities** (i.e., customers) in the system. For example, the three most prominent blocks/nodes in any process-simulation language are a *source* from which transactions are created, a *queue* where they can wait if necessary, and a *facility* where service is performed. Each of these blocks/nodes is defined with all the information needed to drive the simulation automatically. For example, once the interarrival time for the source is specified, a process-oriented language automatically "knows" when arrival events will occur. In effect, each block/node of the model has standing instructions that define *how* and *when* transactions are moved in the simulation network.

Process-oriented languages are internally driven by the same actions used in event-scheduling languages. The difference is that these actions are automated to relieve the user of the tedious computational and logical details. In a way, we can regard process-oriented languages as being based on the input–output concept of the "black box" approach. This essentially means that process-oriented languages trade modeling flexibility for simplicity and ease of use.

Event-scheduling languages (such as SIMSCRIPT, SLAM, and SIMAN) are outdated and are rarely used in practice. Recently, a new language called DEEDS (Elizandro and Taha, 2008) is based on the novice approach of using Excel spreadsheet to drive event scheduling. DEEDS allows the modeling flexibility of event-driven simulation languages while achieving the intuitive nature of a process-oriented language.

The predominant process-oriented commercial package is Arena. It uses extensive user interface to simplify the process of creating a simulation model. It also provides animation capabilities where changes in the system can be observed visually. However, to an experienced simulation professional, these interfaces may appear to reduce the development of a simulation model to a "slow-motion" pace. It is not surprising that some users continue to prefer writing simulation models in higher-level programming languages.

PROBLEM SET 19.7A[2]

1. Patrons arrive randomly at a three-clerk post office. The interarrival time is exponential with mean 5 minutes. The time a clerk spends with a patron is exponential with a mean of 10 minutes. All arriving patrons form one queue and wait for the first available free clerk. Run a simulation model of the system for 480 minutes to determine the following:

   (a) The average number of patrons waiting in the queue.

   (b) The average utilization of the clerks.

   (c) Compare the simulation results with those of the $M/M/c$ queuing model (Chapter 18) and with the spreadsheet *MultiServerSimulator.xls*.

2. Television units arrive for inspection on a conveyor belt at the constant rate of 5 units per hour. The inspection time takes between 10 and 15 minutes, uniformly distributed. Past experience shows that 20% of inspected units must be adjusted and then sent back for reinspection. The adjustment time is also uniformly distributed between 6 and 8 minutes. Run a simulation model for 480 minutes to compute the following:

   (a) The average time a unit takes until it passes inspection.

   (b) The average number of times a unit must be reinspected before it exits the system.

3. A mouse is trapped in a maze and desperately "wants out." After trying between 1 and 3 minutes, uniformly distributed, there is a 30% chance that it will find the right path. Otherwise, it will wander around aimlessly for between 2 and 3 minutes, uniformly distributed, and eventually end up where it started, only to try once again. The mouse can "try freedom" as many times as it pleases, but there is a limit to everything. With so much energy expended in trying and retrying, the mouse is certain to expire if it does not make it within a period that is normally distributed, with a mean of 10 minutes and a standard deviation of 2 minutes. Write a simulation model to estimate the probability that the mouse will be free. For the purpose of estimating the probability, assume that 100 mice will be processed by the model.

4. In the final stage of automobile manufacturing, a car moving on a transporter is situated between two parallel workstations to allow work to be done on both the left and right

---

[2]Work these problems using a simulation language of your choice or a higher-order programming language.

sides of the car simultaneously. The operation times for the left and right sides are uniform between 15 and 20 minutes and 18 and 22 minutes, respectively. The transporter arrives at the stations area every 20 minutes. Simulate the process for 480 minutes to determine the utilization of the left and right stations.

5. Cars arrive at a one-bay car wash facility where the interarrival time is exponential, with a mean of 10 minutes. Arriving cars line up in a single lane that can accommodate at most five waiting cars. If the lane is full, newly arriving cars will go elsewhere. It takes between 10 and 15 minutes, uniformly distributed, to wash a car. Simulate the system for 960 minutes, and estimate the time a car spends in the facility.

BIBLIOGRAPHY

Banks, J., J. Carson, B. Nelson, and D. Nicol, *Discrete-Event System Simulation*, 4th ed., Prentice Hall, Upper Saddle River, NJ, 2005.

Box, G., and M. Muller, "A Note on the Generation of Random Normal Deviates," *Annals of Mathematical Statistics*, Vol. 29, pp. 610–611, 1958.

Elizandro, D., and H. Taha, *Simulation of Industrial Systems: Discrete Event Simulation Using Excel/VBA*, Taylor and Francis, New York, 2008.

Law, A., *Simulation Modeling & Analysis*, 4th ed., McGraw-Hill, New York, 2007.

Rubenstein, R., B. Melamed, and A. Shapiro, *Modern Simulation and Modeling*, Wiley, New York, 1998.

Taha, H., *Simulation Modeling and SIMNET*, Prentice Hall, Upper Saddle River, NJ, 1988.

CHAPTER 20

Classical Optimization Theory

20.1 UNCONSTRAINED PROBLEMS

An extreme point of a function $f(\mathbf{X})$ defines either a maximum or a minimum of the function. Mathematically, a point $\mathbf{X}_0 = (x_1^0, \ldots, x_j^0, \ldots, x_n^0)$ is a maximum if

$$f(\mathbf{X}_0 + \mathbf{h}) \leq f(\mathbf{X}_0)$$

for all $\mathbf{h} = (h_1, \ldots, h_j, \ldots, h_n)$, where $|h_j|$ is sufficiently small for all j. In a similar manner, $\mathbf{X}_0$ is a minimum if

$$f(\mathbf{X}_0 + \mathbf{h}) \geq f(\mathbf{X}_0)$$

Figure 20.1 illustrates the maxima and minima of a single-variable function $f(x)$ defined in the range $a \leq x \leq b$. The points x_1, x_2, x_3, x_4, and x_6 are all extrema of $f(x)$, with x_1, x_3, and x_6 as maxima and x_2 and x_4 as minima. The value $f(x_6) = \max\{f(x_1), f(x_3), f(x_6)\}$ is a **global** or **absolute** maximum, and $f(x_1)$ and $f(x_3)$ are **local** or **relative** maxima. Similarly, $f(x_4)$ is a local minimum and $f(x_2)$ is a global minimum.

Although x_1 (in Figure 20.1) is a (local) maximum point, it differs from remaining local maxima in that the value of f corresponding to at least one point in the neighborhood of x_1 equals $f(x_1)$. In this respect, x_1 is a **weak maximum**, whereas x_3 and x_6 are **strong maxima**. In general, for $\mathbf{h}$ as defined earlier, $\mathbf{X}_0$ is a weak maximum if $f(\mathbf{X}_0 + \mathbf{h}) \leq f(\mathbf{X}_0)$ and a strong maximum if $f(\mathbf{X}_0 + \mathbf{h}) < f(\mathbf{X}_0)$.

In Figure 20.1, the first derivative (slope) of f equals zero at all extrema. This property is also satisfied at **inflection** and **saddle** points, such as x_5. If a point with zero slope (gradient) is not an extremum (maximum or minimum), then it must be an inflection or a saddle point.

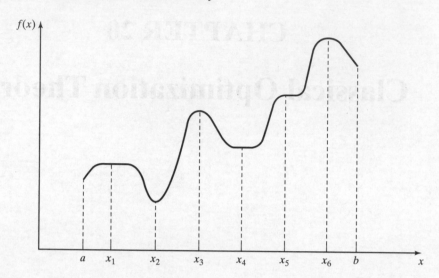

FIGURE 20.1

Examples of extreme points for a single-variable function

20.1.1 Necessary and Sufficient Conditions

This section develops the necessary and sufficient conditions for an *n*-variable function $f(\mathbf{X})$ to have extrema. It is assumed that the first and second partial derivatives of $f(\mathbf{X})$ are continuous for all $\mathbf{X}$.

Theorem 20.1-1   *A necessary condition for $\mathbf{X}_0$ to be an extreme point of $f(\mathbf{X})$ is that*

$$\nabla f(\mathbf{X}_0) = 0$$

Because the necessary condition is also satisfied at inflection and saddle points, it is more appropriate to refer to the points obtained from the solution of $\nabla f(\mathbf{X}_0) = \mathbf{0}$ as **stationary** points. The next theorem establishes the sufficiency conditions for $\mathbf{X}_0$ to be an extreme point.

Theorem 20.1-2   *A sufficient condition for a stationary point $\mathbf{X}_0$ to be an extremum is that the Hessian matrix $\mathbf{H}$ evaluated at $\mathbf{X}_0$ satisfy the following conditions:*

  (i) $\mathbf{H}$ *is positive definite if $\mathbf{X}_0$ is a minimum point.*

  (ii) $\mathbf{H}$ *is negative definite if $\mathbf{X}_0$ is a maximum point.*

Example 20.1-1

Consider the function

$$f(x_1, x_2, x_3) = x_1 + 2x_3 + x_2 x_3 - x_1^2 - x_2^2 - x_3^2$$

The necessary condition $\nabla f(\mathbf{X}_0) = 0$ gives

$$\frac{\partial f}{\partial x_1} = 1 - 2x_1 = 0$$

$$\frac{\partial f}{\partial x_2} = x_3 - 2x_2 = 0$$

$$\frac{\partial f}{\partial x_3} = 2 + x_2 - 2x_3 = 0$$

The solution of these simultaneous equations is

$$\mathbf{X}_0 = \left(\frac{1}{2}, \frac{2}{3}, \frac{4}{3}\right)$$

To determine the type of the stationary point, consider

$$\mathbf{H}|_{\mathbf{X}_0} = \begin{pmatrix} \dfrac{\partial^2 f}{\partial x_1^2} & \dfrac{\partial^2 f}{\partial x_1 \partial x_2} & \dfrac{\partial^2 f}{\partial x_1 \partial x_3} \\[2mm] \dfrac{\partial^2 f}{\partial x_2 \partial x_1} & \dfrac{\partial^2 f}{\partial x_2^2} & \dfrac{\partial^2 f}{\partial x_2 \partial x_3} \\[2mm] \dfrac{\partial^2 f}{\partial x_3 \partial x_1} & \dfrac{\partial^2 f}{\partial x_3 \partial x_2} & \dfrac{\partial^2 f}{\partial x_3^2} \end{pmatrix}_{\mathbf{X}_0} = \begin{pmatrix} -2 & 0 & 0 \\ 0 & -2 & 1 \\ 0 & 1 & -2 \end{pmatrix}$$

The principal minor determinants of $\mathbf{H}|_{\mathbf{X}_0}$ have the values $-2, 4$, and -6, respectively. Thus, as shown in Section D.3, $\mathbf{H}|_{\mathbf{X}_0}$ is negative-definite, and $\mathbf{X}_0 = \left(\frac{1}{2}, \frac{2}{3}, \frac{4}{3}\right)$ represents a maximum point.

In general, if $\mathbf{H}|_{\mathbf{X}_0}$ is indefinite, $\mathbf{X}_0$ must be a saddle point. For nonconclusive cases, $\mathbf{X}_0$ may or may not be an extremum, and the sufficiency condition becomes rather involved, because higher-order terms in Taylor's expansion must be considered.

The sufficiency condition established by Theorem 20.1-2 applies to single-variable functions as follows. Given that y_0 is a stationary point, then

(i) y_0 is a maximum if $f''(y_0) < 0$.

(ii) y_0 is a minimum if $f''(y_0) > 0$.

If $f''(y_0) = 0$, higher-order derivatives must be investigated as the following theorem requires.

Theorem 20.1-3 *Given y_0, a stationary point of $f(y)$, if the first $(n - 1)$ derivatives are zero and $f^{(n)}(y_0) \neq 0$, then*

(i) *If n is odd, y_0 is an inflection point.*

(ii) *If n is even, then y_0 is a minimum if $f^{(n)}(y_0) > 0$ and a maximum if $f^{(n)}(y_0) < 0$.*

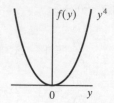 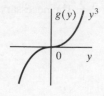

FIGURE 20.2

Extreme points of $f(y) = y^4$ and $g(y) = y^3$

Example 20.1-2

Figure 20.2 graphs the following two functions:

$$f(y) = y^4$$

$$g(y) = y^3$$

For $f(y) = y^4$, $f'(y) = 4y^3 = 0$, which yields the stationary point $y_0 = 0$. Now

$$f'(0) = f''(0) = f^{(3)}(0) = 0, f^{(4)}(0) = 24 > 0$$

Hence, $y_0 = 0$ is a minimum point (see Figure 20.2).

For $g(y) = y^3$, $g'(y) = 3y^2 = 0$, which yields $y_0 = 0$ as a stationary point. Also

$$g'(0) = g''(0), g^{(3)}(0) = 6 \neq 0$$

Thus, $y_0 = 0$ is an inflection point.

PROBLEM SET 20.1A

1. Determine the extreme points of the following functions.
   *(a) $f(x) = x^3 + x$
   *(b) $f(x) = x^4 + x^2$
   (c) $f(x) = 4x^4 - x^2 + 5$
   (d) $f(x) = (3x - 2)^2 (2x - 3)^2$
   (e) $f(x) = 6x^5 - 4x^3 + 10$

2. Determine the extreme points of the following functions.
   (a) $f(\mathbf{X}) = x_1^3 + x_2^3 - 3x_1x_2$
   (b) $f(\mathbf{X}) = 2x_1^2 + x_2^2 + x_3^2 + 6(x_1 + x_2 + x_3) + 2x_1x_2x_3$

3. Verify that the function

$$f(x_1, x_2, x_3) = 2x_1x_2x_3 - 4x_1x_3 - 2x_2x_3 + x_1^2 + x_2^2 + x_3^2 - 2x_1 - 4x_2 + 4x_3$$

   has the stationary points $(0, 3, 1), (0, 1, -1), (1, 2, 0), (2, 1, 1),$ and $(2, 3, -1)$. Use the sufficiency condition to identify the extreme points.

*4. Solve the following simultaneous equations by converting the system to a nonlinear objective function with no constraints.

$$x_2 - x_1^2 = 0$$

$$x_2 - x_1 = 2$$

[*Hint*: min $f^2(x_1, x_2)$ occurs at $f'(x_1, x_2) = 0$.]

20.1.2 The Newton-Raphson Method

In general, the necessary condition $\nabla f(x) \neq 0$ may be highly nonlinear and, hence, difficult to solve. The Newton-Raphson method is an iterative algorithm for solving simultaneous nonlinear equations.

Consider the simultaneous equations

$$f_i(\mathbf{X}) = 0, \, i = 1, 2, \ldots, m$$

Let $\mathbf{X}^k$ be a given point. Then by Taylor's expansion

$$f_i(\mathbf{X}) \approx f_i(\mathbf{X}_k) + \nabla f_i(\mathbf{X}_k)(\mathbf{X} - \mathbf{X}_k), \, i = 1, 2, \ldots, m$$

Thus, the original equations, $f_i(\mathbf{X}) = 0$, $i = 1, 2, \ldots, m$, may be approximated as

$$f_i(\mathbf{X}_k) + \nabla f_i(\mathbf{X}_k)(\mathbf{X} - \mathbf{X}_k) = 0, \, i = 1, 2, \ldots, m$$

These equations may be written in matrix notation as

$$\mathbf{A}_k + \mathbf{B}_k(\mathbf{X} - \mathbf{X}_k) = \mathbf{0}$$

If $\mathbf{B}_k$ is nonsingular, then

$$\mathbf{X} = \mathbf{X}_k - \mathbf{B}_k^{-1}\mathbf{A}_k$$

The idea of the method is to start from an initial point $\mathbf{X}_0$, and then use the equation above to determine a new point. The process may or may not converge depending on the selection of the starting point. Convergence occurs when two successive points, $\mathbf{X}_k$ and $\mathbf{X}_{k+1}$, are approximately equal (within specified acceptable tolerance).

A geometric interpretation of the method is illustrated by a single-variable function in Figure 20.3. The relationship between x_k and x_{k+1} for a single-variable function $f(x)$ reduces to

$$x_{k+1} = x_k - \frac{f(x_k)}{f'(x_k)}$$

The terms may be arranged as $f'(x_k) = \dfrac{f(x_k)}{x_k - x_{k+1}}$—meaning that x_{k+1} is determined from the slope of $f(x)$ at x_k, where $\tan \theta = f'(x_k)$, as the figure shows.

Figure 20.3 demonstrates that convergence is not always possible. If the initial point is a, the method will diverge. In general, it may be necessary to attempt a number of initial points before convergence is achieved.

Example 20.1-3

To demonstrate the use of the Newton-Raphson method, consider the function

$$g(x) = (3x - 2)^2 (2x - 3)^2$$

To determine the stationary points of $g(x)$, we need to solve

$$f(x) \equiv g'(x) = 72x^3 - 234x^2 + 241x - 78 = 0$$

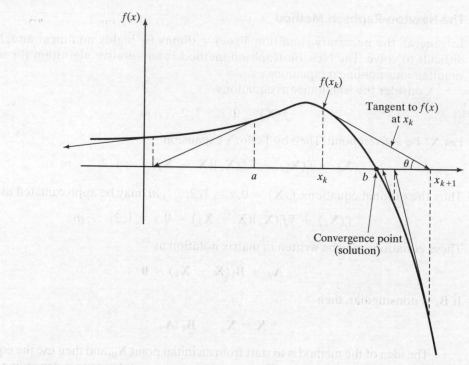

FIGURE 20.3

Illustration of the iterative process in the Newton-Raphson method

Thus, for the Newton-Raphson method, we have

$$f'(x) = 216x^2 - 468x + 241$$

$$x_{k+1} = x_k - \frac{72x^3 - 234x^2 + 241x - 78}{216x^2 - 468x + 24}$$

Starting with $x_0 = 10$, the following table provides the successive iterations:

k	x_k	$\dfrac{f(x_k)}{f'(x_k)}$	x_{k+1}
0	10.000000	2.978923	7.032108
1	7.032108	1.976429	5.055679
2	5.055679	1.314367	3.741312
3	3.741312	0.871358	2.869995
4	2.869995	0.573547	2.296405
5	2.296405	0.371252	1.925154
6	1.925154	0.230702	1.694452
7	1.694452	0.128999	1.565453
8	1.565453	0.054156	1.511296
9	1.511296	.0108641	1.500432
10	1.500432	.00043131	1.500001

The method converges to $x = 1.5$. Actually, $f(x)$ has three stationary points at $x = \frac{2}{3}$, $x = \frac{13}{12}$, and $x = \frac{3}{2}$. The remaining two points can be found by attempting different values for initial x_0. In fact, $x_0 = .5$ and $x_0 = 1$ should yield the missing stationary points (try it!).

Excel Moment

Template *excelNewtonRaphson.xls* can be used to solve any single-variable equation. It requires entering $\frac{f(x)}{f'(x)}$ in cell C3. For Example 20.1-3, we enter

$$=(72*A3^3-234*A3^2+241*A3-78)/(216*A3^2-468*A3+241)$$

The variable x is replaced with A3. The template allows setting a tolerance limit Δ, which specifies the allowable difference between x_k and x_{k+1} that signals the termination of the iterations. You are encouraged to use different initial points, x_0, to get a feel of how the method works.

PROBLEM SET 20.1B

1. Use *NewtonRaphson.xls* to solve Problem 1(c), Set 20.1a.
2. Solve Problem 2(b), Set 20.1a, by the Newton-Raphson method.

20.2 CONSTRAINED PROBLEMS

This section deals with the optimization of constrained continuous functions. Section 20.2.1 introduces the case of equality constraints, and Section 20.2.2 deals with inequality constraints. The presentation in Section 20.2.1 is covered for the most part in Beightler and Associates (1979, pp. 45–55).

20.2.1 Equality Constraints

This section presents two methods: the **Jacobian** and the **Lagrangean**. The **Lagrangean** method can be developed logically from the Jacobian. This relationship provides an interesting economic interpretation of the Lagrangean method.

Constrained derivatives (Jacobian) method. Consider the problem

$$\text{Minimize } z = f(\mathbf{X})$$

subject to

$$\mathbf{g}(\mathbf{X}) = \mathbf{0}$$

where

$$\mathbf{X} = (x_1, x_2, \ldots, x_n)$$
$$\mathbf{g} = (g_1, g_2, \ldots, g_m)^T$$

The functions $f(\mathbf{X})$ and $g(\mathbf{X})$, $i = 1, 2, \ldots, m$, are twice continuously differentiable.

The idea of using constrained derivatives is to develop a closed-form expression for the first partial derivatives of $f(\mathbf{X})$ at all points satisfying $\mathbf{g}(\mathbf{X}) = \mathbf{0}$. The corresponding stationary points are identified as the points at which these partial derivatives vanish. The sufficiency conditions introduced in Section 20.1 can then be used to check the identity of stationary points.

To clarify the proposed concept, consider $f(x_1, x_2)$ illustrated in Figure 20.4. This function is to be minimized subject to the constraint

$$g_1(x_1, x_2) = x_2 - b = 0$$

where b is a constant. From Figure 20.4, the curve designated by the three points A, B, and C represents the values of $f(x_1, x_2)$ satisfying the given constraint. The constrained derivatives method defines the gradient of $f(x_1, x_2)$ at any point on the curve ABC. Point B at which the constrained derivative vanishes is a stationary point for the constrained problem.

The method is now developed mathematically. By Taylor's theorem, for $\mathbf{X} + \Delta\mathbf{X}$ in the feasible neighborhood of $\mathbf{X}$, we have

$$f(\mathbf{X} + \Delta\mathbf{X}) - f(\mathbf{X}) = \nabla f(\mathbf{X})\Delta\mathbf{X} + O(\Delta x_j^2)$$

FIGURE 20.4

Demonstration of the idea of the Jacobian method

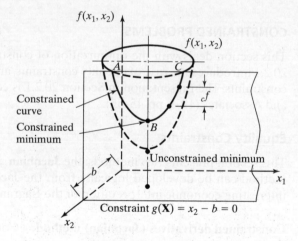

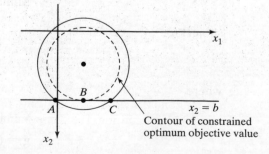

and

$$g(X + \Delta X) - g(X) = \nabla g(X)\Delta X + O(\Delta x_j^2)$$

As $\Delta x_j \to 0$, the equations reduce to

$$\partial f(X) = \nabla f(X) \, \partial X$$

and

$$\partial g(X) = \nabla g(X) \, \partial X$$

For feasibility, we must have $g(X) = 0, \partial g(X) = 0$. Hence

$$\partial f(X) - \nabla f(X) \, \partial X = 0$$

$$\nabla g(X) \, \partial X = 0$$

This gives $(m + 1)$ equations in $(n + 1)$ unknowns, $\partial f(X)$ and ∂X. Note that $\partial f(X)$ is a dependent variable whose value is determined once ∂X is known. This means that, in effect, we have m equations in n unknowns.

If $m > n$, at least $(m - n)$ equations are redundant. Eliminating redundancy, the system reduces to $m \leq n$. If $m = n$, the solution is $\partial X = 0$, and X has no feasible neighborhood, which means that the solution space consists of one point only. The remaining case $(m < n)$ requires further elaboration.

Define

$$X = (Y, Z)$$

such that

$$Y = (y_1, y_2, \ldots, y_m), Z = (z_1, z_2, \ldots, z_{n-m})$$

The vectors Y and Z represent the *dependent* and *independent* variables, respectively. Rewriting the gradient vectors of f and g in terms of Y and Z, we get

$$\nabla f(Y, Z) = (\nabla_Y f, \nabla_Z f)$$

$$\nabla g(Y, Z) = (\nabla_Y g, \nabla_Z g)$$

Define

$$J = \nabla_Y g = \begin{pmatrix} \nabla_Y g_1 \\ \vdots \\ \nabla_Y g_m \end{pmatrix}$$

$$C = \nabla_Z g = \begin{pmatrix} \nabla_Z g_1 \\ \vdots \\ \nabla_Z g_m \end{pmatrix}$$

$J_{m \times m}$ is called the **Jacobian matrix** and $C_{m \times n-m}$ the **control matrix**. The Jacobian J is assumed nonsingular. This is always possible because the given m equations are independent by definition. The components of the vector Y must thus be selected such that J is nonsingular.

The original set of equations in $\partial f(\mathbf{X})$ and $\partial \mathbf{X}$ may be written as

$$\partial f(\mathbf{Y}, \mathbf{Z}) = \nabla_{\mathbf{Y}} f \partial \mathbf{Y} + \nabla_{\mathbf{Z}} f \partial \mathbf{Z}$$

and

$$\mathbf{J} \partial \mathbf{Y} = -\mathbf{C} \partial \mathbf{Z}$$

Given $\mathbf{J}$ is nonsingular, it follows that

$$\partial \mathbf{Y} = -\mathbf{J}^{-1} \mathbf{C} \partial \mathbf{Z}$$

Substituting for $\partial \mathbf{Y}$ in the equation for $\partial f(\mathbf{X})$ gives ∂f as a function of $\partial \mathbf{Z}$—that is,

$$\partial f(\mathbf{Y}, \mathbf{Z}) = (\nabla_{\mathbf{Z}} f - \nabla_{\mathbf{Y}} f \mathbf{J}^{-1} \mathbf{C}) \partial \mathbf{Z}$$

From this equation, the constrained derivative with respect to the independent vector $\mathbf{Z}$ is given by

$$\nabla_c f = \frac{\partial_c f(\mathbf{Y}, \mathbf{Z})}{\partial_c \mathbf{Z}} = \nabla_{\mathbf{Z}} f - \nabla_{\mathbf{Y}} f \mathbf{J}^{-1} \mathbf{C}$$

where $\nabla_c f$ is the **constrained gradient** vector of f with respect to $\mathbf{Z}$. Thus, $\nabla_c f(\mathbf{Y}, \mathbf{Z})$ must be null at the stationary points.

The sufficiency conditions are similar to those developed in Section 20.1. The (constrained) Hessian matrix corresponds to the independent vector $\mathbf{Z}$, and the elements of the Hessian matrix must be the *constrained* second derivatives.

Example 20.2-1

Consider the following problem:

$$f(\mathbf{X}) = x_1^2 + 3x_2^2 + 5x_1 x_3^2$$

$$g_1(\mathbf{X}) = x_1 x_3 + 2x_2 + x_2^2 - 11 = 0$$

$$g_2(\mathbf{X}) = x_1^2 + 2x_1 x_2 + x_3^2 - 14 = 0$$

Given the feasible point $\mathbf{X}^0 = (1, 2, 3)$, we wish to study the variation in $f(= \partial_c f)$ in the feasible neighborhood of $\mathbf{X}^0$.

Let

$$\mathbf{Y} = (x_1, x_3) \quad \text{and} \quad \mathbf{Z} = x_2$$

Thus,

$$\nabla_{\mathbf{Y}} f = \left(\frac{\partial f}{\partial x_1}, \frac{\partial f}{\partial x_3} \right) = (2x_1 + 5x_3^2, 10x_1 x_3)$$

$$\nabla_{\mathbf{Z}} f = \frac{\partial f}{\partial x_2} = 6x_2$$

$$J = \begin{pmatrix} \dfrac{\partial g_1}{\partial x_1} & \dfrac{\partial g_1}{\partial x_3} \\ \dfrac{\partial g_2}{\partial x_1} & \dfrac{\partial g_2}{\partial x_3} \end{pmatrix} = \begin{pmatrix} x_3 & x_1 \\ 2x_1 + 2x_2 & 2x_3 \end{pmatrix}$$

$$C = \begin{pmatrix} \dfrac{\partial g_1}{\partial x2} \\ \dfrac{\partial g_2}{\partial x_2} \end{pmatrix} = \begin{pmatrix} 2x_2 + 2 \\ 2x_2 \end{pmatrix}$$

Suppose that we need to estimate $\partial_c f$ in the feasible neighborhood of the feasible point $X_0 = (1, 2, 3)$, given a small change $\partial x_2 = .01$ in the independent variable x_2. We have

$$J^{-1}C = \begin{pmatrix} 3 & 1 \\ 6 & 6 \end{pmatrix}^{-1} \begin{pmatrix} 6 \\ 2 \end{pmatrix} = \begin{pmatrix} \frac{6}{12} & -\frac{1}{12} \\ -\frac{6}{12} & \frac{3}{12} \end{pmatrix} \begin{pmatrix} 6 \\ 2 \end{pmatrix} \approx \begin{pmatrix} 2.83 \\ -2.50 \end{pmatrix}$$

Hence, the incremental value of constrained f is given as

$$\partial_c f = (\nabla_Z f - \nabla_Y f J^{-1}C)\partial Z = \left(6(2) - (47, 30)\begin{pmatrix} 2.83 \\ -2.50 \end{pmatrix} \right)\partial x_2 = -46.01\partial x_2$$

By specifying the value of ∂x_2 for the *independent* variable x_2, feasible values of ∂x_1 and ∂x_2 are determined for the dependent variables x_1 and x_3 using the formula

$$\partial Y = -J^{-1}C\partial Z$$

Thus, for $\partial x_2 = .01$,

$$\begin{pmatrix} \partial x_1 \\ \partial x_3 \end{pmatrix} = -J^{-1}C\partial x_2 = \begin{pmatrix} -.0283 \\ .0250 \end{pmatrix}$$

We now compare the value of $\partial_c f$ as computed above with the difference $f(X_0 + \partial X) - f(X_0)$, given $\partial x_2 = .01$.

$$X_0 + \partial X = (1 - .0283, 2 + .01, 3 + .025) = (.9717, 2.01, 3.025)$$

This yields

$$f(X_0) = 58, f(X_0 + \partial X) = 57.523$$

or

$$f(X_0 + \partial X) - f(X_0) = -.477$$

The amount $-.477$ compares favorably with $\partial_c f = -46.01\partial x_2 = -.4601$. The difference between the two values is the result of the linear approximation in computing $\partial_c f$ at X_0.

PROBLEM SET 20.2A

1. Consider Example 20.2-1.

   (a) Compute $\partial_c f$ by the two methods presented in the example, using $\partial x_2 = .001$ instead of $\partial x_2 = .01$. Does the effect of linear approximation become more negligible with the decrease in the value of ∂x_2?

   *(b) Specify a relationship among the elements of $\partial \mathbf{X} = (\partial x_1, \partial x_2, \partial x_3)$ at the feasible point $\mathbf{X}_0 = (1, 2, 3)$ that will keep the point $\mathbf{X}_0 + \partial \mathbf{X}$ feasible.

   (c) If $\mathbf{Y} = (x_2, x_3)$ and $\mathbf{Z} = x_1$, what is the value of ∂x_1 that will produce the same value of $\partial_c f$ given in the example?

Example 20.2-2

This example illustrates the use of constrained derivatives. Consider the problem

$$\text{Minimize } f(\mathbf{X}) = x_1^2 + x_2^2 + x_3^2$$

subject to

$$g_1(\mathbf{X}) = \ x_1 + \ x_2 + 3x_3 - 2 = 0$$
$$g_2(\mathbf{X}) = 5x_1 + 2x_2 + \ x_3 - 5 = 0$$

We determine the constrained extreme points as follows. Let

$$\mathbf{Y} = (x_1, x_2) \text{ and } \mathbf{Z} = \ x_3$$

Thus,

$$\nabla_{\mathbf{Y}} f = \left(\frac{\partial f}{\partial x_1}, \frac{\partial f}{\partial x_2}\right) = (2x_1, 2x_2), \ \nabla_{\mathbf{Z}} f = \frac{\partial f}{\partial x_3} = 2x_3$$

$$\mathbf{J} = \begin{pmatrix} 1 & 1 \\ 5 & 2 \end{pmatrix}, \mathbf{J}^{-1} = \begin{pmatrix} -\frac{2}{3} & \frac{1}{3} \\ \frac{5}{3} & -\frac{1}{3} \end{pmatrix}, \mathbf{C} = \begin{pmatrix} 3 \\ 1 \end{pmatrix}$$

Hence,

$$\nabla_c f = \frac{\partial_c f}{\partial_c x_3} = 2x_3 - (2x_1, 2x_2)\begin{pmatrix} -\frac{2}{3} & \frac{1}{3} \\ \frac{5}{3} & -\frac{1}{3} \end{pmatrix}\begin{pmatrix} 3 \\ 1 \end{pmatrix}$$

$$= \frac{10}{3}x_1 - \frac{28}{3}x_2 + 2x_3$$

The equations for determining the stationary points are thus given as

$$\nabla_c f = 0$$
$$g_1(\mathbf{X}) = 0$$
$$g_2(\mathbf{X}) = 0$$

or

$$\begin{pmatrix} 10 & -28 & 6 \\ 1 & 1 & 3 \\ 5 & 2 & 1 \end{pmatrix}\begin{pmatrix} x_1 \\ x_2 \\ x_3 \end{pmatrix} = \begin{pmatrix} 0 \\ 2 \\ 5 \end{pmatrix}$$

The solution is

$$\mathbf{X}_0 \approx (.81, .35, .28)$$

The identity of this stationary point is checked using the sufficiency condition. Given that x_3 is the independent variable, it follows from $\nabla_c f$ that

$$\frac{\partial_c^2 f}{\partial_c x_3^2} = \frac{10}{3}\left(\frac{dx_1}{dx_3}\right) - \frac{28}{3}\left(\frac{dx_2}{dx_3}\right) + 2 = \left(\frac{10}{3}, -\frac{28}{3}\right)\begin{pmatrix} \dfrac{dx_1}{dx_3} \\ \dfrac{dx_2}{dx_3} \end{pmatrix} + 2$$

From the Jacobian method,

$$\begin{pmatrix} \dfrac{dx_1}{dx_3} \\ \dfrac{dx_2}{dx_3} \end{pmatrix} = -\mathbf{J}^{-1}\mathbf{C} = \begin{pmatrix} \frac{5}{3} \\ -\frac{14}{3} \end{pmatrix}$$

Substitution gives $\dfrac{\partial_c^2 f}{\partial_c x_3^2} = \dfrac{460}{9} > 0$. Hence, $\mathbf{X}_0$ is the minimum point.

Sensitivity analysis in the Jacobian method. The Jacobian method can be used to study the effect of small changes in the right-hand side of the constraints on the optimal value of f. Specifically, what is the effect of changing $g_i(\mathbf{X}) = 0$ to $g_i(\mathbf{X}) = \partial g_i$ on the optimal value of f? This type of investigation is called **sensitivity analysis** and is similar to that carried out in linear programming (see Chapters 3 and 4). However, sensitivity analysis in nonlinear programming is valid only in the small neighborhood of the extreme point. The development will be helpful in studying the Lagrangean method.

We have shown previously that

$$\partial f(\mathbf{Y}, \mathbf{Z}) = \nabla_{\mathbf{Y}} f \partial \mathbf{Y} + \nabla_{\mathbf{Z}} f \partial \mathbf{Z}$$

$$\partial \mathbf{g} = \mathbf{J} \partial \mathbf{Y} + \mathbf{C} \partial \mathbf{Z}$$

Given $\partial \mathbf{g} \neq 0$, then

$$\partial \mathbf{Y} = \mathbf{J}^{-1} \partial \mathbf{g} - \mathbf{J}^{-1} \mathbf{C} \partial \mathbf{Z}$$

Substituting in the equation for $\partial f(\mathbf{Y}, \mathbf{Z})$ gives

$$\partial f(\mathbf{Y}, \mathbf{Z}) = \nabla_{\mathbf{Y}} f \mathbf{J}^{-1} \partial \mathbf{g} + \nabla_c f \partial \mathbf{Z}$$

where

$$\nabla_c f = \nabla_{\mathbf{Z}} f - \nabla_{\mathbf{Y}} f \mathbf{J}^{-1} \mathbf{C}$$

as defined previously. The expression for $\partial f(\mathbf{Y}, \mathbf{Z})$ can be used to study variation in f in the feasible neighborhood of a feasible point $\mathbf{X}_0$ resulting from small changes $\partial \mathbf{g}$ and $\partial \mathbf{Z}$.

At the extreme (indeed, any stationary) point $\mathbf{X}_0 = (\mathbf{Y}_0, \mathbf{Z}_0)$, the constrained gradient $\nabla_c f$ must vanish. Thus

$$\partial f(\mathbf{Y}_0, \mathbf{Z}_0) = \nabla_{\mathbf{Y}_0} f \mathbf{J}^{-1} \partial \mathbf{g}(\mathbf{Y}_0, \mathbf{Z}_0)$$

or

$$\frac{\partial f}{\partial \mathbf{g}} = \nabla_{\mathbf{Y}_0} f \mathbf{J}^{-1}$$

The effect of the small change $\partial \mathbf{g}$ on the *optimum* value of f can be studied by evaluating the rate of change of f with respect to $\mathbf{g}$. These rates are usually referred to as **sensitivity coefficients**.

Example 20.2-3

Consider the same problem of Example 20.2-2. The optimum point is given by $\mathbf{X}_0 = (x_{01}, x_{02}, x_{03}) = (.81, .35, .28)$. Given $\mathbf{Y}_0 = (x_{01}, x_{02})$, then

$$\nabla_{\mathbf{Y}_0} f = \left(\frac{\partial f}{\partial x_1}, \frac{\partial f}{\partial x_2} \right) = (2x_{01}, 2x_{02}) = (1.62, .70)$$

Consequently,

$$\left(\frac{\partial f}{\partial g_1}, \frac{\partial f}{\partial g_2} \right) = \nabla_{\mathbf{Y}_0} f \mathbf{J}^{-1} = (1.62, .7) \begin{pmatrix} -\frac{2}{3} & \frac{1}{3} \\ \frac{5}{3} & -\frac{1}{3} \end{pmatrix} = (.0876, .3067)$$

This means that for $\partial g_1 = 1$, f will increase *approximately* by .0867. Similarly, for $\partial g_2 = 1$, f will increase *approximately* by .3067.

PROBLEM SET 20.2B

1. Suppose that Example 20.2-2 is solved in the following manner. First, use the constraints to express x_1 and x_2 in terms of x_3; then use the resulting equations to express the objective function in terms of x_3 only. By taking the derivative of the new objective function with respect to x_3, we can determine the points of maxima and minima.

    (a) Would the derivative of the new objective function (expressed in terms of x_3) be different from that obtained by the Jacobian method?

    (b) How does the suggested procedure differ from the Jacobian method?

2. Apply the Jacobian method to Example 20.2-1 by selecting $\mathbf{Y} = (x_2, x_3)$ and $\mathbf{Z} = (x_1)$.

*3. Solve by the Jacobian method:

$$\text{Minimize } f(\mathbf{X}) = \sum_{i=1}^{n} x_i^2$$

subject to

$$\prod_{i=1}^{n} x_i = C$$

where C is a positive constant. Suppose that the right-hand side of the constraint is changed to $C + \delta$, where δ is a small positive quantity. Find the corresponding change in the optimal value of f.

4. Solve by the Jacobian method:

$$\text{Minimize } f(\mathbf{X}) = 5x_1^2 + x_2^2 + 2x_1 x_2$$

subject to

$$g(\mathbf{X}) = x_1 x_2 - 10 = 0$$

(a) Find the change in the optimal value of $f(\mathbf{X})$ if the constraint is replaced by $x_1x_2 - 9.99 = 0$.

(b) Find the change in value of $f(\mathbf{X})$ in the neighborhood of the feasible point $(2, 5)$, given that $x_1x_2 = 9.99$ and $\partial x_1 = .01$.

5. Consider the problem:

$$\text{Maximize } f(\mathbf{X}) = x_1^2 + 2x_2^2 + 10x_3^2 + 5x_1x_2$$

subject to

$$g_1(\mathbf{X}) = x_1 + x_2^2 + 3x_2x_3 - 5 = 0$$

$$g_2(\mathbf{X}) = x_1^2 + 5x_1x_2 + x_3^2 - 7 = 0$$

Apply the Jacobian method to find $\partial f(\mathbf{X})$ in the neighborhood of the feasible point $(1, 1, 1)$. Assume that this neighborhood is specified by $\partial g_1 = -.01$, $\partial g_2 = .02$, and $\partial x_1 = .01$.

6. Consider the problem

$$\text{Minimize } f(\mathbf{X}) = x_1^2 + x_2^2 + x_3^2 + x_4^2$$

subject to

$$g_1(\mathbf{X}) = x_1 + 2x_2 + 3x_3 + 5x_4 - 10 = 0$$

$$g_2(\mathbf{X}) = x_1 + 2x_2 + 5x_3 + 6x_4 - 15 = 0$$

(a) Show that by selecting x_3 and x_4 as independent variables, the Jacobian method fails to provide a solution and, state the reason.

*(b)** Solve the problem using x_1 and x_3 as independent variables, and apply the sufficiency condition to determine the type of the resulting stationary point.

(c) Determine the sensitivity coefficients, given the solution in (b).

Lagrangean method. In the Jacobian method, let the vector $\boldsymbol{\lambda}$ represent the sensitivity coefficients—that is

$$\boldsymbol{\lambda} = \nabla_{\mathbf{Y}_0}\mathbf{J}^{-1} = \frac{\partial f}{\partial \mathbf{g}}$$

Thus,

$$\partial f - \boldsymbol{\lambda}\,\partial \mathbf{g} = 0$$

This equation satisfies the necessary conditions for stationary points because $\dfrac{\partial f}{\partial \mathbf{g}}$ is computed such that $\nabla_c f = \mathbf{0}$. A more convenient form for presenting these equations is to take their partial derivatives with respect to all x_j. This yields

$$\frac{\partial}{\partial x_j}(f - \boldsymbol{\lambda}\mathbf{g}) = 0, \quad j = 1, 2, \ldots, n$$

The resulting equations together with the constraint equations $\mathbf{g}(\mathbf{X}) = \mathbf{0}$ yield the feasible values of $\mathbf{X}$ and $\boldsymbol{\lambda}$ that satisfy the *necessary* conditions for stationary points.

The given procedure defines the *Lagrangean method* for identifying the stationary points of optimization problems with *equality* constraints. Let

$$L(\mathbf{X}, \lambda) = f(\mathbf{X}) - \lambda\, \mathbf{g}(\mathbf{X})$$

The function L is called the **Lagrangean function** and the elements of the vector λ constitute the **Lagrange multipliers**. By definition, these multipliers have the same interpretation as the sensitivity coefficients of the Jacobian method

The equations

$$\frac{\partial L}{\partial \lambda} = 0, \frac{\partial L}{\partial \mathbf{X}} = 0$$

give the necessary conditions for determining stationary points of $f(\mathbf{X})$ subject to $\mathbf{g}(\mathbf{X}) = \mathbf{0}$. Sufficiency conditions for the Lagrangean method exist, but they are generally computationally difficult.

Example 20.2-4

Consider the problem of Example 20.2-2. The Lagrangean function is

$$L(\mathbf{X}, \lambda) = x_1^2 + x_2^2 + x_3^2 - \lambda_1(x_1 + x_2 + 3x_3 - 2) - \lambda_2(5x_1 + 2x_2 + x_3 - 5)$$

This yields the following necessary conditions:

$$\frac{\partial L}{\partial x_1} = 2x_1 - \lambda_1 - 5\lambda_2 = 0$$

$$\frac{\partial L}{\partial x_2} = 2x_2 - \lambda_1 - 2\lambda_2 = 0$$

$$\frac{\partial L}{\partial x_3} = 2x_3 - 3\lambda_1 - \lambda_2 = 0$$

$$\frac{\partial L}{\partial \lambda_1} = -(x_1 + x_2 + 3x_3 - 2) = 0$$

$$\frac{\partial L}{\partial \lambda_2} = -(5x_1 + 2x_2 + x_3 - 5) = 0$$

The solution to these simultaneous equations yields

$$\mathbf{X}_0 = (x_1, x_2, x_3) = (.8043, .3478, .2826)$$

$$\lambda = (\lambda_1, \lambda_2) = (.0870, .3043)$$

This solution combines the results of Examples 20.2-2 and 20.2-3. The values of the Lagrange multipliers, as given by the vector λ, equal the sensitivity coefficients obtained in Example 20.2-3. The result shows that these coefficients are independent of the specific choice of the dependent vector $\mathbf{Y}$ in the Jacobian method.

PROBLEM SET 20.2C

1. Solve the following linear programming problem by both the Jacobian and the Lagrangean methods:

$$\text{Maximize } f(\mathbf{X}) = 5x_1 + 3x_2$$

subject to

$$g_1(\mathbf{X}) = x_1 + 2x_2 + x_3 \qquad - 6 = 0$$

$$g_2(\mathbf{X}) = 3x_1 + x_2 \qquad + x_4 - 9 = 0$$

$$x_1, x_2, x_3, x_4 \geq 0$$

*2. Find the optimal solution to the problem

$$\text{Minimize } f(\mathbf{X}) = x_1^2 + 2x_2^2 + 10x_3^2$$

subject to

$$g_1(\mathbf{X}) = x_1 + x_2^2 + x_3 - 5 = 0$$

$$g_2(\mathbf{X}) = x_1 + 5x_2 + x_3 - 7 = 0$$

Suppose that $g_1(\mathbf{X}) = .01$ and $g_2(\mathbf{X}) = .02$. Find the corresponding change in the optimal value of $f(\mathbf{X})$.

3. Solve Problem 6, Set 20.2b, by the Lagrangean method, and verify that the values of the Lagrange multipliers are the same as the sensitivity coefficients obtained in Problem 6, Set 20.2b.

20.2.2 Inequality Constraints—Karush-Kuhn-Tucker (KKT) Conditions[1]

This section extends the Lagrangean method to problems with inequality constraints. The main contribution of the section is the development of the general Karush-Kuhn-Tucker (KKT) *necessary* conditions for determining the stationary points. These conditions are also sufficient under certain rules that will be stated later.

Consider the problem

$$\text{Maximize } z = f(\mathbf{X})$$

subject to

$$\mathbf{g}(\mathbf{X}) \leq \mathbf{0}$$

The inequality constraints may be converted into equations by using *nonnegative* slack variables. Let $S_i^2(\geq 0)$ be the slack quantity added to the ith constraint $g_i(\mathbf{X}) \leq 0$ and define

$$\mathbf{S} = (S_1, S_2, \ldots, S_m)^T, \ \mathbf{S}^2 = (S_1^2, S_2^2, \ldots, S_m^2)^T$$

---

[1]W. Karush was the first to develop the KKT conditions in 1939 as part of an M.S. thesis at the University of Chicago. The same conditions were developed independently in 1951 by W. Kuhn and A. Tucker.

where m is the total number of inequality constraints. The Lagrangean function is thus given by

$$L(\mathbf{X}, \mathbf{S}, \boldsymbol{\lambda}) = f(\mathbf{X}) - \boldsymbol{\lambda}\left[\mathbf{g}(\mathbf{X}) + \mathbf{S}^2\right]$$

Given the constraints $\mathbf{g}(\mathbf{X}) \leq \mathbf{0}$, a necessary condition for optimality is that $\boldsymbol{\lambda}$ be non-negative (nonpositive) for maximization (minimization) problems. This result is justified by noting that the vector $\boldsymbol{\lambda}$ measures the rate of variation of f with respect to $\mathbf{g}$—that is,

$$\boldsymbol{\lambda} = \frac{\partial f}{\partial \mathbf{g}}$$

In the maximization case, as the right-hand side of the constraint $\mathbf{g}(\mathbf{X}) \leq \mathbf{0}$ increases from $\mathbf{0}$ to the vector $\partial\mathbf{g}$, the solution space becomes less constrained and hence f cannot decrease, meaning that $\boldsymbol{\lambda} \geq \mathbf{0}$. Similarly for minimization, as the right-hand side of the constraints increases, f cannot increase, which implies that $\boldsymbol{\lambda} \leq \mathbf{0}$. If the constraints are equalities, that is, $\mathbf{g}(\mathbf{X}) = \mathbf{0}$, then $\boldsymbol{\lambda}$ becomes unrestricted in sign (see Problem 2, Set 20.2d).

The restrictions on $\boldsymbol{\lambda}$ hold as part of the KKT necessary conditions. The remaining conditions will now be developed.

Taking the partial derivatives of L with respect to $\mathbf{X}$, $\mathbf{S}$, and $\boldsymbol{\lambda}$, we obtain

$$\frac{\partial L}{\partial \mathbf{X}} = \nabla f(\mathbf{X}) - \boldsymbol{\lambda}\nabla\mathbf{g}(\mathbf{X}) = \mathbf{0}$$

$$\frac{\partial L}{\partial S_i} = -2\lambda_i S_i = 0, \, i = 1, 2, \ldots, m$$

$$\frac{\partial L}{\partial \boldsymbol{\lambda}} = -(\mathbf{g}(\mathbf{X}) + \mathbf{S}^2) = \mathbf{0}$$

The second set of equations reveals the following results:

1. If $\lambda_i \neq 0$, then $S_i^2 = 0$. This result means that the corresponding resource is scarce (i.e., consumed completely).
2. If $S_i^2 > 0$, then $\lambda_i = 0$. This means resource i is not scarce and, hence, it has no effect on the value of f (i.e., $\lambda_i = \frac{\partial f}{\partial g_i} = 0$).

From the second and third sets of equations, we obtain

$$\lambda_i g_i(\mathbf{X}) = 0, \, i = 1, 2, \ldots, m$$

This new condition essentially repeats the foregoing argument, because if $\lambda_i > 0$, $g_i(\mathbf{X}) = 0$ or $S_i^2 = 0$; and if $g_i(\mathbf{X}) < 0$, $S_i^2 > 0$, and $\lambda_i = 0$.

The KKT necessary conditions for maximization problem are summarized as follows:

$$\boldsymbol{\lambda} \geq \mathbf{0}$$

$$\nabla f(\mathbf{X}) - \boldsymbol{\lambda}\nabla\mathbf{g}(\mathbf{X}) = \mathbf{0}$$

$$\lambda_i g_i(\mathbf{X}) = 0, \quad i = 1, 2, \ldots, m$$

$$\mathbf{g}(\mathbf{X}) \leq \mathbf{0}$$

TABLE 20.1   Sufficiency of the KKT Conditions

Sense of optimization	Required conditions	
	Objective function	Solution space
Maximization	Concave	Convex set
Minimization	Convex	Convex set

These conditions apply to the minimization case as well, except that $\boldsymbol{\lambda}$ must be non-positive (verify!). In both maximization and minimization, the Lagrange multipliers corresponding to equality constraints are unrestricted in sign.

Sufficiency of the KKT conditions.   The KKT necessary conditions are also sufficient if the objective function and the solution space satisfy the conditions in Table 20.1.

It is simpler to verify that a function is convex or concave than to prove that a solution space is a convex set. For this reason, we provide a *subset* of sufficiency conditions, which, though not as general as the ones in Table 20.1, are easier to apply in practice. To provide these conditions, we define the generalized nonlinear problems as

$$\text{Maximize or minimize } z = f(\mathbf{X})$$

subject to

$$g_i(\mathbf{X}) \leq 0, \quad i = 1, 2, \ldots, r$$

$$g_i(\mathbf{X}) \geq 0, \quad i = r + 1, \ldots, p$$

$$g_i(\mathbf{X}) = 0, \quad i = p + 1, \ldots, m$$

$$L(\mathbf{X}, \mathbf{S}, \boldsymbol{\lambda}) = f(\mathbf{X}) - \sum_{i=1}^{r} \lambda_i [g_i(\mathbf{X}) + S_i^2] - \sum_{i=r+1}^{p} \lambda_i [g_i(\mathbf{X}) - S_i^2] - \sum_{i=p+1}^{m} \lambda_i g_i(\mathbf{X})$$

The parameter λ_i is the Lagrange multiplier associated with constraint i. The conditions for establishing the sufficiency of the KKT conditions are summarized in Table 20.2.

TABLE 20.2   Subset of KKT Sufficient Conditions

Sense of optimization	Required conditions		
	$f(\mathbf{X})$	$g_i(\mathbf{X})$	λ_i
Maximization	Concave	Convex Concave Linear	$\geq 0 \quad (1 \leq i \leq r)$ $\leq 0 \quad (r + 1 \leq i \leq p)$ Unrestricted $\quad (p + 1 \leq i \leq m)$
Minimization	Convex	Convex Concave Linear	$\leq 0 \quad (1 \leq i \leq r)$ $\geq 0 \quad (r + 1 \leq i \leq p)$ Unrestricted $\quad (p + 1 \leq i \leq m)$

The conditions in Table 20.2 are a subset of the conditions in Table 20.1 because a solution space can be convex without satisfying the conditions in Table 20.2.

Table 20.2 is valid because the given conditions yield a concave Lagrangean function $L(\mathbf{X}, \mathbf{S}, \boldsymbol{\lambda})$ in case of maximization and a convex $L(\mathbf{X}, \mathbf{S}, \boldsymbol{\lambda})$ in case of minimization. This result is verified by noticing that if $g_i(x)$ is convex, then $\lambda_i g_i(x)$ is convex if $\lambda_i \geq 0$ and concave if $\lambda_i \leq 0$. Similar interpretations can be established for all the remaining conditions. Observe that a linear function is both convex and concave. Also, if a function f is concave, then $(-f)$ is convex, and vice versa.

Example 20.2-5

Consider the following minimization problem:

$$\text{Minimize } f(\mathbf{X}) = x_1^2 + x_2^2 + x_3^2$$

subject to

$$g_1(\mathbf{X}) = 2x_1 + x_2 - 5 \leq 0$$
$$g_2(\mathbf{X}) = x_1 + x_3 - 2 \leq 0$$
$$g_3(\mathbf{X}) = 1 - x_1 \leq 0$$
$$g_4(\mathbf{X}) = 2 - x_2 \leq 0$$
$$g_5(\mathbf{X}) = - x_3 \leq 0$$

This is a minimization problem, hence $\boldsymbol{\lambda} \leq \mathbf{0}$. The KKT conditions are thus given as

$$(\lambda_1, \lambda_2, \lambda_3, \lambda_4, \lambda_5) \leq \mathbf{0}$$

$$(2x_1, 2x_2, 2x_3) - (\lambda_1, \lambda_2, \lambda_3, \lambda_4, \lambda_5)\begin{pmatrix} 2 & 1 & 0 \\ 1 & 0 & 1 \\ -1 & 0 & 0 \\ 0 & -1 & 0 \\ 0 & 0 & -1 \end{pmatrix} = \mathbf{0}$$

$$\lambda_1 g_1 = \lambda_2 g_2 = \cdots = \lambda_5 g_5 = 0$$

$$\mathbf{g}(\mathbf{X}) \leq \mathbf{0}$$

These conditions reduce to

$$\lambda_1, \lambda_2, \lambda_3, \lambda_4, \lambda_5 \leq 0$$
$$2x_1 - 2\lambda_1 - \lambda_2 + \lambda_3 = 0$$
$$2x_2 - \lambda_1 + \lambda_4 = 0$$
$$2x_3 - \lambda_2 + \lambda_5 = 0$$
$$\lambda_1(2x_1 + x_2 - 5) = 0$$
$$\lambda_2(x_1 + x_3 - 2) = 0$$
$$\lambda_3(1 - x_1) = 0$$

$$\lambda_4(2 - x_2) = 0$$

$$\lambda_5 x_3 = 0$$

$$2x_1 + x_2 \le 5$$

$$x_1 + x_3 \le 2$$

$$x_1 \ge 1, x_2 \ge 2, x_3 \ge 0$$

The solution is $x_1 = 1, x_2 = 2, x_3 = 0, \lambda_1 = \lambda_2 = \lambda_5 = 0, \lambda_3 = -2, \lambda_4 = -4$. Because both $f(\mathbf{X})$ and the solution space $\mathbf{g}(\mathbf{X}) \le 0$ are convex, $L(\mathbf{X}, \mathbf{S}, \boldsymbol{\lambda})$ must be convex, and the resulting stationary point yields a global constrained minimum. The KKT conditions are central to the development of the nonlinear programming algorithms in Chapter 21.

PROBLEM SET 20.2D

1. Consider the problem:

$$\text{Maximize } f(\mathbf{X})$$

subject to

$$\mathbf{g}(\mathbf{X}) \ge 0$$

Show that the KKT conditions are the same as in Section 20.2.2, except that $\boldsymbol{\lambda} \le \mathbf{0}$.

2. Consider the following problem:

$$\text{Maximize } f(\mathbf{X})$$

subject to

$$\mathbf{g}(\mathbf{X}) = 0$$

Show that the KKT conditions are

$$\nabla f(\mathbf{X}) - \boldsymbol{\lambda} \nabla \mathbf{g}(\mathbf{X}) = \mathbf{0}$$

$$\mathbf{g}(\mathbf{X}) = \mathbf{0}$$

$\boldsymbol{\lambda}$ unrestricted in sign

3. Write the KKT necessary conditions for the following problems.
   (a) Maximize $f(\mathbf{X}) = x_1^3 - x_2^2 + x_1 x_3^2$
       subject to

$$x_1 + x_2^2 + x_3 = 5$$
$$5x_1^2 - x_2^2 - x_3 \ge 2$$
$$x_1, x_2, x_3 \ge 0$$

   (b) Minimize $f(\mathbf{X}) = x_1^4 + x_2^2 + 5x_1 x_2 x_3$
       subject to

$$x_1^2 - x_2^2 + x_3^3 \le 10$$
$$x_1^3 + x_2^2 + 4x_3^2 \ge 20$$

4. Consider the problem

$$\text{Maximize } f(\mathbf{X})$$

subject to

$$\mathbf{g}(\mathbf{X}) = \mathbf{0}$$

Given $f(\mathbf{X})$ is concave and $g_i(\mathbf{X})(i = 1, 2, \ldots, m)$ is a *linear* function, show that the KKT necessary conditions are also sufficient. Is this result true if $g_i(\mathbf{X})$ is a convex *non*linear function for all i? Why?

5. Consider the problem

$$\text{Maximize } f(\mathbf{X})$$

subject to

$$g_1(\mathbf{X}) \geq 0, g_2(\mathbf{X}) = 0, g_3(\mathbf{X}) \leq 0$$

Develop the KKT conditions, and give the stipulations under which the conditions are sufficient.

BIBLIOGRAPHY

Bazarra, M., H. Sherali, and C. Shetty, *Nonlinear Programming Theory and Algorithms*, 3rd ed., Wiley, New York, 2006.

Beightler, C., D. Phillips, and D. Wilde, *Foundations of Optimization*, 2nd ed., Prentice Hall, NJ, 1979.

Fletcher, R., *Practical Methods of Optimization*, 2nd ed., Wiley, New York, 2000.

CHAPTER 21

Nonlinear Programming Algorithms

21.1 UNCONSTRAINED ALGORITHMS

This section presents two types of algorithms for the unconstrained problem: *direct search* and *gradient*.

21.1.1 Direct Search Method

Direct search methods apply primarily to strictly unimodal single-variable functions. Although the case may appear trivial, Section 21.1.2 shows that optimization of single-variable functions is key in the development of the more general multivariable algorithm.

The idea of direct search methods is to identify the **interval of uncertainty** known to include the optimum solution point. The procedure locates the optimum by iteratively narrowing the interval of uncertainty to a desired level of accuracy.

Two closely related search algorithms are presented in this section: **dichotomous** and **golden section**. Both algorithms seek the maximization of a unimodal function $f(x)$ over the interval $a \leq x \leq b$ that includes the optimum point x^*. The two methods start with the initial interval of uncertainty $I_0 = (a, b)$.

General step i. Let $I_{i-1} = (x_L, x_R)$ be the current interval of uncertainty (at iteration 0, $x_L = a$ and $x_R = b$). The following table shows how x_1 and x_2 are determined:

Dichotomous method	Golden section method
$x_1 = \frac{1}{2}(x_R + x_L - \Delta)$	$x_1 = x_R - \left(\frac{\sqrt{5}-1}{2}\right)(x_R - x_L)$
$x_2 = \frac{1}{2}(x_R + x_L + \Delta)$	$x_2 = x_L + \left(\frac{\sqrt{5}-1}{2}\right)(x_R - x_L)$

The selection of x_1 and x_2 guarantees that $x_L < x_1 < x_2 < x_R$.

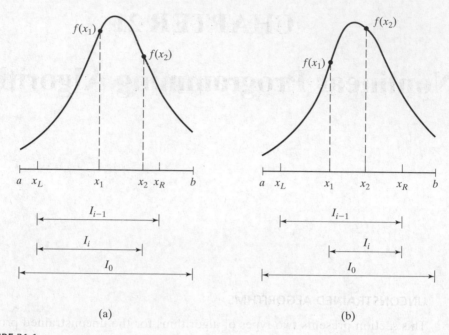

FIGURE 21.1

Illustration of the general step of the dichotomous/golden section search methods

The next interval of uncertainty, I_i, is determined in the following manner:

1. If $f(x_1) > f(x_2)$, then $x_L < x^* < x_2$. Let $x_R = x_2$ and set $I_i = (x_L, x_2)$ [see Figure 21.1(a)].

2. If $f(x_1) < f(x_2)$, then $x_1 < x^* < x_R$. Let $x_L = x_1$ and set $I_i = (x_1, x_R)$ [see Figure 21.1(b)].

3. If $f(x_1) = f(x_2)$, then $x_1 < x^* < x_2$. Let $x_L = x_1$ and $x_R = x_2$; set $I_i = (x_1, x_2)$.

The manner in which x_1 and x_2 are determined guarantees that $I_{i+1} < I_i$, as will be shown shortly. The algorithm terminates at iteration k if $I_k \leq \Delta$, where Δ is a user-specified level of accuracy.

In the dichotomous method, the values x_1 and x_2 sit symmetrically around the midpoint of the current interval of uncertainty. This means that

$$I_{i+1} = .5(I_i + \Delta)$$

Repeated application of the algorithm guarantees that the length of the interval of uncertainty will approach the desired accuracy, Δ.

In the golden section method, the idea is more involved. We notice that each iteration of the dichotomous method requires calculating the two values $f(x_1)$ and $f(x_2)$, but ends up discarding one of them. What the golden section method proposes is to save computations by reusing the discarded value in the immediately succeeding iteration.

Define

$$\left.\begin{array}{l} x_1 = x_R - \alpha(x_R - x_L) \\ x_2 = x_L + \alpha(x_R - x_L) \end{array}\right\} \; 0 < \alpha < 1$$

Then the interval of uncertainty I_i at iteration i equals (x_L, x_2) or (x_1, x_R). Consider the case $I_i = (x_L, x_2)$, which means that x_1 is included in I_i. In iteration $i + 1$, we select x_2 equal to x_1 in iteration i, which leads to the following equation:

$$x_2(\text{iteration } i + 1) = x_1(\text{iteration } i)$$

Substitution yields

$$x_L + \alpha[x_2(\text{iteration } i) - x_L] = x_R - \alpha(x_R - x_L)$$

or

$$x_L + \alpha[x_L + \alpha(x_R - x_L) - x_L] = x_R - \alpha(x_R - x_L)$$

which simplifies to

$$\alpha^2 + \alpha - 1 = 0$$

This equation yields $\alpha = \frac{-1 \pm \sqrt{5}}{2}$. The positive root $\alpha = \frac{-1 + \sqrt{5}}{2} \approx .681$ is selected because $0 < \alpha < 1$.

The design of the golden section computations guarantees an α-reduction in the successive intervals of uncertainty—that is

$$I_{i+1} = \alpha I_i$$

The golden section method converges more rapidly than the dichotomous method because, in the dichotomous method, the narrowing of the interval of uncertainty slows down appreciably as $I \to \Delta$. In addition, the golden section method requires half the computations because it recycles one set of computations from the immediately preceding iteration.

Example 21.1-1

$$\text{Maximize } f(x) = \begin{cases} 3x, & 0 \le x \le 2 \\ \frac{1}{3}(-x + 20), & 2 \le x \le 3 \end{cases}$$

The maximum value of $f(x)$ occurs at $x = 2$. The following table demonstrates the calculations for iterations 1 and 2 using the dichotomous and the golden section methods, with $\Delta = .1$.

Dichotomous method	Golden section method
Iteration 1	*Iteration 1*
$I_0 = (0, 3) \equiv (x_L, x_R)$	$I_0 = (0, 3) \equiv (x_L, x_R)$
$x_1 = 0 + .5(3 - 0 - .1) = 1.45, f(x_1) = 4.35$	$x_1 = 3 - .618(3 - 0) = 1.146, f(x_1) = 3.438$
$x_2 = 0 + .5(3 - 0 + .1) = 1.55, f(x_2) = 4.65$	$x_2 = 0 + .618(3 - 0) = 1.854, f(x_2) = 5.562$
$f(x_2) > f(x_1) \Rightarrow x_L = 1.45, I_1 = (1.45, 3)$	$f(x_2) > f(x_1) \Rightarrow x_L = 1.146, I_1 = (1.146, 3)$
Iteration 2	*Iteration 2*
$I_1 = (1.45, 3) \equiv (x_L, x_R)$	$I_1 = (1.146, 3) \equiv (x_L, x_R)$
$x_1 = 1.45 + .5(3 - 1.45 - .1) = 2.175, f(x_1) = 5.942$	$x_1 = x_2$ in iteration $0 = 1.854, f(x_1) = 5.562$
$x_2 = \frac{3 + 1.45 + .1}{2} = 2.275, f(x_2) = 5.908$	$x_2 = 1.146 + .618(3 - 1.146) = 2.292, f(x_2) = 5.903$
$f(x_1) > f(x_2) \Rightarrow x_R = 2.275, I_2 = (1.45, 2.275)$	$f(x_2) > f(x_1) \Rightarrow x_L = 1.854, I_2 = (1.854, 3)$

Continuing in the same manner, the interval of uncertainty will eventually narrow down to the desired Δ-tolerance.

Excel Moment

Excel template *excelDiGold.xls* handles both methods by entering the letter X in either D5 (dichotomous) or F5 (golden section). The input data include $f(x), a, b,$ and Δ. The function $f(x)$ is entered in cell E3 as

```
=IF(C3<=2,3*C3,(-C3+20)/3)
```

Cell C3 plays the role of x in $f(x)$.

Figure 21.2 compares the two methods. The golden section method requires less than half the iterations of the dichotomous method, in addition to half the calculations at each iteration.

PROBLEM SET 21.1A

1. Use Excel template *excelDiGold.xls* to solve Example 21.1-1 assuming that $\Delta = .01$. Compare the amount of computations and the accuracy of the results with those in Figure 21.2.

2. Find the maximum of each of the following functions by dichotomous search. Assume that $\Delta = .05$.

   (a) $f(x) = \dfrac{1}{|(x - 3)^3|}, \quad 2 \leq x \leq 4$

   (b) $f(x) = x \cos x, \quad 0 \leq x \leq \pi$

   *(c) $f(x) = x \sin \pi x, \quad 1.5 \leq x \leq 2.5$

   (d) $f(x) = -(x - 3)^2, \quad 2 \leq x \leq 4$

   *(e) $f(x) = \begin{cases} 4x, & 0 \leq x \leq 2 \\ 4 - x, & 2 \leq x \leq 4 \end{cases}$

	A	B	C	D	E	F
1			Dichotomous/Golden Section Search			
2	Input data: Type f(C3) in E3, where C3 represents x in f(x)					
3	Δ =	0.1	C3		#VALUE!	Clear Calculations
4	Minimum x =	0	Maximum x =	3		
5	Solution:	Enter x to select>	Dichotomous:	X	GoldenSection:	
6	x* =	2.04001	f(x*) =	5.97002		
7	Clalculations:				Perform calculation	
8	xL	xR	x1	x2	f(x1)	f(x2)
9	0.000000	3.000000	1.450000	1.550000	4.350000	4.650000
10	1.450000	3.000000	2.175000	2.275000	5.941667	5.908333
11	1.450000	2.275000	1.812500	1.912500	5.437500	5.737500
12	1.812500	2.275000	1.993750	2.093750	5.981250	5.968750
13	1.812500	2.093750	1.903125	2.003125	5.709375	5.998958
14	1.903125	2.093750	1.948438	2.048438	5.845313	5.983854
15	1.948438	2.093750	1.971094	2.071094	5.913281	5.976302
16	1.971094	2.093750	1.982422	2.082422	5.947266	5.972526
17	1.982422	2.093750	1.988086	2.088086	5.964258	5.970638
18	1.988086	2.093750	1.990918	2.090918	5.972754	5.969694
19	1.988086	2.090918	1.989502	2.089502	5.968506	5.970166
20	1.989502	2.090918	1.990210	2.090210	5.970630	5.969930
21	1.989502	2.090210	1.989856	2.089856	5.969568	5.970048
22	1.989856	2.090210	1.990033	2.090033	5.970099	5.969989
23	1.989856	2.090033	1.989944	2.089944	5.969833	5.970019
24	1.989944	2.090033	1.989989	2.089989	5.969966	5.970004
25	1.989989	2.090033	1.990011	2.090011	5.970033	5.969996
26	1.989989	2.090011	1.990000	2.090000	5.969999	5.970000
27	1.990000	2.090011	1.990005	2.090005	5.970016	5.969998
28	1.990000	2.090005	1.990003	2.090003	5.970008	5.969999
5	Solution:	Enter x to select>	Dichotomous:		GoldenSection:	X
6	x* =	2.00909	f(x*) =	5.99290		
7	Clalculations:				Perform calculation	
8	xL	xR	x1	x2	f(x1)	f(x2)
9	0.000000	3.000000	1.145898	1.854102	3.437694	5.562306
10	1.145898	3.000000	1.854102	2.291796	5.562306	5.902735
11	1.854102	3.000000	2.291796	2.562306	5.902735	5.812565
12	1.854102	2.562306	2.124612	2.291796	5.958463	5.902735
13	1.854102	2.291796	2.021286	2.124612	5.992905	5.958463
14	1.854102	2.124612	1.957428	2.021286	5.872283	5.992905
15	1.957428	2.124612	2.021286	2.060753	5.992905	5.979749
16	1.957428	2.060753	1.996894	2.021286	5.990683	5.992905
17	1.996894	2.060753	2.021286	2.036361	5.992905	5.987880

FIGURE 21.2

Excel output of the dichotomous and golden section methods applied to Example 21.1-1 (file *excelDiGold.xls*)

21.1.2   Gradient Method

This section develops a method for optimizing twice continuously differentiable functions, called the **steepest ascent** method. The idea is to generate successive points in the direction of the gradient of the function.[1] Termination of the gradient method

---

[1]The Newton-Raphson method in Section 20.1.2 is also a gradient method that locates the optimum indirectly by solving the necessary conditions equations.

occurs at the point where the gradient vector becomes null. This is only a necessary condition for optimality.

Suppose that $f(\mathbf{X})$ is maximized. Let $\mathbf{X}_0$ be the initial point from which the procedure starts, and define $\nabla f(\mathbf{X}_k)$ as the gradient of f at point $\mathbf{X}_k$. The idea is to determine a particular path p along which $\frac{\partial f}{\partial p}$ is maximized at a given point. This result is achieved if successive points $\mathbf{X}_k$ and $\mathbf{X}_{k+1}$ are selected such that

$$\mathbf{X}_{k+1} = \mathbf{X}_k + r_k \nabla f(\mathbf{X}_k)$$

where r_k is the optimal **step size** at $\mathbf{X}_k$.

The step size r_k is determined such that the next point, $\mathbf{X}_{k+1}$, leads to the largest improvement in f. This is equivalent to determining $r = r_k$ that maximizes the function

$$h(r) = f[\mathbf{X}_k + r\nabla f(\mathbf{X}_k)]$$

Because $h(r)$ is a single-variable function, the search method in Section 21.1.1 may be used to find the optimum, provided that $h(r)$ is unimodal.

The proposed procedure terminates when two successive trial points $\mathbf{X}_k$ and $\mathbf{X}_{k+1}$ are approximately equal. This is equivalent to having $r_k \nabla f(\mathbf{X}_k) \approx \mathbf{0}$, or, equivalently, $\nabla f(\mathbf{X}_k) \approx \mathbf{0}$.

Example 21.1-2

Consider the following problem:

$$\text{Maximize } f(x_1, x_2) = 4x_1 + 6x_2 - 2x_1^2 - 2x_1x_2 - 2x_2^2$$

The exact optimum occurs at $(x_1^*, x_2^*) = \left(\frac{1}{3}, \frac{4}{3}\right)$.

The gradient of f is

$$\nabla f(\mathbf{X}) = (4 - 4x_1 - 2x_2, 6 - 2x_1 - 4x_2)$$

The quadratic nature of the function indicates that the gradients at two successive points are orthogonal (perpendicular to one another).

Suppose that we start at the initial point $\mathbf{X}_0 = (1, 1)$. Figure 21.3 shows the successive solution points.

Iteration 1

$$\nabla f(\mathbf{X}_0) = (-2, 0)$$

The next point $\mathbf{X}_1$ is obtained by considering

$$\mathbf{X} = (1, 1) + r(-2, 0) = (1 - 2r, 1)$$

Thus,

$$h(r) = f(1 - 2r, 1) = -2(1 - 2r)^2 + 2(1 - 2r) + 4$$

The optimal step size is obtained using the classical necessary conditions in Chapter 20 (you may also use the search algorithms in Section 21.1.1 to determine the optimum). The maximum value of $h(r)$ is $r_1 = \frac{1}{4}$, which yields the next solution point $\mathbf{X}_1 = \left(\frac{1}{2}, 1\right)$.

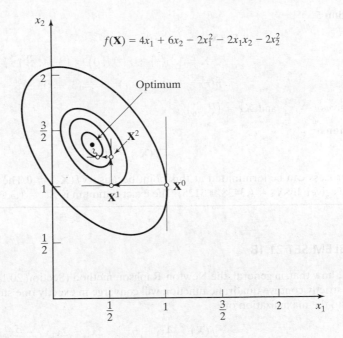

FIGURE 21.3

Maximization of $f(x_1, x_2) = 4x_1 + 6x_2 - 2x_1^2 - 2x_1x_2 - 2x_2^2$ by the steepest-ascent method

Iteration 2

$$\nabla f(\mathbf{X}_1) = (0, 1)$$

$$\mathbf{X} = \left(\tfrac{1}{2}, 1\right) + r(0, 1) = \left(\tfrac{1}{2}, 1 + r\right)$$

$$h(r) = -2(1 + r)^2 + 5(1 + r) + \tfrac{3}{2}$$

Thus, $r_2 = \tfrac{1}{4}$ and $\mathbf{X}_2 = \left(\tfrac{1}{2}, \tfrac{5}{4}\right)$.

Iteration 3

$$\nabla f(\mathbf{X}_2) = \left(-\tfrac{1}{2}, 0\right)$$

$$\mathbf{X} = \left(\tfrac{1}{2}, \tfrac{5}{4}\right) + r\left(-\tfrac{1}{2}, 0\right) = \left(\tfrac{1-r}{2}, \tfrac{5}{4}\right)$$

$$h(r) = -\tfrac{1}{2}(1 - r)^2 + \tfrac{3}{4}(1 - r) + \tfrac{35}{8}$$

Hence, $r_3 = \tfrac{1}{4}$ and $\mathbf{X}_3 = \left(\tfrac{3}{8}, \tfrac{5}{4}\right)$.

Iteration 4

$$\nabla f(\mathbf{X}_3) = \left(0, \tfrac{1}{4}\right)$$

$$\mathbf{X} = \left(\tfrac{3}{8}, \tfrac{5}{4}\right) + r\left(0, \tfrac{1}{4}\right) = \left(\tfrac{3}{8}, \tfrac{5 + r}{4}\right)$$

$$h(r) = -\tfrac{1}{8}(5 + r)^2 + \tfrac{21}{16}(5 + r) + \tfrac{39}{32}$$

Thus, $r_4 = \tfrac{1}{4}$ and $\mathbf{X}_4 = \left(\tfrac{3}{8}, \tfrac{21}{16}\right)$.

Iteration 5

$$\nabla f(\mathbf{X}_4) = \left(-\tfrac{1}{8}, 0\right)$$

$$\mathbf{X} = \left(\tfrac{3}{8}, \tfrac{21}{16}\right) + r\left(-\tfrac{1}{8}, 0\right) = \left(\tfrac{3-r}{8}, \tfrac{21}{16}\right)$$

$$h(r) = -\tfrac{1}{32}(3-r)^2 + \tfrac{11}{64}(3-r) + \tfrac{567}{128}$$

This gives $r_5 = \tfrac{1}{4}$ and $\mathbf{X}_5 = \left(\tfrac{11}{32}, \tfrac{21}{16}\right)$.

Iteration 6

$$\nabla f(\mathbf{X}_5) = \left(0, \tfrac{1}{16}\right)$$

The process can be terminated at this point because $\nabla f(\mathbf{X}_5) \approx \mathbf{0}$. The *approximate* maximum point is given by $\mathbf{X}_5 = (.3438, 1.3125)$. The exact optimum is $\mathbf{X}^* = (.3333, 1.3333)$.

PROBLEM SET 21.1B

*1. Show that, in general, the Newton-Raphson method (Section 20.1.2) when applied to a strictly concave quadratic function will converge in exactly one step. Apply the method to the maximization of

$$f(\mathbf{X}) = 4x_1 + 6x_2 - 2x_1^2 - 2x_1x_2 - 2x_2^2$$

2. Carry out five iterations for each of the following problems using the method of steepest descent (ascent). Assume that $\mathbf{X}^0 = 0$ in each case.

(a) $\min f(\mathbf{X}) = \min f(\mathbf{X}) = (x_2 - x_1^2)^2 + (1 - x_1)$

(b) $\max f(\mathbf{X}) = \mathbf{cX} + \mathbf{X}^T\mathbf{AX}$

where

$$\mathbf{c} = (1, 3, 5)$$

$$\mathbf{A} = \begin{pmatrix} -5 & -3 & -\tfrac{1}{2} \\ -3 & -2 & 0 \\ -\tfrac{1}{2} & 0 & -\tfrac{1}{2} \end{pmatrix}$$

(c) $\min f(\mathbf{X}) = x_1 - x_2 + x_1^2 - x_1x_2$

21.2   CONSTRAINED ALGORITHMS

The general constrained nonlinear programming problem is defined as

$$\text{Maximize (or minimize) } z = f(\mathbf{X})$$

subject to

$$\mathbf{g(X)} \leq \mathbf{0}$$

The nonnegativity conditions, $\mathbf{X} \geq \mathbf{0}$, are part of the constraints. Also, at least one of the functions $f(\mathbf{X})$ and $\mathbf{g(X)}$ is nonlinear, and all the functions are continuously differentiable.

The erratic behavior of the nonlinear functions precludes the development of a single algorithm for the general nonlinear model. Perhaps the most general result applicable to the problem is the KKT conditions (Section 20.2.2). Table 20.2 shows that the KKT conditions are only necessary, unless $f(\mathbf{X})$ and $\mathbf{g}(\mathbf{X})$ are well-behaved functions.

This section presents a number of algorithms that may be classified generally as *indirect* and *direct* methods. Indirect methods solve the nonlinear problem by dealing with one or more *linear* programs derived from the original program. Direct methods deal with the original problem.

The indirect algorithms presented in this section include separable, quadratic, and chance-constrained programming. The direct algorithms include the method of linear combinations and a brief discussion of SUMT, the sequential unconstrained maximization technique. Other important nonlinear techniques can be found in the list of references at the end of the chapter.

21.2.1   Separable Programming

A function $f(x_1, x_2, \ldots, x_n)$ is **separable** if it can be expressed as the sum of n single-variable functions $f_1(x_1), f_2(x_2), \ldots, f_n(x_n)$—that is,

$$f(x_1, x_1, \ldots, x_n) = f_1(x_1) + f_2(x_2) + \cdots + f_n(x_n)$$

For example, any linear function is separable. On the other hand, the function

$$h(x_1, x_2, x_3) = x_1^2 + x_1 \sin(x_2 + x_3) + x_2 e^{x_3}$$

is not separable.

Some (convoluted) nonlinear functions can be made separable using appropriate substitutions. Consider, for example, the case of maximizing $z = x_1 x_2$. Let $y = x_1 x_2$, then $\ln y = \ln x_1 + \ln x_2$, and the equivalent separable problem is

$$\text{Maximize } z = y$$

subject to

$$\ln y = \ln x_1 + \ln x_2$$

The substitution assumes that x_1 and x_2 are *positive* variables because the logarithmic function is undefined for nonpositive values. We can account for the case where x_1 and x_2 can assume zero values by employing the approximations

$$w_1 = x_1 + \delta_1 > 0$$
$$w_2 = x_2 + \delta_2 > 0$$

The constants δ_1 and δ_2 are very small positive values.

This section shows how an approximate solution can be obtained for *any* separable problem by using linear approximation and the simplex method of linear programming. The single-variable function $f(x)$ can be approximated by a piecewise-linear function using mixed integer programming (Chapter 9). Suppose that $f(x)$ is approximated over an interval $[a, b]$, and define $a_k, k = 1, 2, \ldots, K,$ as the kth break-point on the x-axis such that $a_1 < a_2 < \cdots < a_K$. The points a_1 and a_K coincide with end points a and b of the designated interval. Thus, $f(x)$ is approximated as

$$f(x) \approx \sum_{k=1}^{K} f(a_k) w_k$$

$$x = \sum_{k=1}^{K} a_k w_k$$

The nonnegative weights w_k must satisfy the condition

$$\sum_{k=1}^{K} w_k = 1, \, w_k \geq 0, \, k = 1, 2, \ldots, K$$

Mixed integer programming ensures the validity of the approximation by imposing two additional conditions:

1. At most two w_k are positive.
2. If w_k is positive, then only an adjacent w_{k+1} or w_{k-1} can assume a positive value.

To show how these conditions are satisfied, consider the separable problem

$$\text{Maximize (or minimize) } z = \sum_{j=1}^{n} f_j(x_j)$$

subject to

$$\sum_{j=1}^{n} g_{ij}(x_j) \leq b_i, \, i = 1, 2, \ldots, m$$

This problem can be approximated by a mixed integer program as follows. Let[2]

$$\left. \begin{array}{l} a_{jk} = \text{breakpoint } k \text{ for variable } x_j \\ w_{jk} = \text{weight with breakpoint } k \text{ of variable } x_j \end{array} \right\} k = 1, 2, \ldots, K_j, j = 1, 2, \ldots, n$$

Then the equivalent mixed problem is

$$\text{Maximize (or minimize) } z = \sum_{j=1}^{n} \sum_{k=1}^{K_j} f_j(a_{jk}) w_{jk}$$

subject to

$$\sum_{j=1}^{n} \sum_{k=1}^{K_j} g_{jk}(a_{jk}) w_{jk} \leq b_i, \quad i = 1, 2, \ldots, m$$

$$0 \leq w_{j1} \leq y_{j1}, \quad j = 1, 2, \ldots, n$$

---

[2]It is more accurate to replace the index k with k_j to correspond uniquely to variable j. In this instant, we will forsake mathematical accuracy for a simpler notation.

$$0 \le w_{jk} \le y_{j,k-1} + y_{jk}, \quad k = 2, 3, \ldots, K_j - 1, \ j = 1, 2, \ldots, n$$

$$0 \le w_{jK_j} \le y_{j,K_j-1}, \qquad j = 1, 2, \ldots, n$$

$$\sum_{k=1}^{K_j-1} y_{jk} = 1, \qquad j = 1, 2, \ldots, n$$

$$\sum_{k=1}^{K_j} w_{jk} = 1, \qquad j = 1, 2, \ldots, n$$

$$y_{jk} = (0, 1), \qquad k = 1, 2, \ldots, K_j, j = 1, 2, \ldots, n$$

The variables in the approximation problem are w_{jk} and y_{jk}.

The formulation shows how any separable problem can be solved, in principle, by mixed integer programming. The difficulty is that the number of constraints increases rather rapidly with the number of breakpoints. In particular, the computational feasibility of the procedure is questionable because there are no consistently reliable computer codes for solving large mixed integer programming problems.

Another method for solving the approximation model is the regular simplex method (Chapter 3) using **restricted basis**. In this case, the additional constraints involving y_{jk} are dropped. The restricted basis modifies the simplex method optimality condition by selecting the entering variable w_j with the *best* $(z_{jk} - c_{jk})$ that does not violate the adjacency requirement of the w-variables with positive values. The process is repeated until the optimality condition is satisfied or until it is impossible to satisfy the restricted basis condition, whichever occurs first.

The mixed integer programming method yields a global optimum to the approximate problem, whereas the restricted basis method can only guarantee a local optimum. Additionally, in the two methods, the approximate solution may not be feasible for the original problem, in which case it may be necessary to refine the approximation by increasing the number of breakpoints.

Example 21.2-1

Consider the problem

$$\text{Maximize } z = x_1 + x_2^4$$

subject to

$$3x_1 + 2x_2^2 \le 9$$

$$x_1, x_2 \ge 0$$

The exact optimum solution to this problem, obtained by AMPL or Solver, is $x_1 = 0$, $x_2 = 2.12132$, and $z^* = 20.25$. To show how the approximating method is used, consider the separable functions

$$f_1(x_1) = x_1$$

$$f_2(x_2) = x_2^4$$

$$g_1(x_1) = 3x_1$$

$$g_2(x_2) = 2x_2^2$$

The variable x_1 is not approximated because the functions $f_1(x_1)$ and $g_1(x_1)$ are already linear. Considering $f_2(x_2)$ and $g_2(x_2)$, we assume four breakpoints: $a_{2k} = 0, 1, 2$, and 3 for $k = 1, 2, 3$, and 4, respectively. Given $x_2 \leq 3$, it follows that

k	a_{2k}	$f_2(a_{2k}) = a_{2k}^4$	$g_2(a_{2k}) = 2a_{2k}^2$
1	0	0	0
2	1	1	2
3	2	16	8
4	3	81	18

Thus

$$f_2(x_2) \approx w_{21}f_2(a_{21}) + w_{22}f_2(a_{22}) + w_{23}f_2(a_{23}) + w_{24}f_2(a_{24})$$

$$\approx 0w_{21} + 1w_{22} + 16w_{23} + 81w_{24} = w_{22} + 16w_{23} + 81w_{24}$$

Similarly,

$$g_2(x_2) \approx 2w_{22} + 8w_{23} + 18w_{24}$$

The approximation problem thus becomes

$$\text{Maximize } z = x_1 + w_{22} + 16w_{23} + 81w_{24}$$

subject to

$$3x_1 + 2w_{22} + 8w_{23} + 18w_{24} \leq 9$$

$$w_{21} + w_{22} + w_{23} + w_{24} = 1$$

$$x_1 \geq 0, w_{2k} \geq 0, k = 1, 2, 3, 4$$

The values of $w_{2k}, k = 1, 2, 3, 4$, must satisfy the restricted basis condition.

The initial simplex tableau (with rearranged columns to provide a starting solution) is given by

Basic	x_1	w_{22}	w_{23}	w_{24}	s_1	w_{21}	Solution
z	−1	−1	−16	−81	0	0	0
s_1	3	2	8	18	1	0	9
w_{21}	0	1	1	1	0	1	1

The variable $s_1 (\geq 0)$ is a slack. (This problem happened to have an obvious starting solution. In general, one can use artificial variables, Section 3.4.)

From the z-row, w_{24} is the entering variable. Because w_{21} is currently basic and positive, the restricted basis condition dictates that it must leave before w_{24} can enter the solution. However, by the feasibility condition, s_1 must be the leaving variable, which means that w_{24} cannot enter the solution. The next-best entering variable, w_{23}, requires w_{21} to leave the basic solution, a condition that happens to be satisfied by the feasibility condition. The new tableau thus becomes

Basic	x_1	w_{22}	w_{23}	w_{24}	s_1	w_{21}	Solution
z	−1	15	0	−65	0	16	16
s_1	3	−6	0	10	1	−8	1
w_{23}	0	1	1	1	0	1	1

Next, w_{24} is the entering variable, which is admissible because w_{23} is positive. The simplex method shows that s_1 will leave. Thus,

Basic	x_1	w_{22}	w_{23}	w_{24}	s_1	w_{21}	Solution
z	$\frac{37}{2}$	-24	0	0	$\frac{13}{2}$	-36	$22\frac{1}{2}$
w_{24}	$\frac{3}{10}$	$-\frac{6}{10}$	0	1	$\frac{1}{10}$	$-\frac{8}{10}$	$\frac{1}{10}$
w_{23}	$-\frac{3}{10}$	$\frac{16}{10}$	1	0	$-\frac{1}{10}$	$\frac{18}{10}$	$\frac{9}{10}$

The tableau shows that w_{21} and w_{22} are candidates for the entering variable. The variable w_{21} is not adjacent to basic w_{23} or w_{24}, hence it cannot become basic. Similarly, w_{22} cannot enter because w_{24} cannot leave. Thus, the last tableau is the best restricted-basis solution for the approximate problem.

The optimum solution to the original problem is

$$x_1 = 0$$

$$x_2 \approx 2w_{23} + 3w_{24} = 2\left(\tfrac{9}{10}\right) + 3\left(\tfrac{1}{10}\right) = 2.1$$

$$z = 0 + 2.1^4 = 19.45$$

The value $x_2 = 2.1$ approximately equals the true optimum value ($=2.12132$).

Separable convex programming. A special case of separable programming occurs when $g_{ij}(x_j)$ is convex for all i and j, which ensures a convex solution space. Additionally, if $f_j(x_j)$ is convex (minimization) or concave (maximization) for all j, then the problem has a global optimum (see Table 20.2, Section 20.2.2). Under such conditions, the following simplified approximation can be used.

Consider a minimization problem, and let $f_j(x_j)$ be as shown in Figure 21.4. The breakpoints of the function $f_j(x_j)$ are $x_j = a_{jk}, k = 0, 1, \ldots, K_j$. Let x_{jk} define the increment of the variable x_j in the range $(a_{j,k-1}, a_{jk}), k - 1, 2, \ldots, K_j$, and let r_{jk} be the corresponding rate of change (slope of the line segment) in the same range. Then

$$f_j(x_j) \approx \sum_{k=1}^{K_j} r_{jk} x_{jk} + f_j(a_{j0})$$

$$x_j = \sum_{k=1}^{K_j} x_{jk}$$

$$0 \le x_{jk} \le a_{jk} - a_{j,k-1}, k = 1, 2, \ldots, K_j$$

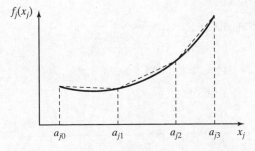

FIGURE 21.4

Piecewise-linear approximation of a convex function

The fact that $f_j(x_j)$ is convex ensures that $r_{j1} < r_{j2} < \cdots < r_{jK_j}$. This means that in the minimization problem the variable x_{jp} is more attractive than x_{jq} for $p < q$. Consequently, x_{jp} will always reach its maximum limit before x_{jq} can assume a positive value.

The convex constraint functions $g_{ij}(x_j)$ are approximated in essentially the same way. Let r_{ijk} be the slope of the kth line segment corresponding to $g_{ij}(x_j)$. It follows that

$$g_{ij}(x_j) \approx \sum_{k=1}^{K_j} r_{ijk}x_{jk} + g_{ij}(a_{j0})$$

The complete problem is thus given by

$$\text{Minimize } z = \sum_{j=1}^{n}\left(\sum_{k=1}^{K_j} r_{jk}x_{jk} + f_j(a_{j0}) \right)$$

subject to

$$\sum_{j=1}^{n}\left(\sum_{k=1}^{K_j} r_{ijk}x_{jk} + g_{ij}(a_{j0}) \right) \leq b_i, i = 1, 2, \ldots, m$$

$$0 \leq x_{jk} \leq a_{jk} - a_{j,k-1}, k = 1, 2, \ldots, K_j, \quad j = 1, 2, \ldots, n$$

where

$$r_{jk} = \frac{f_j(a_{jk}) - f_j(a_{j,k-1})}{a_{jk} - a_{j,k-1}}$$

$$r_{ijk} = \frac{g_{ij}(a_{jk}) - g_{ij}(a_{j,k-1})}{a_{jk} - a_{j,k-1}}$$

The maximization problem is treated in essentially the same way. In this case, $r_{j1} > r_{j2} > \cdots > r_{jK_j}$, which means that, for $p < q$, the variable x_{jp} will always reach its maximum value before x_{jq} is allowed to assume a positive value (see Problem 7, Set 21.2a, for proof).

The new problem can be solved by the simplex method with upper-bounded variables (Section 7.3). The restricted basis concept is not needed because the convexity (concavity) of the functions guarantees correct selection of basic variables.

Example 21.2-2

Consider the problem

$$\text{Maximize } z = x_1 - x_2$$

subject to

$$3x_1^4 + \quad x_2 \leq 243$$

$$x_1 + 2x_2^2 \leq 32$$

$$x_1 \qquad \geq 2.1$$

$$x_2 \geq 3.5$$

The separable functions of this problem are

$$f_1(x_1) = x_1, \qquad f_2(x_2) = -x_2$$

$$g_{11}(x_1) = 3x_1^4, \qquad g_{12}(x_2) = x_2$$

$$g_{21}(x_1) = x_1, \qquad g_{22}(x_2) = 2x_2^2$$

These functions satisfy the convexity condition required for the minimization problems. The functions $f_1(x_1)$, $f_2(x_2)$, $g_{12}(x_2)$, and $g_{21}(x_1)$ are already linear.

The ranges of the variables x_1 and x_2 (estimated from the constraints) are $0 \le x_1 \le 3$ and $0 \le x_2 \le 4$. Let $K_1 = 3$ and $K_2 = 4$. The slopes corresponding to the separable functions are determined as follows.

For j = 1,

k	a_{1k}	$g_{11}(a_{1k}) = 3a_{1k}^4$	r_{11k}	x_{1k}
0	0	0	—	—
1	1	3	3	x_{11}
2	2	48	45	x_{12}
3	3	243	195	x_{13}

For j = 2,

k	a_{2k}	$g_{22}(a_{2k}) = 2a_{2k}^2$	r_{22k}	x_{2k}
0	0	0	—	—
1	1	2	2	x_{21}
2	2	8	6	x_{22}
3	3	18	10	x_{23}
4	4	32	14	x_{24}

The complete problem then becomes

$$\text{Maximize } z = x_1 - x_2$$

subject to

$$3x_{11} + 45x_{12} + 195x_{13} + x_2 \qquad \le 243 \qquad (1)$$

$$x_1 + 2x_{21} + 6x_{22} + 10x_{23} + 14x_{24} \le 32 \qquad (2)$$

$$x_1 \qquad\qquad\qquad \ge 2.1 \qquad (3)$$

$$x_2 \ge 3.5 \qquad (4)$$

$$x_{11} + x_{12} + x_{13} - x_1 \qquad\qquad = 0 \qquad (5)$$

$$x_{21} + x_{22} + x_{23} + x_{24} - x_2 \qquad = 0 \qquad (6)$$

$$0 \le x_{1k} \le 1, \quad k = 1, 2, 3 \qquad (7)$$

$$0 \le x_{2k} \le 1, \quad k = 1, 2, 3, 4 \qquad (8)$$

$$x_1, x_2 \ge 0$$

Constraints 5 and 6 are needed to maintain the relationship between the original and new variables. The optimum solution is

$$z = -.52, x_1 = 2.98, x_2 = 3.5, x_{11} = x_{12} = 1, x_{13} = .98, x_{21} = x_{22} = x_{23} = 1, x_{24} = .5$$

AMPL Moment

AMPL modeling of the *original* nonlinear problem of Example 21.2-2 is very much the same as in linear problems. Obtaining the solution is an entirely different matter because of the "unpredictable" behavior of the nonlinear functions. File *amplEx21.2-2.txt* provides the model. An explanation of the model is given in Appendix C on the website (see Figure C.17).

PROBLEM SET 21.2A

1. Approximate the following problem as a mixed integer program.

$$\text{Maximize } z = e^{-x_1} + x_1 + (x_2 + 1)^2$$

subject to

$$x_1^2 + x_2 \le 3$$
$$x_1, x_2 \ge 0$$

*2. Repeat Problem 1 using the restricted basis method. Then find the optimal solution.

3. Consider the problem

$$\text{Maximize } z = x_1 x_2 x_3$$

subject to

$$x_1^2 + x_2 + x_3 \le 4$$
$$x_1, x_2, x_3 \ge 0$$

Approximate the problem as a linear program for use with the restricted basis method.

*4. Show how the following problem can be made separable.

$$\text{Maximize } z = x_1 x_2 + x_3 + x_1 x_3$$

subject to

$$x_1 x_2 + x_2 + x_1 x_3 \le 10$$
$$x_1, x_2 x_3 \ge 0$$

5. Show how the following problem can be made separable.

$$\text{Minimize } z = e^{2x_1 + x_2^2} + (x_3 - 2)^2$$

subject to

$$x_1 + x_2 + x_3 \leq 6$$

$$x_1, x_2 x_3 \geq 0$$

6. Show how the following problem can be made separable.

$$\text{Maximize } z = e^{x_1 x_2} + x_2^2 x_3 + x_4$$

subject to

$$x_1 + x_2 x_3 + x_3 \leq 10$$

$$x_1, x_2, x_3 \geq 0$$

$$x_4 \text{ unrestricted in sign}$$

7. Show that in separable convex programming, it is never optimal to have $x_{ki} > 0$ when $x_{k-1,i}$ is not at its upper bound.

8. Solve as a separable convex programming problem.

$$\text{Minimize } z = x_1^4 + x_2 + x_3^2$$

subject to

$$x_1^2 + x_2 + x_3^2 \leq 4$$

$$|x_1 + x_2| \leq 0$$

$$x_1, x_3 \geq 0$$

$$x_2 \text{ unrestricted in sign}$$

9. Solve the following as a separate convex programming problem.

$$\text{Minimize } z = (x_1 - 2)^2 + 4(x_2 - 6)^2$$

subject to

$$6x_1 + 3(x_2 + 1)^2 \leq 12$$

$$x_1, x_2 \geq 0$$

21.2.2 Quadratic Programming

A quadratic programming model is defined as

$$\text{Maximize } z = \mathbf{CX} + \mathbf{X}^T \mathbf{DX}$$

subject to

$$\mathbf{AX} \leq \mathbf{b}, \mathbf{X} \geq \mathbf{0}$$

where

$$\mathbf{X} = (x_1, x_2, \ldots, x_n)^T$$

$$\mathbf{C} = (c_1, c_2, \ldots, c_n)$$

$$\mathbf{b} = (b_1, b_2, \ldots, b_m)^T$$

$$\mathbf{A} = \begin{pmatrix} a_{11} & \cdots & a_{1n} \\ \vdots & \vdots & \vdots \\ a_{m1} & \cdots & a_{mn} \end{pmatrix}$$

$$\mathbf{D} = \begin{pmatrix} d_{11} & \cdots & d_{1n} \\ \vdots & \vdots & \vdots \\ d_{n1} & \cdots & d_{nn} \end{pmatrix}$$

The function $\mathbf{X}^{\mathbf{T}}\mathbf{D}\mathbf{X}$ defines a quadratic form (see Section D.3 on the website). The matrix $\mathbf{D}$ is assumed symmetric and negative definite—meaning that z is strictly concave. The constraints are linear, which guarantees a convex solution space.

The solution to this problem is based on the KKT necessary conditions. These conditions (as shown in Table 20.2, Section 20.2.2) are also sufficient because z is concave and the solution space is a convex set.

The quadratic programming problem will be treated for the maximization case. Conversion to minimization is straightforward. The problem may be written as

$$\text{Maximize } z = \mathbf{CX} + \mathbf{X}^{T}\mathbf{DX}$$

subject to

$$\mathbf{G(X)} = \begin{pmatrix} \mathbf{A} \\ -\mathbf{I} \end{pmatrix} \mathbf{X} - \begin{pmatrix} \mathbf{b} \\ \mathbf{0} \end{pmatrix} \leq \mathbf{0}$$

Let

$$\boldsymbol{\lambda} = (\lambda_1, \lambda_2, \ldots, \lambda_m)^{T}$$

$$\mathbf{U} = (\mu_1, \mu_2, \ldots, \mu_n)^{T}$$

be the Lagrange multipliers corresponding to constraints $\mathbf{AX} - \mathbf{b} \leq \mathbf{0}$ and $-\mathbf{X} \leq \mathbf{0}$, respectively. Application of the KKT conditions yields

$$\boldsymbol{\lambda} \geq \mathbf{0}, \mathbf{U} \geq \mathbf{0}$$

$$\nabla z - (\boldsymbol{\lambda}^{T}, \mathbf{U}^{T})\nabla\mathbf{G(X)} = \mathbf{0}$$

$$\lambda_i\left(b_i - \sum_{j=1}^{n} a_{ij}x_j\right) = 0, i = 1, 2, \ldots, m$$

$$\mu_j x_j = 0, \quad j = 1, 2, \ldots, n$$

$$\mathbf{AX} \leq \mathbf{b}$$

$$-\mathbf{X} \leq \mathbf{0}$$

Now

$$\nabla z = \mathbf{C} + 2\mathbf{X}^{T}\mathbf{D}$$

$$\nabla\mathbf{G(X)} = \begin{pmatrix} \mathbf{A} \\ -\mathbf{I} \end{pmatrix}$$

Let $S = b - AX \geq 0$ be the slack variables of the constraints. The conditions reduce to

$$-2X^T D + \lambda^T A - U^T = C$$

$$AX + S = b$$

$$\mu_j x_j = 0 = \lambda_i S_i \quad \text{for all } i \text{ and } j$$

$$\lambda, U, X, S \geq 0$$

Because $D^T = D$, the transpose of the first set of equations can be written as

$$-2DX + A^T \lambda - U = C^T$$

Hence, the necessary conditions may be combined as

$$\begin{pmatrix} -2D & A^T & -I & 0 \\ A & 0 & 0 & I \end{pmatrix} \begin{pmatrix} X \\ \lambda \\ U \\ S \end{pmatrix} = \begin{pmatrix} C^T \\ b \end{pmatrix}$$

$$\mu_j x_j = 0 = \lambda_i S_i, \quad \text{for all } i \text{ and } j$$

$$\lambda, U, X, S \geq 0$$

Except for the conditions $\mu_j x_j = 0 = \lambda_i S_i$, the remaining equations are linear in X, λ, U, and S. Thus, the problem is equivalent to solving a set of linear equations with the additional conditions $\mu_j x_j = 0 = \lambda_i S_i$.

The solution of the system is obtained by using phase I of the two-phase method (Section 3.4.2), with the added restrictions $\lambda_i S_i = 0$ and $\mu_j x_j = 0$. This means that λ_i and s_i cannot be positive simultaneously, and neither can μ_j and x_j. This is the same idea of the **restricted basis** used in Section 21.2.1.

Phase I will render all the artificial variables equal to zero provided the problem has a feasible solution space.

Example 21.2-3

Consider the problem

$$\text{Maximize } z = 4x_1 + 6x_2 - 2x_1^2 - 2x_1 x_2 - 2x_2^2$$

subject to

$$x_1 + 2x_2 \leq 2$$

$$x_1, x_2 \geq 0$$

This problem can be put in the following matrix form:

$$\text{Maximize } z = (4, 6)\begin{pmatrix} x_1 \\ x_2 \end{pmatrix} + (x_1, x_2)\begin{pmatrix} -2 & -1 \\ -1 & -2 \end{pmatrix}\begin{pmatrix} x_1 \\ x_2 \end{pmatrix}$$

subject to

$$(1, 2)\begin{pmatrix} x_1 \\ x_2 \end{pmatrix} \le 2$$

$$x_1, x_2 \ge 0$$

The KKT conditions are given as

$$\begin{pmatrix} 4 & 2 & 1 & -1 & 0 & 0 \\ 2 & 4 & 2 & 0 & -1 & 0 \\ 1 & 2 & 0 & 0 & 0 & 1 \end{pmatrix} \begin{pmatrix} x_1 \\ x_2 \\ \lambda_1 \\ \mu_1 \\ \mu_2 \\ s_1 \end{pmatrix} = \begin{pmatrix} 4 \\ 6 \\ 2 \end{pmatrix}, \mu_1 x_1 = \mu_2 x_2 = \lambda_1 s_1 = 0$$

The initial tableau for phase 1 is obtained by introducing the artificial variables R_1 and R_2 and updating the objective row.

Basic	x_1	x_2	λ_1	μ_1	μ_2	R_1	R_2	s_1	Solution
r	6	6	3	-1	-1	0	0	0	10
R_1	4	2	1	-1	0	1	0	0	4
R_2	2	4	2	0	-1	0	1	0	6
s_1	1	2	0	0	0	0	0	1	2

Iteration 1. The most promising entering variable x_1 can be made basic because $\mu_1 = 0$.

Basic	x_1	x_2	λ_1	μ_1	μ_2	R_1	R_2	s_1	Solution
R	0	3	$\frac{3}{2}$	$\frac{1}{2}$	-1	$-\frac{3}{2}$	0	0	4
x_1	1	$\frac{1}{2}$	$\frac{1}{4}$	$-\frac{1}{4}$	0	$\frac{1}{4}$	0	0	1
R_2	0	3	$\frac{3}{2}$	$\frac{1}{2}$	-1	$-\frac{1}{2}$	1	0	4
s_1	0	$\frac{3}{2}$	$-\frac{1}{4}$	$\frac{1}{4}$	0	$-\frac{1}{4}$	0	1	1

Iteration 2. The most promising variable x_2 can be made basic because $\mu_2 = 0$.

Basic	x_1	x_2	λ_1	μ_1	μ_2	R_1	R_2	s_1	Solution
r	0	0	2	0	-1	-1	0	-2	2
x_1	1	0	$\frac{1}{3}$	$-\frac{1}{3}$	0	$\frac{1}{3}$	0	$-\frac{1}{3}$	$\frac{2}{3}$
R_1	0	0	2	0	-1	0	1	-2	2
x_1	0	1	$-\frac{1}{6}$	$\frac{1}{6}$	0	$-\frac{1}{6}$	0	$\frac{2}{3}$	$\frac{2}{3}$

Iteration 3. The multiplier λ_1 can be made basic because $s_1 = 0$.

Basic	x_1	x_2	λ_1	μ_1	μ_2	R_1	R_2	s_1	Solution
r	0	0	0	0	0	-1	-1	0	0
x_1	1	0	0	$-\frac{1}{3}$	$\frac{1}{6}$	$\frac{1}{3}$	$-\frac{1}{6}$	0	$\frac{1}{3}$
λ_1	0	0	1	0	$-\frac{1}{2}$	0	$\frac{1}{2}$	-1	1
x_2	0	1	0	$\frac{1}{6}$	$-\frac{1}{12}$	$-\frac{1}{6}$	$\frac{1}{12}$	$\frac{1}{2}$	$\frac{5}{6}$

The last tableau gives the optimal feasible solution $(x_1^* = \frac{1}{3}, x_2^* = \frac{5}{6})$. The associated optimal value of z is 4.16.

Solver Moment

Solver template—*excelQP.xls*—solves Example 21.2-3. The data are entered in a manner similar to linear programming (see Section 2.3.1). The main difference occurs in the way the nonlinear functions are entered. Specifically, the nonlinear objective function is entered in target cell D5 as

```
=4*B10+6*C10-2*B10^2-2*B10*C10-2*C10^2
```

The changing cells are B10:C10 $[\equiv (x_1, x_2)]$. Notice that cells B5:C5 are not used at all in the model. For readability, we entered the symbol NL to indicate that the associated constraint is nonlinear. Also, you can specify the nonnegativity of the variables either in the Options dialogue box or by adding explicit nonnegativity constraints.

PROBLEM SET 21.2B

*1. Consider the problem

$$\text{Maximize } z = 6x_1 + 3x_2 - 4x_1 x_2 - 2x_1^2 - 3x_2^2$$

subject to

$$x_1 + x_2 \le 1$$
$$2x_1 + 3x_2 \le 4$$
$$x_1, x_2 \ge 0$$

Show that z is strictly concave, and then solve the problem using the quadratic programming algorithm.

*2. Consider the problem:

$$\text{Minimize } z = 2x_1^2 + 2x_2^2 + 3x_3^2 + 2x_1 x_2 + 2x_2 x_3 + x_1 - 3x_2 - 5x_3$$

subject to

$$x_1 + x_2 + x_3 \geq 1$$

$$3x_1 + 2x_2 + x_3 \leq 6$$

$$x_1, x_2, x_3 \geq 0$$

Show that z is strictly convex, and then solve by the quadratic programming algorithm.

21.2.3 Chance-Constrained Programming

Chance-constrained programming deals with situations in which the parameters of the constraints are random variables and the constraints are realized with a minimum probability. Mathematically, the problem is defined as

$$\text{Maximize } z = \sum_{j=1}^{n} c_j x_j$$

subject to

$$P\left\{ \sum_{j=1}^{n} a_{ij} x_j \leq b_i \right\} \geq 1 - \alpha_i, i = 1, 2, \ldots, m, x_j \geq 0, \text{for all } j$$

The parameters a_{ij} and b_i are random variables, and constraint i is realized with a minimum probability of $1 - \alpha_i, 0 < \alpha_i < 1$.

Three cases are considered:

1. Only a_{ij} is random for all i and j.
2. Only b_i is random for all i.
3. Both a_{ij} and b_i are random for all i and j.

In all three cases, it is assumed that the parameters are normally distributed with known means and variances.

Case 1. Each a_{ij} is normally distributed with mean $E\{a_{ij}\}$, variance $\text{var}\{a_{ij}\}$, and $\text{cov}\{a_{ij}, a_{i'j'}\}$ of a_{ij} and $a_{i'j'}$.

Consider

$$P\left\{ \sum_{j=1}^{n} a_{ij} x_j \leq b_i \right\} \geq 1 - \alpha_i$$

Define

$$h_i = \sum_{j=1}^{n} a_{ij} x_j$$

The random variable h_i is normally distributed with

$$E\{h_i\} = \sum_{j=1}^{n} E\{a_{ij}\} x_j$$

$$\text{var}\{h_i\} = \mathbf{X}^T \mathbf{D}_i \mathbf{X}$$

where

$$\mathbf{X} = (x_1, \ldots, x_n)^T$$

$\mathbf{D}_i = i$th covariance matrix

$$= \begin{pmatrix} \text{var}\{a_{i1}\} & \cdots & \text{cov}\{a_{i1}, a_{in}\} \\ \vdots & \vdots & \vdots \\ \text{cov}\{a_{in}, a_{i1}\} & \cdots & \text{var}\{a_{in}\} \end{pmatrix}$$

Now

$$P\{h_i \leq b_i\} = P\left\{ \frac{h_i - E\{h_i\}}{\sqrt{\text{var}\{h_i\}}} \leq \frac{b_i - E\{h_i\}}{\sqrt{\text{var}\{h_i\}}} \right\} \geq 1 - \alpha_i$$

Letting F be the CDF of the standard normal distribution, it follows that

$$P\{h_i \leq b_i\} = F\left(\frac{b_i - E\{h_i\}}{\sqrt{\text{var}\{h_i\}}} \right)$$

Let K_{α_i} be the standard normal value such that

$$F(K_{\alpha_i}) = 1 - \alpha_i$$

Then the statement $P\{h_i \leq b_i\} \geq 1 - \alpha_i$ is realized if, and only if,

$$\frac{b_i - E\{h_i\}}{\sqrt{\text{var}\{h_i\}}} \geq K_{\alpha_i}$$

This yields the following nonlinear deterministic constraint:

$$\sum_{j=1}^n E\{a_{ij}\}x_j + K_{\alpha_i}\sqrt{\mathbf{X}^T \mathbf{D}_i \mathbf{X}} \leq b_i$$

For the special case where the parameters a_{ij} are independent, $\text{cov}\{a_{ij}, a_{i'j'}\} = 0$, and the last constraint reduces to

$$\sum_{j=1}^n E\{a_{ij}\}x_j + K_{\alpha_i}\sqrt{\sum_{j=1}^n \text{var}\{a_{ij}\}x_j^2} \leq b_i$$

This constraint can be put in the separable programming form (Section 21.2.1) by using the substitution

$$y_i - \sqrt{\sum_{j=1}^n \text{var}\{a_{ij}\}x_j^2}, \text{ for all } i$$

Thus, the original constraint is equivalent to

$$\sum_{j=1}^n E\{a_{ij}\}x_j + K_{\alpha_i}y_i \leq b_i$$

and

$$\sum_{j=1}^{n} \text{var}\{a_{ij}\}x_j^2 - y_i^2 = 0$$

Case 2.   Only b_i is normal with mean $E\{b_i\}$ and variance $\text{var}\{b_i\}$.
Consider the stochastic constraint

$$P\left\{b_i \geq \sum_{j=1}^{n} a_{ij}x_j\right\} \geq \alpha_i$$

As in case 1,

$$P\left\{\frac{b_i - E\{b_i\}}{\sqrt{\text{var}\{b_i\}}} \geq \frac{\sum_{j=1}^{n} a_{ij}x_j - E\{b_i\}}{\sqrt{\text{var}\{b_i\}}}\right\} \geq \alpha_i$$

This can hold true only if

$$\frac{\sum_{j=1}^{n} a_{ij}x_j - E\{b_i\}}{\sqrt{\text{var}\{b_i\}}} \leq K_{\alpha_i}$$

Thus, the stochastic constraint is equivalent to the deterministic linear constraint

$$\sum_{j=1}^{n} a_{ij}x_j \leq E\{b_i\} + K_{\alpha_i}\sqrt{\text{var}\{b_i\}}$$

Case 3.   All a_{ij} and b_i are normal random variables.
Consider the constraint

$$\sum_{j=1}^{n} a_{ij}x_j \leq b_i$$

This may be written

$$\sum_{j=1}^{n} a_{ij}x_j - b_i \leq 0$$

Because all a_{ij} and b_i are normal, $\sum_{j=1}^{n} a_{ij}x_j - b_i$ is also normal. This shows that the chance constraint reduces to the situation in case 1 and is treated in a similar manner.

Example 21.2-4

Consider the chance-constrained problem

$$\text{Maximize } z = 5x_1 + 6x_2 + 3x_3$$

subject to

$$P\{a_{11}x_1 + a_{12}x_2 + a_{13}x_3 \le 8\} \ge .95$$
$$P\{5x_1 + x_2 + 6x_3 \le b_2\} \ge .10$$
$$x_1, x_2, x_3 \ge 0$$

Assume that the parameters $a_{1jj}, j = 1, 2, 3$, are independent and normally distributed random variables with the following means and variances:

$$E\{a_{11}\} = 1, E\{a_{12}\} = 3, E\{a_{13}\} = 9$$
$$\text{var}\{a_{11}\} = 25, \text{var}\{a_{12}\} = 16, \text{var}\{a_{13}\} = 4$$

The parameter b_2 is normally distributed with mean 7 and variance 9.
From standard normal tables in Appendix B (or *excelStatTables.xls*),

$$K_{\alpha_1} = K_{.05} \approx 1.645, \quad K_{\alpha_2} = K_{.10} \approx 1.285$$

For the first constraint, the equivalent deterministic constraint is

$$x_1 + 3x_2 + 9x_3 + 1.645\sqrt{25x_1^2 + 16x_2^2 + 4x_3^2} \le 8$$

and for the second constraint

$$5x_1 + x_2 + 6x_3 \le 7 + 1.285(3) = 10.855$$

The resulting problem can be solved as a nonlinear program (using AMPL or Solver), or it can be converted to a separable program as follows:

$$y^2 = 25x_1^2 + 16x_2^2 + 4x_3^2$$

The problem becomes

$$\text{Maximize } z = 5x_1 + 6x_2 + 3x_3$$

subject to

$$x_1 + 3x_2 + 9x_3 + 1.645y \le 8$$
$$25x_1^2 + 16x_2^2 + 4x_3^2 - y^2 = 0$$
$$5x_1 + x_2 + 6x_3 \le 10.855$$
$$x_1, x_2, x_3, y \ge 0$$

The problem can be solved by separable programming. Also, Excel file *excelCCP.xls* can be used to solve the nonlinear problem directly.

PROBLEM SET 21.2C

*1. Convert the following stochastic problem into an equivalent deterministic model.

$$\text{Maximize } z = x_1 + 2x_2 + 5x_3$$

subject to

$$P\{a_1x_1 + 3x_2 + a_3x_3 \leq 10\} \geq 0.9$$

$$P\{7x_1 + 5x_2 + x_3 \leq b_2\} \geq 0.1$$

$$x_1, x_2, x_3 \geq 0$$

Assume that a_1 and a_3 are independent and normally distributed random variables with means $E\{a_1\} = 2$ and $E\{a_3\} = 5$ and variances $\text{var}\{a_1\} = 9$ and $\text{var}\{a_3\} = 16$, and that b_2 is normally distributed with mean 15 and variance 25.

2. Consider the following stochastic programming model:

$$\text{Maximize } z = x_1 + x_2^2 + x_3$$

subject to

$$P\{x_1^2 + a_2x_2^3 + a_3\sqrt{x_3} \leq 10\} \geq 0.9$$

$$x_1, x_2, x_3 \geq 0$$

The parameters a_2 and a_3 are independent and normally distributed random variables with means 5 and 2, and variance 16 and 25, respectively. Convert the problem into a (deterministic) separable programming form.

21.2.4 Linear Combinations Method

This method deals with the following problem in which all constraints are linear:

$$\text{Maximize } z = f(\mathbf{X})$$

subject to

$$\mathbf{AX} \leq \mathbf{b}, \mathbf{X} \geq \mathbf{0}$$

The procedure is based on the steepest-ascent (gradient) method (Section 21.1.2). However, the direction specified by the gradient vector may not yield a feasible solution for the constrained problem. Also, the gradient vector will not necessarily be null at the optimum (constrained) point. The steepest ascent method thus must be modified to handle the constrained case.

Let $\mathbf{X}_k$ be the *feasible* trial point at iteration k. The objective function $f(\mathbf{X})$ can be expanded in the neighborhood of $\mathbf{X}_k$ using Taylor's series. This gives

$$f(\mathbf{X}) \approx f(\mathbf{X}_k) + \nabla f(\mathbf{X}_k)(\mathbf{X} - \mathbf{X}_k) = (f(\mathbf{X}_k) - \nabla f(\mathbf{X}_k)\mathbf{X}_k) + \nabla f(\mathbf{X}_k)\mathbf{X}$$

The procedure calls for determining a feasible point $\mathbf{X} = \mathbf{X}^*$ such that $f(\mathbf{X})$ is maximized subject to the (linear) constraints of the problem. Because $f(\mathbf{X}_k) - \nabla f(\mathbf{X}_k)\mathbf{X}_k$ is a constant, the problem for determining $\mathbf{X}^*$ reduces to solving the following linear program:

$$\text{Maximize } w_k(\mathbf{X}) = \nabla f(\mathbf{X}_k)\mathbf{X}$$

subject to

$$\mathbf{AX} \leq \mathbf{b}, \mathbf{X} \geq \mathbf{0}$$

Given that w_k is constructed from the gradient of $f(\mathbf{X})$ at $\mathbf{X}_k$, an improved solution point can be secured if and only if $w_k(\mathbf{X}^*) > w_k(\mathbf{X}_k)$. From Taylor's expansion, the condition does not guarantee that $f(\mathbf{X}^*) > f(\mathbf{X}_k)$ unless $\mathbf{X}^*$ is in the neighborhood of $\mathbf{X}_k$. However, given $w_k(\mathbf{X}^*) > w_k(\mathbf{X}_k)$, there must exist a point $\mathbf{X}_{k+1}$ on the line segment $(\mathbf{X}_k, \mathbf{X}^*)$ such that $f(\mathbf{X}_{k+1}) > f(\mathbf{X}_k)$. The objective is to determine $\mathbf{X}_{k+1}$. Define

$$\mathbf{X}_{k+1} = (1 - r)\mathbf{X}_k + r\mathbf{X}^* = \mathbf{X}^k + r(\mathbf{X}^* - \mathbf{X}_k), 0 < r \le 1$$

This means that $\mathbf{X}_{k+1}$ is a **linear combination** of $\mathbf{X}_k$ and $\mathbf{X}^*$. Because $\mathbf{X}_k$ and $\mathbf{X}^*$ are two feasible points in a *convex* solution space, $\mathbf{X}_{k+1}$ is also feasible. In terms of the steepest-ascent method (Section 21.1.2), the parameter r represents step size.

The point $\mathbf{X}_{k+1}$ is determined such that $f(\mathbf{X})$ is maximized. Because $\mathbf{X}_{k+1}$ is a function of r only, $\mathbf{X}_{k+1}$ is determined by maximizing

$$h(r) = f(\mathbf{X}_k + r(\mathbf{X}^* - \mathbf{X}_k))$$

The procedure is repeated until, at the kth iteration, $w_k(\mathbf{X}^*) \le w_k(\mathbf{X}_k)$. At this point, no further improvements are possible, and the process terminates with $\mathbf{X}_k$ as the best solution point.

The linear programming problems generated at the successive iterations differ only in the coefficients of the objective function. Post-optimal analysis procedures presented in Section 4.5 thus may be used to carry out calculations efficiently.

Example 21.2-5

Consider the quadratic programming of Example 21.2-3.

$$\text{Maximize } f(\mathbf{X}) = 4x_1 + 6x_2 - 2x_1^2 - 2x_1x_2 - 2x_2^2$$

subject to

$$x_1 + 2x_2 \le 2$$

$$x_1, x_2 \ge 0$$

Let the initial trial point be $\mathbf{X}_0 = \left(\frac{1}{2}, \frac{1}{2}\right)$, which is feasible. Now

$$\nabla f(\mathbf{X}) = (4 - 4x_1 - 2x_2, 6 - 2x_1 - 4x_2)$$

Iteration 1

$$\nabla f(\mathbf{X}_0) = (1, 3)$$

The associated linear program maximizes $w_1 = x_1 + 3x_2$ subject to the constraints of the original problem. This gives the optimal solution $\mathbf{X}^* = (0, 1)$. The values of w_1 at $\mathbf{X}_0$ and $\mathbf{X}^*$ equal 2 and 3, respectively. Hence, a new trial point is determined as

$$\mathbf{X}_1 = \left(\tfrac{1}{2}, \tfrac{1}{2}\right) + r\left[(0, 1) - \left(\tfrac{1}{2}, \tfrac{1}{2}\right)\right] = \left(\tfrac{1 - r}{2}, \tfrac{1 + r}{2}\right)$$

The maximization of

$$h(r) = f\left(\tfrac{1-r}{2}, \tfrac{1+r}{2}\right)$$

yields $r_1 = 1$. Thus $\mathbf{X}_1 = (0, 1)$ with $f(\mathbf{X}_1) = 4$.

Iteration 2

$$\nabla f(\mathbf{X}_1) = (2, 2)$$

The objective function of the new linear programming problem is $w_2 = 2x_1 + 2x_2$. The optimum solution to this problem yields $\mathbf{X}^* = (2, 0)$. Because the values of w_2 at $\mathbf{X}_1$ and $\mathbf{X}^*$ are 2 and 4, respectively, a new trial point must be determined. Thus

$$\mathbf{X}_2 = (0, 1) + r[(2, 0) - (0, 1)] = (2r, 1 - r)$$

The maximization of

$$h(r) = f(2r, 1 - r)$$

yields $r_2 = \tfrac{1}{6}$. Thus $\mathbf{X}_2 = \left(\tfrac{1}{3}, \tfrac{5}{6}\right)$ with $f(\mathbf{X}_2) \approx 4.16$.

Iteration 3

$$\nabla f(\mathbf{X}_2) = (1, 2)$$

The corresponding objective function is $w_3 = x_1 + 2x_2$. The optimum solution of this problem yields the alternative solutions $\mathbf{X}^* = (0, 1)$ and $\mathbf{X}^* = (2, 0)$. The value of w_3 for both points equals its value at $\mathbf{X}_2$. Consequently, no further improvements are possible. The *approximate* optimum solution is $\mathbf{X}_2 = \left(\tfrac{1}{3}, \tfrac{5}{6}\right)$ with $f(\mathbf{X}_2) \approx 4.16$. This happens to be the exact optimum.

PROBLEM SET 21.2D

1. Solve the following problem by the linear combinations method.

$$\text{Minimize } f(\mathbf{X}) = x_1^3 + x_2^3 - 3x_1x_2$$

subject to

$$3x_1 + x_2 \leq 3$$
$$5x_1 - 3x_2 \leq 5$$
$$x_1, x_2 \geq 0$$

21.2.5 SUMT Algorithm

In this section, a more general gradient method is presented. It is assumed that the objective function $f(\mathbf{X})$ is concave and each constraint function $g_i(\mathbf{X})$ is convex. Moreover, the solution space must have an interior. This rules out both implicit and explicit use of *equality* constraints.

The SUMT (Sequential Unconstrained Maximization Technique) algorithm is based on transforming the constrained problem into an equivalent *unconstrained* problem. The procedure is more or less similar to the Lagrange multipliers method. The transformed problem can then be solved using the steepest-ascent method (Section 21.1.2).

To clarify the concept, consider the new function

$$p(\mathbf{X},t) = f(\mathbf{X}) + t\left(\sum_{i=1}^{m} \frac{1}{g_i(\mathbf{X})} - \sum_{j=1}^{n} \frac{1}{x_j} \right)$$

where t is a nonnegative parameter. The second summation sign accounts for the non-negativity constraints, which must be put in the form $-x_j \leq 0$ to be consistent with the original constraints. Because $g_i(\mathbf{X})$ is convex, $\frac{1}{g_i(\mathbf{X})}$ is concave. This means that $p(\mathbf{X}, t)$ is concave in $\mathbf{X}$. Consequently, $p(\mathbf{X}, t)$ possesses a unique maximum. Optimization of the original constrained problem is equivalent to optimization of $p(\mathbf{X}, t)$.

The algorithm is initiated by arbitrarily selecting an initial *nonnegative* value for t. An initial point $\mathbf{X}_0$ is selected as the first trial solution. This point must be an interior point—that is, it must not lie on the boundaries of the solution space. Given the value of t, the steepest-ascent method is used to determine the corresponding optimal solution (maximum) of $p(\mathbf{X}, t)$.

The new solution point will always be an interior point, because if the solution point is close to the boundaries, at least one of the functions $\frac{1}{g(\mathbf{X})}$ or $-\frac{1}{x_i}$ will acquire a very large negative value. Because the objective is to maximize $p(\mathbf{X}, t)$, such solution points are automatically excluded. The main result is that successive solution points will always be interior points. Consequently, the problem can always be treated as an unconstrained case.

Once the optimum solution corresponding to a given value of t is obtained, a new value of t is generated, and the optimization process (using the steepest-ascent method) is repeated. If t' is the current value of t, the next value, t'', must be selected such that $0 < t'' < t'$.

The SUMT algorithm ends when, for two successive values of t, the corresponding *optimum* values of $\mathbf{X}$ obtained by maximizing $p(\mathbf{X}, t)$ are approximately the same. At this point, further trials will produce little improvement.

Actual implementation of SUMT involves more details than have been presented here. Specifically, the selection of an initial value of t is an important factor that can affect the speed of convergence. Further, the determination of an initial interior point may require special techniques. These details can be found in Fiacco and McCormick (1968).

BIBLIOGRAPHY

Bazaraa, M., H. Sherall, and C. Shetty, *Nonlinear Programming, Theory and Algorithms*, 2nd ed., Wiley, New York, 1993.

Beightler, C., D. Phillips, and D. Wilde, *Foundations of Optimization*, 2nd ed., Prentice Hall, Upper Saddle River, NJ, 1979.

Fiacco, A., and G. McCormick, *Nonlinear Programming: Sequential Unconstrained Minimization Techniques*, Wiley, New York, 1968.

Fletcher, R., *Practical Methods of Optimization*, 2nd ed., Wiley, New York, 2000.

Luenberger, D., *Linear and Nonlinear Programming*, Kluwer Academic Publishers, Boston, 2003.

Rardin, D., *Optimization in Operations Research*, Prentice Hall, NJ, 1998.

APPENDIX A

Statistical Tables[1]

TABLE A.1   Normal Distribution Function

$$F(z) = \frac{1}{\sqrt{2\pi}} \int_{-\infty}^{z} e^{-\left(\frac{1}{2}\right)t^2} dt$$

z	0.00	0.01	0.02	0.03	0.04	0.05	0.06	0.07	0.08	0.09
0.0	0.5000	0.5040	0.5080	0.5120	0.5160	0.5199	0.5239	0.5279	0.5319	0.5359
0.1	0.5398	0.5438	0.5478	0.5517	0.5557	0.5596	0.5636	0.5675	0.5714	0.5753
0.2	0.5793	0.5832	0.5871	0.5910	0.5948	0.5987	0.6026	0.6064	0.6103	0.6141
0.3	0.6179	0.6217	0.6255	0.6293	0.6331	0.6368	0.6406	0.6443	0.6480	0.6517
0.4	0.6554	0.6591	0.6628	0.6664	0.6700	0.6736	0.6772	0.6808	0.6844	0.6879
0.5	0.6915	0.6950	0.6985	0.7019	0.7054	0.7088	0.7123	0.7157	0.7190	0.7224
0.6	0.7257	0.7291	0.7324	0.7357	0.7389	0.7422	0.7454	0.7486	0.7517	0.7549
0.7	0.7580	0.7611	0.7642	0.7673	0.7704	0.7734	0.7764	0.7794	0.7823	0.7852
0.8	0.7881	0.7910	0.7939	0.7967	0.7995	0.8023	0.8051	0.8078	0.8106	0.8133
0.9	0.8159	0.8186	0.8212	0.8238	0.8264	0.8289	0.8315	0.8340	0.8365	0.8389
1.0	0.8413	0.8438	0.8461	0.8485	0.8508	0.8531	0.8554	0.8577	0.8599	0.8621
1.1	0.8643	0.8665	0.8686	0.8708	0.8729	0.8749	0.8770	0.8790	0.8810	0.8830
1.2	0.8849	0.8869	0.8888	0.8907	0.8925	0.8944	0.8962	0.8980	0.8997	0.9015
1.3	0.9032	0.9049	0.9066	0.9082	0.9099	0.9115	0.9131	0.9147	0.9162	0.9177
1.4	0.9192	0.9207	0.9222	0.9236	0.9251	0.9265	0.9279	0.9292	0.9306	0.9319
1.5	0.9332	0.9345	0.9357	0.9370	0.9382	0.9394	0.9406	0.9418	0.9429	0.9441
1.6	0.9452	0.9463	0.9474	0.9484	0.9495	0.9505	0.9515	0.9525	0.9535	0.9545
1.7	0.9554	0.9564	0.9573	0.9582	0.9591	0.9599	0.9608	0.9616	0.9625	0.9633
1.8	0.9641	0.9649	0.9656	0.9664	0.9671	0.9678	0.9686	0.9693	0.9699	0.9706
1.9	0.9713	0.9719	0.9726	0.9732	0.9738	0.9744	0.9750	0.9756	0.9761	0.9767

[1]Spreadsheet *excelStatTable.xls* replaces the (hard-copy) statistical tables of 12 common distributions, including the ones presented in this appendix.

TABLE A.1   Continued

z	0.00	0.01	0.02	0.03	0.04	0.05	0.06	0.07	0.08	0.09
2.0	0.9772	0.9778	0.9783	0.9788	0.9793	0.9798	0.9803	0.9808	0.9812	0.9817
2.1	0.9821	0.9826	0.9830	0.9834	0.9838	0.9842	0.9846	0.9850	0.9854	0.9857
2.2	0.9861	0.9864	0.9868	0.9871	0.9875	0.9878	0.9881	0.9884	0.9887	0.9890
2.3	0.9893	0.9896	0.9898	0.9901	0.9904	0.9906	0.9909	0.9911	0.9913	0.9916
2.4	0.9918	0.9920	0.9922	0.9925	0.9927	0.9929	0.9931	0.9932	0.9934	0.9936
2.5	0.9938	0.9940	0.9941	0.9943	0.9945	0.9946	0.9948	0.9949	0.9951	0.9952
2.6	0.9953	0.9955	0.9956	0.9957	0.9959	0.9960	0.9961	0.9962	0.9963	0.9964
2.7	0.9965	0.9966	0.9967	0.9968	0.9969	0.9970	0.9971	0.9972	0.9973	0.9974
2.8	0.9974	0.9975	0.9976	0.9977	0.9977	0.9978	0.9979	0.9979	0.9980	0.9981
2.9	0.9981	0.9982	0.9982	0.9983	0.9984	0.9984	0.9985	0.9985	0.9986	0.9986
3.0	0.9987	0.9987	0.9987	0.9988	0.9988	0.9989	0.9989	0.9989	0.9990	0.9990
3.1	0.9990	0.9991	0.9991	0.9991	0.9992	0.9992	0.9992	0.9992	0.9993	0.9993
3.2	0.9993	0.9993	0.9994	0.9994	0.9994	0.9994	0.9994	0.9995	0.9995	0.9995
3.3	0.9995	0.9995	0.9995	0.9996	0.9996	0.9996	0.9996	0.9996	0.9996	0.9997
3.4	0.9997	0.9997	0.9997	0.9997	0.9997	0.9997	0.9997	0.9997	0.9997	0.9998
3.5	0.9998									
4.0	0.99997									
5.0	0.9999997									
6.0	0.999999999									

Source: Miller, I., and J. Freund, *Probability and Statistics for Engineers*, Prentice Hall, Upper Saddle River, NJ, 1985.

TABLE A.2 $t_{\alpha,v}$ (Student t) Values

v	$\alpha = 0.10$	$\alpha = 0.05$	$\alpha = 0.025$	$\alpha = 0.01$	$\alpha = 0.005$	v
1	3.078	6.314	12.706	31.821	63.657	1
2	1.886	2.920	4.303	6.965	9.925	2
3	1.638	2.353	3.182	4.541	5.841	3
4	1.533	2.132	2.776	3.747	4.604	4
5	1.476	2.015	2.571	3.365	4.032	5
6	1.440	1.943	2.447	3.143	3.707	6
7	1.415	1.895	2.365	2.998	3.499	7
8	1.397	1.860	2.306	2.896	3.355	8
9	1.383	1.833	2.262	2.821	3.250	9
10	1.372	1.812	2.228	2.764	3.169	10
11	1.363	1.796	2.201	2.718	3.106	11
12	1.356	1.782	2.179	2.681	3.055	12
13	1.350	1.771	2.160	2.650	3.012	13
14	1.345	1.761	2.145	2.624	2.977	14
15	1.341	1.753	2.131	2.602	2.947	15
16	1.337	1.746	2.120	2.583	2.921	16
17	1.333	1.740	2.110	2.567	2.898	17
18	1.330	1.734	2.101	2.552	2.878	18
19	1.328	1.729	2.093	2.539	2.861	19
20	1.325	1.725	2.086	2.528	2.845	20

TABLE A.2   Continued

v	$\alpha = 0.10$	$\alpha = 0.05$	$\alpha = 0.025$	$\alpha = 0.01$	$\alpha = 0.005$	v
21	1.323	1.721	2.080	2.518	2.831	21
22	1.321	1.717	2.074	2.508	2.819	22
23	1.319	1.714	2.069	2.500	2.807	23
24	1.318	1.711	2.064	2.492	2.797	24
25	1.316	1.708	2.060	2.485	2.787	25
26	1.315	1.706	2.056	2.479	2.779	26
27	1.314	1.703	2.052	2.473	2.771	27
28	1.313	1.701	2.048	2.467	2.763	28
29	1.311	1.699	2.045	2.462	2.756	29
Inf.	1.282	1.645	1.960	2.326	2.576	inf.

Source: Abridged by permission of Macmillan Publishing Co. Inc., from *Statistical Methods for Research Workers*, 14th ed., by R. A. Fisher. Copyright © 1970 University of Adelaide.

TABLE A.3 $\chi^2_{a,v}$ (Chi-Square) Values

v	$\alpha = 0.995$	$\alpha = 0.99$	$\alpha = 0.975$	$\alpha = 0.95$	$\alpha = 0.05$	$\alpha = 0.025$	$\alpha = 0.01$	$\alpha = 0.005$	v
1	0.0000393	0.000157	0.000982	0.00393	3.841	5.024	6.635	7.879	1
2	0.0100	0.0201	0.0506	0.103	5.991	7.378	9.210	10.597	2
3	0.0717	0.115	0.216	0.352	7.815	9.348	11.345	12.838	3
4	0.207	0.297	0.484	0.711	9.488	11.143	13.277	14.860	4
5	0.412	0.554	0.831	1.145	11.070	12.832	15.056	16.750	5
6	0.676	0.872	1.237	1.635	12.592	14.449	16.812	18.548	6
7	0.989	1.239	1.690	2.167	14.067	16.013	18.475	20.278	7
8	1.344	1.646	2.180	2.733	15.507	17.535	20.090	21.955	8
9	1.735	2.088	2.700	3.325	16.919	19.023	21.666	23.589	9
10	2.156	2.558	3.247	3.940	18.307	20.483	23.209	25.188	10
11	2.603	3.053	3.816	4.575	19.675	21.920	24.725	26.757	11
12	3.074	3.571	4.404	5.226	21.026	23.337	26.217	28.300	12
13	3.565	4.107	5.009	5.892	22.362	24.736	27.688	29.819	13
14	4.075	4.660	5.629	6.571	23.685	26.119	29.141	31.319	14
15	4.601	5.229	6.262	7.261	24.996	27.488	30.578	32.801	15
16	5.142	5.812	6.908	7.962	26.296	28.845	32.000	34.267	16
17	5.697	6.408	7.564	8.672	27.587	30.191	33.409	35.718	17
18	6.265	7.015	8.231	9.390	28.869	31.526	34.805	37.156	18
19	6.844	7.633	8.907	10.117	30.144	32.852	36.191	38.582	19
20	7.434	8.260	9.591	10.851	31.410	34.170	37.566	39.997	20
21	8.034	8.897	10.283	11.591	32.671	35.479	38.932	41.401	21
22	8.643	9.542	10.982	12.338	33.924	36.781	40.289	42.796	22
23	9.260	10.196	11.689	13.091	35.172	38.076	41.638	44.181	23
24	9.886	10.856	12.401	13.484	36.415	39.364	42.980	45.558	24
25	10.520	11.524	13.120	14.611	37.652	40.646	44.314	46.928	25
26	11.160	12.198	13.844	15.379	38.885	41.923	45.642	48.290	26
27	11.808	12.879	14.573	16.151	40.113	43.194	46.963	49.645	27
28	12.461	13.565	15.308	16.928	41.337	44.461	48.278	50.993	28
29	13.121	14.256	16.047	17.708	42.557	45.772	49.588	52.336	29
30	13.787	14.953	16.791	18.493	43.773	46.979	50.892	53.672	30

Source: This table is based on Table 8 of *Biometrika Tables for Statisticians*, Vol. 1, by permission of Biometrika trustees.

APPENDIX B

Partial Answers to Selected Problems[1]

CHAPTER 1

Set 1.2a

4. (c) 19 minutes
5. (a) Jim's alternatives: Throw curve or fast ball.
   Joe's alternatives: Prepare for curve or fast ball.
   (b) Joe wants to increase his batting average.
   Jim wants to reduce Joe's batting average.

CHAPTER 2

Set 2.1a

1. (a) $-x_1 + x_2 \geq 1$
   (c) $x_2 - x_1 \leq 0$
   (e) $.5x_1 - .5x_2 \leq 0$
3. Unused $M1 = 10$ tons/day
   Unused material of $M2 = 1$ ton/day

Set 2.2a

1. (a and e) See Figure B.1.
2. (a and d) See Figure B.2.

---

[1]Solved problems in this appendix are designated by * in the text.

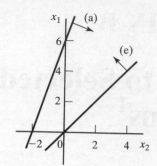

FIGURE B.1

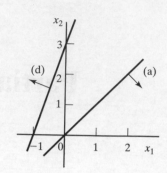

FIGURE B.2

5. Let

x_1 = Number of units of A

x_2 = Number of units of B

Maximize $z = 20x_1 + 50x_2$ subject to M

$$-.2x_1 + .8x_2 \le 0, 2x_1 + 4x_2 \le 240$$

$$x_1 \le 100, x_1, x_2 \ge 0$$

Optimum: $(x_1, x_2) = (100, 25)$, $z = \$6250$

7. Let

x_1 = Dollars invested in A

x_2 = Dollars invested in B

Maximize $z = .05x_1 + .08x_2$ subject to

$$.75x_1 - .25x_2 \ge 0, .5x_1 - .5x_2 \ge 0,$$

$$x_1 - .5x_2 \ge 0, x_1 + x_2 \le 5000, x_1, x_2 \ge 0$$

Optimum: $(x_1, x_2) = (2500, 2500)$, $z = \$325$

14. Let

x_1 = Tons of $C1$ per hour

x_2 = Tons of $C2$ per hour

Maximize $z = 12000x_1 + 9000x_2$ subject to

$$-200x_1 + 100x_2 \le 0, 2.1x_1 + .9x_2 \le 20, x_1, x_2 \ge 0$$

Optimum: $(x_1, x_2) = (5.13, 10.26)$, $z = 153,846$ lb

(a) Optimum ratio $C1:C2 = .5$.

(b) Optimum ratio is the same, but steam generation will increase by 7692 lb/hr.

18. Let

x_1 = Number of HiFi1 units

x_2 = Number of HiFi2 units

Minimize $z = 1267.2 - (15x_1 + 15x_2)$ subject to

$$6x_1 + 4x_2 \le 432, 5x_1 + 5x_2 \le 412.8$$

$$4x_1 + 6x_2 \le 422.4, x_1, x_2 \ge 0$$

Optimum: $(x_1, x_2) = (50.88, 31, 68)$, $z = 28.8$ idle min.

Set 2.2b

1. (a) See Figure B.3.

5. Let

x_1 = Thousand bbl/day from Iran

x_2 = Thousand bbl/day from Dubai

Minimize $z = x_1 + x_2$ subject to

$$-.6x_1 + .4x_2 \le 0, .2x_1 + .1x_2 \ge 14$$

$$.25x_1 + .6x_2 \ge 30, .1x_1 + .15x_2 \ge 10$$

$$.15x_1 + .1x_2 \ge 8, x_1, x_2 \ge 0$$

Optimum: $x_1 = 55, x_2 = 30, z = 85$

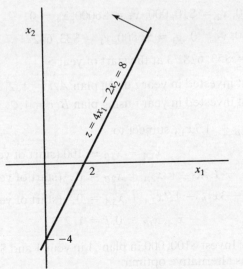

FIGURE B.3

7. Let

$$x_1 = \text{Ratio of scrap A alloy}$$

$$x_2 = \text{Ratio of scrap B alloy}$$

Minimize $z = 100x_1 + 80x_2$ subject to

$$.03 \le .06x_1 + .03x_2 \le .06, .03 \le .03x_1 + .06x_2 \le .05$$

$$.03 \le .04x_1 + .03x_2 \le .07, x_1 + x_2 = 1, x_1, x_2 \ge 0$$

Optimum: $x_1 = .33, x_2 = .67, z = \$86,667$

Set 2.4a

2. Let

$$x_i = \text{Dollars invested in project } i, i = 1, 2, 3, 4$$

$$y_j = \text{Dollars invested in bank in year } j, j = 1, 2, 3, 4$$

Maximize $z = y_5$ subject to

$$x_1 + x_2 + x_4 + y_1 \le 10,000$$

$$.5x_1 + .6x_2 - x_3 + .4x_4 + 1.065y_1 - y_2 = 0$$

$$.3x_1 + .2x_2 + .8x_3 + .6x_4 + 1.065y_2 - y_3 = 0$$

$$1.8x_1 + 1.5x_2 + 1.9x_3 + 1.8x_4 + 1.065y_3 - y_4 = 0$$

$$1.2x_1 + 1.3x_2 + .8x_3 + .95x_4 + 1.065y_4 - y_5 = 0$$

$$x_1, x_2, x_3, x_4, y_1, y_2, y_3, y_4, y_5 \ge 0$$

Optimum solution:

$$x_1 = 0, x_2 = \$10,000, x_3 = \$6000, x_4 = 0$$

$$y_1 = 0, y_2 = 0, y_3 = \$6800, y_4 = \$33,642$$

$$z = \$53,628.73 \text{ at the start of year 5}$$

5. Let $x_{iA} = $ amount invested in year i using plan $A, i = 1, 2, 3$
   $x_{iB} = $ amount invested in year i using plan $B, i = 1, 2, 3$

Maximize $z = 3x_{2B} + 1.7x_{3A}$ subject to

$$x_{1A} + x_{1B} \le 100 \text{ (start of year 1)}$$

$$- 1.7x_{1A} + x_{2A} + x_{2B} = 0 \quad \text{(start of year 2)}$$

$$- 3x_{1B} - 1.7x_{2A} + x_{3A} = 0 \quad \text{(start of year 3)}$$

$$x_{iA}, x_{iB} \ge 0, i = 1, 2, 3$$

Optimum solution: Invest $\$100,000$ in plan A in year 1 and $\$170,000$ in plan B in year 2. Problem has alternative optima.

Set 2.4b

3. Let x_j = number of units of product j, $j = 1, 2, 3$

Maximize $z = 30x_1 + 20x_2 + 50x_3$ subject to

$$2x_1 + 3x_2 + 5x_3 \leq 4000$$
$$4x_1 + 2x_2 + 7x_3 \leq 6000$$
$$x_1 + .5x_2 + .33x_3 \leq 1500$$
$$2x_1 - 3x_2 = 0$$
$$5x_2 - 2x_3 = 0$$
$$x_1 \geq 200, x_2 \geq 200, x_3 \geq 150$$
$$x_1, x_2, x_3 \geq 0$$

Optimum solution: $x_1 = 324.32$, $x_2 = 216.22$, $x_3 = 540.54$, $z = \$41,081.08$

7. Let x_{ij} = Quantity produced by operation i in month j, $i = 1, 2, j = 1, 2, 3$

I_{ij} = *Entering* inventory of operation i in month j, $i = 1, 2, j = 1, 2, 3$

Minimize $z = \sum_{j=1}^{3} (c_{1j}x_{1j} + c_{2j}x_{2j} + .2I_{1j} + .4I_{2j})$ subject to

$$.6x_{11} \leq 800, .6x_{12} \leq 700, .6x_{13} \leq 550$$
$$.8x_{21} \leq 1000, .8x_{22} \leq 850, .8x_{23} \leq 700$$
$$x_{1j} + I_{1, j-1} = x_{2j} + I_{1j}, x_{2j} + I_{2, j-1} = d_j + I_{2j}, j = 1, 2, 3$$
$$I_{1,0} = I_{2,0} = 0, \text{ all variables} \geq 0$$
$$d_j = 500, 450, 600 \text{ for } j = 1, 2, 3$$
$$c_{1j} = 10, 12, 11 \text{ for } j = 1, 2, 3$$
$$c_{2j} = 15, 18, 16 \text{ for } j = 1, 2, 3$$

Optimum: $x_{11} = 1333.33$ units, $x_{13} = 216.67$, $x_{21} = 1250$ units, $x_{23} = 300$ units, $z = \$39,720$.

Set 2.4c

1. Let $x_i(y_i)$ = Number of 8-hr (12-hr) buses starting in period i

Minimize $z = 2\sum_{i=1}^{6} x_i + 3.5 \sum_{i=1}^{6} y_i$ subject to

$$x_1 + x_6 + y_1 + y_5 + y_6 \geq 4, x_1 + x_2 + y_1 + y_2 + y_6 \geq 8,$$
$$x_2 + x_3 + y_1 + y_2 + y_3 \geq 10, x_3 + x_4 + y_2 + y_3 + y_4 \geq 7,$$
$$x_4 + x_5 + y_3 + y_4 + y_5 \geq 12, x_5 + x_6 + y_4 + y_5 + y_6 \geq 4$$

All variables are nonnegative

Solution: $x_1 = 4$, $x_2 = 4$, $x_4 = 2$, $x_5 = 4$, $y_3 = 6$, all others $= 0$.
$z = 49$. Total number of buses $= 20$. For the case of 8-hr shift,
number of buses $= 26$ and comparable $z = 2 \times 26 = 52$. Thus,
(8-hr + 12-hr) shift is better.

5. Let $x_i = $ *Number* of students starting in period i ($i = 1$ for 8:01 A.M., $i = 9$ for 4:01 P.M.)

Minimize $z = x_1 + x_2 + x_3 + x_4 + x_6 + x_7 + x_8 + x_9$ subject to

$$x_1 \geq 2, x_1 + x_2 \geq 2, x_1 + x_2 + x_3 \geq 3,$$
$$x_2 + x_3 + x_4 \geq 4, x_3 + x_4 \geq 4, x_4 + x_6 \geq 3,$$
$$x_6 + x_7 \geq 3, x_6 + x_7 + x_8 \geq 3, x_7 + x_8 + x_9 \geq 3$$
$$x_5 = 0, \text{ all other variables are nonnegative}$$

Solution: $x_1 = x_3 = 2, x_6 = x_7 = x_9 = 1$, total hired $= 8$. Problem has alternative optima.

Set 2.4d

3. Let

$x_{ij} = $ Portion of project i completed in year j

Maximize $z = .05(4x_{11} + 3x_{12} + 2x_{13}) + .07(3x_{22} + 2x_{23} + x_{24})$
$$+ .15(4x_{31} + 3x_{32} + 2x_{33} + x_{34}) + .02(2x_{43} + x_{44})$$

subject, to

$$x_{11} + x_{12} + x_{13} = 1, x_{43} + x_{44} + x_{25} = 1$$
$$.25 \leq x_{22} + x_{23} + x_{24} \leq 1$$
$$.25 \leq x_{31} + x_{32} + x_{33} + x_{34} + x_{35} \leq 1$$
$$5x_{11} + 15x_{31} \leq 3, 5x_{12} + 8x_{22} + 15x_{32} \leq 6$$
$$5x_{13} + 8x_{23} + 15x_{33} + 1.2x_{43} \leq 7$$
$$8x_{24} + 15x_{34} + 1.2x_{44} \leq 7, 8x_{25} + 15x_{35} \leq 7$$
$$\text{all } x_{ij} \geq 0$$

Optimum: $x_{11} = .6, x_{12} = .4, x_{24} = .255, x_{25} = .025, x_{32} = .267,$
$$x_{33} = .387, x_{34} = .346, x_{43} = 1, z = \$523,750$$

Set 2.4e

2. Let $x_s = $ lb of screws/package, $x_b = $ lb of bolts/package, $x_n = $ lb of nuts/package, $x_w = $ *lb* of washers/package

Minimize $z = 1.1x_s + 1.5x_b + \left(\frac{70}{80}\right)x_n + \left(\frac{20}{30}\right)x_w$ subject to

$$y = x_s + x_b + x_n + x_w$$
$$y \geq 1, x_s \geq .1y, x_b \geq .25y, x_n \leq .15y, x_w \leq .1y$$
$$\left(\tfrac{1}{10}\right)x_b \leq x_n, \left(\tfrac{1}{50}\right)x_b \leq x_w$$

All variables are nonnegative

Solution: $z = \$1.12$, $y = 1$, $x_s = .5$, $x_b = .25$, $x_n = .15$, $x_w = .1$

5. Let x_A = bbl of crude A/day, x_B = bbl of crude B/day, x_r = bbl of regular/day x_p = bbl of premium/day, x_j = bbl of jet fuel/day

Maximize $z = 50(x_r - s_r^+) + 70(x_p - s_p^+) + 120(x_j - s_j^+)$

$$- (10s_r^- + 15s_p^- + 20s_j^- + 2s_r^+ + 3s_p^+ + 4s_j^+)$$

$$- (30x_A + 40x_B) \text{ subject to}$$

$x_A \le 2500$, $x_B \le 3000$, $x_r = .2x_A + .25x_B$, $x_p = .1x_A + .3x_B$, $x_j = .25x_A + .1x_B$

$x_r + s_r^- - s_r^+ = 500$, $x_p + s_p^- - s_p^+ = 700$, $x_j + s_j^- - s_j^+ = 400$, All variables ≥ 0

Solution: $z = \$21,852.94$, $x_A = 1176.47$ bbl/day, $x_B = 1058.82$, $x_r = 500$ bbl/day

$x_p = 435.29$ bbl/day, $x_j = 400$ bbl/day, $s_p^- = 264.71$

Set 2.4f

5.

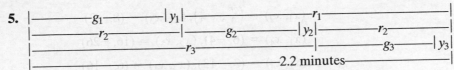

Let g_i, y_i, and r_i be the durations of green, yellow, and red lights for cars exiting highway i. All time units are in seconds. No cars move on yellow.

maximize $z = 3(500/3600)g_1 + 4(600/3600)g_2 + 5(400/3600)g_3$ subject to

$(500/3600)g_1 + (600/3600)g_2 + (400/3600)g_3 \le (510/3600)(2.2 \times 60 - 3 \times 10)$

$g_1 + g_2 + g_3 + 3 \times 10 \le 2.2 \times 60$, $g_1 \ge 25$, $g_2 \ge 25$, $g_3 \ge 25$

Solution: $g_1 = 22$ sec, $g_2 = 45.1$ sec, $g_3 = 34.9$ sec. Booth income = $\$80.33$/hr

CHAPTER 3

Set 3.1a

1. 4 tons/day and 0 ton/day for raw materials $M1$ and $M2$, respectively.

4. Let x_{ij} = units of product i produced on machine j.

Maximize $z = 10(x_{11} + x_{12}) + 15(x_{21} + x_{22})$ subject to

$$x_{11} + x_{21} - x_{12} - x_{22} + s_1 = 5$$

$$-x_{11} - x_{21} + x_{12} + x_{22} + s_2 = 5$$

$$x_{11} + x_{21} + s_3 = 200$$

$$x_{12} + x_{22} + s_4 = 250$$

$$s_i, x_{ij} \ge 0, \text{ for all } i \text{ and } j$$

Set 3.1b

3. Let $x_j = $ units of product $j, j = 1, 2, 3$.

Maximize $z = 2x_1 + 5x_2 + 3x_3 - 15x_4^+ - 10x_5^+$

subject to

$$2x_1 + x_2 + 2x_3 + x_4^- - x_4^+ = 80$$

$$x_1 + x_2 + 2x_3 + x_5^- - x_5^+ = 65$$

$$x_1, x_2, x_3, x_4^-, x_4^+, x_5^-, x_5^+ \geq 0$$

Optimum solution: $x_2 = 65$ units, $x_4^- = 15$ units, all others $= 0, z = \$325$.

Set 3.2a

1. (c) $x_1 = \frac{6}{7}, x_2 = \frac{12}{7}, z = \frac{48}{7}$.

(e) Corner points $(x_1 = 0, x_2 = 3)$ and $(x_1 = 6, x_2 = 0)$ are infeasible.

3. Infeasible basic solutions are as follows:

$$(x_1, x_2) = \left(\frac{26}{3}, -\frac{4}{3}\right), (x_1, x_3) = (8, -2)$$

$$(x_1, x_4) = (6, -4), (x_2, x_3) = (16, -26)$$

$$(x_2, x_4) = (3, -13), (x_3, x_4) = (6, -16)$$

Set 3.3a

3. (a) (A, B) and (H, I) can represent successive simplex iterations because associated corner points are adjacent. The remaining pairs are not adjacent corner points.

(b) (i) Yes. (ii) No, path returns to a previous corner point, A. (iii) No, C and I are not adjacent.

5. (a) x_3 enters at value $1, z = 3$ at corner point D.

Set 3.3b

3.

New basic variable	x_1	x_2	x_3	x_4
Value	3	2	0	16
Leaving variable	x_7	x_7	x_8	x_4

6. (b) $x_2, x_5,$ and x_6 can increase value of z. If x_2 enters, x_8 leaves and $\Delta z = 5 \times 4 = 20$. If x_5 enters, x_1 leaves and $\Delta z = 0$ because x_5 equals 0 in the new solution. If x_6 enters, no variable leaves because all the constraint coefficients of x_6 are less than or equal to zero. $\Delta z = \infty$ because x_6 can be increased to infinity without causing infeasibility.

9. Second-best value of $z = 20$ occurs when s_2 is made basic.

Set 3.4a

3. (a) Minimize $z = (8M - 4)x_1 + (6M - 1)x_2 - Ms_2 - Ms_3 = 10M$

(b) Minimize $z = (3M - 4)x_1 + (M - 1)x_2 = 3M$

6. The starting tableau is

Basic	x_1	x_2	x_3	x_4	Solution
z	-1	-12	0	0	-8
x_3	1	1	1	0	4
x_4	1	4	0	1	8

Set 3.4b

1. Always minimize the sum of artificial variables because the sum represents the amount of infeasibility in the problem.

7. Any nonbasic variable having nonzero objective coefficients at end of Phase I cannot become positive in Phase II because it will mean that the optimal objective value in Phase I will be positive, that is, infeasible Phase I solution.

Set 3.5a

1. (a) $A \rightarrow B \rightarrow C \rightarrow D$.

(b) 1 at A, 1 at B, $C_2^4 = 6$ at C, and 1 at D.

Set 3.5b

1. Alternative basic optima: $\left(0, 0, \frac{10}{3}\right), (0, 5, 0), \left(1, 4, \frac{1}{3}\right)$. Nonbasic alternative optima:

$$\left(\alpha_3, 5\alpha_2 + 4\alpha_3, \frac{10}{3}\alpha_1 + \frac{1}{3}\alpha_3\right), \alpha_1 + \alpha_2 + \alpha_3 = 1, 0 \le \alpha_i \le 1, i = 1, 2, 3.$$

Set 3.5c

2. (a) Solution space is unbounded in the direction of x_3.

(b) Objective value is unbounded because each unit increase in x_3 increases z by 1.

Set 3.5d

1. The most that can be produced is 550 units.

Set 3.6a

2. Let

$x_1 = $ Number of Type 1 hats per day,

$x_2 = $ Number of Type 2 hats per day

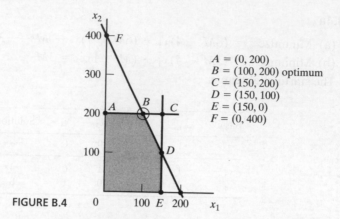

FIGURE B.4

Maximize $z = 8x_1 + 5x_2$ subject to

$$2x_1 + x_2 \leq 400$$

$$x_1 \leq 150, x_2 \leq 200$$

$$x_1, x_2 \geq 0$$

(a) See Figure B.4: $x_1 = 100$, $x_2 = 200$, $z = \$1800$ at point B.

(b) $4 per Type 2 hat in the range $(200, 500)$.

(c) No change because the dual price is $0 per unit in the range $(100, \infty)$.

(d) $1 worth per unit in the range $(100, 400)$. Maximum increase $= 200$ Type 2.

Set 3.6b

3. (a) $0 \leq \frac{c_1}{c_2} \leq 2$.

(b) New $\frac{c_1}{c_2} = 1$. Solution remains unchanged.

Set 3.6c

2. (a) Yes, because additional revenue per min $= \$1$ (for up to 10 min of overtime) exceeds additional cost of \$.83/min.

(b) Additional revenue is \$2/min (for up to 400 min of overtime) $= \$240$ for 2 hr. Additional cost for 2 hr $= \$110$. Net revenue $= \$130$.

(c) No, its dual price is zero because the resource is already abundant.

(d) $D_1 = 10$ min. Dual price $= \$1$/min for $D_1 \leq 10$. $x_1 = 0$, $x_2 = 105$, $x_3 = 230$, net revenue $= (\$1350 + \$1 \times 10 \text{ min}) - \left(\frac{\$40}{60} \times 10 \text{ min}\right) = \$1353.33$.

(e) $D_2 = -15$. Dual price $= \$2$/min for $D_2 \geq -20$. Decrease in revenue $= \$30$. Decrease in cost $= \$7.50$. Not recommended.

6. Let

$$x_1 = \text{radio minutes}, x_2 = \text{TV minutes}, x_3 = \text{newspaper ads}$$

Maximize $z = x_1 + 50x_2 + 10x_3$ subject to

$$15x_1 + 300x_2 + 50x_3 + s_1 = 10,000, \quad x_3 - S_2 = 5,$$

$$x_1 + s_3 = 400, \quad -x_1 + 2x_2 + s_4 = 0, \quad x_1, x_2, x_3 \geq 0,$$

$$s_1, S_2, s_3, s_4 \geq 0$$

(a) $x_1 = 59.09$ min, $x_2 = 29.55$ min, $x_3 = 5$ ads, $z = 1561.36$

(b) From TORA, $z + .158s_1 + 2.879S_2 + 0s_3 + 1.364s_4 = 156.364$. Dual prices for the respective constraints are $.158, -2.879, 0$, and 1.36. Lower limit set on newspaper ads can be decreased because its dual price is negative ($= -2.879$). There is no advantage in increasing the upper limit on radio minutes because its dual price is zero (the present limit is already abundant).

(c) From TORA, $x_1 = 59.9091 + .00606D_1 \geq 0$, $x_3 = 5$, $s_3 = 340.90909 + .00606D_1 \geq 0$, $x_2 = 29.54545 + .00303D_1 \geq 0$. Thus, dual price $= .158$ for the range $-9750 \leq D_1 \leq 56,250$. A 50% increase in budget ($D_1 = \$5000$) is recommended because the dual price is positive.

11. (a) Scarce: resistor and capacitor resource; abundant: chip resource.

(b) Worths per unit of resistor, capacitor, and chips are $\$1.25, \$.25$, and $\$0$.

(e) Change $D_3 = 350 - 800 = -450$ falls outside the feasibility range $D_3 \geq -400$. Hence the problem must be solved anew.

13. (b) Solution $x_1 = x_2 = 2 + \frac{\Delta}{3}$ is feasible for all $\Delta > 0$. For $0 < \Delta \leq 3, r_1 + r_2 = \frac{\Delta}{3} \leq 1 \Rightarrow$ feasibility confirmed. For $3 \leq \Delta < 6, r_1 + r_2 = \frac{\Delta}{3} > 1 \Rightarrow$ feasibility not confirmed. For $\Delta > 6$, the change falls outside the ranges for D_1 and D_2.

Set 3.6d

2. (a) $x_1 = $ Cans of A1, $x_2 = $ Cans of A_2, $x_3 = $ Cans of BK.

Maximize $z = 80x_1 + 70x_2 + 60x_3$ subject to

$$x_1 + x_2 + x_3 \leq 500, x_1 \geq 100, 4x_1 - 2x_2 - 2x_3 \leq 0$$

Optimum: $x_1 = 166.67, x_2 = 333.33, x_3 = 0, z = 36666.67$.

(b) From TORA, reduced cost per can of BK $= 10$. Price should be increased by more than 10 cents.

(c) $d_1 = d_2 = d_3 = -5$ cents. From TORA, the reduced costs for the nonbasic variables are

$$x_3: 10 + d_2 - d_3 \geq 0, \text{satisfied}$$

$$s_1: 73.33 + .67d_2 + .33d_1 \geq 0, \text{satisfied}$$

$$s_3: 1.67 - .17d_2 + .17d_1 \geq 0, \text{satisfied}$$

Solution remains the same.

5. (a) $x_i = $ Number of units of motor $i, i = 1, 2, 3, 4$.

Maximize $z = 60x_1 + 40x_2 + 25x_3 + 30x_4$ subject to

$$8x_1 + 5x_2 + 4x_3 + 6x_4 \leq 8000, x_1 \leq 500, x_2 \leq 500,$$

$$x_3 \leq 800, x_4 \leq 750, x_1, x_2, x_3, x_4 \geq 0$$

Optimum: $x_1 = 500, x_2 = 500, x_3 = 375, x_4 = 0, z = \$59,375$

(b) From TORA, $8.75 + d_2 \geq 0$. Type 2 motor price can be reduced by up to $8.75.

(c) $d_1 = -\$15, d_2 = -\$10, d_3 = -\$6.25, d_4 = -\$7.50$. From TORA,

$$x_4: 7.5 + 1.5d_3 - d_4 \geq 0, \text{ satisfied}$$

$$s_1: 6.25 + .25d_3 \geq 0, \text{ satisfied}$$

$$s_2: 10 - 2d_3 + d_1 \geq 0, \text{ satisfied}$$

$$s_3: 8.75 - 1.25d_3 + d_2 \geq 0, \text{ satisfied}$$

Solution remains the same, but z will be reduced by 25%.

(d) Reduced cost of $x_4 = 7.5$. Increase price by more than $7.50.

Set 3.6e

5. The dual price for the investment constraint $x_{1A} + x_{1B} \leq 100$ is $5.10 per dollar invested for *any* amount of investment.

9. (a) Dual price for raw material A is $10.27. The cost of $12.00 per lb exceeds the expected revenue. Hence, purchase of additional raw material A is not recommended.

(b) Dual price for raw material B is $0. Resource is already abundant, and no additional purchase is warranted.

CHAPTER 4

Set 4.1a

2. Let y_1, y_2, and y_3 be the dual variables.

Maximize $w = 3y_1 + 5y_2 + 4y_3$ subject to

$$y_1 + 2y_2 + 3y_3 \leq 15, 2y_1 - 4y_2 + y_3 \leq 12$$

$$y_1 \geq 0, y_2 \leq 0, y_3 \text{ unrestricted}$$

4. (c) Let y_1 and y_2 be the dual variables.

Minimize $z = 5y_1 + 6y_2$ subject to

$$2y_1 + 3y_2 = 1, y_1 - y_2 = 1$$

$$y_1, y_2 \text{ unrestricted}$$

5. Dual constraint associated with the artificial variables is $y_2 \geq -M$. Mathematically, $M \to \infty \Rightarrow y \geq -\infty$, which is the same as y_2 being unrestricted.

Set 4.2a

1. (a) $\mathbf{AV}_1$ is undefined.

(e) $\mathbf{V}_2\mathbf{A} = (-28 \; -64)$

Set 4.2b

1. (a) Inverse $= \begin{pmatrix} \frac{1}{4} & -\frac{1}{2} & 0 & 0 \\ -\frac{1}{8} & \frac{3}{4} & 0 & 0 \\ \frac{3}{8} & -\frac{5}{4} & 1 & 0 \\ \frac{1}{8} & -\frac{3}{4} & 0 & 1 \end{pmatrix}$

Set 4.2c

3. Let y_1 and y_2 be the dual variables.
    Minimize $w = 30y_1 + 40y_2$ subject to

    $$y_1 + y_2 \geq 5, 5y_1 - 5y_2 \geq 2, 2y_1 - 6y_2 \geq 3$$

    $$y_1 \geq -M(\Rightarrow y_1 \text{ unrestricted}), y_2 \geq 0$$

    Solution: $y_1 = 5$, $y_2 = 0$, $w = 150$.

6. Let y_1 and y_2 be the dual variables.
    Minimize $w = 3y_1 + 4y_2$ subject to

    $$y_1 + 2y_2 \geq 1, 2y_1 - y_2 \geq 5, y_1 \geq 3$$

    $$y_2 \text{ unrestricted}$$

    Solution: $y_1 = 3$, $y_2 = -1$, $w = 5$

8. (a) $(x_1, x_2) = (3, 0)$, $z = 15$, $(y_1, y_2) = (3, 1)$, $w = 14$. Range $= (14, 15)$

9. (a) Dual solution is infeasible; hence, it cannot be optimal even though $z = w = 17$.

Set 4.2d

2. (a) Feasibility: $(x_2, x_4) = (3, 15) \Rightarrow$ feasible.
    Optimality: Reduced costs of $(x_1, x_3) = (0, 2) \Rightarrow$ optimal.

4.

Basic	x_1	x_2	x_3	x_4	x_5	Solution
z	0	0	$-\frac{2}{5}$	$-\frac{1}{5}$	0	$\frac{12}{5}$
x_1	1	0	$-\frac{3}{5}$	$\frac{1}{5}$	0	$\frac{3}{5}$
x_2	0	1	$\frac{4}{5}$	$-\frac{3}{5}$	0	$\frac{6}{5}$
x_5	0	0	-1	1	1	0

Solution is optimal and feasible.

7. Objective value: From primal, $z = c_1x_1 + c_2x_2$, and from the dual, $w = b_1y_1 + b_2y_2 + b_3y_3$. $b_1 = 4, b_2 = 8, c_1 = 2, c_2 = 5 \Rightarrow z = w = 34$.

Set 4.3a

2. (a) Let (x_1, x_2, x_3, x_4) = daily units of SC320, SC325, SC340, and SC370

Maximize $z = 9.4x_1 + 10.8x_2 + 8.75x_3 + 7.8x_4$ subject to

$$10.5x_1 + 9.3x_2 + 11.6x_3 + 8.2x_4 \le 4800$$
$$20.4x_1 + 24.6x_2 + 17.7x_3 + 26.5x_4 \le 9600$$
$$3.2x_1 + 2.5x_2 + 3.6x_3 + 5.5x_4 \le 4700$$
$$5x_1 + 5x_2 + 5x_3 + 5x_4 \le 4500$$
$$x_1 \ge 100, x_2 \ge 100, x_3 \ge 100, x_4 \ge 100$$

(b) Only soldering capacity can be increased because it has a positive dual price $(=.4944)$.

(c) Dual prices for lower bounds are ≤ 0 $(-.6847, -1.361, 0,$ and $-5.3003)$, which means that the bounds have an adverse effect on profitability.

(d) Dual price for soldering is $.4944/min valid in the range $(8920, 10201.72)$, which corresponds to a maximum capacity increase of 6.26% only.

Set 4.3b

2. New fire truck toy is profitable because its reduced cost $= -2$.

3. Parts PP3 and PP4 are not part of the optimum solution. Current reduced costs are .1429 and 1.1429. Thus, rate of deterioration in revenue per unit is $.1429 for PP3 and $1.1429 for PP4.

Set 4.4a

1. (b) No, because point E is feasible, and the dual simplex must stay infeasible until optimum is reached.

4. (c) Add the artificial constraint $x_1 \le M$. Problem has no feasible solution.

Set 4.5a

4. Let Q be the weekly feed in lb $(=5200, 9600, 15000, 20000, 26000, 32000, 38000, 42000,$ for weeks $1, 2, \ldots,$ and 8). Optimum solution: Limestone $=.028Q$, corn $=.649Q$, and soybean meal $=.323Q$. Cost $=.81221Q$.

Set 4.5b

1. (a) Additional constraint is redundant.

Set 4.5c

2. (a) New dual values $= (\frac{1}{2}, 0, 0, 0)$. Current solution remains optimal.

(c) New dual values $= (-\frac{1}{8}, \frac{11}{4}, 0, 0)$. $z - .125s_1 + 2.75s_2 = 13.5$. New solution: $x_1 = 2, x_2 = 2, x_3 = 4, z = 14$.

Set 4.5d

1. $\frac{p}{100}(y_1 + 3y_2 + y_3) - 3 \geq 0$. For $y_1 = 1$, $y_2 = 2$, and $y_3 = 0$, $p \geq 42.86\%$.
3. (a) Reduced cost for fire engines $= 3y_1 + 2y_2 + 4y_3 - 5 = 2 > 0$. Fire engines are not profitable.

CHAPTER 5

Set 5.1a

4. Assign a very high cost, M, to the route from Detroit to dummy destination.
6. (a and b) Use $M = 10,000$. Solution is shown in bold. Total cost $= \$49,710$.

	1	2	3	Supply
Plant 1	600	700	400	
			25	25
Plant 2	320	300	350	
	23	**17**		40
Plant 3	500	480	450	
		25	**5**	30
Excess Plant 4	1000	1000	M	
	13			13
Demand	36	42	30	

(c) City 1 excess cost $= \$13,000$.

9. Solution (in million gallons) is shown in bold. Area 2 will be 2 million gallons short. Total cost $= \$304,000$.

	A1	A2	A3	Supply
Refinery 1	12	18	M	
	4	**2**		6
Refinery 2	30	10	8	
		4	**1**	5
Refinery 3	20	25	12	
			6	6
Dummy	M	50	50	
		2		2
Demand	4	8	7	

Set 5.2a

2. Total cost = $804. Problem has alternative optima.

Day	New	Sharpening service Overnight	Sharpening service 2-day	Sharpening service 3-day	Disposal
Monday	24	0	6	18	0
Tuesday	12	12	0	0	0
Wednesday	2	14	0	0	0
Thursday	0	0	20	0	0
Friday	0	14	0	0	4
Saturday	0	2	0	0	12
Sunday	0	0	0	0	22

5. Total cost = $190, 040. Problem has alternative optima.

Period	Capacity	Produced amount	Delivery
1	500	500	400 for (period) 1 and 100 for 2
2	600	600	200 for 2, 220 for 3, and 180 for 4
3	200	200	200 for 3
4	300	200	200 for 4

Set 5.3a

1. (a) Northwest: cost = $42. Least-cost: cost = $37. Vogel: cost = $37.

Set 5.3b

5. (a) Cost = $1475. (b) $c_{12} \geq 3, c_{13} \geq 8, c_{23} \geq 13, c_{31} \geq 7$.

Set 5.4a

5. Use the code (city, date) to define the rows and columns of the assignment problem. Example: The assignment (D, 3)–(A, 7) means leaving Dallas on Jun 3 and returning from Atlanta June 7 at a cost of $400. Solution is shown in bold. Cost = $1180. Problem has alternative optima.

	(A, 7)	(A, 12)	(A, 21)	(A, 28)
(D, 3)	400	300	300	**280**
(D, 10)	**300**	400	300	300
(D, 17)	300	**300**	400	300
(D, 25)	300	300	**300**	400

6. Optimum assignment: I-*d*, II-*c*, III-*a*, IV-*b*.

CHAPTER 6

Set 6.1a

1. For network (i): (a) 1-3-4-2. (b) 1-5-4-3-1. (c and d) See Figure B.5.

5. Name squares sequentially as A, B, . . . , H starting from top left square on first row. Each square is a node with adjacent squares connected by arcs. Each of nodes D and E has the largest number of emanating arcs and hence must be replaced with the two numbers having the most nonadjacent numbers—namely, the numbers 1 and 8. This problem has more than one solution. See Figure B.6.

Set 6.2a

2. (a) 1-2, 2-5, 5-6, 6-4, 4-3. Total length = 14 miles.

5. High pressure: 1-2-3-7-4. Low pressure: 1-5-6 and 5-9-8. Total length = 49.

Set 6.3a

1. Buy new car in years 1 and 4. Total cost = $8900. See Figure B.7.

4. For arc $(i, v_i) - (i + 1, v_{i+1})$, define $p(q)$ = value(number of item i). Solution: Select one unit of each of items 1 and 2. Total value = $80. See Figure B.8.

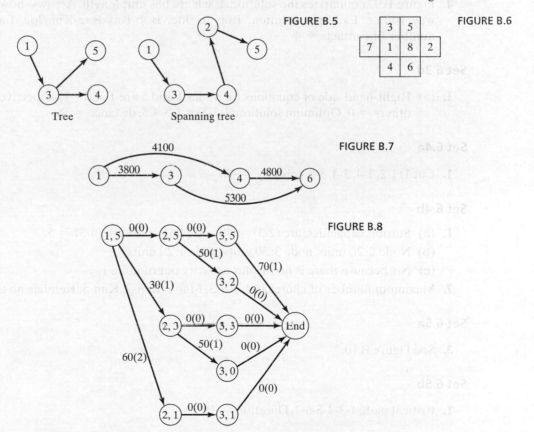

FIGURE B.5

Tree

Spanning tree

FIGURE B.6

3	5	
7	1	8	2
	4	6	

FIGURE B.7

FIGURE B.8

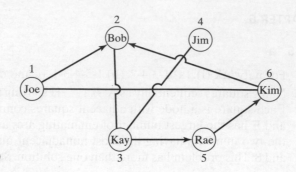

FIGURE B.9

Set 6.3b

1. (c) Delete all nodes but 4, 5, 6, 7, and 8. Shortest distance = 8 associated with routes 4-5-6-8 and 4-6-8.

Set 6.3c

1. (a) 5-4-2-1, distance = 12.
4. Figure B.9 summarizes the solution. Each arc has unit length. Arrows show one-way routes. Example solution: Bob to Joe: Bob-Kay-Rae-Kim-Joe. Largest number of contacts = 4.

Set 6.3d

1. (a) Right-hand side of equations for nodes 1 and 5 are 1 and −1, respectively, all others = 0. Optimum solution: 1-3-5 or 1-3-4-5, distance = 90.

Set 6.4a

1. Cut 1: 1-2, 1-4, 3-4, 3-5, capacity = 60.

Set 6.4b

1. (a) Surplus capacities: arc (2-3) = 40, arc (2-5) = 10, arc (4-3) = 5.
   (b) Node 2: 20 units, node 3: 30 units, node 4: 20 units.
   (c) No, because there is no surplus capacity out of node 1.
7. Maximum number of chores is 4. Rif-3, Mai-1, Ben-2, Kim-5. Ken has no chore.

Set 6.5a

3. See Figure B.10.

Set 6.5b

1. Critical path: 1-3-4-5-6-7. Duration = 19.

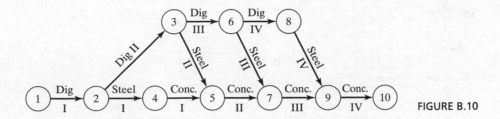

FIGURE B.10

Set 6.5c

3. (a) 20. (b) 3. (c) 0.

5. (a) Critical path: 1-3-6, duration = 45 days.

(b) A, D, and E.

(c) Each of C, D, and G will be delayed by 5 days. E will not be affected.

(d) Minimum equipment = 2 units.

CHAPTER 7

Set 7.1a

2. Points $(1, 0)$ and $(0, 2)$ are in Q, but $\lambda(1, 0) + (1 - \lambda)(0, 2) = (\lambda, 2 - 2\lambda)$ does not lie in Q for $0 < \lambda < 1$.

Set 7.1b

2. (b) Unique solution with $x_1 > 1$ and $0 < x_2 < 1$. See Figure B.11.

(d) An infinite number of solutions.

(f) No solution.

3. (a) Basis because det $\mathbf{B} = -4$.

(d) Not a basis because a basis must include exactly 3 independent vectors.

FIGURE B.11

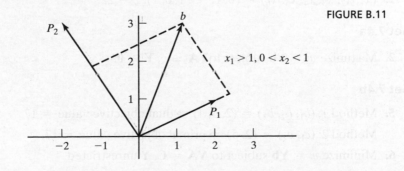

$x_1 > 1, 0 < x_2 < 1$

Set 7.1c

1.

$$\mathbf{B}^{-1} = \begin{pmatrix} .3 & -.2 \\ .1 & .1 \end{pmatrix}$$

Basic	x_1	x_2	x_3	x_4	Solution
z	1.5	−.5	0	0	21.5
x_3	0	.5	1	0	2
x_4	.5	0	0	1	1.5

Solution is feasible but nonoptimal.

4. Optimal $z = 34$.

Maximize $z = 2x_1 + 5x_2$ subject to $x_1 \le 4, x_2 \le 6, x_1 + x_2 \le 8, x_1, x_2 \ge 0$

Set 7.2a

1. (a) $\mathbf{P}_3$ must leave.

(b) $\mathbf{B} = (\mathbf{P}_2, \mathbf{P}_4)$ is a feasible basis.

2. For the basic vector $\mathbf{X}_B$, we have

$$\{z_j - c_j\} = \mathbf{c}_B \mathbf{B}^{-1} \mathbf{B} - \mathbf{c}_B = \mathbf{c}_B \mathbf{I} - \mathbf{c}_B = \mathbf{c}_B - \mathbf{c}_B = \mathbf{0}$$

8. Under nondegeneracy, the number of adjacent extreme points is $n - m$.

10. In case of degeneracy, number of extreme points is less than the number of basic solutions, else they are equal.

11. (a) new $x_j = \frac{1}{\alpha}$ old x_j.

(b) new $x_j = \frac{\beta}{\alpha}$ old x_j.

Set 7.2b

2. (b) $(x_1, x_2, x_3) = (1.5, 2, 0), z = 5$.

Set 7.3a

2. $(x_1, x_2, x_3, x_4, x_5, x_6) = (0, 1, .75, 1, 0, 1), z = 22$.

Set 7.4a

2. Maximize $w = \mathbf{Yb}$ subject to $\mathbf{YA} \le \mathbf{c}, \mathbf{Y} \ge \mathbf{0}$.

Set 7.4b

5. Method 1: $(b_1, b_2, b_3) = (2, 3, 4) \Rightarrow$ dual objective value $= 17$.

Method 2: $(c_1, c_2) = (2, 5) \Rightarrow$ primal objective value $= 17$.

6. Minimize $w = \mathbf{Yb}$ subject to $\mathbf{YA} = \mathbf{C}, \mathbf{Y}$ unrestricted.

Set 7.5a

1. $-\frac{2}{7} \le t \le 1$

2. (a)

Basic solution	Applicable range of t
$(x_2, x_3, x_6) = (5, 30, 10)$	$0 \le t \le \frac{1}{3}$
$(x_2, x_3, x_1) = (\frac{25}{4}, \frac{90}{4}, 5)$	$\frac{1}{3} \le t \le \frac{5}{2}$
$(x_2, x_4, x_1) = (\frac{5}{2}, 15, 20)$	$\frac{5}{2} \le t \le \infty$

5. $\{z_j - c_j\}_{j=1,4,5} = (4 - \frac{3t}{2} - \frac{3t^2}{2}, 1 - t^2, 2 - \frac{t}{2} + \frac{t^2}{2})$. Basis remains optimal for $0 \le t \le 1$.

Set 7.5b

1. (a) $t_1 = 10$, $\mathbf{B}_1 = (\mathbf{P}_2, \mathbf{P}_3, \mathbf{P}_4)$

2. At $t = 0$, $(x_1, x_2, x_4) = (.8, 3.6, 2)$. It remains basic for $0 \le t \le 1.5$. No feasible solution for $t > 1.5$.

CHAPTER 8

Set 8.1a

1. G_5: Minimize s_5^+, $55x_p + 3.5x_f + 5.5x_s - .0675x_g + s_5^- - s_5^+ = 0$.

3. Let x_1 = Number of in-state freshmen, x_2 = Number of out-of-state freshmen, x_3 = Number of international freshmen.

G_i: Minimize s_i^-, $i = 1, 2, \ldots, 5$, subject to $x_1 + x_2 + x_3 + s_1^- - s_1^+ = 1200$,

$$2x_1 + x_2 - 2x_3 + s_2^- - s_2^+ = 0, \quad -.1x_1 - .1x_2 + .9x_3 + s_3^- - s_3^+ = 0,$$

$$.125x_1 - .05x_2 - .556x_3 + s_4^- - s_4^+ = 0, \quad -.2x_1 + .8x_2 - .2x_3 + s_5^- - s_5^+ = 0$$

All variables are nonnegative

5. Let x_j = Number of production runs in shift j, $j = 1, 2, 3$.

Minimize $z = s_1^- + s_1^+$, subject to $-100x_1 + 40x_2 - 80x_3 + s_1^- - s_1^+ = 0$,

$$4 \le x_1 \le 5, 10 \le x_2 \le 20, 3 \le x_3 \le 20$$

Set 8.2a

1. Objective function: Minimize $z = s_1^- + s_2^- + s_3^- + s_4^+ + s_5^+$

Solution: $x_p = .0201$, $x_f = .0458$, $x_s = .0583$, $x_g = 2$ cents, $s_5^+ = 3.048$

Gasoline tax goal is not satisfied.

4. x_1 = lb of limestone/day, x_2 = lb of corn/day, x_3 = lb of soybean meal/day.

Objective function: Minimize $z = s_1^- + s_2^+ + s_3^- + s_4^- + s_5^+$

Solution: $x_1 = 166.08$ lb, $x_2 = 2778.56$ lb, $x_3 = 3055.36$ lb, $z = 0$. Problem has alternative optima. All goals are satisfied, but goals 3 and 4 are overachieved.

7. x_j = Number of units of product j, $j = 1, 2$.

Assign a relatively high weight to the quota constraints.

Objective function: Minimize $z = 100s_1^- + 100s_2^- + s_3^+ + s_4^+$

Solution: $x_1 = 80$, $x_2 = 60$, $s_3^+ = 100$ minutes, $s_4^+ = 120$ minutes.

Production quota can be met with 100 minutes of overtime for machine 1 and 120 minutes of overtime for machine 2.

Set 8.2b

2. G_1 solution: $x_p = .0201$, $x_f = .0458$, $x_s = .0583$, $x_g = 2$, $s_5^+ = 3.048$, all others = 0. Goals G_1, G_2, G_3, and G_4 are satisfied. G_5 is not, and should remain this way because $s_5^+ = 3.048$ was set at G_1.

G_4 problem: Same constraints as G_1 plus $s_1^- = 0$, $s_2^- = 0$, $s_3^- = 0$.

G_4 solution: $x_p = .0201$, $x_f = .0457$, $x_s = .0582$, $x_g = 2$, $s_5^+ = 1.45$. All other variables = 0. Goal G_5 is not satisfied.

G_5 problem: Same as G_4 plus $s_4^+ = 0$.

$G5$ solution: Same as G_4, which means that goal 5 cannot be satisfied ($s_5^+ = 1.45$).

CHAPTER 9

Set 9.1a

3. x_{ij} = Number of bottles of type i assigned to individual j, where $i = 1$ (full), 2 (half full), 3 (empty).

Constraints:

$$x_{11} + x_{12} + x_{13} = 7, x_{21} + x_{22} + x_{23} = 7, x_{31} + x_{32} + x_{33} = 7$$

$$x_{11} + .5x_{21} = 3.5, x_{12} + .5x_{22} = 3.5, x_{13} + .5x_{23} = 3.5$$

$$x_{11} + x_{21} + x_{31} = 7, x_{12} + x_{22} + x_{32} = 7, x_{13} + x_{23} + x_{33} = 7$$

All x_{ij} are nonnegative integers

Solution: Use a dummy objective function.

Status	Number of bottles assigned to individual		
	1	*2*	*3*
Full	1	3	3
Half full	5	1	1
Empty	1	3	3

6. y = Original sum of money. x_j = Amount taken on night j, $j = 1, 2, 3$.

x_4 = Amount given to each mariner by first officer.

Minimize $z = y$ subject to $3x_1 - y = 2, x_1 + 3x_2 - y = 2, x_1 + x_2 + 3x_3 - y = 2,$ $y - x_1 - x_2 - x_3 - 3x_4 = 1.$ All variables are nonnegative integers.

Solution: $y = 79 + 81n, n = 0, 1, 2, \ldots$ Minimum $y = 79$.

10. CD1: 1, 4, 7, and 8 (34 MB). CD2: 2, 3, 5, and 6 (33 MB). Problem has alternative optima.

12. $x_{ij} = 1$ if student i selects course j, and zero otherwise, c_{ij} = associated preference score, C_j = course j capacity. Maximize $z = \sum_{i=1}^{10}\sum_{j=1}^{6} c_{ij}x_{ij}$ subject to

$$\sum_{j=1}^{6} x_{ij} = 2, i = 1, 2, \ldots, 10, \sum_{i=1}^{10} x_{ij} \leq C_j, j = 1, 2, \ldots, 6$$

Solution: Course 1: students (2, 4, 9), 2: (2, 8), 3: (5, 6, 7, 9), 4: (4, 5, 7, 10), 5: (1, 3, 8, 10), 6: (1, 3). Total score = 1775.

Set 9.1b

1. Let $x_j = 1$ if route j is selected and 0 otherwise. Total distance of route (ABC, 3, 2, ABC) = $16 + 14 + 14 + 12 = 42$ miles.

Minimize $z = 42x_1 + 50x_2 + 66x_3 + 52x_4 + 60x_5 + 34x_6$ subject to

$$x_3 + x_5 + x_6 \geq 1, x_1 + x_3 + x_4 + x_5 \geq 1, x_1 + x_2 + x_3 + x_4 + x_6 \geq 1,$$

$$x_2 + x_5 \geq 1, x_2 + x_3 + x_4 \geq 1, x_j = (0, 1), \text{ for all } j.$$

Solution: Select routes (5, 3, 4) and (1, 4, 2), $z = 110$. Customer 4 should be skipped in one of the two routes.

2. Solution: 3-member committee is formed of individuals $a, d,$ and f. Problem has alternative optima.

7. $x_t = 1$ if transmitter t is selected, 0 otherwise. $x_c = 1$ if community c is covered, 0 otherwise. c_t = cost of transmitter t. S_c = set of transmitters covering community c. P_j = population of community j.

Maximize $z = \sum_{c=1}^{15} P_c x_c$ subject to

$$\sum_{t \in S_c} x_t \geq x_c, c = 1, 2, \ldots, 15, \sum_{t=1}^{7} c_t x_t \leq 15$$

Solution: Build transmitters 2, 4, 5, 6, and 7. All but community 1 are covered.

Set 9.1c

2. Let x_j = Number of widgets produced on machine $j, j = 1, 2, 3.$ $y_j = 1$ if machine j is used and 0 otherwise. Minimize $z = 2x_1 + 10x_2 + 5x_3 + 300y_1 + 100y_2 + 200y_3$ subject to $x_1 + x_2 + x_3 \geq 2000, x_1 - 650y_1 \leq 0, x_2 - 850y_2 \leq 0, x_3 - 1250y_3 \leq 0, x_1, x_2, x_3 \geq 600$ and integer, $y_1, y_2, y_3 = (0, 1).$
Solution: $x_1 = 650, x_2 = 600, x_3 = 700, z = \$11,650.$

3. Solution: Site 1 is assigned to targets 1 and 2, and site 2 is assigned to targets 3 and 4. $z = 18$.

10. x_e = Number of Eastern (one-way) tickets, x_u = Number of US Air tickets, x_c = Number of Continental tickets. e_1 and e_2 binary variables. u and c nonnegative integers. Maximize $z = 1000(1.5x_e + 1.8x_u + 2x_c + 5e_1 + 5e_2 + 12u + 7.5c)$ subject to $e_1 \leq x_e/3, e_2 \leq x_e/6, u \leq x_u/6$, and $c \leq x_c/5, x_e + x_u + x_c = 16$.

Solution: Buy 6 tickets on US Air and 10 tickets on Continental. Bonus= 57,800 miles.

Set 9.1d

1. Let x_{ij} = Integer amount assigned to square (i, j). Use a dummy objective function with all zero coefficients.

Constraints:

$$\sum_{j=1}^{3} x_{ij} = 15, i = 1, 2, 3, \sum_{i=1}^{3} x_{ij} = 15, j = 1, 2, 3,$$

$$x_{11} + x_{22} + x_{33} = 15, x_{31} + x_{22} + x_{13} = 15,$$

$$(x_{11} \geq x_{12} + 1 \text{ or } x_{11} \leq x_{12} - 1), (x_{11} \geq x_{13} + 1 \text{ or } x_{11} \leq x_{13} - 1),$$

$$(x_{12} \geq x_{13} + 1 \text{ or } x_{12} \leq x_{13} - 1), (x_{11} \geq x_{21} + 1 \text{ or } x_{11} \leq x_{21} - 1),$$

$$(x_{11} \geq x_{31} + 1 \text{ or } x_{11} \leq x_{31} - 1), (x_{21} \geq x_{31} + 1 \text{ or } x_{21} \leq x_{31} - 1),$$

$$x_{ij} = 1, 2, \ldots, 9, \text{ for all } i \text{ and } j$$

Solution:

2	9	4
7	5	3
6	1	8

Alternative solutions: Exchange rows 1 and 3 or columns 1 and 3.

3. x_j = Daily number of units of product j.

Maximize $z = 20x_1 + 25x_2 + 18x_3$ subject to

$$\begin{pmatrix} 3x_1 + 4x_2 + 5x_3 \leq 150 \\ 4x_1 + 3x_2 + 6x_3 \leq 150 \end{pmatrix} \text{ or } \begin{pmatrix} 3x_1 + 4x_2 + 5x_3 \leq 135 \\ 4x_1 + 3x_2 + 6x_3 \leq 180 \end{pmatrix}$$

$$x_1, x_2, x_3 \geq 0 \text{ and integer}$$

Solution: Produce 18 units of product 1, 24 of product 2, and none of product 3, and use location 1.

12. Define $v = zw, v \leq z, v \leq w, v \geq z + w - 1, 0 \leq v \leq 1, z$ and w binary.

Set 9.2a[2]

2. (a) $z = 14, x_1 = 4, x_2 = 1$.
   (b) $z = 12, x_1 = 0, x_2 = 3$.

3. (a) $z = 14.50, x_1 = 3.5, x_2 = 2$.
   (d) $z = 10.5, x_1 = .5, x_2 = 2$.

9. Equivalent 0-1 ILP:

Maximize $z = 18y_{11} + 36y_{12} + 14y_{21} + 28y_{22} + 8y_{31} + 16y_{32} + 32y_{33}$

subject to $15y_{11} + 30y_{12} + 12y_{21} + 24y_{22} + 7y_{31} + 14y_{32} + 28y_{33} \leq 43$

All variables are binary.

Solution: $z = 50, y_{12} = 1, y_{21} = 1$, all others $= 0$. Equivalently, $x_1 = 2, x_2 = 1$. The 0-1 version required 41 nodes. The original requires 29.

Set 9.2b

1. (a) Legitimate cut because it passes through an integer point and does not eliminate any feasible integer point. You can verify this result by plotting the cut
   on the LP solution space.

2. (a) Optimum integer solution: $(x_1, x_2, x_3) = (2, 1, 6), z = 26$.
   Rounded solution: $(x_1, x_2, x_3) = (3, 1, 6)$ − infeasible.

CHAPTER 10

Set 10.2A

6. Maximize $z = 15(t/100)(53 - 100(t/100)), 10 \leq t \leq 60$
   Demand will reach zero value at $t = 53$. Thus, search can be limited to the range
   $(10, 53)$. Start search at $t = 10\%$.

Set 10.3C

4. Represent a chromosome with a string of ten randomly generated binary
   elements such that card $i = 0(1)$ means it belongs to pile 1(2).

   Fitness $= |36 -$ sum of cards in pile $1| + |36 -$ product of cards in pile $2|$.

   Iteration 0:

   P1: 1011011010, Pile 1: (2, 5, 8, 10), Pile 2: (1, 3, 4, 6, 7, 9),

   $z = |36 - 25| + |36 - 4536| = 11 + 4500 = 4511$

   P2: 0011011111, P3: 0100110101, P4: 11001101111

---

[2]Use TORA integer programming module to generate the B&B tree.

CHAPTER 11

Problem Set 11.1a

3. Each site (plus hotel) represents a city. The cab fare between locations represents distance.

Set 11.2a

1. (a) LP for lower bound:

Minimize $z = 2r_1 + 2r_2 + 2r_3 + 2r_4 + 2r_5$

s.t.

$r_1 + r_2 \leq 125, r_1 + r_3 \leq 225, r_1 + r_4 \leq 155, r_1 + r_5 \leq 215$

$r_2 + r_3 \leq 85, r_2 + r_4 \leq 115, r_2 + r_5 \leq 135$

$r_3 + r_4 \leq 165, r_3 + r_5 \leq 190$

$r_4 + r_5 \leq 195$

all r_i nonnegative

(b) Both *amplAssign.txt* and *amplLP.txt* yield a lower bound of 720 miles. Assignment model solution includes subtours (1-4-1, 2-5-3-2), hence nonoptimal.

6. (a) Each project represents a city. The table below gives the number of distinct employees who enter/leave the manager's office when we switch from project i to project j (i.e., the number of mismatched "x" between column i and column j). The objective is to find a "tour" through all projects that will minimize the total traffic.

	1	2	3	4	5	6
1		4	4	6	6	5
2	4		6	4	6	3
3	4	6		4	8	7
4	6	4	4		6	5
5	6	6	8	6		5
6	5	3	7	5	5	

(b) Lower bound using *solutionAssign.txt* is 26. Although the lower bound happened to be exactly equal to the true minimum tour, the associated assignment solution includes subtours; namely, 1-3-1, 2-4-5-6-2. Optimal tour using *amplCut.txt* is 1-2-6-5-4-3-1.

Set 11.3a

3. See Figure B.12.

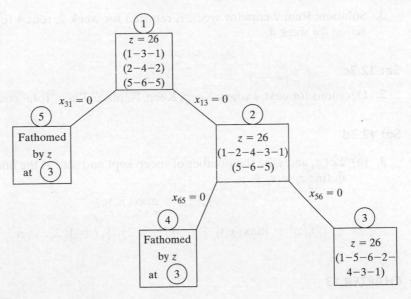

FIGURE B.12

CHAPTER 12

Set 12.1a

1. Solution: Shortest distance = 26 miles. Route: 1-4-6-7.

Set 12.2a

3. Solution: Shortest distance = 17. Route: 1-2-3-5-7.

Set 12.3a

2. (a) Solution: Value = 120. $(m_1, m_2, m_3) = (0, 0, 3), (0, 4, 1), (0, 2, 2),$ or $(0, 6, 0)$.
5. Solution: Total points = 250. Select 2 courses from I, 3 from II, 4 from III, and 1 from IV,
7. Let $x_j = 1$ if application j is accepted, and 0 otherwise. Equivalent knapsack model is

   Maximize $z = 78x_1 + 64x_2 + 68x_3 + 62x_4 + 85x_5$ subject to
   $$7x_1 + 4x_2 + 6x_3 + 5x_4 + 8x_5 \leq 23, x_j = (0, 1), j = 1, 2, \ldots, 5$$

   Solution: Accept all but the first application. Value = 279.

Set 12.3b

1. (a) Solution: Hire 6 for week 1, fire 1 for week 2, fire 2 for week 3, hire 3 for week 4, and hire 2 for week 5.

3. Solution: Rent 7 cars for week 1, return 3 for week 2, rent 4 for week 3, and no action for week 4.

Set 12.3c

2. Decisions for next 4 years: Keep, Keep, Replace, Keep. Total cost = \$458.

Set 12.3d

3. (a) Let x_i and y_i be the number of sheep kept and sold at the end of period i, and define $z_i = x_i + y_i$.

$$f_n(z_n) = \max_{y_n = z_n}\{p_n y_n\}$$

$$f_i(z_i) = \max_{y_i \le z_i}\{p_i y_i + f_{i+1}(2z_i - 2y_i)\}, i = 1, 2, \ldots, n - 1$$

CHAPTER 13

Set 13.3a

2. (a) Total cost per week = \$51.50

(b) Total cost per week = \$50.20, $y^* = 239.05$ lb.

4. (a) Choose policy 1 because its cost per day is \$2.17 as opposed to \$2.50 for policy 2.

(b) Optimal policy: Order 100 units whenever the inventory level drops to 10 units.

Set 13.3b

2. Optimal policy: Order 500 units whenever level drops to 130 units. Cost per day = \$258.50.

4. No advantage if $TCU_1(y_m) \le TCU_2(q)$, which translates to no advantage if the discount factor does not exceed .9344%.

Set 13.3c

1. AMPL/Solver solution: $(y_1, y_2, y_3, y_4, y_5) = (5.17, 6.44, 3.64, 6.03, 3.88)$, cost = \$636.75.

4. Constraint: $\sum_{i=1}^{4} \dfrac{365 D_i}{y_i} \le 150$.

Solver/AMPL solution: $(y_1, y_2, y_3, y_4) = (155.3, 118.82, 74.36, 90.09)$, cost = \$54.71.

Set 13.4a

1. (a) 500 units required at the start of periods 1, 4, 7, and 10.

Set 13.4b

3. Produce 173 units in period 1, 180 in period 2, 240 in period 3, 110 in period 4, and 203 in period 5.

Set 13.4c

1. (a) Yes, because inventory should not be held needlessly at end of horizon.
   (b) (i) $0 \leq z_1 \leq 5, 0 \leq z_2 \leq 6, 0 \leq z_3 \leq 3; x_1 = 3, 1 \leq x_2 \leq 6, 0 \leq x_3 \leq 4$.
   (ii) $5 \leq z_1 \leq 14, 0 \leq z_2 \leq 9, 0 \leq z_3 \leq 5; x_1 = 0, 0 \leq x_2 \leq 9, 0 \leq x_3 \leq 5$.
2. (a) $z_1 = 7, z_2 = 0, z_3 = 6, z_4 = 0$. Total cost = $33.

Set 13.4d

1. Use initial inventory to satisfy the entire demand of period 1 and 4 units of period 2, thus reducing demand for the four periods to 0, 22, 90, and 67, respectively.
   Optimal solution: Order 112 units in period 2 and 67 units in period 4. Total cost = $632.

Set 13.4e

1. Solution: Produce 210 units in January, 255 in April, 210 in July, and 165 in October.

CHAPTER 14

Set 14.1a

1. (a) .15 and .25, respectively. (b) .571. (c) .821.
2. $n \geq 23$.
3. $n > 253$.

Set 14.1b

3. $\frac{5}{32}$.
4. Let p = probability Liz wins. Probability John wins is $3p$, which equals the probability Jim will win. Probability Ann wins is $6p$. Because one of the four wins, $p + 3p + 3p + 3p + 6p = 1$.
   (a) $\frac{3}{13}$.
   (b) $\frac{7}{13}$.
   (c) $\frac{6}{13}$.

Set 14.1c

3. (a) .375. (b) .6.
7. .9545.

Set 14.2a

2. (a) $K = 20$.
3. $P\{\text{Demand} \geq 1100\} = .3$.

Set 14.3a

3. (a) $P\{50 \leq \text{copies sold} \leq 70\} = .6667$.
   (b) Expected number of unsold copies $= 2.67$
   (c) Expected net profit $= \$22.33$

Set 14.3b

1. Mean $= 3.667$, variance $= 1.556$.

Set 14.3c

1. (a) $P(x_1 = 1) = P(x_2 = 1) = .4, P(x_1 = 2) = P(x_2 = 2) = .2, P(x_1 = 3) = P(x_2 = 3) = .4$.
   (b) No, because $P(x_1, x_2) \neq P(x_1)P(x_2)$.

Set 14.4a

1. $\left(\frac{1}{2}\right)^{10}$.
2. .0547.

Set 14.4b

1. .8646.
2. (a) $P\{n = 0\} = 0$.
   (b) $P\{n \geq (1 + 1)\}; P\{n \geq 2\} \simeq .9995$.

Set 14.4c

1. $\lambda = 15$ arrivals/min. $P\{t \leq 8 \text{ sec}\} = .865$.

Set 14.4d

2. .001435.

CHAPTER 15

Set 15.1a

1. Weights for A, B, and C = (.3493, .2573, .3834). Select C.

Set 15.1b

2. CR > .1 for all matrices except **A**. (w_S, w_J, w_M) = (.331, .292, .377). Select Maisa.
4. All matrices are consistent. (w_H, w_P) = (.502, .498). Select H.

Set 15.2a

2. (a) See Figure B.13.
   (b) EV(corn) = −$8250, EV(soybeans) = $250. Select soybeans.
6. (a) See Figure B.14.
   (b) EV(game) = −$.025. Do not play the game.

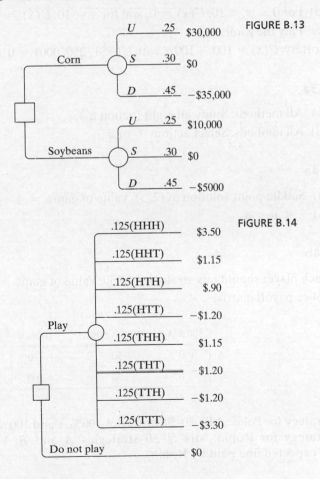

FIGURE B.13

FIGURE B.14

12. Optimum maintenance cycle = 8 years. Cost per year = \$397.50.

15. Optimum production rate = 49 pieces per day.

19. Level must be between 99 and 151 gallons.

Set 15.2b

2. Let z be the event of having one defective item in a sample of size 5.
Answer: $P\{A|z\} = .6097, P\{B|z\} = .3903$.

4. (a) Expected revenue if you self-publish = \$196, 000.
Expected revenue if you use a publisher = \$163, 000.
(b) If survey predicts success, self-publish, else use a publisher.

7. (b) Ship lot to B if both items are bad, else ship lot to A.

Set 15.2c

1. (a) Expected value = \$5, hence there is no advantage.
(b) For $0 \leq x < 10, U(x) = 0$, and for $x = 10, U(x) = 100$.
(c) Play the game.

2. Lottery: $U(x) = 100 - 100p$, with $U(-\$1, 250, 000) = 0$ and $U(\$900, 000) = 100$.

Set 15.3a

1. (a) All methods: Study all night (action a_1).
(b) All methods: Select actions a_2 or a_3.

Set 15.4a

2. (a) Saddle-point solution at $(2, 3)$. Value of game $= 4$.

3. (a) $2 < v < 4$.

Set 15.4b

1. Each player should mix strategies 50-50. Value of game $= 0$.

2. Police payoff matrix:

	100% A	50% A-50% B	100% B
A	100	50	0
B	0	30	100

Strategy for Police: Mix 50-50 strategies 100% A and 100% B.
Strategy for Robin: Mix 50-50 strategies A and B. Value of game $= \$50$ (=expected fine paid by Robin).

Set 15.4c

1. (a) Payoff matrix for team 1:

	AB	AC	AD	BC	BD	CD
AB	1	0	0	0	0	−1
AC	0	1	0	0	−1	0
AD	0	0	1	−1	0	0
BC	0	0	−1	1	0	0
BD	0	−1	0	0	1	0
CD	−1	0	0	0	0	1

Optimal strategy for both teams: Mix AB and CD 50-50. Value of the game = 0.

2. (a) (m, n) = (Number of regiments at location 1, No. of regiments at locations 2). Each location has a payoff of 1 if won and −1 if lost. For example, Botto's strategy $(1, 1)$ against the enemy's $(0, 3)$ will win location 1 and lose location 2, with a net payoff of $1 + (-1) = 0$. Payoff matrix for Colonel Blotto:

	3, 0	2, 1	1, 2	0, 3
2, 0	−1	−1	0	0
1, 1	0	−1	−1	0
0, 2	0	0	−1	−1

Optimal strategy for Blotto: Blotto mixes 50-50 strategies (2-0) and (0-2), and the enemy mixes 50-50 strategies (3-0) and (1-2). Value of the game = −.5, and Blotto loses. Problem has alternative optima.

CHAPTER 16

Set 16.1a

1. (a) Order 1000 units whenever inventory level drops to 537 units.

Set 16.1b

2. Solution: $y^* = 317.82$ gallons, $R^* = 46.82$ gallons.

3. Solution: $y^* = 316.85$ gallons, $R^* = 58.73$ gallons. In Example 14.1-2, $y^* = 319.44$ gallons, $R^* = 93.61$ gallons. Order quantity remains about the same as in Example 14.1-2, but R^* is smaller because the demand pdf has a smaller variance.

Set 16.2a

3. $.43 \le p \le .82$

6. 32 coats.

Set 16.2b

1. Order $9 - x$ if $x < 4.53$, else do not order.

Set 16.3a

2. Order $4.61 - x$ if $x < 4.61$, else do not order.

CHAPTER 17

Set 17.1a

2. S1: Car on patrol
S2: Car responding to a call
S3: Car at call scene
S4: Apprehension made.
S5: Transport to police station

	S1	S2	S3	S4	S5
S1	0.4	0.6	0	0	0
S2	0.1	0.3	0.6	0	0
S3	0.1	0	0.5	0.4	0
S4	0.4	0	0	0	0.6
S5	1	0	0	0	0

Set 17.2a

2.

Initial probabilities:

S1	S2	S3	S4	S5
0	0	1	0	0

Input Markov chain:

	S1	S2	S3	S4	S5
S1	0.4	0.6	0	0	0
S2	0.1	0.3	0.6	0	0
S3	0.1	0	0.5	0.4	0
S4	0.4	0	0	0	0.6
S5	1	0	0	0	0

Output (2-step or 2 patrols) transition matrix ($\mathbf{P}_2$)

	S1	S2	S3	S4	S5
S1	0.22	0.42	0.36	0	0
S2	0.13	0.15	0.48	0.24	0
S3	0.25	0.06	0.25	0.2	0.24
S4	0.76	0.24	0	0	0
S5	0.4	0.6	0	0	0

Absolute 2-step probabilities = $(0\,0\,1\,0\,0)\mathbf{P}^2$

State	Absolute (2-step)
S1	0.25
S2	0.06
S3	0.25
S4	0.2
S5	0.24

$P\{\text{apprehension, S4, in 2 patrols}\} = .2$

Set 17.3a

1. (a) Using *excelMarkovChains.xls*, the chain is periodic with period 3.

(b) States 1, 2, and 3 are transient, State 4 is absorbing.

Set 17.4a

1. (a) Input Markov chain:

	S	C	R
S	0.8	0.2	0
C	0.3	0.5	0.2
R	0.1	0.1	0.8

Steady-state probabilities:

$(\pi_1, \pi_2, \pi_3) = (\pi_1, \pi_2, \pi_3)\mathbf{P}$

$\pi_1 + \pi_2 + \pi_3 = 1$

State	Output Results	
	Steady state	*Mean return time*
S	0.50	2.0
C	0.25	4.0
R	0.25	4.0

Expected revenues = $2 \times .5 + 1.6 \times .25 + .4 \times .25 = \$1,500$

(b) Sunny days will return every $\mu_{SS} = 2$ days—meaning two days on no sunshine.

5. (a) Input Markov chain:

	never	some	always
Never	0.95	0.04	0.01
Some	0.06	0.9	0.04
always	0	0.1	0.9

(b)

	Output Results	
State	Steady State	Mean return time
never	0.441175	2.2666728
some	0.367646	2.7200089
always	0.191176	5.2307892

44.12% never, 36.76% sometimes, 19.11% always

(c) Expected uncollected taxes/year = .12($5000 × .3676 + 12,000 × .1911) × 70,000,000 = $34,711,641,097.07

Set 17.5a

1. (a) Initial probabilities:

1	2	3	4	5
1	0	0	0	0

Input Markov chain:

1	2	3	4	5
0	.3333	.3333	.3333	0
.3333	0	.3333	0	.3333
.3333	.3333	0	0	.3333
.5	0	0	0	.5
0	.3333	.3333	.3333	0

State	Absolute (3-step)	Steady state
1	.07407	.214286
2	.2963	.214286
3	.2963	.214286
4	.25926	.142857
5	**.07407**	**.214286**

(b) $a_5 = .07407$

(c) $\pi_5 = .214286$

(d) $\mu_{15} = 4.6666$.

	$(\mathbf{I} - \mathbf{N})^{-1}$				Mu
	1	2	3	5	
1	2	1	1	.6667	4.6666
2	1	1.625	.875	.3333	3.8333
3	1	.875	1.625	.3333	3.8333
4	1	.5	.5	1.3333	3.3333

5. (a) Input Markov chain:

	A	B	C
A	.75	.1	.15
B	.2	.75	.05
C	.125	.125	.75

(b)

State	Steady state
A	.394737
B	.307018
C	.298246

A: 39.5%, B: 30.7%, C: 29.8%

	$(\mathbf{I} - \mathbf{N})^{-1}$			Mu
	A	C		B
A	5.71429	3.42857	A	**9.14286**
C	2.85714	5.71429	C	8.57143

	1	2		C
A	5.88235	2.35294	A	**8.23529**
B	4.70588	5.88235	B	1.5882

A → B: 9.14 years

A → C: 8.23 years

Set 17.6a

2. (a) States: 1 week, 2 weeks, 3 weeks, Library

Matrix **P**:

	1	2	3	lib
1	0	0.3	0	0.7
2	0	0	0.1	0.9
3	0	0	0	1
lib	0	0	0	1

(b)

$(\mathbf{I} - \mathbf{N})^{-1}$

	1	2	3
1	1	0.3	.03
2	0	1	.01
3	0	0	1

Mu

	lib
1	1.33
2	1.1
3	1

I keep the book 1.33 weeks on the average.

8. (a)

Matrix **P**:

	1	2	3	4	F
1	0.2	0.8	0	0	0
2	0	0.22	0.78	0	0
3	0	0	0.25	0.75	0
4	0	0	0	0.3	0.7
F	0	0	0	0	1

(b)

$(\mathbf{I} - \mathbf{N})^{-1}$

	1	2	3	4
1	1.25	1.282	1.333	1.429
2	0	1.282	1.333	1.429
3	0	0	1.333	1.429
4	0	0	0	1.429

Mu

	F
1	5.29
2	4.04
3	2.76
4	1.43

(c) To be able to take Cal II, the student must finish in 16 weeks (4 transitions) or less. Average number of transitions needed = 5.29. Hence, an average student will not be able to finish Cal I on time.

(d) No, per answer in (c).

CHAPTER 18

Set 18.1a

1. (a) Productivity = 71%.

(b) The two requirements cannot be met simultaneously.

Set 18.2a

1.

Situation	Customer	Server
(a)	Plane	Runway
(b)	Passenger	Taxi
(h)	Car	Parking space

Set 18.3a

1. (b) (i) $\lambda = 6$ arrivals per hour, average interarrival time $= \frac{1}{6}$ hour.

(c) (i) $\mu = 5$ services per hour, average service time = .2 hour.

3. (a) $f(t) = 20e^{-20t}, t > 0$.

(b) $P\{t > \frac{15}{60}\} = .00674$.

7. Jim's payoff is 2 cents with probability $P\{t \leq 1\} = .4866$ and -2 cents with probability $P\{t \geq 1\} = .5134$. In 8 hours, Jim pays Ann $= 17.15$ cents.

10. (a) $P\{t \leq 4 \text{ minutes}\} = .4866$.

(b) Average discount percentage $= 6.208$.

Set 18.4a

1. $p_{n\geq5}(1 \text{ hour}) = .55951$.

4. (a) $p_2(t = 7) = .24167$.

6. (a) Combined $\lambda = \frac{1}{10} + \frac{1}{7}, p_2(t - 5) = .219$.

Set 18.4b

2. (a) $p_0(t = 3) = .00532$.

(c) $p_{n\leq17}(t = 1) = .9502$.

5. $p_0(4) = .37116.$

8. (a) Average order size $= 25 - 7.11 = 17.89$ items.

    (b) $p_0(t = 4) = .00069.$

Set 18.5a

3. (a) $p_{n \geq 3} = .4445.$

    (b) $p_{n \leq 2} = .5555.$

6. (a) $p_j = .2, j = 0, 1, 2, 3, 4.$

    (b) Expected number in shop $= 2$ customers.

    (c) $p_4 = .2.$

Set 18.6a

1. (a) $L_q = 1p_6 + 2p_7 + 3p_8 = .1917$ car.

    (b) $\lambda_{\text{lost}} = .1263$ car per hour. Average number lost in 8 hr $= 1.01$ cars.

    (c) No. of empty spaces $= c - (L_s - L_q) = c - \sum_{n=0}^{8} np_n + \sum_{n=c+1}^{8} (n - c)p_n.$

Set 18.6b

2. (a) $p_0 = .2.$

    (b) Average monthly income $= \$50 \times \mu t = \$375.$

    (c) Expected payment $= \$40 \times L_q = \$128.$

5. (a) $p_0 = .4.$

    (b) $L_q = .9$ car.

    (c) $W_q = 2.25$ min.

    (d) $p_{n \geq 11} = .0036.$

6. (d) Number of spaces is at least 13.

Set 18.6c

1. (a) $p_0 = .3654.$

    (b) $W_q = .207$ hour.

    (c) Expected number of empty spaces $= 4 - L_q = 3.212.$

    (d) $p_5 = .04812.$

    (e) A 40% reduction lowers W_s to about 9.6 minutes ($\mu = 10$ cars/hr).

4. (a) $p_8 = .6.$

    (b) $L_q = 6.34$ generators.

    (c) Probability of finding an empty space cannot exceed .4 regardless of belt capacity. This means that the best utilization of the assembly department is 60%.

7. (a) $1 - p_5 = .962$.

(b) $\lambda_{lost} = \lambda p_5 = .19$ customer per hour.

Set 18.6d

2. For $c = 2$, $W_q = 3.446$ hour and for $c = 4$, $W_q = 1.681$ hour, an improvement of over 51%.

5. Let K be the number of waiting-room spaces. Using TORA, $p_0 + p_1 + \cdots + p_{K+2} \geq .999$ yields $K \geq 10$.

7. (a) $p_{n \geq 4} = .65772$.

(e) Average number of idle computers $= .667$ computer.

Set 18.6e

2. (c) Utilization $= 81.8\%$.

(d) $p_2 + p_3 + p_4 = .545$.

4. (a) $p_{40} = .00014$.

(b) $p_{30} + p_{31} + \cdots + p_{39} = .02453$.

(d) Expected number of occupied spaces $= L_s - L_q = 20.043 - .046 \approx 20$.

(f) Probability of not finding a parking space $= 1 - p_{n \leq 29} = .02467$. Number of students who cannot park in an 8-hour period is approximately 4.

Set 18.6f

2. (a) Approximately 7 seats.

(b) $p_{n \geq 8} = .2911$.

Set 18.6g

1. (b) Average number of idle repairpersons $= 2.01$.

(d) $P\{2 \text{ or } 3 \text{ idle servers}\} = p_0 + p_1 = .34492$.

4. (a) $L_s = 1.25$ machines.

(b) $p_0 = .33342$.

(c) $W_s = .25$ hour.

6. $\lambda = 2$ calls per hour per baby, $\mu = .5$ baby per hour, $R = 5$, $K = 5$.

(a) Number of awake babies $= 5 - L_s = 1$ baby.

(b) $p_5 = .32768$.

(c) $p_{n \geq 2} = .05792$.

Set 18.7a

2. (a) $E\{t\} = 14$ minutes and $var\{t\} = 12$ minutes^2. $L_s = 7.8672$ cars.

4. $\lambda = .0625$ prescriptions per minute, $E\{t\} = 15$ minutes, var$\{t\} = 9.33$ minutes^2.
   (a) $p_0 = .0625$.
   (b) $L_q = 7.3$ prescriptions
   (c) $W_s = 132.17$ minutes.

Set 18.9a

2. Use $(M/M/1):(GD/10/10)$. Cost per hour is $431.50 for repairperson 1 and $386.50 for repairperson 2.

4. (b) $\mu = \lambda + \sqrt{\dfrac{c_2\lambda}{c_1}}$

   (c) Optimum production rate $= 2725$ pieces per hour.

Set 18.9b

2. (a) Hourly cost per hour is $86.4 for two repairpersons and $94.80 for three.
   (b) Schedule loss per breakdown $= \$30 \times W_s = \$121.11$ for two repairpersons and $94.62 for three.

4. Rate of breakdowns per machine, $\lambda = .36125$ per hour, $\mu = 10$ per hour. Model $(M/M/3):(GD/20/20)$ yields $L_s = .70529$ machine. Lost revenue $= \$36.60$ and cost of three repairpersons $= \$60$.

Set 18.9c

1. (a) Number of repairpersons ≥ 5.
   (b) Number of repairpersons ≥ 4.

CHAPTER 19

Set 19.1a

4. (a) $P\{H\} = P\{T\} = .5$. If $0 \leq R \leq .5$, Jim gets $10.00. If $.5 < R \leq 1$, Jan gets $10.00.

7. Lead time sampling: If $0 \leq R \leq .5, L = 1$ day. If $.5 < R \leq 1, L = 2$ days.
   Demand per day sampling: If $0 \leq R \leq .2$, demand $= 0$ unit. If $.2 < R \leq .9$, demand $= 1$ unit. If $.9 < R \leq 1$, demand $= 2$ units. Use one R to sample L. If $L = 1$, use another R to sample demand for one day, else if $L = 2$, use one R to generate demand for day 1 and then another R to generate demand for day 2.

Set 19.2a

1. (a) Discrete.

FIGURE B.15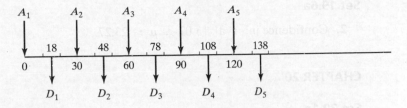

Set 19.3a

4. See Figure B.15.

Set 19.3b

1. $t = -\frac{1}{\lambda} \ln (1 - R)$, $\lambda = 4$ customers per hour.

Customer	R	t (hr)	Arrival time
1	—	—	0
2	0.0589	0.015176	0.015176
3	0.6733	0.279678	0.294855
4	0.4799	0.163434	0.458288

2. $t = a + (b - a)R$.

4. (a) $0 \leq R < .3: d = 0, .3 \leq R < .6: d = 1, .6 \leq R < .8: d = 2, .8 \leq R \leq 1: d = 3$.

9. If $0 \leq R \leq p$, then $x = 0$, else $x = \left(\text{largest integer} \leq \frac{\ln (1 - R)}{\ln q} \right)$.

Set 19.3c

1. $y = -\frac{1}{10} \ln(.0589 \times .6733 \times .4799 \times .4799) = .396$ hour.

6. $t = x_1 + x_2 + x_3 + x_4$, where $x_i = 10 + 10R_i$, $i = 1, 2, 3, 4$.

Set 19.4a

1. In Example 16.4-1, cycle length $= 4$. With the new parameters, cycling was not evident after 50 random numbers were generated. The conclusion is that judicious selection of the parameters is important.

Set 19.5a

2. (a) Observation-based.
   (b) Time-based.

3. (a) 1.48 customers.
   (b) 7.4 hours.

Set 19.6a

2. Confidence interval: $15.07 \leq \mu \leq 23.27$.

CHAPTER 20

Set 20.1a

1. (a) No stationary points.
   (b) Minimum at $x = 0$.
   (e) Inflection point at $x = 0$, minimum at $x = .63$, and maximum at $x = -.63$.
4. $(x_1, x_2) = (-1, 1)$ or $(2, 4)$.

Set 20.2a

1. (b) $(\partial x_1, \partial x_2) = (2.83, -2.5)\, \partial x_2$

Set 20.2b

3. Necessary conditions: $2\left(x_i - \frac{x_n^2}{x_i} \right) = 0, i = 1, 2, \ldots, n - 1$. Solution is

   $x_i = \sqrt[n]{C}, i = 1, 2, \ldots, n.\ \partial f = 2\delta \sqrt[n]{C^{2-n}}$.

6. (b) Solution $(x_1, x_2, x_3, x_4) = \left(-\frac{5}{74}, -\frac{10}{74}, \frac{155}{74}, \frac{60}{74} \right)$, which is a minimum point.

Set 20.2c

2. Minima points: $(x_1, x_2, x_3) = (-14.4, 4.56, -1.44)$ and $(4.4, .44, .44)$.

CHAPTER 21

Set 21.1a

2. (c) $x = 2.5$, achieved with $\Delta = .000001$.
   (e) $x = 2$, achieved with $\Delta = .000001$.

Set 21.1b

1. By Taylor's expansion, $\nabla f(\mathbf{X}) = \nabla f(\mathbf{X}^0) + \mathbf{H}(\mathbf{X} - \mathbf{X}^0)$. The Hessian $\mathbf{H}$ is independent of $\mathbf{X}$ because $f(\mathbf{X})$ is quadratic. Also, the given expansion is exact because higher-order derivatives are zero. Thus, $\nabla f(\mathbf{X}) = \mathbf{0}$ yields $\mathbf{X} = \mathbf{X}^0 - \mathbf{H}^{-1}\nabla f(\mathbf{X}^0)$. Because $\mathbf{X}$ satisfies $\nabla f(\mathbf{X}) = \mathbf{0}, \mathbf{X}$ must be optimum regardless of the choice of initial $\mathbf{X}^0$.

Set 21.2a

2. Optimal solution: $x_1 = 0, x_2 = 3, z = 17$.
4. Let $w_j = x_j + 1, j = 1, 2, 3, v_1 = w_1 w_2, v_2 = w_1 w_3$. Then,

Maximize $z = v_1 + v_2 - 2w_1 - w_2 + 1$

subject to $v_1 + v_2 - 2w_1 - w_2 \le 9$, $\ln v_1 - \ln w_1 - \ln w_2 = 0$,

$\ln v_2 - \ln w_1 - \ln w_3 = 0$, all variables are nonnegative.

Set 21.2b

1. Solution: $x_1 = 1, x_2 = 0, z = 4$.
2. Solution: $x_1 = 0, x_2 = .4, x_3 = .7, z = -2.35$.

Set 21.2c

1. Maximize $z = x_1 + 2x_2 + 5x_3$

   subject to $2x_1 + 3x_2 + 5x_3 + 1.28y \le 10$

   $9x_1^2 + 16x_3^2 - y^2 = 0$

   $7x_1 + 5x_2 + x_3 \le 12$

   $x_1, x_2, x_3, y \ge 0$

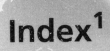

Index[1]

---

[1]Prefixed page numbers deal with index items in chapters and appendixes available on the website. For example, 22.3-7 refers to pages 3 to 7 in chapter 22 and C.4-8 refer to pages 4 to 8 in Appendix C.